REED AND BUSH
WARBLERS

REED AND BUSH
WARBLERS

Peter Kennerley and David Pearson

Illustrated by Brian Small

CHRISTOPHER HELM
LONDON

Published 2010 by Christopher Helm,
an imprint of A&C Black Publishers Ltd, 36 Soho Square, London W1D 3QY

ISBN (print) 978-0-7136-6022-7
ISBN (e-pub) 978-1-4081-2751-3
ISBN (e-pdf) 978-1-4081-3401-6

A CIP catalogue record for this book is available from the British Library

This book is produced using paper that is made from wood grown in managed sustainable forests. It is natural,
renewable and recyclable. The logging and manufacturing processes conform to the environmental regulations
of the country of origin.

Commissioning Editor: Nigel Redman
Project Editor: Jim Martin

Design by Julie Dando at Fluke Art

Printed in Spain by GraphyCems

10 9 8 7 6 5 4 3 2 1

Visit www.acblack.com/naturalhistory to find out more about our authors and their books. You will
find extracts, author interviews and our blog, and you can sign up for newsletters to be the first to
hear about our latest releases and special offers.

CONTENTS

	Plate	Page
FOREWORD by Professor Philip Round		9
ACKNOWLEDGEMENTS		10
Physical features and main habitat types of Eurasia		12
Pacific Ocean showing location of major islands and island groups		13
Provinces of China, India and Pakistan		14
INTRODUCTION		15
TAXONOMY, SPECIES INCLUSION AND SEQUENCE		17
GENUS AND SPECIES ACCOUNTS		19
TOPOGRAPHY OF A BIRD, TERMINOLOGY AND GLOSSARY		25
MIGRATION		28
MOULT STRATEGIES		31
AGEING		34
PHYLOGENETIC RELATIONSHIPS AS REVEALED BY MOLECULAR ANALYSES by Professor Staffan Bensch		35
ORIGINS, DISTRIBUTION AND EXTINCTION OF *ACROCEPHALUS* IN THE PACIFIC OCEAN		41
MAJOR CONTRIBUTORS AND SOURCES		43
COLOUR PLATES		44
SPECIES ACCOUNTS		129

FAMILY LOCUSTELLIDAE

Genus *Bradypterus* | | 129
Little Rush Warbler *Bradypterus baboecala*	1	129
White-winged Swamp Warbler *Bradypterus carpalis*	1	135
Grauer's Swamp Warbler *Bradypterus graueri*	1	138
Dja River Warbler *Bradypterus grandis*	1	140
Bamboo Warbler *Bradypterus alfredi*	2	142
Barratt's Warbler *Bradypterus barratti*	2	144
Knysna Warbler *Bradypterus sylvaticus*	2	147
Cinnamon Bracken Warbler *Bradypterus cinnamomeus*	3	149
Bangwa Forest Warbler *Bradypterus bangwaensis*	3	152
Evergreen Forest Warbler *Bradypterus lopezi*	3, 4	154
Spotted Bush Warbler *Bradypterus thoracicus*	5	159
Baikal Bush Warbler *Bradypterus davidi*	5	165
Long-billed Bush Warbler *Bradypterus major*	6	170
Chinese Bush Warbler *Bradypterus tacsanowskius*	6	173
Brown Bush Warbler *Bradypterus luteoventris*	6	178
Russet Bush Warbler *Bradypterus mandelli*	7	182
Javan Bush Warbler *Bradypterus montis*	7	187
Timor Bush Warbler *Bradypterus timorensis*	7	190
Benguet Bush Warbler *Bradypterus seebohmi*	7	192
Taiwan Bush Warbler *Bradypterus alishanensis*	7	195
Long-tailed Bush Warbler *Bradypterus caudatus*	8	199
Kinabalu Bush Warbler *Bradypterus accentor*	8	202
Chestnut-backed Bush Warbler *Bradypterus castaneus*	8	205

	Plate	Page
Genus *Elaphrornis*		208
Ceylon Bush Warbler *Elaphrornis palliseri*	8	208
Genus *Locustella*		211
Savi's Warbler *Locustella luscinioides*	9	211
River Warbler *Locustella fluviatilis*	9	219
Grasshopper Warbler *Locustella naevia*	10, 11	225
Lanceolated Warbler *Locustella lanceolata*	11	235
Pallas's Grasshopper Warbler *Locustella certhiola*	12	245
Middendorff's Grasshopper Warbler *Locustella ochotensis*	13	258
Styan's Grasshopper Warbler *Locustella pleskei*	13	267
Gray's Grasshopper Warbler *Locustella fasciolata*	14	274
Japanese Swamp Warbler *Locustella pryeri*	15	282
FAMILY ACROCEPHALIDAE		
Genus *Acrocephalus*		288
Moustached Warbler *Acrocephalus melanopogon*	15, 16	289
Sedge Warbler *Acrocephalus schoenobaenus*	16	296
Aquatic Warbler *Acrocephalus paludicola*	16	302
Streaked Reed Warbler *Acrocephalus sorghophilus*	17	307
Black-browed Reed Warbler *Acrocephalus bistrigiceps*	17	311
Manchurian Reed Warbler *Acrocephalus tangorum*	17	317
Blunt-winged Warbler *Acrocephalus concinens*	18	322
Paddyfield Warbler *Acrocephalus agricola*	18	329
Blyth's Reed Warbler *Acrocephalus dumetorum*	19	336
Large-billed Reed Warbler *Acrocephalus orinus*	19	343
Marsh Warbler *Acrocephalus palustris*	19	347
Eurasian Reed Warbler *Acrocephalus scirpaceus*	20, 21	354
African Reed Warbler *Acrocephalus baeticatus*	21	364
Cape Verde Warbler *Acrocephalus brevipennis*	21	369
Lesser Swamp Warbler *Acrocephalus gracilirostris*	22	372
Greater Swamp Warbler *Acrocephalus rufescens*	23	377
Madagascar Swamp Warbler *Acrocephalus newtoni*	23	382
Seychelles Warbler *Acrocephalus sechellensis*	23	385
Rodrigues Warbler *Acrocephalus rodericanus*	23	388
Basra Reed Warbler *Acrocephalus griseldis*	24	391
Great Reed Warbler *Acrocephalus arundinaceus*	24	396
Oriental Reed Warbler *Acrocephalus orientalis*	25	403
Clamorous Reed Warbler *Acrocephalus stentoreus*	26, 27	410
Australian Reed Warbler *Acrocephalus australis*	27	422
Millerbird *Acrocephalus familiaris*	28	428
Cook Islands Warbler *Acrocephalus kerearako*	28	431
Pitcairn Island Warbler *Acrocephalus vaughani*	28	434
Henderson Island Warbler *Acrocephalus taiti*	28	437
Rimatara Warbler *Acrocephalus rimitarae*	28	439
Kiritimati Warbler *Acrocephalus aequinoctialis*	28	441
Southern Marquesan Warbler *Acrocephalus mendanae*	29	444
Northern Marquesan Warbler *Acrocephalus percernis*	29	444
Tahiti Warbler *Acrocephalus caffer*	29	449
Tuamotu Warbler *Acrocephalus atyphus*	30	453
Nightingale Warbler *Acrocephalus luscinius*	30	457

	Plate	Page
Caroline Islands Warbler *Acrocephalus syrinx*	30	460
Nauru Warbler *Acrocephalus rehsei*	30	463
Genus *Hippolais*		465
Icterine Warbler *Hippolais icterina*	31	465
Melodious Warbler *Hippolais polyglotta*	31	471
Olive-tree Warbler *Hippolais olivetorum*	31	476
Upcher's Warbler *Hippolais languida*	32	481
Genus *Iduna*		486
Eastern Olivaceous Warbler *Iduna pallida*	32, 33	486
Western Olivaceous Warbler *Iduna opaca*	32	494
Sykes's Warbler *Iduna rama*	33	498
Booted Warbler *Iduna caligata*	33	503
Dark-capped Yellow Warbler *Iduna natalensis*	34	509
Mountain Yellow Warbler *Iduna similis*	34	514
Genus *Phragamaticola*		516
Thick-billed Warbler *Phragamaticola aedon*	25	516
Genus *Calamonastides*		522
Papyrus Yellow Warbler *Calamonastides gracilirostris*	34	522
Genus *Nesillas*		526
Madagascar Brush Warbler *Nesillas typica*	35	526
Lantz's Brush Warbler *Nesillas lantzii*	35	530
Grande Comore Brush Warbler *Nesillas brevicaudata*	35	532
Moheli Brush Warbler *Nesillas mariae*	35	534
Aldabra Brush Warbler *Nesillas aldabranus*	35	536
FAMILY CETTIIDAE		
Genus *Oligura*		538
Chestnut-headed Tesia *Oligura castaneocoronata*	36	538
Genus *Tesia*		541
Grey-bellied Tesia *Tesia cyaniventer*	36	541
Slaty-bellied Tesia *Tesia olivea*	36	544
Javan Tesia *Tesia superciliaris*	36	547
Russet-capped Tesia *Tesia everetti*	36	549
Genus *Urosphena*		551
Timor Stubtail *Urosphena subulata*	37	551
Bornean Stubtail *Urosphena whiteheadi*	37	554
Asian Stubtail *Urosphena squameiceps*	37	556
Genus *Cettia*		560
Pale-footed Bush Warbler *Cettia pallidipes*	37	560
Sunda Bush Warbler *Cettia vulcania*	38	565
Aberrant Bush Warbler *Cettia flavolivacea*	38	570
Brownish-flanked Bush Warbler *Cettia fortipes*	39	574
Yellow-bellied Bush Warbler *Cettia acanthizoides*	39	580
Hume's Bush Warbler *Cettia brunnescens*	39	584
Chestnut-crowned Bush Warbler *Cettia major*	40	587
Grey-sided Bush Warbler *Cettia brunnifrons*	40	591
Manchurian Bush Warbler *Cettia canturians*	41	595
Japanese Bush Warbler *Cettia diphone*	41	600
Luzon Bush Warbler *Cettia seebohmi*	42	607

	Plate	Page
Palau Bush Warbler *Cettia annae*	42	610
Shade Warbler *Cettia parens*	42	612
Fiji Bush Warbler *Cettia ruficapilla*	42	614
Tanimbar Bush Warbler *Cettia carolinae*	42	617
Bougainville Bush Warbler *Cettia haddeni*	42	619
Cetti's Warbler *Cettia cetti*	40	621
APPENDICES		628
Appendix 1: Sources of original descriptions, type localities and synonyms		628
Appendix 2: Live wing lengths of selected Palearctic migrant species		641
Appendix 3: Principal measurements from museum specimens		646
Appendix 4: Origins, migration status and moult strategies		656
Appendix 5: Comparative field characters of similar species		659
Appendix 6: Scientific names of other bird species mentioned in the text		671
Appendix 7: Recent developments to 2010		672
BIBLIOGRAPHY		676
INDEX		708

FOREWORD

As the authors state, bush warblers and their allies (the quintessential 'little brown jobs'), with their subdued colouring and skulking habits, are not everyone's cup of tea. For equally many though, this group are real 'birdwatchers' birds'. How so? Birders love a challenge: first, you must find your bird; then you must obtain good enough views to identify it. On both counts reed and bush warblers are extraordinarily challenging; and some are hardly less difficult to identify in the hand than in the field. Add to this the fascinating behaviour of many species – the brilliantly varied and mimetic song of the Marsh Warbler; the extraordinary promiscuity of the Aquatic Warbler's mating system; or the magical ability of a wintering or passage Lanceolated Warbler, seemingly cornered in short grass or scrub, to melt away undetected—and you have a recipe for a lifetime's obsession.

My own fascination with this group began as a schoolboy with my first observations of migrant Aquatic Warblers at the edge of a Cornish reedbed. I learned the sublime joys of rising early to commune with these birds that were usually so hard to see, yet became active and cooperative immediately after dawn. Forward a decade or so to my first months in Thailand, where I found the best way of observing the hitherto unseen author of excited chacking notes coming from the bushes was to discard binoculars (they didn't focus close enough), kneel on the ground, and gently part and peer into the undergrowth. Marveling at the small brown feathered creature running mouse-like over the ground, I made my first acquaintance with a Baikal Bush Warbler.

It goes without saying that reed and bush warblers are inadequately treated by existing field guides, which cannot give sufficient attention to geographical variation, and age and moult-related plumage variation among taxa. Even some of the latest generation, otherwise generally very high quality books, have misled when it comes, for example, to the undertail-covert patterns of *Bradypterus*. Up to now, observers have had to work out the best field marks for themselves, gradually gaining experience as they went along. Sometimes it has seemed like one step back for every two steps forward as hypotheses were tested and either discarded or verified. But gradually, the pieces of the puzzle are being assembled. The authors of this work have brought their breadth and depth of field experience in the Palaearctic and in both African and Asian tropics, their acuity of observation, and their erudition to bear.

This book is a giant step forward on what has gone before. It is much more than an essential toolkit for identification as even a rapid perusal of the scholarly yet readable introduction will reveal. This fine work seems certain to realise the authors' goal of inspiring future research work on these warblers.

Philip Round
Assistant Professor, Department of Biology, Mahidol University, Bangkok,
and Regional Representative, The Wetland Trust

Bangkok, October 2009

9

ACKNOWLEDGEMENTS

Plans for this book were conceived by Peter Kennerley (PRK) in the 1980s while living in Hong Kong and Singapore, after becoming fascinated with the complexities of warbler identification in Asia. Ideas then took firmer shape with the involvement of Christopher Helm and Nigel Redman at Pica Press, and the recruitment of Brian Small (BJS) as the artist, and David Pearson (DJP) to provide an African perspective. Whilst the project has been developing over the last ten years we have been assisted and supported by numerous individuals and organisations. We thank every one of these for their advice and constructive criticism, and we extend our sincerest apologies to anyone we may have inadvertently omitted.

PRK is particularly grateful to Paul Leader and Geoff Carey for their good humour and companionship in Hong Kong and during numerous field excursions in search of warblers throughout Asia. Without their input, in particular the use of their many superb photographs and sound recordings, and access to the extensive database of the Hong Kong Ringing Group, this book would be much less complete. He warmly acknowledges the guidance and incisive comments on many of the Asian species provided by Philip Round of the Wetland Trust, Yoshimitsu Shigeta of the Yamashina Institute of Ornithology, Nial Moores of Birds Korea, and Jesper Hornskov. Each has contributed significantly to this work, and he is most grateful to them for replying to seemingly endless questions and requests. He also thanks Chris and Barbara Kightley, proprietors of Limosa Holidays, for enabling him to travel extensively throughout Asia while leading birdwatching tours on their behalf.

DJP is especially indebted to Gerhard Nikolaus for his company and support on various expeditions to ring and observe migrants in northeast Africa and eastern Europe, often at challenging and remote sites. Gerhard has generously supplied information from his explorations in Sudan and Arabia. Much of our biometric and in-hand material on migrant warblers in Africa has been supplied by the Ngulia Ringing Project in Kenya. This was set up and has been organised over many years by Graeme Backhurst and DJP, with essential support from the Kenya Wildlife Service, Ngulia Safari Lodge, and the Wetland Trust.

Per Alström has generously given us an insight of his unpublished research on the phylogenetic links between these warblers. Where possible, we have incorporated his findings, but there is much more to come which will revolutionise the way we view these relationships. Staffan Bensch has given freely of his time and expertise to provide molecular answers in the case of various problematic warbler specimens.

We are grateful to the staff of the NHM, Tring, for allowing ready access to the specimen collection: Robert Prŷs-Jones, Peter Colston, Mark Adams, Michael Walters, Douglas Russell, and Katrina van Grouw. Without their support this book would not have been possible. We have received generous assistance from other collection managers, who have loaned specimens, provided photographs, and in some cases taken measurements under our direction. These include: Mary LeCroy and Paul Sweet at the American Museum of Natural History in New York, USA; Hein van Grouw, Steven van der Mij and René Dekker at the Rijks-museum van Natuurlijke Historie, Leiden, Netherlands; C. S. (Kees) Roselaar at the Zoölogisch Museum, Amsterdam, Netherlands, Sylke Frahnert at the Museum fur Naturkunde, Berlin, Germany; Frederika Woog at the Staatliches Museum fur Naturkunde, Stuttgart, Germany; Till Topfer at the Museum für Tierkunde, Dresden, Germany; and Raffael Winkler at the Naturhistorisches Museum, Basel, Switzerland.

We appreciate the efforts of Effie Warr and Alison Harding, librarians of the Ornithology & Rothschild Libraries at NHM, Tring, and Linda Birch, librarian at the Edward Grey Institute of Field Ornithology, Oxford, for locating many obscure references. Svetlana Gretton, Jevgeni Shergalin and Mike Wilson kindly translated Russian references, and Richard Chandler scanned some of the slides which appear here.

Over the years, many people have responded freely and willingly to our requests for information. Others have been helpful with discussions, supported us on field excursions and assisted in many ways. Without their contributions, this book would be all the poorer. These include: A. Abuladze, AbdulRahman Al-Sirhan, John Allcock, Des Allen, Per Alström, Bernard Amakobe, Vasil Ananian, John Ash, Scott Atkinson, Graeme Backhurst, Neil & Elizabeth Baker, David Bakewell, Staffan Bensch, Herbert Biebach, John Bowler, Mark Brazil, Mike Chalmers, Richard Chandler, Joseph Chernichko, Alice Cibois, Peter Colston, John Cortes, Miles Coverdale, Mike Crewe, Edward Dickinson, Robert Dowsett, Francoise Dowsett-Lemaire, Omar Fadil, Dick Forsman, Kimball Garrett, Kai Gauger, Andrei Gavrilov, Sundev Gombobaatar, Adam Gretton, Ricard Gutiérrez, Karl Schulze-Hagen, Martin Hale, Martijn Hammers, Bill Harvey, Paul Harvey, Dennis Hasselquist, Frank Hawkins, John Holmes, Paul Holt, David Holyoak, Tony Howe, Carol & Tim Inskipp, Colin Jackson, Magnus Jäderblad, Hannu Jännes, Girish Jathar, Praveen Jayadevan, James A. Jobling, Charles Kahindo, David Kelly, Diederik Kok, Victoria Kovshar, Darya Kuznetsova & Viktor Salovarov, Angus Lamont, Laurie Larson, Paul Lehman, Berndt Leisler, Peter Leonard, Mike Leven, Richard Lewthwaite, Åke Lindström, Michel Louette, Ilya Maclean, Takeyoshi Matsuo, Nial Moores/Birds Korea, Pete Morris, Steve Mulkeen, Oliver Nasirwa, Bo Neilsen, Gerhard Nikolaus, Claudien Nsabagasani, Urban Olsson, Kiyoaki Ozaki, Jong-Gil Park, Fabien & Sophie Pékus, Charles Perez, Ian Phillips, Andy Pierce, Verity Picken, Andrew Pierce, Colin Poole/WCS, Vladimir Popenko, Doug Pratt, David Raju, Michael Rank, Pamela Rasmussen, Nigel Redman, Swen Renner, Frank Rheindt, Roger Riddington, Craig Robson, Stephen Rodwell, Steve Rooke, Norbert Roothaert, Frank Rozendaal, Adam Rowlands, Skip Russell, Roger Safford, Geoff Sample, George Sangster, Karl Schulze-Hagen, Mike Smart, Graham Speight, Ian Spence, Frank Steinheimer, Ernst Sutter, Lars Svensson, Rob Timmins/WCS, Colin Trainor, Janette Troop, Mick Turton, Philippe Verbelen, Reinhard Vohvinkel, Grahame Walbridge, Deepal Warakagoda, Ben Warren, David Wells, John Wilson, Sergey Yerochov, Elizabeth Yohannes and Victor Zhukov.

We are indebted to the many individuals who have helped us to locate some of the unique images that appear in this book. In particular, the assistance of Peter Leonard in sourcing images from Africa has been invaluable and greatly appreciated. Although we have not been able to include as many photographs as we would have wished, we are most grateful to all those photographers have generously offered their photographs. Many have loaned copies of photographs and slide transparencies, and allowed unrestricted access to much of their best work. These include AbdulRahman Al-Sirhan, Jason Anderson, Rafael Armada, Nick Athanas, Aurélien Audevard, David Bakewell, Ashley Banwell, Dave Beadle, Antti Below, Amir Ben Dov, Arnoud B. van den Berg/The Sound Approach, Zephne and Herman Bernitz, Leo Berzins, Jiri Bohdal, Nik Borrow, Ian Boustead, Colin Bradshaw, Mark Breaks, Michael Brooke, Robert Brookes, Gary Brown, Boedts Bruno, Sam Chan, Chang Pei-wei, Hugh Chittenden, Katerina Christenson, Marcie Connelly-Lynn, Wojciech Dabrowka, Devashish Deb, Jochen Dierschke, Adriaan Dijksen, James Eaton, Jacques Erard, Hanne & Jens Eriksen, Pekka Fagel, Fang Gu-yun, Augusto Faustino, Bob Flood, Sid and Meggie Francis, Steve Garvie, Peter Ginn, Sundev Gombobaatar, Chris Gooddie, Martin Goodey, Martin Hale, Martijn Hammers, Jens Søgaard Hansen, Hugh Harrop, Jens Hering, Uditha Hettige, Heyi, Akiko Hidaka, John & Jemi Holmes, Jon Hornbuckle, Iva Hristova-Nikolova, Robert Hutchinson, Askar Isabekov, Gary Jenkins, Ian Jones, Arto Juvonen, Neville Kemp, James Kennerley, Kazuyasu Kisaichi, Lior Kislev, Gareth Knass, Shinji Koyama, Ole Krogh, Darya Kuznetsova, Paul Leader, Vincent Legrand, Peter Leonard, Fred Leviez, Li Bin, Liao Pen-shing, Lin Ben Chu, Lin Wen-chong, Åke Lindström, Ferran Lopez, Jim Martin, Takeyoshi Matsuo, Mateusz Matysiak, Stefan McElwee, Pete Morris, Naqeeb Mostafawi/WCS, Steve Mulkeen, Tomi Muukonen, Jyrki Normaja, Rebecca Nason, Robert Newlin, Pekka Nikander, Paul Noakes, Hafizullah Noori/WCS, Daniele Occhiato, Atle Ivar Olsen, Urban Olsson, Stephane Ostrowski/WCS, Kiyoaki Ozaki, Pan Chih-yuan, Pei Wen, Fabien & Sophie Pékus, Jari Peltomäki, Andrew Perkin, Niall Perrins, Raj Kamal Phukan, Michael Pope, Richard Porter, Pascal Provost, AliMadad Rajabi/WCS, Nigel Redman, Johan van Rensberg, George Rezeter, Roger Riddington, Adam Riley, Julian Robinson, Craig Robson, Julian Robinson, Markus Römhild, Philip Round, Steve Round, Peter Ryan, Volker Salewski, Johnny Salomonsson, Viktor Salovarov, Ran Schols, Jonathoń Schrire, Roland Seitre, Sumit K. Sen, Deryk Shaw, Yoshimitsu Shigeta, Tadao Shimba, Arun P. Singh, David Showler, Per Smitterberg, Claire Spottiswoode, Ramki Sreenivasan, Richard Steel, Adoraim Stream, Rajneesh Suvarna, Norman Deans van Swelm, Harri Taavetti, Johannes Tallroth, Warwick Tarboton, Hideo Tani, Amit Thakurta, Ray Tipper, Gaku Tozuka, Peter Usher, Eric VanderWerf, Kevin Vang, Markus Varesvuo, Matthieu Vaslin, Brent Visser, Jaap van der Waarde, Pei Wen, Gehan de Silva Wijeyeratne, Malcolm Wilson, Michelle & Peter Wong, Kelvin Yam, Yang Xianwei, Yuan Xiao and Zhang Yong.

Many individuals have provided invaluable sound recordings. In particular we would like to thank Per Alström, David Bishop, Geoff Carey, Bram Demeulemeester, Dave Farrow, David Fisher, Martijn Hammers, Simon Harrap, Paul Holt, Magnus Jäderblad, Tohru Mano, Nial Moores/Birds Korea, Pete Morris, Craig Robson, Geoff Sample, Steve Smith, Rob Timmins/WCS, Colin Trainor, Dominique Verbelen, Philippe Verbelen and Deepal Warakagoda. In addition, we thank Richard Ranft at the Wildlife Section of the National Sound Archive, London, UK, and Les McPherson at the McPherson Natural History Unit for providing recordings of some of the least known species.

Individual ringers and ringing groups have generously shared their data, much of it previously unpublished. We have included much of this within the In Hand Characters section of the text, and within Appendix 2. Contributors include: Stephen Abbott, John Ash, Graeme Backhurst, Staffan Bensch, Fernando Gavilan, Andrei Gavrilov, Takeyoshi Matsuo, Oliver Nasirwa, Gerhard Nikolaus, Pascal Provost, Roger Riddington, and Stephanie Tyler; Stephen Rumsey and Philip Round/The Wetlands Trust; Norbert Roothaert/the Belgian Ringing Scheme, Royal Belgian Institute of Natural Sciences (Belgian Science Policy) (KBIN); Reinhard Vohwinkel and Werner Prunte/ Ackdenize University, Germany; Juan Carlos Fernández-Ordóñez, Angel Fernández, Antonio España and Valentí Costafreda/PARUS Ringing Group (Grup d'Anellament PARUS in Catalan), Barcelona, Spain; Alejandro Onrubia, Fundación Migres, Algeciras, Cádiz, Spain; Ignacio García Peiró, Departamento de Ecología & Hidrología, Facultad de Biología, Universidad de Murcia, Spain; Javier Blasco Zumeta, Institut 'Cavanilles' de Biodiversitat, Universitat de València, Spain; Pablo Vera Garcia, Jaime Gómez and Juan S. Monrós, and 'Grup d'anellament Pit-roig' and 'Grup Ornitològic l'Ullal', València, Spain; David Cuenca and the Grupo Ornitológico del Estrecho (GOES) (Strait of Gibraltar area, Spain); Ngulia Ringing Group, Kenya (NRG); Kiyoaki Ozaki and Yoshimitsu Shigeta, Bird Migration Research Center, Yamashina Institute for Ornithology, Abiko, Japan; Park Jong-Gil at the National Parks Migratory Birds Center, Seoul, South Korea; and David Melville, Paul Leader and the Hong Kong Ringing Group (HKRG).

We should like to thank Nigel Redman and Jim Martin at A&C Black for their help and encouragement, and Ernest Garcia for his expert copy-editing and valuable comments, which helped improve the text. We are particularly grateful to Julie Dando at Fluke Art who helped enormously with the design and layout of this book. She made numerous suggestions, which have greatly improved the overall presentation, and fielded our numerous requests for corrections and amendments throughout the final stages with great dedication and patience.

Finally, and most importantly, whilst researching and writing this book, PRK has received the unreserved love and support of his wife Susanna, and his sons James and William, for whom this book has occupied a significant part of their lives. As they have grown up, their young minds have questioned pre-conceived ideas and drawn attention to obvious oversights. They have resolved many problems with computers that 'don't work', and their understanding of the latest software developments have greatly assisted in the preparation of this book. Both have helped enormously with the preparation of sonograms and selection of photographs. In recent years, James has assisted with fieldwork, and has corrected numerous errors and contradictions in this text.

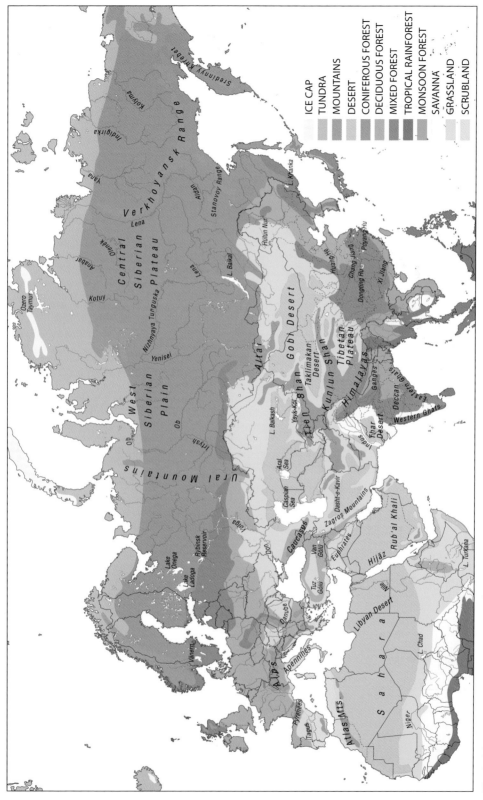

Physical features and main habitat types of Eurasia

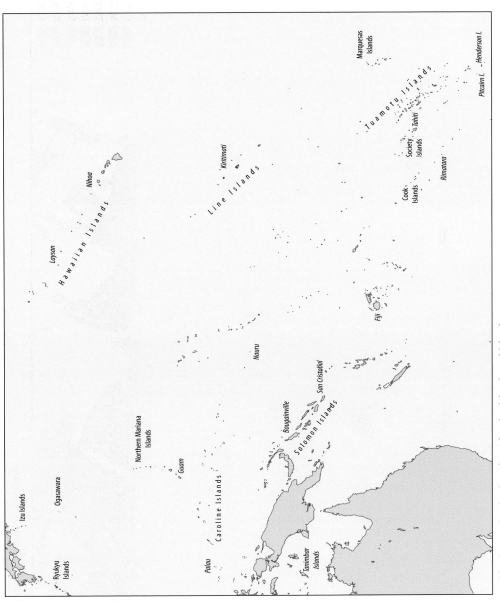

Pacific Ocean showing location of major islands and island groups

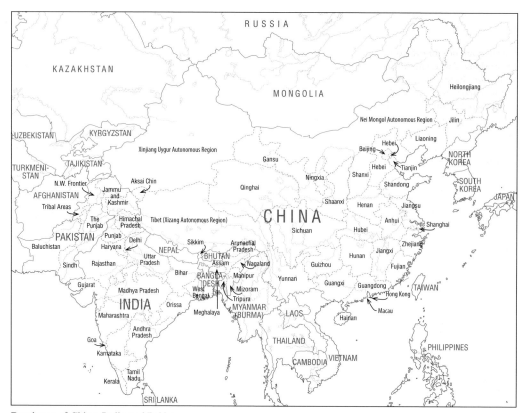

Provinces of China, India and Pakistan

INTRODUCTION

Warblers are not for everyone. These unobtrusive 'little brown jobs', often difficult to locate and observe, can easily be overlooked when more colourful and attractive bird groups beckon. But they offer some of the most demanding challenges in modern birding. With their varied and striking songs and remarkable migrations, representatives of the genera *Acrocephalus, Locustella* and *Hippolais* in particular have long occupied the interest and attention of professional ornithologists and birders alike.

First encounters with these birds can leave a lasting impression. Many will have early memories of chattering Sedge and Eurasian Reed Warbler song at a reedbed on a spring dawn. Others will fondly recall their first view of a Grasshopper Warbler, perhaps perched upon a Rosebay Willowherb, its reeling song rising and falling in volume as its head turns from side to side. Or perhaps reading this will evoke distant memories of your first Savi's Warbler sitting pot-bellied, hunch-backed on a *Phragmites* reed stem swaying gently in the wind. Many of the familiar migrant species can be rediscovered in Africa, in wintering situations and in interesting moult states. Here they are joined by exciting eastern races with unfamiliar plumage tones and measurements. Here too tropical lake edges hold new resident *Acrocephalus* species, while swamps and forested highlands provide an introduction to the *Chloropeta* (now *Iduna*) and African *Bradypterus* warblers.

The Asian *Bradypterus*, often first encountered on a winter visit to Thailand or during a spring visit to the Himalayas, are particularly challenging. Small, brown, usually silent and almost impossible to see, for many this is the time to seek easier quarry. But for those who persevere and clinch a prolonged view, the problems are just beginning. 'What was that?' is a typical reaction. Did it reveal the all-important undertail-covert pattern? Did you even remember to look for it? What of throat spotting and wing structure? Why are the diagnostic characters of a bird that hugs the ground found only on its underparts? More often than not, that first *Bradypterus* will remain unidentified. But the urge to encounter more of these mysterious birds may have been planted!

The study of these warblers, each with its distinctive song, in their breeding haunts can be particularly fascinating. And this can lead us to some of the most wonderful places on the planet; the savannas and mountain forests of east Africa, the unspoilt elfin woodlands in the mountains of Bhutan, the upper slopes of the windswept Tibetan Plateau, remote forests and lakes in Siberia, the vast marshes and deserts of Kazakhstan and sun-drenched islands in the central Pacific and Indian Oceans. Wherever remote places remain in the Old World, these birds are usually to be found.

Songs and calls tend to be immensely important for locating and identifying the reed and bush warblers. Also, by forming effective barriers to hybridisation, vocalisations play a key role in defining species limits. Vocal differences have become better understood as field techniques have improved. The use of sound recordings and playback responses has provided a powerful tool in the study of reed and bush warbler genera, and pointed to distinctions at the species level. In Africa, such studies by Robert Dowsett and his colleagues helped resolve taxonomic issues within the scrub-dwelling *Bradypterus* warblers, and emphasised the close relationship between the African and Eurasian members of the reed warbler complex. Since the 1980s, voice studies in Asia have thrown light on a number of species issues. They have indicated that the widespread *Bradypterus* of the highlands of Taiwan represented a previously undescribed species; that the Pallas's Grasshopper/Middendorff's Grasshopper/Styan's Grasshopper Warbler complex should be separated again as three species; that Manchurian Reed and Paddyfield Warblers should be recognised as distinct species; and that Oriental Reed Warbler should be separated from Great Reed Warbler. And it has only recently been appreciated that Russet Bush and Brown Bush Warblers can be easily separated by their songs.

What further discoveries await us within these complex and challenging groups? New *Acrocephalus* and *Hippolais* (now *Iduna*) taxa were described only recently from the Horn of Africa by John Ash and his colleagues, and in well-studied Hong Kong, Paul Leader continues to catch Styan's Grasshopper-like *Locustella* warblers that defy identification. Since 2006, Philip Round and his colleagues at the Wetland Trust have caught no fewer than three Large-billed Reed Warblers in Thailand. This discovery, of a species previously known from a single specimen collected in Himachal Pradesh, northern India, in 1865, astounded the birding community. How had it managed to elude detection for over 140 years? This renewed interest revealed several birds previously misidentified as Blyth's Reed Warbler in specimen collections, suggesting a Central Asian origin, and finally led to the discovery of the breeding grounds, in northeast Afghanistan and southeast Tajikistan, in 2009. Two species of *Cettia* new to science have been discovered since 1987, in the Lesser Sundas and in the Solomon Islands. In Indonesia, what appears to be Javan Bush Warbler was discovered on Bali in 1989 but may be sufficiently distinct to represent an undescribed taxon; Timor Stubtail was reported from Wetar in 1990 although we still await further details; and a new population of Russet-capped Tesia was found on Adonara, adjacent to Flores, as recently as 2000. Timor Bush Warbler had not been seen since it was found on Gunung Mutis in 1932, but was rediscovered in the mountains of Timor in December 2009 where it was found to be quite numerous. Even more surprising was the discovery of an unknown *Bradypterus* on neighbouring Alor in September 2009. Whether this represents another population of

Timor Bush Warbler or an undescribed species has yet to be established. And we occasionally receive photographs depicting birds that clearly should belong in this book, but which have eluded identification to date. How many more undiscovered species could be lurking on remote islands awaiting discovery and documentation?

Field study and observation can take us only so far in understanding relationships within and between genera. But molecular methods based on DNA comparison have recently led to some surprising discoveries and forced us to rethink the way we view these mysterious warblers. We are particularly indebted to our colleague Staffan Bensch, who accepted an invitation to bring these developments together in a summary that forms part of this Introduction.

DNA work on southeast Asian species in the laboratories of Per Alström, Urban Olsson and their colleagues has unravelled misunderstandings and has led to exciting discoveries that would not be apparent to field birders armed with modern digital cameras and sound recording equipment, or to taxonomists mulling over trays of museum specimens. For example, their investigation of Aberrant Bush and Sunda Bush Warblers suggests that two mainland taxa, *intricata* and *oblita*, which closely resemble and are usually classified with Aberrant Bush Warbler, may actually belong with Sunda Bush Warbler. On the face of it, this situation may appear incongruous; that taxa which appear so similar should not be each others' closest relatives. But their phylogenetic history appears to tell us otherwise.

Who would have thought that Grasshopper and Lanceolated Warblers are not closely related? Mitochondrial DNA comparison by Drovetski *et al.* (2004) indicated that they are seated in different clades, and Grasshopper is more closely related to Chinese Bush Warbler, and better placed within the genus *Bradypterus* as presently defined. The genera *Locustella* and *Bradypterus* are not monophyletic and their boundaries will need redefining

And what are we to make of the remarkable *Acrocephalus* warblers that colonised remote islands in the Pacific Ocean, often thousands of kilometres from the continental homelands of their near relatives? Where did they originate? Alice Cibois and her colleagues have recently uncovered some remarkable relationships. Most surprising are results from the Marquesas, a remote group of islands in the central Pacific, where eight very similar taxa within the distinctive Marquesan Warbler occupy nine islands, or so it has been generally accepted. However, Cibois *et al.* (2007) demonstrated that Marquesan Warbler is not a monophyletic species, but consists of two species which are not closely related and are seated in different clades (Fig. 10). But by occupying a very similar environment they have converged to a point where their appearance, morphology and behaviour suggest they are a single species. Morphological differences between the taxa within each clade are no greater than those between the two clades, and there is no character or combination of characters that could place any taxon within a particular clade. Although virtually identical in appearance, they must be regarded as different species! One clade apparently originated from the southwest and it also includes Tuamotu Warbler, and possibly Tahiti Warbler, while the other clade has its origins with Kiritimati Warbler and Australian Reed Warbler.

These are exciting times for those with a passion for birding into the unknown. The last 30 years have seen our understanding of the reed and bush warblers transformed, and we believe that many more discoveries await. The way is now open for a combination of field and laboratory techniques to revolutionise the taxonomy and systematics of these fascinating birds. By writing this book we hope that we can inspire others to take on these exciting challenges.

Peter Kennerley, David Pearson and Brian Small
August 2009

TAXONOMY, SPECIES INCLUSION
AND SEQUENCE

From the outset we have adopted a pragmatic approach to taxonomic issues. We have been flexible in deciding the scope of this book to ensure the inclusion of the most challenging genera within the Old World reed and bush warbler assemblage. It was recognised that to do so would require us to bring together genera which do not form a naturally cohesive grouping.

Relationships within the large unwieldy family Sylviidae were until recently poorly understood, and distinctions between genera were often superficial. Taxonomy, and decisions on the inclusion or omission of certain genera, soon became problematic. Nevertheless, the inclusion of *Acrocephalus*, *Hippolais*, *Bradypterus*, *Locustella* and *Cettia*, together with their near relatives, was fundamental to this project. Furthermore, we committed ourselves to include all species within the selected genera, and present them in a similar format with comparable detailed treatment. For some groups, such as the *Acrocephalus* endemic to the islands of the Pacific Ocean, this meant that species would be included even where no identification issues arose. Other genera of uncertain affinities that lay on the periphery of the reed and bush warbler assemblage were inevitably excluded. Among these were the primarily Asian genera *Chaetornis*, *Graminicola* and *Schoenicola*, as well as *Megalurus* and allied genera best represented within the Australasian and Wallacean regions.

Family, genus and species sequence within the Old World warblers Sylviidae were addressed by *Peters's Check-list of the Birds of the World* in Volume XI (1986), which included 265 species in 48 genera. Although unprecedented in its scope at the time, its taxonomic approach was quite conservative and differed little from that prevailing throughout much of the twentieth century.

During the initial stages of this book, we were aware of the revision of the *Howard and Moore Complete Checklist of the Birds of the World*, under the editorship of Edward Dickinson, which took into account many of the taxonomic developments of the late 1990s. It was decided to follow the taxonomy and species sequence that Dickinson (2003) adopted, although a few decisions at the species level were modified by our own experience. We have since made further changes in the light of recent publications, notably those based on molecular investigations. Some of these have affected our treatment not only of species level but of genera and families. The work of Charles Sibley and his associates in the 1980s produced a phylogenetic classification for higher avian taxa derived from DNA hybridisation distances. Their findings, published in *Phylogeny and Classification of Birds,* transformed many of the long assumed relationships based on morphological characters. This was hailed at the time as a radical breakthrough and was used as the basis for a companion volume *Distribution and Taxonomy of Birds of the World,* by Sibley & Monroe (1990), which addressed higher-level relationships and also presented a checklist of species-level taxa. Since the 1990s, new techniques for establishing and comparing the DNA sequences of mitochondrial and nuclear genes have further revolutionised taxonomic understanding. Long-established relationships between families, genera and species have been re-examined and many have been overturned. Dickinson (2003) used a family order recommended by Joel Cracraft and his colleagues, which reflected the molecular phylogenetic evidence of the time. More recent DNA findings, such as those of Hackett *et al.* (2008), have considerably modified the picture.

Despite the removal of such groups as the cisticolas, kinglets and white-eyes, the Sibley & Monroe checklist placed over 560 species together in a huge single family Sylviidae, which included the Old World warblers along with various other groups. Dickinson's Sylviidae was more restricted, comprising 265 species in 48 genera, ordered in a sequence not greatly different from the traditional one of Peters. It comprised four sub-families: Megalurinae, Acrocephalinae, Phylloscopinae and Sylviinae. Apart from Japanese Swamp Warbler, which was treated by Dickinson as *Megalurus pryeri* and included in Megalurinae, the species and genera dealt with in this book are all included within Dickinson's Acrocephalinae.

The superfamily Sylvioidea has recently undergone major restructuring. Alström *et al.* (2006) proposed ten families: Cisticolidae, Megaluridae, Acrocephalidae, Timaliidae, Phylloscopidae, Aegithalidae, Cettiidae, Hirundinidae, Pycnonotidae and Alaudidae. This has been further refined with the addition of Sylviidae, Pnoepygidae and Bernieridae, the family proposed for the newly recognised Malagasy warblers (e.g. Jönsson & Fjeldså 2006; Johansson *et al.* 2008; Gelang *et al.* 2009). Five of these families were formed wholly or in part from elements of the Sylviidae *sensu* Dickinson, and only three of these concern us here: Acrocephalidae, Locustellidae (here taking taxonomic priority over Megaluridae) and Cettiidae.

The family Acrocephalidae includes all the reed warblers and contains 54 species in six genera: *Acrocephalus*, *Hippolais*, *Iduna*, *Phragamaticola*, *Calamonastides* and *Nesillas*, all dealt with in this book. *Acrocephalus*, *Hippolais* and *Nesillas* are widely accepted traditional genera. The findings on relationships within *Acrocephalus* and *Hippolais* reported by Leisler *et al.* (1997) and Helbig & Seibold (1999) have, by and large, been adopted here. They recommended the use of *Iduna* as a sister genus to *Acrocephalus* for four former *Hippolais* species; Eastern Olivaceous Warbler, Western Olivaceous Warbler, Sykes's Warbler and Booted Warbler. Also that the distinctive Thick-billed

Warbler should be returned to the monotypic genus *Phragamaticola*, where it was traditionally placed. These views have been supported by the recent work of Fregin *et al.* (2009) who, in addition, recommended the return of Papyrus Yellow Warbler to *Calamonastides*. The two remaining former *Chloropeta* species were found within the *Iduna* clade, and Fregin *et al.* propose including them in this genus. Although their distinctive appearance and their African distribution set them apart from the Palearctic *Iduna* species we follow this recommendation. One species we have not dealt with is Streaked Scrub Warbler *Scotocerca inquieta*. This is usually classified near *Prinia*, within the Cisticolidae, but Barhoum & Burns (2002) considered that it might belong in Acrocephalidae. Fregin *et al.* did not include *Scotocerca* in their review, and its structure, vocalisation and habitat preference make it an uneasy fit within Acrocephalidae.

Also arising from the break up of Sylviidae is Locustellidae: the Locustellid Warblers, comprising 55 species within 12 genera, of which the 33 species in *Bradypterus*, *Elaphrornis* and *Locustella* are treated here in full. Of the omitted genera, *Megalurus* (7), *Cincloramphus* (2), *Eremiornis* (1), *Buettikoferella* (1) and *Megalurulus* (6) are primarily Australasian in their distribution, *Chaetornis* (1) and *Schoenicola* (2) occur in India and Africa, and *Amphilais* (1) and *Dromaeocercus* (2) are restricted to Madagascar (figures in parenthesis refer to the number of species in that genus).

Another new family to emerge from the break up of the Sylviidae was the Cettiidae: the Cettid Warblers, comprising 34 species in eight genera. This group has a primarily Asian distribution and includes the genera *Cettia*, *Urosphena*, *Tesia* and *Oligura*, all treated here in full. The genera *Erythrocercus* (3), *Abroscopus* (3), *Tickellia* (1) and *Phyllergates* (2) were also found to be seated within Cettiidae, an unexpected development of which we were unable to take account. However, unlike other Cettid species, these are brightly plumaged warblers with largely arboreal behaviour. They would not be confused with the less conspicuous members of this family and are not discussed further here.

The Malagasy warblers include Thamnornis Warbler *Thamnornis chloropetoides*, a species that bears a passing resemblance to some *Nesillas*. The former are now placed in the proposed family Bernieridae, with 11 species in eight genera, none of which are discussed further here.

Our sequences of genera and of species within genera do not necessarily follow the findings of molecular genetics, although the sequence indicated by Fregin *et al.* (2009) has been adopted as far as possible for the Acrocephalidae. There have been major recent advances in understanding of the phylogeny of the Locustellidae and the Cettiidae (Alström *et al.* in prep.), but we have been able to take only limited account of these. Generic arrangements within both these families will require major revision. Where possible, we have adopted a pragmatic approach to species sequence based on similarities of morphology and field appearance, and supported rather than led by the molecular data. For the most part, this has resulted in genetically related species being kept together. But as the final word on phylogenetic relationships has yet to be written, it is certain that there will be future rearrangements of species sequence. We hope that by grouping morphologically similar taxa together in the sequence we have adopted, we have achieved a compromise, retaining stability with traditional relationships while bringing together redefined sequences as revealed by molecular methods.

GENUS AND SPECIES ACCOUNTS

Each genus begins with a statement outlining the derivation of the generic name, taken from Jobling (2009); these being either Greek (Gr.) or Latin (L.) in origin. There then follows a brief review of the characters that define that genus, followed by the species accounts. Each of the 112 species treated here is discussed in detail, with particular emphasis on identification, separation of similar species and distribution. To provide a consistent basis for comparison, measurements used within the species accounts have been taken from adult museum specimens except where stated otherwise. As specimens are prone to shrinkage, it is likely that the range and mean values provided here will be slightly below those typically found in a series of live birds. We have also sourced live wing length measurements from ringers and ringing groups throughout Europe, Africa and Asia, and these are presented in Appendix 2.

An initial summary statement on each species is followed by a listing of its races in chronological order of their description, each with a summary of its breeding range. Directional terms are abbreviated here and elsewhere in the species accounts. N, E, SW and C are used, for example, for northern, eastern, southwest and central respectively. S Africa refers to southern Africa, and the country South Africa is always written in full.

Identification

The field identification of each species is discussed in detail and its structural and plumage characters and bare part colours are described. Figures for body length, wing length and tail/wing ratio are given. These are based on museum specimens. Body lengths are mainly taken from the literature but in some cases measured by ourselves. Ranges for wing length and tail/wing ratio encompass all races and both sexes unless otherwise stated. Wing length ranges given here are intended to provide a guide but will be exceeded in some cases in large samples of live wing measurements given in Appendix 2. Useful structural characters often visible in the field include head and body shape, relative bill length, undertail-covert length and position relative to the wing point and tail tip, exposed primary length relative to tertial length (primary projection), relative positions of the primaries, and primary emargination. With the advent of high-definition glass in field telescopes and modern digital photography, the resolution required to examine these characters accurately now exists, and establishing them has become almost routine for some field observers. But the observer's ability to perceive such characters with fleeting views of a quickly moving bird will frequently be the weakest link in the identification chain (e.g. Harrap *et al.* 2008).

Plumage details are given, with emphasis on features most useful in species recognition. Identification is straightforward in a well-marked species such as Aquatic Warbler. However, many reed and bush warblers are relatively nondescript and featureless, so that perception of subtle plumage tones assumes crucial importance. We have attempted to describe these tones as accurately as possible, albeit for a fresh bird in ideal viewing circumstances, i.e. in flat light and stationary. Tones change however with viewing conditions. A bird in sunlight will look very different from the same individual viewed in shade; a worn bird will lose subtle tones that may aid identification when fresh; and even the position and angle of the bird relative to the observer can influence perceived colour.

Bare part colours are described briefly. These are rarely diagnostic but, when used together with plumage and structural characters, minor differences between two similar species, e.g. the presence of dark sides to the tip of the lower mandible, may support identification. Bare part colours remain fairly stable in most species throughout the year. However, in some genera, particularly *Bradypterus*, bill and palate colour can darken considerably at the start of the breeding season, becoming entirely black in males of some species, e.g. Spotted Bush Warbler.

Similar species

Many of the warblers described are exceptionally difficult to identify in the field, particularly when silent. Nondescript and skulking species can often occur alongside one or more equally nondescript, skulking and highly similar confusion species. These separation problems are discussed, often in detail, and the key points of difference from each potential confusion species are reviewed.

Voice

Vocalisations provide the single most useful character for identifying many of the species in this book, and the human ear is the ideal tool to detect and differentiate between similar songs and calls. Many drab and nondescript species have a diagnostic song, and distinctive calls are often useful for separating similar species-pairs, e.g. Eurasian Reed and Blyth's Reed Warblers, particularly on migration when calling birds may occur in atypical habitats. The reeling songs of some *Locustella* species are unique. Similarly, the varied and distinctive songs of the Himalayan *Cettia* enable immediate identification, even when the bird remains hidden. In *Acrocephalus*, song has evolved to reach levels of complexity not found in other groups. To the human ear, this variety is detectable and diagnosable at the species level. Yet attempting to convey this sound as a written transliteration is rarely possible. We have attempted to provide a phonetic description of the song and call of each species where these are known. But individual interpretation of the combinations of letters needed to describe a song varies widely, making it unlikely that the correct sound can be visualised from a written transcription. These difficulties are compounded by the limitations of the English language, making interpretation highly subjective, and taking no account of possible better transcriptions using other languages. For this we apologise.

Where possible, we have attempted to identify distinctive features or trends within song structure, be they characteristic phrases, undulating rhythms or speeds of delivery. The frequency range over which the song is delivered is also given.

Sonograms (sound spectrograms) are now widely used to provide a visual (graphic) representation of songs and calls. Although a sonogram can never replace a sound recording, it does illustrate whether sounds are hard or slurred, inflected up or down or given as a flat monotone, and can also illustrate frequency (pitch), and the length of a sequence or note and intervening pauses. We have largely refrained from attempting to use unfamiliar terminology to describe sections of sound within a sonogram. We avoid the term 'phrase', and usually use 'song sequence' for a continuous burst of song such as might last from one or two to ten or more seconds.

For some songs, notably the mechanical reeling of some *Locustella* and *Bradypterus*, sonograms provide an excellent means of illustrating clearly defined differences (sonogram 1). For others, like the rapid and varied songs of many *Acrocephalus*, interpretation of a complex sonogram becomes much more difficult, and with overlap between species they may be of limited value in species recognition (sonogram 2). We have included a sonogram of the song for most species but we leave it to readers to place their own interpretation upon these. Sonograms were prepared using Raven Lite interactive sound analysis software, version 1.0, published by Cornell University, Laboratory of Ornithology, and are plotted showing frequency (kHz) against time (seconds).

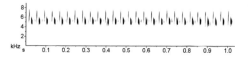

Sonogram 1: song of Grasshopper Warbler *Locustella naevia*. One second of song is illustrated, showing elements that form the characteristic reeling song. The number of elements/second within *Locustella* songs is diagnostic.

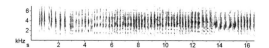

Sonogram 2: song of Eurasian Reed Warbler *Acrocephalus scirpaceus* over a 14-second period. The song is varied and complex, and resembles that of several other *Acrocephalus* species, making it difficult to isolate specific characters that can aid identification. Although the song spans the 1–8kHz frequency range, there is an underlying pattern within the song structure between 3–6kHz, visible as a distinct undulation lasting approximately four seconds.

Moult

Details of the timing of moults in adult and first-year birds are provided where known. Moult cycles are generally well understood for European species but little or no information is available for most African and Asian species, and for endemic island species. In resident species in tropical and temperate latitudes, there is usually a complete moult shortly after the breeding cycle is complete, and this may be followed by a body moult before breeding recommences. Migrant species employ a variety of moult strategies that allow them to make best use of food and habitat resources in the breeding and non-breeding areas. Some species have a complete moult prior to autumn migration, and others moult at a migration stopover area. Many moult after arrival on their wintering grounds, in some cases delaying until shortly before spring migration. Most species have a post-juvenile body moult shortly after fledging, but some migrate with juvenile body plumage retained. Juvenile wing and tail feathers are usually replaced in migrants at a staging or wintering area, often at the same time as in adults. A more detailed review of these strategies is given as a later section of this introduction.

Moult timing may provide a useful pointer to identification. Thus, European breeding Eurasian Reed Warblers have a complete moult shortly after reaching western Africa, so by the time they return to the breeding grounds their primaries are worn and usually lack pale tips. Marsh Warblers also moult in their wintering area, but about three months later, so that pale primary tips are still conspicuous on their return to the breeding grounds. Care is required, however, as different races may moult at different times. Continuing with Eurasian Reed Warbler as an example, some birds of the eastern race *fuscus* moult later in winter than European birds and retain pale primary tips into May. This feature cannot, therefore, be reliably used to separate Marsh and Eurasian Reed Warblers in Asia.

Habitat

Details of each species' preferred habitat are outlined but this usually provides only limited support to identification. Many resident species, particularly island endemics that encounter little or no competition, have adapted to occupy a variety of suitable habitats, although sometimes restricted by introduced vegetation or predators. Most migrant species also occupy a rather wide range of wetland and/or scrub habitat within their breeding and non-breeding ranges. Migrants on passage appear in a variety of situations; after long water crossings almost any coastal habitat becomes temporarily suitable.

Behaviour

Many of the species in this book are renowned for their skulking behaviour and unobtrusive habits, making them hard to locate and difficult to observe. Despite this, their behaviour can often provide important clues to identification. Particular traits may be so stereotyped that members of a closely similar species-group can be confidently identified when plumage and structural characters fail to provide an unequivocal answer. For example, the regular tail dipping of Eastern Olivaceous Warbler is not shown by the similar Western Olivaceous Warbler, or by Sykes's Warbler, and a plain, regularly tail-dipping *Iduna* is almost certainly going to be Eastern Olivaceous. Many of the points made here relate to behaviour that assists in identification but we also include comments on foraging, movement and flight, social behaviour, song behaviour and breeding displays. We briefly mention activities of migrants on their wintering grounds.

Breeding habits

A short summary is given where these are known. Detailed information comes mainly from Europe, South Africa and Australia. Breeding habits from elsewhere in Africa, and throughout Asia, are poorly understood and information is inadequate or non-existent for many species. For example, many Himalayan breeding *Cettia* and *Bradypterus* species are poorly known and the texts prepared by Stuart Baker and published in *The Fauna of British India, including Ceylon and Burma* in the early 1920s remain the most detailed and accurate available, and have not been superseded almost a century later. We include brief details of mating system and territoriality; nest site, structure and placement; clutch size, incubation and fledging; and breeding seasonality. By highlighting what is known and indicating further sources of information we hope to encourage the publication of more breeding observations. No matter how trivial these may appear they could be very significant in a little-known species.

Distribution and maps

Breeding and non-breeding or winter ranges are described in detail and given where possible for each race. For clarity, races are treated here in a geographical order, usually working from north and west to south and east, but there are some exceptions. However, races of migrants tend to overlap in the non-breeding season and their separate ranges can be difficult to define unless races are easily distinguishable. Maps attempt to show the distributions described. Some long-distance migrants occupy more than one non-breeding area in Africa during a protracted southward migration. In such cases the area described and mapped in detail is the southernmost of these, referred to as the wintering range. Published distributional information is sparse for much of tropical Africa, most of Asia and for many of the remote islands. For these we have relied mainly on historical texts, supplemented by recent national checklists and atlas work, by modern regional guides and by published visit reports. The last tend to be dismissed as unsubstantiated sight records, but often contain a wealth of data collected under similar circumstances to the sight records published, for example, in regional and national atlas projects. The vast majority of such sightings are likely to be accurate, particularly those by professional guides familiar with the species in a given region. Data included in tour reports published on the websites of Limosa http://www.limosaholidays.co.uk, Birdquest http://www.birdquest.co.uk and Sunbird http://www.sunbirdtours.co.uk have been widely consulted. Privately published trip reports that appear on a variety of websites on the internet including Surfbirds http://www.surfbirds.com and travellingbirder.com http://www.travellingbirder.com have provided additional supportive data. Museum specimen locations have been used, but these usually lack background information on abundance and frequency of occurrence, and can thus lead to inaccurate distribution assumptions that become established as fact.

For Europe and for Africa, maps are based largely on detail from the handbooks of Snow & Perrins (1998) and Urban *et al.* (1997) respectively. Information from several recently published national and regional atlas projects has also been useful, particularly those of Hagemeijer & Blair (1997) for Europe, Harrison *et al.* (1997) for southern Africa, Barrett *et al.* (2003) for Australia, Dowsett & Dowsett-Lemaire (2006) for Malawi, Dowsett *et al.* (2008) for Zambia and Ash & Atkins (2009) for Ethiopia. Where detailed data is lacking, as for much of central and eastern Asia, ranges shown are approximate and large, broadly shaded areas indicate regions within which we believe a species will occur in suitable habitat. Precise distribution has been difficult to map for species that breed within a narrow altitudinal range in the Himalayas and mountains of western China and then descend to winter at lower elevations. There is no data from outside the breeding season for some of these species and for many races. Furthermore, the accurate depiction of vertical distributions on a two-dimensional map is fraught with difficulty.

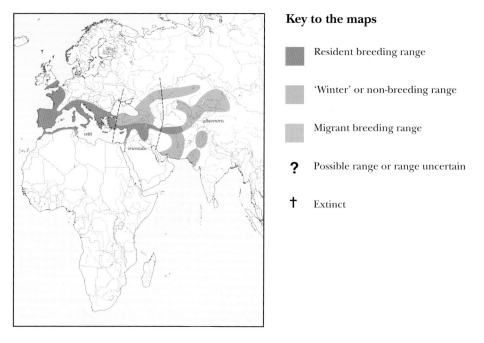

Key to the maps

Resident breeding range

'Winter' or non-breeding range

Migrant breeding range

? Possible range or range uncertain

† Extinct

Cetti's Warbler distribution, showing resident, migrant breeding and winter ranges.

Movements

For migrant species, we give departure and arrival dates for the breeding grounds and wintering grounds, and times and details of passage at intermediate sites. Seasonal terms are always used in a northern hemisphere context. Migration routes and strategies are discussed, and details of informative ringing movements are mentioned. Some Palearctic species interrupt autumn migration with a lengthy stay in the northern tropics before proceeding to final wintering grounds near or south of the equator. In Africa in particular, these stopover areas may be occupied for two to three months and thus constitute a first non-breeding area. Following tradition we reserve the terms 'wintering area' and 'wintering range' for the southernmost non-breeding area occupied prior to spring migration. Vagrancy is summarised, particularly that to western Europe, from where the most detailed information is available.

Description

A full description of the plumage and bare part colours of the adult is provided for each species. This has been based on freshly moulted specimens, augmented by examination of photographs. Where the sexes differ, the description of the adult male is followed by that of the adult female. Plumages of worn adult, first-winter and juvenile are then described in detail where these differ from the fresh adult. Bare part colours have been taken from photographs where available or from our own observations of trapped birds. Otherwise, details on museum specimen labels have been followed.

In polytypic species we have usually described the nominate race, but where the most widely occurring race is not the nominate, we have sometimes described this instead. In a few cases where the nominate and one of the other races differ significantly and in our view represent potential or probable separate species, as for example in Japanese Bush Warbler, descriptions of both races are given.

In hand characters

Examination in the hand provides valuable data that can be difficult or impossible to obtain from field observation. This section is primarily intended as a reference for those who handle and ring birds but it may also be useful to museum workers, to field observers who obtain exceptionally good views and also when examining high resolution photographs. It provides measurements, wing formulae and other structural details, and summarised information on weights. Where appropriate, discussion is included on separation from similar species in the hand and on ageing.

Measurements These are given in millimetres (mm) unless otherwise stated. The principal measurements of wing length, tail length, bill length (to skull unless otherwise stated) and tarsus are tabulated, for males and females separately where possible. They are presented in a standardised format that provides the range (limits), followed by mean value and sample size (n) in parenthesis. This is illustrated by the following example taken from Sedge Warbler.

	Male	Female
Wing	65–71 (67.2; 72)	62–67 (64.7; 37)
Tail	44–51 (47.3; 35)	44–48 (46.7; 14)
Bill	14.1–15.5 (14.8; 63)	13.8–15.4 (14.6; 36)
Tarsus	20.0–22.5 (21.4; 38)	20.1–21.7 (20.8; 23)

Values of tail/wing ratio (given throughout as a percentage) and measurements of bill width and hind claw are then also listed, usually for the sexes combined; also values for tail graduation, the difference in length between the tips of the outermost and the central feathers. In polytypic species, full tabulated measurements are given for the main (usually nominate) race and often for one or two other races. The principal measurements are then given for remaining races in an abbreviated format. Unless otherwise indicated, wing and tail measurements are those of adult birds. A statement is given where juvenile measurements are known to differ from those of adults.

Measurements presented here are almost all from museum specimens. Where insufficient samples were available in collections, data from live birds have occasionally been used and these cases are indicated. Most measurements were taken by DJP from material housed in the Natural History Museum (NHM), Tring, England, (sometimes referred to as BMNH), and supported by specimens on loan from other sources. Specimen data from some referenced published sources (e.g. Cramp 1992, Murphy & Mathews 1928) has been used to supplement our own data where necessary.

Museum measurements were taken as follows. Wing length was the maximum flattened chord (Svensson 1992, method 3), measured to the nearest millimetre with a stopped rule. Due to drying and stiffening, specimen measurements will average 1–2% less than those taken from live birds. Tail length was taken dorsally to the nearest millimetre using fine-tipped dividers, from the point of insertion of the central feathers to the tip of the longest feather. This gave results approximately 1% less than using a thin rule beneath the undertail-coverts as usually recommended for live birds (see e.g. Redfern & Clark 2001), but was found to be quicker and less intrusive with specimens. Our combined measurements should give tail/wing ratios very close to those obtained using standard methods on live birds. Bill length, to skull, was taken with dividers to the nearest 0.5mm. Tarsal length was also measured with dividers to 0.5mm, from the proximal end of the tibiotarsus to the distal edge of the last complete scale before the toes divide. Bill width was measured across the proximal edge of the nostril, estimating to the nearest 0.1mm, and has been found to give measurements about 5% less in specimens than in live birds. Hind claw was measured dorsally with fine-tipped dividers, also estimating to 0.1mm. Appendix 3 summarises our specimen data for each taxon, for each of the principal measurements.

In our species, most measurements from live birds do not distinguish between males and females. However, live measurements are of course those pertinent to ringers, and they are readily available for juvenile/first-winter birds as distinct from adults. We do not usually include them within our in-hand sections, but in Appendix 2 we have assembled wing length data from live birds from selected sources and locations. These are mainly from breeding birds, but data from wintering and passage sites are also included. In some species we give a range of samples to indicate geographical or seasonal variation. The majority of these measurements were supplied by co-workers and colleagues whose measurement of the maximum flattened chord agrees closely with our own. The few cases where measurements from Japan were obtained with the unflattened minimum chord method (Svensson 1992, method 1) are clearly stated.

Structure Wing formula details are tabulated for the main race, and sometimes for other races that show a marked difference. The key features of wing point, second primary length and emargination are then summarised. Details are based on our own measurements or on the authority given. The following example, based upon Sedge Warbler is explained:

p1/pc	p2	p3e	p4	p5	p6	p7	p10
(7)–(1)	0–2	wp	1–4	3.5–7	6.5–8.5	8.5–11	14–19

Figure 1. Wing structure of Sedge Warbler.

Primaries are numbered ascendantly, i.e. the short, outermost primary is p1, and the innermost primary adjacent to the outermost secondary is p10. Primary coverts are denoted by the letters 'pc', emarginated primaries by the letter 'e', and the longest primary that forms the wing point by the letters 'wp'. Where an emarginated primary appears in parenthesis, e.g. p4(e), this indicates that the emargination may be indistinct, restricted to the feather tip, or may not always be present.

The length of each primary is given in millimetres as a range. The range of p1 is given relative to the length of the longest primary covert (pc); where p1 falls short of the longest primary covert tip the difference is given in parenthesis, if it extends beyond the primary coverts then no parentheses are used. In this example (7)–(1) indicates that p1 is always shorter than the tip of the longest primary covert by between 7mm and 1mm. Ranges given for p2 to p10 represent the shortfall from the longest primary (wp). In this example p2 is shown as 0–2mm, meaning that in some birds it falls level with p3 and forms the wing point, while in others it is up to 2mm shorter than wp.

This table is followed by a brief summary of wing structure. In the case of Sedge Warbler, the following data is provided:

'Wing pointed; p1 minute, always < pc. Wing point (p2) p3; p2 = (p3) 3/4 or 4 (sometimes p4/5 in eastern birds); emargination on p3. Notch on inner web of p2 10–13mm from tip in adults, falling at about p8; 8–10mm from tip in juveniles'.

Figures in parenthesis refer to variable values. Thus '(p2) p3' is an abbreviation for: p2 can equal p3 (wp) but often does not.

As another example, in the case of Eurasian Reed Warbler we have: 'p2 = (p3) 3/4 or 4 (sometimes p4/5 in eastern birds)'. This is an abbreviation for: the position of p2 usually falls between the tips of p3 and p4 or level with p4, but may occasionally be as long as p3, or as short as p4/5 in eastern birds.

The size and shape of the tail, bill, feet and claws are outlined briefly, often with species comparisons. Any differences from the main race are mentioned.

Recognition Characters important to the identification are summarised, and comparison is made with measurement and wing formula details of similar species. Diagnostic features of plumage and feather detail and useful differences in bare part colour are emphasised. This section is usually omitted for those species where there are no congeners or potential confusion species.

Ageing For Palearctic species, criteria are given for separating adult from first-year birds during early autumn. Features useful for ageing during late autumn and winter are also provided where established.

Weight The term used to denote the body mass of the bird, measured in grams (g). Extensive weight details are available for many Palearctic migrants, but we have found little or no information for many tropical species. We give data for the great majority of species, taken from the literature, or from the unpublished records of ourselves and the colleagues and correspondents acknowledged. Where data is limited we give a weight range for one or more samples, with mean and sample size shown in parentheses. For well-studied migrants, we present a brief consolidated account including (i) a statement of overall weight range in healthy birds, (ii) typical lean weights (the approximate 90% range for birds with little or no visible subcutaneous fat - score 0–3 on the European Songbird Scale; Kaiser 1993), and (iii) some examples of weights in interesting migratory situations. Maximum and minimum weights are of interest as they show the potential for migratory fuel storage but mean weights can be greatly affected by the high values of a few very fat birds. Weights of lean birds give a more meaningful indication of body size.

Geographic variation

A general summary may be given for polytypic species. Comparison of each race is then made against the form described in detail within the **Description**. This comparison summarises plumage, bare part and structural differences with a view to allowing separation of races in the hand, but with the criteria given racial identification may sometimes be possible in the field. Differences between races can be subtle, and great care must be taken when applying criteria to individual birds or specimens, particularly in an extralimital context or where two or more races mingle outside the breeding season.

Taxonomy and systematics

For each species, an overview of taxonomic and, in some cases, nomenclatural changes that led to the present day treatment is presented, with the aim of explaining and justifying the position we have adopted. For some species, this may be limited to a brief review of taxonomic changes in a historical context that led to the treatment we use. For others, a brief review of the systematic position has been included, making reference to recently published molecular studies that have revealed new phylogenetic relationships. Where the taxonomy, nomenclature and systematics of a species has remained largely stable we use the term 'No issues arising'.

TOPOGRAPHY OF A BIRD, TERMINOLOGY AND GLOSSARY

The topographical terms used in the **Identification** and **Description** sections are illustrated in Figures 2–7.

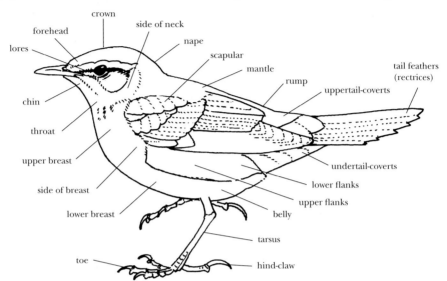

Figure 2. General topography of a typical warbler

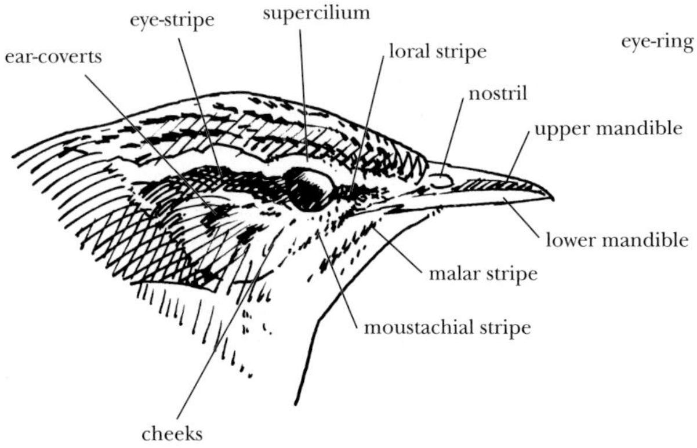

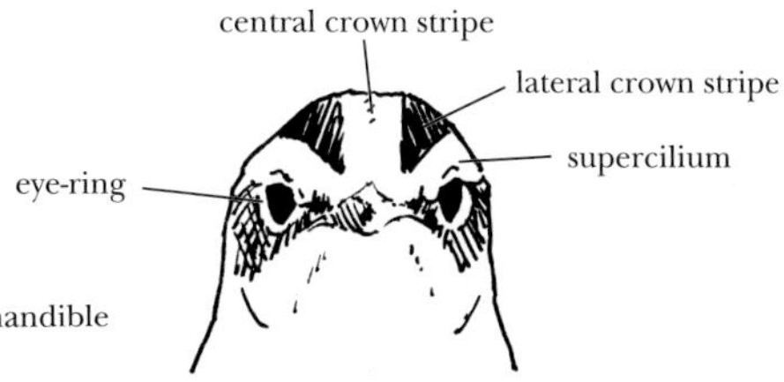

Figure 3. Head topography

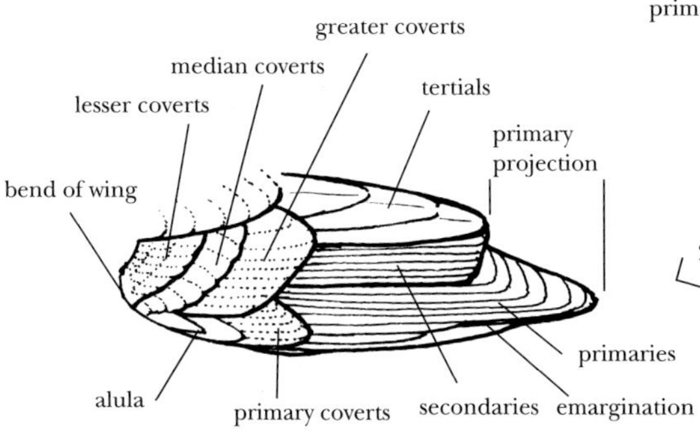

Figure 4. Wing topography

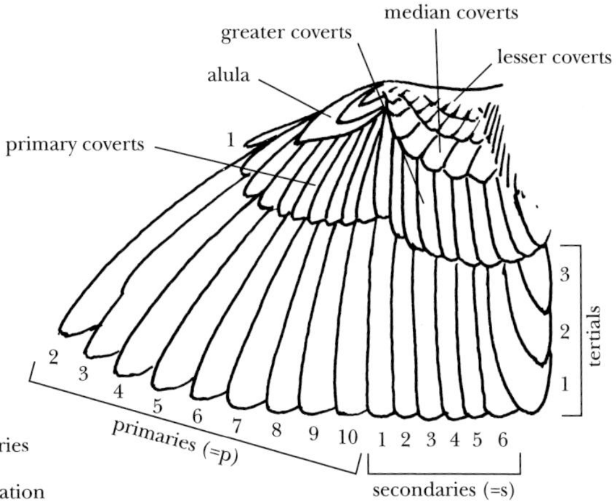

Figure 5. Spread wing (from above)

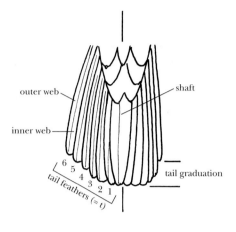

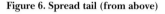

Figure 6. Spread tail (from above)

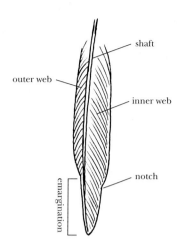

Figure 7. An outer primary (from above)

Glossary

Adult: as a plumage term used for birds which have undergone at least one complete moult

Allopatric: Taxa (usually similar) which occupy mutually exclusive geographical regions, at least during the breeding season.

Ascendantly: Primaries are numbered ascendantly, i.e. from the outermost inwards.

Clade: A monophyletic group in a cladogram.

Cline: A gradual change in one or more characters along a geographical gradient.

Congeneric: Belonging to the same genus.

Conspecific: Belonging to the same species.

Contour feathers: The predominant type of feather covering most of the body.

Convergence: Presence of similar features in non-related taxa, due (e.g.) to similar selection pressures.

Dimorphic: Having two morphs.

Endemic: A taxon that is restricted to an area, at least during the breeding season.

Extant: A species which still exists. The opposite of extinct.

First-winter: Plumage term applied here to birds which have replaced their juvenile body feathers, but retain juvenile wing feathers prior to their first complete moult.

First year: Age term applied to a bird in its first twelve months of life.

Holotype: A type specimen that was expressly designated at the outset by the author.

Juvenile: Term applied to birds in the plumage in which they leave the nest.

Lectotype: A type specimen that is designated in special circumstances to replace a holotype.

Lineage: A single line of ancestry and descent.

Mitochondrial DNA: DNA coding for mitochrondrial genes. Located outside the nucleus of a cell.

Monophyletic: Having a single evolutionary ancestor.

Monotypic genus: A genus with only one species.

Monotypic species: A species without any subspecies.

Morph: Any one of the forms of a polymorphic species, this usually refers to regularly occurring colour variants.

Morphology: External features such as size and shape of the bill, length and shape of wing, plumage, etc.

Mouth: The inside of the bill, often brightly coloured.

Nominate form: The taxon to which a given name applies, as defined by its type.

Nominate subspecies: Synonymous with *Nominate form*.

Nuclear DNA: The main DNA contained in the cell nucleus.

Parapatric: Taxa which have contiguous ranges without overlap or with only limited overlap.

Paraphyletic: From a single evolutionary ancestry, but not including all descendants of the common ancestor.

Phylogeny: The evolutionary history of a taxon.

Pneumatisation: In young birds the bones on the roof of the skull are initially opaque, but during the course of their first autumn they become filled with air. The term ossification has the same meaning.

Polymorphism: A taxon that is polymorphic has more than one morph.

Polytypic species: A species divided into two or more subspecies.

Post-juvenile moult: The moult in which the juvenile plumage is replaced.

Race: Synonymous with subspecies.

Rectrices: The large feathers of the tail; singular rectrix.

Remiges: The large feathers of the wing, includes the primaries, secondaries and tertials.

Sensu lato: 'In the broadest sense', e.g. *Acrocephalus mendanae* (*sensu lato*) refers to the Marquesan Warbler in its broadest sense to encompass all taxa formerly included in this species.

Sensu stricto: 'In the strictest sense', e.g. *Acrocephalus mendanae* (*sensu stricto*) refers to the species in its narrowest sense and encompasses only those taxa now included within Southern Marquesan Warbler.

Sexual dimorphism: The condition in which morphological differences exist between males and females.

Sister taxa: Two taxa that are each other's closest relatives.

Species: A group of interbreeding natural populations that are reproductively isolated from other such groups.

Species group: A group of particularly closely related species within the same genus.

Specific name: The binomial name appertaining to a species.

Subspecies: A population of a given species which differs morphologically from one or more other populations of the same species. The border between species and subspecies, and between one subspecies and another is often arbitrary.

Subspecific name: A name given to a subspecies. Subspecies are designated trinomially, the third term being identical to the second for the nominate race, but relating specifically to the taxon for all other races.

Superspecies: A monophyletic group of very closely related allopatric species

Sympatry: Two taxa are sympatric when they occur in the same geographical area (mainly used for breeding distributions).

Synonym: A different name proposed for the same species or subspecies.

Syntype: All specimens comprising the type series upon which a species or subspecies was described.

Systematics: Often used synonymously with taxonomy, but generally used in a slightly broader sense to include aspects of e.g. phylogeny.

Taxon: Any formally established scientific name, at any level in a taxonomic hierarchy, e.g. a species, subspecies or genus (in this book taxon usually refers to species or subspecies); plural taxa.

Taxonomy: The discipline dealing with classification and nomenclature.

Tongue spots: Spots present on the tongue, usually two or three, on young birds in the nest, and which gradually fade as the bird matures.

Type locality: The location where the type specimen was collected.

Type species: The nominal species that is the type of a genus or a subgenus.

Type specimen: The single specimen that is the type of a nominal species or subspecies.

MIGRATION

General overview

Our understanding of the migrations of the reed and bush warblers has benefited greatly from systematic ringing studies, mostly undertaken in Europe, but increasingly in recent decades in Africa and in southern and eastern Asia. Potential for the capture and monitoring of migrant populations has increased greatly since 1960 due to the development of mist-netting techniques. Warblers are night migrants and tend to be attracted to lights in misty or low overcast conditions. 'Falls' of birds at night at illuminated sites such as Ngulia Lodge in southeast Kenya, Dalton Pass in Luzon in the Philippines, and Fraser's Hill in peninsular Malaysia have added much to our knowledge of certain species and migration flyways. The use of taped song lures to attract and concentrate specific migrants has also proved effective, for example in studying the autumn movements of Aquatic Warbler through northwest Europe.

The reed and bush warblers of tropical Africa, southern Asia and the islands of the Indian and Pacific Oceans are mainly resident, but Palearctic breeders offer some of the most striking examples of passerine migratory behaviour. We consider species that typically travel *c.* 2,000km or more from breeding to wintering grounds as long-distance migrants, those that travel *c.* 500km to 1,500km as short-distance migrants. In addition, altitudinal migrants descend and disperse from breeding grounds in the higher mountains to avoid harsh seasonal conditions, typically moving no further than about 200km. Residents include some highly sedentary species that remain on territory throughout the year.

The great majority of our Palearctic breeders are long-distance migrants. Birds from the Western Palearctic and most from the Central Palearctic migrate to sub-Saharan Africa or India, while those breeding in the Eastern Palearctic (typically in Siberia east of the Yenisey River) migrate to southeast Asia. Most of these winter north of the equator, but in Africa several species migrate much further, and some, such as Marsh Warbler, winter largely in the southern tropics. In Asia, Pallas's Grasshopper Warbler and Oriental Reed Warbler migrate to the equator and Gray's Grasshopper Warbler reaches the Moluccas and New Guinea.

The *Locustella* species all breed in the Palearctic and, except for Japanese Swamp Warbler, they are entirely migratory. The *Hippolais* and Palearctic *Iduna* species are highly migratory, although Eastern Olivaceous Warbler has some less migratory African races. The African *Iduna* and *Calamonastides* yellow warblers are sedentary residents. The genus *Acrocephalus* contains 15 long-distance Palearctic migrants but also many tropical residents. Twelve species are sedentary on Pacific Ocean islands, two on western Indian Ocean islands and one on the Cape Verde Archipelago. A further three resident swamp warblers are restricted to mainland Africa and Madagascar. The Clamorous Reed Warbler, with migrant populations in central Asia, has a string of resident races extending from the Middle East and southern mainland Asia to Indonesia, the Philippines and east to the Solomon Islands. The Australian Reed Warbler and the African Reed Warbler include both resident and short-distance migrant populations. The *Nesillas* warblers of Madagascar and the Comoros are sedentary residents.

All ten African *Bradypterus* species are residents of swamp, bush or forest undergrowth, although Barratt's Warbler performs short seasonal movements in South Africa. The Asian *Bradypterus* include six resident species restricted to the cool montane forests and scrub uplands of the Philippines, Borneo, the Greater Sundas and the Wallacean faunal sub-region. A further four species are altitudinal migrants, breeding in the Himalayas and the mountains of western and southern China and descending to lower elevations with the onset of cooler weather. Another is endemic to the mountains of Taiwan, where birds descend in winter from higher elevations to join those resident lower down. However, two species, Baikal Bush Warbler and Chinese Bush Warbler, are strongly migratory. They breed mainly in southern Siberia and northeast China and winter from northeast India to Burma and northern Indochina.

The *Cettia* and related *Urosphena* and *Tesia* are mainly resident. Cetti's Warbler is largely resident or dispersive in Europe but the Asian races are short- to long-distance migrants, wintering from the Middle East to northwest India. A further ten species breed in the Himalayas and mountains of western and southern China and only perform relatively short altitudinal movements. Elsewhere in Asia, three species are migratory or partially migratory. Manchurian Bush Warbler breeds from southeast Russia and the Korea peninsula to central China and winters from southern China and Taiwan to Vietnam. Some Japanese Bush Warbler populations are resident but others migrate from Sakhalin, the southern Kuril islands and northern Japan south to the Ryukyu islands and Taiwan. Asian Stubtail is also a long distance migrant, breeding in the Russian Far East, northeastern China and Japan and wintering from southern China to Indochina and Burma. Finally, 11 species are sedentary in the montane forests and scrub uplands of the Philippines, Borneo, the Greater Sundas and the Wallacean sub-region, or on islands in the western Pacific.

Long-distance migration

Of our 37 long-distance migrant species, 14 winter in sub-Saharan Africa, 22 in southern and/or southeast Asia, and one, Grasshopper Warbler, in both Africa and India. The breakdown by genera is set out in Table 1.

Table 1. Wintering region of migratory genera, showing the number of long-distance migrant species occurring in each region.

Genus	Species wintering in:		
	Africa	south and/or southeast Asia	Africa and south Asia
Bradypterus		2	
Locustella	2	5	1
Acrocephalus	6	9	
Hippolais	4		
Iduna	2	2	
Phragamaticola		1	
Cettia		2	
Urosphena		1	

In Africa, species such as Eurasian Reed Warbler and Sedge Warbler winter widely from west to east, but others are more regionally confined. The westerly breeding Melodious and Western Olivaceous Warblers winter only in western Africa, and wintering Aquatic Warblers are known only from the wetlands of the west African Sahel. By contrast, the easterly breeding Eastern Olivaceous Warbler (race *elaeica*), Upcher's Warbler and Basra Reed Warbler winter only in eastern Africa. Marsh and River Warblers are also confined to eastern and southern Africa since populations converge from across their wide European and west Asian breeding ranges and migrate via Middle Eastern routes. Seven species migrate only as far as the northern or equatorial tropics: Savi's, Grasshopper, Aquatic, Melodious, Upcher's, Western Olivaceous and Eastern Olivaceous Warblers. Eight species, however, continue on to southern Africa (Table 2). Among these, Eurasian Reed, Sedge and Great Reed Warblers winter over a large latitudinal range, from 17°N in the Sahelian wetlands to 20°S. The other four species spend January to March almost entirely in southern Africa, reaching Botswana, Zimbabwe and northern South Africa; Olive-tree and Icterine Warblers in wooded country, Marsh and River Warblers in moister herbaceous habitat.

Table 2. Migratory species wintering within various latitude ranges in Africa. Species in parentheses indicate relatively small wintering numbers in those latitudes.

Northern (17°N to 5°N)	Equatorial (5°N to 8°S)	Southern (8°S to 20°S)
Savi's Warbler	(River Warbler)	River Warbler
Grasshopper Warbler	Sedge Warbler	Sedge Warbler
Sedge Warbler	(Marsh Warbler)	Marsh Warbler
Aquatic Warbler	Eurasian Reed Warbler	Eurasian Reed Warbler
Eurasian Reed Warbler	Basra Reed Warbler	Basra Reed Warbler
Great Reed Warbler	Great Reed Warbler	Great Reed Warbler
Melodious Warbler	(Icterine Warbler)	Icterine Warbler
Eastern Olivaceous Warbler	(Olive-tree Warbler)	Olive-tree Warbler
Western Olivaceous Warbler	Upcher's Warbler	
	Eastern Olivaceous Warbler	

Passerine migration routes to, from and within Africa have been clarified by recoveries of birds ringed in Europe and, since the 1960s, by observation and ringing at an increasing number of sites in Africa and the Middle East. Species such as Eurasian Reed, Sedge and Great Reed Warblers migrate to the Afrotropics on a broad front, western breeders to the west and eastern breeders to the east and south. But others use surprisingly narrow corridors. Marsh Warbler and River Warbler funnel south in autumn through Ethiopia, where they join eastern species such as Olive-tree Warbler and Basra Reed Warbler in a heavy movement into southern Africa, which is concentrated to the east of the Kenya highlands and Mount Kilimanjaro. Icterine Warbler reaches southern Africa via a route much further west. Some species adopt different routes in spring and autumn. Thus, Great Reed Warbler performs a loop migration to and from southern Africa, with heavy autumn passage through Sudan and a strong return passage through Kenya and Ethiopia. Marsh Warblers cross coastal Sudan and western Ethiopia in autumn, but appear to pass through eastern Ethiopia and more eastern parts of the Arabian peninsula in spring.

Our fourteen African wintering species are all 'early' autumn migrants, reaching the tropics mainly between late August and early October, with only Eurasian Reed and Great Reed Warblers still conspicuous in southwest Europe and the Middle East in October. However, birds that continue on to southern Africa tend to do so after a prolonged stopover in the northern tropics. The main passage through Uganda and Kenya takes place between late October and mid December, and species such as Marsh Warbler and Sedge Warbler reach southern latitudes mainly in December or early January. This two-stage migration from the Palaearctic thus takes three to four months to complete. It is clearly an adaptation to exploit rainfall patterns, birds benefiting from an abundant food supply in the northern tropics during September and October, two months before the rain belt reaches southern Africa. In southeast Kenya, the second stage of this migration has been studied since the 1970s at Tsavo, where thousands of birds attracted to the lights of the isolated Ngulia Safari Lodge have been trapped and ringed annually. This project has provided much of the African information on several of our reed and bush warbler species, notably Marsh Warbler, Basra Reed Warbler, River Warbler, Olive-tree Warbler and Upcher's Warbler.

The return from Africa to the Palearctic is relatively rapid, taking only a month to six weeks. Most birds wintering in western Africa and breeding in western Europe depart in March and early April. Those wintering in southern and eastern Africa, and bound for breeding areas in central Eurasia, leave between late March and late April. Passage continues strongly through northeast Africa and across Arabia until mid or late May.

Some of our species that breed in eastern Europe, western Siberia and central Asia migrate to India, presumably crossing the Hindu Kush mountains and western Himalayas. These include Blyth's Reed and Paddyfield Warblers, Booted and Sykes's Warblers, and the eastern races of Grasshopper Warbler, Moustached Warbler and Cetti's Warbler. Rather more of our migrants, another fourteen species, winter in southeast Asia. These include birds that breed from central Siberia to the maritime regions of Russia including Kamchatka, as well as Mongolia, China and Japan. Most winter in northern tropical latitudes on the mainland, but Lanceolated Warbler, Pallas's Grasshopper Warbler and Oriental Reed Warbler reach the equator in Indonesia. Three species, Streaked Reed Warbler, Middendorff's Grasshopper Warbler and Gray's Grasshopper Warbler only winter on islands to the east of continental Asia.

Most southward migration from central Asia into Pakistan and northwest India takes place in late August and early September. In a situation paralleling that in Africa, migrants destined further south spend some weeks here in lush conditions following the monsoon, and arrive in central and southern India and Sri Lanka from November onwards. Similarly, many migrants reach Thailand by September and early October, but arrivals in Indonesia are not until November. Passage through Japan and coastal China is protracted for some species, beginning in late August and continuing through October and November, and only tailing off towards mid December. Spring departures from India and southeast Asia tend to be very late, during April or early May, a response to the cold winters and low spring temperatures in eastern Siberia which restrict reed growth and leaf opening until early June. A rapid northward passage then brings birds to central Asia and to southern maritime eastern breeding grounds by mid May, but many migrants do not reach Hokkaido and Siberia until early June.

Migration within eastern Asia was studied during the 1960s by the Migratory Animals Pathological Survey (MAPS) project, initiated by the US Army. Over a million birds of more than 1,000 species were trapped and ringed at locations in east and southeast Asia. Some of the most interesting results came from Dalton Pass on Luzon, Philippines, where over 300 Streaked Reed Warblers trapped at lights provided much of what we know of migration in this species (McClure & Leelavit 1972). Otherwise, observer coverage away from regions such as Japan, Hong Kong and the Beidaihe area in China, and Fraser's Hill in Malaysia, has been poor, with few long-term studies in place. This situation is changing in the twenty-first century, with more countries now involved in migration work, but little is yet known of precise migratory routes. Studies at Fraser's Hill have established that, in comparison with other night migrants, *Acrocephalus* and *Locustella* species avoid the highlands, and are greatly outnumbered by birds using coastal routes to Sumatra. Controls of ringed Oriental Reed Warblers have shown that migrants pass through Hong Kong to breed in Japan, and a Black-browed Reed Warbler ringed in Hong Kong was also controlled in Honshu. By contrast, spring passage records indicate that Gray's Grasshopper and Middendorff's Grasshopper Warblers take a direct route north from the Philippines, the former avoiding southeast China and the latter largely bypassing the entire coastline of China en route to Japan and the Sea of Okhotsk.

MOULT STRATEGIES

Moult in residents and migrants

Adult passerines resident in temperate latitudes typically have a complete moult shortly after breeding, referred to as the post-breeding (or definitive pre-basic) moult. Another moult, termed pre-breeding or pre-alternate, may then occur a few months later, before the next breeding season. This involves the contour feathers and perhaps some wing-coverts, but not the flight feathers. Young birds usually moult their juvenile body feathers quickly in a partial post-juvenile (or first pre-basic) moult, but retain their wing and tail feathers throughout the first year of life. In a few species post-juvenile moult is complete, so that young birds and adults may have identical plumage a few weeks after the end of the breeding season.

This pattern may be less clear in tropical residents, especially when breeding is less strictly seasonal. A prolonged potential breeding season is often followed by a protracted complete moult. Some tropical passerines do, however, have a full post-breeding moult into a non-breeding plumage and then a partial moult into breeding body plumage. Juveniles of tropical species commonly moult their flight feathers within a few months of fledging, and a complete and early post-juvenile moult is more common than in temperate breeding species.

In migrants, active moult processes must be fitted into the annual cycle between periods of breeding and migration. Adults of short-distance Palearctic migrants moult fully between breeding and autumn migration. Those of long-distance migrants show a variety of strategies. Some have a rapid and complete adult moult before autumn migration. Others delay the main moult and replacement of flight feathers until they reach the tropics, and complete it on their wintering grounds or at a stopover area on the way south. This may take place between September and December or it may be further delayed until late winter and completed in March or April, shortly before spring migration. Adults which moult in their winter quarters usually replace some contour feathers on the breeding grounds. Those with an early winter moult may also replace their body plumage again during February and March. The categorisation of these winter moults as post-breeding or pre-breeding has little meaning. Thus, Eurasian Reed Warblers in western Africa have a complete moult between September and December, but many of those in Uganda have this moult between December and February, and Marsh Warblers in southern Africa moult between January and March. This appears to represent the same complete plumage transition, variously delayed to exploit optimum food resources.

In most migrant species, young birds replace their juvenile body feathers with a first-winter plumage before autumn migration. In long-distance migrants with a full winter adult moult, the young also have a full moult at much the same time, replacing their juvenile flight feathers and tail and any recently acquired first-winter body plumage. Thus young Eurasian Reed Warblers moult their juvenile body plumage on western European breeding grounds during July to September, then replace their entire plumage in western Africa from October to December. Young birds of some species, including Sedge and Aquatic Warblers and most of the migrant *Locustella* warblers, retain their juvenile body plumage until the complete moult on the wintering grounds. For these species, there is no first-winter plumage as such. They moult directly from juvenile to adult plumage. For migrants in which adults moult completely before autumn migration, the young may have a complete post-juvenile moult at the same time. Or they may moult only juvenile body feathers and retain their flight feathers and tail until a year old.

Moult timing in reed and bush warblers

The timing of moult in adult and first-year reed and bush warblers is summarised in Appendix 4. Information pertaining to resident tropical species is sparse but most moult, or are assumed to moult, shortly after breeding. Juveniles of most species quickly replace any distinctive body plumage. The young of the Asian *Cettia* appear to replace their juvenile wing and tail feathers in a complete moult shortly after fledging. By contrast, young Cetti's Warblers retain some or all of their first (juvenile) flight feathers for a whole year. Most short-distance migrants moult before migration. For example, adults and young of European breeding Moustached Warbler, Japanese Swamp Warbler, Japanese Bush Warbler and Blunt-winged Warbler moult fully on their breeding grounds. On the other hand, some populations of African Reed Warbler and Australian Reed Warbler, and Saharan breeding races of Eastern Olivaceous Warbler, moult after movement to a non-breeding area.

Our long-distance migrants adopt a variety of strategies for accommodating their main and partial moults. Most species within the genera *Acrocephalus, Hippolais, Iduna* and *Locustella* have a complete winter moult, but in some this takes place in a stopover area north of the final wintering destination. There are some interesting comparisons within these genera, and a clear association emerges between the timing of wing moult and the departure latitude of the spring migration. Migrant species are listed in Table 3 according to when and where the complete moult occurs: on the breeding grounds (July–August); soon after reaching the northern tropics (September–December); or in late winter (January–March).

Table 3. Timing of the main moult in migrant reed and bush warblers wintering in the Oriental (O) and Afrotropical (A) Regions. Appearance in more than one column indicates different timing in different races or populations. Parentheses indicate a less common strategy for the species concerned. Where the symbol ? appears, this indicates the timing of the main moult is uncertain. Note that adults of some *Locustella* species have a partial moult of the outer primaries before or during autumn migration but their main moult occurs in late winter.

Main moult occurs:		
Before autumn migration (July–August)	**In northern tropics (September–December)**	**Before spring migration (January–March)**
Savi's Warbler (A)	Chinese Bush Warbler (O)	Baikal Bush Warbler (O)
(Moustached Warbler, race *mimicus*) (O)	Savi's Warbler (A)	River Warbler (A)
Black-browed Reed Warbler (O)	Grasshopper Warbler (A & O)	Lanceolated Warbler (O)
Blunt-winged Warbler, race *concinens* (O)	Moustached Warbler, race *mimicus* (O)	Pallas's Grasshopper Warbler, all races (O)
Oriental Reed Warbler (O)	Sedge Warbler (A)	Middendorff's Grasshopper Warbler (O)
Thick-billed Warbler (O)	Aquatic Warbler (A)	Styan's Grasshopper Warbler (O)
Asian Stubtail (O)	Manchurian Reed Warbler (O)	Gray's Grasshopper Warbler (O)
Manchurian Bush Warbler, race *borealis* (O)	Paddyfield Warbler (O)	Sedge Warbler (A)
?Cetti's Warbler, race *albiventris* (O)	Blyth's Reed Warbler (O)	Streaked Reed Warbler (O)
	Large-billed Reed Warbler (O)	Marsh Warbler (A)
	Eurasian Reed Warbler (A)	Eurasian Reed Warbler, some race *fuscus* (A)
	Basra Reed Warbler (A)	Basra Reed Warbler (A)
	Great Reed Warbler (A)	Great Reed Warbler (A)
	Clamorous Reed Warbler, race *brunnescens* (O)	Icterine Warbler (A)
	Melodious Warbler (A)	Olive-tree Warbler (A)
	Upcher's Warbler (A)	(Upcher's Warbler) (A)
	Eastern Olivaceous Warbler, race *elaeica* (A)	(Eastern Olivaceous Warbler, race *elaeica*) (A)
	Western Olivaceous Warbler (A)	
	Sykes's Warbler (O)	
	Booted Warbler (O)	
	Cetti's Warbler, race *albiventris* (O)	

Most species that moult before autumn migration winter in the Oriental region, while those with an early winter moult are equally distributed between Afrotropical and Oriental wintering regions. Species with a late winter moult, with the exception of *Locustella*, mostly winter in Africa.

Within *Acrocephalus*, the six migrant species that winter in tropical Africa all moult after migration. Aquatic Warblers and most Sedge, Eurasian Reed, Great Reed and Basra Reed Warblers moult in the northern tropics soon after arrival. By contrast, Marsh Warblers, and the most southerly wintering Sedge, Eurasian Reed, Great Reed and Basra Reed Warblers, moult in southern latitudes shortly before spring migration. Three of the nine migrant *Acrocephalus* that winter in tropical Asia, Black-browed Reed, Blunt-winged and Oriental Reed Warblers, moult before migration. A further five moult shortly after arrival in the northern tropics; Moustached Warbler (race *mimicus*), Manchurian Reed, Paddyfield and Blyth's Reed Warblers and Clamorous Reed Warbler (race *brunnescens*). Only Streaked Reed Warbler delays moult until late winter. Oriental Reed Warbler and Black-browed Reed Warbler are both long-distance migrants that winter widely in southeast Asia from Thailand south to the equator, yet moult completely on their breeding grounds. The different strategy of these two species compared with their African wintering counterparts Great Reed Warbler and Sedge Warbler is not easily explained. Examples of the timing of moult and migration in three *Acrocephalus* species are illustrated in Fig. 8.

Figure 8. Comparison of the timing of complete (solid brown) and partial (dotted black) moults relative to periods of migration (solid grey) in adults of three *Acrocephalus* species: Oriental Reed Warbler, Great Reed Warbler and Marsh Warbler.

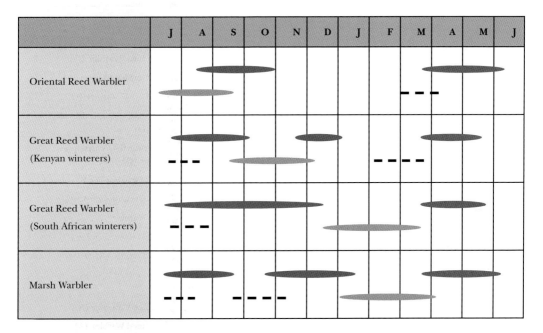

All *Hippolais* and migrant *Iduna* species moult in winter. Most begin when they reach the northern tropics, but Icterine Warbler and Olive-tree Warbler which migrate to southern Africa delay until late winter. Their strategy contrasts with that of the equatorial wintering and much earlier moulting Melodious and Upcher's Warblers.

Apart from the atypical Japanese Swamp Warbler and many European breeding Savi's Warblers, the *Locustella* species have a complete moult in winter. Most moult late, and the four species that winter south to the equator in southeast Asia are commonly still finishing in early April. In Africa, River Warbler which winters south of the equator moults much later than Savi's Warbler which winters in the northern tropics. Several of these *Locustella* species show an interesting moult variation. Adults renew their outer primaries in autumn, but then moult fully in late winter, so that these primaries are replaced twice each year. This supplementary partial primary moult may occur on the breeding grounds or (as in River Warbler) in September–October during a migration stopover. Two *Bradypterus* species, Baikal Bush Warbler and Chinese Bush Warbler, migrate from southern Siberia to winter in southeast Asia. The former has a strategy like the migrant *Locustellas* and moults in late winter; the latter probably moults in autumn, finishing after migration. Within the Cettiidae, the long-distance migrant Manchurian Bush Warbler and Asian Stubtail moult on their breeding grounds, but the migrant eastern race *albiventris* of Cetti's Warbler appears to moult after departure from E Kazakhstan.

In Africa, migrants clearly moult in conditions of plentiful food supply, most doing so in the northern tropics between September and November, or in the southern tropics between January and March. Within *Acrocephalus*, *Hippolais*, *Iduna* and *Locustella* it appears that species that begin a rapid spring migration from southern latitudes gain advantage by delaying moult and setting out with freshly renewed flight feathers. In Asia, few migrants reach the equator and none start spring migration from far south of it. The link between wintering latitude and moult timing is less clear-cut than in Africa. All five *Locustella* species that winter in southeast Asia have a late winter moult, as too apparently does the Baikal Bush Warbler. This could be associated with the lateness of their breeding season. Middendorff's Grasshopper and Lanceolated Warblers return to Hokkaido, their southernmost breeding area, only from the end of May; Pallas's Grasshopper Warbler reaches breeding areas near the Ob River only from the third week of June; and Lanceolated Warbler arrives at its western breeding limit in Finland in early July.

AGEING

First-year reed and bush warblers are usually separable from older birds during the first few months after hatching but are often not distinguishable thereafter. Plumage features, bare part colours and extent of skull ossification can all provide clues to the separation of birds up to a year old from older birds. There is often a distinctive juvenile body plumage, which usually lasts only a few weeks from fledging but is retained until the main winter moult in a few species. The juvenile wing and tail feathers can also show distinctive edges or tips, and these typically remain for a few months. After the breeding season, adults either have abraded plumage, quite distinct from the fresh-looking plumage of young birds, or they are in wing moult. Thus in Palearctic species, ageing is usually straightforward from June to August. But in some species, adults complete a full moult by September or October, and can then be difficult to distinguish from young birds. However, where the latter retain unmoulted juvenile primaries and tail feathers these tend to look less fresh and blackish than in moulted adults, and the tail feathers in particular may be narrower and show slightly frayed or notched tips (castellations) due to abrasion in the nest. In Himalayan species and in some eastern Palearctic migrants the young birds as well as the adults moult completely in early autumn, so that by September or October ageing based on plumage is no longer possible.

Many migrants moult shortly after arrival in the tropics, so that first year and adult birds are then in identical fresh adult plumage. Thus, fully moulted Booted Warblers in India in October and moulted Eurasian Reed Warblers in west Africa in November cannot be aged on plumage. Other migrants retain unmoulted wing and tail feathers to the end of the year, especially in eastern and southern Africa. By November–January, unmoulted first-year birds are becoming increasingly worn. Distinction of these from adults on plumage is then difficult unless some distinctive juvenile character is retained, or a partial adult moult has intervened. Thus, in southeast Asia, the retention of yellow-tinged juvenile body plumage identifies the young in some *Locustella* species up to mid winter. In Africa, adult River Warblers can be distinguished in late autumn by new blacker outer primaries grown during a partial moult in the Ethiopian stopover area. By April, first-year and older birds in all our migrants will have moulted, and will be in the same adult plumage, though the occasional retention of inner flight feathers would indicate a young bird, for example, in Savi's Warbler or Grasshopper Warbler.

The bare part colours of young birds often differ from those of adults, especially leg and iris colours. These differences may persist after distinctive plumage ageing features are lost. The dull dark brown or greyish brown iris of a young bird often develops a richer tint as the bird ages, which may be apparent before the bird is one year old. In some *Acrocephalus* species the iris becomes light brown or reddish brown in older birds. The dark juvenile colour tends to persist throughout the first winter in species such as Eurasian Reed Warbler and Great Reed Warbler, and may then be valuable as an ageing character. Leg colour also pales with age in many *Acrocephalus*. Thus, Eurasian Reed Warblers, Great Reed Warblers and most Marsh Warblers have dark, often greenish grey legs when young, but usually mid brown to pinkish brown legs from one year old. Again, this serves as a supporting ageing character in fully moulted late autumn or winter birds. Tongue spots, if present, can also be indicative of a first-year bird. These may be lost by August–September as in most Marsh Warblers, but usually persist until October–November. In some species however, particularly in *Locustella*, they can be retained in older birds and thus have little ageing value.

In passerines, skull pneumatisation (ossification) can provide an indication of age during the first few months of a bird's life. Birds with a partially pneumatised skull can be reliably determined as first-year. Those with a fully pneumatised double layered skull can be determined as adults during the period when no first-year bird has completed the process. The speed and pattern of this process vary from species to species (Jenni & Winkler 1994). It proceeds broadly from back to front, but leaves 'windows' of single layered skull roof during the later stages. In live birds, incomplete pneumatisation can be detected with practice by wetting and parting the mid line feathers, then with strong light moving the transparent scalp around gently, looking for a line of demarcation between pneumatised and unpneumatised areas (Baird 1963). In the migrant reed and bush warblers, skull examination can usually provide a reliable ageing guide up to about November, and most young *Acrocephalus* and *Locustella* can be determined to December or January.

PHYLOGENETIC RELATIONSHIPS AS REVEALED BY MOLECULAR ANALYSES

By
Professor Staffan Bensch,
Department of Ecology, Lund University, Sweden

Understanding the relationships between species, living and extinct, is a major task for biologists and has been so ever since Linnaeus. Research in this branch of the biological sciences, called systematics, has been guided since Darwin by evolutionary principles. Modern systematists have the goal of classifying organisms into groups that share a common origin. Such groups, which exclude all species more distantly related to the common ancestor, are termed monophyletic. Traditionally, deciphering phylogenetic relationships was based on characters that could be measured or scored directly on the organism, for example details of bones, external structures and shapes, but also details of embryonic development. This works well if the characters used are so called synapomorphies, derived from an ancestral form and shared only between the species that are related. There is, however, no *a priori* and objective way of knowing whether a character is a synapomorphy, unless the true phylogeny is known. More than 100 years ago, the major groups of birds were already classified into Palaeognathous (ostriches and alike) and neognathous (all other extant birds) based on structures of the bony palate (the inside of the beak). This grouping has largely survived the modern DNA-based analyses and demonstrates that old methods in many places were able to identify important events of diversification. However, a large number of phylogenetic relationships drawn from morphological data have proved erroneous. An excellent example of this is the group of Old World reed and bush warblers covered in this book. Morphologically, this is a largely homogenous group of dull-looking insectivorous birds, but nested within them are many species that were traditionally excluded because they did not resemble typical reed and bush warblers.

There are two main situations where character-based reconstructions of species relationships are likely to lead to wrong conclusions. Darwin explained how the evolution of species is shaped by natural selection acting on the heritable variation within species. Closely related species that evolve under different environmental conditions may therefore evolve to look very different. Divergent evolution will hence obscure the relationship between species and may lure researchers to put them on different branches of the phylogenetic tree. On the other hand, species with different evolutionary origins that live under similar conditions are exposed to similar selection pressures and may instead end up looking and behaving similarly. This process is called convergent evolution, and such adaptive similarities have frequently fooled systematists. For example, it has been shown that New World and Old World vultures, sharing the similar ecology of being flying carcass-eating specialists, are not a monophyletic group. Old World vultures share common ancestors with other diurnal birds of prey, except falcons that come from a different branch in the tree of life (Hackett *et al.* 2008). On the other hand, New World vultures although not related to storks as was suggested for some time (Sibley & Ahlquist 1990) form a sister group to other diurnal birds of prey (Seibold & Helbig 1995; Hackett *et al.* 2008).

In order to construct robust phylogenies, the trick is to use many characters that carry the phylogenetic signal, i.e. characters that are unlikely to change due to the act of adaptive evolution. Finding sufficient numbers of such synapomorphic characters, and avoiding the trap of divergent and convergent evolution, severely constrained the ability of pre-DNA scientists to resolve many phylogenetic issues. And discussions were often aggravated as suggested phylogenies differed depending on divergent opinions about which characters to trust.

History and methods of molecular phylogenetics

The introduction of molecular genetic tools from about the 1980s rejuvenated the field of systematics. A bird genome contains about 1.3 billion nucleotides (A, G, T and C). Closely related species may be 99% identical in their DNA, but because the genome is huge, a full knowledge of it would reveal 13 million characters that differed between them. This is orders of magnitude more than can be found using phenotypic traits. However, it is only very recently that even thinking of comparing whole genomes became possible and although whole genome sequencing is becoming progressively both quicker and cheaper, it will be years or decades before phylogenies based on all the characters in the genome will be applied broadly. In 1990, Charles Sibley and Jon Edward Ahlquist published a revised taxonomy of birds that took advantage of the massive information in the genomes (Sibley & Ahlquist 1990). In pair-wise tests, they measured the genetic similarity between species with so called DNA–DNA hybridisation experiments. The more similar the DNA, the higher the temperature required to dissociate hybrid DNA into single-stranded DNA and this was measured by temperature melting curves. This massive work revolutionised the taxonomy of birds and brought several systematic controversies into focus. The use of pair-wise DNA similarities in constructing phylogenies was criticised by cladists because it meant they were no longer based on characters but on crude measures of similarities, and resulted in so called phenetic trees. Moreover, DNA–DNA hybridisation experiments gave little help in resolving finer patterns of relationship, like those between genera within families, and between species within genera. Hence, the work of Sibley & Ahlquist did not contribute much to the understanding of phylogenetic relationships between the species included in this book.

Fortunately, there are ways of analysing the DNA of species that satisfy cladists and that can resolve the fine patterns of phylogenetic relationships. To do this, the same gene sequence needs to be compared, nucleotide by nucleotide, in the focal species group. But what gene to choose from of the 20 thousands or so in the genome? For a number of reasons, logical and incidental, the researchers of molecular systematics in birds focused on analyses of one gene in the mitochondrial genome, the cytochrome *b* gene. The mitochondrial DNA (mtDNA) molecule has many properties that make it suitable for phylogenetic analyses (Ballard & Whitlock 2004). It is a non-recombining molecule inherited by offspring from their mothers, with the result that the sequence will not be affected by hybridisation between taxa carrying different mitochondrial lineages. It has a slightly elevated rate of mutations compared to nuclear DNA which means that it evolves differences more rapidly and can therefore be used to resolve the relationships between closely related species. Certain regions of the mitochondrial genome are very stable in evolutionary terms due to functional constraints and it is therefore possible to design conserved primers for the PCR (Polymerase Chain Reaction) (Kocher *et al.* 1989) which make it possible to obtain the same sequences from the same gene from all the species one wants to study. The mitochondrial genome is, however, only a tiny fraction of the total genome, as little as 0.001% in birds. Of course, most of the genes that make species different are not in the mitochondria but it has nonetheless proved to be very useful for phylogenetic reconstructions of species. It is important to keep in mind that the different genes in the mitochondria are inherited together as one molecule. Hence, even if the whole mtDNA genome of 16,000bp is sequenced, it is essentially just one marker. Robust phylogenies therefore need to be supported by sequences from several nuclear genes.

Phylogenetic analyses based on DNA-sequences have several advantages compared to those based on morphological measurements or DNA similarity estimates. Scientific journals require that DNA sequence data used in publications are deposited in an open database for access by anyone who may then repeat the analysis or include the sequenced species in new analyses. GenBank http://www.ncbi.nlm.nih.gov/Genbank/index.html coordinates this information. With all these sequences in GenBank there is an enormous and steadily increasing amount of reference data for phylogenetic analyses.

Phylogenetic trees constructed from data, be it morphological characters or DNA sequences, are always only hypotheses about the true phylogeny. With limited data (short DNA sequences or few characters) and samples restricted to only some of the species in the group in focus, the generated phylogeny is unlikely to be an accurate reflection of the true one. The literature is swamped with incorrect phylogenetic trees. This is not to say that these studies have been useless or that the researchers have done a bad job. It simply reflects how science works and how knowledge is progressing. A researcher publishes a phylogenetic tree based on some sequence data. This hypothesis will be tested by further analyses of more genes, additional species and by other researchers. If the hypothesis is rejected it will be replaced by a new hypothesis and the process continues. The number of possible trees increases exponentially with the number of species included. With 20 species in an analysis the number of possible trees is more than 10^{21}! Evaluating all these possible alternative trees is an almost endless business and the chance is high that the tree chosen as the best one, by the researcher and by the computer program used, is in parts not identical to the true tree.

When constructing phylogenetic trees, the recognised branching events (nodes) can be evaluated by a statistical procedure known as bootstrapping. This is done by generating a large number of trees (say 1,000) by resampling from the data (the DNA sequences). The original tree is then compared with these resampled trees. In recent years, advanced statistical methods have been developed (parsimony, maximum likelihood or Bayesian inference) to evaluate the robustness of phylogenetic trees based on probability distributions but in essence the interpretations of the statistics are very similar. In the phylogenetic tree of Acrocephalidae (Fig. 10) the node connecting *I. rama* and *I. caligata* has a bootstrap support of 100%. This means that these two species, and only these species, were found to group together in all of the resampled trees. The node that includes the large unstreaked *Acrocephalus* species, has a support value of 71%. Hence, in 29% of the cases the resampled trees were in conflict with this hypothesis; either a species included in this clade fell out, or another from outside broke in. When bootstrap values are lower than 50% the data cannot say anything meaningful about the phylogenetic relationships. It is important to remember that the bootstrap values only show how robust the tree is given the data to hand and not whether it is the true phylogenetic tree. Sequences from other genes may result in different trees and such conflicting information requires data from even more genes until a robust consensus tree can be outlined.

Molecular phylogenies of reed and bush warblers

The species covered here belong to three families in the superfamily Sylvioidea: Acrocephalidae, Locustellidae and Cettiidae (Fig. 9).

Despite considerable efforts put into sequencing representative species of most of the genera supposed to be included within this superfamily, and combining information from the mtDNA cytochrome *b* gene and three nuclear

Figure 9. Abbreviated cladogram of the inferred phylogenetic relationships between the families and genera covered in this book (black print) based on published data (e.g. Alström *et al.* 2006; Jønsson & Fjeldså 2006; Johansson *et al.* 2008; Fregin *et al.* 2009; Gelang *et al.* 2009). The approximate phylogenetic position of untreated genera in the families Locustellidae and Cettiidae, and some of the closely related families within Sylvioidea are also given (grey print).

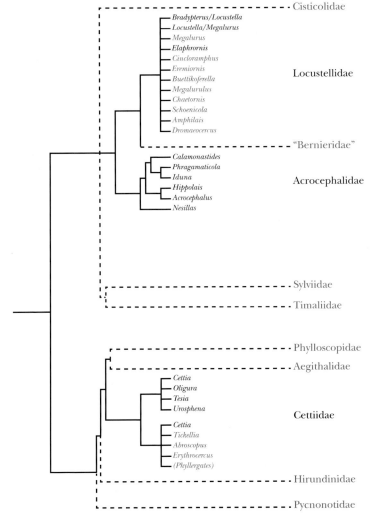

genes, the phylogenetic relationships between families, and genera within families is still far from resolved (Alström *et al.* 2006; Johansson *et al.* 2008). There is quite strong support for the two families Acrocephalidae and Locustellidae making up one clade, together with the Malagasy warblers Bernieridae (Beresford *et al.* 2005; Johansson *et al.* 2008). It is also clear that the bush warblers in the family Cettiidae are quite distantly related to the Acrocephalidae and Locustellidae and they seem to share a common ancestry with Aegithalidae and Phylloscopidae (Alström *et al.* 2006; Johansson *et al.* 2008). This is a beautiful example of how long term evolution can shape the appearance of species to hide their true phylogenetic relationships: few if any ornithologists would have guessed that Cetti's Warbler is more closely related to the Long-tailed Tit than to the Eurasian Reed Warbler! In addition to the three families of Sylvioidea covered here at least eight further families are not treated. How these are related to each other and to the reed and bush warblers will require sequencing of many more nuclear genes. It will be exciting to follow this phylogenetic detective work during the coming years as unexpected relationships are uncovered.

The first molecular phylogeny of species covered by this book was published in 1997 by Bernd Leisler and co-workers (Leisler *et al.* 1997). It was based on full-length cytochrome *b* sequences (1,068 bp) of 25 species of *Acrocephalus*, four *Hippolais* and some representatives of *Locustella* and *Cettia*. These first analyses already suggested that the reed warblers included multiple cases of convergent evolution and adaptive divergence. It is important to know that the problem of constructing phylogenetic trees is not solved by simply having access to DNA sequences. Selecting the statistical method to use is a scientific research field of its own and the choice of method can have a strong effect on the resulting phylogenetic tree. Published papers frequently present trees based on two or more methods. The most frequently used are Maximum Parsimony (MP), UPGMA, Neighbour Joining (NJ), Maximum Likelihood (ML) and Bayesian Inference (BI). To complicate the matter further, the more advanced and supposedly more accurate methods (ML and BI) can be run using numerous additional assumptions that will also influence the results. Adding to the confusion, it is not always clear which of the published trees, even within a single study, represents the best supported hypothesis. The study by Leisler *et al.* (1997) presented phylogenetic trees based on four methods of calculation and, although these differed to some degree, a couple of surprising results emerged. *Hippolais* appeared to be paraphyletic as two of the species (*caligata* and *pallida*) were nested within the genus *Acrocephalus*. Another surprise was the distinct placement of *A. griseldis* basal to all the large unstreaked *Acrocephalus*. That *A. griseldis* was not a subspecies of *A. arundinaceus* had already been proposed on morphological grounds (Pearson & Backhurst 1988), but that it was so distant from *arundinaceus* was truly unexpected.

Figure 10. Phylogenetic tree of the Acrocephalidae based on data from the cytochrome *b* gene and three nuclear genes. Bootstrap values larger than 50% (maximum likelihood) are given under the nodes. Redrawn from Fregin *et al.* (2009).

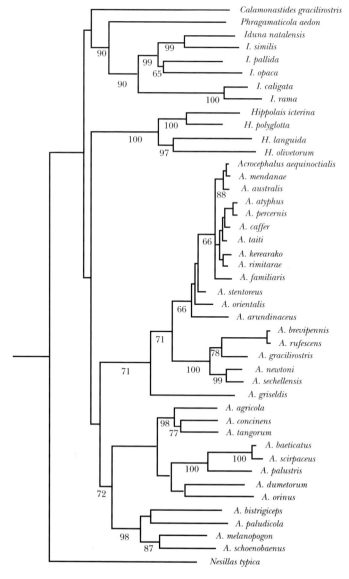

Andreas Helbig and Ingrid Seibold also analysed sequences from the cytochrome *b* gene including a few more species of *Acrocephalus* and *Hippolais* (Helbig & Seibold 1999) and basically supported the findings of Leisler *et al.* A major conclusion from these studies was that the cytochrome *b* gene did not contain enough variation to resolve the major clades within the *Acrocephalus*; the large unstreaked, the small unstreaked and the small streaked clades could not be placed relative to the position of Thick-billed Warbler, Papyrus Swamp Warbler and some of the *Hippolais* warblers. Ten years later, Silke Fregin and co-workers re-examined the phylogeny of this species-group, adding more species and also data from three nuclear genes in addition to cytochrome *b* (Fregin *et al.* 2009). These new results both supported and rejected phylogenetic hypotheses proposed by the previous cytochrome *b* data (Fig. 10).

The placement of *A. griseldis* basal to the large unstreaked *Acrocephalus* was now strongly supported, demonstrating that the initial cytochrome *b* analyses were correct and suggesting that its similarity to *arundinaceus* is either shaped by convergent evolution or maintenance of ancestral traits in the two species. In contrast to the cytochrome *b* results, the *pallida/caligata* clade within *Hippolais* did not now appear to be nested within the *Acrocephalus*. Instead, these species clustered together with *Chloropeta natalensis* and *C. similis* to form a well-supported clade, for which the authors proposed using the available genus *Iduna*. Thick-billed Warbler was placed basal to this clade and was, therefore, also proposed for inclusion in *Iduna*. An additional support for *Iduna* being a monophyletic clade was the presence of four so called 'indels' in the sequenced nuclear genes. Indels are insertions or deletions of several contiguous nucleotides in a gene sequence, and since such changes are supposed to be exceptionally rare, they should carry a reliable phylogenetic signal and be given a high weighting in phylogenetic analyses.

Apart from Thick-billed Warbler, the other 31 species of *Acrocephalus* included in the study by Fregin *et al.* all came out as one monophyletic cluster, and thus very much in line with the traditional pre-DNA taxonomy. The four genes in this study were, however, not sufficient to confidently resolve the branching pattern of the major clades within *Acrocephalus*. The best hypothesis suggests that the large unstreaked species split off first and that the small species then evolved into clades of unstreaked and streaked species. However, analyses of more nuclear genes is needed before this can be firmly established.

In contrast to the relationships within the family Acrocephalidae, which is relatively well resolved (Fregin *et al.* 2009) as shown in Fig. 10, this work is only just beginning for Locustellidae and Cettiidae. A study of the mitochondrial ND2 gene including several species of grass and bush warblers found that the genus *Locustella* was paraphyletic (Drovetski *et al.* 2004). Four of the species (*L. naevia*, *L. lanceolata*, *L fluviatilis* and *L. luscinioides*) clustered with two species of *Bradypterus* (*B. castaneus* and *B. tacsanowskius*). A further finding was that the other group of five species (*L. amnicola*, *L. fasciolata*, *L. certhiola*, *L. ochotensis* and *L. pleskei*) clustered with a species of *Megalurus*, Japanese Swamp Warbler, now recognised as being firmly seated within *Locustella*. More recent analyses using the cytochrome *b* gene together with three nuclear genes have confirmed that the African and Asian *Bradypterus* species make up two separate clades, each containing species from other genera of Locustellidae (Alström *et al.* in prep.). As with the first cytochrome *b* analyses of the *Acrocephalus*, analyses of more nuclear genes will be needed to resolve these relationships, and although it seems clear that neither *Bradypterus* or *Locustella* are monophyletic groups, it is too early for a taxonomic revision as other, not yet sequenced, members of the Locustellidae are involved. The phylogenetic relationships between species within the Cettiidae seem similarly complicated (Alström *et al.* 2006). Cetti's Warbler and three species of Himalayan *Cettia* appear to group with species in the genera *Urosphena* and *Tesia*, whereas Japanese Bush Warbler groups with species included within *Tickellia* and *Orthotomus*. Other eastern Asian *Cettia* as well as five species from the southwestern Pacific also appear to be included in the Japanese Bush Warbler group (Olsson *et al.* 2006; LeCroy & Barker 2006). Hence, we can expect an extensive taxonomic revision of Cettiidae as more sequence data becomes available.

Dating and the molecular clock

Another advantage of DNA-sequence-based phylogenetic analyses compared with analyses based on morphological measurements is that the DNA-distances can give us an indication of when species and clades evolved. This relies on the assumption that mutations in DNA are randomly distributed and not under selection. With time, species that once shared a common ancestor accumulate mutations in their DNA and become progressively more different. That mutations seemed to be accumulating at a rather constant rate over time was first suggested by analyses of proteins (amino acid sequences) in mammals, from which came the concept of a molecular clock (Kumar 2005). Although many later studies have shown that DNA does not always evolve in a clock-like fashion, there is compelling evidence that the mtDNA of mammals and birds contains sufficient clock qualities to be a useful tool in dating speciation events (Fleischer *et al.* 1998; Weir & Schluter 2008). On average, it appears that the mtDNA of two species, for example the cytochrome *b* gene, diverges at a rate of approximately 2% every million years.

The cytochrome *b* sequence distance between *A. arundinaceus* and *A. orientalis* is 5.86%, and assuming a clock that runs at 2% per million years, this suggests that these species shared a common ancestor just under 3 million years ago (5.86/2). But the clock measured as percent of sequence divergence is not linear, because with time, mutations may hit the same nucleotide multiple times. As an example, the sequence divergence in the cytochrome *b* genes between a Great Reed Warbler and a chicken is about 28%, and applying the flat 2% rule, it would correspond to a common ancestor around 14 million years ago. This is just not true as fossils and careful DNA analyses point to chickens and ducks (Galloanserae) having split off from all other modern bird orders (Neoaves) around 100 million years ago (Pereira & Baker 2006). A flat application of the 2% rule only works at relatively recent divergence times (approximately less than 5 million years). Estimating more ancient divergence times requires the use of sophisticated statistical models, known as stochastic lineage sorting, that can account for 'hidden' mutations in the data set. Estimating divergence times between young species and subspecies based on cytochrome *b* gene divergences is also complicated. Because mutations are infrequent and stochastic, the clock has more errors when only short periods have been measured. Also, the mitochondrial gene tree in recently diverged species may not truly reflect the species tree (Arbogast *et al.* 2002). At any time, most species contain multiple mitochondrial lineages, in birds typically showing a within-species divergence of up to one or a few percent (Johns & Avise 1998). Two recently derived species may have fixed different mitochondrial lineages that arose a long time back in their common ancestor, and that was shared between the two species for some time after the speciation event. To conclude, DNA distance is a valuable tool for dating speciation events although it must be interpreted with care. In songbirds that have left so little useful fossil evidence behind, it is often the only tool available for dating.

The radiation of passerines pre-dates the K–T boundary (65 Myr ago) by some 5–10 Myr. Around 60 Myr ago the oscines (true song birds) diverged from the suboscines (Ericson *et al.* 2006). The large number of oscine song birds (around 5,000 species) and their rapid diversification has made it difficult to resolve the phylogenetic branching patterns, and hence we cannot date these events until we have a better knowledge of their phylogeny. For these reasons there is no robust estimate of the divergence time for the families within Sylvioidea. Of the three families covered in this book, only part of the Acrocephalidae radiation has been dated (Price 2008). The oldest split within the *Acrocephalus*, that between the clades of the large and the small species, was estimated from cytochrome *b* sequence data to be around 12 Myr old. Based on sequence divergence within *Cettia*, and *Locustella/Bradypterus*, it seems that these radiations were also initiated around 10–15 Myr ago.

Using DNA to identify species

Broad analyses of mtDNA sequences of birds have demonstrated that taxa differing by 5% or more in the cytochrome *b* gene should be sufficiently differentiated to be considered as good species (Johns & Avise 1998), irrespective of the species concept used. Hence, mtDNA analyses have been helpful to define species where similar taxa are distributed in non-overlapping areas (allopatry). One of the first examples of a Palaearctic warbler where mtDNA analyses took the lead in splitting the species into two was Bonelli's Warbler, which became *Phylloscopus bonelli* and *P. orientalis* (cytochrome *b* divergence 7.9%) (Helbig *et al.* 1995). This has been followed by several examples among reed and bush warblers previously considered to be one species; e.g. *Iduna caligata* and *I. rama* (cytochrome *b* divergence 6.7%), *I. pallida* and *I. opaca* (cytochrome *b* divergence 9.6%). The Pacific *Acrocephalus* warblers as outlined elsewhere in the introduction are also a good example where mtDNA analyses have illuminated our understanding of species distributions. However, resolving their phylogenetic relationships will require more in-depth analyses using multiple nuclear genes.

Before the development of genetic methods, odd specimens in museum collections were a considerable headache to taxonomists of the time. In many cases it was impossible to assess whether these represented rare undescribed species, or non-typical specimens of known species or hybrids. One such problem was the single specimen of *Acrocephalus orinus* at the Natural History Museum, Tring, England, collected in the Himalayan foothills in 1867 by Alan Hume. Several hypotheses about its affinity had been proposed: that it was an unusually small specimen or subspecies of *A. stentoreus*, a hybrid between *A. stentoreus* and some other species, or simply a moulting *A. dumetorum*. After more than 100 years of debate, analysis of partial mitochondrial cytochrome *b* sequences demonstrated that the specimen carried a sequence that was sufficiently different from all known *Acrocephalus* to resurrect its species status (Bensch & Pearson 2002). The finding of a live bird in Thailand in 2006, and analyses of full length cytochrome *b* confirmed a sister relationship with *A. dumetorum* (Round *et al.* 2007), and this sparked an interest among ornithologists to check to what extent it might have been overlooked. Lars Svensson and co-workers searched through the major museum collections among birds labelled as *dumetorum* (Svensson *et al.* 2008). Based on the few characters that appeared to be diagnostic, they identified ten individuals as *orinus* candidates and confirmed their identity by mtDNA analyses. These efforts expanded our knowledge of the morphological characters of this species, as well as its geographic range.

Molecular taxonomy

The Barcode of Life Data System (BOLD; http://www.barcodinglife.org) is a web-based interactive database with the bold goal of building up a reference archive of DNA, morphological and distributional data from all organisms (Ratnasingham & Hebert 2007). The DNA fragment chosen as the reference sequence for the organisms within the animal kingdom is the mitochondrial cytochrome *c* oxidase I (COI) gene. At present it contains information from more than 3,000 species of birds. Because the gene of choice for molecular phylogenetics of birds has traditionally been the cytochrome *b* and not COI, the BOLD database so far contains entries for only some the reed and bush warblers (10 species of *Acrocephalus*, 4 *Hippolais*, 9 *Locustella*, 1 *Bradypterus* and 3 *Cettia*). As data accumulates, it will serve as an invaluable resource for DNA-based species identification, taxonomy and systematics.

ORIGINS, DISTRIBUTION AND EXTINCTION OF *ACROCEPHALUS* IN THE PACIFIC OCEAN

The islands of the Pacific Ocean are oceanic in nature, i.e. they have a volcanic or coralline origin and have never been situated on a continental shelf or attached by a land bridge to a continental landmass. Two basic types of island are recognised; high islands characterised by their mountainous interior, e.g. Mauna Kea on Big Island in the Hawaiian Islands rising to 4,205m, and coralline atolls characterised by the Tuamotu Islands, that typically reach just a few metres above sea level. Consequently, all Pacific islands received their present day flora and fauna entirely by chance, with the exception of those species introduced by humans, particularly to the Hawaiian Islands.

Land birds are poor colonisers of oceanic islands, with species diversity declining with distance from a large landmass. The avifauna of many Pacific islands is characteristically poor and many islands have few or no native land birds. *Acrocephalus* is unique among passerine genera in the extent to which it has spread throughout the Pacific Ocean to colonise, establish and maintain populations on remote atolls and high islands, some of which are extremely small. Only the white-eyes Zosteropidae and monarchs Monarchidae show a comparable number of species within the Pacific Ocean, although neither family occurs so extensively as *Acrocephalus*.

It is interesting to speculate why the spread of *Acrocephalus* has been so successful. What led to colonisation and how did present day distributions become established? The circumstances which pressured ancestral *Acrocephalus*, presumably from Asia, to venture across the Pacific in sufficient numbers to establish permanent populations will never be understood. Many must have failed to make landfall compared with the few which, by chance, came upon an island where conditions were suited to survival. And just how many individuals were required in a landfall to create a population that could flourish?

The initial colonisation(s) – and there is likely to have been more than one – could have occurred as part of an ancestral migration route that perhaps extended south to Australia during a period of severe glaciation, passing close to some of the islands in western Micronesia. Displacement by inclement weather, perhaps a one-off event, may have been responsible for populations becoming established here. But this fails to explain how or why *Acrocephalus* diversity in the Pacific is greater the further east one travels. An alternative hypothesis suggests that a shift in the earth's magnetic field might have affected birds' innate navigational abilities but this would presumably also have affected other groups migrating to and from eastern Asia.

Present day distributions are unlikely to reveal the islands where initial colonisations occurred and it is likely that many intervening islands have been occupied, possibly on more than one occasion, and that subsequent extinctions were frequent in prehistoric times. The present day distribution of *Acrocephalus* within the central and southern Pacific is difficult to understand due to a paucity of prehistoric data.

Is *Acrocephalus* a supertramp genus?

Diamond (1974) coined the term 'supertramp' to describe bird species which demonstrate an ability to colonise small and isolated islands with limited food resources. On many islands, supertramp species are generally the most numerous or, frequently, one of only a handful of land birds present, and they do not have to compete for resources. They are also characterised by their absence from larger islands and from those with a large and varied avifauna where competition is more intense. In other words, they are poorly adapted to competing for limited food and habitat resources. As in the case of the Marquesan Warblers, they may have colonised the same island or archipelago on more than one occasion. The supertramp definition can be applied to *Acrocephalus* species in the Pacific (and also to those species on islands in the Indian Ocean and on Cape Verde in the North Atlantic). Within the Pacific, *Acrocephalus* distribution is greatest along a corridor extending from Australia through southeast Polynesia to the Pitcairn Island Group. These warblers are absent from the larger, species-rich islands of Melanesia and Hawaii.

Present day distributions

The Micronesian region of the western Pacific, south of Japan and east of the Philippines, lies closest to mainland Asia where *Acrocephalus* diversity is particularly high. It is here that species diversity would be expected to be at its highest. Yet this region supports only two species: Nightingale Warbler in the Mariana Islands, and Caroline Islands Warbler in the Caroline Islands. Similarly, the Hawaiian Islands, the most northerly of the Pacific islands, are 'relatively' close to Asia. Yet they are home to just one *Acrocephalus* species, Millerbird, known from just two coralline islands within historical times and now extant only on Nihoa.

Species diversity is no higher in the central Pacific region, which holds just two species: Kiritimati Warbler from Kiribati and Nauru Warbler from the isolated island of Nauru. Elsewhere in the central Pacific and central Polynesia there is a complete absence of *Acrocephalus*, and most other land birds.

It comes as a surprise, therefore, that *Acrocephalus* diversity in southeast Polynesia, the region furthest from Asia and Australia, should be so varied, with eight species occurring: Cook Islands Warbler, Tahiti Warbler, Tuamotu

Warbler, Northern Marquesan and Southern Marquesan Warblers, Rimatara Warbler, Henderson Island Warbler and Pitcairn Island Warbler. Furthermore, these species occur over an extensive region, and populate numerous atolls and high islands. Even more surprising is that recent studies have shown that these species are not all closely related. They did not radiate from a single ancestor but arose as the result of colonisation of this region by ancestral *Acrocephalus* on more than one occasion. Table 4 summarises the distribution of *Acrocephalus* in the Pacific Ocean.

Table 4. Present day distribution and species diversity of *Acrocephalus* inhabiting island groups in the Pacific Ocean.

Hawaiian Islands	Micronesia	Central Pacific	Southeast Polynesia
Millerbird	Nightingale Warbler	Kiritimati Warbler	Cook Islands Warbler
	Caroline Islands Warbler	Nauru Warbler	Pitcairn Island Warbler
			Henderson Island Warbler
			Rimatara Warbler
			Southern Marquesan Warbler
			Northern Marquesan Warbler
			Tahiti Warbler
			Tuamotu Warbler

Phylogenetic relationships

To understand the origin of present day distributions, it is now possible to investigate phylogenetic relationships using molecular methods. It must be borne in mind, however, that oceanic islands are fragile ecosystems and many *Acrocephalus* populations will have become extinct in prehistoric times due to climate change or, perhaps, geological events, leaving gaps in the phylogenetic record.

To-date, few phylogenetic studies have been undertaken on Pacific island *Acrocephalus*, and the only published results come from Cibois *et al.* (2007) who investigated relationships within Marquesan Warbler. By sequencing the mitochondrial genes of this species and comparing with those of *Acrocephalus* populating the Tuamotu Islands, Tahiti and Rimatara, they established a preliminary phylogeny for these species. Their findings provided unexpected evidence for multiple colonisation events of the Marquesas Archipelago, one of the most remote island groups in the southern Pacific Ocean. Marquesan Warbler (*sensu lato*) occurs on nine islands in the archipelago, from where eight races are usually recognised, although morphological differences between them are slight. Cibois *et al.* showed that Marquesan Warbler is polyphyletic, its races falling within two independent lineages, or clades, which they treat as two distinct species: Northern Marquesan Warbler *Acrocephalus percernis*, and Southern Marquesan Warbler which remains *Acrocephalus mendanae*. They established that Northern Marquesan Warbler shares a common ancestry with Tuamotu Warbler, while Tahiti Warbler shares the same lineage but is more distantly related. A second grouping includes Southern Marquesan Warbler which is a sister taxon to Kiritimati Warbler from the central Pacific. In other words, in the Marquesas, the morphologically uniform Marquesan Warbler actually comprises two cryptic species representing two very different lineages.

Cibois *et al.* (2007) concluded that ancestral *Acrocephalus* colonised the Marquesas Archipelago on two occasions. Both events occurred more or less simultaneously approximately 600,000 years ago and probably coincided with one of the severe glacial periods of the mid Pleistocene when sea level in the Pacific was over 100m lower than at present. Lower sea levels would have led to more land area and increased vegetation, thus enhancing the chances of survival and expansion in pioneering *Acrocephalus* populations, with increased likelihood of movements to other islands. Birds from the Tuamotu and Kiribati atolls would appear to have reached the Marquesas at much the same time. When further results are available, it may be possible to correlate colonisations with climatic events elsewhere in the Pacific.

This study also indicated that Australian Reed Warbler is closely related to Henderson Island Warbler and may be derived from a Pacific island ancestor, rather than from continental Asia as has been widely believed. If correct, this may have implications for the origins of some other Asian *Acrocephalus*, in particular Clamorous Reed Warbler, which is already suspected to consist of two or more distinct species.

Extinctions

There are no means of knowing just how many *Acrocephalus* taxa have evolved within the Pacific region and have subsequently become extinct since the initial colonisation event(s) occurred. But islands being fragile environments, it seems likely that the number involved is significant. During the last two centuries, for example, spanning the short history of recorded human activity in the region, no fewer than seven Pacific island *Acrocephalus* taxa have become extinct. These include *A. luscinia yamashinae* from Pagan in the Marianas, *A. luscinia astrolabii* of uncertain origin but possibly from Yap in the Caroline Islands, and *A. familiaris familiaris* from Laysan, in the Hawaiian chain. Within the Society Islands *A. caffer longirostris* has been lost from Moorea, *A. caffer musae* from Raiatea and *A. caffer garretti* from Huahine. In addition, *A. atyphus flavidus* from Napuka in the Tuamotus is also believed to be extinct, although some may still survive.

The impact of human activity in the region must be seen against the background of natural phenomena which will have affected *Acrocephalus* populations over the last 500,000 years or so. Habitat destruction by drought, cyclones, volcanic activity and rising sea levels, as well as the arrival of predators and disease, will have brought about numerous extinctions. But the ability of *Acrocephalus* to behave as a supertramp genus has enabled it to survive such catastrophes and upheavals, and to diversify and expand to become a widespread genus in this hostile environment.

MAJOR CONTRIBUTORS AND SOURCES

Initials in the text refer to the following sources. **Individuals**: AA – A. Abuladze; JSA – John Ash; SB – Staffan Bensch; HB – Herbert Biebach; GJC – Geoff Carey; OF – Omar Fadil; AG – Andrei Gavrilov; JH – Jesper Hornskov; CI – Carol Inskipp; CK – Charles Kahindo; PRK – Peter Kennerley; PJL – Paul Leader; TM – Takeyoshi Matsuo; ON – Oliver Nasirwa; GN – Gerhard Nikolaus; DJP – David Pearson; PP – Pascal Provost; WP – Werner Prünte; PDR – Philip Round/Wetland Trust; SJRR – Stephen Rumsey; YS – Yoshimitsu Shigeta; RV – Reinhard Vohvinkel. **Organisations**: HKRG – Hong Kong Ringing Group; KBIN – Norbert Roothaert/Belgian Ringing Scheme; NHM – Natural History Museum, Tring; NRG – Ngulia Ringing Group; YIO – Yamashina Institute for Ornithology.

PLATE 1: AFRICAN *BRADYPTERUS* I

Little Rush Warbler *Bradypterus baboecala*

Map and text page 129

13–15cm; 14g. Smallest of the swamp-dwelling African *Bradypterus*. Widespread and locally common throughout C, E and S Africa where ten races are resident in wetlands and swamps. Typically skulking, but often attracts attention with its distinctive song, a long accelerating series of loud chirps, typically accompanied by wing-snapping.

a   **Adult *B. b. tongensis*** SE Kenya to lowland E South Africa. Upperparts more rufescent than in nominate form, underparts strongly washed tawny buff and with fainter throat streaking.

b   **Juvenile *B. b. tongensis*** Resembles adult but upperparts richer brown, underparts washed yellowish and dark streaks on throat sharper and narrower.

c   **Adult *B. b. elgonensis*** Highlands of Kenya. Darker, more rufous-brown above than *tongensis*, with darker tawny brown wash on breast, flanks and undertail-coverts, and more prominent streaks on the throat and upper breast.

d   **Adult *B. b. sudanensis*** S Sudan. Similar to *elgonensis* but smaller, with a less conspicuous supercilium and reduced contrast in the wing-covert fringes.

e   **Adult *B. b. msiri*** N and W Zambia to E Angola and NW Botswana. Upperparts dark brown, less rufescent than *tongensis*, but with conspicuous pale tips and fringes to the greater and median coverts. Whiter below than *tongensis* with throat streaks more distinct, and flanks and undertail-coverts darker brown.

f   **Adult *B. b. baboecala*** Resident S South Africa. Upperparts uniform, warm dark brown with well-marked buff supercilium, whitish underparts although with greyish buff breast and warmer and browner flanks. Shows gorget of faint dark brown streaks across lower throat. Marginally the largest race.

White-winged Swamp Warbler *Bradypterus carpalis*

Map and text page 135

16–17cm; 22g. Resident in dense papyrus swamps in C and E Africa. Bulkiest of the African *Bradypterus*, characterised by distinctive whitish band across the median covert tips, and creamy white patch at bend of wing. Upperparts nondescript dark brown apart from a well-marked whitish supercilium that extends behind eye. Whitish underparts show conspicuous blackish streaking, and white tips to undertail-coverts form prominent barring, particularly noticeable during the male's short song flight. Males slightly larger than females and show more extensive white wing-patches.

g   **Adult** Extent of white suggests this is a male.

h   **Juvenile** Resembles adult but overall appears more dusky brown on the upperparts, flanks and belly, less boldly streaked on the breast, and shows a smaller white patch on the wing-coverts.

Grauer's Swamp Warbler *Bradypterus graueri*

Map and text page 138

c. 17cm; 17g. A large, long-tailed *Bradypterus* with a small fragmented range in C Africa, where it is resident in highland swamps. Shows uniform dark olive-brown upperparts and a prominent pale supercilium. Underparts whitish, washed warm, rich brown from upper flanks to undertail-coverts. Both sexes show small, round blackish spots on the chin and upper throat, appearing larger and more prominent on lower throat and breast in male than female. Often sings from top of a reed stem.

i   **Adult**

Dja River Warbler *Bradypterus grandis*

Map and text page 140

c. 18 cm; 18.5g. A large, long-tailed *Bradypterus*, resident in sedge swamps in S Cameroon, Gabon and W Central African Republic. Shows uniform dark olive-brown upperparts and a faint greyish supercilium, most conspicuous above the lores. Chin and throat whitish with short, dark streaks which become longer and more conspicuous on the buffy brown upper breast.

j   **Adult**

PLATE 2: AFRICAN *BRADYPTERUS* II

Bamboo Warbler *Bradypterus alfredi*   Map and text page 142

14cm; 17.5g. This medium-sized, relatively short tailed *Bradypterus* is a poorly known and highly localised resident in bamboo, grassy cover and forest undergrowth in C Africa. The nominate race (not illustrated) has a warm cinnamon tinge to dark olive-brown upperparts and a short inconspicuous greyish supercilium. Below, the whitish throat merges with the greyish breast and flanks, and the greyish brown undertail-coverts show distinctive whitish tips. The simple repetitive song is quite different to that of other African *Bradypterus*.

a   **Adult *B. a. kungwensis*** W Tanzania and NW Zambia. Dark olive-brown above, colder than nominate race, and darker olive-grey below.

b   **Juvenile *B. a. kungwensis*** Resembles adult but underparts washed yellow.

Barratt's Warbler *Bradypterus barratti*   Map and text page 144

15–16cm, 19g. A slim, medium-sized *Bradypterus* resident in bush and scrub in eastern parts of S Africa. Drab and nondescript, with dark brown upperparts and a poorly marked greyish supercilium, but rump and uppertail-coverts are more warmly tinged than mantle, and upperwing-coverts and flight feathers edged rich olive-brown. Underparts pale greyish with soft dusky throat streaks, and with broad brown breast-band, brownish flanks and undertail-coverts.

c   **Adult *B. b. barratti*** NE South Africa. Chin and belly whitish, but throat and upper breast distinctly grey-brown and marked with diffuse gorget of short dusky streaks.

d   **Adult *B. b. godfreyi*** Lowland SE South Africa. Resembles nominate form but slightly darker above, and throat and breast are distinctly darker and greyer, with streaking less distinct and restricted to throat.

e   **Juvenile *B. b. godfreyi*** Slightly more olive above than adult. Supercilium and underparts washed yellow.

f   **Adult *B. b. priesti*** E Zimbabwe. As nominate race but throat and belly centre much whiter.

Knysna Warbler *Bradypterus sylvaticus*   Map and text page 147

c. 14 cm; 21g. This small, largely featureless *Bradypterus* inhabits gloomy undergrowth in coastal forests of South Africa, where it is a scarce resident with a small and fragmented range. Upperparts warm, dark brown to olive-brown, with poorly defined supercilium that reaches just behind eye. Dull greyish brown below with paler throat and belly, usually with some faint streaking or mottling on throat, and dark brown undertail-coverts with slightly paler greyish tips. The race *B. s. pondoensis* (not illustrated) is slightly darker than nominate race, less warmly tinged on the upperparts and wings, and breast and flanks are darker, with mottling confined to throat.

g   **Adult *B. s. sylvaticus*** South Africa from Western Cape Province to SW Eastern Cape Province. Typical adult.

h   **Juvenile** Resembles adult but face and underparts washed strongly with yellow, and throat streaking more pronounced.

46

PLATE 3: AFRICAN *BRADYPTERUS* III

Cinnamon Bracken Warbler *Bradypterus cinnamomeus*

Map and text page 149

14–15cm; 17.5g. A medium-sized *Bradypterus* occurring widely throughout the highlands of E Africa in moist bush and forest edge undergrowth. Often attracts attention with its loud, ringing song.

a **Adult *B. c. cinnamomeus*** Ethiopia to E DR Congo and Malawi. Richly coloured and shows a prominent pale buff supercilium and dark eye-stripe. Upperparts warm brown, becoming brighter cinnamon-brown on uppertail-coverts. The bright cinnamon-brown breast-band, flanks and undertail-coverts contrast with the whitish chin, throat and belly.

b **Juvenile *B. c. cinnamomeus*** Differs from adult by browner, less warmly coloured upperparts, tail and wings. Underparts show distinctive yellow tinge, and lacks distinct breast-band but can show diffuse brownish throat streaks.

c **Adult *B. c. mildbreadi*** Rwenzori Mountains. Closely resembles nominate race, but upperparts are slightly richer rufous-brown, tail darker rufous, and bright cinnamon-brown wash on flanks and breast richer and more extensive.

d **Adult *B. c. nyassae*** E and SE Africa. This distinctive southern race appears duller and lacks warmer tones of nominate *cinnamomeus*. Upperparts uniform dull brown, while underparts are washed tawny brown or tawny buff (rather than cinnamon-brown), this being more extensive and reaching onto belly.

Bangwa Forest Warbler *Bradypterus bangwaensis*

Map and text page 152

14–15cm; 21g. A secretive, medium-sized *Bradypterus* similar to Cinnamon Bracken Warbler, resident in montane thickets and undergrowth in SE Nigeria and W Cameroon. Shows plain dark rufous-brown upperparts and a narrow and inconspicuous warm buff supercilium. Sides of head and neck, breast, flanks and undertail-coverts are rich cinnamon-brown, contrasting with pale cinnamon washed throat and whitish lower breast and belly.

e **Adult**

f **Juvenile** Upperparts paler and browner, less rufous than adult. Underparts tinged yellow, with breast-band and flanks dull olive-brown. Usually shows some indistinct, diffuse dark brown streaks on upper breast and side of neck.

Evergreen Forest Warbler *Bradypterus lopezi*

Map and text page 154

13–15cm; 18g. A medium-sized, highly variable *Bradypterus*, resident in montane forest in tropical Africa, where eight races occur, treated here within two distinct groupings; the *lopezi* group (comprising *lopezi*, *manengubae*, *camerunensis* and *barakae*) in W and C Africa, and the *mariae* group (including *mariae*, *usambarae*, *granti*, *ufipae* and *boultoni*) in E and S central Africa. Structure similar to Cinnamon Bracken Warbler although tail is proportionately shorter and narrower in most races.

lopezi group

g **Adult *B. l. lopezi*** Restricted to Bioko. Upperparts uniform warm, dark brown with narrow cinnamon-buff supercilium. Chin, throat, centre of lower breast and belly cinnamon-buff, contrasting with the rich, warm brown breast, flanks and undertail-coverts.

h **Juvenile *B. l. lopezi*** Upperparts dull olive-brown. Supercilium, chin to throat and centre of lower breast and belly washed olive-yellow, with indistinct dull olive-brown streaking on upper breast and side of throat. Side of breast, flanks and undertail-coverts olive-brown.

i **Adult *B. l. manengubae*** Confined to Mount Manenguba, Cameroon. The darkest race. Upperparts rich, dark brown with faint russet tinge, slightly darker above than *camerunensis* and much more intensely coloured below. Underparts deep tawny brown, darkest on flanks and undertail-coverts, rather paler on throat and belly centre.

Continued on Plate 4

Evergreen Forest Warbler *Bradypterus lopezi* (cont. from Plate 3)

Map and text page 154

lopezi group

a   **Adult *B. l. camerunensis*** Restricted to Mount Cameroon. Similar to *lopezi* (see Plate 3), but overall colour tone less saturated. Upperparts dark brown, tinged cinnamon, with narrow, warm buff supercilium, and pale cinnamon-buff cheeks with dark brown mottling. Underparts slightly paler than *lopezi* with chin and throat pale cinnamon-buff, darkening to cinnamon-brown on flanks and upper breast, which usually show diffuse brown streaking. Unlike *lopezi,* belly is whitish.

b   **Juvenile *B. l. camerunensis*** Upperparts dark olive-brown, lacking cinnamon tinge of adult. Supercilium and underparts washed pale yellow, although breast and flanks are suffused olive-brown, becoming darker olive-brown on lower flanks and undertail-coverts, and usually with indistinct and diffuse olive-brown streaking on upper breast.

c   **Adult *B. l. barakae*** E DR Congo to SW Uganda. A distinctive race with dark russet-brown upperparts. Supercilium and underparts bright rufous-cinnamon, slightly paler on throat, and becoming whitish on centre of lower breast and belly. Rear flanks and undertail-coverts dark olive-brown.

mariae group

d   **Adult *B. l. mariae*** Kenya and N Tanzania. Upperparts rich, dark olive-brown with narrow greyish supercilium. Upper breast olive-grey, usually with a few fine dark streaks on throat and upper breast. Throat and belly centre paler grey-buff, lower flanks and undertail-coverts dark olive-brown.

e   **Juvenile *B. l. mariae*** Resembles adult, but has throat and belly centre tinged yellow and dark brown tone to flanks and undertail-coverts is less intense than adult shows.

f   **Adult *B. l. usambarae*** SE Kenya to N Mozambique. Resembles *mariae* but upperparts less russet and slightly paler brown. Underparts paler, with chin and throat whitish, breast washed dull cinnamon-brown, becoming greyish olive-brown on flanks and undertail-coverts, and with a slightly more extensive and paler belly patch.

g   **Adult *B. l. granti*** Malawi to NW Mozambique. Overall appearance warmer and paler than *mariae,* with upperparts appearing more tawny brown. Underparts tinged cinnamon-buff with whitish belly.

h   **Adult *B. l. ufipae*** N Zambia to SW Tanzania. Upperparts tawny brown, similar to *granti,* but with slightly paler and more prominent supercilium. Breast and flanks show intense cinnamon-brown wash, usually with diffuse darker streaking on lower throat and upper breast, and a whitish belly.

i   **Adult *B. l. boultoni*** Angola. Coloration resembles *ufipae,* but cinnamon-tinged breast and flanks are more extensive, and whitish belly centre more restricted. Often shows distinct dark streaking on lower throat and upper breast.

PLATE 5: SPOTTED BUSH & BAIKAL BUSH WARBLERS

Spotted Bush Warbler *Bradypterus thoracicus*

Map and text page 159

12–13cm; 11g. The most numerous and widespread *Bradypterus* in the Himalayas and mountains of W China, where three subtly different races occur, differing in the intensity of the upperpart colour and extent and tone of grey on underparts. A small, dark warbler with a short, graduated tail, long and pale-tipped undertail-coverts and a thin, fine bill. All races show gorget of blackish spots across lower throat and upper breast, although this feature is variable in extent and shared with several related Asian species. Song is one of the most distinctive sounds above the tree line of the higher mountains.

a   **Adult *B. t. thoracicus*** Widespread from C Himalayas to W China. Entire upperparts dark russet-brown, although crown often shows a hint of chestnut, and side of head is washed grey.

b   **Juvenile *B. t. thoracicus*** Differs from adult in its dull olive-brown upperparts with faint darker scaling on crown and mantle, and contrasting warm brown fringes to wing-coverts and flight feathers. Supercilium as adult, but dull greyish sulphur, and ear-coverts dull olive-brown with fine whitish streaks. Underparts oily-yellow with band of diffuse, dull olive-brown spots on upper breast, on some extending as diffuse striations onto sides of breast and upper flanks. Undertail-coverts dull olivaceous-brown with greyish yellow tips, narrower than those of adult.

c   **Adult *B. t. kashmirensis*, buff morph** Restricted to W Himalayas. Upperparts as typical morph *kashmirensis*. Differs in having underparts, supercilium and side of head washed warm buff, and usually lacks throat spotting but occasionally shows hint of a narrow necklace of fine spotting.

d   **Adult *B. t. kashmirensis*, typical morph** Closely resembles nominate form and *przevalskii* but upperparts slightly paler and less richly washed, and ear-coverts and nape sides paler grey. Differs in having greyish white supercilium, which can appear almost white in front of eye. Spots across lower throat variable in extent and colour, usually small and brown but larger and dark grey on some individuals. Breast slightly paler grey than *thoracicus* and flanks and undertail-coverts paler fulvous-brown, the latter prominently tipped whitish.

e   **Juvenile *B. t. kashmirensis*** As juvenile *thoracicus* but underparts slightly yellower and breast spotting tends to appear less distinct.

f   **Adult *B. t. przevalskii*** Birds from NC China appear slightly paler and more rufescent above than nominate *thoracicus*, but many from SC China are inseparable. Tends to show better-defined and more contrasting head pattern with a pale grey or greyish white supercilium, slightly greyer and paler ear-coverts, and the upper breast is washed light ash-grey, slightly paler than nominate form, and tending towards brown rather than grey on the breast sides and flanks.

Baikal Bush Warbler *Bradypterus davidi*

Map and text page 165

12cm; 10g. This diminutive *Bradypterus* is a long-distance migrant, breeding in S Siberia, NE and C China, and wintering in Thailand and the Indochina region. Two races recognised, both with a short but strongly graduated tail and long, full and conspicuously pale-tipped undertail-coverts. Closely resembles Spotted Bush Warbler at all times of the year but readily separated by different song.

g   **Adult *B. d. davidi*, May** Breeds E Siberia to NE China, with isolated population in C China. Upperparts dull reddish brown with buffy white supercilium. Shows small blackish spots on lower throat, usually forming a conspicuous gorget across pale greyish brown lower throat and upper breast. On some birds, extensive pale tips to undertail-coverts may almost obscure darker brown bases, so undertail-coverts appear almost entirely pale.

h   **Adult *B. d. davidi*, non-breeding, January** Resembles breeding adult but brown tones slightly colder and supercilium slightly paler. Underparts lack prominent gorget of breeding adult although a narrow band of faint small spots is usually visible across lower throat.

i   **Juvenile *B. d. davidi*** Upperparts resemble fresh adult or slightly duller olive-brown, but supercilium dull sulphur-yellow. Underparts pale primrose-yellow to dull olive-yellow with band of diffuse olive-brown mottling across breast. Undertail-coverts olive-brown with conspicuous yellow tips.

j   **Adult *B. d. suschkini*, June** Breeds Siberia from Russian Altai to region of Lake Baikal. Overall paler and greyer than nominate *davidi*, with warm olive-brown fringes to wing-coverts and edges to primaries and secondaries. Lacks reddish brown upperparts except on fore-crown. Supercilium marginally paler, distinctly greyer, and slightly more conspicuous, particularly behind eye. Shows slightly greyer breast and belly, and the underpart spotting is variable, on some spots coalescing to form dense charcoal-grey band across lower throat and upper breast.

k   **Adult *B. d. suschkini*, non-breeding, February** Resembles adult breeding but greyish brown wash on breast more pronounced and spotting is indistinct.

Long-billed Bush Warbler *Bradypterus major*

Map and text page 170

14cm; 13g. Breeds at high elevations in W Himalayas in Pakistan and NW India, and the Kun Lun Mountains in W China, where two races are recognised. Largest *Bradypterus* in mainland Asia, with longest and finest bill but otherwise shares similar structure. Upperparts dull mousy brown with contrasting chestnut edges to tail and wings, and shows prominent whitish supercilium.

a   **Adult *B. m. major*, fresh** Breeds N Pakistan and NW India. Most show small greyish brown spots across lower throat, sometimes extending onto upper breast. Underparts washed light peachy buff, becoming pale warm buff to olive-buff on flanks and undertail-coverts, lacking paler tips shown by most mainland *Bradypterus*.

b   **Adult *B. m. major*, worn, July** Appears paler, greyer and more uniform than fresh adult with mousy brown upperparts and closed wing. Underparts silvery white with little or no contrast between throat and breast, and dark spotting usually conspicuous across lower throat.

c   **Juvenile *B. m. major*** Upperparts dull olive-brown with olive yellow supercilium and dull olive-yellow ear-coverts, faintly mottled with brown. Underparts washed yellow, appearing palest on chin and throat, and with olive-brown mottling across dull sulphur-yellow breast.

d   **Adult *B. m. innae*, worn** Breeds Kun Lun Mountains. Paler and colder than nominate form, although rump and uppertail-coverts often slightly warmer than mantle. Shows greyish ear-coverts and paler supercilium, giving head a more contrasting appearance. Underparts white and unmarked although some show faint grey or greyish brown wash across breast, and light spotting across lower throat, never as pronounced as nominate *major*.

Chinese Bush Warbler *Bradypterus tacsanowskius*

Map and text page 173

13cm; 11.5g. A long-distance migrant, breeding in SE Siberia, N Mongolia, NE China and eastern edge of the Tibetan Plateau, and wintering from Nepal and NE India to N Thailand and Indochina. Structure similar to Long-billed and Brown Bush Warblers, longer tailed than Baikal Bush Warbler. Upperparts uniform greyish olive-brown, contrasting slightly with browner fringes to wing-coverts, tertials and edges to primaries and secondaries, which form warmer wing-panel. Head lacks supercilium and eye-stripe but lores greyish white, merging with eye-ring to form a pale triangular patch in front of eye. Breast sandy grey, often with distinct ochreous wash, and some show faint and diffuse spots across lower throat, sometimes absent. Flanks and undertail-coverts washed warm brown, with diffuse pale creamy or buff tips to longest undertail-coverts. Distinctive song provides useful identification character.

e   **Adult worn, June** A poorly marked individual lacking spotting on throat and breast.

f   **Adult worn, May** A well-marked bird with conspicuous throat spots, most appear less well marked.

g   **Adult fresh, November** Following complete moult, separation of adult and first-year birds in wintering area is uncertain. The conspicuous spotting on this individual suggests it may be an adult.

h   **Juvenile** Upperparts uniform dull olivaceous-brown, slightly darker than adult. Loral wedge as adult but dull sulphur-yellow. Underparts dull sulphur-yellow with mottled, dull brown breast-band, extending as diffuse brown striations along flanks and merging with ochreous-brown lower flanks and undertail-coverts.

Brown Bush Warbler *Bradypterus luteoventris*

Map and text page 178

13cm; 12g. Breeds in tall grass and dwarf bamboo above the tree line from E Himalayas to mountains of E China. Small and particularly nondescript with similar structure to Chinese Bush Warbler. Upperparts uniform warm brown including unmarked head which, at best, shows an indistinctly paler eye-ring and loral region. Underparts whitish, lightly washed paler brown on breast, flanks and undertail-coverts. Lower mandible pale. Its distinctive 'clacking reel' song separates it from other *Bradypterus*.

i   **Adult** Always show unmarked throat and plain undertail-coverts.

j   **Juvenile** Resembles adult but underparts washed cream or pale yellow, with breast heavily tipped warm brown, creating broad, mottled band on lower throat and breast. Side of breast, flanks, vent and undertail-coverts washed warm brown to fulvous-brown.

PLATE 7: RUSSET BUSH WARBLER COMPLEX

Russet Bush Warbler *Bradypterus mandelli*

Map and text page 182

13–14cm; 12g. Ranges widely from E Himalayas to E China, N Thailand and Indochina region, with three similar races. Structure similar to Brown Bush and Chinese Bush Warblers although bill slightly heavier. Drab and non-descript, with uniform, rich, dark russet-brown upperparts and a faint greyish white supercilium not reaching behind eye. Undertail-coverts greyish brown with buffy white to greyish white tips. Distinctive song is a repetitive series of nasal buzzing notes.

a   **Adult *B. m. mandelli,* May** Breeds E Himalayas from Darjeeling to N Burma. Shows greyish brown underparts, becoming drab russet-brown on side of breast, flanks and ventral region. In the breeding season, a row of dark brown spots extends across the lower throat and upper breast, and the bill is entirely black.

b   **Juvenile *B. m. mandelli*** Upperparts resemble adult, but underparts warmer brown. Darker brown tips to breast and throat feathers merge to form indistinct striations extending onto side of breast and upper flanks. Undertail-coverts dull russet-brown, narrowly tipped dull buff, less conspicuous than on adult.

c   **Adult *B. m. melanorhynchus,* May** Breeds C and SE China. Underparts darker and greyer than in nominate race. During the breeding season shows a necklace of small, dark spots across lower throat and upper breast.

d   **Adult *B. m. melanorhynchus,* February** This bird shows a yellowish lower mandible and conspicuous gape flange and lacks spotting on upper breast, suggesting it may be a first-winter bird.

e   **Adult *B. m. idoneus*** Restricted to Da Lat Plateau in S Vietnam. Lacks distinct russet tones to rich brown upperparts. Underparts paler than other races; breast lacks buffy or greyish tones, and lower throat spotting indistinct or absent.

Javan Bush Warbler *Bradypterus montis*

Map and text page 187

14cm; 14g. Endemic to the upper montane regions of Java and Bali. Closely resembles Russet Bush Warbler, with similar structure but slightly larger. Upperparts unmarked dark rufescent-brown. Greyish supercilium poorly marked, merging with greyish brown ear-coverts. Throat pale grey, becoming slate-grey on breast, and dark rufescent-brown on lower flanks and undertail-coverts, the latter showing broad, pale buff tips.

f   **Adult breeding** Shows well-defined gorget of dark grey spots on lower throat and upper breast, sometimes extending onto breast side.

g   **Juvenile** Differs from adult by browner side to head, showing little or no contrast with crown and upperparts. Underparts with creamy yellow wash, most pronounced on chin, throat and belly. Lacks necklace of spots across lower throat.

Timor Bush Warbler *Bradypterus timorensis*

Map and text page 190

14cm; 11g. Restricted to montane grassland with scattered forest in W Timor and Alor. Structure as Javan Bush Warbler. Upperparts uniform cinnamon-brown, head with long, greyish white supercilium, becoming greyer and less obvious behind eye. Breast pale grey with band of indistinct greyish brown spots across lower throat. Shows pale brown flanks and slightly darker brown undertail-coverts with inconspicuous pale tips.

h   **Adult**

Benguet Bush Warbler *Bradypterus seebohmi*

Map and text page 192

14cm; 12g. A rare and localised *Bradypterus*, endemic to montane grasslands of N Luzon, Philippines. Structure as Russet Bush Warbler. Upperparts dark russet-brown, with short, pale supercilium and paler, greyer sides to head. Upper breast ash-grey with diffuse dark brown striations, becoming warm brown on upper flanks and sepia-brown on lower flanks. Undertail-coverts dark brown with narrow whitish tips.

i   **Adult**

Taiwan Bush Warbler *Bradypterus alishanensis*

Map and text page 195

14cm; 10g. Endemic to the highlands of C and N Taiwan where it occurs in montane forest undergrowth and dwarf bamboo above the treeline. Structure similar to Russet Bush Warbler. Upperparts uniform dull russet-brown with poorly defined greyish brown supercilium. Shows white chin and throat, brown breast and greyish white belly although tone varies. Flanks dull russet-brown but undertail-coverts slightly warmer with narrow, pale brown tips.

j   **Adult** Blackish spotting is usual on chin and throat, but is absent on this poorly marked individual, perhaps a first-year bird.

k   **Adult** A well-marked bird with extensive spotting on breast, typical of males in the breeding season. Underpart variation during the breeding season is greater than in related species.

Long-tailed Bush Warbler *Bradypterus caudatus*

Map and text page 199

16.5–18cm; 23g. A large, long-tailed *Bradypterus* restricted to montane forest in hills of N Luzon and Mindanao, Philippines, where three races occur. Much larger with a proportionately longer tail than mainland *Bradypterus*. Upperparts and side of head dull uniform rufescent-brown with poorly defined greyish white supercilium barely extending behind eye. Underparts dull, with greyish white chin and throat, upper breast greyish with necklace of diffuse, dusky striations. Flanks rufescent-brown, becoming darker and richer towards ventral region and under-tail-coverts, which lack pale tips.

a **Adult *B. c. caudatus*** Resident in hills in N Luzon. Tail particularly long with weak, filamentous structure.

b **Adult *B. c. unicolor*** Resident in hills in C, E and S Mindanao. Resembles nominate *caudatus* but darker below, and shows faint greyish wash on side of head. Underparts show greater contrast between white chin, greyish throat and breast, and rich rufous-brown lower flanks, belly and undertail-coverts. Also differs from nominate *caudatus* by proportionately shorter and more robust tail.

Kinabalu Bush Warbler *Bradypterus accentor*

Map and text page 202

15cm; 14g. A large, drab and nondescript *Bradypterus* endemic to montane forest on three high peaks in N Borneo. Structure similar to Long-tailed Bush Warbler but with proportionately shorter tail. Upperparts and side of head uniform dark rufescent-brown although ear-coverts washed dull greyish brown on some birds. Thin, buffy brown supercilium extending to rear of eye. Flanks dull rusty brown, darkening to richer brown on vent and undertail-coverts. Usually located by its distinctive repetitive buzzing song.

c **Adult** Whitish throat contrasts with greyish breast marked with a band of brownish or blackish spots of varying extent and prominence. This well-marked individual shows bold and extensive underpart spotting.

d **Adult** A poorly marked bird with spotting restricted to chin, throat and upper breast.

e **Juvenile** Resembles adult, although upperparts generally duller and often with faint scaly or mottled effect. Supercilium barely contrasts with side of head. Underparts darker than adult, with pale sandy buff chin and throat merging with darker, browner breast and flanks. Breast spotting restricted to small, dark brown smudges which extend as indistinct striations down breast.

Chestnut-backed Bush Warbler *Bradypterus castaneus*

Map and text page 205

14–15cm; 19g. A large *Bradypterus* of montane forests of Sulawesi, Buru and Seram in the Moluccas of Indonesia, with each island home to an endemic race. Similar in size and structure to Kinabalu Bush Warbler but proportionately slightly shorter tailed and with relatively stout bill.

f **Adult *B. c. castaneus*** Restricted to Sulawesi. Upperparts vary from dull rufescent-brown to chestnut-brown although side of head slightly greyer and shows greyish white supercilium reaching to rear of ear-coverts Upper breast unmarked slate-grey, contrasting with greyish white chin and throat and warm chocolate-brown lower breast and upper flanks. Lower flanks, vent and undertail-coverts dull sepia-brown and unmarked.

g **Adult *B. c. disturbans*** Occurs on Buru. Differs from nominate form in having warmer, browner upperparts, lacking chestnut tone, and browner side to head. Underparts warmer and slightly paler than nominate form, with grey restricted to a band across the upper breast. Edges to secondaries and primaries warm brown as upperparts.

Ceylon Bush Warbler *Elaphrornis palliseri*

Map and text page 208

15cm; 14g. Endemic to scrub and montane forest in the higher hills of S Sri Lanka. Small and stocky with relatively short but strongly graduated tail. Upperparts uniform dull olive-brown, becoming slightly paler and greyer on head, which shows an indistinct supercilium. Chin and throat vary from pale cream to bright yellowish buff, usually sharply demarcated from greyish brown cheeks. Breast and upper flanks washed greyish brown, becoming faint primrose-yellow on lower belly, and rich brown on the undertail-coverts. Male shows dark ruby red iris, female has white iris.

h **Adult** Female illustrated with white iris.

i **Juvenile** Slightly darker and more rufescent above than adult, lacking grey tones to head. Underparts duller and browner than adult, with chin and throat dull creamy white to sulphur-yellow, and breast deep sulphur-yellow, heavily tipped olive-brown.

Savi's Warbler *Locustella luscinioides*

Map and text page 211

13–14cm; 15g. A long-distance migrant, breeding in *Phragmites* reedbeds from W Europe to SC Asia and wintering in W and NE Africa. A medium-sized, slightly stocky warbler with strongly curved outer primaries and deep-based undertail-coverts almost reaching to tip of broad and markedly graduated tail. Readily recognisable reeling song is a characteristic wetland sound.

a   **Adult *L. l. luscinioides*, fresh, September** Breeds Europe and N Africa. Shows uniform warm brown upperparts and narrow, pale supercilium. Underparts whitish with pale, warm brown breast and flanks. Undertail-coverts warm brown, usually with narrow, paler tips.

b   **Adult *L. l. luscinioides*, worn, June** Some birds, in particularly those breeding in the Danube delta and around the northern Black Sea, show fairly prominent band of fine spots across the lower throat, usually absent on freshly moulted adults in W Europe in autumn. These birds may be of the poorly defined form *sarmatica*.

c   **Juvenile *L. l. luscinioides*, July** Closely resembles fresh adult. Upperparts slightly warmer and brighter, and brown wash on breast and flanks more extensive, but differences slight and probably not consistent. Most readily separated from freshly moulted adult by yellow base to lower mandible and grey-brown rather than rich brown iris.

d   **Adult *L. l. fusca*, fresh, December** Breeds SC Asia. Differs from nominate by dull olive-brown to greyish brown upperparts, paler and colder buffy brown wash to breast and flanks, and undertail-coverts slightly paler with narrow whitish tips, usually more conspicuous and contrasting than on nominate birds. Birds resembling *fusca* occasionally breed in Europe, particularly Spain.

e   **Juvenile *L. l. fusca*** Closely resembles adult *fusca* but base of lower mandible yellow, not pink.

River Warbler *Locustella fluviatilis*

Map and text page 219

14cm; 16g. A long-distance migrant, breeding in riparian woodland and lush, dense vegetation from C Europe to W Siberia and wintering in E and S Africa. Structure similar to Savi's Warbler but longer and flatter forehead creates attenuated head shape; also has longer primary projection. Shows considerable plumage variation, not related to age, and two colour morphs. Majority are brown morph but 10–20% are yellow morph. Both show upper breast and flanks washed olive-brown with row of small, dark brown spots across lower throat that broaden and expand to form obvious gorget of broad, diffuse striations of variable extent on upper breast. Brown bases to undertail-coverts contrast with greyish white tips. Distinctive, stridulating, insect-like song readily recognisable.

f   **Adult, brown morph, fresh, May** Upperparts uniform dark olive-brown with variable greenish tinge, slightly browner wings, long outer primary with pale brown outer web, an indistinct whitish supercilium and faintly mottled ear-coverts. Shows variation in intensity and extent of underpart streaking, with some having narrow, faint streaks confined to lower throat and upper breast border.

g   **Adult, brown morph, fresh, May** Singing male with broad dark streaking extending from throat to upper breast. During the breeding season, body plumage of adults becomes abraded, appearing duller, and wing and tail feathers become browner.

h   **Adult, brown morph with suspended primary moult, November** A particularly well-marked individual with extensive streaking on underparts. After partial moult in NE Africa, late-autumn adults have fresh, rich olive-brown body and head, and darker newly moulted outer primaries contrasting with retained older, paler inner primaries and secondaries.

i   **Juvenile, yellow morph** Shows yellowish wash to supercilium, chin, throat and underparts, and more greenish upperparts; this feature is not age-related. Yellow-tinged birds occur alongside predominant brown morph.

Grasshopper Warbler *Locustella naevia*

Map and text page 225

12–13 cm; 12.5g. The most widespread European *Locustella*, ranging from W Europe to C Asia. Frequents a broad range of dry and damp habitats with thick low-lying vegetation, ranging from scrubby edges of open woodland to fens and reedbeds with sedges and scattered bushes. A small, dark olive-brown warbler with streaked upperparts and variable underpart colour. Distinctive structure with a fine, slender bill, fairly long and graduated tail, and long, deep undertail-coverts. Appearance highly variable with three races. Closely resembles Lanceolated Warbler but slightly larger and with longer tail, and lacks conspicuous fine streaking on breast, and contrasting 'tramline' pattern on mantle. Unlike Lanceolated, shows diffuse tertial fringes and long, poorly defined dark streaks on the undertail-coverts. Characteristic high-pitched reeling song resembles that of Savi's and Lanceolated Warblers.

a **Adult *L. n. naevia*, brown morph, fresh** Occupies European breeding range. Underparts greyish white with light brown wash extending across breast and along the flanks. With few exceptions, olive tones to upperparts are shown by both morphs of the nominate form. Underpart streaking variable in extent, and is almost absent in this individual.

b **Juvenile *L. n. naevia*, yellow morph, fresh, August** Shows conspicuous sulphur-yellow wash to underparts, and diffuse streaking confined to lower throat and sides of upper breast. Upperparts show distinct olive wash as adult.

c **Adult *L. n. naevia*, brown morph, worn** Similar to fresh adult, but worn primaries lack pale tips. Shows particularly well-marked underparts, with extensive fine streaking across breast and diffuse striations along flanks. Most birds are less well marked.

d **Adult *L. n. naevia*, yellow morph, fresh** Underparts show dull sulphur-yellow wash, usually slightly paler, less intense than juvenile yellow morph in autumn. This individual shows a fairly well-marked band of spots across lower throat. In spring, most adults less well marked, often restricted to just an indistinct row of fine, diffuse circular spots across the lower throat.

e **Adult *L. n. obscurior*, fresh, May** Restricted to the Caucasus Mountains. Compared with *naevia*, olive-brown tones to upperparts are largely suppressed and replaced with a greyish brown wash.

f **Adult *L. n. straminea*, brown morph, fresh** Breeds W Siberia and C Asia. Upperparts of brown morph lack olive tones and are distinctly paler and greyer than upperparts of *naevia*, with bolder, more contrasting dark centres to mantle feathers.

g **Adult *L. n. straminea*, grey morph, fresh** The most widespread morph. Underpart markings are variable in all morphs and often absent, but when present *straminea* tends to show small, neat spots across lower throat.

h **Juvenile *L. n. straminea*, yellow morph, fresh** Browner above than adult and lacking olive tones typical of *naevia*. Underparts slightly paler than juvenile yellow morph *naevia*, washed purer ochreous or primrose-yellow rather than slightly oily yellow of *naevia*.

i **Adult *L. n. straminea*, grey morph, fresh** A particularly cold and pale individual, lacking streaking and spotting on the underparts. Such birds occur throughout the range of *straminea* but predominate towards N and E Kazakhstan and W China.

j **Adult *L. n. straminea*, fresh, May** An unusual, fresh individual from the Indian wintering grounds on a very late date. Combination of light, bright buff wash across the underparts and distinctly brown upperparts is unique amongst specimens held at NHM, Tring, and such birds appear unknown within breeding range.

Continued on Plate 11

PLATE 11: GRASSHOPPER & LANCEOLATED WARBLERS

Grasshopper Warbler *Locustella naevia* **(cont. from Plate 10)**   Map and text page 225

a   **Adult *L. n. naevia*, brown morph, fresh, December** Strongly marked bird with diffuse streaking on side of neck and across lower throat, but not approaching the crisp, blackish streaking shown by Lanceolated Warbler.

b   **Adult *L. n. straminea*, brown morph, May** Spring *straminea* shows plainer underparts than *naevia*, usually lacking spotting or streaking on lower throat and breast, making separation from Lanceolated Warbler fairly straightforward.

c   **Adult *L. n. straminea*, yellow morph, May** An exceptionally well-marked bird showing a conspicuous band of small spots across the lower throat. Such well-marked birds are unusual.

Lanceolated Warbler *Locustella lanceolata*   Map and text page 235

12cm; 10.5g. The smallest and most heavily marked *Locustella*, breeding from E Finland to E Siberia. Closely resembles Grasshopper Warbler, but differs in its conspicuous fine streaking on the breast and flanks, and dull olive-brown upperparts with broad blackish feather centres that form a series of 'tramlines' along the mantle. Shows a distinctive gorget of fine streaks on the breast, and long, fine 'lanceolate' streaks along the flanks, while the sharply demarcated tertial fringes and crisp, blackish streaks on the undertail-coverts also separate it from Grasshopper. Does not have a yellow morph. Behaviour and habitat overlap with Grasshopper Warbler. Song is a reeling trill, similar to Grasshopper Warbler.

d   **Adult *L. l. lanceolata*, fresh, June** A well-marked bird showing fine spots extending from chin to lower throat, a gorget of fine, crisp streaks across the breast, and larger, broader streaks along the flanks. The whitish underpart tone accentuates the streaking. Upperparts strongly streaked, with the black feather centres forming long 'tramlines' extending from fore-crown to mantle. Such well-marked birds are not unusual.

e   **Adult *L. l. hendersonii*, fresh, June** Closely resembles the nominate form but tends to appear less clearly marked, but some individuals may be inseparable. Streaking on crown, mantle and rump slightly less crisp, and underpart colour more variable.

f   **Adult *L. l. hendersonii*, fresh, June** Strongly toned birds with reddish ochre flanks and breast are unusual. Poorly developed spotting occurs more frequently in *hendersonii*, and flank streaking is faint and occasionally absent. Dark centres to undertail-coverts are most obvious on the shorter outer feathers, and may be diffuse or absent on longer feathers.

g   **Juvenile *L. l. lanceolata*, fresh, September** Young birds leave the breeding grounds in juvenile plumage. All show the characteristic 'tramline' pattern on upperparts and a gorget of fine streaks across the breast. There is individual variation, particularly in the prominence of the underpart streaking, and this individual shows particularly broad flank streaking.

h   **Juvenile *L. l. hendersonii*, fresh, October** Most juveniles have white underparts that accentuate the streaking, but some show a faint yellow wash and others a warmer ochre tinge on the chin, throat and breast.

i   **Juvenile *L. l. lanceolata*, fresh, October** Classic juvenile showing dark 'tramlines' on upperparts, dark centres to tertials contrasting crisply with paler fringes, fine dark streaking on white breast and longer, broader streaks on the browner flanks. Note also the proportionately shorter tail and bill than Grasshopper.

Pallas's Grasshopper Warbler *Locustella certhiola* Map and text page 245

12–14cm; 15g. A common and widespread *Locustella*, breeding in wetlands, damp woodlands, and moist over-grown habitats throughout the temperate C and E Palearctic, where five distinct races occur. Winters in Sri Lanka, E India and throughout SE Asia. Size and structure similar to Grasshopper Warbler but slightly stockier and with proportionately shorter tail, often held slightly spread, even in flight, exaggerating its apparent size. Combination of pale supercilium, distinctive rusty brown rump and uppertail-coverts, well-marked and contrasting mantle feathering, and pale tips to four outer pairs of rectrices is common to all races, making this the most distinctive and straightforward of the *Locustella* warblers to identify. Juveniles difficult to assign to race, all sharing yellowish tone to underparts and dark spotting across lower throat and upper breast.

a **Adult *L. c. certhiola*, fresh, June** Breeding range centred on Lake Baikal region to E Mongolia and NC China. Mantle streaked rusty brown and black, contrasting with chestnut-brown rump that sometimes shows indistinct, blackish feather centres. Uppertail-coverts with large, black spot close to tip. Tail dark grey-brown with pale tips except for two central pairs. Crown blackish with dull ash-grey fringes. Tertials blackish with narrow, crisp, warm brown to pale greyish white fringes, usually becoming white at tips of inner webs adjacent to feather shafts, forming small indentation. Chin and throat whitish, usually unmarked but some show small, indistinct spots on lower throat. Breast lightly washed pale tan. Undertail-coverts pale sandy buff with large diffuse whitish tips.

b **Adult *L. c. minor*, fresh, June** Smallest and most richly coloured race, breeding in SE Siberia and NE China, to east of *certhiola*. Resembles nominate *certhiola* but more contrasting, with warmer and brighter rufous-brown fringes to upperparts and wing-coverts. Tertials slightly warmer and more richly coloured and some lack white notch against shaft on inner two.

c **Juvenile *L. c. minor*, September** Differs from adult by slightly duller rump and large dark spots near tips of uppertail-coverts less crisply defined. Tail often with conspicuous pale tips on all feathers. Supercilium, ear-coverts and underparts variably washed yellow, sometimes indistinct, usually yellowish buff on breast and flanks. Shows a row of small spots across lower throat and band of blackish arrowheads on upper breast and upper flanks. Juvenile *certhiola* probably not safely distinguishable from juvenile *minor*.

d **Adult *L. c. centralasiae*, fresh, June** The palest race, breeding in arid regions from E Kazakhstan to C Mongolia and NW China. Closely resembles *sparsimstriata* but upperparts slightly paler and less contrasting. Mantle and scapulars show relatively small, diffuse blackish centres and broad, dull tan fringes, and closed wing appears paler and less well marked than other races, with flight feathers edged warm tawny brown. Mid brown (rather than blackish) tertials usually lack whitish notch at tip. Crown fringed pale sandy brown (rather than greyish), and rump warm cinnamon-brown and unmarked. Underparts whitish to pale rusty buff, and undertail-coverts with pale tips, appearing almost white on some.

e **Juvenile *L. c. centralasiae*, September** Separated from juvenile *certhiola*, *minor* and *rubescens* by paler, browner upperparts that lack darker, warmer and richer chestnut fringes, and rump and uppertail-coverts uniform, lacking prominent dark centres. Extent of spotting across upper breast and intensity of yellow wash to underparts variable.

f **Adult *L. c. sparsimstriata*, fresh, June** The westernmost race, and also the largest, breeding SW Siberia. Closely resembles *centralasiae* but slightly darker, with pale ash-grey, rather than pale brown fringes to crown, and with darker sandy brown upperparts that lack rufous tones. Never as heavily marked and contrasting as *certhiola* (although beware intergrades). Rump and uppertail-coverts unmarked or with darker, poorly defined spots, and tail warm sepia-brown with whitish tips. Underparts as *centralasiae*, although more inclined to show faint, indistinct spots across lower throat.

g **Adult *L. c. rubescens*, typical bird, fresh, June** Breeds C to E Siberia to north of other races. Darker and browner than other races, lacking warmer, richer tones of nominate *certhiola* and *minor*, but brownish supercilium remains prominent. Upperparts with small blackish centres extending to feather tip and broad, cold brown fringes, so mantle appears heavily striped. Rufous-brown uppertail-coverts always show large, blackish spot towards tip. Crown finely streaked, with blackish feather centres contrasting with mid grey fringes, Underparts pale greyish white, although upper breast washed light buff to warm brown, and usually shows scattering of small, dark spots across lower throat. Undertail-coverts warm rufous-cinnamon, darker than other races, conspicuously and broadly tipped buffy white.

h **Adult *L. c. rubescens*, dark bird, September** In east of range a minority appear much darker than typical *rubescens*, with darker brown upperparts, conspicuously dark brown flanks and less prominent supercilium.

i **Juvenile *L. c. rubescens*, September** Generally darker than juveniles of other races, with darker undertail-coverts showing contrastingly paler tips. Compared with adult, upperpart streaking less pronounced, with smaller blackish feather centres and slightly warmer tawny brown fringes extending to tip, so mantle appears mottled rather than streaked. Usually shows whitish spot on inner web at tip of inner two pairs of tertials, sometimes on longest. Underparts dull sulphurous yellow, becoming sulphurous buff across breast, and with a band of brown arrowheads across lower throat and upper breast.

PLATE 13: STYAN'S & MIDDENDORFF'S GRASSHOPPER WARBLERS

Styan's Grasshopper Warbler *Locustella pleskei*   Map and text page 267

15–16cm; 20g. A large *Locustella*, restricted during the breeding season to small offshore islands with lush, sub-tropical vegetation fringing the Pacific coast of Japan, the Sea of Japan and the Yellow Sea. In winter known only from the Deep Bay region of Hong Kong and the Red River delta region of northern Vietnam. Structure resembles Middendorff's Grasshopper Warbler but averages larger, with a proportionately larger, heavier bill, and longer, broader, heavily graduated tail. Upperparts variable in colour, usually pale greyish brown and entirely unmarked, occasionally showing faint, diffuse and obscure mottling. Supercilium whitish, less prominent than Middendorff's Grasshopper, and outer four pairs of tail feathers tipped whitish. Underparts whitish with a pale grey-brown wash across breast and brown suffusion on flanks. Undertail-coverts typically unmarked, pale creamy buff, occasionally rich buff with dark shaft streaks, and tipped dull creamy white. Outermost long primary lacks obvious pale outer web of Middendorff's Grasshopper Warbler.

a   **Adult, fresh, April** A freshly moulted individual showing brownish upperparts with unusually prominent but still diffuse lines on mantle. During the breeding season upperparts become paler, greyer and entirely uniform.

b   **Adult, slightly worn, November** Following partial post-breeding moult, slightly worn birds appear slightly paler and greyer than fresh adult. Some show indistinct spots across lower throat but it remains unclear whether these are worn adults or juveniles.

c   **Juvenile, July** Resembles adult, but the chin, throat, upper breast and supercilium with variable yellow wash, pale in some, richer ochre-yellow in others, but usually reduced to a creamy or pale yellowish wash to the throat and belly by early winter. Shows ill-defined spotting across lower throat. Yellow wash and throat spotting mostly lost by early winter.

Middendorff's Grasshopper Warbler *Locustella ochotensis*   Map and text page 258

14–15cm; 18g. A long-distance migrant, breeding in coastal regions and islands fringing the Sea of Okhotsk, and wintering in the Philippines and N Borneo. Structure as Pallas's Grasshopper Warbler but averages slightly larger. Resembles a pale, poorly marked Pallas's Grasshopper with particularly prominent pale supercilium. Differs by plainer, browner upperparts with diffusely darker feather centres, some appearing unmarked, and uniform rump and uppertail-coverts. Underparts whitish with faint warm brown wash across upper breast, and undertail-coverts pale creamy buff.

d   **Adult *L. o. ochotensis*, fresh, June** Southern race, breeding in S Kuril Islands, S Sakhalin and N Hokkaido, appears warmer and plainer than northern breeders. Adults returning to breeding grounds show poorly marked, diffuse mantle streaking.

e   **Adult *L. o. ochotensis*, worn** Before complete moult in late winter, feather fringes are heavily abraded and mantle shows little or no mottling, so tawny brown rump, uppertail-coverts and upper surface of tail appear conspicuously warmer and brighter than mantle.

f   **Juvenile, July** Upperparts duller, more olive toned than adult, often with slightly darker striations along mantle. Supercilium and underparts washed yellowish and becoming dull brown along flanks, and with band of small, oily brown spots across lower throat. Undertail-coverts yellowish buff with paler tips. By December, the stronger yellow tones are subdued due to wear and bleaching.

g   **Adult *L. o. subcerthiola*, fresh, June** Differs from nominate race by reduced contrast between dull greyish brown to olive-brown mantle, and rump, uppertail-coverts and upper surface of tail. Northernmost breeders, such as bird depicted here, are slightly greyer and colder with diffuse mottling on mantle and scapulars, paler fringes to wing-coverts, and dull ash-brown rump and uppertail-coverts that are slightly browner than mantle.

h   **Hybrid Middendorff's Grasshopper Warbler × Pallas's Grasshopper Warbler** Some birds appear too well marked for Middendorff's Grasshopper Warbler and may be hybrids/intergrades with Pallas's Grasshopper Warbler. Such birds are frequent in the lower Amur River region and northern Sakhalin, but are rarely encountered on migration or in winter. Care is required to eliminate these from races *centralasiae* and *sparsimstriata* of Pallas's Grasshopper Warbler.

68

Gray's Grasshopper Warbler *Locustella fasciolata*　　　　　Map and text page 274

16–17cm; 27g. The largest *Locustella*, breeding in cool, temperate forest from C Siberia to N Japan, and wintering from S Philippines to New Guinea. Shows characteristic flat, attenuated head with straight and relatively strong bill, long deep-based undertail-coverts, and long, graduated tail. Two races, both showing pale creamy brown outer web to outermost long primary and uniform tail feathers, lacking pale tips. Has a loud and distinctive bulbul-like song, quite unlike any other in this genus.

a　　**Adult *L. f. fasciolata*, fresh, June** Upperparts unmarked, rich warm brown to olive-brown. Head shows a long, thin greyish white supercilium and greyish ear-coverts. Breast and upper flanks nondescript dull grey, some showing indistinct mottled striations on sides of upper breast. Some birds from NE China are browner on breast and resemble *amnicola*. Lower flanks pale brown, merging with unmarked, warm buff to light rufous-brown undertail-coverts.

b　　**Adult *L. f. fasciolata*, fresh** Underpart colour of nominate form is variable, this individual is paler than most.

c　　**Juvenile *L. f. fasciolata*, August** Upperparts resemble adult but may show slightly darker, diffuse striations running length of mantle. Head browner, with narrower, less conspicuous buffy yellow supercilium, and warm olive-brown ear-coverts with narrow yellowish buff streaks. Entire underparts washed yellow, lacking greyer tones of adult. Breast usually lightly mottled olive-brown to ochre-yellow, on some birds the breast is suffused with a broad band of olive-brown. Flanks dull olive-brown, becoming pale buff to yellowish buff on lower flanks and belly, and the unmarked undertail-coverts are warmer yellowish or peachy buff.

d　　**Juvenile *L. f. fasciolata*, August** A well-marked juvenile with a strong olive-brown wash on breast and faint barring on chin and throat.

e　　**Adult *L. f. amnicola*, fresh, June** Differs from nominate *fasciolata* by richer, browner upperparts that lack olive tones, and brownish rather than grey ear-coverts. Underparts variable, with most lacking greyish wash of nominate race, and breast usually dull olive-buff, sometimes faintly mottled, and contrasting with whitish or pale buffy white chin and throat. Side of breast darkens to buffy brown or greyish brown, becoming warm fulvous-brown on flanks and vent. Undertail-coverts warm peachy buff or cinnamon-buff, slightly brighter than nominate form and usually unmarked

f　　**Juvenile *L. f. amnicola*, August** Resembles nominate *fasciolata* but shows warmer and browner fringes to the wing-coverts, and appears to lack yellow in supercilium and underparts, with lower throat and upper breast varying between olive-brown and buffy brown. Assignation of individuals to either race becomes problematic from late autumn onwards, as young birds become worn, and juveniles of nominate race may lose the yellow wash.

Japanese Swamp Warbler *Locustella pryeri*   Map and text page 282

13–14cm; 14g. A poorly known, highly localised resident and short-distance migrant, frequenting marshes, swamps and *Phragmites* reedbeds in N Japan and NE and E China. Compared with other *Locustella*, shows a relatively short and stubby bill, short undertail-coverts, a long and narrow tail, and shorter, more rounded wings. Upperparts heavily streaked, with warmly coloured fringes contrasting with black feather centres, but side of head plain with poorly defined supercilium. Underparts pale and unmarked, with whitish throat contrasting with the pale brown breast, warmer brown flanks and undertail-coverts. Tail rich brown and unmarked but with darker feather shafts.

a   **Adult *L. p. pryeri*, fresh** Upperparts including crown and nape warm chestnut-brown with black feather centres, and extensive black centres and rich chestnut-brown fringes to the tertials and wing-coverts. Shows poorly defined greyish supercilium that merges with the pale lores. Warm brown flanks and paler undertail-coverts contrast with pale greyish breast and belly.

b   **Adult *L. p. pryeri*, worn** Upperparts appear darker and contrast becomes more pronounced, with broad, parallel blackish streaking along mantle, and fine, dark streaking on the rump and uppertail-coverts. Warm brown edges to wing feathers match fringes of upperparts.

c   **Adult *L. p. sinensis*, fresh** Longer tailed, and lacks the darker and richer tones of nominate *pryeri*. Upperparts paler, with warm sandy brown to greyish brown fringes accentuating contrast with black centres, but supercilium more subdued emphasising open-faced appearance. Closed wing edged bright sandy buff. Underparts paler than nominate, with silky grey breast and belly, and flanks and undertail-coverts washed uniform bright buff, paler but warmer than in nominate *pryeri*.

d   **Adult *L. p. sinensis*, worn** Black feather centres on upperparts, tertials and wings become more pronounced, and underparts appear whiter.

Moustached Warbler *Acrocephalus melanopogon*   Map and text page 289

12–13cm; 10g. A small, streaked *Acrocephalus*, largely resident in marshes and reedbeds in S Europe and NW Africa, but W and C Asian breeders migrate to winter from Middle East to NW India. Structure more compact than Sedge Warbler with shorter primary projection, but tail slightly longer, fuller, and with a more graduated tip; when nervous, tail is characteristically held cocked above the back. Nominate birds generally darker and more warmly coloured than Sedge Warbler. Shows bolder, more sharply defined head pattern, with dark crown, long and broad whitish supercilium that ends squarely on the nape, paler greyish ear-coverts, and prominent blackish eye-stripe and moustachial line just below eye. Streaked upperparts with rich rufous-brown fringes and black centres, but rump unmarked rufous-brown. Closed wing dull tawny brown, warmer than in Sedge. Underparts washed tawny buff, more deeply on flanks and undertail-coverts, but chin and throat whitish. Legs dark grey to blackish.

e   **Adult *A. m. melanopogon*, fresh** Upperparts edged rich rufous-brown with narrow blackish mantle streaks, although nape warm rufous and unmarked, forming a contrasting shawl around rear and side of neck.

f   **Adult *A. m. melanopogon*, worn** Crown and ear-coverts appear darker when worn, and upperpart streaking becomes more pronounced as contrast between blackish feather centres and narrower, paler fringes increases.

g   **Juvenile *A. m. melanopogon*** Closely resembles spring adult, with almost uniform black crown, conspicuous whitish supercilium and streaked upperparts. Edges of wing feathers and tertials slightly paler and buffier than adult, and tertial fringes narrower. Upper breast washed warm buff and usually shows row of faint greyish spots.

h   **Adult *A. m. mimicus*, fresh** Slightly larger, conspicuously paler and less richly coloured than nominate race, and with longer primary projection, so appearance more reminiscent of Sedge Warbler. Upperparts, including side of neck olive-brown rather than rufous-brown, and crown brown and distinctly streaked. Tawny brown wash on side of breast and flanks duller, less extensive than on nominate form.

i   **Juvenile *A. m. mimicus*** Closely resembles adult but upperparts and wing feather edges slightly paler and buffier, and usually shows an indistinct band of small spots across the upper throat.

j   **Adult *A. m. albiventris*** Closely resembles *mimicus*, but upperparts slightly darker and greyer, flanks slightly deeper ochre-brown and undertail-coverts paler.

Continued on Plate 16

PLATE 16: MOUSTACHED, AQUATIC & SEDGE WARBLERS

Moustached Warbler *Acrocephalus melanopogon* (cont. from Plate 15)   Map and text page 289

a   **Juvenile *A. m. mimicus*** Some juvenile *mimicus* closely resemble Sedge Warbler but upperparts, breast sides and flanks darker tawny brown and with less contrasting closed wing pattern. Head shows streaked brown crown, and broad square-cut whitish supercilium. Chin and throat whitish, contrasting with dark brown cheeks and ear-coverts, and shows only indistinct spots on lower throat. Primary projection much shorter than Sedge, and legs dark grey.

Aquatic Warbler *Acrocephalus paludicola*   Map and text page 302

13 cm; 11g. Rare and highly localised, breeding in low open marshy tracts dominated by sedge, mostly in C and E Europe, but some east to S Ural Mountains. Winters in W Africa. Shows small bill, narrow pointed tail feathers, and long primary projection. A distinctive warbler with conspicuous broad black stripes extending along tawny buff mantle and scapulars, becoming finer on rump and uppertail-coverts but still obvious. Head shows broad buff supercilium and well-defined central crown stripe, separated by broad blackish lateral crown stripes, but lores usually pale and unmarked. Underparts yellowish buff, palest on throat and belly. Legs pinkish.

b   **Adult, worn, spring** Dark streaks conspicuous on side of breast and flanks. Greater coverts and tertials with contrasting pale buff fringes, and pale buff panel on closed secondaries.

c   **Adult, heavily worn, August** Upperparts and wing feather appear much greyer, with buff fringes to upperparts and wing-coverts narrow or absent, supercilium and underparts usually whiter, and underpart streaking reduced.

d   **Juvenile, autumn** Brighter and fresher than worn adult, with conspicuously pale lores. Head stripes and upperpart fringes more contrasting golden-buff than adult. Shows narrow necklace of fine greyish streaks across lower throat, and often with occasional longer streaks along flanks.

Sedge Warbler *Acrocephalus schoenobaenus*   Map and text page 296

13 cm; 11g. Breeds in wetlands, marshes and waterside habitats from W Europe to W Siberia, and winters throughout sub-Saharan Africa. A small *Acrocephalus* with a fine bill, long primary projection and rather short tail. Upperparts conspicuously streaked light olive-brown or buffish from crown to mantle and scapulars but with unmarked, more warmly tinged rump and uppertail-coverts. Head shows streaked crown and prominent pale buff or whitish supercilium. Underparts pale buff to whitish, tinged browner on rear flanks. Legs brownish grey to flesh-grey.

e   **Adult, fresh, December** Upperparts rich olive-brown and with warm buff edges to flight feathers and fringes to wing-coverts and tertials contrasting sharply with blackish feather centres.

f   **Adult, worn, spring** Upperparts rather paler and duller, and wing feather edges faded buff.

g   **Juvenile, autumn** Brighter and fresher than worn and faded adult. Upperparts brighter buff and with sharper, darker mantle streaks. Supercilium and underparts washed yellowish buff, with necklace of small dark spots across lower throat and upper breast, usually conspicuous, occasionally tiny or absent.

h   **Hybrid Sedge Warbler × Eurasian Reed Warbler** Known hybrids between Sedge and Eurasian Reed Warblers in W Europe superficially resemble Black-browed Reed Warbler (Plate 17), but should be separable by long primary projection shown by both parents.

PLATE 17: STREAKED, BLACK-BROWED & MANCHURIAN REED WARBLERS

Streaked Reed Warbler *Acrocephalus sorghophilus*
Map and text page 307

12cm; 8g. An extremely rare *Acrocephalus* which probably breeds along the Amur River in SE Siberia and NE China, and winters in the Philippines. Frequents willow scrub, reedbeds and marshes. Small and slim, with a delicate, fine-tipped bill, fairly long primary projection and rather short tail. Crown and mantle warm straw to sandy brown with fine brown streaking, rump and uppertail-coverts plain warm brown. Head shows conspicuous pale supercilium bordered by narrow dark brown to blackish band along crown side, and small dark spot in front of eye. Underparts pale buff with warmer flanks and whitish throat and undertail-coverts. Legs pale grey.

a   **Adult, fresh, spring** Upperpart streaking and dark sides to crown less contrasting and conspicuous, but closed wing more contrasting, with warm straw fringes to coverts and tertials, and warm brown edges to flight feathers. Breast washed sandy buff, becoming warmer on flanks.

b   **Adult, worn, February** By late winter, overall appearance paler than fresh adult, with mantle and scapulars paler sandy brown, upperpart streaking more conspicuous, and head pattern more pronounced with dark side to crown contrasting with paler supercilium. Fringes to wing-coverts faded and closed wing appears less contrasting. Underparts paler with sandy buff wash confined to flanks.

c   **Juvenile, autumn** Young birds resemble adults but are paler, brighter buff with darker feather centres and more pronounced streaking. Lores unmarked or with small dark spot just in front of eye.

Black-browed Reed Warbler *Acrocephalus bistrigiceps*
Map and text page 311

12cm; 9g. The most numerous and widespread of the smaller *Acrocephalus* in E Asia, breeding in reedbeds, marshes, damp meadows and edges of moist forest from SE Siberia to NE China and Japan, and wintering in SE Asia. A small warbler with a small fine bill, rounded crown and rather short tail, but with a relatively short primary projection. Upperparts dull olive-brown, becoming warmer on rump, and head shows conspicuous pale supercilium and bold blackish stripes along crown sides. Underparts drab and unmarked, paler than upperparts. Bill dark grey with unmarked pink lower mandible, and legs dull grey.

d   **Adult, summer** Typical adult on the breeding grounds, with dull brown upperparts and slightly warmer rump and uppertail-coverts contrasting with paler creamy white underparts.

e   **Adult, fresh, September** Some freshly moulted birds in autumn show a warm rufous tone to the upperparts, a bright buff supercilium and warmly washed underparts.

f   **Adult, fresh, autumn** Slightly duller appearance typical from October onwards when young birds only separable from adults by greyer iris.

g   **Adult, worn** By the end of the breeding season the upperparts become duller and darker as the warmer feather fringes are lost.

Manchurian Reed Warbler *Acrocephalus tangorum*
Map and text page 317

12cm; 8g. A scarce, poorly known migrant which breeds in extensive reedbeds in NE China and extreme SE Siberia, and winters in the Indochina region and Thailand. A small unstreaked *Acrocephalus* with a relatively long and strong bill and long, narrow tail feathers. Shows a bold pale supercilium bordered by narrow dark line along side of crown and dark eye-line. Plumage seasonally variable, with upperparts and wings uniform brown, and underparts paler with whitish throat. Lower mandible unmarked and legs reddish brown.

h   **Adult, worn** Adults in spring are worn and faded, with greyish brown to sandy brown upperparts contrasting with warm brown rump, uppertail-coverts and tail. Narrow blackish sides to crown remain conspicuous. Underparts whitish, slightly warmer pale buff on flanks. Iris pale greyish brown.

i   **Adult, fresh body and worn wings, September** Shows warm brown upperparts and edges to wing-coverts and tertials, and appears much brighter than worn adult, but retains older worn flight feathers. This individual has also retained the middle tertial. Underparts whitish, washed peachy buff on flanks.

j   **First-winter, September** When fresh, upperparts rich rufous brown and underparts washed deep peachy buff. Retains pale supercilium and dark side to crown, although often tipped brown and less obvious than shown here. These rich tones soon lost as feather tips abrade and fade, and by early winter usually resembles adult.

Paddyfield Warbler *Acrocephalus agricola*   Map and text page 329

12–13cm; 9.5g. A small, unstreaked *Acrocephalus*, breeding in *Phragmites* reedbeds from the W Black Sea to C Asia and NW China, and wintering in the Indian subcontinent. A small warbler with a proportionately smaller bill than other W Palearctic *Acrocephalus*, a short primary projection but rather long tail. Shows plain, warmly coloured upperparts, but colour and tone affected by wear and bleaching. Head with diffuse dusky brown band along side of crown and prominent pale supercilium, and usually shows distinctive pale half-collar extending onto side of nape. Underparts variable but paler than upperparts. Always shows small dark smudge near tip of pale lower mandible.

a   **Adult, spring, May** Typical adult on the breeding grounds, with warm brown upperparts, whitish underparts and warm creamy buff wash on flanks.

b   **Adult, spring** A slightly warmer, more richly toned bird.

c   **Adult, fresh, November** After the complete moult in early autumn, upperparts and wings bright cinnamon-brown, and underparts washed orange-cinnamon, most strongly on side of breast, flanks and undertail-coverts, but chin and throat whitish. Dark sides to crown may be obscured by brown tips.

d   **Adult, fresh, particularly bright rufous bird, November** A minority of freshly moulted birds in early autumn show an intense orange-brown wash on the underparts and appear strikingly different to adults on the breeding grounds and first-winter birds. These warmer, richer colours are soon lost and by early winter they resemble typical adults.

e   **Adult, worn, autumn** By late summer, worn and bleached adults can be extremely pale, with warmer tones restricted to rump and uppertail-coverts, and underparts largely white, with any warmer tones restricted to lower flanks.

f   **First-winter, autumn** Although some are initially warm cinnamon-brown above, these tones are soon lost and first-winter birds then resemble breeding adults, but are fresher with broader fringes to wing-coverts and tertials, and pale primary tips. The pale half-collar and dark side to crown are usually quite pronounced.

Blunt-winged Warbler *Acrocephalus concinens*   Map and text page 322

12–13cm; 8.5g. Three races breed locally in widely separated areas of E China, NE India to NW Burma, and the NW Himalayas. Chinese breeders winter Indochina region to Thailand but other races are resident or altitudinal migrants. Breeds in *Phragmites* or other tall emergent waterside vegetation, but also on dry bushy hillsides in China and Kashmir. Bill longer and stouter, and wing shorter than Paddyfield Warbler, with very short primary projection so tail appears relatively long. A small, unstreaked *Acrocephalus* with uniform warm brown upperparts, head and wings. Shows a short pale supercilium extending to rear of eye, occasionally just beyond, brown lores and lacks dark border along crown side. Underparts warm buff with pale throat. Lower mandible pink, usually unmarked but occasionally with indistinct greyish sides.

g   **Adult A. c. concinens, fresh** In autumn, upperparts warm brown or fulvous-brown contrasting with paler underparts with warm brown wash across breast and brighter fulvous-brown flanks. Lower breast, belly and undertail-coverts creamy brown.

h   **Adult A. c. concinens, worn, spring** Typical adult from Chinese breeding grounds. Resembles fresh adult but upperparts duller and browner, and underparts paler.

i   **Adult A. c. haringtoni, fresh** Breeding birds of NW Himalayas are warmer and brighter than nominate *concinens* with cinnamon-brown to russet-brown upperparts, warmest on rump, uppertail-coverts and tail. Underparts washed cinnamon-buff, with stronger warm apricot wash on side of breast, flanks and undertail-coverts. Supercilium similar in shape to nominate race but faintly washed cinnamon and less contrasting.

j   **Adult A. c. haringtoni, worn** Slightly paler than fresh adult, with cinnamon washed rump and uppertail-coverts showing greater contrast with mantle, and a stronger creamy brown wash below. Warmer and brighter than worn nominate. Lower mandible often shows dark sides towards tip.

k   **Adult A. c. stevensi** Birds from NE India closely resemble *haringtoni* but upperparts slightly darker and, in particular, shows rufous-brown rather than buff underparts with little contrast between throat and side of head.

PLATE 19: BLYTH'S REED, LARGE-BILLED REED & MARSH WARBLERS

Blyth's Reed Warbler *Acrocephalus dumetorum*

Map and text page 336

13cm; 11.5g. A small, nondescript *Acrocephalus* that closely resembles Eurasian Reed and Marsh Warblers. Breeds in scrub and woodland, often far from wetlands, from S Finland east to C Siberia and C Asia, and winters in the Indian subcontinent. Structure differs from Eurasian Reed and Marsh Warblers by shorter primary projection, emargination on fourth primary, and longer bill than Marsh. Appearance differs by uniform olive-brown upperparts that lack warmer tone even to rump, pale supercilium well-marked in front of eye, less contrasting dark centres to tertials, and underparts paler with whitish chin and throat. Legs dark, usually reddish brown, never pale. Distinctive song slow and repetitive, and includes considerable mimicry.

a   **Adult, fresh, November** After complete moult in autumn, upperparts cold olive-brown and primaries show slightly paler tips. Underparts creamy white with breast and flanks lightly washed brownish grey. Lower mandible usually shows poorly defined dark subterminal smudge at sides near tip.

b   **Adult, worn, breeding** Upperparts duller and slightly greyer than fresh adult, and worn primaries lack pale tips. Underparts colder, lacking brownish wash except on lower flanks.

c   **First-winter, September** Slightly warmer and browner above and buffier below than fresh adult. Rump and uppertail-coverts uniform with mantle, and although browner than fresh adult, lacks rufescent tone of Eurasian Reed Warbler. Lower mandible pinkish and usually lacks dusky sides to tip.

Large-billed Reed Warbler *Acrocephalus orinus*

Map and text page 343

13–14cm; 10.5g. Only known to breed in riparian scrub in high mountain valleys in NE Afghanistan and SE Tajikistan, and winters in Thailand. Specimens and unconfirmed sight records suggest it probably winters widely throughout the Indian subcontinent. Closely resembles Blyth's Reed Warbler, separable in the hand by longer and heavier bill with unmarked pinkish lower mandible, slightly shorter primary projection and longer tail.

d   **Adult** Shows plain olive-brown upperparts with short pale supercilium broadening onto pale lores. Underparts whitish with buffy wash on breast, flanks and undertail-coverts.

Marsh Warbler *Acrocephalus palustris*

Map and text page 347

13cm; 11.5g. Breeds in low rank, herbaceous vegetation, often far from wetlands, from W Europe to W Siberia, and migrates to winter in E and S Africa. Shows long primary projection with regularly spaced primary tips, and a slightly shorter and more robust bill than Eurasian Reed Warbler. Upperparts plain, rather bright olive-brown with short, pale supercilium and well-marked whitish eye-ring. Underparts lightly washed creamy buff, contrasting with paler throat. Legs often pale. Rapid, flowing song includes considerable mimicry.

e   **Adult, fresh, April** After complete late winter moult, typical spring adult shows uniform olive-brown upperparts, buff-washed underparts and contrastingly pale throat. Pale tertial fringes well-defined and dark primaries feathers show conspicuous pale tips.

f   **Adult, fresh, April** Another fresh adult showing slightly warmer, clean olive-brown upperparts with greenish tinge. Note lack of contrast between mantle and rump, bright olive tertial fringes contrasting with darker centres, and pale primary tips.

g   **Adult, fresh, June** Singing male showing characteristic raised fore-crown feathers. Mouth yellow and legs typically pale brown. Adults are still fresh when they return to the breeding grounds and often retain slight yellowish tinge to pale buff underparts.

h   **Adult, December** After partial late autumn moult, freshly moulted body feathers contrast with worn greyish brown wings and tail.

i   **First-winter, August** Young birds in autumn are slightly brighter than worn adults, with warm brown fringes to tertials and greater coverts contrasting with darker centres. Rump and uppertail-coverts often slightly warmer than mantle, but rarely as rufescent-brown as Eurasian Reed Warbler shows. Legs darker brown than most adults.

80

Eurasian Reed Warbler *Acrocephalus scirpaceus*   Map and text page 354

12–14cm; 11g. The most widespread of the small, unstreaked *Acrocephalus*, frequenting *Phragmites* reeds in wetlands from NW Africa and W Europe to C Asia, locally S through Arabian Peninsula, and also in mangroves along Rea Sea and Gulf of Aden coasts. Winters in W, C and E Africa. Shows typical slim *Acrocephalus* structure, with attenuated head shape and fine bill, and long primary projection. Resident birds in south of range significantly smaller than northern migrant breeders. Upperparts brown with tone and hue varying geographically and with season, but usually with warmer rump and uppertail-coverts, and short, pale supercilium extending to rear of eye. Underparts pale, ranging from whitish in worn birds to olive-buff or cinnamon-buff on fresh individuals, and with whitish throat. Leg colour usually dark in young birds, becoming browner and paler in adults. Song slow and varied but only with slight mimicry.

a   **Adult *A. s. scirpaceus*, fresh, winter** By December, upperparts warm olive-brown, becoming cinnamon-brown on rump and uppertail-coverts. Underparts washed warm buff, strongest on breast and flanks, but throat contrastingly white. Dark tertial centres contrast with warm buff fringes, and shows pale tips to primaries.

b   **Adult *A. s. scirpaceus*, worn, spring** Adults returning to W Europe are duller brown above but retain contrasting warm cinnamon-brown rump and uppertail-coverts. Primaries slightly worn with pale tips faint or lost, and dark tertial centres less prominent. Underparts paler than fresh adult, with warmer tones most obvious on flanks. Mouth orange, (cf. Marsh Warbler Plate 19). Note paler legs shown by this individual.

c   **First-winter *A. s. scirpaceus*, August** In autumn, much brighter than worn adult, appearing rusty or cinnamon-tinged above so contrast with rump reduced, and with buffier, less distinct supercilium. Warm buff wash to underparts more extensive than worn adult. Shows typical dark greenish grey legs.

d   **Adult *A. s. fuscus*, fresh** An extremely grey individual from the E African wintering grounds, with uniform appearance to upperparts, lacking warmer tawny brown rump and uppertail-coverts, and with underparts whitish. These birds may originate from the east of the range.

e   **Adult *A. s. fuscus*, fresh, spring** A typical breeding bird from C Asia, showing rather bright olive-brown upperparts with contrasting tawny brown rump and uppertail-coverts, and greyish tinge to nape. Primaries fresh with conspicuous pale tips, and usually shows pale tips to at least the outer three pairs of rectrices, most conspicuous on the outermost. Underparts whitish with pale buff wash restricted to sides of upper breast.

f   **Adult *A. s. fuscus*, worn** By late summer, adult appears duller and slightly greyer brown above, whiter below, and pale tips to abraded primaries and rectrices usually lost. Note browner legs on this bird.

g   **First-winter *A. s. fuscus*** Resembles fresh adult but slightly warmer and brighter. Readily separated from adult in early autumn by brighter appearance and unworn feathers, especially primaries and tail.

h   **Adult *A. s. fuscus*, small local bird, Arabia, April** Duller and more heavily abraded than larger *fuscus* on passage, with worn wings lacking pale tips.

Continued on Plate 21

PLATE 21: AFRICAN REED, EURASIAN REED & CAPE VERDE WARBLERS

African Reed Warbler *Acrocephalus baeticatus*   Map and text page 364

11.5–13cm; 10.5g. Resident or a short distance migrant, breeding in marshy habitats locally in sub-Saharan Africa where five races occur. A small, slim *Acrocephalus* with structure similar to Eurasian Reed Warbler, but wings shorter and more rounded and emargination on fourth primary. Size and appearance varies regionally, with S African birds similar in size to Eurasian Reed Warbler, but those from C and E Africa approximately 10% smaller. All races show uniform warm brown upperparts, short and narrow supercilium reaching to rear of eye, whitish throat and pale underparts, ranging from warm cinnamon-brown to creamy buff.

a   **Adult *A. b. hallae*** SW African race, paler and slightly greyer than nominate *baeticatus*.

b   **Adult *A. b. baeticatus*** A large race, breeding in S Africa. Similar in size and coloration to nominate race of Eurasian Reed Warbler, with warm brown upperparts, brighter cinnamon-brown rump, and warm buff wash on flanks and breast.

c   **Juvenile *A. b. baeticatus*** Closely resembles adult but slightly more rufescent above so contrast between mantle and rump less obvious.

d   **Adult *A. b. suahelicus*** Closely associated with coastal mangroves in E Africa from Tanzania to Kwazulu-Natal in South Africa. Upperparts warmer and darker than nominate, and underparts extensively washed warm rufescent-brown, contrasting with whiter throat.

e   **Adult *A. b. cinnamomeus*** The smallest race, occurring widely throughout W, C and E Africa. Shows rich cinnamon-brown upperparts, more strongly tinged on mantle than nominate *baeticatus*, becoming bright cinnamon-brown on rump and fringes to wing-coverts and tertials. Upperparts of birds from Malawi and Mozambique resemble *suahelicus*, while birds from Lake Chad slightly browner, less rufescent above. Underparts show rich buff wash to breast and flanks contrasting with paler throat.

f   **Adult *A. b. guiersi*** Birds from Senegal are considerably paler and slightly larger than *cinnamomeus*, with colder brown upperparts and head with greyish tinge. Underparts whitish with faint brown wash to side of upper breast and flanks.

Eurasian Reed Warbler *Acrocephalus scirpaceus* (cont. from Plate 20)   Map and text page 354

g   **Adult *A. s. avicenniae*, fresh, November** Smallest race, resident in mangroves fringing S Red Sea and Gulf of Aden. Differs from migrant Palearctic races by shorter, more rounded wing with shorter primary projection and emargination on fourth primary (as African Reed Warbler). Overall coloration similar to some *fuscus* with olive-brown upperparts contrasting with tawny tinge to rump and uppertail-coverts, and fringes to greater coverts and tertials olive-buff. Underparts off-white, with breast washed creamy buff, and buff flanks.

h   **Adult *A. s. avicenniae*, worn, July–August** Upperparts paler and greyer than fresh adult, and supercilium whiter. Underparts creamy white with a slight buff suffusion on flanks.

Cape Verde Warbler *Acrocephalus brevipennis*   Map and text page 369

14–15cm; 16g. A rare resident restricted to Santiago, São Nicolau and Fogo in the Cape Verde Islands, where it occurs in remnant native scrub, along watercourses and in areas of cultivation, particularly sugar cane, maize and coffee plantations interspersed with fruit trees. Larger, more heavily built than Eurasian Reed Warbler, with a short rounded wing, graduated tail tip, long bill and robust grey legs.

i   **Adult, worn, February** Upperparts dull olive-brown with warm wash to rump and uppertail-coverts. Head shows greyish cast to crown and nape and short greyish white supercilium. Underparts show whitish chin and throat contrasting with grey-brown breast and flanks. Lower mandible unmarked orange-yellow.

j   **Fresh, February** Upperparts uniform warm brown, with short, whitish supercilium extending to rear of eye. Chin and throat whitish, contrasting with pale, greyish brown to pinkish buff underparts. It is uncertain why warm brown and dull olive-brown birds occur together in February; warm brown birds may be juveniles.

Lesser Swamp Warbler *Acrocephalus gracilirostris*

Map and text page 372

14–16cm; 16.5g. Resident in wetlands with tall reeds, papyrus and rank grass in sub-Saharan Africa. Appearance and size vary considerably, with eight races recognised. Larger than Eurasian Reed Warbler with longer, more robust bill, short rounded wings, rather long graduated tail and strong dark legs. Upperparts uniform rich warm brown to dark olive-brown, and head with short, well-marked pale supercilium usually extending behind eye. Underparts paler, ranging from pale grey-buff or whitish to greyish brown, usually with warmer wash to lower flanks and undertail-coverts.

a Adult *A. g. gracilirostris* Widespread in South Africa. Shows uniform warm brown upperparts and contrasting appearance to head, with pronounced greyish white supercilium, pale ear-coverts and dark eye-stripe. Underparts with whitish throat, pale greyish buff breast with diffuse greyish brown striations to sides, and warm buff flanks and undertail-coverts.

b Adult *A. g. cunenensis* Occurs locally in regions with low rainfall from W Angola to N South Africa. Differs from nominate race by paler, less warmly tinged upperparts, and whiter underparts.

c Adult *A. g. leptorhynchus* Widespread in lowlands of E Africa from SE Ethiopia and S Somalia to Mozambique and E South Africa. Resembles nominate race but smaller and differs by slightly paler and duller nape and mantle, contrasting with warm rump and uppertail-coverts. Underparts buffy white with cinnamon tinge to lower flanks and undertail-coverts, paler than nominate but less so than *cunenensis*.

d Juvenile *A. g. leptorhynchus* Much brighter more rufescent above than adult, supercilium and underparts washed cinnamon-buff. Juvenile of nominate race similar in appearance but larger.

e Adult *A. g. parvus* Restricted to highland regions from SW Ethiopia to N Tanzania where size varies considerably; a larger individual from Kenya illustrated but birds in N Tanzania smaller, similar in size to *leptorhynchus*. Upperparts darker than nominate race with rich brown head, and mantle tinged greyish, and supercilium and ear-coverts subdued. Underparts greyish brown with whiter chin and throat, but warmer on undertail-coverts.

f Adult *A. g. winterbottomi* Restricted to N Zambia and E Angola. Upperparts darker and greyer above than nominate race, and underparts mostly whitish, with indistinct streaking on breast and throat.

g Adult *A. g. neglectus* Restricted to W Chad, possibly this race also N Nigeria and N Central African Republic. Resembles nominate race with similar warm brown upperparts and head pattern, but smaller, and underparts washed grey-buff, less whitish.

PLATE 23: GREATER SWAMP WARBLER & INDIAN OCEAN *ACROCEPHALUS*

Greater Swamp Warbler *Acrocephalus rufescens*   Map and text page 377

16–18cm; 20g. A large *Acrocephalus*, resident in swamps, papyrus and reedbeds in sub-Saharan Africa where four races occur. Larger and longer billed than Lesser Swamp Warbler, with short rounded wings, relatively long tail and robust dark legs. All races show uniform brown upperparts with short pale supercilium in front of eye and pale, unmarked lores. Underparts vary from whitish to dusky greyish brown, with browner rear flanks and undertail-coverts.

a **Adult A. r. rufescens** Resident W Africa from Ghana and Nigeria to NW Angola. Upperparts uniform olive-brown with slightly warmer brown rump and uppertail-coverts. Underparts with pale creamy buff chin and throat contrasting with greyish brown wash on breast, becoming warmer buff-brown towards breast sides and darker tawny brown on rear flanks and undertail-coverts.

b **Juvenile A. r. rufescens** Closely resembles adult but upperparts slightly warmer, more richly toned and wing and tail feathers with broader and brighter edges. Underparts darker, washed tawny buff, with sides cinnamon-brown.

c **Adult A. r. senegalensis** Restricted to NW Senegal and Gambia. Shows greyer crown and upperparts than nominate *rufescens* and less warmly toned rump. Underparts whitish with buffy grey wash restricted to lower flanks, vent and undertail-coverts.

d **Adult A. r. ansorgei** Ranges through much of C and E Africa south to N Zimbabwe and N Namibia. Distinctly larger, darker and greyer than nominate *rufescens*. Upperparts cold brown, slightly paler tawny brown on rump and uppertail-coverts. Supercilium and lores dingy and inconspicuous, merging with side of head. Underparts suffused greyish brown, with tawny tinge to lower flanks and undertail-coverts. Throat paler than breast with diffuse dusky streaking.

Madagascar Swamp Warbler *Acrocephalus newtoni*   Map and text page 382

18cm; 17g. A widespread resident in marshes, swamps and lake edges throughout Madagascar. Structure resembles Lesser Swamp Warbler with fairly long bill, short rounded wings, long, narrow graduated tail and robust, dark grey legs. Upperparts dull olive-brown, with a narrow pale supercilium above dark eye-stripe. Underparts with variable bold blackish streaking to whitish throat and olive-buff breast, and with greyish brown flanks and undertail-coverts.

e **Adult** A typical, boldly streaked individual.

f **Adult** A particularly poorly marked bird with underpart streaking absent.

g **Juvenile** Warmer brown above than adult, with brighter tone to rump and warm buff supercilium. Underparts warmer buff with throat streaks browner, less conspicuous, and flanks and undertail-coverts tinged cinnamon.

Seychelles Warbler *Acrocephalus sechellensis*   Map and text page 385

14cm; 16g. Rare resident in dense scrub vegetation and woodland on granitic islands in the Seychelles. A rather bulky warbler with a proportionately long bill and short tail, and with short wings and strong, dark legs. Shows uniform drab brown upperparts with a slight greenish or yellowish tinge, and a short inconspicuous supercilium and dark loral line on the otherwise plain head. Underparts yellowish buff with paler throat and undertail-coverts, often with a few faint breast streaks.

h **Adult**

Rodrigues Warbler *Acrocephalus rodericanus*   Map and text page 388

13.5cm; 12g. Rare resident inhabiting scrub and woodland on Rodrigues in the Mascarene Islands. Much smaller, less bulky, than Seychelles Warbler but with proportionately longer tail and finer bill, so overall length similar. Shows pale olive-brown upperparts with contrasting pale yellow cheeks, ear-coverts, lores and short pale yellow supercilium, giving side of head a plain appearance. Entire underparts washed pale lemon-yellow.

i **Adult**

Great Reed Warbler *Acrocephalus arundinaceus*   Map and text page 396

18–20cm; 28g. The largest Palearctic *Acrocephalus*, breeding in reedbeds from W Europe to C Asia, where two races occur, and wintering in sub-Saharan Africa. Has bulky, almost thrush-like structure with a large, robust bill, long primary projection, fairly long and ample tail and stout legs. Upperparts unmarked olive-brown to buffy brown, often warmly tinged, especially on rump and uppertail-coverts. Shows a prominent pale supercilium extending behind eye and broad above darker lores. Underparts pale, with whitish throat often faintly streaked, and breast, flanks and undertail-coverts with a variable buff wash. Song slow, loud and raucous.

a   **Adult *A. a. arundinaceus*, fresh** In early winter following complete moult, upperparts rich warm olive-brown with brighter rufescent wash on rump and uppertail-coverts, and pale tips to primaries. Lower edge of throat shows faintly darker streaks. Breast sides and flanks warm buff. Leg colour variable, usually brownish, paler in older birds.

b   **Adult *A. a. arundinaceus*, worn** Breeding birds reaching Europe usually show duller brown upperparts but greater contrast between darker mantle and paler rufous-brown rump and uppertail-coverts. Worn primaries usually lack paler tips. Underparts paler than fresh adult and throat streaking often lost. This singing bird shows characteristic head shape with fore-crown feathers raised.

c   **Juvenile *A. a. arundinaceus*** Upperparts cinnamon-brown, warmer and browner than heavily worn autumn adult but generally paler and buffier above than fresh adult. Underparts more extensively warm buff, and throat lacks streaking. Most have extensive post-juvenile moult into similar first-winter plumage. Legs dark greyish, darker than adult.

d   **Adult *A. a. zarudnyi*** Differences from nominate race are most pronounced in C Asian breeding birds, when paler and colder tone to olive-brown upperparts and wing feather edges are most apparent, and underparts are whiter with paler buff wash restricted to flanks. After complete winter moult many are warmer and browner than the individual illustrated and resemble nominate *arundinaceus*. Juvenile and first-winter *zarudnyi* warmer than autumn adult and not safely separable from nominate.

Basra Reed Warbler *Acrocephalus griseldis*   Map and text page 391

15–16cm; 16g. A localised breeding bird, restricted to marshes of S Iraq, and wintering in E and SE Africa. Much smaller and slimmer than Great Reed Warbler, with long and slim bill, long primary projection and strong dark grey legs. Upperparts plain olive-brown, but head shows narrow, pale supercilium extending behind eye, and contrasting dark eye-stripe. Shows unstreaked whitish throat, while underparts vary from whitish to pale buff.

e   **Adult, fresh** In December, after complete moult, upperparts appear uniform cold olive-brown and lack warmer rump and uppertail-coverts. Breast and flanks washed buff.

f   **Adult, worn** Adults returning to breeding grounds in April appear duller and greyer above but retain conspicuous whitish tips to primaries. Supercilium and underparts paler than fresh adult.

g   **Juvenile** Differs from fresh adult by warmer brown tinge to upperparts, more prominent pale brown edges to tertials and wing-coverts that contrast with darker centres, and brighter brown edges to flight feathers. Underparts show extensive warm buff wash and paler throat.

Oriental Reed Warbler *Acrocephalus orientalis* Map and text page 403

18–19cm; 22g. This eastern counterpart of Great Reed Warbler is an abundant breeding bird in *Phragmites* reed-beds from E Mongolia and SE Siberia to N and E China, Korea and Japan, and winters throughout SE Asia. Structure as Great Reed Warbler but slightly smaller and with proportionately shorter primary projection. Appearance closely resembles Great Reed Warbler with olive-brown upperparts, slightly warmer and paler rump and uppertail-coverts, conspicuous pale supercilium and contrasting darker eye-stripe, and conspicuous whitish tips to outer three pairs of tail feathers. Underparts variable, usually with whitish chin and throat and buff wash across breast and flanks, but streaks on lower throat and upper breast sides generally more pronounced than on Great Reed Warbler. Song resembles that of Great Reed Warbler.

a   **Adult, October, fresh** From September onwards, following complete moult on breeding grounds by juveniles and adults, plumage identical but they remain readily separable by iris colour; pale brown in adult and greyish brown in young birds. Shows warm olive-brown upperparts, extensive bright buff wash to underparts and conspicuous dark streaking on lower throat and upper breast.

b   **Adult, May, worn** Typical breeding bird with dull olive-brown upperparts and buff wash restricted to lower flanks, vent and undertail-coverts. Usually retains indistinct streaking on lower throat and upper breast, generally absent on Great Reed Warbler at this season.

c   **Adult, July** After breeding, adults are extremely worn and faded. Like this bird, most will have lost throat streaking and warmer plumage tones, although rump and uppertail-coverts often slightly brighter.

Black-browed Reed Warbler *Acrocephalus bistrigiceps* (see Plate 17) Map and text page 311

d   **Adult, May** Typical adult, included here to illustrate size and structural differences with larger Oriental Reed and Thick-billed Warblers.

Thick-billed Warbler *Phragamaticola aedon* Map and text page 516

18–19cm; 24g. A large, warmly coloured warbler breeding in woodland, scrub and rank undergrowth in C and SE Siberia, N Mongolia and NE China, and wintering from N Indian subcontinent to SE Asia. Shows distinctive structure with short, thick bill, domed crown, relatively short and rounded wings, and long, narrow and graduated tail. Upperparts including head and closed wing warm brown, with brighter more richly toned reddish brown rump, uppertail-coverts and tail. Head plain, lacking supercilium and eye-stripe but shows pale unmarked lores. Underparts pale sandy brown, with creamy white chin and throat, and warmer buff undertail-coverts. Bill pale greyish brown with paler unmarked lower mandible. Legs greyish.

e   **Adult *P. a. aedon*, May** Shows warm fulvous-brown upperparts, and underparts lightly washed pale buff on breast, warming and darkening slightly towards flanks and undertail-coverts.

f   **Adult *P. a. stegmanni*, May** Closely resembles nominate but upperparts including tail marginally darker, more rufescent or cinnamon-brown, and underparts extensively washed bright buff. There is considerable overlap and many within range of *stegmanni* not safely separable from nominate *aedon*.

g   **Adult, fresh** Throughout the range, in both autumn and spring, some birds are paler, less richly coloured than typical birds, with duller olive-brown upperparts, wings and tail, and whitish underparts with warmer tones restricted to upper breast and flanks, but chin, lower breast and belly white. Birds with this appearance include known young birds, but it is uncertain whether adults can also resemble this. From October onwards, following complete moult by both adults and juveniles, there are no established plumage features by which they can be separated, although iris colour remains reliable; dark brown in adults and greyish brown in young birds.

Clamorous Reed Warbler *Acrocephalus stentoreus*   Map and text page 410

The most widespread *Acrocephalus*, frequenting reedbeds, papyrus swamps and mangroves across warmer temperate and tropical latitudes from Egypt and coasts of the Arabian Peninsula to C Asia, the Indian subcontinent, the Philippines, and many islands of Indonesia and Melanesia east to the Solomon Islands. Ten mostly resident races occur, but *brunnescens* from C Asia migrates to winter in Pakistan and N India. Shows marked geographical variation in size, bill structure and coloration. Size varies from medium-sized *sumbae* in N Australasia to large *brunnescens* in C Asia which approaches Great Reed Warbler in size and bulk. All races share proportionately long, slim bill that accentuates attenuated head structure, relatively long tail, and much shorter primary projection than Oriental Reed and Great Reed Warblers. All races show brownish upperparts and less pronounced head pattern than Great Reed Warbler, with supercilium usually narrow and poorly defined, and eye-stripe often indistinct or absent. Underpart colour variable but paler than upperparts and most races lack throat streaking. Bill dark grey with pale lower mandible, and legs dark grey to pinkish grey. Song is loud and raucous but delivered in short, stereotyped bursts.

Larger races Typically 18–20cm; 24g.

a   **Adult *A. s. stentoreus*** Fairly large, with long, narrow and laterally compressed bill, restricted to Egypt. Upperparts warm olive-brown with narrow pale buff supercilium above lores, and indistinct eye-stripe. Whitish throat contrasts with light fulvous-brown breast, darkening to tawny brown on lower flanks and vent, becoming paler buff on undertail-coverts.

b   **Juvenile *A. s. stentoreus*** Much brighter than adult, with warm rufous-brown to dull cinnamon upperparts including rump and closed wings, and cinnamon-buff supercilium. Underparts washed pale rufous-brown, palest on throat, more intense on breast and upper flanks, and approaching closed wing colour on lower flanks.

c   **Adult *A. a. levantinus*, typical morph** Closely resembles nominate *stentoreus*, but slightly darker and browner, less warmly coloured and with longer wing and proportionately longer tail. Upperparts uniform dull brown, sometimes with indistinct olive wash. Throat and belly whitish, contrasting with dull cinnamon-brown breast and flanks.

d   **Adult *A. s. levantinus*, dark morph** Distinctive dark sepia-brown appearance with slightly warmer throat is unique to this race.

e   **Adult *A. s. brunnescens*, fresh** This large migrant race, breeding in C Asia, shows a heavier bill, longer primary projection, and paler and less warmly coloured appearance than nominate *stentoreus*, and more closely resembles the sympatric Great Reed Warbler. Upperparts uniform olive-brown with narrow pale supercilium usually extending behind eye. Whitish chin and throat contrast with pale fulvous-brown breast and flanks.

f   **Adult *A. s. brunnescens*** Smaller resident *brunnescens* occur in mangroves fringing the coasts of the Red Sea, Arabian Gulf and Persian Gulf. They tend to appear drabber than C Asian birds, with grey-tinged crown and mantle contrasting with slightly warmer rump, and with whiter underparts. While there is overlap, larger migratory *brunnescens* rarely appear so pallid.

g   **Adult *A. s. amyae*** A large resident race, restricted to NE India to SW China. Similar in size and structure to *brunnescens* but, when fresh, differs by slightly richer, browner upperparts, narrower and less prominent supercilium, and more strongly washed pale gingery buff underparts. When worn, these differences become less apparent.

h   **Adult *A. s. meridionalis*** Endemic to Sri Lanka. Similar in size to *brunnescens* but darker and more richly coloured, and slightly darker above than *amyae* with rufescent tinge. Underparts whitish with fulvous-brown flanks, and some show indistinct dusky striations on lower throat and breast sides.

i   **Adult *A. s. lentecaptus*** Restricted to Borneo, Lombok and Sumbawa. A large race, similar in size to *meridionalis*. Upperparts dark warm brown, and supercilium often conspicuous, extending behind the ear-coverts. Underparts washed orange-cinnamon, with contrasting whitish throat.

Continued on Plate 27

PLATE 27: CLAMOROUS REED & AUSTRALIAN REED WARBLERS

Clamorous Reed Warbler *Acrocephalus stentoreus* **(cont. from Plate 26)**   Map and text page 410

Smaller races Typically 14–15cm; *c.* 16g.

a   **Adult** *A. s. harterti* Resident in the Philippines. Much smaller, shorter billed and shorter-winged than *brunnescens*, from which it differs by darker, richer toned upperparts and poorly marked supercilium. Underparts variable, some with extensive fulvous-brown wash contrasting with whitish throat, others resemble *siebersi*, appearing paler with light brown wash on breast, intensifying on flanks and contrasting with whitish belly. Some show indistinct breast streaking.

b   **Adult** *A. s. siebersi* Restricted to Java. Shows dark, warm brown upperparts similar to *lenticaptus*, but underparts less strongly washed, appearing similar in colour and pattern to *brunnescens* and *amyae*, but often with indistinct striations at side of upper breast.

c   **Adult** *A. s. celebensis* A small race, only known from Sulawesi. Upperparts warm rufescent-brown. Underparts contrastingly pale, typically creamy white but intensifying to warm creamy brown on flanks.

d   **Adult** *A. s. sumbae* The smallest race, similar in size to Australian Reed Warbler and *celebensis*. Widespread, occurring on many islands from Buru in the Moluccas, and Sumba and Timor in the Lesser Sundas, east through Melanesia to the Solomon Islands. Across this range shows marked variation in coloration. Some are darker as bird illustrated here, with rich warm brown upperparts, short and indistinct buff supercilium, pale buff throat and cinnamon-buff underparts. Others are paler and resemble *celebensis*, but it remains unclear how much variation is due to wear and bleaching.

Australian Reed Warbler *Acrocephalus australis*   Map and text page 422

15–16cm; 18g. An unstreaked *Acrocephalus*, breeding in wetlands with reeds, sedges and other emergent vegetation in SW and SE Australia, mainly near coast, but locally inland and north to tropical W Australia and NE Queensland. Some are resident but most southern breeders migrant to north after breeding. Similar in size and structure to smaller races of Clamorous Reed Warbler, with slender bill, short primary projection and relatively long, broad tail. Appearance variable but all show brown upperparts, short supercilium most conspicuous above lores, a rather diffuse darker loral stripe and paler underparts.

e   **Adult** *A. a. australis* Widespread throughout SE and E Australia. Upperparts rufescent brown, slightly warmer and paler on rump and uppertail-coverts. Throat whitish, often with indistinct dusky streaking across lower edge, and warm buff on breast, darkening towards flanks.

f   **Adult** *A. a. gouldi*, **fresh, May** Slightly larger than nominate *australis* and with longer, broader based bill. Appears darker than nominate race with warmer, richly toned upperparts, and shows extensive cinnamon-buff wash to underparts, palest on throat and most intense on lower flanks.

g   **Adult** *A. a. gouldi*, **worn, September** Duller above and paler below than fresh adult, and more closely resembles nominate race.

Millerbird *Acrocephalus familiaris*   Map and text page 428

14cm; 18g. Resident in low scrub and bushes on Nihoa in the Hawaiian Islands. A small *Acrocephalus* with a rather short, fine bill, rounded crown and relatively long tail.

a   **Adult, fresh** Upperparts uniform brown or olive-brown with dark lores and a narrow, poorly marked supercilium. Underparts paler, with creamy white throat, breast whitish to pale grey-brown, becoming warmer and browner on flanks, and pale undertail-coverts.

b   **Adult, worn** Upperparts greyer and slightly paler, and underparts whiter.

Cook Islands Warbler *Acrocephalus kerearako*   Map and text page 431

16cm; 22.5g. Resident on Mangaia and Mitiaro in the Cook Islands in woodland, bushy scrub, reedbeds and gardens. A plain, medium-sized *Acrocephalus* with a rather long and slender bill and relatively long tail.

c   **Adult *A. k. kerearako*** Birds on Mangaia show warm brown to olive-brown upperparts, and slightly brighter, richer brown edges to wing-coverts and flight feathers. Head shows yellowish buff ear-coverts, narrow supercilium above dark lores, and a poorly defined eye-stripe. Underparts washed yellowish buff with creamy white chin and throat. Race *kaoko* on Mitiaro differs by slightly paler yellower underparts, often with indistinct grey-brown streaking on throat and upper breast, while sides of breast and lower flanks are tinged paler brown.

Pitcairn Island Warbler *Acrocephalus vaughani*   Text page 434

17cm; 25g. Resident in forest, scrub and gardens on Pitcairn. A fairly stocky *Acrocephalus* with a moderately long bill, sloping forehead and rounded crown, relatively short wings and long tail. Male slightly larger than female. Adults usually show random, asymmetrical pattern of white feathers in wings and tail, less frequently on head and mantle.

d   **Adult** Upperparts mottled ash-grey with paler rump, and short, narrow whitish supercilium above lores. Wing shows conspicuous white fringes to wing-coverts and tertials that contrast with blackish centres, and randomly placed white remiges and rectrices contrast with typical black feathers. Underparts pale yellowish or creamy white.

e   **Juvenile** Browner than adult, with strong buff wash below, especially on flanks and undertail-coverts. Rarely shows white feathering.

Henderson Island Warbler *Acrocephalus taiti*   Text page 437

17cm; 26g. Endemic to Henderson Island where resident in climax forest. A fairly large *Acrocephalus* resembling Pitcairn Island Warbler, and adult usually shows random and asymmetrical pattern of white and black remiges and rectrices.

f   **Adult** Upperparts variably mottled pale grey with conspicuous whitish feather fringes, palest on rump and uppertail-coverts, giving frosted appearance. Underparts largely white.

Rimatara Warbler *Acrocephalus rimitarae*   Text page 439

17cm; 26.5g. Restricted to Rimatara where resident in bushy forest undergrowth, reedbeds and damp vegetation. A large *Acrocephalus*, not separable from Pitcairn Island Warbler except by range.

g   **Adult** Crown to mantle mottled dull olive-brown to grey-brown, becoming slightly paler on rump. Fringes to wing-coverts white, in some birds forming conspicuous wing-panel. Black and white remiges and rectrices mixed randomly in wings and tail. Underparts creamy white, tinged yellow on breast and belly.

Kiritimati Warbler *Acrocephalus aequinoctialis*   Map and text page 441

16cm; 25g. Resident on Kiritimati and Teraina in the Republic of Kiribati. Similar in structure to Pitcairn Island Warbler but slightly smaller. Upperparts grey with contrastingly paler rump and uppertail-coverts and dark grey tail. Tips to greater and median coverts form two narrow whitish wing bars, and edges to remiges form pale wing-panel.

h   **Adult *A. a. aequinoctialis*** Occurs on Kiritimati. Shows conspicuous long, white supercilium and whitish underparts with pale grey mottling on breast.

i   **Adult *A. a. pistor*** Found only on Teraina. Slightly larger than nominate race from which it differs by indistinct greyish supercilium, and light grey wash to underparts, often with indistinct streaking across lower throat and upper breast.

PLATE 29: PACIFIC ISLAND *ACROCEPHALUS* II

Southern Marquesan Warbler *Acrocephalus mendanae*

Northern Marquesan Warbler *Acrocephalus percernis*

20–22cm. Two morphologically indistinguishable species, each with four races, restricted to nine islands in the Marquesas. Highly adaptable, occurring widely in scrub, gardens, cultivation and secondary forest. Large and bulky, with long, strong bill and sloping forehead giving attenuated appearance to head. All taxa share dull greenish upperparts with yellowish rump and uppertail-coverts, and blackish tail edged and tipped yellow. Head shows long, broad yellowish supercilium that contrasts with the bold olive-green eye-stripe. Side of head and underparts yellow, varying in intensity, tone and hue. Shows blackish flight feathers fringed pale yellow or whitish. The extent to which the appearance of these species overlaps, or whether any diagnostic characters exist, has yet to be established.

Southern Marquesan Warbler   Map and text page 444

a   **A. m. mendanae** Restricted to Hiva Oa and Tahuata. Closely resembles *A. p. percernis* with same size and structure, but yellow underparts slightly paler, although extent of overlap not yet established.

b   **A. m. fatuhivae** Endemic to Fatuhiva. Structure as *percernis*, but with slightly longer, finer bill. Supercilium, ear-coverts and underparts slightly paler yellow than *mendanae*, and shows straw-yellow to bright warm buff rump and uppertail-coverts, which merge with similarly toned flanks and undertail-coverts. Crown, nape and mantle paler green when fresh, lacking olive tones typical of *mendanae* and *A. p. percernis*. Wing-coverts, primaries and secondaries narrowly edged and fringed white rather than yellow.

Northern Marquesan Warbler   Map and text page 444

c   **A. p. percernis** Occurs only on Nuku Hiva. Size and structure as *A. m. mendanae*, but differs by more intense yellow wash to supercilium, side of head and underparts, always appearing richer yellow than straw-yellow underparts of *A. m. mendanae*. Upperparts slightly greener, with brighter yellowish fringes.

d   **A. p. aquilonis** Endemic to Eiao. Size and structure similar to *A. p. percernis* but marginally smaller and with slightly smaller bill. Upperparts slightly darker with indistinct brownish tone, and underparts richer yellow.

e   **A. p. idae** The smallest race, restricted to Huahuna. Distinctly smaller than *percernis*, with shorter, more slender bill. Overall slightly paler than *percernis*.

Tahiti Warbler *Acrocephalus caffer*   Map and text page 449

20–22cm. Restricted to thick secondary forest in valleys on slopes of interior Tahiti in the Society Islands. A large *Acrocephalus*, showing a long, heavy bill, low sloping forehead, short rounded wings and strong legs and feet. Plumage variable and two colour morphs occur.

f   **Adult, typical morph** Upperparts dark greyish brown with conspicuous creamy white feather fringes, broadest on rump and uppertail-coverts. Shows prominent pale supercilium contrasting with dark grey crown and narrow blackish eye-stripe. Supercilium, side of head and neck, and entire underparts creamy white to pale yellow. Blackish wing and tail feathers fringed and edged creamy white. Bill dark grey with conspicuous pinkish sides to lower mandible, and legs dark grey.

g   **Adult, typical morph, fresh** Fringes to upperparts and wing feathers broader and yellower, so appears paler than worn adult. Supercilium, side of the head and underparts variably washed pale creamy buff to pale primrose-yellow.

h   **Adult dark morph** Entirely brownish black including bill, legs and feet.

i   **Juvenile, typical morph** Dull olive green above and lacks conspicuous pale fringes. Supercilium, side of head and neck, and underparts washed sulphur-yellow. Fringes to wing-coverts, and edges to flight feathers paler than upperparts.

Tuamotu Warbler *Acrocephalus atyphus*   Map and text page 453

18–19cm. Resident on at least 40 atolls in the Tuamotu Archipelago, where six races with two colour morphs occur; a grey-and-white morph and warm brown morph, sometimes on same island. Widespread on most atolls where it frequents thick coastal scrub, cultivation, woodland and plantations. A large *Acrocephalus* with a long, rather thin bill, low forehead and relatively short wings. Many birds show random white feathering in the body plumage, wings and tail, usually restricted to occasional feathers and fringes on mantle or tips of tail feathers, but occasionally an entire tail feather is white.

a   **Adult *A. a. atyphus*, grey-and-white morph** The most widespread race, occurring on 30 or more atolls. This morph lacks warmer tones and shows enhanced contrast between paler and darker areas, with supercilium appearing conspicuous behind eye, and darker eye-stripe better defined. Upperparts rather cold greyish brown, with paler fringes to greater and median coverts, tertials and secondaries showing contrast with closed wing. Underparts whitish, washed pale grey across upper breast, washed pale cream on flanks and undertail-coverts.

b   **Adult *A. a. atyphus*, brown morph** Shows dull rufescent-brown upperparts, warmer creamy buff supercilium that extends over ear-coverts, and poorly defined darker eye-stripe, often little more than a small dark spot in front of eye. Underparts white with warm peachy buff wash restricted to breast sides, flanks and undertail-coverts. Closed wing more uniform than on grey-and-white morph although pale edges to tertials and secondaries can form pale wing-panel.

c   **Adult *A. a. ravus*** Restricted to six atolls in SE Tuamotus. Structure as nominate form. Upperparts slightly but consistently browner than grey-and-white morph of nominate form, and conspicuous supercilium shows variable yellowish wash. Side of head and underparts washed warm yellowish straw or paler with subdued yellow tone. Edges to wing-coverts, tertials and secondaries whitish, forming pale wing-panel.

d   **Adult *A. a. eremus*, brown morph** Confined to Makatea. Structure resembles nominate form but with slightly larger decurved bill. Upperparts more rufescent than nominate, and underparts washed pale cinnamon-brown, palest on throat and breast.

Nightingale Warbler *Acrocephalus luscinius*   Map and text page 457

18–19cm; 34g. Resident on Saipan, Alamagan and Agiguan in the Mariana Islands, where two races occur. Inhabits forest edge, scrub, grassland and wetland fringes. A large *Acrocephalus* with an extremely long, slender bill showing conspicuous dull pink lower mandible, and grey legs.

e   **Adult *A. l. luscinius*, fresh** Occurs on Saipan and Alamagam. Shows plain olive-brown upperparts with conspicuous pale supercilium and narrow dark eye-stripe. Underparts with whitish throat, pale creamy buff breast and warm peach wash on flanks.

f   **Adult *A. l. luscinius*, worn** Appearance more contrasting than fresh adult, with crown, mantle and wings duller greyish brown, and supercilium, side of head and underparts pale greyish white.

Caroline Islands Warbler *Acrocephalus syrinx*   Map and text page 460

16cm. Widespread resident throughout the Caroline Islands in Micronesia, occupying a wide range of habitats from montane rain forest to lowland cultivation and coastal scrub. A rather large, robust *Acrocephalus* with short wings and long slender bill. Legs dark greyish.

g   **Adult** Upperparts warm brown, more richly coloured than Nightingale Warbler, and with grey wash on crown and nape, and brighter rusty brown rump. Shows conspicuous whitish supercilium, narrow dark eye-stripe and pale side to head. Underparts show white throat contrasting with pale cinnamon-brown wash to breast and darker, more richly coloured lower flanks.

Nauru Warbler *Acrocephalus rehsei*   Text page 463

15cm. Restricted to Nauru in the W Pacific, where it occurs widely in scrub and bushes, remnant forest and gardens. A medium-sized, warmly coloured *Acrocephalus*, smaller than similar Caroline Islands Warbler with a slightly shorter bill and less attenuated head structure.

h   **Adult** Upperparts dark rufescent-brown, slightly brighter on rump and uppertail-coverts. Supercilium, side of head and throat washed pale rusty brown, becoming warmer and darker on breast, flanks and undertail-coverts.

PLATE 31: ICTERINE, MELODIOUS & OLIVE-TREE WARBLERS

Icterine Warbler *Hippolais icterina*

Map and text page 465

13.5cm; 13g. Breeds in open woodland from NW and E Europe to W Siberia, and winters in sub-Saharan Africa, mainly south of equator. A medium-sized warbler with a long primary projection similar to tertial length, and well-spaced primary tips. Tail slim and square-cut, and lacks white in feather tips. Upperparts greenish olive, contrasting with yellow underparts, and often a pale yellow or whitish panel in the closed wing. Shows yellow supercilium, side to head and lores giving distinctive open-face pattern in which dark eye is prominent. Lower mandible pinkish yellow and unmarked, legs dark grey or blue-grey.

a   **Adult fresh, April** Distinctive, with bright greenish olive upperparts, lemon-yellow underparts and con-spicuous pale wing-panel.

b   **Adult worn, July** Compared with fresh adult, upperparts slightly duller, yellow underparts paler, pale pri-mary tips lost, and pale wing-panel inconspicuous or absent. Worn birds closely resemble Melodious Warbler in late summer but long primary projection remains diagnostic.

c   **Juvenile, August** Duller than fresh adult, with browner upperparts and paler yellow underparts, especially on throat and abdomen. Pale wing-panel and primary tips less prominent than on fresh adult.

d   **Pale variant** A small minority lack yellow and green plumage tones. Upperparts greyish olive and under-parts whitish but supercilium usually retains faint yellow. Still shows pale wing-panel.

Melodious Warbler *Hippolais polyglotta*

Map and text page 471

13cm; 11g. Breeds in woodland and bushy growth in SW Europe and NW Africa and winters in tropical W Africa. Neater and more compact than slightly larger Icterine Warbler, and with slightly rounded tail. Always shows much shorter primary projection, extending between half and two-thirds of exposed tertial length. Plumage closely resembles Icterine Warbler and shares similar open-face pattern, but overall slightly warmer with olive or greenish olive upperparts and yellow or yellowish buff underparts. Wings typically appear uniform, even when fresh, and a pale panel, if present, is never as prominent as in Icterine Warbler. Legs are typically brownish grey. As in Icterine Warbler, pale variants occasionally occur, lacking yellow and green in plumage.

e   **Adult fresh, winter** From late November, fresh upperparts olive-brown or greenish brown. Closed wing usually uniform, lacking paler fringes or pale wing-panel, but showing pale primary tips. Underparts rich yellow with slight buff suffusion.

f   **Adult worn, summer** Birds returning to Europe are quite worn and primaries lack pale tips. Upperparts slightly duller than fresh adult, but side of head and underparts still rich yellow. During summer upper-parts become duller brown to greyish brown, and underparts fade to paler yellow or whitish.

g   **Juvenile, August** Upperparts browner than fresh adult, supercilium and underparts paler buff-yellow. Yellow wash extensive on some birds, on others limited to throat and breast. Edges to tertials and secondar-ies drab yellowish buff to greyish white and may form faint wing-panel, usually lost to abrasion by August. Separation from worn adult difficult from August onwards.

Olive-tree Warbler *Hippolais olivetorum*

Map and text page 476

15cm; 16g. The largest *Hippolais*, breeding in olive groves, orchards and open woodland in Mediterranean region of SE Europe and S Turkey, and wintering mainly in S Africa. A large, slim warbler with an attenuated structure, accentuated by long primary projection of similar length to tertials, long, strong bill and long tail. Shows distinc-tive greyish upperparts, with conspicuous whitish panel in closed wing, but head poorly marked, with short whitish supercilium, and darker grey lores and cheeks suggesting hooded appearance. Underparts greyish white. Tail often shows distinct whitish edges and fresh outer feathers are broadly fringed white at tip of inner web. Shows conspicu-ous orange-yellow lower mandible, and robust dark grey legs.

h   **Adult fresh, May** Upperparts drab brownish grey with slightly warmer grey-buff rump and uppertail-coverts. Wings slightly darker, showing conspicuous pale panel formed by buffy white edges to secondaries, outer tertial and tips of greater coverts. Underparts tinged cream, often with greyish wash to breast and flanks.

i   **Adult worn, August** With wear, wings and tail become browner and contrast with duller, greyer upperparts. Pale wing-panel reduced to a narrow band along edge of outer tertial and inner secondaries, but often lost by August. Most have partial moult during migration, after which contrast between grey upperparts and faded brown wings and tail is more pronounced.

j   **Juvenile, July** Resembles fresh adult but slightly paler and browner, with pale sandy buff rather than whitish wing-panel, and pale edges and tips to outer tail feathers less well defined. Replaces body feathering and inner greater coverts in post-juvenile moult before autumn migration, after which first-winter bird resem-bles adult.

PLATE 32: UPCHER'S WARBLER & OLIVACEOUS WARBLERS

Upcher's Warbler *Hippolais languida*

Map and text page 481

14cm; 12g. Breeds among scrub in dry hills and semi-deserts of SW and C Asia, and winters in E Africa. Similar in size to Icterine Warbler but with longer bill and relatively long and bulky tail. Primary projection approximately two-thirds of tertial length, and tip of middle tertial falls close to longest. Greyish upperparts often contrast with darker tail. Shows conspicuous pale supercilium above dusky loral line, and whitish underparts. Lower mandible pinkish or yellowish, and legs grey. Often sits prominently on top of a small bush, slowly lowering and raising slightly spread tail and moving it randomly from side to side.

a   **Adult fresh, February** Shows light grey-brown or sandy grey upperparts, conspicuous whitish supercilium to just behind eye and variably diffuse dusky loral line. Underparts clean, whitish or with faint creamy wash. Tail blackish with narrow white edge and white fringes to outer feather tips. Often shows conspicuous pale wing-panel.

b   **Adult worn, July** On breeding grounds, appears faded and brown tones are lost. Upperparts duller grey and underparts dingy white. Tends to lose pale wing-panel and white tail feather tips.

c   **First-winter, August** Resembles fresh adult, but wing and tail feathers less dark. Shows distinct pale buff panel in closed wing, and pale fringes to wing-coverts, but pale tips to tail feathers poorly defined.

Eastern Olivaceous Warbler *Iduna pallida*

Map and text page 486

11.5–13cm; 9.5g. Breeds in dry bushy habitats, orchards, olive groves and oases from Mediterranean region of SE Europe and Middle East to SC Asia, throughout Sahara from SE Morocco to Sudan, and N Somalia. Resident or dispersive south to W Africa, but migratory race *elaeica* winters NE and E Africa. A small, slim warbler with an attenuated head structure and short undertail-coverts. Less bulky than Upcher's Warbler and much smaller than Olive-tree. Slender bill, narrower and less bulky than in Western Olivaceous Warbler. African races show short primary projection but this is longer, more than half of tertial length, in migratory race *elaeica*. All races show unmarked pinkish yellow lower mandible and slender grey-brown legs. Has distinctive, persistent tail dipping habit, usually calling at same time.

Saharan races (See Plate 33 for Palearctic race *I. p. elaeica*)

d   **Adult *I. p. pallida*, fresh** Breeds NE Sahara from Egypt to N Sudan. Upperparts buffy brown. Shows pale edges to wing feathers, and pale fringes at tail feather tips. Underparts washed pale creamy buff.

e   **Adult *I. p. pallida*, worn** Upperparts slightly duller and greyer, underparts dingy white and wings lack paler feather fringes.

f   **Adult *I. p. reiseri*, fresh** Restricted to NW Sahara. Size and structure as nominate *pallida*, and with similar pale wing-panel. Differs in slightly paler and sandier buff-brown upperparts, more ochreous rump, and cleaner creamy white wash to underparts.

g   **Adult *I. p. reiseri*, worn** Slightly greyer than fresh adult, with more uniform appearance to wing.

h   **Adult *I. p. laeneni*, fresh** Resident in S Sahara. Closely resembles *reiseri* but slightly smaller.

i   **First-winter, probably *I. p. alulensis*** Coastal Sudan, August. A small grey-brown form with short primary projection and prominent pale edges to wing-coverts.

Western Olivaceous Warbler *Iduna opaca*

Map and text page 494

13.5cm; 11g. Breeds in olive groves, scrub covered hillsides and bushy river valleys in Iberia and Maghreb region of NW Africa, and migrates to tropical W Africa. More bulky and with longer tail than Eastern Olivaceous Warbler. Head with swollen, broad-based bill and low fore-crown giving attenuated profile. Appearance rather uniform, with pale brown upperparts, a poorly marked pale supercilium, usually pale lores and buffy white underparts, and always lacks pale wing-panel. Tail similar in colour to upperparts but outer feathers usually show brownish white fringes at tip. Legs brownish or pinkish grey, stouter than Eastern Olivaceous. Shows no distinctive tail movements.

j   **Adult fresh, December** Upperparts light brown, similar to race *reiseri* of Eastern Olivaceous, and lacking olive tinge of race *elaeica*. Shows short sandy buff supercilium and pale lores, so head appears bland with 'open-faced' appearance similar to Melodious Warbler. Underparts with light buff wash, most pronounced on breast sides and flanks.

k   **Adult worn, June** Upperparts drabber greyish brown, underparts dingy white. Usually shows faint dusky spot in front of eye, so loses 'open-faced' expression of fresh adult. Resembles pale variant Melodious Warbler.

l   **First-winter** Resembles fresh adult but paler, especially on top and sides of head. Fringes to wing-coverts and flight feathers paler. Tail feathers paler and browner with tips lacking distinct pale fringes.

PLATE 33: SYKES'S, BOOTED & EASTERN OLIVACEOUS WARBLERS

Sykes's Warbler *Iduna rama*

Map and text page 498

12cm; 9g. Plainest and drabbest of the small grey-brown *Iduna*, closely resembling Booted and Eastern Olivaceous Warblers. Breeds among scattered bushes in arid grassland and semi-deserts of SW and SC Asia, and migrates to winter throughout the Indian subcontinent. A small, pale warbler with slender *Acrocephalus*-like structure, accentuated by short, straight-sided bill, rather flat crown, short undertail-coverts and relatively long tail. Primary projection shorter than Booted and Eastern Olivaceous Warblers, approximately 30% of tertial length. Upperparts pale greyish brown or sandy grey, with short pale supercilium contrasting with darker loral spot. Wing plainer than Eastern Olivaceous Warbler, always lacking pale wing-panel, and with less contrast between tertial centres and fringes than Booted shows. Underparts white or buffy white. Outer tail feathers edged and bordered whitish around tip and on distal part of inner web. Pinkish lower mandible sometimes with dark smudge near tip, but not as distinct as in Booted. Legs light brownish or pinkish, paler and less grey than in *elaeica* Eastern Olivaceous. Tail tends to be flicked erratically, showing no deliberate movements.

a   **Adult, fresh, December** Upperparts light greyish brown, lacking warm tones of Booted or olive-grey of *elaeica* Eastern Olivaceous, and lacks pale wing-panel. Shows poorly marked head pattern, occasionally with indistinct darker shadow over supercilium, not as obvious as on Booted. Underparts whitish with faint buff tinge to breast.

b   **Adult, worn, May** Slightly paler and greyer brown above and whiter below. Wings uniformly brown and primaries lack distinct pale tips.

c   **First-winter, August** Resembles freshly moulted adult but by August often worn. Differs by paler sandy brown upperparts with paler brown wing and tail feathers. Usually lacks faint dark line above lores.

Booted Warbler *Iduna caligata*

Map and text page 503

11.5cm; 9g. Breeds in open scrub and forest edge from E Finland to C Siberia and C Asia and winters in Indian subcontinent. Smallest *Iduna* with rather *Phylloscopus*-like structure, accentuated by small and narrow bill with 'pinched in' sides, short undertail-coverts and shorter tail than Sykes's Warbler. Primary projection short, 30–40% of tertial length. Conspicuous narrow supercilium, dusky loral line, and usually a narrow and diffuse dark line above supercilium. Upperparts pale ochreous brown to warm olive-brown, the plain wing lacking pale wing-panel but with contrasting darker centres and paler fringes to tertials. Underparts whitish to light cinnamon-buff. Outermost tail feather has narrow whitish outer edge, which broadens and extends around tip onto distal portion of inner web. Pale lower mandible shows dark smudge at tip, absent or faint and diffuse on Sykes's and Eastern Olivaceous Warblers. Legs pinkish grey to light grey-brown. Tends to flick tail in an erratic manner.

d   **Adult, fresh, December** Upperparts warm olive-brown, sometimes with rufous tinge not seen in Sykes's Warbler. Underparts washed buff or cinnamon-buff, contrasting with whitish throat and belly. Brighter edges to tertials, greater coverts and tail feathers contrast with darker centres more than in Sykes's.

e   **Adult, worn, May** By spring, warmer tones lost and appearance more uniform, with upperparts drab mid brown to greyish brown, and contrast between darker centres and paler fringes to tertials less apparent. Underparts dingy white with buff confined to side of breast and flanks.

f   **First-winter, August** Upperparts pale olive-brown, lacking warm tone of fresh adult. Supercilium and underparts with pale creamy buff wash absent on Sykes's. Shows contrasting brown centres and light buff edges to remiges, wing-coverts and tertials, more prominent than on adult, and more contrasting than young Sykes's shows.

Eastern Olivaceous Warbler *Iduna pallida* (cont. from Plate 32)

Map and text page 486

Palearctic race *I. p. elaeica*

g   **Adult *I. p. elaeica*, fresh** Upperparts greyish brown with slight olive cast, with narrow creamy supercilium extending just beyond eye, and small dusky spot on otherwise pale lores. Closed wing shows narrow buff edges and tips to flight feathers, forming faint wing-panel, and a pale line across tips of bunched secondaries. Underparts with creamy buff wash to side of breast and flanks, and whitish or greyish white throat and belly. Outermost tail feathers with narrow pale outer edge and outer two pairs with well-demarcated whitish fringes at tips, extending onto distal inner web.

h   **Adult *I. p. elaeica*, May** Slightly paler than fresh adult, and pale wing-panel less conspicuous.

i   **First-winter *I. p. elaeica*, August** Resembles fresh adult in overall colour and appearance, including pale panel on secondaries. Oten with paler fringes to greater coverts so wing appears more contrasting.

PLATE 34: AFRICAN YELLOW WARBLERS

Dark-capped Yellow Warbler *Iduna natalensis*

Map and text page 509

13–14cm; 11.5g. Widespread resident and local migrant, frequenting forest edges and bush-lined streams from C and E Africa to E South Africa, where four races occur. Size and structure suggest a *Hippolais* or *Acrocephalus* warbler, but bill very broad, crown rather rounded and wings short. All races show distinctive yellowish olive-brown upperparts and strikingly yellow underparts. Has short, narrow yellow supercilium contrasting with darker lores. Edges to flight feathers and tips of greater coverts yellowish green, giving closed wing more contrasting appearance than upperparts. Crown colour varies between races.

a   **Adult *I. n. natalensis*** S Tanzania and E Zambia to E South Africa. Top of head dark olive-brown rather than blackish, contrasting slightly with yellowish olive-brown upperparts. Underparts rich yellow with olive wash to side of breast.

b   **Adult *I. n. major*** Gabon and Angola to N and C Zimbabwe. Differs from *natalensis* by yellowish olive-brown crown, matching mantle colour. Upperparts paler than *natalensis*, and wing and tail feathers browner (less blackish) with yellower edges. Shows bright yellow side of breast.

c   **Adult *I. n. massaica*** Ethiopia to E DR Congo and N Tanzania. Shows distinctive blackish brown crown and loral-line, contrasting with yellow side of head, short yellow supercilium and yellowish olive-brown upperparts.

d   **Juvenile *I. n. massaica*** Differs from adult by light cinnamon-brown upperparts with darker brown crown. Supercilium and eye-ring yellow-ochre, and underparts rich tawny buff rather than yellow.

Mountain Yellow Warbler *Iduna similis*

Map and text page 514

13cm; 11g. Resident in forest edge, scrub and bushy habitat in highlands of E Africa, usually occurring at higher elevations than Dark-capped Yellow Warbler. Size, structure and appearance closely resemble race *major* of Dark-capped Yellow Warbler, uniform dark olive-green upperparts contrasting with bright yellow underparts.

e   **Adult** Closed wing lacks the contrast between dark feather centres and olive-green edges shown by Dark-capped Yellow Warbler.

f   **Juvenile** Yellow and green plumage tones suppressed. Differs from adult by browner, cinnamon-tinged upperparts, and duller warm buff underparts, although throat and breast may be yellow-tinged. Edges to flight feathers and wing-coverts warm buff.

Papyrus Yellow Warbler *Calamonastides gracilirostris*

Map and text page 522

c. 13.5cm; 10.5g. Localised resident of papyrus and swamps in C and E Africa. Medium-sized warbler with olive green crown and head side, and warm brown or olive-brown upperparts. Lacks clear supercilium or eye-stripe, and shows bland 'open-faced' expression. Underparts yellow, brightest on chin, throat, centre of breast and belly.

g   **Adult *C. g. gracilirostris*** E DR Congo to W Kenya. Upperparts warm brown with flight feathers edged cinnamon-brown, giving contrasting appearance to closed wing. Lower flanks to undertail-coverts washed cinnamon-brown. Eyes dark reddish brown.

h   **Adult *C. g. bensoni*** Lake Mweru in N Zambia and adjacent SE DR Congo. Slightly darker, more olive-brown above than nominate race, and lacks warm tinge on wings, uppertail-coverts and lower underparts. Shows indistinct yellowish supercilium and darker lores, and has pale yellow iris.

PLATE 35: *NESILLAS* BRUSH WARBLERS

Madagascar Brush Warbler *Nesillas typica*　　　Map and text page 526

17–18cm; 18g. Resident in forest understorey and dense undergrowth on Madagascar, with three races, and the Comoro Islands, where two races occur. Large, slim warbler with short wings, long graduated tail, low crown and longish robust bill. Coloration varies racially but all show dark olive-brown upperparts, short paler supercilium usually fairly conspicuous above narrow, dark eye-stripe, and underparts with diffuse but conspicuous brown or buff streaks on breast.

a　　**Adult *N. t. typica*** Widespread in humid regions of S and C Madagascar. Upperparts olive-brown tinged greenish, with narrow, pale buff supercilium and dark lores. Underparts pale yellowish buff, tinged olive-brown on breast, and with soft olive-grey streaks extending from chin to upper breast. Flanks light olive-brown, becoming warmer olive-brown on vent and undertail-coverts.

b　　**Adult *N. t. longicaudata*** Only found on Anjouan in the Comoro Islands. Paler than nominate race, differing by paler olive-brown upperparts and slightly paler, greyer crown. Streaks on breast and throat narrower and mostly confined to upper breast.

c　　**Adult *N. t. obscura*** Restricted to limestone massifs in W Madagascar and locally in north. Distinctly darker, longer-winged and larger-billed than nominate race, with dark olive-brown upperparts and indistinct greyish supercilium. Underparts much darker than nominate, showing little or no yellow tinge.

Lantz's Brush Warbler *Nesillas lantzii*　　　Map and text page 530

17cm; 17g. Resident in spiny forest and coastal scrub in semi-desert of SW Madagascar. Size and structure as Madagascar Brush Warbler including long graduated tail. Much paler than Madagascar Brush Warbler, with pale greyish brown upperparts and conspicuous buffy white supercilium above narrow, dark eye-stripe. Underparts buffy white, with faint and diffuse dusky streaks on throat and lower breast.

d　　**Adult**

Grande Comore Brush Warbler *Nesillas brevicaudata*　　　Map and text page 532

15–16cm; 16g. Resident in higher altitude forest and thickets on Grande Comore, Comoro Islands. Shows distinctive *Nesillas* structure but tail shorter than other species. Upperparts warm olive-brown, becoming more rufescent on rump. Underparts darker and browner than nominate Madagascar Brush Warbler, but throat pale. Throat and upper breast streaking forms conspicuous and contrasting dark brown striations.

e　　**Adult**

Moheli Brush Warbler *Nesillas mariae*　　　Map and text page 534

15–16cm; 15.5g. Resident in forest and thick scrub on Moheli, Comoro Islands. Smaller and less robust than Madagascar Brush Warbler, with shorter tail, more slender bill and finer legs. Upperparts paler and greener than other *Nesillas*. Underparts yellowish buff with warmer flanks and undertail-coverts, sometimes with faint and diffuse greyish streaks on throat and upper breast. Supercilium poorly defined, most prominent over lores. Shows narrow reddish orbital ring.

f　　**Adult**

Aldabra Brush Warbler *Nesillas aldabranus*　　　Map and text page 536

18–20cm. Formerly occurred in dense coastal scrub on Aldabra, now considered extinct. A large *Nesillas* with a proportionately long and graduated tail and long, stout bill. Upperparts pale brown, slightly greyer on head, and warmer on rump and wing feather edges. Underparts pale buff with whitish throat and faint streaks on upper breast.

g　　**Adult**

PLATE 36: TESIAS

Chestnut-headed Tesia *Oligura castaneocoronata*

Map and text page 538

c. 8cm; 9g. A brightly coloured warbler that frequents dense undergrowth, dark ravines and gullies in montane forest from the Himalayas to W China and the N Indochina region. Descends to lower elevations outside the breeding season. Tiny, with an extremely short tail that barely extends beyond the wing-tips giving an apparent tail-less appearance, exaggerated by its upright stance and energetic, highly animated behaviour. Readily identified by red head with distinctive pale spot behind the eye, drab olive-green upperparts, bright yellow chin and throat, and dull greenish fringes to yellow underparts forming indistinct band across breast. Simple but powerful song often reveals presence of unseen bird in dense cover.

a   **Adult *O. c. castaneocoronata*** Red on head extends to cover crown and upper nape.

b   **Juvenile *O. c. castaneocoronata*** Differs from adult by dark olive-brown upperparts and uniform rich orange-brown underparts.

c   **Adult *O. c. abadiei*** Differs from nominate by slightly duller appearance and less extensive red on head, being replaced with dull green on nape and rear crown.

Grey-bellied Tesia *Tesia cyaniventer*

Map and text page 541

8–8.5cm; 10g. A minute, 'tail-less' and drably coloured warbler that inhabits dense undergrowth and the forest floor at lower elevations from the Himalayas to N Vietnam, where some are resident and others descend to adjacent foothills and lowlands. Structure and behaviour similar to Chestnut-headed Tesia but tail shorter, not extending beyond wing-tips. Upperparts dull green with a distinctive brighter green supercilium and dark grey eye-stripe. Underparts grey, appearing greyish white on chin, mid grey on breast and dark grey on flanks.

d   **Adult**

Slaty-bellied Tesia *Tesia olivea*

Map and text page 544

7.5–8cm; 9g. A diminutive 'tail-less' warbler of montane forest from the Himalayas to N Burma and N Indochina region, often occurring alongside Grey-bellied and Chestnut-headed Tesias, but also breeding at lower elevations. Always active and keeps close to the forest floor. Structure and behaviour as Grey-bellied Tesia. Upperparts dull moss-green except for slightly iridescent, bright golden-yellow cap on crown and nape. Side of head and underparts uniform bluish grey.

e   **Adult *T. o. olivea***

f   **Adult *T. o. chiangmaiensis*** Closely resembles nominate race, differing principally by slightly duller crown and nape, which lack iridescence.

Javan Tesia *Tesia superciliaris*

Map and text page 547

8.5–9cm. A tiny, 'tail-less', drably coloured warbler, endemic to montane forest in the mountains of W Java, Indonesia, where it frequents dense undergrowth and the forest floor. Behaviour and structure as Grey-bellied and Slaty-bellied Tesias, but legs thicker and feet exceptionally large, possibly an adaptation for clinging onto moss-covered tree trunks when feeding. Upperparts including crown dull olive-green. Shows grey supercilium, ear-coverts and underparts, and a broad, dark charcoal-grey eye-stripe.

g   **Adult**

Russet-capped Tesia *Tesia everetti*

Map and text page 549

8.5–9cm. A minute, 'tail-less' and drably coloured warbler, endemic to Flores and Sumbawa in the Lesser Sundas of Indonesia. Structure and behaviour as other *Tesia* species, and has large feet like Javan Tesia. Upperparts dull brown, although crown and nape distinctive rich russet-brown and sides to head slightly paler reddish brown. Some show a narrow, slightly paler and poorly defined reddish brown supercilium.

h   **Adult *T. e. everetti*** Typical adult from Flores.

i   **Adult *T. e. sumbawana*** Birds on Sumbawa differ from nominate form by brownish grey rather than reddish sides to head, and a duller russet tone to crown.

PLATE 37: STUBTAILS & PALE-FOOTED BUSH WARBLER

Timor Stubtail *Urosphena subulata*
Map and text page 551

8–9cm. A tiny, unobtrusive warbler of the forest floor, with mouse-like behaviour and a barely audible song, restricted to Timor, Wetar and Babar in the E Lesser Sundas of Indonesia. Shows large head with a low, flat forehead and crown exaggerated by the long, fine bill, a proportionately small, round body and a minute tail. Upperparts uniform dull olive-brown to slightly warmer brown. Has contrasting head pattern with long, pale supercilium extending to side of nape, bold olive-brown eye-stripe, and slightly mottled paler ear-coverts and cheeks. Underparts whitish with dull greyish wash across breast and faint diffuse striations along flanks. Undertail-coverts dull straw, but appear darker in dull light conditions on forest floor.

a   **Adult** *U. s. subulata* Typical bird from Timor with dull olive-brown upperparts and whitish underparts.

b   **Adult** *U. s. advena* Birds on Babar closely resemble nominate, differing by slightly warmer rusty tone to upperparts, blackish upper mandible and slightly longer wing.

Bornean Stubtail *Urosphena whiteheadi*
Map and text page 554

8–9cm. An infrequently encountered, unobtrusive warbler that inhabits the forest floor in submontane and montane forest of N Borneo. Structure as Timor Stubtail. Upperparts uniform deep sepia-brown. Head shows striking pattern with blackish crown and eye-stripe, bold bright buff to golden-brown supercilium, and paler mottled ear-coverts. Underparts white or greyish white with prominent dark feather fringes giving conspicuous mottled appearance to breast and upper flanks. Lower flanks and undertail-coverts dull brown. Legs conspicuously pale pink. High-pitched song is almost inaudible.

c   **Adult** Typical adult.

d   **Adult** A slightly browner, more sullied individual.

Asian Stubtail *Urosphena squameiceps*
Map and text page 556

9–10cm; 9g. A small, short-tailed, largely terrestrial warbler, breeding in the warm temperate regions of Japan, NE China and SE Siberia, and wintering from S China to Indochina and Burma. Structure as other *Urosphena* but tail slightly longer, extending just beyond wing tip. Typically forages amongst leaf litter, with body held close to the ground. Upperparts uniform warm brown. Head shows prominent long creamy white supercilium extending onto side of nape and contrasting with dark brown eye-stripe and warm brown, slightly scaly crown. Underparts whitish on chin and throat, becoming pale greyish brown to peachy brown on breast and belly, and slightly brighter peachy brown on flanks and undertail-coverts. Song is a distinctive, high-pitched stridulating buzz, reminiscent of some *Locustella* and *Bradypterus* species, usually delivered from a low branch.

e   **Adult** Typical adult.

f   **Adult** Slightly cleaner individual with whiter supercilium.

g   **Adult** A particularly warmly toned individual. Birds with brighter upperparts, more strongly washed brown flanks, and breast pale peachy brown have been described as the race *ussuriana* from the Russian Far East, but differences are inconsistent and such birds occur throughout the range.

Pale-footed Bush Warbler *Cettia pallidipes*
Map and text page 560

11–12cm; 8.5g. A resident or short-distance altitudinal migrant frequenting undergrowth in foothills from the NW Himalayas to S China and N Vietnam, with an isolated population in the Andaman Islands. Has stocky, *Urosphena*-like structure but shows more rounded head, finer bill and longer tail than Asian Stubtail. Upperparts vary from dull olive-brown to dull rufous-brown, and head shows contrasting pale buff supercilium, sharply defined dark brown eye-stripe and paler, faintly mottled ear-coverts. Underparts of nominate form silky white with faint pinkish buff suffusion on breast and subdued greyish brown wash to flanks and ventral region. Legs conspicuously pale pinkish white, paler than any other *Cettia*.

h   **Adult** *C. p. pallidipes* Himalayan foothills from NW India to Bhutan. Typical bird with whitish lower flanks and belly.

i   **Adult** *C. p. laurentei* Burma to S China, N Thailand and N Vietnam. Differs from nominate by slightly warmer upperparts, greyish brown wash on upper breast and lower flanks, and warm buffy wash on undertail-coverts.

j   **Adult** *C. p. osmastoni* Restricted to South Andaman Island. Differs from *laurentei* by slightly warmer side to head, warmer and more extensive buff to ochre-brown wash to breast, becoming dark greyish brown towards lower flanks and warm buff on undertail-coverts, but differences are slight and subtle.

PLATE 38: SUNDA BUSH & ABERRANT BUSH WARBLERS

Sunda Bush Warbler *Cettia vulcania*

Map and text page 565

12–13cm. A common resident of montane forest on many larger islands of SE Asia, where eight isolated races occur. A neatly proportioned *Cettia* with a rounded body, short and rounded wings often held loose at sides, rather large domed head, and relatively long, rounded tail. Appearance varies between races but all share uniform brownish upperparts, a prominent supercilium, dark eye-stripe and mottled ear-coverts. Birds in moist forests of the Greater Sundas are darker than those of the drier Lesser Sundas. Often adopts a perky and upright stance, and its distinctive song remains fairly consistent throughout range.

a **Adult *C. v. vulcania*** When fresh, birds on Java and Bali show warm olive-brown upperparts, with contrasting dull creamy brown supercilium, and edges of primary coverts, secondaries and primaries dull rusty brown. Underparts whitish with warm peachy buff wash to breast and upper flanks, darkening to dull greyish brown on lower flanks, vent and undertail-coverts.

b **Adult *C. v. vulcania*** Worn birds are slightly duller above and paler below, and supercilium appears paler and more contrasting.

c **Adult *C. v. flaviventris*** Birds on Sumatra are darker and browner above than nominate race, with richer brown edges to wing feathers forming bright panel in closed wing. Supercilium slightly narrower, washed pale rusty brown, and side of head appears mottled darker rufous-brown. Underparts strikingly darker, with breast washed rich, warm sepia, and sides and flanks darker rufous-brown, although belly and vent with faint buffy yellow wash.

d **Adult *C. v. flaviventris*** When worn, shows slightly greyer upperparts and paler underparts.

e **Adult *C. v. oreophila*** Birds on Borneo generally duller than nominate race, with mahogany-brown upperparts, although warm fringes and edges to wing feathers, form brighter patch in closed wing. Underparts with whitish throat, grey-brown wash across breast and side of neck, becoming dark sepia-brown along flanks and darkest across ventral region.

f **Adult *C. v. oreophila*** A paler individual, slightly warmer above and lacking greyish wash to underparts.

g **Adult *C. v. everetti*** Birds on Timor differ from Greater Sundas races by paler greyish brown upperparts with a slight olive wash, and conspicuous whitish supercilium. Underparts much paler, with breast white, washed pale grey, darkening to pale peachy grey at sides. Slightly smaller than nominate race.

Aberrant Bush Warbler *Cettia flavolivacea*

Map and text page 570

12–13cm; 7.5g. An altitudinal migrant, with five races breeding from the W Himalayas to the mountains of W and SW China, Burma and N Indochina, and wintering at lower elevations nearby. Structure similar to Sunda Bush Warbler, and slightly longer tailed than other Himalayan *Cettia*. The only Himalayan *Cettia* with dull, oily olive-brown or drab brown upperparts, a conspicuous yellowish supercilium extending to rear of ear-coverts and mostly yellow-tinged underparts. Confusion with juveniles of other Himalayan *Cettia* showing yellow underparts is a potential pitfall. Race *intricata* may belong with Sunda Bush Warbler.

h **Adult *C. f. flavolivacea*** Richly coloured adult with conspicuous yellow underparts, typical of breeding birds from the Himalayas.

i **Adult *C. f. stresemanni*** Birds from Meghalaya and W Assam closely resemble nominate form, but are marginally darker green and slightly browner above, and yellow tone to supercilium and underparts appears slightly subdued and more sullied. Differences are slight and it may not be possible to assign a particular individual to this race.

j **Adult *C. f. flavolivacea/stresemanni*** Occasional birds lack yellow on supercilium and underparts, which then appear paler buffy white to dull olive-grey.

k **Adult *C. f. intricata*** Birds from N and E Burma and C China closely resemble *stresemanni*. They differ by the slightly darker and browner upperparts with any olive tone largely subdued, yellow underparts that appear paler and faded, and flanks washed warmer buff.

l **Adult *C. f. intricata*** A particularly richly toned individual from W China, with warm brown wash to breast and flanks. Such birds are unusual and presumably represent an extreme example of colour saturation.

m **Adult *C. f. weberi*** Birds of Nagaland, Mizoram, Manipur and W Burma show warmer, less olivaceous upperparts than nominate form, and yellow and ochre tones to underparts are subdued or absent.

Brownish-flanked Bush Warbler *Cettia fortipes*　　　　Map and text page 574

11–12cm; 7.5g. The most widespread *Cettia* in continental Asia with four races breeding in the Himalayan foothills and low mountains from Pakistan to SE China and Taiwan. Resident or descends to lower elevations outside breeding season. A small, nondescript warbler with a distinctly rounded crown, plump and deep-bellied structure, short and rounded wings typically held slightly spread and drooped along sides of body, and relatively long tail often held slightly cocked. Upperpart colour varies from uniform warm russet-brown to dull cold olive-brown. All races show an indistinct supercilium, most conspicuous in front of eye, a short dark eye-stripe, and warm rusty brown edges to primaries and secondaries that contrast with the darker, drabber upperparts. Underparts typically dull and sullied but show individual and racial variation.

a　　**Adult *C. f. fortipes*, fresh** Upperparts rich brown, usually with slight rusty wash. Underparts washed rich buffy brown in centre of breast, becoming paler towards belly, rusty brown on upper flanks, and darker rich sepia-brown on lower flanks and undertail-coverts.

b　　**Adult *C. f. fortipes*, worn** Upperparts slightly paler and greyer than fresh adult, and contrast with browner wings. Underparts paler, with breast varying from dull greyish brown to whitish, and flanks appear paler, more buff toned than fresh adult.

c　　**Adult *C. f. davidiana*** Differs from nominate by warmer sandy brown upperparts, lacking rich, dark rusty tones of nominate race, but contrasting with warmer reddish brown crown. Supercilium dull buffy grey, diffuse and poorly defined, and side of head pale. Underparts paler than nominate form, with whitish chin, throat and belly contrasting with pale sandy grey breast and flanks.

d　　**Adult *C. f. robustipes*** Overall appearance duller, less contrasting, than other races, with olive-brown upperparts and slightly paler underparts, usually with slight ochre suffusion, most pronounced on belly, flanks and ventral region.

e　　**Adult *C. f. pallida*, fresh** Palest and greyest race, breeding in the drier W Himalayas. Upperparts dull greyish brown with an olivaceous wash, much greyer and paler than nominate form, with warmer tones on closed wing, rump and uppertail-coverts showing greater contrast. Underparts with faint greyish brown wash across breast, warming to dull fulvous-brown on lower flanks, vent and undertail-coverts.

f　　**Adult *C. f. pallida*, worn** Worn *pallida* shows considerable variation. Most retain brown tone to upperparts but palest birds appear frosty grey on crown, nape, mantle and scapulars, lacking warmer tones. Underparts can be almost entirely white, with faint grey wash restricted to breast sides, flanks and undertail-coverts.

g　　**Adult *C. f. davidiana*** This interesting bird was caught in Hong Kong in November. The warm brown upperparts and faint yellow suffusion to the underparts was unlike typical *davidiana* in autumn, and suggested Yellow-bellied Bush Warbler. Its true identity was revealed using DNA analysis.

Yellow-bellied Bush Warbler *Cettia acanthizoides*　　　　Map and text page 580

10–11cm; 6g. A diminutive *Cettia*, frequenting thick bamboo understorey in upper montane forest up to tree line in C and E China and Taiwan. Winters nearby at lower elevations. Structure as Brownish-flanked Bush Warbler but bill smaller and finer. An attractive warbler with subtle plumage tones. Shows pale greyish brown mantle, well-marked whitish supercilium, often flushed primrose-yellow in front of eye, and warmer brown crown. Underparts with delicate pale primrose-yellow wash on breast and belly, darkening to warm buffy yellow on flanks. Song is a remarkable and unmistakable wind-up followed by a long descending trill, lasting up to one minute.

h　　**Adult *C. a. acanthizoides*** Typical adult with conspicuous yellow wash to underparts.

i　　**Adult *C. a. concolor*** Birds in Taiwan tend to appear slightly warmer than nominate form. Upperparts and crown pale rusty brown, contrasting with greyish wash on nape. Underparts show greater variation in than nominate race, and some show reduced yellow wash.

j　　**Adult *C. a. concolor*** A particularly dull individual, perhaps a first-autumn bird. Note similarity to some Brownish-flanked Bush Warblers.

Hume's Bush Warbler *Cettia brunnescens*　　　　Map and text page 584

10–11cm. Replaces Yellow-bellied Bush Warbler in the Himalayas, where it occupies the same niche. Diminutive size and structure as Yellow-bellied Bush Warbler and shares similar appearance, but song quite different. Differs by paler and greyer underparts, with yellowish wash restricted to side of upper breast and flanks. Lower flanks suffused warm buff or buffy yellow and undertail-coverts pale apricot to warm buff.

k　　**Adult** Typical adult with greyish breast and warmer, yellow and buff tones restricted to flanks.

l　　**Adult** An extremely pale individual, lacking yellow wash to underparts.

PLATE 40: HIMALAYAN & CHINESE *CETTIA* II & CETTI'S WARBLER

Chestnut-crowned Bush Warbler *Cettia major*
Map and text page 587

13cm; 12.5g. Largest of the Himalayan *Cettia*, breeding up to the tree line in understorey and scrub, from NW India east to the mountains of C China. A large and robust warbler with similar structure to other *Cettia*. Upperparts uniform drab grey-brown or olive-brown but with distinctive chestnut-brown crown and nape contrasting with paler supercilium and dark eye-stripe. Underpart colour variable, upper breast typically greyish, forming dull greyish brown smudge on breast sides and flanks, and contrasting with white throat and belly.

a   **Adult *C. m. major*** Breeds from Himalayas to C China. Typical adult with dusky underparts and contrasting supercilium.

b   **Adult *C. m. major*** Some birds, perhaps breeding adults, show a warmer reddish brown supercilium, particularly in front of eye.

c   **Juvenile *C. m. major*** Overall much darker than adult and lacks chestnut cap. Upperparts uniform dull greyish brown with slight olive wash. Head pattern poorly marked. Underparts with greyish wash to breast and flanks contrasting with whiter throat and belly.

Grey-sided Bush Warbler *Cettia brunnifrons*
Map and text page 591

10–11cm, *c.* 8g. A small and lively *Cettia*, widespread in montane forest in the Himalayas and mountains of C China, and wintering in adjacent foothills and lowlands. Size and structure as Brownish-flanked Bush Warbler, and tail is often flicked upwards and held slightly cocked, particularly by singing males. Shows distinctive head pattern with warm chestnut cap, bold whitish supercilium and blackish eye-stripe. Uniform dull rufescent-brown upperparts contrast with whitish underparts, with pale ash-grey wash on breast and flanks and brownish olive wash to ventral region and undertail-coverts. Highly repetitive song is particularly distinctive.

d   **Adult *C. b. brunnifrons*** Typical singing male.

e   **Juvenile *C. b. brunnifrons*** Much darker and drabber than adult. Head shows indistinct greyish olive supercilium, lacking distinctive chestnut crown and contrasting facial appearance. Little contrast between dull brownish olive upperparts and dull greyish brown underparts.

f   **Adult *C. b. umbratica*** Closely resembles nominate form. Birds breeding in NE Burma and China show slightly darker, browner upperparts, lacking rufous tones to rump and uppertail-coverts, and edges to primaries and secondaries less contrasting and similar in colour to upperparts.

g   **Adult *C. b. whistleri*** Tends to be slightly paler, less intensely coloured than nominate, with marginally paler chestnut crown, and rufescent wash to upperparts is less noticeable and sometimes absent.

Cetti's Warbler *Cettia cetti*
Map and text page 621

13–15cm; Male 15g, female 12g. A large, skulking *Cettia* of damp, bushy and waterside habitats, breeding from W and SW Europe to C Asia, where three races occur. European populations resident or dispersive, but Asian breeders mostly migratory, wintering from Middle East to Pakistan. Shows robust, dumpy body, a proportionately large head with distinctly rounded crown, short and fine bill, and relatively long, broad tail often held slightly cocked. Males average *c.* 10% larger than females. All races drab and featureless, with uniform brown upperparts and eye-stripe, greyish side to head and supercilium, and plain unmarked underparts. Distinctive song is loud, explosive and abrupt.

h   **Adult *C. c. cetti*** The smallest and darkest form with dark rufescent-brown upperparts, and ash-grey supercilium and ear-coverts. Underparts dull, with drab ash-grey breast and flanks, dull rufescent-brown lower flanks, and undertail-coverts grey-brown with narrow pale tips. Juveniles similar but with paler eye-ring.

i   **Adult *C. c. orientalis*** Distinctly larger than nominate race. Upperparts warmer, paler rufous-brown than nominate, and supercilium paler and better marked. Underparts differ from nominate by light greyish wash to breast and side of neck, becoming white towards throat and belly, pale greyish brown along flanks, and pale grey-brown undertail-coverts show wider, paler tips.

j   **Adult *C. c. albiventris*** The largest and palest race with upperparts light tan, considerably paler than nominate race and slightly paler than *orientalis*. Side of head and supercilium greyish white. Underparts cleaner and paler than other races, with chin, throat and belly white to greyish white, showing little contrast with delicate pale grey breast and flanks. Ventral region pale brown, contrasting with paler undertail-coverts, which often appear uniformly whitish, or show a faint brown tinge and broader white tips.

PLATE 41: MANCHURIAN BUSH & JAPANESE BUSH WARBLERS

Manchurian Bush Warbler *Cettia canturians*

Map and text page 595

15–18cm; male 22g, female 13g. Male is largest *Cettia*. A large, warmly coloured warbler breeding in dense thickets and bushy undergrowth in N and E China, the Korean Peninsula and adjacent regions of SE Siberia, and wintering from Taiwan and SE China to NW Thailand, Indochina and N Philippines. Shows characteristic domeheaded, short-winged and long-tailed appearance, and pronounced sexual dimorphism, with sexes readily separable on size and bill structure. Shows brown upperparts with warmer chestnut fringes to tertials and wings, contrasting head pattern with pale supercilium and mottled ear-coverts, and whitish underparts.

a   **Adult *C. c. canturians*, male, winter** Large size and bulky structure readily identifies male. When fresh, upperparts warm brown, with cinnamon-brown crown, long pale buff supercilium, dark brown eye-stripe, and whitish underparts often lightly washed pale brown.

b   **Adult *C. c. canturians*, female, winter** As fresh male, but distinctly smaller. Both sexes may show brighter chestnut crown. At this time of year it is uncertain whether *borealis* and nominate *canturians* can be separated.

c   **Adult *C. c. canturians*, male, summer** When worn in late summer, upperparts including crown slightly paler greyish brown, but warmer and browner closed wing then shows greater contrast with mantle.

d   **Adult *C. c. borealis*, male, summer** During breeding season, nape and mantle appear colder and greyer than nominate form, contrasting with warmer cinnamon-brown forehead and crown, and brown edges to primaries and secondaries.

e   **Adult *C. c. borealis*, female, summer** As male, but distinctly smaller. Underparts pale greyish white, with warmth restricted to pale sandy grey lower flanks.

Japanese Bush Warbler *Cettia diphone*

Map and text page 600

14–16cm; male 16g, female 11g. A widespread and familiar but nondescript warbler, breeding in woodland, thickets, dense undergrowth and edges of wetlands throughout Japan and locally in South Korea. Mainly resident or dispersive, but some migrate to winter in S Japan and Taiwan. Structure as Manchurian Bush Warbler but bill finer, less robust, males are much smaller with sexual dimorphism less pronounced. Plumage varies considerably due to racial differences. All forms show drab greyish or brownish upperparts, a conspicuous supercilium and dull greyish white underparts, but only nominate and *restricta* show warmer brown tone to crown. Closed wing, with greenish bronze feather edges, appears brighter than upperparts. Its cheerful whistling song heralds the arrival of spring in Japan.

f   **Adult *C. d. diphone*, worn** Restricted to the southern Izu Islands, Ogasawara Islands and Iwo Islands of S Japan where other races absent. Shows proportionately longer tail and paler legs than other races. When fresh, upperparts and crown uniform warm brown, becoming paler and greyer than fresh adult when worn, but usually retaining brown wash on crown and bronze panel in closed wing.

g   **Adult *C. d. restricta*** Birds breeding in S Ryukyu Islands are more warmly and richly coloured than other races, with brown upperparts and brighter cinnamon-brown crown. Some resemble female Manchurian Bush Warbler, but differ by light sandy brown supercilium and ear-coverts, and greenish bronze edges to closed wing. Underparts whitish or with breast and flanks lightly washed sandy buff.

h   **Adult *C. d. cantans*, winter** The most widespread race, occurring throughout the main Japanese islands. When fresh, upperparts dull brownish grey, showing little or no contrast with crown, but greenish bronze closed wing usually noticeable. Underparts whitish, with dull greyish wash across breast. Worn adult in summer slightly paler and greyer but retains bronze edges to wing feathers.

i   **Adult *C. d. riukiuensis*, summer** The northernmost race, breeding on Sakhalin and wintering to south including Ryukyu Islands and Taiwan. Closely resembles *cantans* but upperparts slightly paler and greyer, lacking brownish tone, enhancing contrast with greenish bronze closed wing. Underparts paler than *cantans*, with faint grey tinge to breast, flanks and undertail-coverts. During the breeding season becomes progressively paler and greyer.

j   **Juvenile *C. d. cantans/riukiuensis*** Differs from adult by uniform pale olive-brown upperparts, warm brown wing and tail, creamy yellow supercilium, and ear-coverts washed pale sulphur-yellow and mottled pale olive-brown. Underparts show pale primrose-yellow chin and throat, and pale sulphur-yellow breast, belly and undertail-coverts, usually with faint brownish mottling on side of breast.

PLATE 42: PACIFIC ISLAND & MELANESIAN *CETTIA*

Luzon Bush Warbler *Cettia seebohmi*

Map and text page 607

12cm; 12g. A dark, medium-sized, skulking *Cettia* restricted to scrub and grass-covered hills of NW Luzon, Philippines. Structure similar to Brownish-flanked Bush Warbler but tail proportionally longer. Shows dark rufous-brown upperparts with slightly warmer crown and wing, whitish supercilium and dark brown eye-stripe. Underparts variable, some with uniform greyish throat and breast, others paler with whitish throat, greyish white breast, darker and browner flanks, and dull cinnamon-brown lower flanks and undertail-coverts.

a   **Adult** Paler individual with whitish throat and greyish white breast.

Palau Bush Warbler *Cettia annae*

Map and text page 610

14–15cm. A fairly large, nondescript *Cettia* resident in scrub and forest undergrowth on five islands in the Palau Archipelago, SW Pacific. Appears round-headed with a robust body but shows proportionally shorter tail and longer bill than Asian *Cettia*. Male larger than female. Upperparts drab olive-brown, head with long pale olive-yellow supercilium, dark eye-stripe and lightly mottled, pale olive-yellow ear-coverts. Underparts pale olive-yellow, often with slight mottling across upper breast, becoming warm buff on lower flanks and undertail-coverts.

b   **Adult**

Shade Warbler *Cettia parens*

Map and text page 612

11–12cm; male 19g, female 14g. A poorly known *Cettia* of thick forest undergrowth, endemic to San Cristobal in the Solomon Islands. Structure as Palau Bush Warbler but smaller and shorter tailed. Upperparts uniform dull chestnut-brown with long cinnamon-buff supercilium and darker eye-stripe, and mottled cinnamon-brown ear-coverts. Warmer toned individuals may appear rusty brown on crown and nape, slightly brighter than mantle. Underparts dark, with dull cinnamon-brown breast and belly, cinnamon-buff chin and throat, and deeper cinnamon-brown lower flanks and undertail-coverts.

c   **Adult**

Fiji Bush Warbler *Cettia ruficapilla*

Map and text page 614

12–13cm; 13g. A widespread but elusive *Cettia*, occurring on four islands in Fiji, each with an endemic race. Size and structure similar to Shade Warbler but with proportionally longer, thinner bill. All races show warm brown upperparts, long supercilium and chestnut crown. Underparts with white chin and throat and contrasting dull greyish brown breast and flanks, often with indistinct greyish striations on side of upper breast and flanks. Duetting song is one of the characteristic bird sounds of Fiji.

d   **Adult** *C. r. ruficapilla* Restricted to Kandavu. Warm chestnut-brown ear-coverts and supercilium with chestnut crown, and poorly defined eye-stripe. Upperparts warm brown, occasionally with slight olive wash. Race *funebris* of Taveuni is similar but ear-coverts brighter chestnut, and supercilium slightly paler and more conspicuous.

e   **Adult** *C. r. badiceps* Restricted to Viti Levu. Differs from nominate by contrasting head pattern with warm chestnut crown, long creamy white supercilium and narrow blackish eye-stripe. Upperparts duller olive-brown.

f   **Adult** *C. r. castaneoptera* Restricted to Vanua Levu. Resembles *badiceps* but supercilium washed slightly with buff, especially in front of eye, and upperparts slightly browner, less olive. Slightly larger than *badiceps*.

Tanimbar Bush Warbler *Cettia carolinae*

Map and text page 617

11–13cm; male 19.5g, female 14.5g. A nondescript, medium-sized *Cettia* endemic to Yamdena in the Lesser Sundas of Indonesia. Structure resembles Fiji Bush Warbler. Differs from Asian *Cettia* by longer bill and relatively short tail. Unmarked upperparts dull brown with warmer brown panel in the closed wing. Head shows rufous-brown crown, dull cinnamon-buff supercilium, greyish ear-coverts and dark brown eye-stripe. Underparts greyish white, contrasting with duller grey side to breast and browner flanks.

g   **Adult**

Bougainville Bush Warbler *Cettia haddeni*

Text page 619

13cm; 25g. An elusive, dark warbler inhabiting montane forest in the mountains of Bougainville in the Solomon Islands. Bulky structure atypical for *Cettia*, with proportionally short tail, long and heavy bill with broad base, and large, robust legs. Upperparts featureless dark brown although edges of flight feathers and tail tinged chestnut. Head shows dull chestnut-brown crown, slightly paler warm brown ear-coverts, dark lores and a poorly defined supercilium that barely contrasts with the crown. Breast and belly dark grey with darker diffuse mottling, and paler chin and throat.

h   **Adult**

Genus *Bradypterus* Swainson, 1837

[Gr. *bradus* slow, sluggish; -*pteros*-winged (*pteron* wing)]

A genus comprising 23 species, 13 of which breed in eastern and southern Asia and ten in Africa. All are small to medium-sized warblers, most with drab dark brown plumage, which live near the ground among dense vegetation in swamps, forest edges and undergrowth. Most are residents, although some of the Asian species are altitudinal migrants and two are long-distance migrants that breed in the southeastern Palearctic.

Bradypterus warblers are characterised by short, rounded wings, usually with a large or fairly large first primary, and long graduated tails comprising either ten or twelve rectrices, which often tend to become badly frayed. Their bills are narrow and fine-tipped, and quite small in many of the Asian species. The legs are typically thin with long slender toes. Relative to *Locustella* warblers, *Bradypterus* have a narrower tail, their wings much shorter and their undertail-coverts less long. The rictal bristles are shorter than in the superficially similar *Cettia* warblers. Most species have plain, nondescript plumage and a subdued head pattern, but several show spotted or streaked throats and/or pale tips to dark undertail-coverts. They tend to forage partly on the ground and build cup-shaped nests attached loosely to vegetation.

Molecular genetic studies have shown that, within the Locustellidae, the African and Asian *Bradypterus* are not closely related. The African *Bradypterus* are placed in one lineage together with some of the *Megalurus* grass warblers (not covered in this book) while the Asian *Bradypterus* form part of another lineage which also includes the western (European) *Locustella* warblers (Olsson *et al.* 2006; Alström *et al.*, in prep,). The African *Bradypterus* are larger, stronger-legged and larger-billed than most of the Asian species. They tend to have ringing, often melodious songs, whereas those of Asian species usually consist of repeated buzzing or reeling phrases. Comparison of MtDNA has indicated that the Bamboo Warbler of C Africa, which also has a repetitive mechanical song, is in fact more closely allied with the Chinese Bush Warbler of Asia than with the other African *Bradypterus* species (Kahindo 2005). The African *Bradypterus* include a fine-billed swamp-dwelling group exemplified by the wide-ranging Little Rush Warbler, and a stouter-billed forest/scrub-dwelling group of which Cinnamon Bracken Warbler and Barratt's Warbler are typical species. The Knysna Warbler of South Africa, whose affinities have been debated, lies outside the main African scrub-dwelling group (Alström *et al.*, in prep.). Another Cape breeding species, Victorin's Warbler, formerly considered to belong with *Bradypterus*, is now removed to the more distant family Macrosphenidae, and is not discussed further here.

In Asia, several species occurring on the continental mainland and some of the island forms were formerly included within the genus *Tribura*. These are characterised by small bills, slender legs and toes with weak claws, low tapering crowns and longish undertail-coverts. They include two long distance migrant species, Baikal Bush Warbler and Chinese Bush Warbler, which show a smaller first primary and a less rounded wing-tip than the Himalayan and S China breeding species. Three further species, Long-tailed Bush Warbler of the Philippines, Kinabalu Bush Warbler of northern Borneo and Chestnut-backed Bush Warbler of the Moluccas, are resident in montane forest. All are distinctly larger and stockier than the *Tribura* group, with more rounded crowns, stronger bills and legs, and broad primaries that lack notches and emarginations.

LITTLE RUSH WARBLER
Bradypterus baboecala   Plate 1

Sylvia baboecala Vieillot, 1817. *Nouv. Dict. Hist. Nat.* nouv. éd. 11: 172. Based upon 'La Caqueteuse' of Levaillant 1802, *Hist. Nat. Oiseaux Afrique* 3, page 61, plate 121, figure 1. Knysna district, Cape Province.

A widespread and locally common resident of wetlands and swamps, occurring throughout C, E and S Africa. Recent DNA studies confirm that two cryptic species are involved (Alström *et al.* in prep.). Following Watson *et al.* (1986) and Urban *et al.* (1997), ten races are recognised.

B. b. baboecala (Vieillot, 1817). S South Africa.
B. b. abyssinicus (Blundell & Lovat, 1899). Ethiopia.
B. b. centralis Neumann, 1908. S Nigeria and S Cameroon, NE DR Congo to Rwanda, Burundi, SW Uganda and N Tanzania.
B. b. msiri Neave, 1909. SE DR Congo, N and W Zambia to adjacent E Angola and probably SW Tanzania, merging with *tongensis* in Caprivi and N Botswana.

B. b. elgonensis Madarász, 1912. Highlands of E Uganda and W and C Kenya.
B. b. transvaalensis Roberts, 1919. C Zimbabwe, upland NE and E South Africa, W Swaziland and Lesotho.
B. b. benguellensis Bannerman, 1927. Plateau of W Angola.
B. b. tongensis Roberts, 1931. SE Kenya, E Tanzania, E and S Zambia, Malawi, NE and E Zimbabwe, Mozambique, E Swaziland and lowland NE and E South Africa.
B. b. chadensis Bannerman, 1936. Lake Chad.
B. b. sudanensis Grant & Mackworth-Praed, 1941. S Sudan.

IDENTIFICATION Length 13–15cm. Wing 50–62mm. Tail/wing 102–124%.

A skulking, dark brown warbler of swamps and marshes, with a gorget of faint streaks across the throat and a longish rounded tail. It usually attracts attention with its distinctive song, a long accelerating series of loud chirps, typically accompanied by wing snaps. Occurs sympatrically in African swamps with three other more localised *Bradypterus* species; White-winged Swamp Warbler, Grauer's Swamp Warbler and Dja River Warbler. Sexes alike.

Structure The smallest of the swamp-dwelling African

Bradypterus. A slim warbler with short rounded wings, a longish graduated tail and rather short undertail-coverts. The bill is long, but slim and fine-tipped, the head profile somewhat attenuated. The wing shows a large first primary, wing point formed by p4–6 and a primary projection about 30% of exposed tertial length. The tail has 12 broad rounded feathers.

Plumage and bare parts Adults of nominate *baboecala* are uniformly warm, dark brown above, although slightly more rufescent on the rump and uppertail-coverts. An inconspicuous buff supercilium above dusky lores fades shortly behind the eye. A short dark eye-stripe contrasts with paler brown cheeks and ear-coverts. The whitish throat and belly contrast with a greyish buff breast and the breast sides and flanks are browner, becoming tawny on the lower flanks and undertail-coverts. There is a gorget of faint dark brown streaks across the lower throat. The tail is dark brown, with all except the central feathers showing distinctly paler brown tips. The wings appear warm, dark brown with paler fringes creating a scaly pattern on the lesser and median coverts. Pale tips to the greater coverts create a lighter bar across the closed wing.

Juveniles resemble adults but are tinged yellowish below and show more sharply defined throat streaks.

The bill is blackish but with a paler greyish base to the lower mandible. The legs are pale pinkish.

Other races appear broadly similar, with slight differences affecting colour tone and the prominence of the throat streaking. The race *elgonensis* is generally more warmly toned above and *chadensis* is also more rufous-brown and lacks throat streaking. Throat streaks are fainter in *tongensis* and *msiri* than in the nominate race, but are more pronounced in the smaller northern races, including *centralis*, *elgonensis*, *sudanensis* and *abyssinicus*.

SIMILAR SPECIES Two swamp-dwelling *Bradypterus* overlap geographically with Little Rush Warbler in C and E Africa. White-winged Swamp Warbler is sympatric at some sites, but Grauer's Warbler appears to be separated by habitat and altitude. In W Africa, the range of Little Rush meets that of Dja River Warbler in Cameroon, but the two probably occupy different habitats. Broad-tailed Warbler is another species of moist rank grassland similar to Little Rush and overlapping with it throughout much of Africa. Confusion could also arise with migrant River Warbler, but in Africa this is a bird of herbaceous undergrowth rather than swamps and wetlands and it should be easily separable by its long pointed wings and long pale-tipped undertail-coverts.

White-winged Swamp Warbler has a song remarkably like that of nominate Little Rush Warbler, but much lower pitched than songs of *elgonensis* and *centralis* (with which it occurs sympatrically). It is readily separated by its larger size, darker appearance, bold breast spots and prominent white 'shoulder' markings.

Grauer's Swamp Warbler is rather larger than Little Rush Warbler. It has a more clearly defined whitish supercilium and heavier breast marking. Its song is quite different.

Dja River Warbler is much larger, with a long tail of ten feathers. It shows bold throat streaking and has a distinctive song.

Broad-tailed Warbler has a broad rounded tail, short wings and fine bill like Little Rush Warbler, but has paler upperparts, greyish white rather than tawny brown undertail-coverts and lacks throat streaks. The tail is even broader-based and shows prominent white feather tips from below.

VOICE Birds in S and coastal E Africa have a very different song from those in the Kenya highlands and Rwanda. In nominate *baboecala* and *tongensis* (which reaches SE Kenya), the song consists of a series of 8–18 rather deep loud notes, all on the same pitch. Delivery is slow and hesitant at first but speeds up towards the end before ceasing abruptly; '*turr – turr – turr-turr – turr-turr-turrturrturturturtur*', with wing snaps often accompanying the rapid phase.

Song of Little Rush Warbler recorded within breeding range of *B. b. tongensis*, Lake Jipi, Kenya, January. (David Fisher)

Song of Little Rush Warbler recorded within breeding range of *B. b. tongensis*, Natal, South Africa, September. (Gibbon 2003)

In *elgonensis* (and *centralis* in SW Uganda and Rwanda) the song is similar in form to the southern races but much higher pitched and sounds reedy or insect-like. It consists of a series of up to 25 sharp '*zrip*' or '*zri*' notes on the same pitch, given over a period of about 15 seconds. It begins slowly and hesitantly, the first few notes being given at about one per second. It accelerates over the next few seconds as the interval between notes decreases and then fades away, regularly followed by a few sharp wing snaps: '*zri – zri – zri – zri – zri – zri - zri-zri-zrizrizizizizizizizizizi…prrrrt…prrrrt… prrrrt*'.

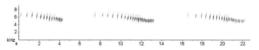

Song of Little Rush Warbler recorded within breeding range of *B. b. elgonensis*, Lake Naivasha, Kenya, August. (Chappuis 2000)

Birds in Cameroon, although assigned to *centralis*, sound like southern birds rather than those of SW Uganda and Rwanda.

Song of Little Rush Warbler recorded within breeding range of *B. b. centralis*, Buea, southwest Cameroon, December. (Chappuis 2000)

The call of southern birds is a single '*chirp*' or a bleating '*pee-et*', that of the race *elgonensis* a nasal '*pink*'.

MOULT Primary moult occurs in Zimbabwe between September and March (Manson 1985). In S Zambia it is recorded in February, April and August and is sometimes irregular.

HABITAT Inhabits tall reedbeds, rushes and swamp vegetation by permanent water, mainly in areas with higher rainfall. In southern Africa, it favours reeds and reed mace

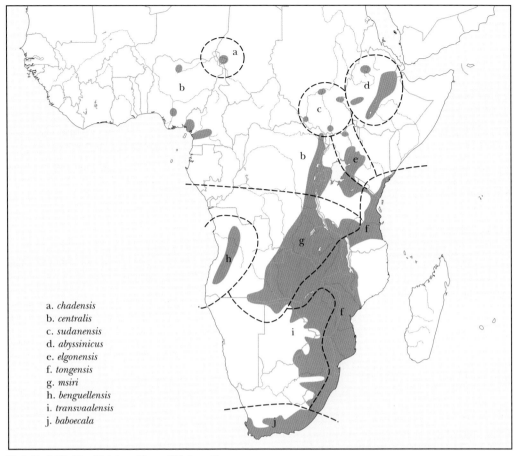

a. *chadensis*
b. *centralis*
c. *sudanensis*
d. *abyssinicus*
e. *elgonensis*
f. *tongensis*
g. *msiri*
h. *benguellensis*
i. *transvaalensis*
j. *baboecala*

Little Rush Warbler. Mainly resident within breeding range.

and occurs along estuaries, rivers and streams. In eastern Africa, it occurs mainly in sedge and papyrus, around lake edges and dams and in small highland swamp patches. It is occasionally found in dry stands of elephant grass. Throughout its range, it readily exploits man-made swamp habitats. In Kenya it occurs in both low humid coastal sites and in the highlands where it ranges up to 2,300m.

BEHAVIOUR Shy and usually difficult to see. It forages among low vegetation close to the water, or while running on the ground, but may occasionally emerge near the top of a sedge stem. It often gives its characteristic territorial song in a low fluttering flight above reeds or along trails within beds of sedge or papyrus, with the tail bouncing and drooping. Otherwise, it is reluctant to fly and when it does this is only for short distances. Several birds will often sing and display in a small area simultaneously.

BREEDING HABITS Territorial, but often forms loose breeding colonies. Apparently monogamous. The nest is usually placed in the base of a sedge tussock or in a sheaf of dead rushes, usually less than 70cm above water. It is a deep, tightly woven construction of dry reeds, weeds and grasses that may trail out untidily below. The cup is lined with finer fibres and rootlets. The usual clutch size is 2–3 eggs. No information is available on incubation or fledging periods. Breeding tends to be associated with the rains. Laying has

been recorded in June–August in Cameroon, April–May in Chad, August–September in Ethiopia, April–November in DR Congo and East Africa, March–May in Malawi and November–March in Zambia and Zimbabwe. Within South Africa, it occurs in September–March in Northern Province and KwaZulu-Natal and August–December in Western Cape.

DISTRIBUTION Wide-ranging in Africa south of the Sahara. It has a fragmented distribution in W and NE Africa, where it is quite scarce and localised, but is more widespread and locally common in central and E Africa, mainly in highlands and coastal areas. It is common and widespread in much of southern C Africa and the wetter eastern and southern parts of S Africa.

B. b. chadensis Confined to Lake Chad, where it is rare.

B. b. centralis Known in W Africa only from small populations in N Nigeria (Kano) and S Nigeria (Onitsha) and from SW Cameroon (coastal areas east to Nyong River). This race is more widespread In C Africa, in NE and E DR Congo, Rwanda and Burundi, extending to SW Uganda and NW Tanzania and (this race or *elgonensis*) locally to N Tanzania at Lake Victoria, Ngorongoro and Mbulu.

B. b. sudanensis Occurs locally in S Sudan along the Nile Valley, and reaches SW Ethiopia in Gambela.

B. b. abyssinicus Locally common in Ethiopia in the western highlands north to Lake Tana, extending east to the Awash valley.

B. b. elgonensis Confined to Mount Elgon and the highlands of W and C Kenya, where it is common but local.

B. b. tongensis Ranges from coastal Kenya north to the Tana River, and lowland NE and E Tanzania to Malawi, E and S Zambia, NE and E Zimbabwe, Mozambique and E Swaziland and in E South Africa through E Limpopo and Mpumalanga Provinces to the midlands of KwaZulu-Natal and coastal East Cape.

B. b. msiri Ranges from the highlands of S and SW Tanzania and SE DR Congo through N, C and W Zambia to adjacent areas of E and SE Angola, the Caprivi Strip (Namibia) and the W Okavango swamps in N Botswana.

B. b. benguellensis Confined to the plateau of W Angola.

B. b. transvaalensis Occurs widely on the Zimbabwe Plateau and through interior E South Africa from the Gauteng highveld to the KwaZulu-Natal uplands, Free State and Griqualand East, also reaching lower parts of Lesotho.

B. b. baboecala Confined to South Africa where it is locally common in West Cape south of Berg River and through S East Cape to Great Kei River.

MOVEMENTS Mainly sedentary. Local movements occur in Zimbabwe during the winter months and in South Africa in response to seasonal water level changes.

DESCRIPTION *B. b. baboecala*
Plumage Adult Forehead to nape and upperside of neck warm, dark olive-brown. Supercilium buff, narrow, extending back to above middle of ear-coverts. Lores and upper ear-coverts dark olive-brown. Lower ear-coverts and cheeks paler olive-brown with fine buffish shaft streaks. Mantle and scapulars tawny-brown, becoming more rufous-brown on rump and uppertail-coverts. Tail dark brown, tips of all except central feathers with broad paler brown fringes and all feathers with regular narrow darker barring. Chin and throat whitish, washed with buff; lower throat with a gorget of short dark brown streaks. Upper breast suffused grey-buff. Centre of lower breast and belly whitish, washed grey-buff. Sides of breast and flanks olive-brown, becoming more tawny-brown on lower flanks and undertail-coverts. Upperwing-coverts dark brown; lesser and median coverts tipped buffy brown to give pale scaly appearance; greater coverts edged and tipped light tawny-brown to form a distinct pale wing-bar. Tertials and flight feathers dark brown with tawny-brown edges. Underwing-coverts buff.

Juvenile Similar to adult but richer brown above. Underparts washed yellowish, dark streaks on throat sharper and narrower.

Bare Parts Upper mandible black. Lower mandible blackish with pale greyish base. Tarsi and toes brownish pink or flesh. Iris brown.

IN HAND CHARACTERS
Measurements *B. b. baboecala*

	Male	Female
Wing	58–62 (60.1; 9)	58–62 (59.2; 6)
Tail	63–71 (67.4; 9)	63–66 (64.2; 5)
Bill	15–17.5 (16.1; 9)	15–17 (16.0; 6)
Tarsus	22–24 (23.2; 9)	21–23.5 (22.1; 6)

Sexes combined:
Tail/wing ratio: 102–119% (111%; 15)
Bill width: 2.8–3.4 (3.1; 10)
Hind claw: 5.2–7.2 (6.5; 10)
Tail graduation: 28–34 (30.3; 12)

Other races (sexes combined)
B. b. tongensis: *wing* 53–59 (57.0; 20); *tail* 59–65 (62.5; 21); *bill* 14.5–17 (15.8; 23). Smaller than *baboecala*.
B. b. msiri: *wing* 54–61 (58.5; 4); *tail* 67–74 (69.8; 4)
B. b. centralis: *wing* 54–57 (55.5; 8) (n = 3)
B. b. elgonensis: *wing* 53–58 (56.4; 11); *tail* 60–64 (62.4; 7); *bill* 14–15.5 (14.5; 8); *tarsus* 20–21.5 (21.0; 8).
B. b. abyssinicus: *wing* 56–60 (57.6; 5).
B. b. sudanensis: *wing* 50–55 (53.0; 7) The smallest race.

Structure *B. b. baboecala*

Wing formula (n = 10):

p1/pc	p2	p3e	p4e	p5e	p6e	p7	p10
12–17	7–9	1.5–3	0–1	wp	0–2	1–3	3.5–6

Wing strongly rounded with large p1. Wing point p(4) 5 (6); p2 < ss tips, p3 = p6–8; emargination on p3–6.

Figure 11. Wing of Little Rush Warbler *B. b. baboecala*.

Tail rather long, strongly graduated; 12 feathers, broad and rounded (Fig. 12).
Bill long, slender, concave-sided with fine tip.
Tarsi rather strong; claws quite small.

a   b   c

Figure 12. Comparison of tail structure of (a) Little Rush Warbler, (b) White-winged Swamp Warbler and (c) Grauer's Swamp Warbler.

Other races As nominate race, but *msiri* shows a relatively longer tail: tail/wing 115–124% (n = 4).

Recognition The shorter wing (< 60mm) separates it from White-winged Swamp Warbler and Dja River Warbler within the range of those species. The 12 tail feathers (ten in Dja River and White-winged Swamp) are broad and rounded (narrower in Grauer's Swamp Warbler). Supercilium and breast streaks are subdued (not bold as in Grauer's Swamp).

Weight
B. b. baboecala: 11.2–17g (14.0; 83).
B. b. transvaalensis: 11.2–15.0g (13.6; 49) (Manson 1985).
B. b. elgonensis: 10.4–15g (12.1; 26) (Urban *et al.*1997).

GEOGRAPHIC VARIATION Mainly clinal, involving colour tone and throat streaking. There is also a trend of decreasing size, from the largest birds in South Africa to the smallest in Sudan. The Zambian race *msiri* and the isolated Angolan *benguellensis* are darker and colder above and whiter below, with indistinct throat streaking. The birds of the central and E African highlands have the strongest throat streaking and are warmly tinged above, *elgonensis* of Kenya being the most tawny-brown or rufescent race. There are also significant differences in song (see **Voice** and **Taxonomy and Systematics**). The isolated Lake Chad population is distinctive, warmly coloured and without throat streaking. The racial identity of birds from N Nigeria (Kano) has not been established.

B. b. baboecala (S South Africa) Described above. The largest race.

B. b. transvaalensis (Zimbabwe Plateau, upland E South Africa) Upperparts as those of nominate race, but underparts whiter, the flanks and undertail-coverts lighter, less tawny-brown.

B. b. tongensis (SE Kenya to lowland E South Africa) Upperparts more rufescent than in the nominate race. Underparts washed more strongly with tawny-buff; throat streaks fainter.

B. b. msiri (N and W Zambia to adjacent SW Tanzania, E Angola and NW Botswana) Upperparts darker brown, less rufescent, than in *tongensis*, flanks and undertail-coverts also darker brown. Wing-covert fringes pronounced. Whiter below than *tongensis* (resembling

transvaalensis) with throat streaking more pronounced and usually extending onto the upper breast and flanks.

B. b. benguellensis (W Angola) Like *msiri*, but larger and darker.

B. b. centralis (Nigeria, Cameroon, E DR Congo to S Uganda and N Tanzania) Upperparts dark olive-brown. Underparts whitish but throat and upper breast well streaked; flanks and undertail-coverts olive-brown.

B. b. elgonensis (Kenya highlands) Darker, more rufous-brown above than *tongensis* or *centralis*, with tawny-brown flanks and undertail-coverts (like *tongensis*) and a tawny-brown wash across the breast. Throat and upper breast with prominent streaks.

B. b. abyssinicus (Ethiopia) Similar to *centralis* but upperparts lighter olive-brown, more cinnamon-tinged. Underparts more strongly washed with tawny-brown.

B. b. sudanensis (S Sudan) Closely resembles *abyssinicus*, but smaller.

B. b. chadensis (Lake Chad) Upperparts more rufous-brown than in *centralis*, sides and lower underparts browner. Throat lacks streaking or spotting. Larger than *centralis*.

TAXONOMY AND SYSTEMATICS The very different voices of two morphologically similar forms in Kenya have long suggested that two cryptic species are involved. Recent DNA study has confirmed this, showing that *tongensis* and *elgonensis/centralis* are, in fact, located on different branches of the African swamp-dwelling warbler clade, the former closely related to White-winged Swamp Warbler, the latter to Grauer's Swamp Warbler (Alström *et al.*, in prep.). But vocal and molecular comparison of Little Rush Warbler races throughout Africa is needed to fully resolve this situation.

▲ Adult *B. b. baboecala*, Western Cape, South Africa, October. Note the well-marked supercilium and fine breast-streaks; also the short wings, rather long broad tail and pinkish legs (Jonathon Schrire).

▲ Probably juvenile *A. b. baboecala*, Mpumalanga, South Africa, March. Note the short tail, the deep tawny brown upperparts and undertail-coverts, the sullied underparts and supercilium, and the buff-tipped greater and median coverts (Johan van Rensberg).

▲ Adult *B. b. baboecala*, Western Cape, South Africa, August (Peter Ryan).

▲ Adult *B. b. centralis*, SW Uganda, August. A small dark brown race showing sharp breast streaks. Note the broad-tipped tail feathers typical of this species (Augusto Faustino).

▲ Adult *B. b. tongensis*, NE KwaZulu-Natal, South Africa, September. This race is warmer above and buffer below than *baboecala*, with less distinct breast streaks and less prominent supercilium (Hugh Chittenden).

▲ Adult *B. b. elgonensis*, Nairobi, Kenya, April. This small, warmly toned race has well-marked breast streaks (Peter Usher).

▲ Adult *B. b. transvaalensis*, Gauteng, South Africa, September. Similar to *baboecala* but paler below. This bird shows a greyer head and dark brown legs (Niall Perrins).

WHITE-WINGED SWAMP WARBLER
Bradypterus carpalis   Plate 1

Bradypterus carpalis **Chapin, 1916.** *Bull. Amer. Mus. Nat. Hist.* 35: 27, figure 4. Faradje, upper Uele district, Belgian Congo.

A resident of swamps and wetlands in C and E Africa. Currently treated as monotypic, but the distinctive characters of a population recently discovered in Zambia suggest these birds merit recognition as a subspecies.

IDENTIFICATION Length 16–17cm. Wing 66–71mm. Tail/wing 95–107%.

A large dark warbler of dense papyrus swamps. Conspicuous whitish patches on the wing-coverts are diagnostic and heavily streaked underparts and white tips to the undertail-coverts are distinctive. Sexes similar but males are larger than females and show more extensive white patches in the wing.

Structure The largest African *Bradypterus*. It has a low domed crown and a long bill that is larger than that of Little Rush Warbler or Grauer's Swamp Warbler, but narrower and fine-tipped. The wing is particularly short and rounded, with a very large first primary, the wing point formed by p5–7 and a very short primary projection. The bulky and strongly graduated tail is relatively shorter than those of Little Rush or Grauer's Swamp Warblers and has ten broad feathers. The legs are long, the toes and claws very strong.

Plumage and bare parts Adults are characterised by a distinctive whitish band across the median covert tips that forms a creamy white patch at the bend of the dark brown wing, unique amongst African *Bradypterus*. It also shows a well-marked whitish supercilium that extends well behind the eye and contrasts with a dark loral stripe and dark brown upper cheeks and ear-coverts. Otherwise the very dark brown upperparts appear nondescript. The underparts are whitish, becoming olive-brown on the flanks and marked with distinctive and bold blackish streaking on the throat and breast, which broadens and forms long diffuse dark lines along the flanks. The undertail-coverts are dark brown with white tips forming prominent barring. This often eye-catching feature is best noticed when the male gives a short song-flight or when it turns to descend from a reed after singing.

Juveniles resemble adults but are less boldly streaked on the breast and more generally dusky brown on flanks and belly, and show a smaller white patch on the wing-coverts.

The bill is black with a bluish grey or yellowish base to the lower mandible. The legs and feet vary from pinkish brown to dull flesh.

SIMILAR SPECIES White-winged Swamp Warbler can occur with Little Rush Warbler and with both Greater Swamp and Lesser Swamp Warblers. It may also meet Grauer's Swamp Warbler in the Rwanda highlands.

Little Rush Warbler has a similar song structure to White-winged Swamp Warbler (see below). It is smaller, however, and has a slimmer bill, much smaller legs and feet and 12 tail feathers. It is less dark above than White-winged Swamp, has much less prominent supercilium and throat streaking, and lacks the white patches on the wings and pale tips to the undertail-coverts.

Grauer's Swamp Warbler has a dark-spotted throat and well-marked supercilium, but is browner, less dark above than White-winged Swamp, and lacks the white wing and undertail-covert markings. Bill is smaller and legs and feet less stronger, and it has a longer, narrower tail than White-winged Swamp, with 12 feathers. Song is quite different.

Greater Swamp and **Lesser Swamp Warblers** are similar in size to White-winged Swamp Warbler, but have plain olive-brown to warm brown upperparts and wings and lack the white wing patches and white tips to the undertail-coverts. Both also show stronger, heavier bills and blackish legs.

VOICE The song, audible up to several hundred metres, is a succession of short loud notes, starting slowly, accelerating and then fading: '*tsyik, tsyik, tsyik-tsyik- tyer-tyer-tyer- turturturturturturtur*', within a frequency range of 2–4kHz. As song ceases, it is often followed by a few loud wing snaps (Zimmerman *et al.* 1996). Each sequence lasts 4–5 seconds with the introductory notes clearly spaced, but with individual notes more difficult to discern as the delivery accelerates. This accelerating 'bouncing ball' song pattern resembles that of Little Rush Warbler and the song is similar in pitch to that of the southern and coastal E African races of that species. However, the song of Little Rush Warblers (races *centralis* and *elgonensis*) that occur sympatrically with White-winged Swamp in the C and E African highlands is weaker and much higher-pitched.

Song of White-winged Swamp Warbler, Namulongwe, Uganda, March. (Chappuis 2000)

The call is a loud '*chip*' or '*cluck*'.

MOULT No information available.

HABITAT Confined to swamps at medium elevation where it prefers the interior of dense papyrus. In Rwanda it is also found in swamps of mixed papyrus and *Miscanthidium* reed and may even move into elephant grass and broad-leaved sedges if preferred areas are drained. It ranges from 1,290m to 2,050m in C Africa, but is absent from the higher forest swamps occupied by Grauer's Swamp Warbler. It occurs between 1,100m and 1,300m at Lake Victoria in Kenya and at 930–960m in Zambia.

BEHAVIOUR Extremely secretive and difficult to see. Typically creeps through the lower layers of papyrus and among old decaying vegetation with small mouse-like movements. It is usually reluctant to fly across open spaces. However, males often make short display flights in the more open areas within papyrus immediately after singing and this can be a good opportunity to observe them.

BREEDING HABITS No information available. Egg laying in DR Congo probably occurs between April and September, while in Kenya it takes place during April.

DISTRIBUTION Has a restricted and fragmented range in C and E Africa, where it is locally common to abundant in the river systems of C and E Rwanda, but it is apparently absent from most of Uganda's swamplands. Although not yet threatened, the cutting of papyrus and swamp drainage may be affecting some populations. In NE DR Congo, it is known from NE Uele District at Faradje and north of Nzoro, and from Shari River in E Ituri. In E DR Congo it occurs at Lwiro in Kivu District. It breeds widely through N, C and E Rwanda to C and E Burundi and adjacent NW Tanzania, including the Mulindi valley, Rugezi swamp and

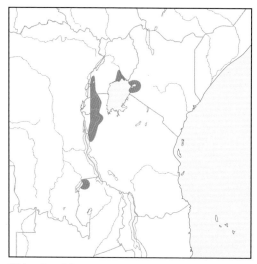

White-winged Swamp Warbler. Resident within breeding range.

the Akagera-Nyabarongo-Akanyaru and Malagarizi River systems. In Uganda, it is known only from Toro, W Ankole and Kigezi in the southwest and Namolonge in the south. Its range extends to Lake Victoria in W Kenya, where it occurs from Yala swamp, Lake Kanyaboli and Usengi east to Kisumu and Kendu Bay. A distinctive population was discovered recently at Lake Mweru in N Zambia. It occurs here in dense papyrus swamp from the mouth of the Luapala River to Chibilikila and near Mwense and appears to be common, with perhaps two pairs/ha recorded (Leonard & Beel 1999).

MOVEMENTS Believed to be sedentary.

DESCRIPTION
Plumage – Adult male Forehead to nape blackish brown. Supercilium buffish white, fairly broad and prominent above lores, tapering off behind eye to reach rear of ear-coverts. Lores, upper cheeks and ear-coverts dark brown, ear-coverts with fine whitish shaft streaks. Mantle to uppertail-coverts very dark olive-brown, slightly paler on rump. Tail dark brown or blackish brown. Chin to belly whitish, sides of breast washed olive-grey. Throat and upper breast marked with bold blackish brown triangular streaks. Flanks olive-brown with darker streaking. Undertail-coverts dark greyish brown with broad white fringes. Upperwing-coverts dark brown or blackish brown; lesser coverts fringed white, those at bend of wing being mainly white; median coverts narrowly tipped greyish white; alula feathers edged white; greater coverts narrowly edged olive-brown. Tertials and flight feathers blackish brown, narrowly edged olive-brown.
Adult female Resembles male but has white on wing restricted to fringes of lesser coverts.
Juvenile Differs from adult in having throat buffy white and remainder of underparts sullied grey-buff, darker and browner on flanks and belly. Breast spots browner, broader

and more diffuse. Upperparts slightly darker than in adult. Pale wing patches reduced, with edges to lesser coverts creamy white, tips of median coverts brown.
Bare parts Upper mandible black, cutting edges bluish grey or yellowish. Lower mandible blackish with bluish grey or yellowish base. Tarsi and toes pinkish brown or dull flesh. Iris brown.

IN HAND CHARACTERS
Measurements

	Male	Female
Wing	70–74 (71.4; 17)	66–69 (68.4; 14)
Tail	69–79 (n = 11)	66–74 (n = 5)
Bill	18–19.5 (n =11)	17–18.5 (n = 5)
Tarsus	27–30 (n = 9)	26–29 (n = 4)

(Urban *et al.* 1997).

Sexes combined (n = 3):
Tail/wing ratio: 95–107% (100%; 7)
Bill width: 3.2–4.0 (3.6; 6)
Hind claw: 9.0–9.7 (9.3; 7)
Tail graduation: 25–29 (26.3; 3)

Structure

Wing formula (n = 3):

p1/pc	p2	p3e	p4e	p5e	p6e	p7	p10
20–25	9–10	4–5	1.5–3	0–1	wp	1	4

Wing similar to Little Rush Warbler (Fig. 11), or slightly more rounded; with large p1 (*c.* 70% p2). Wing point p(5) 6; p2 < ss tips, p3 near p10; slight emargination on p3–6.
Tail strongly graduated (t6 *c.* 60% t1); ten feathers, broad and rounded (Fig. 12).
Bill long, deep but rather narrow; concave-sided with fine tip.
Tarsi and toes long and strong; claws large.
Recognition Readily distinguished by very dark upperparts and white tips to wing-coverts and undertail-coverts. Larger than Little Rush Warbler and Grauer's Swamp Warbler, with longer wing (usually > 62mm) and ten (not 12) tail feathers. Supercilium more prominent and breast markings bolder than in Little Rush Warbler.
Weight W Kenya, 18.5–27g (22.3; 82) (ON unpublished data).

GEOGRAPHIC VARIATION Birds from Kenya appear to be identical to those of E DR Congo and W Uganda. However, birds from the newly discovered population in N Zambia are darker, more blackish, on the upperparts and tail and have darker flanks and blacker throat streaks.

TAXONOMY AND SYSTEMATICS Treated as a monotypic species, but see **Geographic Variation** above. Alström *et al.* (in prep.) have demonstrated, by comparing DNA, that this species is closely related to Little Rush Warbler of the race *tongensis*, as their songs suggest.

▲ Adult, Luapala, Zambia, January. Note the blackish upperparts, white wing-covert markings, bold black breast spotting and white-tipped undertail-coverts. Zambian birds appear blacker above than those of East Africa (Peter Leonard).

▲ Adult, Ruhoma Swamp, SW Uganda, February (Gareth Knass).

▲ Adult, Lake Bunyonyi, Uganda, July. Note the broad tail and light brown legs (Pete Morris).

137

GRAUER'S SWAMP WARBLER
Bradypterus graueri   Plate 1

Bradypterus graueri Neumann, 1908. *Bull. Brit. Orn. Club* 21: 56. Western Kivu Volcanoes, Belgian Congo. 2,200 meters.

A resident of highland swamps with a restricted range in the Albertine Rift of C Africa. Considered ENDANGERED by BirdLife International due to its small and fragmented range, within which many sites are being lost to cultivation. Monotypic.

IDENTIFICATION Length *c.* 17cm. Wing 56–61mm. Tail/wing *c.* 121%.

A rather large, long-tailed *Bradypterus* with dark upperparts, a heavily spotted breast and a prominent pale supercilium, readily seen when the male is singing from the top of a reed stem. Sexes similar, although the female has reduced breast spotting.
Structure The bill is long and fine-tipped, but stouter than in Little Rush Warbler and with a less flattened forehead this gives it a less attenuated head profile. The wings are short and strongly rounded, with a large first primary, the wing-tip formed by p4–7 and a very short primary projection. The tail is strongly graduated and contains 12 feathers. It is narrower than that of Little Rush Warbler but relatively longer.
Plumage and bare parts Adults have dark olive-brown upperparts, slightly more warmly tinged on the rump and uppertail-coverts. A conspicuous whitish supercilium extends from the bill base to the rear of the ear-coverts, bordered below by a dark brown eye-stripe. The remaining ear-coverts and cheeks are mottled whitish and dark brown. At rest, the plain closed wing appears uniform with the upperparts. The underparts are largely whitish but washed rich warm brown from the upper flanks to the undertail-coverts. Both sexes show small round blackish spots on the chin and upper throat, while the male has larger and more prominent spots on the lower throat and breast than the female.

Juveniles are tinged pale yellow below and show narrower breast spots.

The bill is black with a paler greyish lower mandible. The legs and feet are pale brown.

SIMILAR SPECIES Grauer's Swamp Warbler overlaps geographically with two other swamp-dwelling *Bradypterus* species, Little Rush Warbler and White-winged Swamp Warbler, but these rarely occur sympatrically with it and could be readily separated by song. It more closely resembles the allopatric Dja River Warbler.
Little Rush Warbler of the race *centralis* is slightly smaller and has a broader tail. It shows a shorter, less distinct supercilium and its throat marking is less bold than in Grauer's Swamp Warbler.
White-winged Swamp Warbler is larger than Grauer's Swamp Warbler, with a shorter tail of just ten broad feathers. It appears generally darker, shows distinctive white lesser coverts and white-tipped undertail-coverts and has a streaked (not spotted) throat.
Dja River Warbler is a slightly larger bird with a less prominent supercilium and darker legs. It also differs in having ten tail feathers.

VOICE The song consists of a few repeated loud guttural notes followed by a rapid dry trill: '*tchew-tchew-tchew-trrrrrrrrr*', within a frequency range of 2–7kHz. The entire sequence lasts for approximately 1.5 seconds, followed by

a pause of 2–4 seconds. Pairs often duet, one bird (the male?) calling '*tchew-tchew-tchew*', the other responding with an excited chatter. When displaying, the song may be repeated without pause.

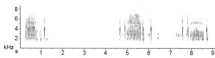

Song of Grauer's Swamp Warbler, Nyungwe, Rwanda, October. (Chappuis 2000)

Alarm and contact notes are not recorded.

MOULT No information available.

HABITAT Restricted to altitudes between 1,950m and 2,600m, where it occurs in swampy areas dominated by various vegetation types, including short-grass and mosses, medium-sized sedges, rushes and ferns, tall grass and sedges and dense scrub. Some of the swamps occupied are small and surrounded by forest, while others are larger and some distance from forest. In Rwanda, it is usually absent from the papyrus swamps inhabited by White-winged Swamp Warbler and is generally found at higher altitudes. In Rugezi swamp, Rwanda, where both species occur, Grauer's Swamp Warbler avoids the papyrus area used by White-winged Swamp Warbler (Van de weghe 1983).

BEHAVIOUR Highly vocal and readily found if present. Often sings in full view from the tops of reeds and sedges and may display while perched with rapidly fluttering wings, calling constantly. It makes short low flights over wet ground with snapping wings. It dwells mainly in the lower strata of the vegetation, feeding on small beetles, caterpillars, spiders and small seeds, but it will often appear in the open, sometimes on floating vegetation. Noted in groups of 10–12 birds outside the breeding season (Van de weghe 1983).

BREEDING HABITS Monogamous and highly territorial, with territories of 0.1–0.5ha (Dowsett-Lemaire 1990). Nests have been found in Rwanda in Rugezi Swamp and in Kabatwa Swamp in the Volcanoes National Park. The latter was a small cup-shaped structure of *Poa leptocrada* and other sedges, built among foliage 0.3–0.4m above the ground (C. Nsabagasani; CK pers. comm.). Appeared to be breeding in Uganda from February to May (Mwambu 1999).

DISTRIBUTION Confined to highlands on either side of the Albertine rift where it occupies a small and highly fragmented area in E DR Congo, SW Uganda, Rwanda and N Burundi. Within its range in DR Congo it occurs in the highlands west of Lake Edward, the highlands west of Lake Kivu at Mumba and Nyawarongo, and at Kahuzi Swamp. In Uganda it is known only from Mubwindi and Ruhizha Swamps in the Bwindi-Impenetrable Forest, Muchuyu Swamp and a few smaller sites. In Rwanda it breeds in the north in Rugezi swamp and in marshes between the Virunga volcanoes, and in the southwest in swamps in Nyungwe Forest. In N Burundi it breeds at Rwegura and north of Teza. It can be very common at some sites. A density of 13 birds per hectare was recorded at Kamiranzovu Swamp, Rwanda based on surveys of singing birds (BirdLife International 2008). The global population of the species is estimated to be less than 10,000 individuals, about half of these in Rwanda (BirdLife International 2000, 2004). Overall numbers are threatened by habitat loss. The major breeding site at Rugezi Swamp is unprotected, and is being degraded and encroached upon by agriculture. Many smaller sites are being drained.

Grauer's Swamp Warbler. Resident within breeding range.

MOVEMENTS Believed to be sedentary.

DESCRIPTION

Plumage Adult male Forehead to nape dark olive-brown. Supercilium narrow, buffish white, from bill base to above rear of ear-coverts. Lores and below eye to ear-coverts dark olive-brown. Cheeks tawny-buff, finely mottled dark brown. Mantle and scapulars olive-brown, grading to warmer tawny-brown on rump and uppertail-coverts. Tail dark tawny-brown. Chin and throat whitish; breast washed tawny-brown. Chin and upper throat with small circular dark brown spots; lower throat and upper breast with larger blacker spots. Belly whitish. Flanks, vent and undertail-coverts tawny-brown. Upperwing-coverts dark brown; lesser and median coverts broadly fringed light olive-brown, greater coverts broadly edged tawny-brown, alula fringed paler buffy brown. Tertials and flight feathers dark brown with diffuse broad tawny-brown edges.

Adult female As male but with smaller spots restricted to breast and throat almost pure white.

Juvenile Similar to adult but underparts mainly white,

washed pale yellowish; brown flanks tinged cinnamon, spots on breast narrower.

Bare parts Upper mandible black. Lower mandible greyish. Tarsi and toes pale brown or flesh. Iris brown to dark brown.

IN HAND CHARACTERS

Measurements

	Male	Female
Wing	56–61 (58.4; 7)	56–59 (57.5; 5)
Tail	71–75 (72.9; 7)	66–69 (67.4; 5)
Bill	15–16.4 (15.7; 7)	14.5–15.3 (14.9; 5)

(Urban *et al.* 1997)

Tarsus: 1 ♂ 24, 1 ♀ 23.5

Tail/wing ratio (n = 13, sexes combined): mean 121%. (n = 1, unsexed): bill width 3.2; hind claw 8.0; tail graduation 39.

Structure

Wing formula (n = 1):

p1/pc	p2	p3e	p4e	p5e	p6e	p7e	p10
15	9	2	wp	wp	wp	1	5

Wing similar to Little Rush Warbler (Fig. 11); strongly rounded with large p1. Wing point p4–7; p2 < ss tips; emargination on p3–7.

Tail long, strongly graduated; 12 feathers, rather narrow and pointed (Fig. 12).

Bill longer and stouter than in Little Rush Warbler, concave-sided with fine tip.

Tarsi and toes stronger than in Little Rush Warbler.

Recognition Distinguished from Little Rush Warbler by prominent whitish supercilium, bold blackish breast spots and narrower tail feathers. Tail/wing ratio often ≥ 120%, higher than in Little Rush Warbler.

Weight 15–19g (16.9; 15) (Urban *et al.* 1997).

GEOGRAPHIC VARIATION None recorded.

TAXONOMY AND SYSTEMATICS No issues arising.

▲ Adult, Nyungwe Forest, Rwanda, July. Freshly moulted bird, showing the long, narrow tail, a prominent whitish supercilium, whitish throat and bold black breast spots (Peter Ryan).

▲ Adult, Nyungwe Forest, Rwanda, June. A worn bird with bold breast spots. Note the frayed pointed tail and strong pale brown legs (Malcolm Wilson).

DJA RIVER WARBLER
Bradypterus grandis   Plate 1

Bradypterus grandis Ogilvie-Grant, 1917. *Ibis*, page 78. Bitye, Ja (=Dja) River, southern Cameroon.

A poorly known *Bradypterus* with a restricted range in S Cameroon, Gabon and SW Central African Republic where it is resident in dense sedge swamp. Considered NEAR THREATENED by BirdLife International due to its small population and restricted range. Monotypic.

IDENTIFICATION Length *c.* 18cm. Wing 64–67mm. Tail/wing *c.* 115%.

A rather large and long-tailed swamp-dwelling warbler with dark brown upperparts, greyish underparts and dark throat streaks. Typically skulking, its presence usually revealed by its distinctive song. Sexes alike.

Structure A large *Bradypterus*, with a fairly strong bill, robust legs and strong toes. The wings are short and very rounded with a long first primary, wing point at p4–7 and an extremely short primary projection. It has a proportionately long and strongly graduated tail with only ten rectrices, which can show narrow and very worn looking tips.

Plumage and bare parts The entire upperparts are uniform dark olive-brown, the only contrast being with the slightly more warmly toned edges to the wing-coverts and flight feathers. It has a narrow and poorly marked greyish supercilium, most conspicuous above the lores. Below, a whitish throat and belly centre contrast with a buffy brown breast, which darkens to tawny-brown on the flanks and undertail-coverts. The chin and upper throat show short dark streaks which become longer and more conspicuous on the lower throat and upper breast.

The blackish bill shows a greyish base below. The legs are greyish brown.

SIMILAR SPECIES Within its restricted range in W Africa, it is only likely to be confused with Little Rush Warbler. The similar Grauer's Swamp Warbler is confined to C Africa and the two species are unlikely to meet.

Little Rush Warbler is much smaller than Dja River Warbler. It has a finer bill and a more rounded tail of 12 feathers. Throat streaking is less prominent.

Grauer's Swamp Warbler is slightly smaller than Dja River Warbler, but resembles it in plumage, structure and song and may well be closely related. It shows a more conspicuous supercilium and paler legs and has 12 rectrices.

VOICE The song has a similar structure to that of Grauer's Swamp Warbler. It consists of brief loud repeated sequences of *c.*1.5 seconds, separated by pauses of 5–8 seconds. Each sequence consists of 2–4 introductory notes and a short loud descending trill; *psuit-psuit-psuit-its-struuuuuuuuuu* (Christy & Clarke 1994), or a slightly higher pitched '*tsweet – tsweet - tsweet its-struuuuuuuuuuu*' within a frequency range of 1.5–3.5kHz.

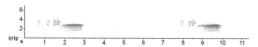

Song of Dja River Warbler, Lope reserve, Gabon, December. (Chappuis 2000)

MOULT No information available.

HABITAT Inhabits swamps with tall dense sedge *Rhynchospora*

corymbosa, at altitudes between 400m and 800m. It typically occupies isolated swamps within forest, or between forest and savanna and these are sometimes extremely small. It has also been recorded in tall elephant grass *Pennisetum* and in dense low growth in abandoned plantations.

BEHAVIOUR Secretive and usually keeps close to the ground, where it moves about in dense growth with short hops. It rarely flies, but when it does, it flaps heavily and briefly over sedge tops with the tail spread. Display flight over the territory is accompanied by a curious wing-snapping noise.

BREEDING HABITS Unknown.

DISTRIBUTION Has a small and restricted known range within Cameroon, Gabon and the Central African Republic. Recorded from just eight widely spaced localities, but it may have a more extensive distribution in its specialised and inaccessible marsh habitat in the forests of N Gabon and SE Cameroon and perhaps N DR Congo. In SE Cameroon it is known from Bitye on the Dja River, the Nki Reserve and Lobeke, where a population of at least 100 pairs was estimated (Dowsett-Lemaire & Dowsett 2000). It appears to be more widespread in S Gabon where it is known from Mimongo and M'bigou in Massif Chaillu, the Lopé Faunal Reserve and Langhoué. In Central African Republic it was discovered recently in Dzangha-Ndoki National Park in the extreme southwest.

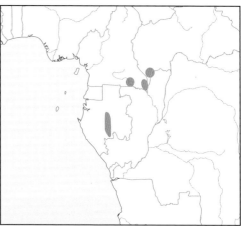

Dja River Warbler. Resident within breeding range.

MOVEMENTS Believed to be sedentary.

DESCRIPTION

Plumage – Adult Forehead to nape plain dark olive-brown. Supercilium greyish buff, narrow and inconspicuous. Lores, cheeks and ear-coverts dark brown. Mantle and scapulars to uppertail-coverts olive-brown, slightly rufescent. Tail dark tawny-brown. Chin and throat white, washed grey-buff and spotted dark brown. Upper breast more strongly washed with brown and with prominent short dark brown streaks. Lower breast and belly white, washed grey-buff. Sides of breast, long flank feathers and undertail-coverts tawny-brown. Upperwing feathers dark brown; lesser coverts fringed lighter olive-brown, median and greater coverts edged and tipped warm brown, alula fringed pale buff-brown, remiges edged warm brown. Underwing-coverts light brown.

Juvenile An immature (presumably juvenile) was described as lighter than the adult above, whiter below with no brownish breast-band, throat and upper breast spotted blackish (Urban *et al.* 1997).

Bare parts Upper mandible black. Lower mandible grey. Tarsi and toes greyish brown. Iris brown.

IN HAND CHARACTERS

Measurements 3 males, 1 unsexed: *wing* 64–67 (65.8); *tail* 72–77 (75.3); *bill* 16.5–17 (16.7); *tarsus* 24–26 (25.3); bill width (n = 1) 3.8.

Structure

Wing formula (n = 1):

p1/pc	p2	p3e	p4e	p5e	p6e	p7	p10
19	9	2	wp	wp	wp	wp	6

Wing similar to Little Rush Warbler (Fig. 11); strongly rounded with large p1. Wing point p4–7; p2 < ss tips; emargination on p3–6.

Tail long and strongly graduated; feathers quite broad but with narrow tips.

Bill longish, but broader than in Grauer's Swamp Warbler and Little Rush Warbler

Tarsi long and strong.

Recognition Much larger than Little Rush Warbler (wing > 62mm), with a broader bill and longer tail of only ten tail feathers.

Weight 18.5g (n = 1) (Dunning 2007)

GEOGRAPHIC VARIATION None known.

TAXONOMY AND SYSTEMATICS No issues arising.

▲ Adult, Langoue Bai, Gabon, June. This singing male shows the drab brown plumage and the long, narrow graduated tail (Adam Riley).

▲ Adult, Langoue Bai, Gabon, January. Note the large, broad blackish breast streaks, well-marked but short and narrow supercilium, and the mid-brown leg colour (Adriaan Dijksen).

BAMBOO WARBLER
Bradypterus alfredi   Plate 2

Bradypterus alfredi Hartlaub, 1890. *J. Ornithol.* 38: 152. Njangalo (=Nyangabo). Northeastern Congo Free State.

A little known and very localised resident of bamboo, grassy cover and forest undergrowth in C Africa. Polytypic with two races recognised:

B. a. alfredi Hartlaub, 1890. W Ethiopia, SE Sudan, W Uganda, E DR Congo.

B. a. kungwensis Moreau, 1942. W Tanzania, NW Zambia.

IDENTIFICATION Length 14cm. Wing 55–65mm. Tail/wing 87–98%.

A skulking medium-sized warbler, rather dark brown above with a poorly marked supercilium. The underparts are greyish, with conspicuous pale tips on the undertail-coverts. Voice is quite different from that of other African *Bradypterus*. Sexes alike.

Structure Similar to that of other scrub-dwelling African *Bradypterus* but the strongly graduated tail of 12 broad rounded feathers is relatively short and it has a rather long bill. The wing is strongly rounded, with a large first primary, wing point formed by p4–6 and a very short primary projection.

Plumage and bare parts An overall dingy appearance suggests Evergreen Forest Warbler. The adult of nominate *alfredi* is dark olive-brown above with a slightly warmer cinnamon tinge. It shows a short and poorly marked greyish supercilium. Below, the whitish throat merges with the greyish breast and flanks. The central underparts are dingy white, the undertail-coverts greyish brown with distinctive white fringes. Birds of the race *kungwensis* are colder dark olive-brown above and darker olive-grey below.

The bill is blackish with a greyish lower mandible. The legs and feet are dark brown.

SIMILAR SPECIES Two common *Bradypterus* species, Cinnamon Bracken Warbler and Evergreen Forest Warbler, overlap the range of Bamboo Warbler. Both are readily distinguished by their songs.

Cinnamon Bracken Warbler is generally found at higher elevations than Bamboo Warbler. It is distinctly brighter and warmly coloured above and has a more prominent supercilium. It also shows a warmly coloured breast-band and contrasting white belly, but has plain undertail-coverts. Longer-tailed than Bamboo Warbler.

Evergreen Forest Warbler of the race *ufipae* overlaps locally with Bamboo Warbler in NW Zambia. It differs in its larger size and longer-tailed structure, and is more warmly coloured with a whiter belly. The race *barakae* could occur with Bamboo Warbler in E DR Congo and W Uganda but should be readily separable by its bright cinnamon head-sides and underparts and long narrow tail of ten feathers.

VOICE The simple song is a repeated series of 20 or more hard, nasal disyllabic notes; '*tchuu-ka, tchuu-ka, tchuu-ka...*', delivered at about 2.5 notes per second within a frequency range of 2–4kHz. This gives it a quality and structure reminiscent of some of the Asian *Bradypterus* or a slowed down *Locustella* song. It is quite different from the melodious trill of Cinnamon Bracken Warbler and the repeated whistles of Evergreen Forest Warbler.

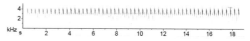

Song of Bamboo Warbler, Menilunga, Zambia, October. (Chappuis 2000)

The call-note is a short '*whitt*' or '*ticc*', recalling that of Common Redstart (G. Nikolaus).

MOULT No information available.

HABITAT Occurs in a variety of habitats, both within and outside forest, including bamboo, high grass and dense ground cover below montane forest, and grassy secondary growth in forest clearings. In DR Congo and Ethiopia it inhabits a mosaic of riverine marshland, *Combretum/Terminalia* savanna and crops, sometimes near villages. In Zambia it frequents the ground layer of moist evergreen forest, including regrowth and riparian strips. It ranges from 1,200m to 1,460m in Zambia, 1,200m to 2,500m in DR Congo and Uganda and from 1,800m to 2,300m in Tanzania, but occurs as low as 525m in Ethiopia. It overlaps locally in Zambia with Evergreen Forest Warbler.

BEHAVIOUR Rarely seen and easily overlooked unless vocal. It tends to remain within thick cover and close to the ground.

BREEDING HABITS Unknown.

DISTRIBUTION This is a rare and localised species for reasons that are obscure. There are three discrete populations, with two recognised races.

B. a. alfredi Known from W Ethiopia at Didessa, Bulchra Forest and Gambela and SE Sudan in the Imatong Mountains. Further south, it is found in E DR Congo from the plateau west of Lake Albert and the Rwenzori Mountains south to the highlands northwest of Baraka and in W Uganda in Bugoma forest and the E Rwenzoris (Mubuku Valley).

B. a. kungwensis Described from the Kungwe-Mahare highlands of W Tanzania. It is scarce in a few localities in NW Zambia in N Mwinilunga District and also recorded at Kasangu north of Lake Mweru. It seems likely that it will be found in the intervening Katanga highland region of SE DR Congo.

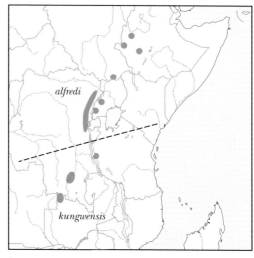

Bamboo Warbler. Resident within breeding range.

MOVEMENTS Believed to be sedentary.

DESCRIPTION *B. a. kungwensis*
Plumage – Adult Top of head dark olive-brown. Supercilium poorly marked, pale grey-buff extending from bill to just behind eye. Lores, cheeks and ear-coverts olive-brown, ear-coverts with a few grey-buff streaks. Mantle and scapulars to uppertail-coverts dark olive-brown. Tail dark brown above with faint narrow blackish transverse barring, grey-brown below. Chin and throat dirty white. Upper breast, side of breast and flanks dark olive-grey. Belly and centre of lower breast greyish white. Undertail-coverts greyish brown, broadly tipped greyish white. Lesser and median coverts dark olive-brown. Rest of upperwing-coverts blackish brown with olive-brown edges. Remiges blackish brown, outer webs of tertials tinged olive-brown, flight feathers with narrow olive-brown edges. Underwing-coverts olive-grey.
Juvenile Similar to adult but underparts washed yellowish.
Bare parts Upper mandible black. Lower mandible slate-grey. Tarsi and toes brown. Iris brown.

IN HAND CHARACTERS
Measurements *B. a. kungwensis*

	Male	Female
Wing	55–62 (58.8; 5)	56–62 (59.0; 4)
Tail	53, 53, 58 (n = 3)	51, 55, 57 (n = 3)
Bill	16–18 (17.1; 4)	16, 16.5 (n = 2)
Tarsus	24, 24, 26 (n = 3)	24, 25, 26 (n = 3)

(Includes data from Urban *et al.* 1997)

Sexes combined:
Tail/wing ratio: 87–98% (n = 3)
Bill width: 4.0, 4.2 (n = 2)
Hind claw: 5.8–6.3 (6.0; 4)
Tail graduation: 23.0 (n = 1)

B. a. alfredi (sexes combined): *wing* 58–65 (61.3; 4); (1 female): *tail* 61; *bill* 16.5; *tarsus* 24.

Structure *B. a. kungwensis*

Wing formula (n = 4):

p1/pc	p2	p3e	p4e	p5e	p6(e)	p7	p10
12–13	8–9	2–3	wp	wp	wp	1	4–5

Wing similar to Cinnamon Bracken Warbler (Fig. 13); strongly rounded with large p1 (*c.* 60% p2). Wing point p4–6; p2 < ss tips, p3 = p8/9; emargination on p3–5 (slightly on p6).
Tail relatively short, strongly graduated; feathers broad and rounded (Fig. 14).
Bill broad-based with rather narrow tip; slightly concave-sided.
Tarsi and toes rather long but slender; claws small, gently curved.
Recognition Shows dark olive-brown upperparts and greyish underparts with a whitish throat and belly centre. Separated from more warmly coloured Cinnamon Bracken Warbler by shorter tail (< 60mm); from the brightly coloured race *barakae* of Evergreen Forest Warbler by shorter tail with broader feathers; and from both of these by the whitish fringes to grey-brown undertail-coverts.
Weight *B. a. alfredi*: 14–17.5g (15.8; 5) (GN, unpublished data; Dunning 2007).

GEOGRAPHIC VARIATION Two similar races, separated by slight colour differences.
B. a. kungwensis (W Tanzania, NW Zambia) Described above.
B. a. alfredi (W Ethiopia, SE Sudan, W Uganda, E Congo) Differs from *kungwensis* in having the upperparts and wing feather edges tinged cinnamon rather than dark olive-brown, and the breast and flanks washed paler olive-grey.

TAXONOMY AND SYSTEMATICS Bamboo Warbler was allied with the Knysna Warbler of South Africa, based upon structural similarities including its broad and shortish tail (Hall & Moreau 1970). This relationship is not, however, supported by other structural features and the two species have completely different songs. Moreover, mtDNA studies have indicated that Bamboo Warbler is only distantly related to other African *Bradypterus*, and appears to be closer to some Asian species (CK *in litt.*).

BARRATT'S WARBLER
Bradypterus barratti   Plate 2

Bradypterus barratti Sharpe, 1876. *Ibis*, page 53. Neighbourhood of Mac Mac goldfields, Lydenburg district, Transvaal.

A resident of bush and scrub with a restricted range in eastern parts of S Africa. Polytypic, with four races recognised:

B. b. barratti Sharpe, 1876. NE South Africa (Limpopo, Mpumalanga) to Swaziland and Lebombo Mountains on the S Mozambique border.

B. b. godfreyi (Roberts, 1922). Lowland E South Africa (coastal Eastern Cape and lowland KwaZulu-Natal).

B. b. priesti Benson, 1946. E Zimbabwe and adjacent Mozambique to Mount Gorongoza.

B. b. cathkinensis Vincent, 1948. Highland E South Africa (interior KwaZulu-Natal to Griqualand West in Eastern Cape) and Lesotho.

IDENTIFICATION Length 15–16cm. Wing 61–69mm. Tail/wing 100–108%.

A rather uniform dull brown *Bradypterus* with greyish underparts and soft dusky throat streaks. It resembles Knysna Warbler with which it can occur during the austral winter on the southeast coast of South Africa and the two are easily confused.

Sexes alike.

Structure A slim medium-sized warbler showing the strongly rounded wing and well-graduated tail typical of the genus. It has a large first primary (p1), a wing point formed by p4–6 and a very short primary projection. The tail is relatively long and consists of 12 rather broad, rounded feathers. The bill is strong and rather long.

Plumage and bare parts The adult has the top and sides of the head dark brown, with a poorly marked greyish supercilium. The upperparts and wing feather edgings are rich olive-brown, more warmly tinged on the rump and uppertail-coverts. The underparts are pale greyish, with a broad brown band across the breast and brown flanks and undertail-coverts, and with short dusky throat streaks that extend onto the breast in the nominate race. The throat and belly centre are whiter in the race *priesti*.

The juvenile is rather more olive above and has the supercilium and underparts tinged yellow.

The bill is blackish. The legs fleshy brown.

SIMILAR SPECIES The similar Knysna Warbler overlaps with Barratt's Warbler in South Africa. Two other *Bradypterus* species of forest or forest edge scrub, Evergreen Forest Warbler and Cinnamon Bracken Warbler, have ranges in Africa to the north of Barratt's Warbler.

Knysna Warbler is only slightly smaller than Barratt's and has a similar broad and rounded although somewhat shorter tail. It is slightly darker olive-brown or chocolate brown above and darker and greyer on the throat, and shows only faint throat streaking. The songs of the two species are similar, but that of Knysna is louder, with longer, more clearly defined opening notes.

Evergreen Forest Warbler has a narrower tail of just ten feathers, lacks throat streaking and has a very different song. The race which breeds closest to Barratt's, *B. l. granti* in Malawi, is warmer, tawny-brown above than Barratt's (of the race *priesti*) and tinged cinnamon below.

Cinnamon Bracken Warbler has broad tail feathers like

Barratt's and a similar trilling song. It ranges south to Malawi, where the race *nyassae* is a more warmly coloured bird than the *priesti* race of Barratt's Warbler. It also shows a more pronounced supercilium and has a paler, unstreaked throat.

VOICE The song begins with two or three high pitched '*tseee*' notes that lead into a quick succession of lower and louder ringing notes, forming an even trill within frequency range 2–6kHz: '*tseee tseee tchui-tchui-tchui-tchui-tchui-tchui-tchu-tchu-tchu-tchu…*'. The entire sequence lasts 2–4 seconds, the terminal trill of approximately 20 '*tchu*' calls being given within less than two seconds. Successive song sequences are separated by some 5–8 seconds. The speed of the terminal trill varies between individuals. The song is similar in form to that of Cinnamon Bracken Warbler but a little drier and faster.

Song of Barratt's Warbler, Natal, South Africa, March. (Gibbon 2003)

The call is a harsh '*trrk*' or '*chrr*', sometimes drawn out into a rattling *trrr-r-rrrrrrrk*'.

MOULT No information available.

HABITAT Mainly a bird of highlands, breeding at 1,500m to 2,200m in Zimbabwe and above 1,370m in the Drakensberg, but found at much lower elevations in the interior forests of Eastern Cape and near the coast of KwaZulu-Natal. It inhabits dense tangled vegetation, usually near water, particularly favouring undergrowth along streams in temperate forest. It is fairly adaptable and able to occupy small patches of secondary vegetation. It occurs in rank growth along paths and clearings in evergreen forest, in pockets of valley bottom or hillside scrub and in bushy gullies in upland mist forest. In the E Zimbabwe highlands it is found in *Philippia* heathland. In Lesotho it favours dense *Buddleia* scrub (Urban *et al.* 1997).

BEHAVIOUR Usually seen alone or in pairs. It generally forages low down, climbing with agility among vegetation and running mouse-like on the ground. It is usually detected by its frequent calls. The male sings near the nest during the early stages of breeding.

BREEDING HABITS A monogamous, solitary nester and territorial. The nest is built close to the ground among tangled vegetation and consists of a bulky cup of leaves, stems and grasses. The usual clutch size is two eggs. No information available on incubation and fledging periods. The nestlings are fed by both parents. Breeding occurs between October and December in Zimbabwe and in late November and December in Mpumalanga. In KwaZulu-Natal, it occurs between September and November.

DISTRIBUTION Widespread in temperate areas of S Africa and common in suitable habitat throughout much of its range. The two northern populations, *priesti* (Zimbabwe) and nominate *barratti* (NE South Africa) are well separated, but within South Africa the highland and lowland races appear to have a continuous range.

B. b. priesti Breeds locally in the highlands of E Zimbabwe and occurred historically in adjacent W Mozambique, including Mount Gorongoza.

B. b. barratti Ranges in NE South Africa from Zoutpansberg, Limpopo Province and through Mpumalanga, where common in the highveld and in patches of relict forest in the escarpment region. It extends to Swaziland, the Lebombo Mountains on the S Mozambique border and N KwaZulu-Natal.

B. b. godfreyi Occurs widely through lowland SE South Africa, on the edges of interior forests from KwaZulu-Natal to Great Fish River, Eastern Cape.

B. b. cathkinensis Breeds on the edges of high altitude forests, from the KwaZulu-Natal/Mpumalanga border, along the Drakensberg and through Lesotho to bordering Griqualand West, Eastern Cape.

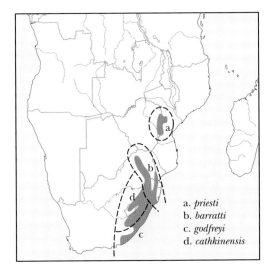

a. *priesti*
b. *barratti*
c. *godfreyi*
d. *cathkinensis*

Barratt's Warbler. Mostly resident within breeding range.

MOVEMENTS Abandons highland breeding localities during the colder winter months. Birds from Zimbabwe disperse, most probably moving east to the Mozambique lowlands (Irwin 1981). Birds from the Drakensberg and KwaZulu-Natal uplands move to the coast and there are coastal records in winter as far west as East London.

DESCRIPTION *B. b. priesti*
Plumage – Adult Forehead to nape and upper sides of neck olive-brown. Supercilium grey-buff, narrow and rather inconspicuous, extending back to behind eye. Lores, cheeks and ear-coverts olive-brown. Mantle and scapulars to rump rich olive-brown, becoming more warmly tinged on uppertail-coverts. Tail rich, dark olive brown, matching upperparts. Chin and throat greyish white, merging with dull olive-brown upper breast. Throat and upper breast with short dark grey-brown streaks. Centre of lower breast and belly greyish white. Flanks, vent and undertail-coverts dull olive-brown. Lesser and median coverts rich olive-brown. Primary coverts, greater coverts and alula dark brown with olive-brown fringes showing little contrast. Remiges dark brown with richer olive-brown edges, those of primaries slightly warmer, giving more rufescent appearance to closed wing. Underwing-coverts greyish brown.
Juvenile Upperparts more olive, less warmly tinged than in adult. Supercilium and underparts washed strongly with yellow.
Bare Parts Upper and lower mandibles black. Tarsi and toes dark brownish to flesh. Iris brown or hazel.

IN HAND CHARACTERS
Measurements *B. b. priesti*

	Male	Female
Wing	62–66 (63.7; 6)	61–62 (61.7; 3)
Tail	62–71 (67.0; 6)	63–65 (64.3; 3)
Bill	15–16 (15.4; 4)	15–15.5 (15.1; 3)
Tarsus	23–24 (23.4; 6)	22–23.5 (22.7; 3)

Sexes combined:
Tail/wing ratio: 100–108% (104%; 9)
Bill width: 3.6–4.2 (3.9; 6)
Hind claw: 6.2–7.0 (6.5; 10)
Tail graduation: 30–35 (31.6; 8)
B. b. barratti (sexes combined): *wing* 62–65 (63.6; 5); *tail* 63–68 (66.2; 5); *bill* 14.5–16 (15.7; 5); *tarsus* 22–23 (22.5; 4).
B. b. godfreyi (sexes combined): *wing* 62–67 (64.6; 17) (Urban *et al.* 1997); *tail* 67–72 (69.3; 6); *bill* 15–16 (15.4; 6); *tarsus* 21.5–13 (22.4; 6).
B. b. cathkinensis (1 ♂): *wing* 69; *tail* 76; *bill* 16; *tarsus* 21.

Structure *B. b. priesti*

Wing formula (n = 9):

p1/pc	p2	p3e	p4e	p5e	p6e	p7	p10
14–18	10–14	2–4	wp	wp	wp	0.5–1	5–7

Wing similar to Cinnamon Bracken Warbler (Fig. 13); strongly rounded with rather large p1. Wing point p4–6; p2 < ss tips, p3 = p8–9; emargination on p3–6.

Tail strongly graduated (t6 = 50–60% t1); 12 feathers, rather broad and rounded.

Bill quite strong with slightly concave sides; rather longer than in Cinnamon Bracken Warbler.

Tarsi strong; claws rather small.

Recognition A dark brown warbler, greyish below but with pale throat and dusky throat/breast streaks. Usually separable from Knysna Warbler by longer tail (> 61mm; tail/wing > 100%) and longer tarsus (> 21mm); throat streaks are sharper and more distinct.

Weight *B. b. priesti*: unsexed, 16.1–22.2g (18.8; 36) (Manson 1990).

GEOGRAPHIC VARIATION
Variation involves differences in plumage tone, extent of throat streaking and size. The Zimbabwe race *priesti* is much paler below than those of South Africa.
B. b. priesti (E Zimbabwe) Described above.
B. b. barratti (NE South Africa) Upperparts as in *priesti*, but the throat and belly are greyer (less whitish). Streaking extends from the throat to the chin and further onto the breast.
B. b. godfreyi (Lowland SE South Africa) Resembles *barratti*, but slightly darker above. The underparts are more grey-buff, with streaking less distinct and confined to the throat.
B. b. cathkinensis (Highland E South Africa) Similar to *barratti* but more olive-brown above. Slightly lighter below, with streaking confined to the throat and upper breast. Larger than other races.

TAXONOMY AND SYSTEMATICS Barratt's Warbler has often been treated as conspecific with Evergreen Forest

Warbler (e.g. by White 1965; Hall & Moreau 1970; Watson 1986). However, it differs in voice and in the number and shape of the tail feathers from all the forms grouped here under *B. lopezi*. It was regarded by Dowsett and Dowsett-Lemaire (1993) as forming a superspecies with Cinnamon Bracken Warbler.

▲ Adult *B. b. barratti*, W KwaZulu-Natal, South Africa, April. Note the long and rather broad graduated tail, and the drab brown plumage with more warmly tinged wings. This race has well-streaked greyish underparts (Hugh Chittenden).

▲ Adult *B. b. barratti*, Limpopo, South Africa, December (Niall Perrins).

KNYSNA WARBLER
Bradypterus sylvaticus   Plate 2

Bradypterus sylvaticus **Sundevall, 1860**. In: *Grill, Svenska Vetenskaps-Akad. Handlingar, Stockholm*, ser. 2(10): 30. Knysna.

A rare resident, endemic to South Africa where confined to southern coastal forests. Considered VULNERABLE by BirdLife International due to its small fragmented range, with the population apparently declining due to habitat loss. Polytypic with two races recognised:

B. s. sylvaticus Sundevall, 1860. S Western Cape Province to SW Eastern Cape east to Port Elizabeth.

B. s. pondoensis Haagner, 1909. SE Eastern Cape.

IDENTIFICATION Length 14cm. Wing 56–63mm. Tail/ wing 87–100%.

A rather small, featureless *Bradypterus* with dark brown upperparts, which inhabits gloomy undergrowth and is usually detected by its song. Sexes similar.

Structure Shows the short rounded wing typical of the genus, with a fairly large first primary and a wing point formed by p4–6. The tail of 12 feathers is broad and fan-shaped, but rather shorter and less strongly graduated than in most African *Bradypterus*. The bill is quite long, but slim.

Plumage and bare part Adults show uniform, warm dark brown or olive-brown upperparts, including the closed wings and tail. There is a poorly defined supercilium which reaches to just behind the eye. The male shows a dark loral triangle, bordered below by a short white stripe and emphasising a narrow whitish eye-ring. The underparts are drab, dull greyish brown with a paler throat and central abdomen and usually some faint streaking or mottling on the throat. Dark brown undertail-coverts show paler greyish tips. The female resembles the male but lacks the dark loral spot and has a paler throat (Visser & Hockey 2002).

Juveniles are washed yellowish below and show more pronounced throat streaking.

The bill is dark brown with a paler base to the lower mandible and the legs are pale brown.

SIMILAR SPECIES Within its restricted range, Knysna Warbler is only likely to be confused with Barratt's Warbler, which is quite similar in structure and coloration and they can occur together outside the breeding season in East Cape Province.

Barratt's Warbler is slightly larger than Knysna Warbler with a proportionately longer tail. It is also paler, particularly on the throat and central underparts, and shows more distinct throat streaking. The two species have similar but readily distinguishable songs

VOICE The song consists of a sequence of thin, high-pitched notes, increasing in tempo and volume, which often lead into a lower reedy reel or trill descending from 7–4kHz: '*wit wit wit wit-wit-wit-witwitwitrrrrrrrrrrrrrr*'. Each sequence lasts some 4–9 seconds and is typically followed by a pause of similar length before being repeated.

The song is similar in structure to that of Barratt's Warbler, but louder, the notes sharper and more clearly defined.

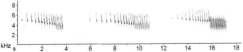

Song of Knysna Warbler, Cape Town, Cape Province, South Africa, September. (Gibbon 2003)

Calls include a low '*brrit*', a soft '*trr-up*' and a loud '*peeeit*'; also a repetitive '*prrrit prrrit prrrit*' in alarm (Urban *et al.* 1997).

MOULT No information available.

HABITAT Requires dense low vegetation and shows a distinct preference for tangled thickets along streams. It occurs over drainage lines in fynbos forest patches, on the edges of temperate evergreen forest and in small forest patches; also in thickets of introduced bramble *Rubus*.

BEHAVIOUR It creeps through thick low vegetation and feeds close to or on the ground, where it moves with a slow, hunched, mouse-like walk, scratching the ground and fluttering its wings to disturb debris. It sings mainly from within dense thickets but occasionally from an exposed perch.

BREEDING HABITS A solitary, territorial and apparently monogamous breeder. The nest is well concealed in a thicket or in matted twigs below the leaf canopy, typically 0.5–1.2m above ground. It is built by the female. It is a loose bulky construction with a small neat cup composed of leaves, pine needles and grass strands and lined with fine vegetable fibres (Visser & Hockey 2002). The clutch comprises 2–3 eggs, which are incubated by the female for 12–13 days. The chicks are fed by both parents for 12–14 days with food collected close to the nest. Breeding takes place during September and October.

DISTRIBUTION Occupies a small and fragmented range in coastal South Africa where it is vulnerable and highly localised. It is threatened by destruction of forests and riparian undergrowth, and by clearance of brambles. The population is estimated at only a few thousand and continues to decline (BirdLife International 2008).

B. s. sylvaticus Local in coastal Western Cape between the Cape Peninsula and Knysna. There are three population centres within its range: on the eastern slopes of Table Mountain, on the southern slopes of Langeberg Mountains near Swellendam, and between Tsitsikama and Sedgefield.

B. s. pondoensis Restricted to coastal forests in Eastern Cape, from Dwesa Nature Reserve east to Port St Johns. It was formerly known in coastal S KwaZulu-Natal, between Wentworth and Umhlanga Rocks, but appears to have been extirpated there by habitat destruction. It may still occur in Oribi Gorge.

Knysna Warbler. Resident within breeding range.

147

MOVEMENTS Apparently sedentary. Previous reports of seasonal movements to winter in Kwazulu-Natal have been called into doubt (Berruti *et al.* 1993).

DESCRIPTION *B. s. sylvaticus*

Plumage – Adult Forehead to nape dark olive-brown. Supercilium pale buff-brown, poorly defined, extending from bill base to just behind eye. Lores and ear-coverts dark brown, the latter with fine whitish streaks. Lores bordered below by short whitish stripe. Cheeks brown, mottled with buff. Mantle and scapulars to uppertail-coverts dark olive-brown, warmly tinged, especially on rump and uppertail-coverts. Tail blackish brown with warm brown feather edges. Chin and throat greyish white with faint olive-brown mottling that extends to the upper breast. Breast, flanks and sides of belly olive-brown. Centre of belly greyish white. Undertail-coverts warm brown, barred and tipped pale greyish. Lesser and median coverts warm olive-brown. Greater coverts, primary coverts, alula and tertials dull dark brown with warm olive-brown fringes. Flight feathers blackish brown with paler warm brown edges. Underwing-coverts greyish white, mottled brown.

Juvenile Resembles adult, but face and underparts washed strongly with yellow. Throat streaking more prominent.

Bare parts Upper mandible dark horn. Lower mandible paler horn, yellowish near base. Mouth yellow. Tarsi olive-brown or flesh-brown. Iris brown.

IN HAND CHARACTERS

Measurements Races and sexes combined (n = 6):

Wing	56–63 (59.8)
Tail	49–60 (55.3)
Bill	15–16 (15.4)
Tarsus	20–20.5 (20.2)

Tail/wing ratio: 87–100% (94%; 6)
Bill width: 3.4–4.0 (3.6; 6)

Hind claw: 5.9–6.6 (6.3; 6)
Tail graduation: 15–20 (18.2; 6)

Structure

Wing formula (n = 6):

p1/pc	p2	p3e	p4e	p5e	p6(e)	p7	p10
10–15	9–11	2–4	wp	wp	wp	2–2.5	5–8

Wing similar to Cinnamon Bracken Warbler (Fig. 13); strongly rounded with fairly large p1. Wing point p4–6; p2 = ss tips; emargination on p3–5, sometimes on p6.

Tail rather short, graduated; 12 feathers, broad and rounded.

Bill quite strong with slightly concave sides; narrower than in Barratt's Warbler.

Tarsi rather short; claws small.

Recognition Usually separable from Barratt's Warbler by shorter tail (< 62mm; tail/wing < 100%) and shorter tarsus (< 21mm); also by fainter, more diffuse throat streaks.

Weight (Unsexed, n = 1) 21g (Hockey *et al.* 2005).

GEOGRAPHIC VARIATION The two races are very similar, differing only in colour and extent of underpart streaking.

B. s. sylvaticus (South Africa from S Western Cape to SW Eastern Cape east to Port Elizabeth) Described above.

B. s. pondoensis (SE Eastern Cape) Darker than the nominate race, less warmly tinged on the upperparts and wings. The breast and flanks are also darker and mottling on the underparts is confined to the throat.

TAXONOMY AND SYSTEMATICS Although placed in a superspecies with Bamboo Warbler by Hall & Moreau (1970), Knysna Warbler appears to have little in common with that species apart from its realtively short tail. Its song is similar to that of Barratt's and Cinnamon Bracken Warblers, but recent DNA study places it apart from the main scrub-dwelling group of African *Bradypterus* (Alström *et al.*, in prep.).

▲ Adult *B. s. sylvaticus*, Cape Town, South Africa, November. Bird at nest, showing the drab brown plumage, plain head, and diffusely streaked breast (Brent Visser).

▲ The same bird feeding its young. Note the short wings, relatively short tail, obscure supercilium and pale brown legs (Brent Visser).

CINNAMON BRACKEN WARBLER
Bradypterus cinnamomeus   Plate 3

Sylvia (Salicaria) cinnamomea Rüppell, 1840. *Neue Wirbelthiere Fauna Abyssinien, Vögel*, page 111, plate 42, figure 1. (labeled *Curruca (Sylvia) cinnamomea.* Entschetqab, Semien Province, Abyssinia.

An Afrotropical resident that ranges widely through the highlands of E Africa in moist bush and forest edge undergrowth. Polytypic, with four races recognised:

B. c. cinnamomeus (Rüppell, 1840). Ethiopia, Kenya, N Tanzania, Uganda (except Mount Morongole and Ruwenzoris), E DR Congo (except Ruwenzoris), Rwanda and Burundi.

B. c. nyassae Shelley, 1893. NE Tanzania (Usambaras and Ngurus), SW Tanzania, SE DR Congo, NE Zambia and Malawi.

B. c. mildbreadi Reichenow, 1908. The Rwenzori Mountains in Uganda and DR Congo.

B. c. cavei Macdonald, 1939. SE Sudan, NE Uganda (Mount Morongole).

IDENTIFICATION Length 14–15cm. Wing 58–67mm. Tail/wing 103–121%.

A richly coloured, medium-sized *Bradypterus* with a prominent pale supercilium, warm brown upperparts and a whitish throat and belly. It is a skulking bird of bracken, briars and forest edge vegetation, but commonly attracts attention with its loud ringing song. Sexes alike.

Structure Has the moderately long but strong bill typical of the scrub-dwelling group of African *Bradypterus* and shows a distinctly rounded head profile. The wings are short and rounded with a large first primary, a primary projection no more than about 20% and a wing point usually formed by p5–6. The tail is rather long and strongly graduated, with either ten or 12 feathers. These are broad and rounded, but can appear narrower when worn.

Plumage and bare parts Adults have a conspicuous pale buff supercilium, which extends from the bill to above the ear-coverts and contrasts with a dark olive-brown crown and head side. A blackish stripe through the lores continues as a short dark stripe behind the eye. Otherwise, the upperparts and wing feather edgings are rich warm brown, with a brighter rufous or russet tinge to the tail and uppertail-coverts. Below, a broad cinnamon-brown band across the breast and bright cinnamon-brown flanks and undertail-coverts contrast with the whitish chin, throat and central underparts. The bill is dark horn, the legs light brown. The distinctive southern race *nyassae* is duller, with less warmly tinged upperparts and shows paler flanks and a paler, more diffuse breast-band. Juveniles are browner above, less warmly coloured, and show a distinctive yellow tinge below. They lack a distinct breast-band but can show diffuse brownish throat streaks.

The bill is dark horn and the legs and feet are mid brown.

SIMILAR SPECIES Cinnamon Bracken Warbler overlaps throughout much of its range with Evergreen Forest Warbler. The two are largely segregated, Cinnamon Bracken preferring more open habitats and avoiding the dense forest interior preferred by Evergreen Forest. It also overlaps, in similar habitat, with the more restricted and much rarer Bamboo Warbler. Its range is separate from that of the similar S African Barratt's Warbler.

Evergreen Forest Warbler shows great racial variation. Several differing forms occur within the range of Cinnamon Bracken Warbler. In Kenya and E Tanzania, races *mariae* and *usambarae* are darker olive-brown to russet-brown above and dingier below than Cinnamon Bracken Warbler, and with less white on the throat and belly. In Malawi, Zambia and SW Tanzania, however, birds of the forms *granti* and *ufipae* resemble Cinnamon Bracken more closely in plumage pattern and colour. The brightly coloured race *barakae* of E DR Congo to W Uganda shows extensive rufous cinnamon below but lacks the pale supercilium and white throat of Cinnamon Bracken. All races of Evergreen Forest Warbler have ten rather narrow pointed tail feathers and their songs are quite different from that of Cinnamon Bracken Warbler.

Bamboo Warbler is darker olive-brown above than Cinnamon Bracken Warbler and greyer below, with white more restricted on the throat and belly. It has a fainter supercilium, and shows broad whitish fringes to the undertail-coverts.

Barratt's Warbler appears more uniform and less brightly coloured than Cinnamon Bracken Warbler. It has a dull and poorly marked supercilium and a streaked greyish white throat.

VOICE The loud song consists of a few clearly separated, high-pitched slurred notes at a frequency of 2–8kHz, followed by a slow ringing trill: '*twee twee tr-ur-ur-ur-ur-urrrr*' or '*chee woy woy chichichichichichi*'. There is individual variation, with some birds giving a slower '*wee chyoo-chyoo-chyoo-chyoo*'. Each sequence usually lasts 1–2 seconds, about half of this occupied by the faster 6–10 notes of the trill. Consecutive sequences are separated by intervals of about 5 seconds. A second bird will sometimes join in to perform a duet with a few slurred whistles (Urban *et al.* 1997).

Song of Cinnamon Bracken Warbler recorded within breeding range of *B. c. cinnamomeus*, Mount Kenya, Kenya, September. (Chappuis 2000)

Contact and alarm calls include a low-pitched scolding '*trrr*', a soft '*seep*' and a high '*schreep*'. In addition, a sharp '*pie*' call has been recorded from Rwanda (Dowsett & Stjernstedt 1979; Dowsett-Lemaire 1990).

MOULT Begins in March or April in Zambia.

HABITAT Mainly a montane bird. It inhabits dense undergrowth in forest edges and clearings, brushy bamboo stands and montane forest with a broken canopy. It is, however, not dependent on forest and occurs along overgrown roadsides, in thick cover in open plantations and in tall thick grass, montane scrub and bracken, marsh edges and overgrown gardens. In Malawi, it penetrates small patches of forest with an herbaceous understorey where Evergreen Forest Warbler is absent (Dowsett-Lemaire 1983). In S Sudan and Ethiopia it occurs above 1,800m and in Kenya and Rwanda mainly above 2,000m. In the Ruwenzoris it ranges from 2,100m to above 3,000m in moist valley bottoms. It reaches the heath zone above 3,000m on Mount Kilimanjaro and above 3,600m in Ethiopia. In Malawi it occurs down to 1,300m but ranges to 2,800m on Mount Mulanje.

BEHAVIOUR Poorly studied. A secretive species, usually found singly or in pairs. It is highly vocal but usually difficult to see, keeping within dense ground cover, where it forages for small insects with mouse-like movements. It responds positively to playback of the song.

BREEDING HABITS Believed to be monogamous, solitary and territorial. The nest is built close to the ground, in a grass tuft, brambles or other tangled vegetation. It is a bulky construction of dry grass and leaves, covered outside with plant down and feathers and the deep cup is lined with fine grass and down. The usual clutch is 2–3 eggs. No information is available on incubation or fledging periods. Breeding takes place in May and October in Ethiopia, May in Sudan, from August to February in central Kenya and N Tanzania, between February and June in E DR Congo and November to February in Malawi. The few East African records suggest that it is a dry season breeder (Brown & Britton 1980).

DISTRIBUTION Has a wide but patchy distribution within E Africa, occurring in most highland areas from N Ethiopia south to Malawi. A bird of edge habitat, it is not badly threatened by forest destruction.

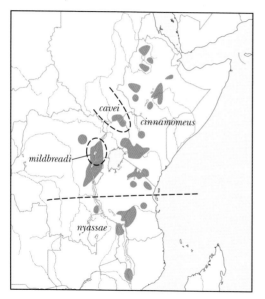

Cinnamon Bracken Warbler. Resident within breeding range.

B. c. cinnamomeus Common but locally distributed in Ethiopia on both sides of the rift, north to the Simien Mountains and east to Harar. Common in Kenya from Mount Elgon to the W and C Highlands; also on Mount Nyiru and in the Chyulu Hills. In N Tanzania it ranges from the Crater Highlands to Mount Kilimanjaro, the Pares and the Usambaras. Further west, it is very common in E DR Congo in N Kivu and S Kivu districts; also in Rwanda and Burundi and in SW Uganda.

B. c. cavei Common in the Imatong and Dongatona Mountains, SE Sudan, and in nearby NE Uganda on Mount Morongole and (presumably this race) Mount Moroto.

B. c. mildbreadi Common in the Rwenzori Mountains along the E DR Congo/Uganda border

B. c. nyassae Occupies southern parts of the species range. It is known in E Tanzania in the Nguru and Uluguru Mountains; in S Tanzania on the Ufipa Plateau, from Njombe to Mbeya and Ilembo and on Mount Kungwe; and in SE DR Congo in the Marungu highlands. It is common in N Malawi on the Nyika Plateau and N Viphya Plateau (the former partly in NE Zambia); and in S Malawi on Mount Mulanje.

MOVEMENTS Believed to be sedentary.

DESCRIPTION *B. c. cinnamomeus*
Plumage – Adult Forehead to nape and upper sides of neck rather dark olive-brown. Supercilium prominent, pale cinnamon-buff, from the bill base to above the middle of the ear-coverts, broadest above the eye. A narrow whitish eye-ring, merging with supercilium. Lores blackish, continuing as a faint dusky stripe behind the eye. Ear-coverts and cheeks olive-brown, flecked cinnamon-buff. Mantle and scapulars to rump rich warm brown, becoming brighter cinnamon-brown or rufous-brown on uppertail-coverts. Tail feathers dark rufous-brown. Chin and throat buffy white, sides washed with cinnamon. Lower side of neck pale cinnamon. Band across upper breast, sides of breast, flanks and undertail-coverts cinnamon-brown. Centre of lower breast and belly whitish. Lesser, median and greater coverts rich warm brown. Primary coverts and alula dark brown, fringed cinnamon-brown. Tertials and secondaries dark brown with broad cinnamon-brown edges. Primaries dark brown with narrower paler cinnamon edges. Underwing-coverts brown, edged cinnamon.
Juvenile Differs from adult in having the upperparts, tail and wing feathers browner, less rufous. Underparts tinged yellow, especially on belly, with side of breast and flanks olive-brown (not cinnamon). Upper breast and lower throat with diffuse olive-brown streaking. No distinct breast-band.
Bare Parts Upper and lower mandibles dark horn. Tarsi and toes mid brown. Iris hazel.

IN HAND CHARACTERS
Measurements *B. c. cinnamomeus*

	Male	Female
Wing	60–66 (63.0; 23)	58–64 (61.3; 6)
Tail	68–74 (71.0; 6)	63–71 (67.5; 6)
Bill	14–15 (14.4; 6)	14.5–15.5 (15.1; 6)
Tarsus	23.5–25 (24.3; 6)	23–24 (23.7; 6)

Sexes combined:
Tail/wing: 107–114% (111%; 12)
Bill width: 3.6–4.2 (3.8; 12)
Hind claw: 5.5– 6.9 (6.2; 18)
Tail graduation: 29–35 (31.3; 12)
 Juvenile wing *c.* 3mm shorter than in adult, tail *c.* 6mm shorter.
B. c. cavei: *wing*, ♂ 61–65 (63.6; 5), ♀ 58–63 (61.6; 6); *tail*, ♂♀ 63–69 (64.4; 8); Tail/wing 99–106% (103%; 8).
B. c. mildbreadi: *wing*, ♂ 59–64 (61.0; 4), ♀ 58–63 (59.3; 6); *tail*, ♂♀ 62–69 (64.5; 4).
B. c. nyassae: *wing*, ♂ 63–67 (65.2; 6), ♀ 60–64 (62.3; 6); *tail*, ♂ 73–78 (75.8; 5), ♀ 70–71 (70.3; 4); *bill*, ♂ 14.4–15.5 (15.1; 7), ♀ 15–15.5 (15.2; 3); Tail/wing 103–121% (114%; 11).

Structure *B. c. cinnamomeus*

Wing formula (n = 9):

p1/pc	p2	p3e	p4e	p5e	p6e	p7e	p10
15–19	8–12	2–4	0–2	wp	wp	0–1	4–6

Wing rounded with large p1 (*c.* 60% p2). Wing point p(4) 5–6 (7); p2 < ss tips, p3 = p8–10; emargination on p3–7.

Figure 13. Wing of Cinnamon Bracken Warbler.

Tail medium-long, strongly graduated (t6 *c.* 40% t1); ten or 12 feathers, broad and rounded (Fig. 14).

Bill rather short, strong-based; sides slightly concave.

Tarsi strong; toes short, claws rather small.

Other races Similar, but *cavei* has a shorter tail.

Recognition Shows cinnamon-brown or rufous-brown upperparts and a prominent pale supercilium. Distinguished from Evergreen Forest Warbler by broader tail feathers (*c.* 15mm wide at one-third length from tip; *c.* 10mm in Evergreen Forest); and from all races except *ufipae* by broad cinnamon breast-band combined with extensively white throat and belly.

Weight

B. c. cinnamomeus: (n = 59) 14.5–25g (17.5).

B. c. nyassae: (n = 20) 16–22g (18.5) (Urban *et al.* 1997).

GEOGRAPHIC VARIATION The races *cavei* and *mildbreadi* differ only slightly from nominate *cinnamomeus*, but the southern breeding race *nyassae* is distinctive.

B. c. cinnamomeus (Ethiopia to E DR Congo and Malawi – except the Rwenzori Mountains) Described above.

B. c. cavei (SE Sudan, NE Uganda) Darker above than nominate *cinnamomeus*, with a more distinct russet wash on the rump, uppertail-coverts and tail. The breast-

band is also broader, with white more restricted on the lower breast.

B. c. mildbreadi (Rwenzori Mountains) Similar to the nominate race but the upperparts are slightly richer rufous-brown and the tail is darker rufous.

B. c. nyassae (NE Tanzania, SW Tanzania, SE DR Congo, NE Zambia and Malawi) The brown upperparts are duller, less warmly tinged than in the nominate race. The sides of the breast and flanks are drab tawny-brown or tawny-buff rather than cinnamon-brown, and much duller. The breast is washed drab tawny-buff and this is much more extensive than on the nominate form, reaching onto the upper belly, although the throat and lower belly remain whitish.

TAXONOMY AND SYSTEMATICS Cinnamon Bracken Warbler has been considered to form a superspecies with Barratt's Warbler of S Africa, mainly on the basis of their similar songs (Dowsett & Forbes-Watson 1993, Urban *et al.* 1997). These two, together with Evergreen Forest Warbler, occupy similar ecological niches. Each species exhibits geographic variation throughout its range and there is considerable overlap in appearance between them, which makes it difficult to decide where some races should be placed. The taxon *ufipae*, treated here under Evergreen Forest Warbler, was regarded as a race of Cinnamon Bracken Warbler by some authors, including White (1965). The Bangwa Forest Warbler has also traditionally been treated as a W African race of Cinnamon Bracken Warbler but we prefer to regard it as a separate species.

▲ Adult *B. c. cinnamomeus*, Bale Mountains, Ethiopia, November. Shows the bright cinnamon plumage, longish graduated tail and prominent supercilium (Fred Leviez).

▲ Adult *B. c. cinnamomeus*, Bale Mountains, Ethiopia, January. The tail feathers are broader than those of Evergreen Forest Warbler (Dave Beadle).

▲ Adult *B. c. cinnamomeus*, Rwanda, June. Bright cinnamon flanks and breast contrast with the paler throat and whitish belly. Note the short wings and rather short bill (Malcolm Wilson).

151

BANGWA FOREST WARBLER
Bradypterus bangwaensis   Plate 3

Bradypterus bangwaensis Delacour, 1943. *Ibis* 85: 39.
New name for *Bradypterus casteneus* Reichenow, 1900,
preoccupied by *Turdinus castaneus* Büttikofer, 1893. Bango
Mountains and Bangwa, Cameroon.

A resident of montane thicket and undergrowth in SE
Nigeria and W Cameroon. Considered to be NEAR THREAT-
ENED by BirdLife International due to its small geographic
range and the degradation and clearance of its habitat.
Monotypic.

IDENTIFICATION Length 14–15cm. Wing 60–66mm.
Tail/wing 92–106%.

A secretive, medium-sized *Bradypterus* with dark rufous-
brown upperparts and bright rufous- cinnamon breast
and flanks. Sexes similar but female slightly smaller than
male.
Structure Similar in size and structure to Cinnamon
Bracken Warbler but the heavily graduated tail of 12
broad rectrices is somewhat shorter. The wing is short and
strongly rounded, with a long first primary (p1), the wing
point formed by p4–7 and a particularly short primary
projection. The bill is longer and the legs and feet larger
than in Cinnamon Bracken Warbler.
Plumage and bare parts The entire upperparts are unmarked dark rufous-brown, including the rump and
uppertail-coverts and the closed wing. The upper tail is
also dark rufous- or russet-brown. A narrow and rather
inconspicuous warm buff supercilium extends back behind
the eye, above dark brown lores and a short dark brown
eyestripe. The sides of the head and neck and the breast,
flanks and undertail-coverts are rich cinnamon. These
contrast with a pale cinnamon-washed throat and a whitish
lower breast and belly.

The bill is blackish brown with a paler lower mandible.
The legs are brownish.

SIMILAR SPECIES Evergreen Forest Warbler occurs
alongside Bangwa Forest Warbler on Mount Manenguba.
The latter is unlikely to be confused with any other species
within its range.
Evergreen Forest Warbler (race *manengubae*) is darker and
browner above than Bangwa Forest Warbler and has a
poorly marked supercilium. It is deep tawny brown below,
only slightly paler on the throat and belly. It also has ten
narrower, more pointed, tail feathers.

VOICE The song is quite different from that of Cinnamon
Bracken Warbler but resembles Evergreen Forest Warbler
song in structure and tempo (Dowsett-Lemaire 1989).
It consists of up to 30 identical two note phrases within
a frequency range of 1.5–5kHz given over a period of
5–10 seconds, slowly increasing in volume: '*piya-piya-
piya-piya-piya-piya-piya-piya-piya-piya...*', or a slightly slower
pitched '*weriya-weriya-weriya-weriya-weriya-weriya-weriya...*',
or an even slower '*werdyu-werdyu-werdyu-werdyu-werdyu-
werdyu-...*', in which the notes in each phrase are more
distinct. These sequences are repeated, typically with
intervals of about 4–6 seconds between them. The female
will duet with the male, giving a series of high-pitched
whistled notes.

The alarm call, a rattling '*krrrr,*' is quite different from
the loud clicking calls of Evergreen Forest Warbler.

Song of Bangwa Forest Warbler, eastern Nigeria. (Chappuis
2000)

MOULT No information available.

HABITAT Occurs among tangled shrubs and thick herbage
in forest edges and clearings and along forest tracks, and
among bracken and brambles at higher altitudes. It also
frequents dense secondary growth and thickets, including
bamboo, under open-canopy forest. Often found in rank
herbage and tall thick grass along streams. On Mount
Manenguba it occurs in more scrubby edge habitat than
Evergreen Forest Warbler which is mainly confined to
forest interior (Dowsett-Lemaire & Dowsett 1999). Occurs
from 1,600–2,300m in Nigeria and from 1,900–2,950m in
Cameroon.

BEHAVIOUR Usually in pairs. Keeps close to the ground
in dense cover. Responds to playback of tapes of Evergreen
Forest Warbler (*camerunensis*) song but not to that of
Cinnamon Bracken Warbler (Dowsett-Lemaire 1989).

BREEDING HABITS Laying recorded in Cameroon in
October–November and occasionally March–April. No
other data available.

DISTRIBUTION Has a small and fragmented range
restricted to montane regions of SE Nigeria and W
Cameroon and is under threat from forest clearance. In
Nigeria, it is common on the Mambilla Plateau and is also
known from the Obudu Plateau, Gotel Mountains, Chappell
Wadi and Leinde Fadali. On Mount Oku in Cameroon, it
is reported as abundant above 2,400m but scarce at lower
elevations due to bush clearance. Elsewhere in Cameroon,
its range includes the Banso Mountains, Kumbo, the Sabga
Pass, the region between Mbengwi and Tinachong, the
Bamenda Highlands, Bamboutos Mountains, the Bamileke
Plateau and Mount Manenguba, where it is common.

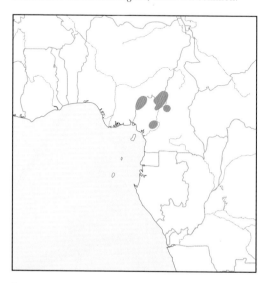

Bangwa Forest Warbler. Resident within breeding range.

MOVEMENTS Believed to be sedentary.

DESCRIPTION

Plumage – Adult Forehead and crown dark rufous-brown. Supercilium narrow, tawny-buff, extending from bill base to above middle of ear-coverts. Lores dark brown. Short stripe behind eye dark brown; otherwise ear-coverts and cheeks rufous-brown with buff streaking or mottling. Mantle to uppertail-coverts dark rufous-brown. Tail dark russet above, darker and greyer below. Chin and throat white, washed cinnamon-buff. Upper breast, lower sides of neck, sides of breast, flanks, vent and undertail-coverts bright rufous-cinnamon. Centre of lower breast and belly greyish white. Lesser and median coverts dark rufous-brown. Greater coverts, primary coverts and alula dark brown with dark rufous-brown fringes. Remiges dark brown with broad rufous-brown edges matching colour of upperparts. Underwing-coverts rufous-cinnamon.

Juvenile Upperparts paler and browner, less rufous, than adult. Underparts tinged yellow, although breast-band and flanks dull olive-brown, usually with some indistinct, diffuse and darker brown streaking on the upper breast and sides of the neck.

Bare Parts Upper mandible blackish brown. Lower mandible slightly paler. Tarsi brown.

IN HAND CHARACTERS
Measurements

	Male	Female
Wing	62–66 (64.1; 13)	60–63 (62.0; 6)
Tail	60–67 (63.5; 13)	57–63 (60.0; 6)
Bill	15.5–17 (16.2; 13)	15–16 (15.3; 5)
Tarsus	24.5–26 (25.2; 12)	23.5–25.5 (24.2; 5)

Tail/wing ratio: 92–106% (99%; 19)
Bill width: 3.5–4.3 (3.9; 18)
Hind claw: 6.5–7.6 (7.0; 17)
Tail graduation: 21–27 (24.0; 13)

Structure

Wing formula (n = 10):

p1/pc	p2	p3e	p4e	p5e	p6e	p7e	p10
14–19	12–15	4–7	1–2	wp	wp	0–0.5	3.5–5

Wing similar to Cinnamon Bracken Warbler (Fig. 13); strongly rounded with large first primary (*c.* 70% p2). Wing point p5–7; p2 < ss tips, p3 = p10/ss; slight emargination on p3–7.

Tail medium, strongly graduated; feathers broad and rounded.

Bill strong as in Cinnamon Bracken Warbler, but slightly longer; concave-sided.

Tarsi stronger than in Cinnamon Bracken Warbler, toes and claws longer.

Recognition Distinguished from *camerunensis* race of Evergreen Forest Warbler by bright cinnamon breast-band and flanks, contrasting with pale throat and whitish belly; also by having 12 broad tail feathers.

Weight ♂: 18–27g (21.0; 5) (Urban *et al.* 1997; Dunning 2007)

GEOGRAPHIC VARIATION None known.

TAXONOMY AND SYSTEMATICS Formerly treated as a race of Cinnamon Bracken Warbler which it resembles in plumage and tail structure. Due to its geographical isolation and its very different song, Dowsett-Lemaire & Dowsett (1989) elevated it to species status, and we follow this treatment here. Urban *et al.* (1997) included it as a race of Evergreen Forest Warbler. But its 12 broad tail feathers are quite unlike those of the races grouped within Evergreen Forest Warbler, and it occurs alongside one of these (*manengubae*) in Cameroon. Alström *et al.* (in prep) have recently established that its closest relative is Cinnamon Bracken Warbler.

▲ Adult, Cameroon, February. The rufous-cinnamon breast-band and flanks contrast with the whitish throat and belly (Jaap van der Waarde).

EVERGREEN FOREST WARBLER
Bradypterus lopezi   Plates 3 and 4

Phlexis lopezi **Alexander, 1903.** *Bull. Brit. Orn. Club.* 13: 48. Moka, Fernando Po.

A resident of mid- or high elevation forest in W, E and S central Africa. Consists of two groups of races that have sometimes been considered two species, *B. lopezi* and *B. mariae* (e.g. by Benson *et al.* 1970). But the songs, tail structure and tail/wing ratios of the two groups are similar and following Dowsett & Dowsett-Lemaire (1989, 1993) and Urban *et al.* (1997) we treat this complex as a single variable species. Polytypic, with nine races recognised:

The *lopezi* group:
B. l. lopezi (Alexander, 1903). Bioko.
B. l. barakae Sharpe, 1906. Highlands of E DR Congo, Rwanda and SW Uganda.
B. l. camerunensis Alexander, 1909. Mount Cameroon.
B. l. manengubae Searle, 1949. Mount Manenguba.

The *mariae* group:
B. l. mariae Madarász, 1905. Kenya (except Taita Hills) and N Tanzania (Oldeani to Kilimanjaro).
B. l. usambarae Reichenow, 1917. SE Kenya (Taita Hills), E and S Tanzania (Usambaras and North Pares to Mbeya, Njombe, Mount Rungwe and Songea), NE Zambia and N Malawi (Nyika Plateau) and N Mozambique at Unango.
B. l. granti Benson, 1939. Malawi (south of Nyika), and Mount Chiperone, N Mozambique.
B. l. ufipae (Grant & Mackworth-Praed, 1941). SW Tanzania (Ufipa Plateau, Mbisi forest), SE DR Congo (Marungu Plateau), N and NW Zambia.
B. l. boultoni Chapin, 1948. W Angola.

IDENTIFICATION Length 13–15cm. Wing, *lopezi* group 54–62mm, *mariae* group 58–70mm. Tail/wing *c.* 100% in most races (*c.* 105% in *ufipae*, 110–115% in *barakae*).

A medium sized, dingy brown or cinnamon-brown warbler which skulks in forest undergrowth and is more often heard than seen. It overlaps geographically with both Cinnamon Bracken Warbler and Bangwa Forest Warbler, but is largely separated by habitat from these species; Evergreen Forest Warbler frequenting the dim forest interior rather than of edges and clearings. Sexes alike.
Structure A slim *Bradypterus* with a medium-length, fairly strong bill, very short rounded wings and a strongly graduated tail of ten feathers, which usually appears worn and frayed. In most races, the tail is proportionately shorter than that of Cinnamon Bracken Warbler and has narrower feathers. The wing has a large first primary, a wing point formed by p4–7 and an extremely short primary projection.
Plumage and bare parts In the *mariae* group in E and S central Africa, adults have rather dark olive-brown upperparts, tinged cinnamon or russet, especially on the rump and uppertail-coverts. There is a narrow and inconspicuous greyish supercilium above dark brown lores and head sides. The underparts are olive-grey, cinnamon-grey or greyish white, palest on the throat and belly centre and becoming browner on the lower flanks and undertail-coverts. The edges to the wing feathers are rich dark olive-brown and the closed wing appears uniform with the mantle and scapulars. Juveniles resemble adults, but have the throat and belly centre tinged yellow and the rich brown tone of

the undertail-coverts less intense. In S Tanzania and Zambia, the race *ufipae* shows a more intense cinnamon wash on the breast and flanks and a whitish belly, giving it an appearance close to that of Cinnamon Bracken Warbler.

In W Africa, adults are warm, dark brown above and show a narrow, sometimes obscure, paler supercilium. The breast, flanks and undertail-coverts are rich warm brown to deep tawny brown, the throat and belly paler, often cinnamon-tinged. In C Africa, the distinctive form *barakae* is dark russet-brown above with the supercilium and underparts bright cinnamon, with a smaller pale belly patch.

The bill is dark grey with a pale grey or brownish grey lower mandible. The legs and feet are pale brown or pinkish brown.

SIMILAR SPECIES Birds of the *mariae* group can occur alongside Cinnamon Bracken Warbler in E Africa, mainly in mid-altitude forest edge situations. The race *barakae* could also meet Cinnamon Bracken Warbler in C Africa, while in Cameroon the race *manengubae* and the Bangwa Forest Warbler both occur on Mount Manenguba. The allopatric Barratt's Warbler of S Africa has in the past been treated as conspecific with Evergreen Forest Warbler.
Cinnamon Bracken Warbler is more brightly coloured than Evergreen Forest Warbler and has a more prominent pale supercilium. Its whiter throat and belly are matched only in the Zambian race *B. l. ufipae* and they distinguish it readily in C Africa from *B. l. barakae*. Cinnamon Bracken Warbler has broader tail feathers and its trilling song differs from the piercing whistled calls of the various races of Evergreen Forest Warbler.
Bangwa Forest Warbler is more rufous above and brighter cinnamon-brown below than races *manengubae* and *camerunensis* of Evergreen Forest Warbler, and shows extensive white on the throat and belly. It has ten tail feathers but these are broad and rounded. Its song resembles that of Evergreen Forest Warbler, but the call is different (Dowsett-Lemaire & Dowsett 1989).
Barratt's Warbler is a more uniform dull olive-brown than most races of Evergreen Forest Warbler and shows a streaked throat. It also differs in its broader tail feathers and trilling song.

VOICE The various races produce a similar song throughout the range, a series of loud repeated notes or short phrases maintained for several seconds to form a song sequence. Despite variation in pitch and dialect, the general pattern and song structure remain constant. Individuals may have several song types and the female may join in to duet with a few high-pitched '*wheeeeooo*' whistles towards the end of the male's song. Sequences are usually repeated after a short pause.

On Bioko, nominate *lopezi* gives a cheerful fluty song sequence varying between 2–4kHz and lasting about two seconds, followed after a pause of 1–2 seconds by a slightly different sequence. This series of sequences is repeated three to five times before a longer pause, so that a complete cycle lasts 12–20 seconds; '*tweeer-tweeer-tweeer – teuwe-teuwe-teuwe-teuwe – chewir-chiwer-chewir – …*'.

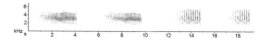

Song of Evergreen Forest Warbler recorded within breeding range of *B. l. camerunensis*, Mount Cameroon, Cameroon. (Chappuis 2000)

B. l. camerunensis gives a loud series of some 6–20 single, double or triple notes within a frequency range spanning 2–5kHz but increasing in volume. This is reminiscent of the song of Wood Lark: '*chee-chee-chee-CHEE-CHEE-...*', '*chewi-chewi-chewi-CHEWI-CHEWI-CHEWI*', '*chitrip-chitrip-chitrip-CHITRIP-CHITRIP-CHITRIP-...*', '*chuchui-chuchui-chuCHUi-chuCHUi-chuCHUi-,weecha-weecha-weecha-weecha-...*' and other variations, usually delivered at three to eight notes per second and lasting 2–5 seconds.

Song of Evergreen Forest Warbler recorded within breeding range of *B. l. lopezi*, Bioko, February. (Chappuis 2000)

In Kenya, the song of *mariae* is simpler and consists of some 12–20 identical notes on the same pitch, but increasing in volume; '*whe-whe-whe-whe-whe-whe-whe-whe-WHE-WHE-WHE*'. Each sequence lasts about 2–3 seconds, followed by a pause of several seconds before being repeated.

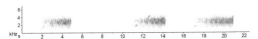

Song of Evergreen Forest Warbler recorded within breeding range of *B. l. mariae*, Mount Kenya, March. (David Pearson)

Call notes include a soft '*chick*' or '*tchic, tchi-tchic*' (*mariae*), a similar but longer series of 3-8 '*chick*' notes (*camerunensis*, Dowsett-Lemaire 1989), a hard, sharp '*TCHEW*' or '*chiCHEW*', a vigourous '*weet-weet, weet-weet...*', a vigorous '*pirr*' and a '*yoop-yoop-ipp*' (*lopezi* in alarm; Eisentraut 1973).

MOULT Begins in February in Malawi.

HABITAT Typically inhabits dense shrubby understorey within montane forest, including bamboo thickets growing under the canopy and it can often be found in rank herbage along gullies and streams. In West Africa it also occurs on plantations of spaced trees, tall thick grass, shrubby thickets, bracken and brambles. But on Mount Manenguba, the race *manengubae* is a bird of the forest interior. In Malawi, it has adapted locally to pine plantations with a good layer of dense ground cover. It ranges from 1,700m to 2,400m in DR Congo and Rwanda and from 1,700m to 3,000m in Kenya, but occurs as low as 800m on Mount Cameroon. In Tanzania and Malawi it is most common between 1,700m and 2,400m, but breeds locally as low as 950m.

BEHAVIOUR Usually occurs in pairs or family parties but is secretive and hard to locate. Although it can be inquisitive, it is difficult to observe even when calling and attracted by song playback. It hops and creeps in low shady vegetation and creeper tangles with the tail partly raised, usually remaining close to the ground. It gleans small insects and snails from leaves and bark, occasionally from the ground. It rarely flies and when it does so it typically flits quickly between patches of cover no more than a metre or two apart. Where it occurs together with Cinnamon Bracken Warbler, for example in forest-edge situations on the Nyika Plateau (Malawi) it is usually the dominant species (Dowsett-Lemaire 1989).

BREEDING HABITS Solitary, territorial and monogamous. The nest is built close to the ground in thick undergrowth, or hidden in a grass tussock. It is a compact structure built from leaf skeletons and other plant fragments, or of grass stalks and blades. The cup is lined with long dry plant threads. The usual clutch is 2–3 eggs (Urban *et al.* 1997). It breeds at the end of the dry season, continuing into the rains. Eggs are laid mainly in October–November in Bioko, October–November in Cameroon, March–April in E DR Congo, October in Angola and September to January in Tanzania and Malawi.

DISTRIBUTION Occurs in three widely separated regions of Africa: (1) Cameroon and Bioko, (2) Angola, (3) E DR Congo to Kenya and south to N Zambia and Malawi. It is not uncommon in the west of its range on Bioko and on Mount Cameroon and is often locally common in the east. It is dependent in most areas on the presence of mid-altitude or highland forest. Densities of about one pair per 2ha were found in several Malawi forests (Dowsett-Lemaire 1983).

B. l. camerunensis Restricted to Mount Cameroon, where common.

B. l. manengubae Restricted to Mount Manenguba, Cameroon.

B. l. lopezi Locally common on Bioko in the Moka valley and northern highlands.

B. l. barakae Locally common in eastern C Africa on either side of the Albertine rift. It occurs in E DR Congo in the Kivu Volcanoes, Itombwe Mountains, highlands northwest of Lake Tanganyika, and Upemba National Park; in the Ruwenzori Mountains (DR Congo/Uganda border); in SW Uganda in the Bwindi–Impenetrable Forest; and in N Rwanda.

B. l. mariae Locally common in W and C Kenya, from Mount Elgon and the Nandi, Mau and Molo forests to the Aberdares, Mount Kenya and Limuru; in SE Kenya in the Chyulu Hills; and in NE Tanzania from the Crater Highlands to Arusha National Park and Mount Kilimanjaro.

B. l. usambarae Ranges from SE Kenya in the Taita Hills, and through Tanzania from the Pares and Usambaras southwest to the southern highlands and Songea, and to Mount Unango in N Mozambique. Intergrades with *granti* on the Nyika Plateau (NE Zambia/N Malawi) where it is quite common.

B. l. granti Locally common in N Malawi on the Viphya Plateau and occasional in highlands south to Ntchisi. Fairly common in the C and S Malawi highlands, and on Mount Chiperone in NW Mozambique.

B. l. ufipae Common in Zambia in upland evergreen forests in Northern Province, down the Machinga escarpment to Mkushi River, and through the Copperbelt west to N Mwinilunga. It extends to adjacent SE DR Congo, including the Marungu highlands, and to Mbisi forest and the Ufipa Plateau in SW Tanzania.

B. l. boultoni Restricted to W Angola where it is common on Mount Soque, Mount Moco, Mombolo, and the Benguela Plateau.

MOVEMENTS Mainly sedentary. Altitudinal movements appear to take place in Tanzania and Malawi where birds have been noted at 600m or lower during the cool non-breeding season.

DESCRIPTION *B. l. mariae*
Plumage – Adult
Forehead to nape dark olive-brown. Supercilium narrow,

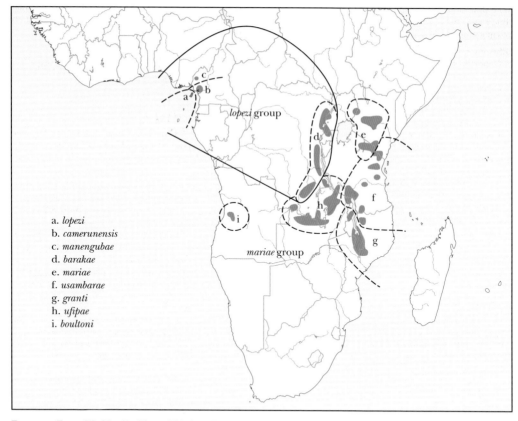

a. *lopezi*
b. *camerunensis*
c. *manengubae*
d. *barakae*
e. *mariae*
f. *usambarae*
g. *granti*
h. *ufipae*
i. *boultoni*

Evergreen Forest Warbler. Resident within breeding range.

dingy grey-brown, extending from bill base to above fore-part of ear-coverts. Lores and below eye to ear-coverts dark brown, lower ear-coverts flecked grey-buff. Cheeks mottled dark olive-brown and grey-buff, each feather with a dark tip. Mantle and scapulars to uppertail-coverts rich dark olive-brown, tinged russet on rump and uppertail-coverts, with darker fringes to body feathers producing a faint scaly effect. Tail feathers dark olive-brown. Chin and throat grey-buff. Upper breast and upper flanks olive-grey, merging with olive-brown lower flanks and undertail-coverts. Sometimes a few short, fine dark streaks on upper breast. Centre of lower breast and belly grey-buff. Lesser, median and greater coverts rich dark olive-brown Primary coverts, alula and remiges dark brown, edged olive-brown. Remiges blackish brown, broadly and diffusely edged dark olive-brown. Closed wing uniform dark olive-brown as mantle and scapulars. Underwing-coverts dark grey-brown.

Juvenile Similar to adult, but chin to throat and centre of lower breast and belly washed olive-yellow. Sides of breast, flanks and undertail-coverts olive-brown, less greyish.

Bare parts Upper mandible black. Lower mandible horn. Tarsi brownish flesh. Iris brown.

***B. l. camerunensis* Plumage – Adult** Forehead to nape dark brown. Supercilium narrow, warm buff, from bill base to above fore part of ear-coverts. Lores and below eye to ear-coverts dark brown. Cheeks cinnamon-buff mottled dark brown. Mantle and scapulars dark brown, tinged cinnamon. Tail feathers dark russet brown. Chin and throat pale cinnamon-buff. Upper breast and upper flanks pale

cinnamon-brown, merging with darker tawny-brown lower flanks and undertail-coverts. Upper breast with diffuse darker brown streaks. Centre of lower breast and belly whitish. Lesser, median and greater coverts dark warm brown, matching upperparts. Primary coverts, alula and remiges dark brown, edged warmer brown. Remiges blackish brown, with broad diffuse warm brown edges, matching upperparts. Underwing-coverts dark warm brown.

Juvenile Upperparts including closed wings and tail dark olive-brown, without cinnamon tinge. Supercilium pale yellowish. Underparts washed pale yellow, breast and flanks suffused olive-brown, lower flanks and undertail-coverts dark olive-brown.

Bare parts Upper mandible dark grey. Lower mandible light grey. Tarsi pale brown. Iris brown.

IN HAND CHARACTERS
Measurements *B. l. mariae*

	Male	Female
Wing	59–66 (62.5; 13)	58–63 (61.0; 6)
Tail	58–67 (63.6; 13)	55–63 (59.2; 6)
Bill	14.5–16 (15.5; 12)	14.5–16.5 (15.3; 6)
Tarsus	24–26 (24.9; 12)	23.5–25 (24.2; 6)

Sexes combined:
Tail/wing ratio: 95–105% (100%; 19)

Bill width: 3.6–4.2 (3.9; 10)

Hind claw: 5.8–6.7 (6.4; 10)

Tail graduation: 26–31 (28.6; 11)

Other races (sexes combined)

B. l. usambarae: *wing* 61–65 (62.4; 17); *tail* 57–70 (62.5; 13).

B. l. granti: *wing* 60–65 (61.9; 11); *tail* 59–68 (62.7; 9).

B. l. ufipae: *wing* 64–70 (66.7; 9); *tail* 66–74 (70.3; 8); *bill* 15.5–17.5 (16.8; 9); *tarsus* 24.5–26.5 (25.4; 9). Large with a relatively long tail.

B. l. boultoni: *wing* 64–68 (66.1; 14); *tail* 65–73 (68.7; 14). Larger than *mariae* and *usambarae*.

B. l. camerunensis: *wing* 54–60 (57.2; 15); *tail* 54–61 (55.5; 6); *bill* 14.5–16 (15.4; 19); *tarsus* 21.5–24 (22.9; 19). All measurements except bill smaller than in *mariae*.

B. l. manengubae: (1 ♂, 1 ♀): *wing* 58–59; *tail* 55; *bill* 16; *tarsus* 23.5.

B. l. lopezi: *wing* 58–62 (59.6; 5); *tail* 53–64 (58.8; 5).

B. l. barakae: *wing* 56–60 (57.8; 5); *tail* 58–70 (64.8; 5); *bill* 13.5–15 (14.3; 6); *tarsus* 22–22.5 (22.8; 5). A small race. Bill smaller than in *camerunensis* but tail much longer.

Wings of males generally average *c.* 1mm longer than in females, tails *c.* 3mm longer.

Structure *B. l. mariae*

Wing formula (n = 10):

p1/pc	p2	p3e	p4e	p5e	p6e	p7e	p10
14–20	9–12	2–4	wp	wp	wp	wp	4–6

Wing similar to Cinnamon Bracken Warbler (Fig. 13); strongly rounded with large p1 (*c.* 60–65% p2). Wing point p4–7; p2 < ss tips, p3 = p8–10; emargination on p3–7.

Tail medium, strongly graduated (t5 *c.* 50% t1); ten rather narrow feathers (Fig. 14).

Bill as in Cinnamon Bracken Warbler, strong based with sides slightly concave.

Tarsi strong; toes short, claws small.

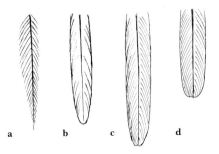

a   b   c   d

Figure 14. Comparison of central tail feathers of (a) Evergreen Forest Warbler *B. l. barakae*, (b) Evergreen Forest Warbler *B. l. mariae*, (c) Cinnamon Bracken Warbler and (d) Bamboo Warbler.

Other races Similar to *mariae*, except that races *ufipae* (mean 105%) and especially *barakae* (mean 112%), have a higher tail/wing ratio.

Recognition All races have narrower tail feathers than Cinnamon Bracken Warbler (*c.* 10mm wide at one-third of length from tip compared to *c.* 15mm in Cinnamon Bracken). Except in *barakae*, the tail/wing ratio is usually < 105%, shorter than in Cinnamon Bracken Warbler. Most

races are darker olive-brown or cinnamon-brown below than Cinnamon Bracken Warbler, with less extensive white on throat and abdomen.

Weight Data from Urban *et al.* (1997)

B. l. mariae: 15.1–20.8g (18.9: 21)

B. l. granti and *B. l. usambarae*: 12.2–19.9g (16.9; 29)

B. l. ufipae: 17–24g (20.2; 17)

B. l. camerunensis: 14–19.5g (17.7; 14)

B. l. lopezi: 16–20g (17.7; 12)

B. l. barakae: 15–18.5g (17.0; 9)

GEOGRAPHIC VARIATION Complex, involving plumage colour and pattern, size and tail length. There are nine well-differentiated races that have been treated as two groups.

The *lopezi* group:

Three similar W African races (*lopezi*, *camerunensis* and *manengubae*) are small, dark brown above and warm brown below with a paler throat and abdomen. In C Africa, the race *barakae* is also a small bird but longer-tailed and is extensively bright cinnamon-brown below.

B. l. camerunensis (Mt. Cameroon) Described Above. Less dark than *manengubae*, less brightly coloured than *lopezi*. Similar overall to *ufipae* (within the *mariae* group) but the breast-band is broader and the upperparts are darker.

B. l. manengubae (Mt. Manenguba) Slightly darker above than *camerunensis* and much more intensely coloured below. The entire upperparts are rich dark brown with a russet tinge. The paler supercilium is obscure. The underparts are deep tawny-brown, darkest on the flanks and undertail-coverts, rather paler on the throat and belly centre.

B. l. lopezi (Bioko) More richly coloured than *camerunensis*. The entire upperparts including the wing feather edges are dark cinnamon- or russet-brown. The supercilium and chin to throat are pale warm brown, becoming deeper cinnamon-brown on the breast and upper flanks and dark russet-brown on the lower flanks and undertail-coverts, with a restricted pale area on the belly centre.

B. l. barakae (E DR Congo to SW Uganda) Distinctive in coloration. The upperparts, including wings and uppertail are brighter and darker, more russet-brown than in *camerunensis* and *lopezi*. The supercilium and the underparts are bright rufous-cinnamon, although slightly paler on the throat and becoming whitish, washed cinnamon-buff, on the centre of the lower breast and belly. The rear flanks and undertail-coverts are dark olive-brown.

The *mariae* group:

These five races have sometimes been treated within the species *B. mariae*. Collectively, they range from Kenya to Malawi and Zambia with an isolated population in W Angola. They show a trend towards decreasing colour saturation from north to south, with birds in Kenya (race *mariae*) more olive-brown with darker underparts. To the south and southwest, they become paler and warmer brown with a paler throat and abdomen, with Zambian *ufipae* as warmly toned as W African *camerunensis*. These races are all larger than W African birds, *ufipae* and Angolan *boultoni* being larger than the other three.

B. l. mariae (Kenya and N Tanzania) Described above.

B. l. usambarae (SE Kenya, E and S Tanzania to N Mozambique) Resembles *mariae* but the pale areas on the underparts are whiter and more extensive, with greyish olive-brown restricted to the sides, flanks and undertail-coverts. The entire breast is extensively washed cinnamon-brown although the chin and throat are whitish. The upperparts are slightly less dark, less russet than in *mariae*.

B. l. granti (Malawi to NW Mozambique) Similar to *usambarae* but warmer, more tawny above, with the underparts tinged cinnamon-buff. Paler overall than *mariae*.

B. l. ufipae (N Zambia to SE DR Congo and SW Tanzania) Differs from *usambarae* in having the brown breast-band, flanks and undertail-coverts washed cinnamon-buff. These contrast with the paler chin, throat, lower breast and belly, which are whitish with a warm buff tinge. The supercilium is paler, rather more prominent and the upperparts are more tawny-brown than in *usambarae*, closely matching the tone of *granti*. A large race.

B. l. boultoni (Angola) Similar in coloration to *ufipae*, but the cinnamon-tinged breast-band and sides are more extensive and the whitish belly centre more restricted. Shows more distinct dark streaking on lower throat and upper breast

TAXONOMY AND SYSTEMATICS The *lopezi* and *mariae* groups of races were treated as separate species by, for example, Mackworth-Praed & Grant 1952, Chapin 1954 and Benson *et al.* 1970. However, White (1965) not only combined these but lumped them with the S African Barratt's Warbler under one species *B. barratti*, a treatment then followed by Hall & Moreau (1970) and Watson *et al.*

(1986). However, the *barratti* group of races have 12 (not ten) tail feathers, broader than those of the *lopezi* and *mariae* groups, and their trilling song is quite different. Dowsett & Dowsett-Lemaire (1980) separated *B. mariae* from *B. barratti* and then later (Dowsett & Dowsett-Lemaire 1989) treated the *mariae* and *lopezi* groups as conspecific (under *B. lopezi*). This was the treatment adopted by Urban *et al.* (1997) and which we broadly follow here.

In W Africa, Urban *et al.* (1997) regarded *manengubae* as a synonym of *bangwaensis*, but Dowsett-Lemaire & Dowsett (1999) described the presence of both taxa on Mount Manenguba, and we treat them here as separate species. The Zambian *ufipae* has been difficult to place. Its plumage pattern is much like that of Cinnamon Bracken Warbler and no race of *B. cinnamomeus* exists within its range. It was treated as a race of Cinnamon Bracken Warbler by many twentieth century authors, and White (1965) regarded *ufipae* as a synonym of *B. cinnamomeus nyassae*. However, it has ten rather narrow tail feathers and its song is of the *lopezi-mariae* type. Dowsett & Sternstedt (1979) showed that it was better treated as a race of Evergreen Forest Warbler, a course adopted by Urban *et al.* (1997) and which we have followed here. DNA study will undoubtedly shed further light on relationships within the *lopezi-mariae-barratti* complex. Molecular work has already indicated that *barakae* is not closely related to the W African races of *B. lopezi* (CK *in litt.*).

▲ ▶ Adult *B. l. camerunensis*, Mt Cameroon, March. Shows the cinnamon-tinged upperparts, breast and flanks, whitish belly centre and well-marked buffy supercilium. Note the very short wings and the narrow graduated tail (Nik Borrow).

▲ Adult *B. l. barakae*, Nyungwe, Rwanda, January. A richly coloured race with bright rufous-cinnamon underparts and a longish tail with particularly narrow pointed feathers (Jason Anderson).

▲ Adult *B. l. usambarae*, Udzungwa Mts, Tanzania, June (Andrew Perkin).

SPOTTED BUSH WARBLER
Bradypterus thoracicus   **Plate 5**

Dumeticola thoracica **Blyth, 1845**. *J. Asiatic Soc. Bengal,* 14: 584. Nepal.

The most numerous and widespread *Bradypterus* in the Himalayas and mountains of W China, where it is an altitudinal or short-distance migrant, descending to the lowlands after the breeding season. The northerly breeding Baikal Bush Warbler was formerly included within Spotted Bush Warbler. Polytypic, with three races recognised:

B. t. thoracicus (Blyth, 1845). C and E Himalayas to W and S China.

B. t. przevalskii (Sushkin, 1925). C China (Sichuan to N Qinghai, SW Gansu and S Shaanxi).

B. t. kashmirensis (Sushkin, 1925). W Himalayas.

IDENTIFICATION Length 12–13cm. Wing 51–59mm. Tail/wing 83–94%.

A small, dark warbler with a relatively short tail. As its name implies, it has a gorget of blackish spots across the lower throat and upper breast, although this feature is shared by several related Asian species. Undoubtedly the best means of identifying Spotted Bush Warbler is by its distinctive and readily recognisable song, one of the most distinctive sounds of the Himalayas and the mountains of C China above the tree line. Sexes alike.

Structure A small *Bradypterus* with a proportionately short but strongly graduated tail, long and deep undertail-coverts and a thin, fine bill. The wing is well rounded, with a fairly long outermost primary. The wing point is formed by p5, and usually p4, and falls well short of the longest uppertail- and undertail-coverts, and p3–5 are all emarginated. Despite this, the primary projection is quite long at *c.* 75% of the tertial length

Plumage and bare parts A drab and nondescript *Bradypterus* with a distinctive gorget of blackish spots that extend across the lower throat and onto the upper breast, a feature shared by several related Asian species which it closely resembles. The entire upperparts including the wings and tail are dark russet-brown, the crown is slightly warmer with a hint of chestnut. When fresh the crown and mantle feathers have slightly darker tips, giving a delicately scaled appearance. The dark head shows a narrow, dull grey supercilium, most conspicuous in front of the eye but merging with the crown sides behind. A dark eye-stripe is most contrasting across the lores but becomes narrower and more diffuse above the ash-grey ear-coverts, giving the side of the head an appearance quite distinct from that of the other mainland *Bradypterus*. Apart from a white chin and throat and a whitish belly, the underparts are dull and there is considerable individual variation, although this may be related to sex, age and time of year. On most birds, the characteristic gorget of blackish spots is conspicuous but neither as extensive, nor the spots as large, as shown by Baikal Bush Warbler. However, there is considerable variation, some birds showing indistinct paler grey spots that show little contrast with the breast, while others have large spots that merge to form a solid band across the uppermost breast. The grey tone of the breast also varies, being entirely dark ash-grey in some birds, while in others a grey centre merges with dull mouse-brown sides. Grey upper flanks grade into dark fulvous-brown lower flanks and undertail-coverts, the latter with broad buffy-white tips that contrast with the darker bases, creating a barred appearance.

The juvenile resembles the adult but the upperparts appear more olive-brown, less rufous and there is a dull yellow tinge to the supercilium and underparts.

The bill is entirely black with a small whitish tip. The legs and feet are deep plumbeous-pink.

SIMILAR SPECIES Several of the Asian *Bradypterus* warblers closely resemble Spotted Bush Warbler in appearance and share similar plumage tones and structure. Two species, Baikal Bush and Chinese Bush Warblers breed sympatrically or allopatrically with it in the mountains of C China and separation is discussed under the accounts for these species. In the Himalayas, the range of Spotted Bush overlaps that of both Brown Bush Warbler, which also breeds above the tree line, and Russet Bush Warbler, which breeds at lower elevations.

Russet Bush Warbler shares much of its range with Spotted Bush Warbler, from Bhutan east to Sichuan Province in C China, but breeds below the tree line so the two species are unlikely to come into contact. Outside the breeding season, however, they are likely to overlap. Song is the best means of separating them, Russet Bush Warbler having a distinctive, repetitive, nasal buzzing '*zee-bit, zee-bit, zee-bit…*', or '*cree-ut, cree-ut, cree-ut…*' with each sequence repeated about once per second. Calling birds should also be separable, Russet Bush giving a rather soft quiet '*quip, quip*', similar to the call of Radde's Warbler and quite different from the harsher '*chut*' or '*shtak*' of Spotted Bush Warbler. Russet Bush is distinctly longer-tailed and shorter-winged than Spotted Bush, but this may not always be apparent. Both species have long, dark brown and pale-tipped undertail-coverts, greyish underparts and dark, warm brown upperparts, and both show a gorget of blackish spots across the lower throat when breeding. The brown upperparts of Russet Bush are rather richer and darker than those of Spotted Bush, but this distinction is marginal. In the past, this has led to confusion and belief that Spotted Bush Warbler bred beyond its known range, including in the mountains of SE China.

In the breeding season, separation is straightforward with good views. Russet Bush lacks a prominent supercilium and grey head sides. The centre of the breast and belly are usually dark grey, becoming warm rusty brown on the flanks and vent, while in Spotted Bush they tend to be paler grey, with less extensive brown. Russet Bush shows a row of indistinct fine brown spots across the lower throat and top of the breast that become larger and slightly darker as they extend down the breast and form diffuse striations that fade across the lower breast and flanks. The extent and prominence of these striations varies greatly between individuals, but the fine gorget across the lower throat is paler and less conspicuous than in Spotted Bush.

Outside the breeding season, the extent of spotting is more variable in both species, and separation more difficult

Brown Bush Warbler is quite unlike typical Spotted Bush Warbler and the two species are unlikely to be confused, having distinct differences in plumage and song. However, the poorly known buff-bellied morph of the *kashmirensis* race of Spotted Bush Warbler more closely resembles Brown Bush Warbler. These species have repeatedly been confused but should be separable with care. Both share a similar warm buff wash to the supercilium, side of the head and breast, light fulvous-brown flanks and lack throat spotting, so appear very similar. The main differences on a silent bird are that the upperparts are slightly paler in Brown Bush

Warbler and the undertail-coverts lack the conspicuous white tips shown by *kashmirensis*.

Outside the breeding season, it is uncertain whether Brown Bush and Spotted Bush Warblers come into contact. However, this seems likely in NW India and Nepal, when trapping provides the only reliable means of separating them.

VOICE The song of nominate *thoracicus* and the race *przevalskii* is a far-carrying and monotonous, rhythmic '*trick-he-dee, trick-he-dee…, trick-he-dee, trick-he-dee…*' or '*tri-tri-tri-tree, tri-tri-tri-treez… tri-tri-tri-treez, tri-tri-tri-treez…*' repeated continuously within a frequency range of 4–7kHz. Two identical phrases, each lasting approximately 0.5 seconds, followed by a brief pause and two further phrases, form a sequence. This song sequence is often delivered without a break for several minutes.

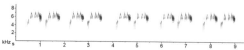

Song of Spotted Bush Warbler recorded within breeding range of *B. t. przevalskii*, Bau Mu Ping, Sichuan Province, China, June. (Peter Kennerley)

The song of *kashmirensis* differs slightly from that of the other forms. It retains the rhythmic and monotonous quality but has a slightly different quality which Alström *et al.* (2008) consider to be sufficient to act as a barrier to pair formation. It is described by Rasmussen & Anderton (2005) as 'a rhythmic, mechanical buzzy and clicking series; each starting with 1–2 quick, mid-pitch, rather musical clicks, then a few very short, extremely high clicks, then a short, abrupt humming buzz and another set of clicks and a buzz, before starting again with hardly a break…'. Phrases are not delivered in pairs as in races *thoracicus* and *przevalskii*. It was transcribed by Alström *et al.* as '*tre-tre-tre-triptreez-trip-treez, tre-tre-tre-trip-treez-trip-treeez, tre-tre-tre-trip-treez-trip-treeez…*' There is slight individual variation, mainly in the number of introductory elements (Alström *et al.* 2008). While the difference is perceptible, it is not as distinct as that between Spotted Bush and Baikal Bush Warblers.

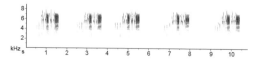

Song of Spotted Bush Warbler recorded within breeding range of *B. t. kashmirensis*, Manali, Himachal Pradesh, India, June. (Per Alström)

Calls include a subdued and quiet '*chut*' and a rather more attention-seeking '*shtak*'. They are only uttered occasionally outside the breeding season but may develop into an excited chatter when several birds are together. It is not known whether there is any regional or racial variation between calls.

MOULT No data.

HABITAT Breeds at and above the tree line to over 3,700m in the C and E Himalayas, and to above 3,200m where high rainfall extends the tree line in W China. Frequents grasslands and pastures interspersed with low scrub and thickets, including bamboo, azalea, dwarf rhododendron, dwarf juniper, Barberry *Berberis*, bracken and other dense

herbage. In optimal habitat, it can occur at high densities with several birds audible at once. However, this habitat is threatened by increasing numbers of foraging herbivores and by the use of scrub for fuel. At lower elevations, some breed in forest glades up to 200m below the tree line.

In the W Himalayas, the race *kashmirensis* breeds in similar habitat above the tree line between 3,200m and 4,000m. Alström *et al.* (2008) state that it occurs in moist, tall herbaceous alpine vegetation, at places also dominated by tussock grass *Danthonia cashmeriana*, mainly at 3,350–3,920m, but also down to 3,100m below the tree line, in open herbaceous patches.

There are few records outside the breeding season and so the full range of wintering habitats is unknown. In the lowlands of the Terai in Nepal, immediately south of the Himalayas, it then occurs fairly commonly in damp grass-lands, *Phragmites* swamps, dense grass thickets and thick, rank herbage along damp ditches and water channels.

BEHAVIOUR Typically skulking and difficult to observe outside the breeding season, but perhaps less elusive than most other *Bradypterus*. In the early morning, it occasionally feeds in the open beside dense cover and patient observation can produce prolonged views. It typically flicks its wings nervously above the back while hopping on the ground and rarely remains stationary, darting into cover on signs of disturbance, but often reappearing quickly. Males sing occasionally in the wintering grounds but are rarely seen. During the breeding season, they tend to sing from a favoured perch within a dense scrub patch. On still mornings they may emerge to sing in the open before creeping back down a stem and into cover. After a pause of several minutes, singing is likely to commence again. Where grass is cropped short by grazing herbivores, males will fly low and fast between favoured bushes within the territory.

BREEDING HABITS Little data available. In Sichuan, singing males return to breeding grounds by mid May and are numerous in the mountains at Bei Mu Ping, above Wolong, in early June. No data is available for other races and regions but these are presumed not to differ greatly. The nest is a domed structure, placed in a tuft of grass or well concealed near the ground in a low bush. It is loosely constructed from coarse grasses and lined with finer grasses and the occasional feather. A clutch of 3–4 eggs is laid between May and July (Ali & Ripley 1973). No data is available on incubation, fledging or number of broods raised.

DISTRIBUTION As a breeding bird, Spotted Bush Warbler is confined to high mountains around the southern and eastern periphery of the Himalayas and Tibetan Plateau, from Kashmir east to the Chinese provinces of Sichuan, Qinghai, Gansu and Shaanxi.

Breeding

B. t. kashmirensis Breeds from 2,000–3,200m in the NW Himalayas. It occurs in Kashmir but appears to be absent from Pakistan-administered territory there (Roberts 1992). The breeding range follows the western flank of the Himalayas east to at least the region of Kumaon in Uttarakhand and possibly to W Nepal, where there is one record of a racially indeterminate bird (Inskipp & Inskipp 1991). As it is otherwise absent from Nepal to the west of the Kali Gandaki Valley, it is possible that this breeding season record may be referable to *kashmirensis*.

B. t. thoracicus Nominate *thoracicus* breeds from 2,400–

4,300m through the C and E Himalayas and into the mountains of W China. It ranges from C Nepal east of the Kali Gandaki Valley, through Sikkim, Bhutan and Assam, India, and north into adjacent regions of S Tibet. It is considered a rare summer visitor to Bhutan (Spierenburg 2005), known mainly from specimens collected there in the 1930s, but there have been few summer visits to its breeding altitudes and it may be overlooked there. It may also breed in N Burma, where it was reported as common in July in the Adung Valley above the tree line (Smythies 1968). In China, Cheng (1987) considered the range to follow the mountains east through N Yunnan and into S and C Sichuan north to the region of Sungpan (but see *B. t. przevalskii* below).

B. t. przevalskii Unclear due to intergradation with nominate *thoracicus*. Cheng (1987) restricted *przevalskii* to the provinces of Qinghai, Gansu, and the Qinling Shan in S Shaanxi, with no overlap with the nominate form. However, territorial males showing the characters of *przevalskii* have been examined in the hand at Bei Mu Ping, near Wolong, within Cheng's range for the nominate form (PRK pers. obs.). Others, including Vaurie (1959) and Watson *et al.* (1986) consider *przevalskii* to have a substantially larger range, including Sichuan and N Yunnan and possibly the SE and C Tibetan Plateau and N Burma. Further research is required to establish the northern limit of nominate *thoracicus* in Sichuan and the extent of intergradation with *przevalskii*.

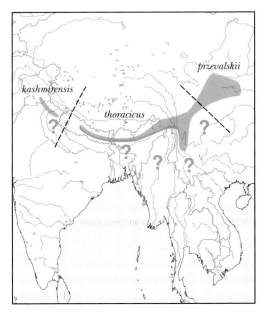

Spotted Bush Warbler. Breeding range and non-breeding distribution.

Non-breeding Spotted Bush Warbler is virtually unknown outside the breeding season but it is assumed to descend to the lowlands and foothills below the mountains of its breeding range. Sight records come mostly from E Nepal, including the Koshi Barrage and Chitwan (Inskipp & Inskipp 1991) and more recently from Koshi Tappu (PRK pers. obs.). Further east, there are winter records

from Assam, Bangladesh, Yunnan Province in China and probably also Burma. As yet, no birds have been assigned to a particular race, but those in Nepal and NE India are assumed to belong to the nominate form which breeds directly to the north. The wintering ranges of *kashmirensis* and *przevalskii* are unknown but are assumed to lie in the lowlands and foothills of the western Himalayas and C China respectively. There are no reports from Thailand where Baikal Bush Warbler is common in winter.

MOVEMENTS All races are believed to be altitudinal migrants, descending to winter in the foothills. However, there are no recorded movements of ringed Spotted Bush Warblers and very few winter records, with none west of Nepal where *kashmirensis* would be expected to occur. It will be difficult to differentiate between wintering birds and passage migrants in the foothills.

DESCRIPTION B. t. thoracicus
Plumage – Adult fresh, breeding Forehead to nape dark reddish brown, slightly darker brown tips giving a distinct scaly effect. Supercilium dull grey, narrow and poorly defined; most conspicuous before and over eye; tinged russet-brown behind eye, indistinct and tapering away. A dark brown loral line, narrow and diffuse, sometimes does not reach the bill base. Behind eye, a dark brown spot extends as a narrow line below the supercilium to the rear of the ear-coverts. Ear-coverts ash-grey with dull brown tips and pale shaft streaks, giving a mottled brown effect towards the upper edges, but greyer with more obvious pale shafts towards the lower edges. Eye-ring poorly defined, merging with supercilium above eye, appearing as thin pale crescent below it. Mantle to uppertail-coverts dark russet-brown, duller than crown, with darker tips forming faint scaling on mantle and scapulars. Tail feathers dark russet-brown without contrast between centres and fringes, often finely and diffusely barred darker brown; tips of outer two or three pairs sometimes narrowly tipped warm buff.

Chin white, unmarked. Throat white, usually with fine blackish streaks towards the sides and larger, better-defined blackish spots across the lower edge. Still larger spots form a distinct gorget across the upper breast. Breast with variable dark ash-grey wash. In the best-marked birds this extends to the lower breast and sides of breast, and merges with the greyish lower ear-coverts; in others, it is restricted to the breast centre, merging with the dull mouse-brown sides of lower breast. Upper flanks ash-grey, merging with dark fulvous-brown lower flanks. Belly and vent washed creamy white. Undertail-coverts dark fulvous-brown with broad buffy white tips (2–5mm wide). Upperwing rather uniform. Lesser and median coverts dark russet-brown. Alula, greater coverts and tertials with narrow russet-brown fringes, barely contrasting with darker centres. Edges of primary coverts and secondaries dull russet-brown, matching upperparts. Edges of primaries paler and brighter, especially towards bases, creating a slight pale panel on the closed wing. Underwing-coverts pale grey-buff to pale grey.

Adult non-breeding Not known to differ from breeding adult.

Juvenile Top of head and upperparts dull olive-brown with faint darker scaling on crown and mantle. Supercilium as adult, but dull greyish sulphur. Loral line and eye-line dark brown as in adult. Ear-coverts dull olive-brown with fine whitish streaks. Eye ring poorly defined. Chin dull creamy white, unmarked. Throat often with an oily-yellow wash and tiny olive-brown spots at the sides. A narrow gorget of small, diffuse spots across lower throat, becoming a band of diffuse, dull olive-brown spots on the upper breast. Extent of spotting variable: on some individuals extending to sides of breast and upper flanks as diffuse striations, more restricted on others. Belly dull greyish yellow. Lower flanks, vent and undertail-coverts dull olivaceous-brown, the last with greyish yellow tips, narrower than those of the adult. Upperwing-coverts, alula and tertials dull brown with warm brown fringes, warmer and brighter than upperparts. Edges to secondaries and primaries warm brown, lacking russet tones of the adult. Tail dull olive-brown with slightly warmer fringes.

Bare parts During the breeding season, upper and lower mandibles entirely black with small whitish tips. Tarsi deep plumbeous-pink; toes paler brownish pink. Iris of adult rich, dark brown.

IN HAND CHARACTERS
Measurements *B. t. thoracicus*

	Male	Female
Wing	51–59 (55.1; 14)	52–56 (54.1; 8)
Tail	46–52 (49.0; 10)	43–50 (47.5; 8)
Bill	12–14 (12.9; 14)	12.5–13.5 (13.2; 7)
Tarsus	19–21 (20.3; 13)	19.5–21 (19.9; 6)

Sexes combined:
Tail/wing ratio: 83–94% (89%; 21)
Bill width: 2.8–3.2 (3.0; 16)
Hind claw: 5.0–7.7 (6.3; 16)
Tail graduation: 17–23 (20.9; 16)
B. t. przevalskii (sexes combined): *wing* 53–57 (54.8; 4); *tail* 48, 50 (n = 2); *bill* 13, 13.2 (n = 2); *tarsus* 19.8, 20.0 (n = 2).
B. t. kashmirensis (sexes combined): *wing* 55–57 (56.2; 5); *tail* 45–50 (47.8; 5); *bill* 13–14.5 (14.0; 5); *tarsus* 19–20.5 (20.0; 5). Bill thus appears slightly longer than other races.

Structure *B. t. thoracicus*

Wing formula (n = 12):

p1/pc	p2	p3e	p4e	p5e	p6	p7	p10
7–11	7–10	0.5–2.5	0–0.5	wp	1–2.5	2.5	6.5–8.5

Wing short and rounded with fairly small p1. Wing point p(4) 5; p2 = p9/10 to < ss tips; emargination on p3–5.

Figure 15. Wing of Spotted Bush Warbler.

Tail rather short, strongly graduated; 12 feathers, broad and rounded (tl *c.* 11mm wide) (Fig. 19).
Bill small and narrow, concave-sided with fine tip.
Tarsi slender, but slightly longer than in Chinese Bush and Brown Bush Warblers; toes slender, claws small and

weak.
B. t. przevalskii Wing point usually at p4, with p3 and p5 subequal and p6 2–4 shorter; p5 may lack emargination.
B. t. kashmirensis Wing as in nominate *thoracicus*.
Recognition Nominate race shows combination of dark rich brown upperparts, greyish head sides and underparts, dark and boldly pale-tipped undertail-coverts and conspicuous black spotting on throat and breast. All races are separable from Baikal Bush Warbler by more rounded wing (Baikal Bush has wing point at p3–4) and emargination on p5. From other mainland Asian *Bradypterus* by shorter tail (usually < 52mm, below range for Russet Bush, Chinese Bush and most Brown Bush Warblers). From Russet Bush also by fine-tipped bill.
Weight Range 9.0–13.4g (10.8; 3) (Dunning 2007).

GEOGRAPHIC VARIATION Three subtly different races are recognised, which differ in the intensity of the upperpart colour and the extent and tone of grey on the underparts. The nominate form shows darker, richer and more saturated plumage tones, while the western form *kashmirensis* is slightly paler. There does not appear to be a clear divide between the nominate form and the race *przevalskii* which seem to show a cline of characters in C China where many individuals cannot be assigned to a particular taxon. In addition, there are minor differences in wing length and wing structure between these races, summarised under **In Hand Characters** above.
B. t. thoracicus (C and E Himalayas to W and S China) Described above.
B. t. przevalskii (C China including Sichuan to N Qinghai, SW Gansu and S Shaanxi) Closely resembles the nominate form, with many individuals not reliably separable. In the northern part of the range, including Qinghai, Gansu and S Shaanxi Provinces in C China, *przevalskii* appears warm dark brown, slightly paler and more rufescent above than nominate *thoracicus* but lacks the slightly contrasting rufous crown found in southern populations, also assigned to *przevalskii*. Other differences, all of a minor nature and not appearing consistently within the range of *przevalskii* include the better-defined and more contrasting head pattern with a pale grey or greyish white supercilium in front of and over eye, becoming washed light buff and less obvious behind eye, and the dark brown and better defined loral and eye-lines that form a narrow but contrasting dark stripe from the bill base to the rear of the ear-coverts. The ear-coverts are slightly greyer and paler and the upper breast is washed light ash-grey, again slightly paler than in the nominate race and tending towards brown rather than greyish on the breast sides and flanks. The extent of spotting on lower throat and breast is variable between and within both taxa and the conspicuous whitish tips (up to 3mm in length) to the undertail-coverts are found in both races. There is individual variation within China and the above differences are rarely present on all individuals and many appear inseparable from nominate *thoracicus*. This led Alström *et al.* (2008) to treat *przevalskii* as a synonym of *thoracicus*.
B. t. kashmirensis (W Himalayas) Closely resembles the nominate form and *przevalskii*. The upperparts are slightly paler and less richly washed, and the ear-coverts and nape sides slightly paler grey. It differs in having a greyish white supercilium, which can appear almost white in front of and above the eye. Spots across the

lower throat are variable in extent and colour, usually small and brown but larger and dark grey on some individuals. The breast is slightly paler grey than in *thoracicus* and the flanks and undertail-coverts paler fulvous-brown, the latter still prominently tipped whitish.

This race is unique in also having a distinctive buff-breasted morph in which the breast and supercilium are warm buff and grey tones are entirely suppressed. It usually lacks throat spotting but occasionally shows a hint of a narrow necklace of fine spotting. This morph closely resembles Brown Bush Warbler and has been mistaken for it in museum collections. It occurs sympatrically with typical birds and there is no difference in the song between it and typical *kashmirensis*. Alström *et al.* (2008) found it occurring alongside typical grey-breasted birds and estimated that about one in ten birds observed were of this morph.

TAXONOMY AND SYSTEMATICS Round & Loskot (1994) proposed that Spotted Bush Warbler (including races *thoracicus*, *kashmirensis* and *przevalskii*) and Baikal Bush Warbler (with races *davidi* and *suschkini*) should be treated as distinct species, based upon differences in morphology and vocalisations. This conclusion has recently been supported by the findings of Alström *et al.* (2008) and has been adopted here. Further discussion can be found within the Baikal Bush Warbler account.

In addition to treating Spotted Bush and Baikal Bush Warblers as distinct species, Alström *et al.* (2008) suggested that the taxonomic status of *kashmirensis* requires revision. They acknowledge that (except for the distinctive buff-breasted morph) it is poorly differentiated from the *thoracicus* group in biometrics and morphology, but consider differences between the songs of *kashmirensis* and *thoracicus/ przevalskii* sufficient to act as a barrier to mating if these taxa were to meet. They support this assumption with data on the cytochrome *b* divergence between these taxa,

which approaches that found between *thoracicus* and *davidi* in C China. As *kashmirensis* is diagnosably different from *thoracicus* (including *przevalskii*) and *B. davidi* (including *suschkini*) they propose that *Bradypterus thoracicus* (*sensu lato*) be treated as two separate species: *B. thoracicus*, which they consider to be monotypic, and *B. kashmirensis*.

We have taken a cautious approach to these findings and decided to retain *kashmirensis* as a race of Spotted Bush Warbler until further research is undertaken. We acknowledge that the genetic divergence is as great as that found between Spotted and Baikal Bush Warblers in C China, but note that other morphological and biometric distinctions are lacking. The mechanism for the isolation of *thoracicus* from *kashmirensis* appears to rely solely upon vocalisations. While differences in song are perceptible to the human ear, they do not approach those between the songs of Spotted Bush and Baikal Bush Warblers.

Yen (1933) collected a distinctive specimen from the Yao Shan range, Guangxi (Kwangsi) Province, China, which he named *Tribura thoracica saturata*. He recognised its similarity to *Tribura thoracica melanorhyncha* (= Russet Bush Warbler *B. mandelli melanorhynchus*), but noted that it differed in its darker colour, particularly on the breast and flanks, which he described as 'dirty brown rather than grey and olive-grey'. Compared with nominate *thoracicus*, he described the upperparts of *saturata* as much darker. With a wing length of 49mm, *saturata* is clearly too small to belong within the Spotted Bush Warbler complex and plumage characters and wing length fall within the recognised range for Russet Bush Warbler, which is known to occur in the Yao Shan. The location of the type specimen is now unknown. Without reference to this and in the absence of other evidence, we have chosen not to recognise the validity of *saturata*, which we believe to be Russet Bush Warbler in breeding plumage and showing a gorget of dark spotting across the lower throat.

▲ Adult *B. t. przevalskii*, China, July. Male from north-central China showing conspicuous grey wash to breast and side of head, and band of blackish spots across lower throat and upper breast. In the breeding season the entire bill and inside of upper mandible become black (Fang Gu Yun).

◀ Adult *B. t. przevalskii*, Sichuan, China, July. Upperparts show fine, dark fringes to crown and mantle, and warm buff flanks (Heyi).

◀ Adult *B. t. przevalskii*, Sichuan, China, March. Seen from below, the characteristic broad pale tips to the undertail-coverts are clearly visible (Li Bin).

◀▲ Adult *B. t. kashmirensis*, Uttarakhand, India, July. Distinctive buff morph shows warm brown upperparts and a buff-brown wash across the underparts, which is unique to *kashmirensis*. On this individual, buff wash is restricted to side of head, flanks and side of breast, on others it extends fully across the belly and breast (Devashish Deb/ birdpoints.com).

BAIKAL BUSH WARBLER
Bradypterus davidi   Plate 5

Tribura thoracica davidi La Touche, 1923. *Bull. Brit. Orn. Club* 43: 168. Chinwangtao, northeastern Chihli, China.

A long-distance migrant that breeds in the mountains of S Siberia and NE and C China and winters in Thailand, the Indochina region and possibly elsewhere. Closely resembles Spotted Bush Warbler and until recently treated as a race of that species, but clearly separated by its different song and wing structure. Polytypic, with two races recognised:

B. d. davidi (La Touche, 1923). E Siberia from the NW Amur River region south to NE China, with an isolated population in C China.

B. d. suschkini (Stegmann, 1929). Siberia from the Russian Altai east through Sayan Mountains to the region of Lake Baikal.

IDENTIFICATION Length 12cm. Wing 50–57mm. Tail/wing 80–90%.

A small, drab, unstreaked brown *Bradypterus* warbler that shows conspicuous pale-tipped undertail-coverts and often a spotted throat. Sexes alike.

Structure A diminutive warbler with a strongly graduated tail and long, full undertail-coverts that extend beyond the outermost rectrices. The tail is proportionately shorter than in other Asian *Bradypterus* species, with the exception of the closely related Spotted Bush Warbler. The short wings are rather less rounded than in Spotted Bush Warbler, with wing point formed by p3 and p4 only and the first primary is relatively short. The fifth primary (p5) lacks emargination.

Plumage and bare parts Closely resembles the similar Spotted Bush Warbler at all times of year. The entire upperparts of breeding adults including the tail, wing-coverts and fringes to the remiges are uniform dull reddish brown, although the crown of fresh birds in spring is slightly darker than the mantle and shows marginally darker feather tips, creating a faintly scaly appearance. Shows buffy white supercilium, broadest above the lores but narrows and merges with the crown sides over the ear-coverts. This is bordered by a short, dark eye-stripe, restricted in most birds to a dark spot immediately in front of and behind the eye. The dull brown ear-coverts show little contrast with the crown or upperparts, a character useful in separation from Spotted Bush Warbler.

The underparts are conspicuously paler than the upperparts, particularly the chin and throat which are whitish. The breast is pale greyish brown, darkening to warm buffy brown near the carpal bend. After pre-breeding moult, rows of small blackish spots usually form a conspicuous gorget across the lower throat, becoming larger and bleeding into diffuse striations into the upper breast. The lower flanks are warmer buffy brown, the undertail-coverts similar but with conspicuous broad pale tips. These tips usually create a series of pale and dark bands or rear-pointing arrowheads and the pale tips may be so extensive that they almost obscure the darker brown bases, so the undertail-coverts appear almost white. After the post-breeding moult, the supercilium is slightly paler and more contrasting, the upperparts rather greyer and throat spotting much reduced or entirely absent.

Juveniles have the supercilium and underparts washed with yellow and usually show a mottled brownish breast-band.

During the breeding season the bill is entirely black, but outside the breeding season the lower mandible is pale yellowish-pink, becoming slightly darker on the sides towards the tip. The legs and feet are fleshy pink.

Of the two races, nominate *davidi* is warmer and richer brown above than *suschkini*, in which the reddish tones are subdued, except on the forehead.

SIMILAR SPECIES Although superficially resembling many of the nondescript *Acrocephalus* and *Locustella* warblers occurring in East Asia, the combination of small size, unstreaked upperparts, long and deep, whitish tipped undertail-coverts, and relatively short strongly graduated tail combine to give this diminutive warbler a particularly distinctive character, rather resembling an unstreaked Lanceolated Warbler. These characters, combined with the lack of streaking, are exclusive to the smaller *Bradypterus*. It occurs alongside two similar species; overlapping with Chinese Bush Warbler within its breeding range in S Siberia and with Chinese Bush and Spotted Bush Warblers outside the breeding season. Separation from these species will depend on a combination of plumage and structural characters, biometrics and song. All these species are difficult to view well under the most favourable field conditions, making it extremely difficult to establish the true plumage colours. Whenever possible, birds should be trapped, when in-hand examination should establish the identification.

Spotted Bush Warbler (particularly nominate *thoracicus*) is warmer, darker and richer brown above than Baikal Bush Warbler. It shows a less prominent and darker grey supercilium and dark grey ear-coverts which merge with the dark grey sides to the neck. The throat and breast are also darker than on Baikal Bush and the belly is greyer. The black spotting on the throat and upper breast of Spotted Bush Warbler typically forms a well-defined necklace. This feature is variable in both species, but in Spotted Bush Warbler it is set against the dark grey upper breast, while on Baikal Bush the upper breast is never dark or grey. The song of Spotted Bush is a distinctive '*trick-he-dee, trick-he-dee, trick-he-dee...*', repeated continuously and quite different from the nasal, buzzing phrases of Baikal Bush Warbler (see **Voice**).

In the hand, wing shape is key to separation. The wing point falls at p4 in both species, but Spotted Bush shows a more rounded wing, particularly in the nominate race, and a slightly larger first primary. Round & Loskot (1994) showed that in nominate race of Spotted Bush the outermost primary (p1) extends 7.0–11.5mm beyond the primary coverts, the tip of p2 falls opposite the tips of the secondaries or innermost primaries, and p3 falls short of the wing point on p4 by 0.5–2.0mm. By contrast, in Baikal Bush Warbler, p1 is much shorter, extending 5.4–8.0mm beyond the primary coverts in race *davidi*, and 3.8–7.2mm in *suschkini*. The tip of p2 falls opposite the tips of p6–8, and p3 lies within 1.0mm of the wing point and frequently forms the wing point with p4. Emarginations are present on p3–p5 in Spotted Bush but only on p3–4 in Baikal Bush Warbler.

Chinese Bush Warbler is distinctly paler than Baikal Bush Warbler, especially during the breeding season. It lacks the darker, chestnut-brown upperparts of Baikal Bush, appearing paler, uniform greyish brown above, usually with a hint of olive, particularly on the fringes of the wing-coverts, tertials and edges to the remiges, which appear warmer and browner than the upperparts. It has a uniform appearance to the head and lacks a prominent supercilium and eye-stripe. The lores form a pale greyish white triangle in front of the eye that merges with the eye-ring. Breeding adults lack prominent throat spotting and many are entirely unmarked. Some have an row of tiny diffuse spots across the lower throat, but never approaching the gorget of blackish spots shown by Baikal Bush. Chinese Bush Warbler is slightly larger longer-winged and proportionately longer-tailed than Baikal Bush. The songs of the two species share a similar structure but differ in pitch, duration of phrases and intervening pauses, and volume. That of Chinese Bush is harsher, louder and generally carrying further (see **Voice**). Small differences in wing structure are evident in the hand, in particular Chinese Bush usually has emargination on p5, which is lacking in Baikal Bush (see Chinese Bush Warbler for further distinctions).

Outside the breeding season some Baikal Bush Warblers show dark earth-brown upperparts and the gorget of spots then becomes diffuse, indistinct and in some, possibly first-winter plumage, entirely absent. Separation then requires greater emphasis on the colour and pattern of the underparts and undertail-coverts, and on head pattern and structure.

VOICE The song has an almost mechanical quality. It comprises a series of regular monotonous, rasping or buzzing phrases '*dzzzzzzr, dzzzzzzr, dzzzzzzr…*', forming a sequence reminiscent of the reeling songs of some European *Locustella* warblers. Each phrase lasts for about 0.5 seconds followed by a pause of approximately one second or slightly less between phrases. These phrases are distinctly higher pitched, between 5–7kHz, and slightly shorter than in the otherwise similar song of Chinese Bush Warbler, and they are separated by shorter pauses. The song sequence can continue for several minutes without a break, especially in the early morning. Comparison of sonograms shows little difference between the songs of nominate *davidi* and *suschkini*.

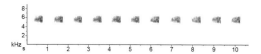

Song of Baikal Bush Warbler, recorded within range of *B. d. suschkini*, Lake Baikal, Siberia, Russia, June (Geoff Carey).

At least two calls are given. A series of loud and rapid chacking notes, usually given when alarmed, closely resembles that given by Lanceolated Warbler (Round 2008). A sharp, metallic '*pwit*' or '*thwik*' repeated occasionally, is more frequently heard and is presumably a contact call.

MOULT Adults appear to have an early autumn moult, which often involves partial renewal of the primaries. Birds in Thailand in November–December were mostly in suspended moult and showed a variable mix of primaries, some with new outer feathers, others with new inner primaries (PDR, *in litt.*). One bird in late November was beginning active primary moult and another in late December was in mid moult. There appears to be a complete moult of body, wing feathers and tail in winter quarters between March and early May, shortly before northward departure (Round 2008). This presumably involves both adult and first year birds.

Young birds undergo a post-juvenile body moult, and in some at least this is delayed or protracted. Autumn migrants in N China retain the distinctive yellowish juvenile

underparts into early October, but those trapped in Hong Kong in mid to late October have completed moult to first-winter plumage. The yellow juvenile plumage tones are absent during the winter months.

HABITAT In the Altai and Sayan Mountains in S Russia, where it ranges up to 1,200m, it breeds in valleys with a mixture of deciduous woodland, scrubby thickets by streams and glade edges in forested taiga, typically among tangles of bird cherry, birches and grass. To the east, it frequents similar habitats including grassy meadows with a scattering of trees and bushes.

In winter in Thailand it frequents small patches of scrub around damp rice paddies, flooded grassland, marshes and dry scrub, suggesting it occupies a wide diversity of habitats and is probably far more numerous than records suggest. Records from the Mai Po Marshes in Hong Kong are of birds trapped in *Phragmites* reedbeds.

BEHAVIOUR Resembles that of other *Bradypterus*. Extremely shy, but perhaps the easiest of its genus to observe away from the breeding areas, when it often works its way along the base of scrub bordering rice paddies and damp grassland, flicking its wings nervously and darting back into cover at the slightest disturbance. Birds may perch in the open to sing in the early morning and occasionally remain in view for several minutes, particularly when challenging a rival male. Sings on the wintering grounds and on northward migration, as well as throughout the breeding season.

BREEDING HABITS Males on migration in spring regularly sing but rarely remain for more than one day.

Once established on breeding territories, males sing throughout the day and night until pair formation. The nest is built close to the ground among fallen twigs or piles of dead branches. It is a domed structure of coarse grasses with a side entrance, lined with finer grasses. A clutch of 4–6 eggs is laid and incubated by the female. No data is available on the fledging period. Birds breeding in China possibly raise two broods.

DISTRIBUTION
Breeding
B. d. davidi Breeds from the region of Chita oblast in SE Transbaikalia, east into W Amurland and south in the Da Hinggan Ling in the Nei Mongol Autonomous Region of NE China. From here it extends south through the NE provinces of Heilongjiang, Jilin, Liaoning and into N Hebei, and probably into neighbouring Shanxi where singing birds have been heard at Pangquanguo Nature Reserve. Singing males are also regularly encountered in the mountains of C China, from the Wolong Nature Reserve region of C Sichuan, north and east to S Gansu and S Shaanxi Provinces (Round & Loskot 1994; PRK pers. obs.). It is unclear whether these represent an isolated breeding population or whether there is a continuous distribution, in suitable habitat, throughout the hills of northern China to southern Shanxi Province. Birds breeding in Sichuan closely approach the breeding range of Spotted Bush Warbler, the two species being separated here by altitude, with Spotted Bush breeding at or above the tree-line and Baikal Bush Warbler at lower elevations in moist valleys with lush vegetation.

B. d. suschkini Breeds in a narrow belt through the mountains of southern C Siberia. From western limit at *c.* 85°E in the foothills of the northern Russian Altai Mountains it ranges through the Sayan Mountains into northernmost Mongolia and southern part of the Lake Baikal region. It is considered to be scarce in the Altai and Sayan Mountains but more numerous in the Baikal region, where it breeds up to 1,200m.

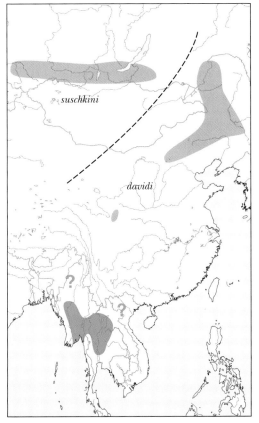

Baikal Bush Warbler. Breeding range and winter distribution.

Non-breeding The winter distribution is poorly known. It is a common visitor to N and C Thailand, south to Bangkok (Round & Loskot 1994; Round 2008). These birds are referable to *suschkini* (Round & Loskot 1994), but the range of this race outside Thailand is unknown. Round & Loskot also mention a specimen from Bengal, India, and also include Burma, and Assam in NE India within its range. However Rasmussen & Anderton (2005) have questioned the identity of this specimen and do not include the species for the Indian subcontinent. The wintering area of the nominate form has yet to be discovered. It has been suggested that it lies east of that of *suschkini*, in Indochina or southernmost China although there is no evidence to support this. The only records from China south of the Yangtze River are from Hong Kong, where four birds have been trapped at the Mai Po Marshes; three between mid October and early November which were presumably migrants, and one on 30 January 2004. Wintering in SE China is clearly unusual.

MOVEMENTS There are very few records away from the breeding or wintering grounds. In E China, it is a scarce passage migrant in coastal Hebei Province in late May and early June and again in late September and early October. La Touche (1925–30) recorded just two spring migrants from Qinhuangdao (Chinwangtao), on 31 May and 1 June 1917, in seven years' residence, while Hemmingsen failed to record it from Beidaihe (Hemmingsen & Guildal 1968). There are some recent records from Beidaihe and Happy Island (JH, *in litt.*) which have slightly increased the spread of dates in both spring and autumn, but it remains a scarce, though doubtless overlooked, migrant through NE China. Together with the three late autumn records from Hong Kong, this suggests that small numbers may migrate through SE China. The western breeding race *suschkini* presumably migrates through Sichuan and other Chinese provinces to the east of the Tibetan Plateau to reach Thailand and the Indochinese countries.

Birds reach Thailand from October and remain until late April and early May, with the latest reported near Bangkok on 12 May (Round 2008).

Migrants return to the breeding grounds in NE China from late May onwards but arrive much later in Russia, reaching S Transbaikalia in mid June and the western limit in the Altai Mountains in late June, where Dement'ev & Gladkov (1954) noted the earliest arrival on 26 June.

DESCRIPTION *B. d. davidi*

Plumage – Adult fresh (May to July) Forehead to nape dull reddish brown with fine darker feather tips creating an indistinct scaly appearance. Supercilium buffy white, extending from bill base to ear-coverts; narrow over lores, broadest over eye, then tapering to a point and merging with crown sides. A dark greyish brown loral spot in front of eye sometimes almost forms a fine line to the bill base. An indistinct, narrow dark brown line extends behind the eye, becoming progressively less distinct above the ear-coverts. Eye-ring narrow, pale buff, merging above the eye with the supercilium; more conspicuous below eye, contrasting with darker ear-coverts. Ear-coverts pale greyish brown, with paler shaft streaks forming fine, indistinct streaking. Sides of neck, mantle, scapulars and uppertail-coverts dull reddish brown, slightly paler than the crown, with indistinct darker tips creating a faint scaly effect on the mantle and scapulars. Rump slightly paler warm sandy brown, contrasting with mantle and uppertail-coverts. Upper surface of tail dull reddish brown with slightly darker shafts and usually with fine, diffuse cross-barring, underside dull greyish brown. Chin white, throat and upper breast washed pale brownish grey. Lower breast pale greyish brown, darkening to olivaceous-brown on the sides near the carpal bend. Upper throat often with faint darker spots. Lower throat with clear gorget of dark grey spots, these being larger on upper breast and merging to form a band of diffuse striations that fade across the lower breast. Belly white. Flanks and vent warm buffy brown, sometimes with ill-defined paler fringes. Undertail-coverts warm buffy brown with broad pale tips (up to 7mm) that can almost obscure brown bases; these are pale buff on the outermost, almost white on the central pair. Lesser and median coverts dull reddish brown, lacking darker centres and closely resembling mantle and scapulars. Primary and greater coverts and tertials dull brown with broad warm reddish brown fringes, slightly warmer than mantle. Secondaries and primaries grey-brown with warm brown edges matching tertial fringes. Alula dark grey-brown with pale brown fringe. Underwing-coverts light sandy brown to mid brown.

Adult non-breeding As adult breeding but overall appearance duller, with brown tones colder and grey tones enhanced.

Forehead and crown dull chocolate-brown. Supercilium thin, pale brown, whitest and most conspicuous above and behind eye. Ear-coverts and sides of nape greyish brown with fine white shaft streaks. Upperparts from forehead to tail uniform reddish brown and lacking indistinct warmer brown fringes. Edges to wing-coverts, tertials and remiges warm chestnut-brown. Underparts whitish with greyish sides to neck, becoming a light brown wash on flanks. Gorget of small round black spots usually present across lower throat but variable in both size and intensity and absent in some birds. Undertail-coverts dark brown with broad and sharply demarcated white tips.

Juvenile Upperparts and edges to tail feathers, wing-coverts and remiges similar to those of fresh adult. Supercilium as in adult but dull sulphur-yellow. Chin and throat pale primrose-yellow and unmarked. Breast duller olive-yellow, with a band of diffuse mottling, typically broadest towards sides, but sometimes reduced or absent. Upper flanks dull olive-yellow, becoming darker olive-brown on lower flanks and vent. Undertail-coverts olive-brown with conspicuous yellow tips.

Bare parts In breeding adult, upper and lower mandibles are entirely black. In non-breeding birds, upper mandible dark grey with a fine pink cutting edge, lower mandible yellowish at base, otherwise pale pink with slightly darker sides towards tip. Tarsi and toes fleshy pink; claws paler pinkish white. Iris warm brown in adult, grey-brown in immature.

IN HAND CHARACTERS

Measurements

B. d. davidi (1 ♂, 1 ♀): *wing*, ♂ 55, ♀ 51; *tail*, ♂ 44; *bill*, ♂12.7, ♀ 12.5; *tarsus*, ♂ 19.3, ♀ 19.0. (1 ♂): bill width 2.8, tail graduation 19. Also, live wing length 51–57 (52.9; 8) (Round & Loskot 1994).

B. d. suschkini Live data: *wing* 50–55 (53.0; 31); *tail* 43–46 (44.8; 4) (PDR unpublished data).

Structure *B. d. davidi*

Wing formula (n = 2):

p1/pc	p2	p3e	p4e	p5	p6	p7	p10
6–7	5–8	wp	wp	0.5–2	3–4	5	9–10

Wing short and rounded with small p1. Wing point p(3) 4; p2 = p6/7–8/9; emargination on p3–4 only (Round & Loskot 1994).

Figure 16. Wing of Baikal Bush Warbler.

Tail short, strongly graduated; feathers narrower than in Spotted Bush Warbler.
Bill, leg and foot structure as Spotted Bush.
B. d. suschkini As nominate *davidi* but p1 typically shorter, 4–7mm > pc compared to 5.5–8mm in *davidi* (Round & Loskot 1994).

Recognition Brown upperparts less rich and dark than

in Spotted Bush Warbler and underparts less greyish. Distinguished structurally from Spotted Bush by less rounded wing with shorter p1 (Spotted Bush has wing point at p4–5, p5 emarginated and p1 7–11mm > pc). From Chinese Bush Warbler by warmer brown, less olive plumage (especially nominate *davidi*), more contrasting face pattern and shorter tail (< 50mm); in breeding season, also by bold blackish throat spots.

Weight Thailand, 8.9–11.7g (10.1; 32). (PDR unpublished data)

GEOGRAPHIC VARIATION Two races are recognised, which resemble each other.

B. d. davidi (E Siberia south to NE China, with isolated population in C China) Described above.

B. d. suschkini (Siberia from Russian Altai to region of Lake Baikal) Supercilium is marginally paler and distinctly greyer than in nominate *davidi*, also slightly longer and more conspicuous, particularly behind the eye. Ear-coverts are tinged greyer and this sometimes extends as a diffuse greyish collar across the nape. The forehead and crown are warm chestnut-brown with faint narrow darker tips producing a scaly effect. Upperparts, including the fringes to the wing-coverts and edges to the primaries and secondaries, are warm olive-brown, slightly paler and less rich than in the nominate form. The breast and belly are slightly greyer than in the nominate form and the dull buffy-grey flanks less bright. Spotting is variable, but tends to form a diffuse charcoal-grey gorget across the upper breast.

In winter, the upperparts are slightly more drab, dull earth-brown and quite different from the dull reddish brown which nominate *davidi* retains. In addition, greater differences in the underpart colour and patterning become apparent. The lower throat and breast usually develop a paler greyish brown wash, and spotting becomes light and indistinct. It was this non-breeding plumage that was previously associated with the form *shanensis*.

TAXONOMY AND SYSTEMATICS The migratory northern taxa, *davidi* and *suschkini*, were formerly treated as races of Spotted Bush Warbler, which was regarded as a wide-ranging species, breeding from S Siberia to the Himalayas and China. However, song is quite different from that of the Himalayan taxa *kashmirensis*, *thoracicus* and *przevalskii*. Round & Loskot (1994) recommended that they should be treated within a separate species *B. davidi* and we have followed this treatment here. Spotted Bush Warbler is thus recognised as a species breeding exclusively around the western, southern and eastern periphery of the Tibetan Plateau. Northerly breeding Baikal Bush Warbler becomes a separate species with two migratory races, *davidi* and *suschkini*.

An additional form, *shanensis*, was described by Ticehurst (1941) on the basis of a specimen collected in October 1937 at Maymyo, Burma. This form was subsequently recognised as wintering commonly in N Thailand, and Watson *et al.* (1986) suggested it might breed in the mountains of N Burma. However, by comparing plumage, biometrics and song, Round & Loskot (1994) demonstrated that *shanensis* was inseparable from *suschkini,* apparent minor differences being attributable to differences between the non-breeding and breeding plumages of *suschkini*. Consequently, *shanensis* becomes a synonym of *suschkini*.

▲ ▲ Adult *B. d. davidi*, Hebei, China, May. Shows warm brown upperparts, conspicuous pale supercilium, and small blackish spots on lower throat and upper breast, which form distinctive gorget. Male has an entirely black bill during breeding season (Peter Kennerley).

▲ ▲ Adult *B. d. suschkini*, Lake Baikal, Siberia, June. Differs from nominate by slightly paler, less richly toned upperparts, paler and distinctly greyer supercilium, and greyer ear-coverts, side of nape, breast and belly. Throat spotting is variable, typically forming a diffuse dark grey gorget across the upper breast (Paul Leader).

▲ ▲ First-winter *B. d. davidi*, Hong Kong, October. Drabber than adult with poorly defined supercilium, browner breast and lacks spotting on lower throat. Note yellowish-pink base to lower mandible (James Kennerley).

▲ ▲ First-winter *B. d. suschkini*, Chiang Mai, Thailand, January. Resembles first-winter of nominate race but paler and greyer, particularly on sides of breast, and supercilium usually paler and more conspicuous. Typically lacks spotting on lower throat at this time of year but some may show slight trace (Peter Kennerley).

LONG-BILLED BUSH WARBLER
Bradypterus major   Plate 6

Dumeticola major **Brooks, 1872**. *J. Asiatic Soc. Bengal* 41(2): 77. Kashmir.

A poorly known species breeding at high altitude in the W Himalayas in Pakistan and NW India, and in the Kun Lun Mountains in W China. The most range-restricted and least known *Bradypterus* on continental Asia and considered NEAR THREATENED by BirdLife International due to agricultural expansion, overgrazing and destruction of habitat for firewood. Polytypic, with two races recognised:

B. m. major (Brooks, 1872). NW Himalayas from N Pakistan to NW India.
B. m. innae (Portenko, 1955). Kunlun Mountains and W Altun Shan in SW China.

IDENTIFICATION Length 14cm. Wing 54–63mm. Tail/wing 92–107%.

A slim, drab and fairly nondescript warbler with dull mousy brown upperparts and contrasting chestnut-edged tail and wings, but otherwise few distinguishing features which set it apart from other Asian *Bradypterus* species. It most closely resembles Chinese Bush Warbler but is readily separated from this and all other similar species by its repetitive but highly distinctive song. Sexes alike.

Structure The largest of the six *Bradypterus* occurring on the Asian mainland. It also has the longest and finest bill of any of these species, but otherwise shares their general structure, including long and deep undertail-coverts, a heavily graduated tail and distinctly rounded wings. The first primary (p1) extends 4–8mm beyond the primary coverts and the wing point is formed by p4, often together with p3 and p5; these primaries are also emarginated.

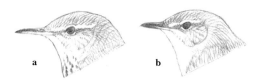

a   b

Figure 17. Comparison of head and bill of (a) Long-billed Bush Warbler and (b) Chinese Bush Warbler.

Plumage and bare parts The head shows a distinctive whitish supercilium extending from the fore-crown to the rear of the ear-coverts. Below this, the lores are pale and unmarked and it lacks a distinct eye-stripe above the pale, faintly mottled ear-coverts. The crown, nape and mantle are dull mouse-brown, the mantle usually slightly warmer than the crown, while the rump and uppertail-coverts are contrastingly warmer and browner. The edges to the primaries and secondaries and the tertial fringes are chestnut-brown and form a warm panel in the closed wing. The tail fringes are also warm chestnut-brown. There is usually a narrow gorget of greyish brown spots across the lower edge of the whitish throat. This is variable, being almost absent on some birds while on others the dark spots extend onto the upper breast. The pale breast and central underparts are washed light peachy buff, while the flanks and undertail-coverts are pale warm buff to olive-buff. The undertail-coverts lack the paler tips shown by Chinese Bush, Baikal Bush and Spotted Bush Warblers.

The juvenile shows a distinctly dull olive-brown tone to the upperparts and is washed pale yellowish below.

The bill is blackish although the lower mandible is fleshy pink towards the base and may be entirely pale in young birds. The legs and feet are deep yellowish pink.

SIMILAR SPECIES Has the most westerly breeding range of the Himalayan *Bradypterus* and is only likely to come into contact with Chinese Bush and Spotted Bush Warblers. The extent of overlap is unknown, particularly outside the breeding season.

Chinese Bush Warbler is a long-distance migrant that may occur alongside Long-billed Bush Warbler during migration and in the winter months, when their ranges are largely unknown. Although similar in proportions it is a smaller bird, with a shorter bill and shorter wings and tail. Its overall appearance and particularly its uniform, dull grey-brown upperparts, resemble those of Long-billed Bush, but it lacks the distinctive chestnut-brown fringes to the wing feathers and tail that the latter shows. Differences in head pattern are probably diagnostic: on Chinese Bush, the supercilium is poorly defined or absent, and the pale lores and fore-supercilium merge with the whitish eye ring to create a plain and pale, open-faced expression. In contrast, Long-billed Bush Warbler has a long pale supercilium, clearly visible behind the eye.

The necklace of spots across the lower throat of Chinese Bush is generally less conspicuous than in Long-billed Bush and is frequently absent, although there may be some overlap in this character as the extent to which this changes outside the breeding season is unknown and it may be absent in both species. Differences in undertail-covert colour and pattern are a further useful feature: on Chinese Bush these are darker brown and broadly tipped pale cream, while on Long-billed Bush Warbler, they appear pale and uniform. While these tips are not as conspicuous in Chinese Bush as those of Baikal Bush and Spotted Bush Warblers, but are often visible on singing birds.

In the hand, Long-billed Bush Warbler is longer-billed, longer-winged and longer-tailed than Chinese Bush. There is no overlap in major measurements and bill length alone is sufficient to distinguish it all the other *Bradypterus* of continental Asia (see **In Hand Characters**).

Spotted Bush Warbler of the western Himalayan race *kashmirensis* is likely to occur within the breeding range of Long-billed Bush. Singing birds are readily separable, the '*trick-he-dee, trick-he-dee...*' song of Spotted Bush being quite different from that of Long-billed Bush (see **Voice**). Silent birds are problematic, particularly if giving only brief views among thick grass and bushy undergrowth. Spotted Bush is significantly smaller and rather more compact than Long-billed Bush, with a proportionately shorter tail and a considerably shorter bill. The rich, dark reddish brown upperparts are much darker than those of Long-billed Bush Warbler and the contrasting greyer ear-coverts are a useful feature. Although both species have a conspicuous supercilium, this is less prominent on Spotted Bush and becomes diffuse behind the eye. Both species show a necklace of spots across the lower throat, but this tends to be larger and more conspicuous on Spotted Bush. The conspicuous broad whitish tips to the dark brown undertail-coverts of Spotted Bush are entirely lacking in Long-billed Bush and this provides the best single separation character. The distinctive buff-bellied morph of *kashmirensis* has no comparable plumage in Long-billed Bush, is distinctly smaller, and they are unlikely to be confused.

VOICE The song is a repetitive two-note, mechanical and insect-like '*pikha, pikha, pikha, pikha...*', given within a frequency range of 4–5kHz. Each phrase is repeated three to four times per second. Song sequences may last just a few seconds or continue without a pause for several minutes. The song carries far in the still mountain air and at long range can sound like a faint '*tik, tik, tik, tik...*', with the descending '*ha*' phrase being inaudible. This distinctive song should preclude confusion with all similar species. It is not known whether the song of the race *innae* differs from that of the nominate form.

Song of Long-billed Bush Warbler recorded within breeding range of *B. m. major*. Naltar Valley, Pakistan, June. (Dave Farrow)

The call is a grating '*trrrr*'.

MOULT No information available.

HABITAT Breeds on open bush- and shrub-covered slopes from 2,400m to the tree line. In the Naltar Valley, Gilgit, Roberts (1992) noted a preference for weedy embankments between terraced cultivation. He recorded it away from cultivation, at 2,400–2,500m, in sheltered glades with thickets of wild gooseberry *Ribes grossularia* on the edge of spruce forest, but it was absent higher up the valley. In the Kaghan Valley, at 2,700–3,050m, it occurs on forest edge with patches of Dwarf Elder *Sambucus ebulus*.

BEHAVIOUR Poorly understood and not known to differ from other *Bradypterus*. It is a skulking bird and most reluctant to fly. When flushed, it flies only a short distance before dropping back into cover. Its presence would be overlooked were it not for the distinctive song given on the breeding grounds. The behaviour is mouse-like as it creeps through the grassy undergrowth. It frequently flicks its wings and tail when nervous.

BREEDING HABITS Information from Kashmir and Ladakh is mainly from Osmaston (1926, 1930) and Koelz (1939) respectively. There are only a few subsequent records; it was reported by Williams & Delaney (1979) from the Suru Valley in Ladakh in July 1977, and by Roberts (1992) from the Naltar Valley, Gilgit. More recent surveys in formerly occupied areas have failed to find singing birds.

The climate on the breeding grounds moderates to give only a brief summer-breeding opportunity. Singing males defend territories from early June onwards and song can still be heard late in July. No dates are available for egg laying but Osmaston (1926) reported nests with unincubated eggs in the Suru valley in early July and Buchanan (1903) found nests with eggs and newly hatched young in the Sind Valley in July. The nest is an untidy structure of dried grasses, usually raised off the ground and situated amongst dense grass at the base of a thorny bush, bramble or honeysuckle. The usual clutch is 3–4 eggs.

DISTRIBUTION
Breeding
B. m. major Known only from the extreme W Himalayan range and appears virtually endemic to the western extremity of the Tibetan Plateau. Breeds at up to 3,300m in Ladakh and Kashmir in NW India and at 2,400m in Gilgit, Pakistan. There are no reports from Chitral, west

of Gilgit, or from elsewhere in Pakistan. Recorded by Bates & Lowther (1952) from the higher slopes on the northern side of the Vale of Kashmir, including the Sind valley between Sonamarg and Baltal. Breeds in the Suru Valley, Ladakh, where it was considered to be common between Kargil and Parkachik (Osmaston 1926, 1930) and recorded at Guntung (Koelz 1939). Reported to be very common in parts of Kashmir by Stuart Baker (1924). The only recent record comes from Sanku in July 1977. It was not found during surveys in 1980 and 1983, raising concerns that the breeding range may be contracting due to habitat destruction caused by changing agricultural practices and overgrazing.
B. m. innae Breeds to the north of the nominate form in the Kun Lun Mountains in the extreme W Xinjiang Uygur Autonomous Region, China, but its current status and range limits here are largely unknown. An extensive search of this region by PJL and GJC in June–July 2003, including a locality where specimens had been collected in the past, failed to locate any birds. Overgrazing had clearly had an adverse impact and most of the suitable habitat had been destroyed. A juvenile recorded from the adjacent E Pamir Mountains of Tajikistan (Flint *et al.* 1984) may indicate that breeding occurs to the north of the established range.

Non-breeding After the breeding season, it is assumed that all birds descend to a more favourable climate in the foothills or plains of northwest India and N Pakistan to avoid severe climatic conditions. Stuart Baker (1924) reported that it 'descended in winter to between 4,000–7,000 feet', but there are no recent reports at this season. A bird photographed near Solan in Himachal Pradesh, India, at an elevation of 1,250m in late September 2004 was outside the known breeding range and may have been a wintering bird.

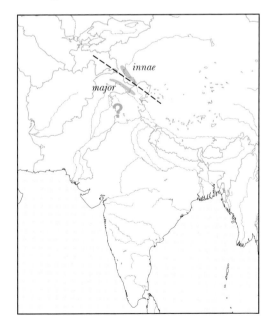

Long-billed Bush Warbler. Breeding range (non-breeding distribution unknown).

MOVEMENTS No information available.

DESCRIPTION *B. m. major*

Plumage – Adult fresh

Forehead to nape uniform dull mousy brown. Supercilium long, narrow but clearly defined, pale creamy buff to creamy white, from bill base, tapering onto sides of nape. Dark loral line fine and variable, sometimes little more than spot in front of the eye. Eye-line cold brown, widening towards rear of ear-coverts. Cheeks and ear-coverts cold brown flecked white, appearing finely mottled or streaked. Whitish eye-ring narrow and poorly defined, upper edge blending with supercilium. Mantle and scapulars dull mouse-brown, slightly warmer than crown. Rump and uppertail-coverts dull chestnut-brown, conspicuously warmer than mantle. Tail feathers dark brown with dull mousy brown fringes. Chin and throat white with a gorget of small black spots across the lower throat; these often extending onto upper breast, becoming larger and forming upward-pointing arrowheads. Upper breast otherwise white, darkening to dull peachy buff across centre of lower breast. Peachy buff wash becoming more intense towards breast sides, darkening to dull ochreous-brown to buffy brown along the flanks and across the ventral region. Belly white, washed dull ochreous-buff. Undertail-coverts uniform ochreous-buff to olive-buff and lack contrasting white tips. Lesser, median and greater coverts dull brown with slightly warmer, brighter fringes. Tertials dark brown with broad, crisply defined chestnut-brown fringes. Secondaries and primaries dull dark brown, broadly edged chestnut-brown, creating a conspicuous chestnut panel in the closed wing. Alula dark brown with contrasting whitish fringe. Underwing-coverts buffy white.

Adult worn Variable. Upperparts and closed wing mousy brown, rather paler, greyer, more uniform than in fresh adult. Underparts silvery white with little or no contrast between throat and breast, buff wash restricted to sides of breast and flanks; undertail-coverts pale buff or whitish. Dark spotting usually remains across the lower throat.

Juvenile Differs from adult in having entire upperparts including crown dull olive-brown; supercilium olive yellow; ear-coverts dull olive-yellow, mottled brown. Underparts washed yellow; palest on chin and throat, dull olive-yellow on breast, usually with dull olive-brown mottling, and paler sulphur-yellow on belly, vent and undertail-coverts.

Bare parts Upper mandible dark grey to black. Lower mandible fleshy pink, usually with darker tip in adult, entirely pale in immature birds. Tarsi and toes deep yellowish pink. Iris pale brown or hazel on specimens from Kashmir.

IN HAND CHARACTERS

Measurements *B. m. major*

	Male	Female
Wing	55–62 (59.0; 32)	54–63 (58.4; 10)
Tail	54–63 (59.0; 30)	55–62 (58.3; 9)
Bill	16.5–18.5 (17.4; 30)	16.5–18 (17.3; 9)
Tarsus	21–23.5 (22.2; 30)	21–22 (21.8; 8)

Sexes combined:
Tail/wing ratio: 92–107% (100%; 43)
Bill width: 3.1–3.5 (3.3; 13)
Hind claw: 5.0–6.2 (5.7; 10)
Tail graduation: 19–25 (23.5; 10)

Structure

Wing formula (n = 10):

p1/pc	p2	p3e	p4e	p5e	p6	p7	p10
4–8	5–10	0–2	wp	0–1	0.5–3	2.5–5	7–11

Wing similar to Spotted Bush Warbler (Fig. 15); short and rounded with small p1. Wing point p4 (5); p2 = p9–10; emargination on p3–5.

Tail longish, strongly graduated; 12 feathers, rather narrow but round-tipped.

Bill long, slender, concave-sided and fine-tipped.

Tarsi stronger than in Spotted Bush or Chinese Bush Warblers; claws rather short and curved.

Recognition Paler than Spotted Bush and Baikal Bush Warblers; rather greyer than Chinese Bush Warbler. Distinguished from all of these by prominent supercilium and plain undertail-coverts. Also by much longer bill (> 16mm) and longer tarsus (> 21mm) and usually by longer wing (> 58mm).

Weight 13g (del Hoyo *et al.* 2006).

GEOGRAPHIC VARIATION Two races occur, which are similar in size and structure. Plumage differences between them appear consistent, with no intergrades documented.

B. m. major (NW Himalayas in N Pakistan and NW India) Described above.

B. m. innae (Kun Lun Mountains, SW China) Generally paler than in the nominate race. The supercilium is white, tinged pale cream, the ear-coverts pale grey with brown tips creating a pale mottled effect. These features give the head a slightly colder, more contrasting appearance than in the nominate form. The upperparts are slightly colder and paler than in nominate *major*, the rump and uppertail-coverts only slightly warmer than the mantle. The entire underparts from chin to undertail-coverts are usually white and unmarked. Some birds may show a faint greyish or greyish brown wash across the breast and light spotting across the lower throat or on the upper breast but, if present, is not as pronounced as in nominate *major*.

TAXONOMY AND SYSTEMATICS A specimen collected in Qinghai Province, China, was described by Stresemann (1931) as a new race of Long-billed Bush Warbler, which he named *Tribura major netrix*. This individual is now recognised as a typical Chinese Bush Warbler.

CHINESE BUSH WARBLER
Bradypterus tacsanowskius   Plate 6

Locustella tacsanowskia **Swinhoe, 1871**. *Proc. Zool. Soc. London.* p. 355. Transbaikalia.

A long-distance migrant that breeds in open woodland and scrub in SE Siberia, N Mongolia, NE China and the eastern edge of the Tibetan Plateau. It winters from Nepal and NE India to N Thailand and Indochina. One of just two *Bradypterus* species with breeding ranges extending north into southern Siberia, the other being Baikal Bush Warbler. Monotypic.

IDENTIFICATION Length 13cm. Wing 53–60mm. Tail/wing 95–105%.

A drab and nondescript warbler with greyish olive-brown upperparts and pale ochre-tinged underparts. Song provides the single most useful identification character, both for locating Chinese Bush Warbler and distinguishing it from similar species. Sexes alike.

Structure A typical *Bradypterus*, similar in size, shape and proportions to Brown Bush and Russet Bush Warblers and proportionately longer tailed than Baikal Bush and Spotted Bush Warblers. It has a long and fine bill, gradually sloping forehead and relatively flat crown, long and deep undertail-coverts and a long, broad and heavily graduated tail. Wing structure is distinctly rounded with the first primary p1 extending 4–8mm beyond the primary coverts and the wing point is formed by p3, sometimes together with p4, both of which are emarginated, sometimes also p5. The primary projection is short, typically 5–6mm, and falls well short of the longest uppertail- and undertail-coverts.

Plumage and bare parts Overall appearance is paler and greyer than other Asian *Bradypterus* except Long-billed Bush Warbler. Shows plain head pattern which lacks a supercilium and eye-stripe, and greyish white lores merge with the eye-ring to form a pale triangular patch in front of the eye. The upperparts from the fore-crown to uppertail-coverts are uniform greyish brown, the tail slightly warmer and browner. The wing-coverts, tertials and edges to the primaries and secondaries show brown fringes, often with a hint of olive, and form a warmer panel on the closed wing.

The underparts are whitish with a strong warm brown wash on the flanks and undertail-coverts. The sandy grey breast can have a distinct ochreous wash, which adults of other Asian *Bradypterus* lack. Adults can sometimes show a necklace of diffuse spots across the lower throat that merge and fade into the upper breast, but are sometimes absent. The warm brown undertail-coverts have paler creamy tips, but these can be poorly defined and lack the clear definition and contrast shown by Baikal Bush, Spotted Bush and Russet Bush Warblers. Observing the undertail-coverts on these species, which skulk close to the ground in thick cover, is a major challenge and the best opportunities are perhaps offered by singing males.

During the breeding season the male has an entirely black bill. At other seasons, the bill is pale grey with a pale yellowish pink lower mandible, becoming slightly darker towards the tip. The legs and feet are dull pink.

SIMILAR SPECIES Breeds sympatrically with Baikal Bush Warbler in S Siberia and with Spotted Bush Warbler on the eastern slopes of the Tibetan Plateau. Its range outside the breeding season is poorly known but it probably occurs alongside these and several closely related *Bradypterus*

species including Russet Bush, Brown Bush and possibly Long-billed Bush Warbler.

Baikal Bush Warbler is sympatric with Chinese Bush Warbler during the breeding season across S Siberia and NE China. In winter, both occur in N Thailand along the Mekong River and probably also in neighbouring E Burma and Laos. Nominate Baikal Bush Warbler is always warmer, browner and more richly coloured than Chinese Bush but birds of the race *suschkini* are dull earth-brown and closer to Chinese Bush in overall upperpart colour, particularly outside the breeding season. Baikal Bush differs from Chinese Bush in its more contrasting head pattern, with an obvious supercilium, dark loral spot and a darker line behind the eye. In the breeding season, Baikal Bush shows a gorget of distinctive black throat spots which Chinese Bush lacks. In winter, however, these spots are indistinct or lacking, reinforcing the apparent resemblance of *suschkini* to Chinese Bush. Undertail-covert patterning provides an extremely reliable means of separating these species. In Baikal Bush, the individual feathers are dark brown with conspicuous broad white tips, giving evenly spaced pale and dark bands or barring, whereas the pale tips in Chinese Bush are shorter, less contrasting and easily overlooked.

Structural distinctions include the proportionately shorter tail of Baikal Bush that gives it a smaller, more compact appearance. On average, Baikal Bush has a slightly shorter wing but there is considerable overlap in measurement and wing structure, although Baikal Bush always lacks an emarginated p5. The song of Baikal Bush resembles that of Chinese Bush, but the buzzing phrases are distinctly higher pitched, shorter, and separated by shorter pauses.

Spotted Bush Warbler is very similar to Baikal Bush, and many of the characters used to distinguish the latter from Chinese Bush Warbler are equally applicable. Spotted Bush of the race *przevalskii* breeds sympatrically with Chinese Bush in the mountains of the NE Tibetan Plateau, but usually at higher altitude. Wintering ranges of Spotted Bush and Chinese Bush probably also overlap in the foothills of the Himalayas. Spotted Bush is considerably darker and richer brown than Chinese Bush. It shows a distinct greyish supercilium and dark greyish sides of the head and breast, which Chinese Bush lacks. Shows gorget of black spots and contrasting pale undertail-covert tips that are also lacking in Chinese Bush.

Song provides the best means of separation, that of Spotted Bush Warbler being a far-carrying and repetitive three note '*trick-i-dee, trick-i-dee, trick-i-dee...*', delivered at approximately one phrase per second, and quite different from the nasal buzzing of Chinese Bush.

Brown Bush Warbler breeds to the south of Chinese Bush, but outside the breeding season both species could occur together in the lowlands of Burma and N Thailand, Laos and S China, although there are few wintering reports of either species from that region. Brown Bush is readily separated by its overall warmer and browner appearance. The entire upperparts are warm tan-brown, lacking the grey and olive tones of Chinese Bush, and the head is remarkably nondescript and featureless apart from a creamy white eye-ring. Underparts are largely white, with warm brown tones restricted to the flanks and undertail-coverts. It lacks throat spotting and noticeable pale tips to the undertail-coverts. Their songs are quite different, that of Brown Bush being a rapid, continuous clicking reel, '*tik, tik, tik, tik, tik...*'.

Long-billed Bush Warbler is not known to overlap with

Chinese Bush but may do so outside the breeding season. It has dull grey-brown upperparts, but differs in having a conspicuous whitish supercilium and uniform pale ochreous-brown undertail-coverts, and its throat spots tend to be more conspicuous. Although similar in proportions to Chinese Bush, Long-billed Bush is substantially larger, with wing length often above 60mm. The distinctive song, a repetitive '*pikha, pikha, pikha, pikha*' is quite different to that of Chinese Bush.

VOICE The song comprises a far-carrying nasal, rasping buzz that can have an almost crackling, electrical quality, while also suggesting the reeling song of the European-breeding *Locustella* warblers. It is lower in pitch than that of Baikal Bush Warbler, within a frequency range of 4–8kHz, but particularly energetic at 5–7kHz. Song sequences are short, usually lasting 1–2 seconds and uttered irregularly at intervals of up to 20 seconds, although pauses are shorter, typically 5–7 seconds. In calm conditions the song carries up to 600m.

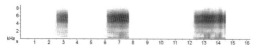

Song of Chinese Bush Warbler, Laoye Shan, Qinghai Province, China, June. (Geoff Carey)

Song of Chinese Bush Warbler, Chita region, Siberia, Russia, June. (Veprintsev 2007)

The call is a soft grating '*chack*'. Other calls occasionally heard include a '*chirr*' or '*thaaa*', uttered rapidly and continuously.

MOULT Little information available. The adult probably has a complete moult in early autumn. A bird trapped in N Thailand in late November was completing moult with p1 and p2 still growing (PDR *in litt.*).

HABITAT Breeds in extensive areas of dense scrub and low bushes in woodland glades and clearings, or in open riverside vegetation adjacent to woodland. In S Siberia, prefers riverside forest with glades and dense bushy undergrowth, but some breed at higher elevations, in dry mountain valleys with scattered scrub. In NW Qinghai Province, China, it is highly localised and restricted by the availability of suitable habitat, much of which is severely degraded due to cutting for firewood and by overgrazing. On the Tibetan Plateau it breeds at higher elevations than in Siberia, up to 2,500m or above. It favours light, open birch and pine woodland with a dense understorey but also breeds at lower density in scattered patches of thorn scrub interspersed with areas of short open grassland.

Wintering birds are believed to frequent dense undergrowth close to wetlands or similar damp localities. In Thailand, it occurs in dense damp grass interspersed with thick scrub and bushes close to the Mekong River (PDR *in litt.*). Stuart Baker (1924) noted that in Burma it frequented paddy fields, stubble and grass.

BEHAVIOUR Extremely skulking and difficult to observe. In fact, this species is so infrequently encountered that almost nothing is known of its behaviour. Song is most frequently heard in the early morning and late evening but often during the night and up to mid morning. Singing birds appear occasionally and can be encouraged into view in calm conditions. Although such appearances are usually fleeting, prolonged views are occasionally given. Identifying a silent bird outside the breeding range is not recommended unless supported by examination in the hand.

BREEDING HABITS It returns to the breeding grounds in late May and early June. Males are believed to commence singing immediately upon arrival and continue until at least mid July, possibly longer. The nest is a neat construction placed on the ground in deep grass at the base of a dense bush or shrub. The usual clutch size is five eggs, but the incubation and fledging periods remain unknown. It is not known whether a second brood is raised but the late arrival on the breeding grounds makes this unlikely.

DISTRIBUTION
Breeding Breeds in the warm steppe-taiga forest region along the southern edge of C and E Siberia and in neighbouring regions of Mongolia and NE China. In Russia, it is believed to range west to *c.* 93°E in the Krasnoyarsk region and along the upper Yenisey River. From here it extends eastwards in a narrow belt, through the Irkutsk region and the southern end of Lake Baikal, into the catchments of the Ussuri and Amur Rivers to the region of Lake Khanka. In Mongolia, it has been recorded breeding in the SW Khangai Mountains in the north and possibly also in the Kentai Mountains in the east, towards the border with China.

In China, it is largely restricted to warmer, drier regions of the north, although even here there are few records. Breeding is regular in Heilongjiang, the Hulun Nur region and Da Hinggan Mountains of the Nei Mongol Autonomous Region and at several localities in NE Qinghai Province, including Laoye Shan, Yao Shui Quan (Yŭo-schüi-tsuăn) and Ma Yi Guo. Further south, there are occasional reports from the mountainous regions of NW Hebei, S Shaanxi, C and N Sichuan and N Yunnan Provinces, although these fall outside the recognised breeding range.

Non-breeding There are very few records outside the breeding season. Limited information suggests the core wintering range may lie in Burma, where it was reported as being 'very common' in Lower Burma by Stuart Baker (1924) and 'not uncommon' in the Sittang Plain (Smythies 1968). But the only additional Burmese record listed by Smythies was of a single bird in the Yoma foothills of Yamethin district. Until recently there was just a single record from Thailand, from the northwest (Lekagul & Round 1991), but in 1996 a bird was trapped in the north in late November at Mae Taeng, followed by several more in December near Chiang Saen, close to the Mekong River (PDR *in litt.*), suggesting that this region may hold a significant wintering population. To the west, it is reported by Rasmussen & Anderton (2005) as fairly common in NW Bengal and in W Assam, India, where recorded in February from the Kaziranga National Park. Not known from Bhutan but wintering apparently extends into the lowland Terai of E Nepal, from where there are late February and March records (Inskipp & Inskipp 1991).

MOVEMENTS There are very few reports of Chinese Bush Warbler on migration. It appears to avoid the coastal regions of S and E China and observations from the wetlands of the lower Yangtze River, Shanghai and Shaweishan have failed to produce any records. La Touche (1925–30) did not record it at Chinwangtao (Qinhuangtao) nor did Hemmingsen

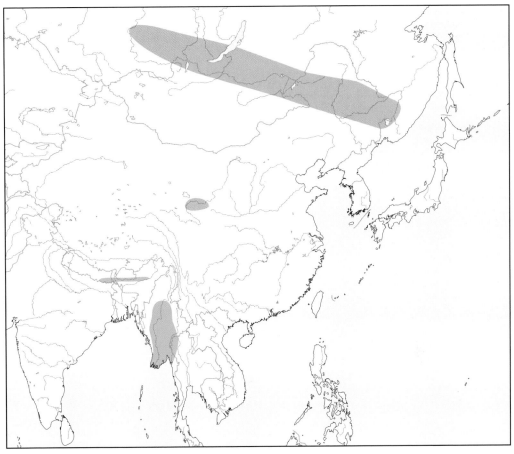

Chinese Bush Warbler. Breeding range and winter distribution.

& Guildal (1968) at Beidaihe in Hebei Province. It has since been reported from Beidaihe, the Yang He River and Happy Island in Hebei Province in late May and from mid to late September. A presumed migrant was collected on 23 August at Pe on the Tsang Po in Tibet (Xizang Autonomous Region).

From this limited data it seems likely that migration to the breeding grounds takes place overland through C and W China with birds spreading to the eastern and western limits of the breeding range and largely avoiding the coastal regions.

DESCRIPTION

Plumage – Adult fresh, breeding

Forehead to nape dull greyish brown. Lores pale sandy grey, forming a pale wedge between the bill base and rear of eye, merging above and below eye with the pale eye-ring. Occasionally shows a poorly defined darker line between bill and eye. No supercilium or eye-line behind the eye, sides of crown merging with uniform grey-brown ear-coverts. Mantle, scapulars, rump and uppertail-coverts unmarked dull greyish brown with faint olivaceous wash, slightly warmer and browner than crown and nape. Tail slightly warmer brown than upperparts, with darker brown shafts and usually showing fine, diffuse barring. Underside of tail dark greyish brown, darker than undertail-coverts.

Chin and throat white, often with an indistinct line of small spots forming a diffuse gorget across lower throat, but usually not extending onto upper breast, although some birds appear entirely unmarked below. Breast buffy brown to pale sandy grey with a slight yellowish or ochre-tinged wash, this appearing strong and conspicuous in some individuals, paler and less obvious in others. Belly white. Flanks grey-brown, darkening and becoming warmer brown posteriorly. Undertail-coverts brown, slightly warmer and darker than flanks and with diffuse but distinctly paler creamy white tips. Closed wing uniform and unmarked. Lesser, median and greater coverts, alula and tertials grey-brown as mantle with narrow, warmer olive-brown fringes. Edges to remiges warm brown, slightly brighter than upperparts, lacking olivaceous wash and appear as a warmer brighter panel. Underwing-coverts pale buff.

Adult, non-breeding Usually lacks spots on lower throat but is otherwise not known to differ from fresh adult.

Juvenile Entire upperparts dull olivaceous-brown, slightly darker, more oily, than those of adult. Pale loral wedge dull sulphur-yellow. Chin, throat and belly dull sulphur-yellow, paler than breast and flanks. Upper breast with dull brown feather tips forming mottled band and darker brown striations at sides, these merging to form a strong ochreous-brown wash on flanks and vent. Undertail-coverts ochreous-brown, slightly paler than lower flanks; longest with indistinct paler tips.

Bare parts Upper and lower mandibles of male black during breeding season. Otherwise, upper mandible pale grey with pink cutting edge. Lower mandible pale yellowish pink at base, becoming pale pink towards tip and with a slightly darker smudge on the sides towards the tip. Mouth yellowish pink. Tarsi and toes dull pink. Iris of adult dark chocolate-brown.

IN HAND CHARACTERS
Measurements

	Male	Female
Wing	53–58 (55.3; 12)	54–60 (55.9; 9)
Tail	52–61 (55.1; 11)	52–60 (56.4; 9)
Bill	13–14.5 (14.0; 10)	13–14 (13.5; 9)
Tarsus	18.5–19.5 (19.1; 12)	18–20 (19.0; 9)

Sexes combined:
Tail/wing ratio: 95–105% (99%; 20)
Bill width: 2.8–3.4 (3.1; 24)
Hind claw: 4.6–7.0 (6.0; 20)
Tail graduation: 19–25 (22.1; 15)

Structure

Wing formula (n = 11):

p1/pc	p2	p3e	p4e	p5(e)	p6	p7	p10
4–8	5–7	wp	0–0.5	0–1	1.5–3	3–5	8–9.5

Wing short and rounded with small p1. Wing point p3–4 (5); p2 = p7–9; emargination on p3–4, usually also on p5.

Figure 18. Wing of Chinese Bush Warbler.

Tail long, strongly graduated, with 12 broad rounded feathers (Fig. 19).

Bill small and narrow, concave-sided with fine tip.

Tarsi slender; toes long and slender with small, weakly curved claws.

Recognition More olive-toned and with a plainer head than other *Bradypterus* with which likely to occur. Paler than all

except Long-billed Bush Warbler, which has a prominent supercilium and much longer bill (> 16mm). Distinguished from Baikal Bush and Spotted Bush Warblers by longer tail (> 52mm); and from Spotted Bush, Brown Bush and Long-billed Bush Warblers by having wing point at p3–4 rather than p4–5. Usually shows emargination on p5 unlike Baikal Bush Warbler.

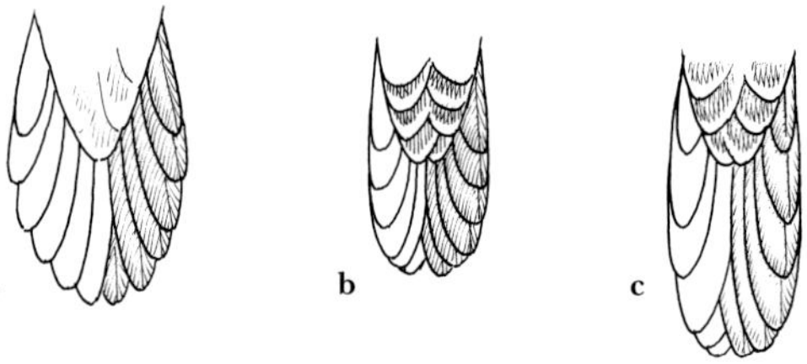

a　　　　　　　　b　　　　　　　c

Figure 19. Comparison of tail shape and undertail-covert pattern of (a) Chinese Bush Warbler (b) Spotted Bush Warbler and (c) Russet Bush Warbler.

Weight Range 9.8–12.4g (11.4: 7) (PDR unpublished data).

GEOGRAPHIC VARIATION None recorded but see **Taxonomy and Systematics**.

TAXONOMY AND SYSTEMATICS Appears to show no regional variation but two additional races have been described in the past. Based on a specimen collected by Beick on 13 July 1930 at Yüo-schüi-tsuän, birds breeding in N Qinghai were considered to be a race of Long-billed Bush Warbler and named *Tribura major netrix* by Stresemann (1931). It was subsequently realised that these were Chinese Bush Warblers and they are now considered synonymous with the nominate form.

In addition, a bird collected on 24 June 1931 at Yaoschan (Yao Shan), Guangxi Province, China, was described by Yen (1933) as a new subspecies of Chinese Bush Warbler, which he named *Tribura tacsanowskia chui*. It has not been possible to examine this specimen, which Yen described as being 'slightly darker than nominate *tacsanowskius*, but with the throat, breast and centre of the belly whiter, less rusty and the flanks rustier and less olive' stating it to be appreciably smaller than nominate *tacsanowskius*, approaching the size of Baikal Bush Warbler.

Regular surveys of the hills and forests throughout southern China since 1984, including a survey of the Yao Shan in June 1994, failed to locate any *Bradypterus* (Lewthwaite 1996). Brown Bush and Russet Bush Warblers occur widely throughout the hill ranges of S China and Russet Bush Warbler is known from the Yao Shan. Without access to comparative material from S China, it seems likely that Yen concluded that his bird was unique, rather than belonging to the more widespread Russet Bush Warbler. Until this specimen is located, its identity remains uncertain.

▲ Adult, Khentii Province, Mongolia, June. Rarely ventures away from thick cover except when singing; this exceptional photograph captures the character of this skulking species well. Overall appearance quite variable, and none of the five individuals in these photographs are alike. Note fairly conspicuous pale supercilium, and underparts that are slightly paler than the upperparts. The pale bill suggests this is a female (Sundev Gombobaatar).

▲ Adult, Tuv Province, Mongolia, June. An exceptionally uniform individual, lacking contrast between the upperparts and underparts, and no spots on lower throat. Black bill suggests this is a male (Sundev Gombobaatar).

▲ Adult, Hebei, China, May. Shows particularly dark brown upperparts with little contrast between the upperparts and flanks. Note short pale supercilium only extending to rear of eye, pale line below eye and dark loral spot, giving a distinctive 'pointed' appearance to the lores, which all birds share (Jens Søgaard Hansen).

▲ Adult, Qinghai, China, June. Birds from the eastern edge of the Tibetan Plateau show slightly paler, greyish brown upperparts and the sandy grey breast often shows a slight ochreous wash. Males from this region often show a band of small spots across the lower throat, seemingly absent on most Mongolian birds. Pale base to lower mandible is indicative of a female (Peter Kennerley).

▲ ▶ Adult, Gun Galuut, Mongolia, June. Note plain, unmarked appearance. Underparts show extensive drab brown wash to breast and flanks that contrast with paler throat. Fresh body plumage contrasts with worn and faded primary tips, suggesting this was replaced in a late winter moult, whereas the older primaries were presumably replaced the previous autumn in a complete moult (Jyrki Normaja).

BROWN BUSH WARBLER
Bradypterus luteoventris   **Plate 6**

Tribura luteoventris **Hodgson, 1845.** *Proc. Zool. Soc. London:* 30. Nepal.

A skulking warbler, breeding in tall grass and dwarf bamboo above the tree line from the E Himalayas to E China, with some descending to sea level outside the breeding season. In the past, this species and Russet Bush Warbler were treated as races of *B. luteoventris*, making the historical published accounts on the distribution of this species difficult to interpret. Monotypic.

IDENTIFICATION Length 13cm. Wing 49–57mm. Tail/wing 100–118%.

A small and nondescript warbler with warm brown upperparts, lightly washed paler brown across the breast and with a whitish belly, unmarked undertail-coverts and unspotted lower throat. Four similar *Bradypterus* species occur within its range; Russet Bush and Spotted Bush Warblers as breeding species, and Baikal Bush and Chinese Bush Warblers during the winter months. If seen well it can be distinguished from all of these by its unmarked throat and plain undertail-coverts, while its distinctive 'clacking reel' song separates it readily from Russet Bush and Spotted Bush Warblers. Sexes alike.

Structure Shows the short wings, strongly graduated tail, flat crown and short bill typical of Asian *Bradypterus*. Similar in structure to Russet Bush and Chinese Bush Warblers but appears longer tailed than Spotted Bush and Baikal Bush Warblers. The tail is similar in length to the wing, averaging slightly shorter than in Russet Bush Warbler. The wing is short and rounded. It has a long first primary (p1), extending 6–11mm beyond the primary coverts, much longer and wider than p1 on Chinese Bush Warbler but overlapping with Russet Bush Warbler. The wing point is formed by p4–5 and p3–5 are emarginated.

Plumage and bare parts Shows the most warmly toned upperparts of the Asian mainland *Bradypterus*. The entire upperparts are uniform warm brown, with little or no contrast between the mantle and scapulars, the centres and fringes of the tertials and wing-coverts and the centres and edges of the flight feathers. The plain, almost unmarked head adds to this nondescript appearance, a narrow, pale buff eye-ring being the most conspicuous feature. A faint supercilium reaches only to the rear of the eye, barely contrasting with the crown and lores. The unmarked and uniformly warm brown lores tend to merge with the forehead and there is no hint of a contrasting eye-stripe. The ear-coverts are slightly darker but show minimal contrast with the nape and crown. The creamy white chin and throat contrast with a warm sandy brown wash across the breast and warm tan breast sides and flanks. During the breeding season it lacks the necklace of fine spotting on the lower throat and upper breast shown by other Asian mainland *Bradypterus*. The belly is silky white and the undertail-coverts contrastingly warm tan-brown to greyish brown, appearing uniform and lacking the pale tips prominent on most mainland *Bradypterus*.

The bill is black above, with an unmarked pinkish yellow lower mandible, sometimes darker towards the tip. The legs and feet are pinkish grey to plumbeous-grey.

SIMILAR SPECIES With its warm brown upperparts, lack of throat spotting and uniform undertail-coverts,

Brown Bush Warbler is actually one of the most readily recognisable *Bradypterus*. With care it can be separated from all the mainland species if these features can be seen.

Russet Bush Warbler overlaps with Brown Bush Warbler throughout its range although they are usually separated by altitude during the breeding season, Brown Bush breeding above the tree line and Russet Bush below it. Both species do, however, occur together, particularly outside the breeding season when they descend to lower elevations. Each has a distinctive and diagnostic song which provides the easiest means of separation, that of Russet Bush being a characteristic, far-carrying repetitive ' *cree-ut, cree-ut, cree-ut...*' or ' *zreee-ut* or *zreee-ut...*'. Otherwise, Russet Bush differs in its considerably darker and duller appearance with uniform, russet-brown upperparts and a greyer breast, which Brown Bush never shows. During the breeding season, it usually shows a gorget of fine spots across the lower throat and upper breast but these tend to be absent in winter, especially in first-winter birds. It also has dark greyish brown undertail-coverts with conspicuous, broad pale tips and, although this feature may be difficult to observe, once seen it is sufficient to rule out Brown Bush.

Chinese Bush Warbler may occur alongside Brown Bush Warbler outside the breeding season from the E Himalayas to Burma and northernmost Thailand, although this has not been firmly established. Separation of these species relies on the distinctly colder, greyer brown appearance of the upperparts of Chinese Bush, especially on the crown and nape. It shows a sandy grey wash across the upper breast, often tinged faintly ochre or yellow, and sandy grey to grey-brown flanks; quite different from the whiter breast and warm tan-washed flanks of Brown Bush. The colour and pattern of the undertail-coverts also differs; in Chinese Bush these are mid brown with broad pale but diffuse creamy tips, while on Brown Bush they are warmer brown and lack paler tips. Chinese Bush develops an indistinct gorget of small throat spots before breeding but it is uncertain whether this is retained throughout the year. Some birds, probably in their first-year, certainly lack this feature in winter. Neither Chinese Bush or Brown Bush Warbler are known to sing outside the breeding season and their calls are not well understood and, at present, of little use in their separation.

VOICE The song is a quiet but very distinctive reeling that may carry for 100m or more across open, windswept summits on the breeding ground. It is a rapid, continuous clacking reel, ' *tik, tik, tik, tik, tik...*', with approximately ten notes delivered per second, the pause between each ' *tik*' note being sufficient to perceive it as distinct from the previous one. Individual phrases cover a range of 2–6kHz, although the rapid delivery creates the impression of constancy in pitch, tone and speed of delivery. It has a noticeable ventriloquial quality as the singing bird turns its head, sounding nearby at times and quite distant at others. Song may continue without pause for several minutes and can be heard at any time during daylight hours but it is uncertain whether it is given at night. It is reminiscent of the 'reeling' of European *Locustella* warblers and has also been likened to the sound of a fishing reel being wound. There is much individual variation, some songs sounding distinctly higher pitched than others, but it seems that no regional differences are involved.

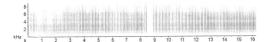

Song of Brown Bush Warbler, Wu Yi Shan, Fujian Province, China, June. (Geoff Carey)

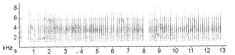

Song of Brown Bush Warbler, Gantey La, Bhutan, April. (Peter Kennerley)

A variety of calls are attributed to Brown Bush Warbler but whether all are from this skulking species is difficult to establish. Those regularly heard include a soft, rapidly repeated '*chut, chut*' and an occasional rasping, grating '*tchrrrrk*' and it is also reported to give a sharp, high-pitched '*tink, tink, tink...*' and a harsh '*tchack, tchack, tchack*'.

MOULT No data available.

HABITAT During the breeding season, it occurs above the tree line where it occupies extensive tracts of tall grass and dwarf bamboo, typically 1–2m in height. Here it prefers gentle slopes rather than steep hillsides. There is often a scattering of emergent bushes and shrubs and the occasional tree within breeding territories. It breeds up to 3,300m in the eastern Himalayas and mountains of W China, but lower if suitable habitat is available. In eastern China, in the isolated hill ranges of Guangdong and Fujian Provinces it is restricted to the highest summits and upper slopes above 1,900m. Here, the few trees are low and windswept and barely exceed the height of the bamboo, so that the habitat mimics that found over 1,000m higher in the Himalayas and W China.

Usually separated altitudinally from Russet Bush Warbler, the latter breeding on bushy slopes 500m or more below the lower level at which Brown Bush occurs. In view of past confusion with Russet Bush Warbler, historical reports of Brown Bush Warblers breeding below the tree line should be viewed with caution and if the song is not described, the identification has been assumed to be unproven. Reports of Brown Bush Warbler breeding in bushes, bracken and grass in pine forest at 1,200–1,600m in the Khasi Hills, Meghalaya, India, (Ali & Ripley 1973) probably refer to Russet Bush Warbler. Outside the breeding season it has been recorded in winter in Hong Kong alongside Russet Bush Warbler in thick rank grassland with occasional scattered trees and bushes in a broad secluded valley at *c.* 200m.

BEHAVIOUR Skulking and difficult to observe unless singing. Virtually nothing is known of behaviour outside the breeding season. When seen in the open, it is particularly nervous, adopting a horizontal posture while scurrying mouse-like across or near the ground between bushes.

Singing males are more visible, clinging near the top of a tall grass stem. They typically sing half hidden on top of a swathe of wind-blown bamboo, with just the head and upper body visible, showing a determination to remain there regardless of how hard the wind tries to displace them. They adopt a vertical posture, with the tail held vertically downwards and the bill slightly above the horizontal, while the head is rotated from side to side. The mandibles remain open throughout the song sequence in the manner of the European *Locustella* warblers. Song is most intense during

early morning and evening, but up to early July activity is little diminished during the middle of the day. Singing birds occasionally emerge from cover and may even run around on the ground, unconcerned by the presence of observers. The wings are then drooped by the flanks and flicked rapidly and repeatedly across the back, while the tail is held slightly raised. Unlike Russet Bush Warbler, this species has not been reported to sing during the winter months.

BREEDING Due to past confusion with Russet Bush Warbler, there are no accurate breeding data. Singing males occupy breeding territories from late April onwards in Bhutan and from mid May in SE China, where they remain up to at least the end of August.

DISTRIBUTION Poorly understood. Most records published prior to 1952 do not differentiate between Brown Bush and Russet Bush Warblers so that specific distributions are difficult to unravel retrospectively. Only where there are specimens of Brown Bush Warbler, or references to the distinctive song, has it been possible to determine its historical distribution. With more observers becoming familiar with the song in recent years, the breeding range has become better understood.

Breeding Breeds widely throughout the E Himalayas, in the hills of W China and, locally, into S and E China. Recorded from Nepal by Hodgson, who obtained specimens from the northern hills in the nineteenth century (Inskipp & Inskipp 1991) but there are no reliable subsequent records and it is believed to be extirpated there (CI *in litt.*). It breeds in Darjeeling and Bhutan, where it is localised and considered a rare resident (Spierenburg 2005) but it is possibly overlooked, since at least ten singing birds were heard in dwarf bamboo at *c.* 3,000m on Gantey La, Bhutan, in April 2002 (PRK pers. obs.). Local and scarce through the E Indian states, including Arunachal Pradesh, Meghalaya, Assam, Nagaland and possibly Manipur. In the Chin Hills, W Burma, it is reportedly common in March and April on Mount Victoria from 2,135–2,745m and was heard singing near Mindat and at Ramhtlo (Robson *et al.* 1998). Earlier reports from the Chin Hills and N Burma (Smythies 1968) do not preclude confusion with Russet Bush Warbler.

In W China, it breeds in the mountains of SE Tibet (Xizang Autonomous Region) and adjacent parts of N Yunnan Province, but is unrecorded from the higher mountains to the south in Xishuangbanna. Singing birds occur widely in Sichuan Province, including the summit regions of Emei Shan and Bau Mu Ping below Ba Long Shan, where it overlaps with Spotted Bush Warbler. Further east, the range is fragmented and restricted to higher peaks in isolated hill ranges south of the Yellow River (Huang Ho). Known breeding areas include the Qinling Shan in Shaanxi Province, Luoshan in Henan Province and Huangshan in Anhui Province. There are localised records from Hubei, Hunan and Guizhou Provinces but some of these may be erroneous due to confusion with Russet Bush Warbler. In SE China, it is restricted to summit regions above 1,900m and known only from Ba Bao Shan in Guangdong Province and Wu Yi Shan in Fujian Province (Lewthwaite (1996), although it may be more widespread since much of this region is poorly known.

Non-breeding Due to its elusive behaviour, its distribution in winter is also poorly understood. It was stated to winter in the foothills of the Himalayas (Ripley 1982) but there are no winter records from Nepal, Bhutan or India. It probably occurs locally from the E Himalayan foothills to the coastal hills of SE China. A specimen collected by Smythies at

1,500m in the S Chin Hills in Burma on 5 December 1938 was presumably a wintering bird. From China, the only winter records are from Hong Kong: three individuals were trapped at Sha Lo Tung in the NE New Territories, on 25 January 1992, 3 December 1994 and 18 November 1995 and single birds were seen there on 26 October and 4 November 1995, as well as two on 25 November 1995 (Carey *et al.* 2001). It would seem unlikely that the small breeding population at Bao Bo Shan in N Guangdong Province could account for so many records in one locality and it is likely that undiscovered breeding populations occur more widely across S China than is currently believed and that these winter throughout the hill ranges fringing the Guangdong coastline.

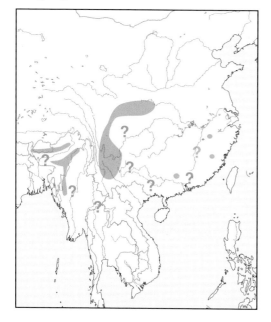

Brown Bush Warbler. Breeding range and non-breeding distribution.

MOVEMENTS An altitudinal migrant that leaves the higher breeding grounds during the northern winter. There are no definite reports of birds on migration and little is known of its timing or direction. The Hong Kong records span the period 26 October to 25th January and may include passage birds as well as wintering individuals. Inskipp & Inskipp (1991) mention single birds in a reedbed at Sukla Phanta, Nepal, on 4–5 May, which could have either been wintering or on passage.

DESCRIPTION
Plumage – Adult fresh
Forehead to nape warm brown. Supercilium narrow and indistinct, buffy brown, fading immediately behind eye, merging with unmarked warm brown lores. Ear-coverts warm brown, slightly darker than crown but showing no discernible eye-line. A narrow pale buff eye-ring, contrasting slightly with side of head. Mantle, scapulars, rump and uppertail-coverts unmarked warm brown, concolorous with crown. Tail slightly darker than uppertail-coverts, with distinctly darker feather shafts. Chin, throat and belly silky-white, sometimes with faint creamy wash. Centre of breast white, lightly tinged warm sandy brown. Sides of breast and

upper flanks rich sandy brown, darkening slightly to warm fulvous-brown on lower flanks and vent. Undertail-coverts uniform warm fulvous-brown. Lesser, median and greater coverts warm brown, lacking contrasting darker centres. Primary coverts and tertials with slightly darker brown centres and broad, warm brown fringes. Secondaries and primaries with warm brown edges, the darker brown webs not visible unless the wing is spread. Alula grey-brown with pale sandy brown fringe to outer web. The closed wing thus presents a uniform appearance. Underwing-coverts tawny-buff.

Adult, worn Not known to differ from the fresh adult.
Juvenile Upperparts and closed wing warm brown, similar to those of fresh adult. Chin and throat white, strongly washed cream or pale yellow. Breast pale yellow, heavily tipped warm brown, creating a broad, mottled band extending from lower throat to upper belly. Sides of breast, flanks, vent and undertail-coverts washed warm brown to fulvous-brown, unmarked. Belly white with faint yellowish wash.
Bare parts Upper mandible dark grey to black with thin yellow cutting edge. Lower mandible pinkish yellow and unmarked, but during breeding season sometimes slightly greyer at sides towards tip. Tarsi, toes and claws pinkish grey to plumbeous grey. Iris dark brown, but not known whether colour changes with age.

IN HAND CHARACTERS
Measurements

Sexes combined:

Wing	49–57 (52.7; 55)
Tail	51–62 (56.9; 52)
Bill	12.4–14.5 (13.3; 52)
Tarsus	17.5–20 (19.1; 45)

Tail/wing ratio: 100–118% (108%; 51)
Bill width: 2.8–3.2 (3.0; 9)
Hind claw: 5.2–6.8 (5.9; 18)
Tail graduation: 25–29 (26.6; 16)

Structure

Wing formula (n = 10):

p1/pc	p2	p3e	p4e	p5e	p6	p7	p10
6–11	6–9	0.5–1	0–0.5	wp	0.5–1.5	1–3	4.5–7

Wing structure as Russet Bush Warbler (Fig. 20); short and rounded with fairly small p1. Wing point p(4) 5; p2 = p10 to < ss tips; emargination on p3–5.

Tail longish, broad-based, strongly graduated; 12 feathers, quite broad and rounded (less narrow at tip than in Russet Bush Warbler; t1 10–11mm wide).

Bill straight, narrow and concave-sided, slightly finer-tipped than in Russet Bush.

Tarsi and toes slender; claws small and weakly curved.
Recognition Separated from similar Russet Bush Warbler by unspotted whitish throat, whitish or buffy breast without grey tinge and brighter tawny-buff flanks and undertail-coverts, the latter without distinctly paler tips. Bill finer at tip, with lower mandible pale (usually blackish at tip in Russet Bush). On wing, p3 usually only 0.5–1mm shorter than p4 (usually 1.5–3mm shorter in Russet Bush). Tail/wing ratio usually < 1.1 (usually > 1.1 in Russet Bush).

Distinguished from Chinese Bush Warbler by warmer coloration and by more rounded wing (Chinese Bush has wing point at p3–4 and often lacks emargination on p5). From Baikal Bush Warbler by more rounded wing and much longer tail.

Weight Range 11.8–13.2g (n = 3) (Dunning 2007; HKRG unpublished data).

GEOGRAPHIC VARIATION None recorded but see **Taxonomy and Systematics** below.

TAXONOMY AND SYSTEMATICS Prior to 1952, Brown Bush and Russet Bush Warbler were treated as races of a single species, *B. luteoventris and* no serious attempts were made to distinguish them, resulting in many specimens being incorrectly labelled. In his major work on Bush Warblers, Delacour (1952) recognised the distinction between the paler *B. luteoventris*, which he treated as a monotypic species and the darker *B. mandelli* (= *B. seebohmi*), which he recognised as a polytypic species incorporating four races.

Within Brown Bush Warbler, the form *saturatus* was described by Ticehurst (1941) on the basis of a specimen from W Burma. It was subsequently renamed *B. l. ticehursti* by Deignan (1943) as the name *saturatus* was already assigned. The upperparts of this bird are described as 'mummy-brown'* instead of rufous-brown and the flanks and undertail-coverts are said to lack the rufous tinge of *luteoventris*'. However, the upperparts, flanks and undertail-coverts of typical *luteoventris* also lack rufous coloration, implying perhaps that Ticehurst was comparing the *ticehursti* specimen with *B. mandelli* (= *B. seebohmi*), at that time considered a race of *B. luteoventris*. A further report of *ticehursti* came from a single specimen from N Thailand, but recent examination shows this to be a dark *mandelli* (Dickinson *et al.* 2000). The race *ticehursti* is no longer considered valid.

* Mummy-brown was a pigment made from the ground-up remains of Egyptian mummies, both human and feline, white pitch and Myrrh. Since it contained ammonia and particles of fat, it was likely to affect other colours that it was used with, and its composition and quality varied considerably. It was popular in the sixteenth and seventeenth centuries and continued to be produced until the early years of the twentieth century when the supply of mummies ran out.

▲ Adult, Wu Yi Shan, Fujian, China, May. Singing males often emerge from dense grass or dwarf bamboo and sit on a prominent perch, particularly when other males are singing nearby (Pete Morris).

▲ ▶ Adult, Hong Kong, January. Has the most uniform appearance of any *Bradypterus*. Upperparts warm brown, becoming a less saturated warm tan on flanks and warm sandy brown on breast. Lacks supercilium and eye-stripe, has pale, unmarked lores, and lacks spotting on throat or breast (Paul Leader).

RUSSET BUSH WARBLER
Bradypterus mandelli   **Plate 7**

Dumeticola mandelli **Brooks, 1875**. *Stray Feathers,* 3(4): 284-287. Sikkim.

The most wide-ranging of the Asian *Bradypterus*, breeding from the E Himalayas to E China and the N Indochinese countries, where it is largely resident although some undertake altitudinal migration to coastal regions. The identification and taxonomy of Russet Bush Warbler and closely related island taxa is complex but was recently revised by Dickinson *et al.* (2000), who advocated that four island forms are better treated as distinct species. This recommendation has been adopted and three races of Russet Bush Warbler are recognised, with a distribution restricted to the Asian mainland.

B. m. mandelli (Brooks, 1875) Himalayan foothills of N India from Darjeeling to E Arunachal Pradesh and N Burma.

B. m. melanorhynchus (Rickett, 1898) Hills of S China from C Sichuan east to Fujian and south to S Guangdong and Hong Kong.

B. m. idoneus (Riley, 1940) Da Lat Plateau, S Annam, Vietnam.

IDENTIFICATION Length 13–14cm. Wing 49–57mm. Tail/wing 105–122%.

An exceptionally drab and nondescript warbler with rich, dark russet-brown upperparts and flanks, pale-tipped undertail-coverts and, in breeding adults, a grey breast with small blackish spots extending across the lower throat and sometimes onto the upper breast. Best located and identified by its distinctive song, a repetitive series of nasal buzzing notes. Sexes alike.

Structure Shows a fairly flat crown with a shallow sloping forehead, a slender body with a long and graduated tail and long, deep undertail-coverts. The wings are short and rounded, with the first primary (p1) extending up to 11mm beyond the primary coverts and the wing point falling at p4–5. The tip of the closed wing reaches only to the base of the uppertail-coverts, which reinforces the long-tailed appearance. The bill is fairly broad and deep based and appears proportionately heavier than in other mainland *Bradypterus*.

Plumage and bare parts The entire upperparts including wings and tail are uniform, dull russet-brown. Even the head is poorly marked, with just a faint greyish white supercilium above the lores but not reaching behind the eye. There is no hint of an eye-stripe and the ear-coverts are russet-brown, matching the tone of the crown and nape. On the underparts, most birds in China show an extensive grey wash to the breast, but on Himalayan birds these greyer tones are less obvious and replaced with warmer and less contrasting greyish brown. However, young birds in China can also lack the greyer tone to the breast so this feature cannot be used to assign individuals to race outside the breeding season. Following the pre-breeding body moult, a variable and sometimes quite conspicuous gorget of dark spots develops along the upper breast, with smaller and less obvious spots extending onto the lower edge of the throat. The sides of the breast, flanks and ventral region are drab russet-brown, similar to the upperparts in colour, while the belly is greyish white. Undertail-covert pattern in *Bradypterus* is an important diagnostic feature and in Russet Bush Warbler these are dark greyish brown and the

longest show broad buffy white to greyish white tips, which contrast against the grey underside of the tail and russet-brown ventral region.

In the breeding adult, the bill is entirely black, but outside the breeding season the lower mandible becomes paler yellowish pink to greyish pink with darker shading at the sides towards the tip. The legs and feet are dull plumbeous-pink.

SIMILAR SPECIES Within its range on mainland Asia, Russet Bush Warbler may occur alongside Brown Bush Warbler throughout the year and with Chinese Bush, Spotted Bush and Baikal Bush Warblers outside the breeding season. Of these species, Brown Bush most closely resembles Russet Bush Warbler in appearance but the two are readily separated during the breeding season by their distinctive songs. The remaining species differ from Russet Bush Warbler in structure, morphology and vocalisations, but actually seeing any of these species in the wintering areas sufficiently well to establish the identification is challenging.

Brown Bush Warbler occurs sympatrically with Russet Bush Warbler throughout much of its range, but usually breeds at higher elevations so there is little overlap during the summer. Outside the breeding season, they are more likely to occur together at lower elevations and have been trapped almost simultaneously at the same location in Hong Kong. Their distinctive songs provide the single best means of separation, that of Brown Bush being a continuous clacking reeling '*tik, tik, tik, tik, tik...*', with approximately ten phrases per second. Silent birds are more challenging. Both species show a plain, unmarked head, but Brown Bush has considerably paler and warmer brown upperparts and paler underparts. The breast is also warm brown, lacking the grey tone of Russet Bush and shows no trace of spotting, even in the breeding season. The undertail-coverts always lack the pale tips characteristic of Russet Bush Warbler.

In structure, Brown Bush is slightly shorter-tailed than Russet Bush. It has a shorter, narrower and finer bill with a yellowish lower mandible, whereas in Russet Bush the lower mandible is entirely black during the breeding season, becoming largely yellowish pink in winter.

Spotted Bush and **Baikal Bush Warblers** closely resemble each other and share many characters with Russet Bush Warbler. In fact, these species have been thoroughly confused with Russet Bush Warbler in the past, mistakenly extending the breeding range of Spotted Bush Warbler into E China. The breeding range of Russet Bush Warbler is sympatric with that of Spotted Bush Warbler from Bhutan east to Sichuan and overlap between the two is known to occur, at least occasionally, outside the breeding season, e.g. at Hong Kong. The songs of these three species are quite distinct and completely diagnostic, and calls may also be of useful in their separation (see **Voice**).

Both species share features with Russet Bush Warbler, including russet-brown upperparts, greyish underparts, long and pale-tipped undertail-coverts and a strongly graduated tail. All three species have a necklace of dark spots across the lower throat during the breeding season. The best distinction lies in the colour and pattern of the underparts. During the breeding season, Spotted Bush shows greyish sides to the head (browner in Russet Bush) and the breast is washed extensively grey (usually more restricted grey to greyish brown in Russet Bush, darkening to rusty brown on the lower flanks). During the breeding season, Spotted Bush and Baikal Bush Warblers tends to show larger, darker and more extensive throat spotting.

In the hand, Spotted Bush and Baikal Bush Warblers are shorter-tailed and longer-winged than Russet Bush, giving a very different tail/wing ratio.

VOICE The song comprises a series of repeated nasal buzzing notes, variously described as '*cree-ut, cree-ut, cree-ut...*' (Smythies 1986), '*zreee-ut, zreee-ut, zreee-ut...*' or '*zree-ut, zree-ut, zree-ut...*' (Round 1983) or '*zee-bit, zee-bit, zee-bit...*' (Kennerley & Leader 1993). Notes are delivered at approximately two per second and song sequences may continue for 20 seconds or longer. Pitch and delivery varies between individuals, within a frequency range of 4–6kHz, although this may be attributable to individual sequence than consistent regional variation. Examination of sonograms reveals that an individual sequence of the song of *melanorhynchus* contains a greater number of elements, up to 40, compared with about 24 in nominate *mandelli*, giving the former its more buzzing quality. To the human ear, this difference is barely perceptible, the slightly longer buzzing section to the song of *melanorhynchus* being difficult to discern. It is uncertain whether analysis of sound recordings is a reliable means of separating the races and further investigation is required.

Song of Russet Bush Warbler, recorded within breeding range of *B. m. mandelli*, Trongsa, Bhutan, April. (Peter Kennerley)

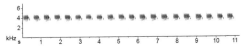

Song of Russet Bush Warbler, recorded within winter range of *B. m. melanorhynchus*, Sha Lo Tung, Hong Kong, China, March. (Geoff Carey)

The song of the isolated race *idoneus* on the Da Lat Plateau, South Annam, Vietnam, differs slightly from that of the other two races. Although the repetitive structure and delivery of the song are very similar, with approximately one note per second followed by a brief pause, it has a rattling and piercing quality rather than the nasal buzzing quality apparent in the songs of the other two forms.

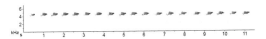

Song of Russet Bush Warbler, recorded within breeding range of *B. m. idoneus*, Cong Troi, Da Lat Plateau, South Annam, Vietnam, January. (Craig Robson)

Calls include an explosive '*pwit*' and a rapid, rasping series of notes '*tink-tink-tink-tink-tink-tink*' (Round 1992). Another call, given by foraging birds, resembles the soft '*quip*' call of Radde's Warbler.

MOULT No data available.

HABITAT During the breeding season, it frequents degraded upland grasslands, grass-covered hillsides, thickets of scrub and bushes in young secondary growth and agricultural margins, and similar open habitats with rank undergrowth. This naturally uncommon habitat has expanded greatly due to upland forest clearance, especially

across S and E China in the later twentieth century and it appears that Russet Bush Warbler has expanded its range to utilise new areas of suitable habitat. In Bhutan, it avoids the extensive forest that covers much of the country but breeds in open scrub adjacent to forest and also in thick scrub by open cultivated plots, sometimes close to human habitation (PRK pers. obs.).

Outside the breeding season, it occurs in rank and overgrown habitats similar to those used when breeding but may be present at lower elevations. For example, in Hong Kong, it has been recorded from *c.* 1,000m down to sea level, with most records below 250m and exceptionally, one was trapped for ringing in a *Phragmites* reedbed at sea level.

BEHAVIOUR This is an elusive species that frequents dense undergrowth and rarely remains visible for more than a few seconds, so there are no detailed accounts of behaviour. Males rarely sing in the open and the distinctive '*cree-ut*' song is typically delivered from deep within thick cover. However, a singing bird may remain visible for several minutes when coaxed into view. Males sing throughout the day, although activity appears greatest in the early morning and late evening and erratic and occasional at other times. They do not appear to sing at night. It exhibits typical mouse-like *Bradypterus* behaviour, rarely flying and preferring to walk through thick grasses. Consequently, it is exceptionally difficult to catch as it will frequently walk under a mist-net rather than fly into it. Other aspects of its behaviour, such as the characteristic nervous flicking of wings across the back, are not known to differ from those of other *Bradypterus*.

BREEDING HABITS Little known. Singing males are present on presumed breeding territories from early April onwards. Breeds at high densities in suitable habitat and Round (1992) recorded at least 20 individuals singing in July on grassy deforested hillsides at Doi Ang Khang in N Thailand.

There appears to be no account of the breeding behaviour, nest or eggs, although Stuart-Baker (1924) described the nesting behaviour of Brown Bush Warbler in India at a time when *mandelli* was still treated as a race of this species. His description of the birds suggests he was encountering both Brown Bush and Russet Bush Warblers, but his description of the breeding habitat appears to favour Russet Bush rather than Brown Bush Warbler. He described the nest as being placed in a low bush or tangle of weeds, creepers, raspberry or blackberry vines, or a *Daphne* bush. It is usually situated close to the ground but may be up to *c.* 1m up in a large bush. The nest is a deep cup constructed from grasses and an occasional leaf and lined with finer grass and grass stems. Typically four eggs are laid, occasionally three or five. No data is available on the incubation or fledging periods.

DISTRIBUTION Incompletely understood due to past confusion with Brown Bush Warbler. Dickinson *et al.* (2000) established a historical range based on museum specimens showing diagnostic characters for this species. Recordings of the distinctive song have recently established presence in regions from where there are no previous records.
Breeding
B. m. mandelli The nominate race breeds in the Himalayan foothills from Darjeeling in N India, through Sikkim (where reportedly it was quite numerous in the late nineteenth century), to Bhutan where it is localised

and confined to the centre and east at *c.* 2,000–2,200m (Spierenburg 2005). In the NE Indian states of Arunachal Pradesh and southern Assam (including Meghalaya and south to the Lushai Hills) it breeds from 1,000–2,200m but it appears to be absent from Bangladesh (Rasmussen & Anderton 2005).

It is unclear which race breeds in Burma. But as the known distribution of *mandelli* includes NE India, it seems likely that this race extends into N Burma, where Smythies (1986) accurately described the song of Russet Bush Warbler from hill savanna in the Chin Hills and elsewhere in N Burma.

B. m. melanorhynchus Cheng (1987) only included *melanorhynchus* as occurring in China, but many of the specimens he examined may have been misidentified Brown Bush Warblers. However, birds observed in Sichuan and in E and SE China showed the characters of this race (PRK pers. obs., and others). This form is probably widespread on the grassy and scrub-covered hills of south and east China extending northwest to the region of Emei Shan, Sichuan Province. There are no reports across much of S and C China, suggesting it is either absent or local there. However, the absence of records there may simply be due to a lack of visits by experienced observers that know the song. In E and SE China, a region regularly visited by experienced observers, reports are numerous from the hills of Guangdong and Fujian Provinces and it is occasionally reported from the provinces of W Guangxi, S Hunan and Nan Gong Shan and nearby hills in Xishuangbanna, S Yunnan Province (Lewthwaite 1996). Russet Bush Warbler occurs widely, but again locally, in N Vietnam where singing birds have been reported from several locations including Tam Dao. Although the race occurring here is unknown, it is expected that these will also prove to be *melanorhynchus*.

Round (1992) considered the birds breeding in N

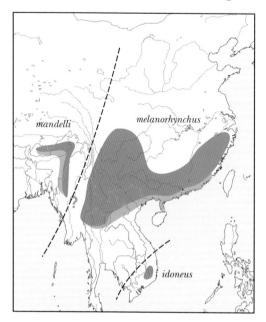

Russet Bush Warbler. Mostly resident but some disperse to lower elevations outside the breeding season.

Thailand to show characters of *melanorhynchus*. Here it breeds on Doi Ang Khang in the northwest and has been found during the breeding season on several peaks in the north, including Doi Pha Hom Pok, Doi Chiang Dao, Huai Nam Dang and Doi Inthanon, from 1,300–1,900m (Round 1992).

B. m. idoneus Restricted to the Da Lat Plateau in South Annam, in S Vietnam, where it is believed to be resident.

Non-breeding Poorly known and much of the historical published material is unreliable due to past confusion with Brown Bush Warbler. Some males sing during the winter months, as in Hong Kong, but many are silent outside the breeding season. It is assumed to winter below the breeding range, in the foothills of the Himalayas and the mountains of C and S China. It is probably quite widespread below the E Himalayas, where Stuart-Baker described it as descending to the foothills and even into the adjacent plains. In SE China it has been found in coastal hills, but the only recent data come from Hong Kong, where it is a regular winter visitor in small numbers. It probably occurs throughout the coastal hills of Fujian, Guangdong and Guangxi Provinces, but is unrecorded due to lack of observers. Elsewhere in China, it was heard in song at Ruili, Yunnan Province, in November 2000 (JH, *in litt.*). It is believed to winter in the hills of N Thailand, although there are no reports outside the breeding season.

MOVEMENTS Poorly understood, with very few systematic observations and no ringing recoveries. The only precise data comes from Hong Kong, where it is a scarce visitor, recorded annually during the winter months since 1989 (Carey *et al.* 2001). Most records are of singing birds and it may well be more numerous and widespread here than these suggest. First arrivals take place in mid October but there is a usually an influx in early to mid November. Small numbers remain widespread throughout the grass and scrub-covered hills below 250m until mid March, when singing ceases, presumably when birds return to breeding areas in the uplands of Guangdong Province. In recent years, singing males have occasionally been heard in Hong Kong in April on grass-covered slopes at *c.* 1,000m, which may be breeding.

DESCRIPTION *B. m. mandelli*
Plumage – Adult fresh
Forehead, crown and nape rich dark brown. Supercilium dull grey-buff, most conspicuous over lores to rear of eye; rarely extending behind eye. Lores dark brown, forming a solid area between bill and eye. Usually a small brown spot behind eye, but no distinct eye-line. Ear-coverts dull rusty brown, finely flecked pale buff. Eye-ring pale buff, merging above eye with supercilium, usually conspicuous and contrasting below eye. Mantle and scapulars to rump and uppertail-coverts unmarked rich russet-brown. Tail feathers dark brown with broad, diffuse dark rusty brown fringes. Chin and throat white. A row of indistinct fine brown spots forms a necklace across lower throat. Below these, larger, darker spots merge with the greyish brown upper breast to form diffuse striations, which become less clear and merge into lower breast and flanks. The extent and prominence of striations is variable but a fine necklace is usually present across the lower throat and is usually visible on upper breast. Sides of breast and upper flanks pale greyish or fulvous-brown, darkening to warm russet-brown on lower flanks and across vent. Belly white to pale grey. Undertail-coverts dark russet-brown, narrowly

tipped greyish white. Lesser and median coverts dark brown with slightly paler fringes. Greater coverts and tertials dark brown with broad, diffuse dark russet-brown fringes. Edges to primary coverts, secondaries and primaries dark russet-brown. Alula dark brown with narrow, contrasting paler fringe. Underwing-coverts tawny-brown. Outside the breeding season some birds appear browner on the breast and lack spotting on the lower throat. These birds may be in their first year.

Adult worn Not known to differ from fresh adult.

Juvenile Upperparts as fresh adult. Chin white. Throat white with light buff wash, each feather tipped dark brown. Breast warm buff, slightly darker than throat but showing similar dark feather tips which merge to form indistinct striations which extend to sides of breast and upper flanks. Lower flanks and vent washed dull russet-brown, contrasting with greyish white belly. Undertail-coverts dull russet-brown, narrowly tipped dull buff.

Bare parts In breeding adult, upper and lower mandibles entirely black. Outside breeding season, upper mandible black, lower mandible greyish pink with darker shading at sides towards tip. In presumed immature birds, upper mandible black with fine yellowish pink cutting edge, entire lower mandible pale yellowish-pink, sometimes with slight darkening at the sides towards the tip. Tarsi, toes dull plumbeous-pink, claws whitish. Iris rich reddish brown.

IN HAND CHARACTERS
Measurements *B. m. mandelli*

Sexes combined:

Wing	50–57 (53.1; 18)
Tail	55–65 (59.7; 17)
Bill	13–15 (13.9; 16)
Tarsus	17.5–19.5 (18.7; 18)

Tail/wing ratio: 105–122% (111%; 18)
Bill width: 2.8–3.7 (3.3; 13)
Hind claw: 5.0–6.3 (5.7; 10)
Tail graduation: 25–35 (29.9; 9)
B. m. melanorhynchus (sexes combined): *wing* 49–53 (50.8; 6); *tail* 53–61 (56.8; 4); *bill* 12.7–14.0 (13.3; 6); *tarsus* 17.5–19.5 (18.2; 5). Thus slightly smaller than nominate *mandelli*.
B. m. idoneus (n = 1, unsexed): *wing* 51; *tail* 59; *tarsus* 18.

Structure *B. m. mandelli*

Wing formula (n = 10):

p1/pc	p2	p3e	p4e	p5e	p6	p7	p10
6.5–10.5	7–11	1–3	0–0.5	wp	0–1	1–4	5–7

Wing short and rounded with fairly small p1. Wing point usually p4–5 (6); p2 near or below ss tips; emargination on p3–5.

Tail long, broad-based, strongly graduated; 12 feathers, broad (t1 10–11mm wide) but narrowed at tip (Fig. 19).

Bill fairly strong; less fine than in Spotted Bush Warbler and slightly broader-tipped than in Brown Bush Warbler.

Tarsi and toes slender, but slightly stronger than in Brown Bush.

Other races similar in structure to *mandelli*.

Figure 20. Wing of Russet Bush Warbler.

Recognition Separated from similar Brown Bush Warbler by more buffy or greyish throat and breast, with distinct dusky spots and by duller, darker warm brown flanks and undertail-coverts, the latter with pale tips. Lower mandible usually blackish (pale in Brown Bush). Structurally very similar to Brown Bush, but wing usually has p3 1.5–3mm shorter than p4 (0.5–1mm shorter in Brown Bush). Tail/wing ratio frequently > 1.1 (usually < 1.1 in Brown Bush) but this difference is slight.

Distinguished from Chinese Bush Warbler by richer russet-brown coloration and more rounded wing (Chinese Bush has wing–point at p3–4). From Spotted Bush Warbler by longer tail (> 54mm) and browner (less greyish) underparts. From Baikal Bush Warbler by much longer tail and more rounded wing.

Weight *B. m. melanorhynchus*: 10.3–13.6g (12.2; 7) (HKRG unpublished data).

GEOGRAPHIC VARIATION Slight racial variation involves small differences in size and plumage tone. Three races are recognised.

B. m. mandelli (Himalayas from Darjeeling to Arunachal Pradesh and N Burma) Described above.

B. m. melanorhynchus (China from mountains of C Sichuan east to Fujian and Guangdong Provinces, also Hong Kong) Resembles nominate race but slightly paler above and distinctly greyer below. Some show slight rufescent tinge on crown and nape but this is variable. Others are slightly duller and greyer on rump and uppertail-coverts. Supercilium poorly marked, dull greyish white in front of the eye, barely extending beyond rear of eye. Underparts darker and greyer than in nominate race and especially race *idoneus*. Closed wing and tail dark rich brown, slightly duller than in nominate race. Slightly smaller, and the bill averages shorter, but there is overlap (see **In Hand Characters**).

B. m. idoneus (Da Lat Plateau, S Annam, Vietnam) Slightly darker brown above than nominate *mandelli*, lacking the rich russet tones of the other two races, and paler below. Supercilium usually more contrasting, whitish and well marked above the lores but fading to pale dull straw behind the eye. Chin, throat and belly cleaner and whiter, and breast washed cold pale brown, lacking the buffy or greyish tones of the other races. Upper breast and lower throat lightly spotted. Breast sides and upper flanks washed dull cold brown.

TAXONOMY AND SYSTEMATICS Originally described by Brooks (1875) as *Dumeticola mandelli* from a specimen collected by Mandelli from Sikkim, but Seebohm treated *mandelli* as synonymous with several other E Asian *Bradypterus*. As more specimens came to light during the late nineteenth and early twentieth centuries from localities throughout the Asian mainland and islands of Asia, the treatment of Asian *Bradypterus* became thoroughly confused. Many taxa were included within the umbrella of a wide-ranging *Bradypterus luteoventris*. Delacour (1942) maintained this position but subsequently realised that two taxa, *luteoventris* and *mandelli* (= *seebohmi*), occurred together in China at Kuatan in Fujian Province and revised the existing arrangement (Delacour 1952). This left Brown Bush Warbler *B. luteoventris* as a monotypic species, while Russet Bush Warbler became a polytypic species *B. seebohmi*, which at the time was considered to be the oldest name. Within Russet Bush Warbler he included the insular forms from the Philippines and Indonesia, but overlooked the distinctive Taiwan birds.

Dickinson *et al.* (2000) reviewed relationships between the taxa comprising the Russet Bush Warbler complex. They concluded that *mandelli* was the oldest valid name for the mainland taxon and placed the mainland populations

of Russet Bush Warbler within *B. mandelli*, including races *melanorhynchus* from E China and *idoneus* of S Vietnam. They then addressed the position of each of the other forms within the complex. Based upon differences in vocalisations (which became apparent only during the 1990s), geographical isolation and minor differences in morphology, they concluded that it was preferable to treat each island population as a distinct species. The name *B. seebohmi* was retained for birds from the mountains of northern Luzon, now renamed Benguet Bush Warbler. Newly described birds from the hills on Taiwan became Taiwan Bush Warbler *B. alishanensis*. The two Indonesian taxa were also considered to be distinct from the mainland species: Javan Bush Warbler *B. montis* (from Java and Bali) and Timor Bush Warbler *B. timorensis* (from Timor). This arrangement has been adopted here.

▲ ▶ Adult *B. m. melanorhynchus*, Hong Kong, November. Separated from Brown Bush Warbler by darker appearance, with uniform dull russet-brown upperparts and flanks, faint greyish white supercilium above the lores, grey breast and broad pale tips to the undertail-coverts. During the breeding season usually shows a band of blackish spots across the lower throat (Peter Kennerley).

▲ Adult B. *m. melanorhynchus*, Hong Kong, December. A duller individual with less pronounced russet tones (Paul Leader).

JAVAN BUSH WARBLER
Bradypterus montis   **Plate 7**

Stasiasticus montis **Hartert, 1896**. *Novit. Zool.* 3: 540. Mount Arjuno, eastern Java.

A poorly known *Bradypterus* restricted to montane habitats on Java and Bali. Until recently treated as a race of the wide-ranging Russet Bush Warbler but now regarded as a distinct monotypic species (Dickinson *et al.* 2000).

IDENTIFICATION Length 14cm. Wing 52–56mm. Tail/wing 102–113%.

An undistinguished warbler with a relatively long and strongly graduated tail, long and deep undertail-coverts and proportionally short wings. With its dark brown upperparts and grey head sides and underparts it is quite unlike any other warbler occurring on Java and Bali, where this is the only *Bradypterus*. Sexes alike.

Structure Similar to Russet Bush Warbler of mainland Asia, but slightly larger and with a rather longer bill, longer wings and longer tail. The tail is broad across the base and strongly graduated, the individual feathers being broad and strong. The legs and feet are rather larger than in Russet Bush Warbler.

Plumage and bare parts The entire upperparts, including the wings and tail, are unmarked dark rufescent-brown. There is a poorly marked greyish supercilium which is most prominent in front of the eye but fades over the ear-coverts. The sides to the head and the lores are dark greyish brown and contrast with the dark rufescent-brown crown. A dark mark is usually visible just behind the eye, in some birds extending to form an indistinct eye-stripe.

Adults show a white chin and pale grey throat, grading into the darker slate-grey breast and pale brownish grey belly. A gorget of well-defined dark grey spots crosses the lower throat and upper breast and extends as smudged striations onto the breast sides and flanks. The slate-grey upper flanks merge into dark rufescent-brown lower flanks and undertail-coverts, the latter showing broad, pale buff tips.

The juvenile closely resembles the adult but differs in the browner sides to the head, which show little or no contrast with the crown and upperparts and which are slightly less rufescent than in the adult. The underparts have a yellowish wash, most pronounced on the chin, throat and belly, but broken by a dull chocolate-brown band across the breast. The flanks, vent and undertail-coverts are also dull chocolate-brown, the latter narrowly tipped pale brown, much less conspicuously than on the adult. Unlike the adult, it lacks the gorget of spots across the lower throat, although some show indistinct brown streaks below the breast-band.

The bill is entirely black during the breeding season and possibly throughout the year, but the lower mandible is a paler deep straw in young birds. The legs and feet are reported to be plumbeous-brown on Java but pale pink on Bali.

SIMILAR SPECIES No other *Bradypterus* occur on Java and Bali and confusion with other species within its restricted range is unlikely. Only the structurally and morphologically distinct Sunda Bush Warbler, which is resident in upper montane forest from 2,000m to the tree line and within the range of Javan Bush Warbler, is a potential source of confusion.

Sunda Bush Warbler is resident on Java and Bali and overlaps with Javan Bush Warbler above the tree line where it inhabits stunted forest and alpine grasslands with scattered ericaceous shrubs and *Casuarina* trees. Although the two species share similar habitat, there are so few similarities between them that confusion should not arise. Singing birds are readily separable; the song of Sunda Bush being a cheerful, fluty '*suuueeeuuu*', quite unlike the harsh, monotonous, repetitive song of Javan Bush. Sunda Bush is a more demonstrative species, often appearing high in a bush to sing or call and readily revealing itself, even when feeding. Compared with Javan Bush Warbler, it is a smaller and more compact bird, with short undertail-coverts and a proportionally shorter tail that lacks the strongly graduated structure of Javan Bush. The upperparts of Sunda Bush Warbler are an unremarkable dull, olive-brown, lacking the dark russet-brown appearance and grey sides to the head of Javan Bush Warbler. The supercilium of Sunda Bush Warbler is pale and conspicuous, providing a ready distinction from Javan Bush Warbler where it is grey, indistinct and poorly marked. The characteristic dark spotting across the throat and breast of Javan Bush Warbler is absent from the uniform underparts of Sunda Bush Warbler. Likewise, the prominent pale tips to the rufescent-brown undertail-coverts of Javan Bush Warbler are also absent in Sunda Bush Warbler.

VOICE The song is a simple, repetitive, rasping '*cree-ut, cree-ut, cree-ut …*' uttered at a frequency of *c.* 4kHz and at rate of approximately two notes per second with a gap of about 0.25 seconds between each. The song from Javan birds is extremely similar to that of Russet Bush Warbler in northern Thailand and China and, as in that species, it is a conspicuous, loud and penetrating sound, sometimes audible at distances of up to 300m. Song sequences may last just a few seconds while others continue without interruption for several minutes.

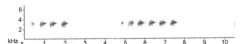

Song of Javan Bush Warbler, Gunung Bromo, Java, Indonesia, April. (Magnus Jäderblad)

The song of the bird on Bali differs from that on Java but retains the repetitive buzzing character characteristic of the Russet Bush Warbler complex. Each note is slightly longer than that of the Java bird, lasting for approximately 0.5 seconds and is followed almost immediately by the next. Each note has a slightly more piercing and nasal, buzzing quality than the Java bird, and is described as a repetitive '*zeeurt, zeeurt, zeeurt…*'. Phrases are introduced with a buzzing '*zee*' at a frequency of *c.* 4.5 kHz but this quickly develops a distinct nasal quality as the frequency drops to *c.* 2.5kHz. It is uncertain whether this difference between the Java and Bali birds reflects individual variation rather than a consistent difference between populations.

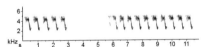

Song of Javan Bush Warbler, Bedugul Botanical Garden, Bali, Indonesia, March. (Magnus Jäderblad)

The call is a soft and quiet '*tuk*', occasionally uttered by foraging birds.

MOULT No information available.

HABITAT On Java it is most numerous at or above the tree line where grasslands predominate. On Gunung Bromo it is restricted to grassy slopes with scattered low scrub, where stunted *Casuarina* trees around the rim of the caldera form the most prominent vegetation. This scrub and the open grassland resembles the breeding habitat of Russet Bush Warbler in continental Asia.

On Bali singing birds have been recorded from tree-covered hillsides with a light understorey of ferns, at *c.* 1,200m, not a habitat in which the Javan birds have yet been recorded. This was well below the height of the surrounding volcanic peaks, and birds may have also been present on the grassy slopes above the tree-line, as in C Java.

BEHAVIOUR Not known to differ from Russet Bush Warbler but seldom observed. An inveterate skulker, usually remaining on or close to the ground in thick cover, its presence revealed by the occasional call. It prefers rank grassland and can be easier to observe than *Bradypterus* species resident in montane forest. It may appear in an isolated bush to investigate a disturbance within the territory. Singing birds are most vocal in the late evening and early morning.

On Bali, a bird remained in view close to the observer for several minutes. It was not shy and was believed to have a nest nearby. It stayed close to the ground, within the cover of a light understorey of loose ferns, occasionally descending and appearing to run across the ground and over fern fronds. It carried small insects which it continued to collect throughout, while giving the occasional call.

BREEDING HABITS No information available.

DISTRIBUTION On Java, confined to the upper slopes of the highest mountains in the centre and east of the island. It was originally described from specimens collected on Gunung Ardjuno, south of Surabaya in E Java. Subsequently, it has been found on several of the higher peaks west to Gunung Soembing and including Gunung Sindoro and Gunung Lawu and east to Gunung Bromo. It should be expected on other apparently suitable peaks within its range from where records are currently lacking. The altitudinal

Javan Bush Warbler. Resident within breeding range.

range extends from *c.* 1,800m on Gunung Lawu up to *c.* 3,300m and close to the summit of Gunung Soembing. Known on Bali in forested hills near Bedugul and Lake Bratan at 1,200m (Kennerley 1989).

MOVEMENTS Believed to be resident throughout the year and no seasonal or altitudinal movements reported.

DESCRIPTION
Adult fresh Forehead to nape dark rufescent-brown. Supercilium poorly defined, restricted to a faint grey line from the bill base, fading over the ear-coverts. Lores darker greyish brown, forming a dark line from bill base to eye. There is a faint hint of a darker eye-line, most noticeable immediately behind eye. Pale eye-ring inconspicuous. Ear-coverts uniform grey, contrasting with crown and nape. Mantle, scapulars, rump and uppertail-coverts uniform dark rufescent-brown, slightly darker than crown. Tail dark rufescent-brown. Chin white. Throat white with variable grey wash. Upper breast and upper flanks slate-grey, joining with grey sides of neck and head. A gorget of small, round, dark grey spots forms an obvious necklace across the lower throat and extends as dark grey blotches across the upper breast, merging into blurred striations on breast sides and flanks and fading on lower breast. Flanks are fulvous-brown but richer rufescent-brown posteriorly. Belly white, washed greyish brown, much paler than flanks and breast. Vent and undertail-coverts rufescent-brown, the latter with broad, pale buff tips to the longer feathers.

Closed wing uniform dark rufescent-brown, fringes of lesser, median and greater coverts, alula and tertials showing little or no contrast with centres. Secondaries and primaries dark grey-brown, with rufescent brown edges closely matching upperpart colour.
Juvenile Upperparts similar to adult but usually browner, less rufescent. Ear-coverts and sides of head dark brown with paler sandy buff shafts forming indistinct streaking. Chin and throat white, tinged yellowish. Breast washed dull chocolate-brown as a broad band that intensifies on the flanks and ventral region. Lower throat and upper breast unspotted but sometimes with indistinct brown streaks, extending as faint striations to lower breast. Belly pale yellow, contrasting with flanks and breast. Undertail-coverts dull brown, narrow pale brown tips less conspicuous than in adult.
Bare parts In breeding adult, upper and lower mandibles entirely black. It is unknown whether the non-breeding adult has a pale base to the lower mandible. In immature birds, lower mandible deep straw-brown, darkening with age. Tarsi and toes reported as plumbeous-brown on Java, pale pink on Bali. Iris dull greyish brown.

IN HAND CHARACTERS
Measurements

Sexes combined:

Wing	52–56 (53.1; 14)
Tail	53–61 (58.5; 13)
Bill	13.5–15 (14.4; 14)
Tarsus	19.5–22 (20.7; 14)

Tail/wing ratio: 102–113% (108%; 14)
Bill width: 3.4–4.0 (3.7; 13)
Hind claw: 5.2–6.7 (5.9; 14)
Tail graduation: 25–36 (30.6; 12)

Structure Wing similar to Russet Bush Warbler (Fig. 20); short and rounded with fairly small p1. Wing point p4–5 (6); p2 < ss tips; emargination on p3–5.

Tail with 12 feathers, rather long; strongly graduated.

Bill rather strong; larger and deeper than in Russet Bush Warbler.

Tarsi and toes stronger than in Russet Bush Warbler.

Weight *c*. 14g (del Hoyo *et al.* 2006).

GEOGRAPHIC VARIATION None recognised at present. Field observations on Bali (Kennerley 1989) suggested that the supercilium, ear-coverts, crown and upperparts match those of *B. montis* on Java, but that underpart colour and pattern differ. On Bali, the breast and flanks were pale brown, more fulvous than the upperparts, rather than grey as in Javan birds. Also, the spots across the lower throat were indistinct and did not extend onto the upper breast. The undertail-coverts appeared to lack pale tips. If these reported differences prove to be correct and consistent, Bali birds may warrant recognition as a distinct taxon.

TAXONOMY AND SYSTEMATICS Following a detailed analysis and comparison of the morphological differences and vocal distinctions between the taxa comprising the Russet Bush Warbler complex, plus the isolated position of *montis* on the summits of the mountains of Java and Bali, Dickinson *et al.* (2000) concluded that Javan Bush Warbler should be treated as a species *B. montis*, distinct from *B. mandelli* of the Asian mainland. We have adopted this recommendation here. Furthermore, we do not recognise the Bali birds as being different from the Java birds, so *B. montis* remains monotypic. However, this taxonomic status requires further study and may yet change.

For example, vocal differences are slight and the song of Javan Bush Warbler closely resembles that of Russet Bush Warbler from China. Playback experiments on Gunung Bromo on Java by Rozendaal (1989) established that Javan Bush Warbler responded strongly to the song of Russet Bush recorded in Sichuan Province, China. If Javan and Russet Bush Warblers were to come into contact again, pair formation might well occur as vocal barriers to breeding do not appear to be established. However, this situation is most unlikely to arise since the closest populations of Russet Bush Warbler to Java are in S Vietnam. Intervening populations presumably existed during the Pleistocene, when Java was connected to adjacent landmasses, but have long since become extinct.

Regarding the birds on Bali, the song differs slightly from both *montis* on Java and Russet Bush Warbler in continental Asia. However, sonograms (see Dickinson *et al.* 2000) reveal that the difference is small and indicate a close relationship to both Javan and Russet Bush Warblers. A recent comparison of mtDNA from the Javan Bush Warblers on Java and Bali revealed only a small sequence divergence, in the region of 0.6–0.7%. It also showed only a 1.3% difference between these taxa and nominate Russet Bush from Darjeeling, India (M. Jäderblad, *in litt.*). This small divergence may suggest that Javan Bush and Russet Warblers may not yet have diverged sufficiently to be recognised as distinct species.

TIMOR BUSH WARBLER
Bradypterus timorensis   Plate 7

Bradypterus montis timorensis Mayr, **1944**. The birds of Timor and Sumba. *Bull. Amer. Mus. Nat. Hist.* 83(2): 158. Mount Mutis, western Timor.

Known from just two old specimens, collected in W Timor, Indonesia, until rediscovered in December 2009. Another population was found at two sites on neighbouring Alor in September 2009. Formerly treated as a race of Javan Bush Warbler, or of the wider-ranging Russet Bush Warbler, but now considered to represent a distinct species (see Dickinson *et al.* 2000). Considered NEAR THREATENED by Birdlife International due to livestock grazing and grass burning in the restricted areas of suitable habitat. Perhaps polytypic.

IDENTIFICATION Length 14cm. Wing *c.* 54mm. Tail/wing *c.* 120%.

The only *Bradypterus* on Timor and Alor. Structure resembles that of Javan Bush Warbler but upperparts warm cinnamon- brown and underparts paler. Sexes believed to be alike.
Structure Does not appear to differ structurally from other species in the Russet Bush Warbler complex, having a relatively long and graduated tail, long undertail-coverts and short rounded wings.
Plumage and bare parts Shows distinctive, uniform cinnamon-brown upperparts, including the closed wings and tail. Only the head shows contrast, with a long, whitish supercilium that becomes greyer and less obvious over the darker and duller brownish grey ear-coverts. It has a bland facial expression resulting from the lack of an eye-stripe and the pale unmarked lores, although there is a dark spot immediately in front of the eye and another just behind the eye. The underparts are whitish, with a pale grey breast and pale brown flanks. The undertail-coverts are slightly darker brown and show inconspicuous pale tips. A faint gorget of greyish brown spots extends across the lower throat and merges with diffuse grey striations on the upper breast. The bill is dark with a pale lower mandible. The legs of the two specimens are pale, more so than on specimens of Javan Bush Warbler.

SIMILAR SPECIES Two small, drab, nondescript and skulking warblers are resident on Timor although neither is likely to be mistaken for Timor Bush Warbler. Differences in structure and behaviour alone should be sufficient to prevent confusion with Sunda Bush Warbler and Timor Stubtail. The much larger Gray's Grasshopper Warbler, although unrecorded from Timor during the northern winter, shows a similar structure but is a substantially larger bird, and unlikely to be confused with Timor Bush Warbler.
Sunda Bush Warbler of the race *everetti* occurs throughout Timor up to 2,300m. Although not a bird of the forest floor and often skulking, it frequently feeds in trees and shrubs up to 2–3m above the ground. It has a typical round-crowned *Cettia* structure but is smaller, shorter tailed, lacks the long undertail-coverts and appears less attenuated than Timor Bush Warbler. It shows a conspicuous whitish supercilium and pale greyish brown upperparts, distinctly paler than the cinnamon-brown upperparts of Timor Bush Warbler. The underparts are white, washed pale grey, darkening to pale peachy grey at the sides and it always lacks the small

row of spots across the lower throat present on Timor Bush Warbler.
Timor Stubtail is a tiny warbler with an extremely short tail and usually appears tail-less; these features alone should preclude confusion with Timor Bush Warbler. Plumage differences further emphasise the distinctions. It shows a long and conspicuous greyish or buffish supercilium extending to the side of the nape, contrasting with the dull olive-brown crown and darker eye-stripe. Upperparts dull olive-brown and underparts pale greyish white, often with a dull greyish wash across the breast, and always lacks the gorget of spotting across the lower throat.
Gray's Grasshopper Warbler is a common winter visitor to Sulawesi and the Moluccas, and probably occurs on Timor and Alor. Frequents forest edge and secondary scrub from sea level to at least 600m, and could overlap with Timor Bush Warbler. Significantly larger and darker than Timor Bush Warbler and with a larger, heavier bill. Upperparts olive-brown to warm brown, lacking the cinnamon-brown tone of Timor Bush. Also separated by the grey-brown supercilium, breast and flanks, and warm peachy buff or cinnamon-buff undertail-coverts that lack pale tips.

VOICE Song structure resembles that of Russet Bush and Javan Bush Warblers, but tone and quality differ slightly. On Timor it comprises a repetitive, mechanical and rather hollow-sounding monosyllabic '*dzrrrp, dzrrrp, dzrrrp, dzrrrp…*', delivered at 2–3 per second within a frequency range of 3.5–5kHz, with an energy peak at *c.* 4kHz. Typically, 3–10 notes are given in rapid succession over a 2–3 second period followed by a short pause lasting 2–5 seconds before the next sequence.

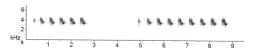

Song of Timor Bush Warbler, Mount Ramelau, Timor-Leste, Indonesia, December. (Colin Trainor)

The song given by birds on Alor is recognisably similar to that of the Timor, but is slightly faster and higher pitched, giving it a more piercing and nasal quality. Typically delivered at a rate of *c.* 3 notes per second within a frequency range of 4–5kHz, but with an energy peak at 4–4.5kHz, slightly higher than that of the Timor bird.

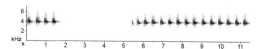

Song of Timor Bush Warbler, Alor, Indonesia, September. (Philippe Verbelen)

The call is unknown.

MOULT No information available.

HABITAT On Timor, birds at Mount Ramelau frequented a 2.5km section of an upland river valley at 1,720–2,050m dominated by grasses *Themeda* mixed with low sedges and weeds, typically < 1m in height, and borders of *Eucalyptus* woodland and cultivated land with a dense tangled understorey. The habitat on Timor is intensively grazed by a large number of cattle and horses, and regularly burnt. This severely limits the extent of suitable habitat available (Verbelen & Trainor in prep.).

On Alor, recorded from 860–1,250m on steep scrub-covered slopes and ridges above broad upland valleys, but was absent from plateau above the valleys. Apparently suitable habitat is extensive and includes a mosaic of shifting agriculture and tree crops, with substantially less impact of cattle grazing and wildfire burning than occurs on Timor (Verbelen & Trainor in prep.).

BEHAVIOUR No information available.

BREEDING HABITS Singing males on Alor occupy small territories, typically 50–100m apart, and occur at fairly high densities. Verbelen & Trainor (in prep.) estimate territory size at 1–3ha.

DISTRIBUTION Described from two specimens collected on Gunung Mutis in W Timor, Indonesia, at 1,800m in March 1932 by G. Stein. Apart from an unconfirmed sight record from Same, East Timor, in August 1972 (White & Bruce 1986), there were no subsequent records until rediscovered in the Hatu Builico valley below Mount Ramelau on Timor-Leste in December 2009 by Colin Trainor. Here it was surprisingly numerous, with 18 individuals heard within a relatively small area.

In September 2009, Philippe Verbelen discovered a previously unknown population of Timor Bush Warbler at two sites, Mainang and Subo-Manmas, on nearby Alor, where no *Bradypterus* had previously been recorded. With large areas of apparently suitable habitat available, it may occur more widely than these observations suggest.

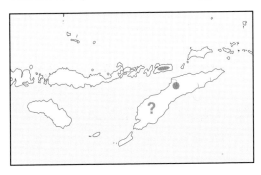

Timor Bush Warbler. Resident within breeding range.

MOVEMENTS Believed to be resident.

DESCRIPTION

Adult fresh Forehead to nape pale cinnamon-brown. Supercilium dull greyish white, extending from bill base to rear of ear-coverts. Lores plain greyish white apart from a small, dark brown spot immediately in front of eye and a similar dark brown spot behind the eye; eye-line poorly defined. Pale eye-ring inconspicuous. Ear-coverts pale grey, tipped cinnamon-brown, appearing faintly mottled. Mantle, scapulars, rump and uppertail-coverts pale cinnamon-brown, concolorous with crown. Tail feathers dull rufescent-brown with diffuse brighter cinnamon-brown fringes.

Chin and throat white, malar region with indistinct darker spotting. Upper breast pale grey with indistinct darker grey striations, most conspicuous towards throat, forming a gorget of small dark grey spots. Flanks pale rusty brown with indistinct, diffuse but slightly darker brown striations. Lower breast and belly white, unmarked. Vent and undertail-coverts dull rust-brown, the latter with narrow and inconspicuous pale tips. Lesser, median and greater coverts, alula and tertials pale cinnamon-brown, similar to upperpart colour, with little contrast between fringes and centres. Secondaries and primaries drab dark brown, broadly edged pale cinnamon-brown.

Juvenile Undescribed.

Bare parts Upper mandible black. Lower mandible pale. Legs and feet pale pink. Iris colour unknown.

IN HAND CHARACTERS

Measurements (1 ♂, 1♀, mean values): *wing* 53.5; *tail* 64.5; *bill* 14.6; *tarsus* 19.5; *tail/wing* 121%; *hind claw* 6.4 (Dickinson *et al.* 2000).

Structure Wing similar to Russet Bush Warbler (Fig. 20); short and rounded with small p1. Wing point p5, with p4 and p6 subequal; p2 < ss tips; emargination on p3–5.

Tail of 12 feathers long and strongly graduated.

Bill and tarsi as Russet Bush Warbler.

Weight *c.* 11g (del Hoyo *et al.* 2006).

GEOGRAPHIC VARIATION None documented. As yet, the Alor bird has not been collected and no detailed description is available. However, based upon differences in song frequency, Verbelen & Trainor (in prep.) propose that birds from Alor are recognised as a new subspecies, distinct from the Timor bird.

TAXONOMY AND SYSTEMATICS Described by Mayr (1944) as a race of Javan Bush Warbler, but included by Delacour (1953) within a wide-ranging Russet Bush Warbler extending from E India and SE China to Timor. Based upon structural and morphological differences from its geographically closest near relative, Javan Bush Warbler, and mainland populations of Russet Bush Warbler, together with its geographical isolation, Dickinson *et al.* (2000) proposed that *timorensis* should be recognised as distinct at the species level. This position has been adopted here, but it is acknowledged that further research is required to establish molecular relationships and phylogeny.

BENGUET BUSH WARBLER
Bradypterus seebohmi   Plate 7

Lusciniola seebohmi **Ogilvie-Grant, 1895.** *Bull. Brit. Orn. Club,* 4: 40. Lepanto Mountains, northern Luzon, Philippines.

An extremely rare and localised *Bradypterus*, endemic to N Luzon, Philippines. Until the 1990s, known only from a single specimen collected in 1894 in the mountains of Lepanto. In recent years, small numbers have been discovered near Mount Polis. Formerly regarded as conspecific with Javan Bush, Timor Bush and Russet Bush Warblers but, following Dickinson *et al.* (2000), treated here as a monotypic species.

IDENTIFICATION Length 14cm. Wing *c.* 52mm. Tail/wing *c.* 120%.

A poorly known and rarely seen *Bradypterus* of the montane grasslands of Luzon, almost invariably located and identified by song. Singing males may sit in partial view, perched on a tall grass stem or side of a small bush, when its plain and nondescript dark brown appearance provides few clues to its identification. Sexes alike.

Structure Not known to differ from the closely related Russet Bush Warbler. They share the same attenuated structure, with a long and strongly graduated tail, long and deep undertail-coverts, short rounded wings that barely reach the uppertail-coverts; a relatively small, flat-crowned head, and rather fine and delicate legs and feet. The quite deep-based bill has a rather stubby appearance.

Plumage and bare parts The upperparts, including the wings and tail, are uniform dark russet-brown. Only the head shows contrast, with a short, pale supercilium above the lores and, at best, a darker spot on either side of the eye, but it is otherwise plain and lacks a darker eye-stripe. The sides to the head usually appear slightly paler and greyer, contrasting with the crown. Perhaps the single most conspicuous feature is the unmarked white chin which contrasts with the otherwise dark head. The throat and upper breast show a light ash-grey wash, which becomes darker on the lower breast, but paler and warmer brown on the belly. Short, dark brown striations form a diffuse and restricted gorget across the lower throat and upper breast. The upper flanks are greyish brown, becoming rich sepia-brown on the lower flanks and vent, while the long dark brown undertail-coverts show narrow whitish tips.

The bill is black with a pale pinkish straw lower mandible, but this may vary seasonally and with age. Legs and feet deep plumbeous-brown.

SIMILAR SPECIES Benguet Bush Warbler forms part of a group of very similar *Bradypterus* species closely allied to Russet Bush Warbler of the Asian mainland, with which it shares structural and plumage characters including dull, uniform rich brown upperparts and pale tips to the long, dark brown undertail-coverts. Two potential confusion species occur within its range in northern Luzon: Long-tailed Bush Warbler and Luzon Bush Warbler and their separation is discussed below.

Long-tailed Bush Warbler is the only other *Bradypterus* occurring in Luzon where it is resident in the montane forests of the north and frequents the forest floor. It is not known to occur in the rank grasslands where Benguet Bush Warbler is found. This is a larger, more thickset bird with longer wings and a proportionately longer tail, up

to *c.* 24mm longer than that of Benguet Bush. This has a loose structure which often gives it a frayed or damaged appearance. The upperparts are brighter and more rufescent than those of Benguet Bush, and the breast greyish brown, darkening to deep cinnamon-brown on the belly and lower flanks. It shows rich rufous-brown undertail-coverts which lack pale tips. The supercilium is even more obscure than that of Benguet Bush Warbler.

Luzon Bush Warbler is a *Cettia* with a similar distribution and habitat preference to Benguet Bush Warbler. It is much commoner, however, and generally not such a skulking and secretive species. If seen well, this is a distinctly smaller bird with bolder behaviour, relatively short undertail-coverts and tail lacks strong graduation. It shows a conspicuous pale supercilium, warm brown crown, greyish brown upperparts and greyish white underparts.

VOICE The song comprises a rapid repetition of a nasal '*reeep…reeep…reeep*' note resembling a metallic zipping sound, with approximately two phrases given per second at a frequency of *c.* 4 kHz. Like Russet Bush Warbler, the song is loud and far-carrying. Some birds give a rather quiet and feeble song that does not attract attention and can be easily overlooked. Initially it seems to have difficulty starting the song, and after commencing with one or two quiet '*reeep…reeep*' notes it may cease singing for a second or two before further sequences are given, usually between three and five, before a pause of several seconds. This hesitant delivery can continue throughout the entire song sequence, but once started, most birds will sing continuously for up to 20 seconds without a break, then pause briefly before recommencing.

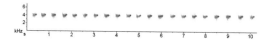

Song of Benguet Bush Warbler, between the village of Bay-yo and the town of Bontoc, Mount Polis, Luzon, Philippines, April. (Magnus Jäderblad)

The call is unknown.

MOULT No information available.

HABITAT The type specimen was collected in a thick patch of coarse grass at 1,800m. This description resembles the typical habitat of the closely related Russet Bush Warbler of continental Asia. Recent observations of Benguet Bush Warbler are of singing males on steep, grass-covered hillsides and in ravines and gullies, again with tall rank grass.

BEHAVIOUR Nothing recorded of behaviour on Luzon but probably similar to Russet Bush Warbler.

BREEDING No information available.

DISTRIBUTION Known only from the mountains of Lepanto in N Luzon, Philippines. Following its initial discovery in 1894, there were no further reports until the 1990s, when it was rediscovered in the Mount Polis region. It has since been reported regularly here and between the village of Bay-yo and the town Bontoc in the Central Mountains. With deforestation having removed much of Luzon's accessible montane forests, large areas of apparently suitable rank grassland habitat have become available, raising the possibility that Benguet Bush Warbler may expand its range.

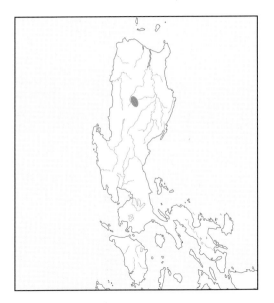

Benguet Bush Warbler. Resident within breeding range.

MOVEMENTS Believed to be resident throughout the year and no seasonal or altitudinal movements reported.

DESCRIPTION

Adult, fresh Forehead to nape dull russet-brown. Supercilium greyish white, tinged warm brown, most conspicuous from bill base to eye, fading over ear-coverts. Loral spot dark greyish brown, not reaching bill base. There is a smaller dark spot behind the eye but no eye-line. Ear-coverts dull brown with faintly paler streaking, slightly paler and colder than crown. Eye-ring poorly defined, merging with supercilium and showing little contrast with ear-coverts. Mantle, scapulars, rump and uppertail-coverts uniform dark, rich russet-brown, lacking warm tones. Tail feathers dark brown with broad, diffuse russet-brown fringes.

Chin white. Throat white with ash-grey tinge, merging with strong ash-grey wash on upper breast. A gorget of short, smudged, dark brown striations extends across the lower throat and upper breast. Sides of breast and upper flanks greyish brown, darkening to rich sepia-brown on lower flanks and vent. Centre of belly whitish with warm brown wash. Undertail-coverts dull russet-brown with narrow whitish tips. Lesser and median coverts as uppertarts. Fringes to greater coverts, tertials and alula uniform dull russet-brown, merging with ill-defined, slightly darker centres. Secondaries and primaries dark brown, edged dull russet-brown.

Juvenile Undescribed.

Bare parts Upper mandible black. Lower mandible pale pinkish straw, but this may vary seasonally and with age. Tarsi and toes deep plumbeous-brown. Iris colour unknown.

IN HAND CHARACTERS

All data based upon a single female specimen.

Measurements 1 ♀: *wing* 52; *tail* 62; *bill* 14.2; *tarsus* 19.7; tail/wing 119% ; hind claw 6.4 (Dickinson *et al.* 2000).

Structure Wing similar to Russet Bush Warbler (Fig. 20); short and rounded with small p1. Wing point p5, with p4 and p6 subequal; p2 < ss tips; emargination on p3–5.

Tail of 12 feathers, long and strongly graduated.

Bill and tarsi as Russet Bush Warbler.

Recognition Separated from Long-tailed Bush Warbler by much smaller measurements, e.g. wing *c.* 10mm shorter and tail *c.* 24mm shorter than Long-tailed Bush Warbler. Also by pale-tipped greyish brown undertail-coverts.

Weight *c.* 12g (del Hoyo *et al.* 2006).

GEOGRAPHIC VARIATION None recorded.

TAXONOMY AND SYSTEMATICS The difficulties involved in *Bradypterus* identification are encapsulated in the history of *Bradypterus seebohmi*. This is a classic case of a complex of poorly understood but morphologically similar and closely related taxa being thoroughly confused both in the specimen trays and in the field. The resulting disarray has only recently been revised (Dickinson *et al.* 2000). An understanding of this background is useful here to establish the changes to the nomenclature of this taxon since its discovery.

It was originally collected in the mountains of Lepanto, northern Luzon, on 28 December 1894 by John Whitehead and described by Ogilvie-Grant (1895) who named it *Lusciniola seebohmi*. During the late nineteenth century and early twentieth century, similar *Bradypterus* were being discovered and described from NE India, E China, Indochina and Java. But the difficulty in identifying *Bradypterus* specimens and the lack of comparable material in accessible collections made specific identification of isolated individuals difficult. This confused situation remained unresolved until Delacour (1943) made the first real attempt to pull together available specimen material from continental Asia and the islands to the south and east. His conclusion, based solely on morphology, was that a single, wide-ranging species was involved, which he considered to be *B. luteoventris*. He recognised four races within this species: the nominate ranging from Nepal east to central China, *melanorhynchus* from SE China, *idoneus* from S Annam and *seebohmi* from Luzon.

Other interpretations appeared as additional information emerged. Birds resembling nominate *luteoventris* were known to occur at Kuatan, Fujian Province, China, alongside *melanorhynchus*. In addition, specimens from Taiwan came to light that closely resembled *idoneus*. Revising his position, Delacour (1952) then considered *B. luteoventris* to be a monotypic species defined by a paler upperpart colour. The remaining forms, *seebohmi*, *melanorhynchus* and *idoneus* from the mainland, *montis* from Java, and the recently described *timorensis* from Timor, all showed consistent morphological features, with the upperpart colour (darker than in *luteoventris*) playing a crucial role in the new arrangement. Delacour did not discuss the birds from Taiwan, which he included within *melanorhynchus* from southeastern China. He treated all these darker-backed forms under the name *Bradypterus seebohmi*; this name at the time being believed to have taxonomic priority. The name Russet Bush Warbler was given to this complex and the situation remained unchallenged for the next 30 years.

Following a detailed review of the taxonomy of the Russet Bush Warbler complex, based upon biometric and morphological distinctions together with geographical isolation, Dickinson *et al.* (2000) concluded that:

(a) Populations of mainland Asia, still known as Russet Bush Warbler, were specifically distinct from those on islands to the south and should be treated under the name *B. mandelli*, this name having taxonomic priority and based upon the type specimen from Sikkim. Within Russet Bush Warbler, three races should be recognised; the nominate form, *melanorhynchus* and *idoneus*.

(b) The name *B. seebohmi* should be restricted to the Benguet Bush Warbler of N Luzon. Dickinson *et al.* (2000) treated this as a monotypic species, citing the low wing/tail ratio (making it unlikely to be a good disperser) and its isolation in a biogeographic sub-region renowned for high levels of endemism.

(c) Although vocalisations are similar, the populations resident on Java and Bali, and on Timor, show slight morphological divergence from the continental Asian taxa.

These should be considered two distinct species: Javan Bush Warbler *B. montis* (including birds from Bali which may yet be recognised as a distinct taxon) and Timor Bush Warbler *B. timorensis*. This position may require further revision if additional data from Timor becomes available.

(d) The *Bradypterus* resident in the mountains of Taiwan merited specific status based upon its distinct vocalisations. It was described as Taiwan Bush Warbler *B. alishanensis* (Rasmussen *et al.* 2000) and recognised as being endemic to Taiwan.

TAIWAN BUSH WARBLER
Bradypterus alishanensis   Plate 7

Bradyptereus alishanensis Rasmussen, Round, Dickinson & Rozendaal, 2000. *Auk* 117(2): 279–289. Taiwan.

A little-known *Bradypterus* endemic to the highlands of C and N Taiwan. Previously treated under Russet Bush Warbler *B. mandelli* (formerly *B. seebohmi*), either within the race *idoneus* (Delacour 1952) or within *melanorhynchus* (Watson 1986; Cheng 1987). Not recognised as a distinct taxon until separated from Russet Bush Warbler and given species status by Rasmussen *et al.* (2000), who demonstrated distinct differences in territorial songs between Taiwan and continental birds. Monotypic.

IDENTIFICATION Length 14cm. Wing *c.* 54mm. Tail/wing *c.* 110%.

A nondescript and uniform drab brown warbler, the only *Bradypterus* occurring on Taiwan but part of the wide-ranging Russet Bush Warbler complex. The penetrating and far-carrying song is a distinctive and readily recognisable sound of the hills of Taiwan. Sexes alike.

Structure Very similar to Russet Bush Warbler, with short and rounded wings reaching only to the base of the uppertail-coverts and long, deep undertail-coverts extending well beyond the primary tips. The tail is long, broad-based and strongly graduated, the bill short but quite fine. The feet are proportionately slightly larger than those of Russet Bush Warbler.

Plumage and bare parts The entire upperparts including the closed wings and tail are uniform dull russet-brown and lack contrast. An indistinct paler region above the lores merges with the equally indistinct eye-ring, while the lores are slightly darker, giving the head a plain appearance. A paler supercilium may sometimes be visible behind the eye, but is often absent. The brown sides to the head are more extensive than on Russet Bush Warbler and extend to the lower malar regions, leaving a narrow and not particularly conspicuous whitish throat patch. Some birds show dark spotting on the chin and throat, but this is more typically limited to faint and diffuse brown spotting on the throat centre and occasionally on the upper breast. Usually, the breast is paler brown than the flanks, which are dull russet-brown and similar to the upperparts, but contrasts with the greyish white belly. This russet-brown tone extends to the undertail-coverts, which are plain apart from narrow, pale brown tips to the longest feathers. These are relatively inconspicuous compared with the broader, paler and more contrasting tips on Russet Bush Warbler.

A melanistic morph has been described based on one individual (Kuroda 1938). This was, however, an exceptionally dark brown bird which may represent the extreme end of individual variation. It was much darker above and below than typical russet-brown birds. The upperparts and flanks were uniform smoky-brown, while the sides of the head showed a faint grey wash.

The bill is typically entirely black in adults but some (possibly immature birds) show an entirely pale or pale-based lower mandible. The legs and feet are pale pink.

SIMILAR SPECIES No similar species occur on Taiwan. However, the allopatric Russet Bush Warbler, which is an altitudinal migrant in SE China, could conceivably cross the Taiwan Strait and reach Taiwan. Their separation is discussed below.

Russet Bush Warbler is quite variable in appearance and some can closely resemble Taiwan Bush, particularly those of the race *melanorhynchus* which breeds in SE China. Compared with Taiwan Bush Warbler, the upperparts of Russet Bush Warbler tend to be darker, richer russet-brown while the breast is greyer in adults but brownish in young birds. In addition, the white throat of Russet Bush appears more conspicuous. Both species show spotting on the throat and upper breast which is variable in extent, but usually more prominent and extensive on Russet Bush. On Russet Bush, spotting is heaviest across the upper breast and less so on the throat. In contrast, Taiwan Bush never shows the large, dark spots that some Russet Bush show and the spotting, when present, is most obvious in the centre of the throat, with very few spots extending onto the upper breast. The flanks of Russet Bush are darker and closely resemble the upperpart colour, lacking the cinnamon tones often present in Taiwan Bush. The undertail-coverts of Russet Bush are also darker grey-brown with broader and more contrasting pale tips.

There are subtle structural differences between these species but most of little use in the field. Russet Bush Warbler shows a slightly heavier, deeper and broader-based bill, but the shorter, more pointed wing and rounded tips to the rectrices are only apparent in the hand.

VOICE The song has a characteristic simple, repetitive structure but differs markedly from that of Russet Bush Warbler. Each sequence consists of four or five components. A short monotone whistle, perhaps rising slightly in pitch, is followed by a series of three or four rather flat, hollow sounding clicks that almost merge into each other but are sufficiently separated to be perceived as distinct notes. The song can be transcribed as '*whuuu, trr, trr, trr, whuuu, trr, trr, trr, whuuu, trr, trr, trr, whuuu...*' and always starts and finishes with the monotone whistle. There is individual variation in pitch and delivery within a frequency range of 3–4kHz, even between birds in adjacent territories, but the tempo, rhythm and structure of the song remains consistent.

The song is slightly lower in pitch than that of Russet Bush and each note is slightly longer, so that there are usually three notes every two seconds while Russet Bush generally gives four. Each note lasts approximately one second followed by a brief pause, typically about half a second, before the next begins. The song may be repeated just two or three times before stopping or may continue without pausing for a minute or longer. A minimum of ten note sequences is usually given before there is a break.

Song of Taiwan Bush Warbler. An Ma Shan, Taiwan, May. (Geoff Carey)

A number of different calls are given, the most frequent being a series of raspy '*ksh, ksh, ksh...*' notes. These may be uttered continuously, sometimes becoming very rapid and intense in alarm.

MOULT No information available.

HABITAT Frequents a variety of habitats throughout its altitudinal range but requires a luxuriant understorey of thick grasses, tangled shrubs and ferns. At lower elevations, breeds on slopes in both coniferous and deciduous woodland provided there is thick undergrowth. At higher elevations, up to and above the tree line, it sings on hillsides covered in tall grass and dwarf bamboo, similar to the habitat favoured by Brown Bush Warbler in China.

BEHAVIOUR There are no known behavioural differences between Taiwan Bush Warbler and other closely related *Bradypterus* in the Russet Bush Warbler complex. The song may be heard on breeding territories from late March onwards, when it is given most frequently from pre-dawn to mid morning and again in the evening and it has been reported on moonlit nights (Kuroda 1938). It is also heard in non-breeding localities during the winter months (Rasmussen *et al.* 2000), although we have not heard it during visits to known breeding locations in December, January and February.

BREEDING HABITS Available information comes mainly from Hachisuka & Udagawa (1951), who noted activities consistent with breeding behaviour between mid May and the end of June. However, males occupying woodland breeding territories below 1,000m are in song from late March onwards and breeding may begin earlier at these lower elevations. Birds have been recorded in song at Hsitou in June and carrying food in August (Rasmussen *et al.* 2000), suggesting that breeding continues much later than recorded by Hachisuka & Udagawa. The nest is built close to the ground, often in a *Miscanthus* clump. A clutch of two eggs is laid.

DISTRIBUTION Endemic to the mountains of C and N Taiwan where it occurs widely above 1,200m to the tree line at *c.* 3,000m (Hachisuka & Udagawa 1951). Some breed at slightly lower elevations, to just below 1,000m where suitable habitat exists in broadleaf forest. Throughout its range it is generally common and widespread, leading Rasmussen *et al.* (2000) to suggest that the lack of competition in Taiwan has enabled it to occupy a wider range of habitats and a greater altitudinal range than its congeners on the mainland. It is believed to be mainly resident, although some birds probably descend to lower elevations outside the breeding season.

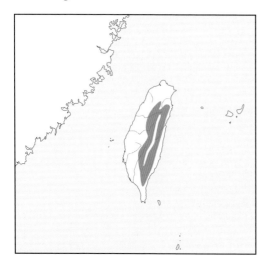

Taiwan Bush Warbler. Resident within breeding range, although birds breeding at higher altitude are believed to descend during cold weather.

MOVEMENTS Considered to be resident in the mountains of Taiwan by Hachisuka & Udagawa (1951). However, winter temperatures in the central mountains frequently drop below freezing for extended periods and birds probably vacate higher territories during the colder months. Those breeding at lower altitudes may be resident but to-date we have no evidence to suggest whether they remain or move elsewhere. Robson (2000) noted that seven Brown Bush Warblers were trapped at Kao Ping Hsi, near Kaohsiung, Taiwan, in November 1999, which would represent the first records for Taiwan. However, given the very similar structure and morphology of Taiwan Bush and Brown Bush Warblers, it is possible these birds were Taiwan Bush Warblers, perhaps young birds lacking throat spotting, which had descended from breeding grounds. Such behaviour occurs regularly in Russet Bush and Brown Bush Warblers in SE China, where both reach the coast after vacating breeding territories in the hills of Guangdong and Fujian Provinces.

DESCRIPTION
Plumage – Adult fresh Forehead to nape dull rufous-brown. Crown feathers narrowly tipped slightly darker to give a faintly scaly appearance. Supercilium pale buff, dull and poorly defined, extending from bill base to upper edge of eye and merging with slightly paler eye-ring, but faint and often absent behind eye. Lores with narrow dark brown line from bill base to eye; in some individuals this is restricted to a small dark spot in front of eye. Otherwise pale buff lores merge with supercilium. No hint of dark line behind eye. Ear-coverts dull rufous-brown with indistinct white to pale buff shaft streaks. Malar region dull rufous-brown, merging with lower ear-coverts and sides of throat. Mantle, scapulars, rump and uppertail-coverts uniform dull rufous-brown. Tail dark brown with broad, diffuse, rufous-brown fringes, similar to upperpart colour and with numerous narrow and faintly darker brown cross-barring.

Chin and centre of throat white. Usually a row of spots across lower throat, variable in extent and intensity, sometimes ill-defined and pale brown around edge of throat with a few larger, darker and crisper spots towards centre, while in other birds these appear more distinct and blackish, reaching malar region and edge of upper breast. Upper breast dull greyish brown, slightly colder than upperparts. Lower breast warm, rusty brown, paler than upperparts. Flanks and vent dull rufous-brown, darkening posteriorly. Lower breast and belly white, sometimes with pale buff wash and contrasting with darker flanks. Undertail-coverts dark rufous-brown with conspicuous warm tan to warm buff tips. Underside of tail pale grey-brown, paler than upper surface and contrasting with darker, browner undertail-coverts.

Lesser and median coverts dull rufous-brown with ill-defined darker brown centres. Greater and primary coverts, tertials and alula dull brown with broad warm rusty brown fringes. Primaries and secondaries dull brown, edges warm rusty brown.
Juvenile Resembles adult but breast brownish and lacks spots.
Bare parts During breeding season, upper and lower mandibles of adults black. In winter, upper mandible black, lower mandible variable, either entirely black or dull pink with darker sides towards tip, occasionally entirely pale. Difference may be age-related, as lower mandible entirely pale in known immatures of other *Bradypterus*. Tarsi and toes pale pink, claws slightly darker. Iris dull reddish brown, not known to vary with age.

IN HAND CHARACTERS

Measurements (Sexes combined, mean values, n = 11): *wing* 54.1; *tail* 60.3; *bill* 14.2; *tarsus* 19.8; tail/wing 111%; hind claw 6.8 (Dickinson *et al.* 2000).

Structure Wing similar to Russet Bush Warbler (Fig. 20); short and rounded with small p1. Wing point p5, with p4 and p6 subequal.

Tail of 12 feathers fairly long, strongly graduated.

Bill and tarsi as Russet Bush Warbler.

Recognition Separation from Russet Bush requires care. Slightly larger than the Chinese race *melanorhynchus* of Russet Bush Warbler but measurements overlap. Russet Bush Warbler has slightly heavier, deeper and broader-based bill, shorter and more pointed wing and rounded tips to the rectrices. Plumages similar, although the upperparts of Taiwan Bush are slightly less dark or richly toned and flanks often with a cinnamon wash. Whiter throat and smaller throat spotting not extending onto upper breast of Taiwan Bush also useful.

Weight *c.* 10g (del Hoyo *et al.* 2006).

GEOGRAPHIC VARIATION None recorded.

TAXONOMY AND SYSTEMATICS Although discovered on Mount Ari (= Ali Shan) in 1917, the *Bradypterus* on Taiwan were only described as a distinct endemic taxon by Rasmussen *et al.* (2000), who accorded them specific status. It is worth summarising the circumstances that led up to this.

The Taiwan *Bradypterus* were for a long time believed to belong within a wide-ranging *B. luteoventris* that extended from Nepal to eastern China and south through Vietnam to the Philippines and Java. Subtle plumage differences were recognised between specimens from this extensive range, but these were poorly understood. Delacour (1943) attempted to pull material together from continental Asia and the islands of southern and eastern Asia and define a logical order. He concluded that within a single species *B. luteoventris* there were four races, nominate *luteoventris* from Nepal east to central China, *melanorhynchus* in southeastern China, *idoneus* in southern Annam and *seebohmi* in Luzon, Philippines, but he seems to have overlooked the existence of the Taiwan birds. When specimens came to light subsequently, these were considered to most closely resemble *idoneus*.

Delacour (1952) later revised his position, concluding that Brown Bush Warbler was a monotypic species defined by a paler upperpart colour. The remaining darker, more rufous taxa, *seebohmi, melanorhynchus, idoneus, montis* and the recently described *timorensis*, he treated as being conspecific under the name Russet Bush Warbler (then *B. seebohmi*). He included the Taiwan birds within *idoneus* although Hachisuka & Udagawa (1951) thought them closest to *melanorhynchus*. The decision to include them within *melanorhynchus* was taken by Watson *et al.* (1986), who were subsequently followed by Cheng (1987). By the late 1980s, many observers recognised that the distinctive song of the *Bradypterus* breeding in the mountains of Taiwan was quite different from that of both Brown Bush Warbler and Russet Bush Warbler on the Chinese mainland and elsewhere.

With vocal distinctions now important in establishing species limits within this nondescript *Bradypterus* group, there came a realisation that the Taiwan population deserved recognition not only as a distinct taxon but also as a full species.

▲ Adult, Huangguan Shan, Taiwan, April. Note the characteristic long, graduated tail and rounded wing structure, characters shared with all species in the Russet Bush Warbler complex (James Eaton/Birdtour Asia).

▲ ▶ Adult, Taiwan, May. Males will often sit in an exposed position when singing, but they are otherwise extremely difficult to see. Extent of spotting on chin and throat is variable; some can show more conspicuous dark spotting than this bird does, while on others it may be faint or absent (Pete Morris).

▲ Adult, Nantou County, Taiwan, July. This singing male lacks throat spotting (Liao Pen-shing).

▲ Juvenile, Yushan National Park, Taiwan. June. Note brown wash across breast, pale base to lower mandible and conspicuous gape flange, which point to this being a juvenile (Liao Pen-shing).

LONG-TAILED BUSH WARBLER
Bradypterus caudatus   Plate 8

Pseudotharrhaleus caudatus Ogilvie-Grant, 1895. *Bull. Brit. Orn. Club* 4: 40. Lepanto Mountains, northern Luzon, Philippines.

Endemic to the Philippines, where it inhabits montane forest floor undergrowth in the hills of N Luzon and Mindanao. Polytypic, with three races recognised.

B. c. caudatus (Ogilvie-Grant, 1895). N Luzon.
B. c. unicolor (Hartert, 1904). C, E and S Mindanao.
B. c. malindangensis (Mearns, 1909). Mount Melindang, NW Mindanao.

IDENTIFICATION Length 16.5–18cm. Wing *c.* 61–62mm. Tail/wing, *B. c. caudatus c.* 130%, *B. c. unicolor c.* 115%.

A relatively large and exceptionally skulking *Bradypterus* characterised by its proportionately long tail and dark rufescent-brown upperparts. Shares similarities in behaviour, vocalisations and habitat with the allopatric Kinabalu Bush and Chestnut-backed Bush Warblers. Sexes alike.

Structure A proportionately long-tailed *Bradypterus* that displays a characteristic horizontal stance, long and deep undertail-coverts and a long and fine bill. Due to the long tail, the wings appear exceptionally short and rounded, with a long first primary (p1) and the wing point formed by p5–7. The strongly graduated tail has twelve feathers. In the nominate form the tail is particularly long with a weak filamentous structure and often appears frayed and tattered.

The two races on Mindanao have a more robust tail, which is proportionately shorter than in nominate birds, giving them a more neatly proportioned appearance.

Plumage and bare parts Rather drab and featureless. The entire upperparts, including wings and tail, are dull uniform rufescent-brown. The dark rufescent-brown head is marked by a greyish white supercilium, most obvious above the lores but almost vanishing just behind the eye, while the slightly darker eye-stripe shows little contrast and is difficult to discern in the dull forest light. The underparts are equally featureless. It shows a greyish white chin and throat that merge into the greyer upper breast. Most have a poorly defined gorget of diffuse, dusky striations across the upper breast. The flanks are dull rufescent-brown, becoming darker and richer towards the ventral region and undertail-coverts, which are uniform and lack the pale tips shown by the *Bradypterus* species of the Russet Bush Warbler complex.

The bill is black, although some birds show a paler, straw-brown base to the lower mandible. The legs and feet are dark brown, but occasionally appear blackish.

SIMILAR SPECIES On Luzon, where Benguet Bush Warbler is the only likely confusion species, there is little or no overlap in habitat, and identification is fairly straightforward. Luzon Bush Warbler may occur alongside it within montane forest but is quite different in appearance, structure and behaviour. On Mindanao, there are no potentially confusing warbler species, and here the challenge comes from the unrelated Bagobo Babbler which shares the same mossy understorey in montane forest, and is quite similar in appearance.

Benguet Bush Warbler is known only from the Lepanto Mountains of N Luzon, where it is rare and localised.

It occurs among coarse grasses and scattered bushes in open and cleared areas where Long-tailed Bush Warbler is unlikely to be found. Being *Bradypterus*, both species exhibit similar secretive and furtive behaviour but if seen well, plumage and structural differences are diagnostic. Appears smaller and slimmer than Long-tailed Bush, with a much shorter tail. It is warm brown above and lacks the dark, rich rufescent tones. It shows a whitish throat and a greyish breast with darker striations, but has pale-tipped greyish brown undertail-coverts, unlike the plain rufous-brown undertail-coverts of Long-tailed Bush Warbler.

Luzon Bush Warbler can occur alongside Long-tailed Bush Warbler in NW Luzon. This is a typical small *Cettia*, skulking at times but noisy and demonstrative at others. It tends to keep deep within scrub and undergrowth but can appear on the edge of dense foliage several metres above ground. It is considerably smaller than Long-tailed Bush, with a shorter, less graduated tail. The head is more rounded and the short, weak bill accentuates this effect. The wings are typically held over the back, not drooped across the flanks in *Bradypterus* manner and the whole appearance is neater, less elongated than in Long-tailed Bush. It differs from Long-tailed Bush Warbler by its conspicuous pale supercilium, warm brown crown, olive-brown upperparts and pale underparts. The legs and feet are warm brown, not dark as in Long-tailed Bush Warbler.

Bagobo Babbler occurs in forest undergrowth in montane forest on Mindanao where it is known from Mount Busa, Mount Apo and Mount Kitanglad, where Long-tailed Bush Warbler also occurs. It has recently been found to be common in some surveyed areas and may well be widespread throughout forest in the mountains of Mindanao. Kennedy *et al.* (2000) considered it to be 'unquestionably the most secretive bird in the Philippines' but its song establishes its presence. This is a high-pitched, almost inaudible insect-like series of four or more '*seeeeep seep seep seep*' notes, repeated at intervals of four to five seconds (Kennedy *et al.* 2000), quite different to the thin, buzzing song of Long-tailed Bush Warbler (see **Voice** below).

Shares secretive behaviour with Long-tailed Bush Warbler. Even if seen well, the plumages of these two species are extraordinarily similar although the white throat of Bagobo Babbler is slightly more extensive than that of Long-tailed Bush Warbler. Structural differences are more useful with Bagobo Babbler being slightly larger than Long-tailed Bush Warbler with a larger, heavier and wider-based bill and longer wings and tail. The tail lacks the loosely webbed structure of Long-tailed Bush Warbler and appears not to be held cocked above the back.

VOICE The characteristic song of Long-tailed Bush Warbler on Luzon is a repetition of a single thin buzzing sequence that may continue for several minutes without pausing, but is more frequently interspersed with longer pauses before singing recommences. Each sequence lasts approximately one second and is followed by the next sequence 1–2 seconds later. Each has two or more components, commencing with a sharp '*tzp, tzp*', followed by a longer more buzzing '*trrzz*', at a frequency of *c.* 6kHz. The final component of each sequence may be extended into a slurred but piercing '*eet*', so the entire sequence becomes '*tzp- tzp-trrzz-eet, tzp-tzp-trrzz tzp-eet, tzp-tzp-trrzz-eet*', rising in inflection at the end. It may take several attempts for a bird to become fully engaged in this song. Initially, a quieter, less buzzing '*t'tzee, t'tzee, t'tzee*' or '*tzee, tzee, tzee*' may be heard, with intervals of about three seconds between sequences. Harrap (1994) described the song of Luzon birds as comprising two short units followed by a longer, harsher and more buzzing unit; '*trp, trp, trzz*', similar in speed of delivery to the normal song of Kinabalu Bush Warbler but higher pitched and slightly shorter, with the last unit more clearly monosyllabic.

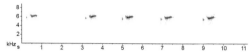

Song of Long-tailed Bush Warbler, recorded within breeding range of *B. c. caudatus*, Mount Polis, Luzon, Philippines, April. (Pete Morris)

The song of the race *unicolor* on Mindanao is slightly higher pitched than that on Luzon, at 7–8kHz, a thicker, more buzzy '*trrrrrrrrzz*' than given by the Luzon bird. However, variation within each island appears to overlap with that between the two islands. On Mindanao, *unicolor* gives either a single or a two-part song phrase, although the first component may be missing and if given is always very quiet '*ti*', barely audible and difficult to separate from the following '*trrrrrrrrzz*'. Each sequence is slightly shorter in duration than that given by Luzon birds. The pause between them is variable, just over a second in some birds, five seconds or longer in others.

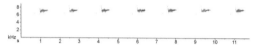

Song of Long-tailed Bush Warbler, recorded within breeding range of *B. c. unicolor*, Mount Pasian, Mindanao, Philippines, April. (Pete Morris)

The song of *malindangensis* is not known to differ from *unicolor*.

Luzon birds give an explosive '*pwit, pwit, pwit...*call, repeated continuously at approximately one second intervals. The calls of Mindanao birds are not known to differ from those on Luzon.

MOULT No data available.

HABITAT Requirements appear very similar to those of the related Kinabalu Bush Warbler in Sabah. It occurs above 700m in moist montane forest, on or close to the ground in light undergrowth or among ferns, mosses, fallen and rotting tree trunks and moss-covered boulders.

BEHAVIOUR Primarily terrestrial, living in the undergrowth close to and on the forest floor in montane mossy forest, sometimes adjacent to degraded areas of secondary forest. It runs and hops over the forest floor, often at great speed, and can be mistaken for a small rodent. Most of the time, however, it skulks quietly within deep cover and rarely forages in the open. When relaxed, it hops with its tail cocked slightly above the back and wings drooped across the flanks, occasionally flicking its wings. If disturbed in an exposed situation and it becomes agitated, it continuously flicks its wings, before darting back into deep cover, often giving the repeated explosive '*pwit*' call.

Males sing throughout the year. The song is most frequently heard in the early morning and evening, but often continues until midday in cool overcast weather. A singing male may climb slowly into view in bushes and low trees in mouse-like fashion, creeping along branches until it reaches a suitable position, which can be on an exposed branch. It

then adopts a fairly upright posture with the bill angled above the horizontal and tail held vertically below the body.

BREEDING HABITS Poorly known. Recently fledged birds have been found in April, May and September and breeding may occur throughout the year. The nest and eggs remain undescribed.

DISTRIBUTION Endemic to the Philippines where it is restricted to the upper slopes of a small number of forested mountains on the two largest islands, Luzon and Mindanao. Apparently uncommon within its restricted range on each island but this status may be due, in part, to its skulking behaviour.

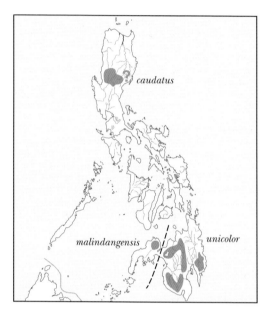

Long-tailed Bush Warbler. Resident within breeding range.

B. c. caudatus The nominate form is restricted to the forested mountains of northern Luzon above 700m. Originally described from Mount Datu in the Lepanto Mountains, it is now known to occur quite widely on suitable forested peaks in Benguet, Ifugao and Nueva Vizcaya Provinces in NW Luzon. Also recorded from Aurora Province in NE Luzon but its distribution here is poorly known. Mount Polis remains the best-known locality for encountering this species.

B. c. unicolor In Mindanao, the race *unicolor* was originally considered to be endemic to Mount Apo but is now known to occur more widely in montane forest above 1,000m. Recent records come from several forested peaks surrounding Mount Apo, including Mount Busa in the south, Mount Pasian in the east and Mount Kitanglad in the centre of the island. It seems likely that it is more widespread within the mountain ranges than the limited number of known localities would suggest.

B. c. malindangensis The race *malindangensis* is known only from Mount Malindang in NW Mindanao, ranging from about 700m to the summit at 2,425m.

MOVEMENTS Believed to be sedentary; no movements have been recorded.

DESCRIPTION *B. c. caudatus*

Plumage – Adult fresh Forehead to nape dark rufescent-brown with indistinct charcoal-grey feather fringes creating faint scaling. Supercilium narrow, greyish white, extending from bill base to rear of eye, but barely discernible over ear-coverts. Lores dull brown to black, forming a well-defined line between bill base and eye. An indistinct blackish spot immediately behind the eye fades into an indistinct eye-line. Ear-coverts greyish brown, darker at upper edges, becoming paler, greyer and with faint mottling towards lower edges. Lower ear-coverts merge imperceptibly into malar region, sides of throat and sides of neck. Poorly defined, narrow whitish eye-ring, merging above eye with supercilium but barely discernible below eye. Mantle and scapulars dark rufescent-brown with grey fringes, but these are less clear and contrasting than on crown. Rump and uppertail-coverts unmarked dark rufescent-brown, slightly brighter than crown and mantle. Tail uniform dark rufescent-brown, strongly graduated with loosely webbed, weak structure.

Chin and throat greyish white. Upper breast slate-grey with a row of indistinct grey striations that merge into lower throat and upper breast. Sides of breast and upper flanks around carpal bend washed slate-grey, merging with warmer, rufescent-brown wash on sides of neck. Lower breast, lower flanks and vent rich warm burnt sienna. Belly slightly paler than flanks and lower breast. Undertail-coverts uniform burnt sienna. Closed wing uniform dark rufescent-brown, with little or no contrast between webs and fringes of tertials, wing-coverts, secondaries and primaries. Diffuse fringes to alula, tertials, secondaries and primaries may be slightly warmer-toned than the upperwing-coverts. Underwing-coverts dark rufous-brown.

Juvenile Darker rufescent-brown overall. Throat pale brown rather than whitish.

Bare parts Upper mandible black. Lower mandible blackish in some birds, deep straw-brown in others. Tarsi and toes dark brown. Iris reddish brown or brown.

IN HAND CHARACTERS

Measurements

B. c. caudatus (1 ♂): *wing* 62; *tail* 88; *bill* 16.5; *tarsus* 26; bill width 4.0; hind claw 8.5; tail graduation 48.

B. c. unicolor (1 ♂, 1 ♀): *wing* 61–62; *tail* 71; *bill* 17.5; *tarsus* 25–27; bill width 3.8–4.2; hind claw 7.7–8.3; tail graduation 42–45.

Structure *B. c. unicolor*

Wing formula (n = 2):

p1/pc	p2	p3	p4	p5	p6	p7	p10
9–11	13–14	7	0.5–2	wp	wp	0–2	6

Wing structure similar to Kinabalu Bush Warbler (Fig. 21); short and strongly rounded, with fairly large p1 and p2 falling far short of wing point. Wing point p5–6 (7); p2 < ss tips, p3 near ss tips; leading pp broad, with no emarginations.

Tail long, very strongly graduated; 12 feathers, rather narrow and readily frayed.

Bill rather large and strong, sides slightly concave. Tarsi long and strong; claws strong, well curved.

B. c. caudatus Tail much longer than in *unicolor* with weaker filamentous structure. Wing particularly rounded (1 specimen examined), with p1 15mm > pc and wing point at p6–7. Based on these three birds examined (2 *unicolor*, 1 *caudatus*) it seems that nominate *caudatus* may have a significantly more rounded wing than *unicolor*, with a longer p1.

Recognition The longer tail eliminates Kinabalu Bush and Chestnut-backed Bush Warblers.

Weight Races combined: 21–28g (22.9; 7) (Dunning 2007).

GEOGRAPHIC VARIATION Three races are recognised. The nominate form shows well marked differences in structure, plumage and vocalisations from the two races endemic to Mindanao, which closely resemble each other.

B. c. caudatus (N Luzon) Described above.

B. c. unicolor (C, E and S Mindanao) Slightly darker above than nominate *caudatus*. It differs most conspicuously by its darker underparts, with the white chin contrasting sharply with the greyish throat and breast, while dark feather fringes and tips create an indistinct mottled effect to the breast. The lower flanks, belly and undertail-coverts are richer rufous-brown than in *caudatus*. This race and *malindangensis* also differ from nominate *caudatus* by their proportionately shorter tails and shorter first primaries. Slight differences in song structure and delivery are discussed within Voice above.

B. c. malindangensis (Mount Melindang, NW Mindanao) Closely resembles *unicolor* but sides of head are slightly darker and the throat is paler.

TAXONOMY AND SYSTEMATICS It is most unlikely that birds from Luzon and Mindanao will come into contact since they are resident and isolated from each other, and separated by inhospitable lowland forest. The known differences may already be sufficient to justify giving specific status to Mindanao birds but should be supported by molecular evidence which is currently lacking. It is certain that birds on Luzon and Mindanao have developed unique plumage and structural characters that enable them to be readily separated. Although the songs of nominate *caudatus* and *unicolor* are quite similar, Harrap (1994) noted that *unicolor* on Mount Kitanglad, Mindanao, reacted poorly, if at all, to playback of the song of nominate *caudatus* from Mount Polis, Luzon, but responded well to recordings of their own songs, supporting suggestions that they may be distinct at the species level.

Within Mindanao, differences between *malindangensis* and *unicolor* are poorly marked, and Ripley & Rabor (1961) recommended that all Mindanao birds be united within a single taxon. We agree that *malindangensis* is poorly defined and barely separable, but have continued to recognise it as a valid race.

KINABALU BUSH WARBLER
Bradypterus accentor   Plate 8

Androphilus accentor Sharpe, 1888. *Ibis*, p. 390, pl. 9, fig. 2. Mount Kinabalu, Sabah, Borneo.

An endemic resident confined to the forested upper slopes of three peaks in N Borneo. It often appears unconcerned by the presence of people and has a well-deserved reputation for being 'friendly', at times approaching and even walking over the feet of resting hill walkers, which has given rise to its alternative name of Friendly Bush Warbler. Monotypic.

IDENTIFICATION Length 15cm. Wing 58–61mm. Tail/ wing 95–102%.

This medium-sized, dark rufous-brown warbler is the only *Bradypterus* occurring on Borneo, where it frequents the lower undergrowth in upper montane forest and often feeds on the ground. It is readily recognised by its distinctive far-carrying and repetitive buzzing song and singing birds often sit on the side of a bush or on low emergent vegetation, when the contrasting whitish throat and boldly spotted upper breast are conspicuous. Unlike other *Bradypterus*, feeding birds appear to seek disturbed open ground. Sexes alike.

Structure Rather stocky for a *Bradypterus*, but shares a horizontal and attenuated structure, with long undertail-coverts and rather slim bill, with other Asian montane *Bradypterus*. The short wings are usually held slightly open and drooped loosely across the flanks and are flicked continuously, accentuating the rather plump body shape. The wings are strongly rounded with a long first primary (p1) and wing point formed by p5–6. The strongly graduated tail, with only ten rectrices, is frequently held slightly cocked above the back.

Plumage and bare parts Drab and nondescript, the entire upperparts including the closed wings and tail uniform dark rufescent-brown. There is usually a thin, pale buffy brown supercilium and a dark line across the lores, but it lacks a clearly defined eye-line behind the eye. The dull greyish brown ear-coverts show fine pale buff streaking, giving a slightly paler appearance to the sides of the head. The chin and throat are whitish, conspicuously paler than the greyish brown breast, while the belly appears rusty buff. The throat and upper breast are copiously but variably marked with blackish spots, which sometimes extend onto the lower breast and occasionally reach to the upper belly. The flanks are dull rusty brown, darkening to richer brown on the vent and undertail-coverts.

The bill is black, although some birds show a paler base to the lower mandible, while that of juveniles is entirely greyish pink. The legs and feet are dark reddish brown.

SIMILAR SPECIES Kinabalu Bush Warbler resembles Long-tailed Bush Warbler of the Philippines and Chestnut-backed Bush Warbler of the Wallacean sub-region, but as neither of these species occurs in Borneo, there is no possibility of confusion. Sunda Bush Warbler represents an unlikely confusion species on the high peaks of Sabah, where both can occur together in the montane forest of Mount Kinabalu.

Sunda Bush Warbler is a vocal and conspicuous warbler whose distinctive song, a pleasantly undulating whistled '*chee-hu-ueeoo*', is quite different from the repetitive nasal buzzing of Kinabalu Bush Warbler. It is a typical small and neatly proportioned *Cettia* with a rather large rounded head, proportionately short tail, short undertail-coverts and perky, upright stance. Although it can be secretive, it is just as likely to be demonstrative and conspicuous, often feeding and singing in the open in low trees and bushes in clearings or along roadsides. It differs from Kinabalu Bush Warbler by its greyish brown upperparts, long whitish supercilium, paler unspotted underparts and fleshy brown, not dark, legs.

VOICE The repetitive song of Kinabalu Bush Warbler is one of the characteristic sounds of the higher montane forests of northern Borneo, where it can be loud and far-carrying in the still, moisture-laden mountain air, frequently being audible up to 500m or more. Song bursts may last for just a few seconds or continue without a pause for several minutes. Approximately 40 phrases are given per minute, each lasting about one second, and separated by breaks of *c.* 0.5 seconds.

The song is recognisably similar to those of many other Asian *Bradypterus* and consists of a series of short sequences repeated continuously, within a frequency range of 5–7kHz. Each comprises a repetitive, nasal, rasping '*trrzzz*', given in combination with a brief and much quieter and weaker '*trp*'. Song structure does, however, vary between individuals. While all males include the rasping '*trrzzz*' sequence in the song, the emphasis on the '*trp*' varies individually. On some it appears as a single note after the '*trrzzz*'; so the phrase becomes '*trrzzz-trp...*' with a pause of approximately 0.5 seconds between phrases. Other birds may include one or two '*trp*' phrases that can precede the rasp, becoming a repetitive '*trp trp trrzzz, trp trp, trp trp trrzzz...*'. Harrap (1994) described a variation of this song from Mount Kinabalu that he considered to be weaker and mellower than the normal song. It was lower in pitch and delivered at a much slower pace, approximately 20 phrases per minute, each phrase consisting of two brief calls followed by two longer buzzing notes; '*tu di dzu-yu, tu di dzu-yu, tu di dzu-yu...*'.

Song of Kinabalu Bush Warbler, Mount Kinabalu, Sabah, Malaysia, July. (Peter Kennerley)

Sonograms show that the song resembles that of Long-tailed Bush Warbler in overall structure and speed of delivery. However, the song of Long-tailed Bush is slightly higher pitched with a shorter, faster final phrase.

Calls are weak, only audible at close range. They include various subdued '*chit*' or '*chut*' notes, given singly and intermittently.

MOULT No information available.

HABITAT Frequents the floor and lower levels of damp montane and upper montane forest with dark, damp gullies, moss covered *Leptospermum* trees and stumps, fallen logs and boulders. There is usually a light understorey of saturated mosses and small ferns.

BEHAVIOUR Not shy, but unobtrusive, spending most time on or near the ground. Typically appears briefly, scurrying rodent-like, then disappearing under a log or behind a rock or fern frond, often to reappear several metres away. At times it can be very confiding and apparently unconcerned by nearby observers, hence the alternative name of Kinabalu

Friendly Warbler. It forages through undergrowth, hopping over moss-covered logs and boulders, continually wing flicking. Singing birds are easier to find and observe. Males perch up to a metre above the ground, often in full view, but will disappear quickly if disturbed by an unexpected movement. It may sing from the same twig for several minutes, drooping the wings across the flanks and slightly cocking the tail. It sings throughout the year but less frequently and persistently during the northern winter, although this may reflect the poorer weather conditions prevailing at this time (PRK pers. obs.).

BREEDING HABITS Little information. The nest and eggs are undescribed.

DISTRIBUTION Endemic to N Borneo where it shows the characteristic relict distribution of a species marooned in a cooler montane 'island' environment surrounded by unsuitable humid tropical rainforest. It occurs in montane forest on the upper slopes of just three neighbouring peaks in Sabah, E Malaysia. It is best known from Mount Kinabalu, the highest peak in SE Asia, where it occurs between 1,800m and 3,800m (Smythies & Davison 1999). It is particularly numerous from 2,300–2,900m, but becomes less common in stunted upper montane forest above 3,000m. It reaches the tree line around 3,600m but is absent in higher alpine scrub. Also known from Gunung Tamboyukan (between 1,825–2,356m) to the north of Mount Kinabalu and Gunung Trus Madi (between 2,200–2,336m) to the south, where it has been collected at 2,315m (Smythies 1975) but it was recorded here at 1,770m (Fogden 1965). These mountains are considerably lower than Mount Kinabalu but support upper montane forest at the altitudes where Kinabalu Bush Warbler is numerous on Mount Kinabalu. There are no records from the hill ranges further south and it is apparently absent from the Kelabit Uplands, the main upland massif of Borneo. Much of its preferred habitat occurs in National Parks where there are no immediate or apparent threats to its long-term survival and reports of a recent decline appear to be unfounded.

Kinabalu Bush Warbler. Resident within breeding range.

MOVEMENTS Believed to be resident.

DESCRIPTION
Plumage – Adult fresh Forehead to nape dull rufescent-brown, with slightly darker brown fringes creating faint mottling. Supercilium pale buffy brown, indistinct and narrow, extending from bill base to rear of eye. A dull greyish brown loral line is usually present but there is little or no hint of a darker line behind eye. Ear-coverts greyish brown, finely streaked pale buff to white. Eye-ring concolorous with supercilium and ear-coverts. Mantle and scapulars to rump and uppertail-coverts dull, rich rufescent-brown with slightly darker brown fringes on mantle and scapulars. Tail feathers dark brown, contrastingly darker than upperparts, with dull rufescent-brown fringes.

Chin white, usually unmarked. Throat greyish white, with numerous black spots, larger and more conspicuous towards upper breast. Breast greyish brown with conspicuous but variable dark brown or blackish spotting, extending to the lower breast on most but restricted to the upper breast in some, and extending to the sides of breast and occasionally the upper belly on others. Belly warm buff to dark rusty brown. Sides of breast and upper flanks washed dull rusty brown, darkening to dull rufous-brown on lower flanks, vent and undertail-coverts.

Lesser and median coverts uniform rufescent-brown as upperparts, lacking darker centres. Greater coverts, alula and tertials blackish brown with dark rufous-brown fringes, slightly warmer than mantle. Secondaries and primaries blackish, edged dark rufous-brown. Underwing-coverts dark russet-brown.

Juvenile Similar to adult, but upperparts and closed wing generally duller and drabber. Supercilium dull buff above lores, barely contrasting with sides of head and not extending beyond eye. Crown and ear-coverts show a scaly or mottled effect, more pronounced than on adult. Underparts darker than in adult. Chin and throat pale sandy buff, merging with darker, browner breast and flanks. Breast spotting less conspicuous and more restricted, typically to small dark brown smudges which form indistinct striations down breast.

Bare parts Upper mandible black. Lower mandible black in some, perhaps adults in breeding condition, pale grey to straw-brown in others. Lower mandible of immature slightly paler greyish pink. Tarsi and toes dark reddish brown. Iris dark brown.

IN HAND CHARACTERS
Measurements

Sexes combined:

Wing	58–61 (59.4; 5)
Tail	55–61 (58.0; 5)
Bill	15–16 (15.6; 4))
Tarsus	22–23.5 (23.0; 4)

Tail/wing ratio: 95–102% (98%; 5)
Bill width: 3.4–3.7 (3.6; 4)
Hind claw: 6.2–6.8 (6.6; 5)
Tail graduation: 23–27 (25.4; 5)

Structure

Wing formula (n = 5):

p1/pc	p2	p3	p4	p5	p6	p7	p10
9–12	11–17	6–7	1–2	wp	wp	0–0.5	4–6

Wing short and strongly rounded with large p1 (*c.* 60%

of p2). Wing point p5–7; p2 < ss tips, p3 near ss tips; leading pp broad, with no emarginations.

Figure 21. Wing of Kinabalu Bush Warbler.

Tail rather short, strongly graduated; ten feathers, narrow but rounded.

Bill fairly narrow but strong; sides slightly concave.

Tarsi rather slender; much less substantial than in Long-tailed Bush Warbler; claws well curved.

Recognition Wing similar to Long-tailed Bush Warbler; short and strongly rounded with long p1 (*c.* 60% p2) and p2 tip falling well short of ss tips. Tail lacks filamentous, loose and frayed structure of Long-tailed Bush Warbler, which has a proportionately longer tail with 12, rather than ten rectrices. **Weight** *c.* 14g (del Hoyo *et al.* 2006).

GEOGRAPHIC VARIATION None recorded.

TAXONOMY AND SYSTEMATICS The mountains of N Borneo lie close to the S Philippines where the endemic Long-tailed Bush Warbler occurs in the montane forests of Mindanao. Kinabalu Bush and Long-tailed Bush Warblers have many features in common and are quite similar in appearance, leading Delacour (1942–43) to conclude that they are closely related. Harrap (1994) noted a similarity between the songs of the two.

Other *Bradypterus* occurring in the Sundaic and Wallacean regions include Javan Bush, Benguet Bush and Timor Bush Warblers. These species, which form part of the Russet Bush Warbler complex, show a preference for montane grassland habitats and are quite different in plumage and structure from Kinabalu Bush Warbler. Chestnut-backed Bush Warbler of Sulawesi, Seram and Buru appears to share morphological and vocal similarities with Kinabalu Bush Warbler, but its true affinities are uncertain.

▲ ▶ ▲ Adult, Mount Kinabalu, Sabah, Malaysia, May. Distinctly larger and heavier than mainland *Bradypterus* with darker, richer reddish brown upperparts and flanks, contrasting with grey throat, breast and sides of head and conspicuous black spots on lower throat and upper breast (James Eaton/Birdtour Asia).

CHESTNUT-BACKED BUSH WARBLER
Bradypterus castaneus   Plate 8

Turdinus castaneus **Büttikofer, 1893**. *Notes Leyden Mus.*, 15: 260–261. Minahassa, northern Celebes.

Restricted to Sulawesi and the nearby islands of Buru and Seram in the Moluccas, Indonesia, where it frequents the understorey of damp montane forest. Polytypic, with three distinctive insular races recognised, but their relationship is unclear and more than one species may be involved.
B. c. castaneus (Büttikofer, 1893). Sulawesi.
B. c. disturbans (Hartert, 1900). Buru, Molucca Islands.
B. c. musculus (Stresemann, 1914). Seram, Molucca Islands.

IDENTIFICATION Length 14–15cm. Wing *c.* 54–60mm. Tail/wing *c.* 95%.
  This medium sized, drab rufous-brown warbler is the only *Bradypterus* occurring within the montane forests of Wallacea and is readily overlooked. It is almost invariably located by its unobtrusive, insect-like buzzing song which lacks the harsh rasping quality of most other *Bradypterus* songs. If seen well, its whitish supercilium, pale throat and contrastingly darker grey and unmarked breast should confirm the identification. Sexes alike.
Structure A chunky *Bradypterus*, similar in size and structure to Kinabalu Bush Warbler but proportionately shorter tailed. It possesses a relatively stout bill, relatively long legs and strongly rounded wings with a long first primary (p1) and the wing point formed by p5–7, and sometimes also p4. Smaller and much shorter tailed than Long-tailed Bush Warbler of the Philippines.
Plumage and bare parts A drab and nondescript *Bradypterus* which is rarely seen in the gloom of the forest floor. The nominate race has rufescent-brown to chestnut-brown upperparts, including the wings and tail. The head shows a darker grey-brown crown and a long and fairly distinctive greyish white supercilium, most prominent in front of the eye but reaching the rear of the ear-coverts. Below this there is a conspicuously darker eye-stripe. It has an indistinct pale grey eye-ring and greyish brown ear-coverts that fade to mottled grey towards the sides of the throat. If seen well, the contrastingly paler greyish white chin and throat are usually conspicuous, but the uniform and unmarked slate-grey upper breast often appears much darker. The lower breast and adjacent flanks are warm chocolate-brown, darkening to sepia-brown on the belly, lower flanks and undertail-coverts.
  Young birds are generally duller and more uniform in their appearance and lack the dark eye-stripe (J. Bowler *in litt*).
  The bill is black with a yellowish base to the lower mandible. The legs and feet are dark reddish-brown.

SIMILAR SPECIES No *Bradypterus*, *Cettia* or *Urosphena* species occur within the range of Chestnut-backed Bush Warbler and there is little likelihood of confusing it with other resident species. Few warblers from northeast Asia reach the Wallacean region during the northern winter with Gray's Grasshopper Warbler being the most likely to occur.
Gray's Grasshopper Warbler frequents forest edge and secondary scrub from the lowlands to *c.* 600m, but is unlikely to occur in montane forest and would probably not overlap with Chestnut-backed Bush Warbler. It is considerably larger than Chestnut-backed Bush with a proportionately longer

and broader tail, longer wings and a more substantial bill. It shows a conspicuous long, pale supercilium and a dark eye-stripe. Its olive-brown upperparts are significantly duller than the warm rufescent-brown of Chestnut-backed Bush on Sulawesi, although closer to the upperpart colour of the race *disturbans* on Buru. The breast and flanks are washed dull olive-brown or, in young birds, dirty sulphur-yellow, again duller and quite different from Chestnut-backed Bush. The legs are pinkish, much paler than those of Chestnut-backed Bush Warbler.

VOICE On Sulawesi, the song is short, repetitive and high-pitched and can be difficult to discern from background insect noise. Each sequence is a short, quiet and buzzing '*tzeeeuuutzeee*', which rises and falls in pitch within a frequency range of 6–9kHz. It lasts for approximately one second and is repeated at intervals of between two and five seconds. This sequence is sometimes extended with an additional '*uuu*' which forms a terminal flourish, becoming '*tzeeeuuutzeeeuuu*'. A less frequently heard variation is a thin, feeble repeated '*tzee*', having the quality of a Coal Tit call. This may be a subsong or a preliminary introduction to the main song.

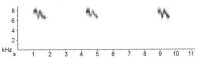

Song of Chestnut-backed Bush Warbler, recorded within breeding range of *B. c. castaneus*, central Sulawesi, Indonesia, July. (K. D. Bishop)

  The song of the race *musculus* on Seram is a frequently repeated '*zit-oh-zit, zit-oh-zit...*'. (J. Bowler *in litt*), and very different to that of the nominate form on Sulawesi. This is supported by the observations of Rheindt & Hutchinson (2007), who describe the song as having a similar structure to that of the nominate race although the notes have a distinctly different quality and spacing. The song of the race *disturbans* on Buru has not been recorded. However, Rheindt & Hutchinson (2007) commented that its song sounded distinct from that of the other two races.
  The usual call is a loud, high-pitched and rather nasal '*pzwit, pzwit...*', with a pause of one or two seconds between each call. An adult calling to a fully fledged juvenile bird on Seram gave a continuous soft '*chit, chit, chit, chit...*' (J. Bowler *in litt*).

MOULT No information available.

HABITAT On Sulawesi it is most frequently encountered in the ground layer of unlogged montane mossy forest. It does, however, tolerate adjacent secondary forest, degraded scrubland and areas of thick grass and low shrubs adjacent to forest. Within the preferred forest habitat, it frequents damp moss-covered rocks and trunks with tangles of dense scrub and vines.
  On Buru, it occurs in montane forest essentially similar to that on Sulawesi, but has also been reported from rank grassland (Coates & Bishop 1997).
  On Seram, it is known only from montane forest, where said to be common at lower levels in a mixture of oak *Lithocarpus* and *Castanopsis*, meranti and the conifers *Agathis* and *Dracydium*, with a dense layer of damp moss and ferns. It is frequently associated with stands of dense bamboo on clay subsoil and is reportedly much less numerous in limestone areas with thin undergrowth (Bowler & Taylor 1989).

BEHAVIOUR Extremely skulking and frustratingly elusive, but not particularly shy. Like other montane *Bradypterus*, it is largely terrestrial and usually seen close to, or walking on the forest floor. The tail is often held slightly cocked and the wings are continuously flicked across the back. It is most active at dawn and dusk when it may emerge onto logging tracks, but it scuttles mouse-like back into cover if disturbed. When singing, it will perch on a low branch of a bush, sometimes in full view, and remain stationary for several minutes if undisturbed.

BREEDING HABITS The nest and eggs are undescribed. An adult was observed collecting grubs for a fully-fledged juvenile on 7 August (Bowler & Taylor 1989).

DISTRIBUTION Confined to Sulawesi and the nearby islands of Buru and Seram in the Moluccas, Indonesia.

B. c. castaneus The nominate form has an extensive distribution in montane forest throughout Sulawesi above 950m, with some reaching 3,500m. In the north, it is widespread and numerous in the accessible areas in Dumoga-Bone National Park and it has been recorded from the forest ridge on Gunung Kabila at 1,400m. It also occurs in forest undergrowth below the summit of Gunung Muajat at 1,780m (Rozendaal & Dekker 1989). In the centre of the island, it is numerous above 1,300m in Lore Lindu National Park.

B. c. disturbans The race *disturbans* is only known from Buru where it has been recorded between 750m and *c.* 2,000m, but its distribution within the island has not been studied.

B. c. musculus The easternmost race *musculus* is restricted to the highest mountain range on Seram, where it is known from Gunung Binaia at 2,490m and Gunung Kobipoto at 1,500m. Here it was described as being common between 1,000m and 1,750m (Bowler & Taylor 1989) but recorded down to 850m on Gunung Binaia.

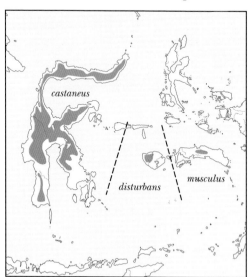

Chestnut-backed Bush Warbler. Resident within breeding range.

MOVEMENTS All races believed to be resident and there are no known instances of movements within or between islands.

DESCRIPTION *B. c. castaneus*
Plumage – Adult fresh Forehead, crown and nape dark brown with distinct darker greyish fringes giving a faintly scalloped appearance. Supercilium greyish white, narrow and well defined, extending to rear of ear-coverts; most conspicuous between bill base and rear of eye, then narrowing before merging with sides of crown. Lores dark greyish brown to blackish, forming a distinct line from bill to eye. There is usually a dark brown smudge or spot behind eye, but no distinct eye-line. Ear-coverts greyish brown, fading to mottled grey towards their lower edges and the sides of the throat. An indistinct pale grey eye-ring joins the supercilium above the eye but is barely discernible below it. Mantle and scapulars uniform rufescent-brown to chestnut-brown, contrasting with the darker, greyer crown and nape. Greyish fringes often visible on mantle, creating faintly scalloped appearance, but less obvious than on head. Rump and uppertail-coverts warm chestnut-brown and unmarked. Tail uniform warm chestnut-brown. Chin and centre of throat whitish, lightly washed pale grey. Side of throat pale ash-grey, slightly darker tips creating faint mottling which increases across the malar region to merge with lower ear-coverts. Upper breast and sides of breast uniform slate-grey, warming to dark rufous-brown on lower breast and upper flanks. Belly, lower flanks, vent and undertail-coverts deep sepia-brown. Lesser and median coverts and tertials chestnut-brown, similar to upperpart colour and lacking darker centres. Primary coverts, greater coverts and alula with slightly darker brown centres and chestnut-brown fringes. Flight feathers dark grey; secondaries edged bright chestnut-brown, primaries edged slightly paler, creating a brighter rufescent bronze panel on the closed wing. Underwing-coverts grey-brown.
Juvenile Not described.
Bare parts Upper mandible black. Lower mandible deep warm straw. Tarsi and toes dark reddish-brown.

IN HAND CHARACTERS
Measurements
B. c. castaneus (2 ♀♀): *wing* 54, 58; *tail* 50, 57; *bill* 16, 17; *tarsus* 25, 26; bill width 4.0; hind claw 7.0, 7.3; tail graduation 28.
B. c. disturbans (1 unsexed): *wing* 60; *bill* 17.5; *tarsus* 25.

Structure *B. c. castaneus*

Wing formula (n = 2):

p1/pc	p2	p3	p4	p5	p6	p7	p10
13–14	10–11	3–4	0–0.5	wp	wp	wp	4–7

Wing structure similar to Kinabalu Bush Warbler (Fig. 21); short and strongly rounded, with large p1. Wing point p5–7; p2 < ss tips, p3 = p9–10; leading pp broad with no emarginations.

Tail fairly short, strongly graduated; 12 feathers, narrow and loosely structured.

Bill rather narrow but deep; sides slightly concave.

Tarsi long and strong; claws well curved.
Weight *B. c. castaneus*: 19g (n = 1) (Dunning 2007).

GEOGRAPHIC VARIATION Three races recognised. The nominate form is the most widespread and shows no variation within its range in the hills of Sulawesi. Birds on Buru closely resemble those on Sulawesi, but those on Seram show substantial differences.
B. c. castaneus (Sulawesi) Described above.

B. c. disturbans (Buru) Differs from the nominate form in having warmer and browner upperparts, with chestnut tones reduced or absent. The edges to secondaries and primaries are warm brown, giving a uniform appearance to the upperparts. The side of the head is brown, lacking the greyish appearance of the nominate race, but the fine whitish supercilium remains conspicuous. The underparts are warmer and slightly paler than nominate form, with grey restricted to a band across the upper breast.

Bare parts as nominate race but the lower mandible is deep straw at the base, darkening slightly towards tip.

B. c. musculus (Seram) Distinctly darker than the nominate race. Differs by the darker sooty-brown upperparts which lack warmer brown or chestnut tones, and the supercilium is greyish and inconspicuous. The side of the head is greyish and merges with the grey underparts.

TAXONOMY AND SYSTEMATICS Rheindt & Hutchinson (2007) commented that differences in plumage and song between the nominate race and *musculus* are likely to be sufficient to justify their recognition as distinct species. But until the appearance and, in particular, the song of the race *disturbans* on Buru are compared and its relationship with the other taxa fully established, a decision to split them would be premature. In addition, the relationship between Chestnut-backed Bush Warbler and the *Bradypterus* resident in the montane forests of SE Asia requires investigation.

Drovetski *et al.* (2004) examined the phylogeny of *Locustella* and related genera, including *Bradypterus*, in Asia, using mtDNA. They found an unexpectedly close relationship between Chestnut-backed Bush Warbler and *Locustella*. They concluded this species to be more closely related to Eurasian Grasshopper Warbler than that species was to its assumed nearest relative, Lanceolated Warbler.

▲ ▶ Adult *B. c. musculus*, Seram, Indonesia, August. Characterised by uniform chestnut-brown upperparts and unmarked slate-grey upper-breast and side of head, contrasting with warm chocolate-brown to sepia-brown flanks, belly and undertail-coverts. Typically keeps close to the ground in lush montane forest (Robert Hutchinson/Birdtour Asia).

Genus *Elaphrornis* Legge, 1879

[Gr. *elaphros* small, nimble; *ornis* bird]

A monotypic genus containing just one resident species, Ceylon Bush Warbler, endemic to Sri Lanka. It has previously been included within *Bradypterus*, although when described by Legge he believed it to be related to the babblers and placed it within the Timaliidae. It shares structural similarities with Kinabalu Bush Warbler and Chestnut-backed Bush Warbler but is slightly larger, with a strong deep bill and long legs. The sexes are dimorphic; the iris is ruby red in the male, white or cream in the female.

CEYLON BUSH WARBLER
Elaphrornis palliseri   Plate 8

Brachypteryx palliseri **Blyth**, 1851. *J. Asiatic Soc. Bengal*, 20: 178. Ceylon. Above 3,500 feet.

Endemic to the higher hills of S Sri Lanka where it is considered NEAR THREATENED by BirdLife International due to its restricted range. Different in appearance and structure from Asian *Bradypterus* species and does not appear to have close affinities with them. Monotypic.

IDENTIFICATION Length *c.* 14cm. Wing 58–65mm. Tail/wing 98–107%.

A stocky featureless warbler with olive-brown upperparts and yellowish underparts. No closely related warblers occur on Sri Lanka. Sexes similar, but iris colour differs.

Structure Heavy-bodied, with a relatively short but strongly graduated tail. It has short rounded wings with a very large first primary (p1) and wing point formed by p5–7. It is slightly larger than the *Bradypterus* of continental Asia and appearance suggests a small babbler. The legs are quite long and the bill appears deep based and strong.

Plumage and bare parts Drab and nondescript. The entire upperparts of the adult, including the wing-coverts, flight feather edges and tail are uniform dull olive-brown. There is a faintly paler stripe above the dull brown loral line, but the supercilium and eyestripe are indistinct or absent behind the eye. The sides of the head are slightly paler and greyer than the upperparts. The underparts are drab and uniform, although the chin and throat are slightly paler, varying from pale cream to bright yellowish buff, and usually sharply demarcated from the greyish brown cheeks. Otherwise, the underparts vary from pale cream to yellowish buff, with a greyish brown suffusion on the breast and flanks, becoming pale primrose-yellow on the lower belly. The vent and undertail-coverts are deep umber.

Young birds are slightly darker above than adults, and faintly rufescent. The creamy white throat is tinged olive-brown and lacks sharp definition with the cheeks, and the upper breast tends to be browner.

The bill is dark brown to blackish, with a pale straw base to the lower mandible. The legs and feet are pale yellowish brown. Sexes can be separated by iris colour, rich ruby red in the male, white to pale cream in the female.

SIMILAR SPECIES There are no similar species in the mountains of Sri Lanka with which Ceylon Bush Warbler could be confused.

VOICE The song consists of a short sequence of thin, high-pitched squeaky and slightly slurred notes. The entire song sequence, described as '*swee-swee-seee – see-see - see-see*' has a rapid delivery and lasts about one second. It initially increases, in frequency, falls and then increases again, within a range of 2–8kHz. This is immediately followed by two pairs of notes, sometimes slurred together to form a terminal flourish. The quiet delivery and high frequency of parts of this song makes it difficult to discern amongst background noise and it is only occasionally repeated, and is so easily overlooked.

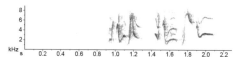

Song of Ceylon Bush Warbler, Horton Plains, Sri Lanka, April. (Deepal Warakagoda)

The most frequently heard call is a single sharp and high pitched, dry '*tsick*', repeated at intervals of about two seconds, although several calls are occasionally given in rapid succession. This call is occasionally interspersed with a lower pitched and almost sparrow-like '*chrup*' call.

MOULT Little information. Baker (1997) considered adults to have a complete post-breeding moult, probably in October and November, followed by partial pre-breeding moult. Juveniles are said to have a partial post-juvenile moult of the head and body feathers and probably some wing-coverts (Baker 1997).

HABITAT A bird of the hills and mountains, most numerous above 1,500m and extending to the tree line just below 2,000m. It inhabits undergrowth in montane forest, secondary scrub and occasionally tea plantations adjacent to forest. It is apparently never found away from tree cover and is absent from montane grassland. It requires a thick understorey of ferns, dwarf bamboo, nillu *Strobilanthes* and elephant grass. At higher elevations, trees less than 10m tall may not form a complete canopy and it appears to prefer this open forest.

BEHAVIOUR Unobtrusive, spending much time on or close to the ground, creeping through and below dense undergrowth. Its behaviour resembles that of a small rodent or wren-babbler *Pnoepyga*. It frequently appears and then disappears behind fallen logs, thick vegetation or moss-covered boulders. Quite vocal, the progress of individuals or pairs being revealed by regular calling. When foraging, it continuously flicks its wings and raises the tail slightly. Singing birds may droop their wings across the flanks, giving a rather plump-bodied impression not apparent at other times.

It rarely flies when alarmed and then usually flutters weakly from one scrub patch to the next, occasionally flitting across a trail. More frequently seen as it scurries across the ground, rarely pausing in the open. If undisturbed it will feed within undergrowth on the edge of a track or clearing and can be quite confiding. It responds well to song playback when it may approach a stationary observer and sing from an exposed perch.

BREEDING HABITS Breeds between February and May and sometimes again in September. Nest building takes place from February and is carried out by both sexes. The nest is a large, solid structure constructed from grass, leaves and moss, placed in a dense tangle of ferns and twigs within 1m of the ground. The cup is deep, lined with fine plant fibres. A nest in Horton Plains National Park in early March was in a tangle of ferns within a metre of the roadside (PRK pers. obs.). The usual clutch is 2–3 eggs. No details of incubation or fledging are available.

DISTRIBUTION Endemic to the highlands of S Sri Lanka where resident and widespread, mainly above 1,500m, but occasionally down to *c.* 1,000m. It is particularly numerous in the Horton Plains National Park at *c.* 2,000m and occurs up to the tree line.

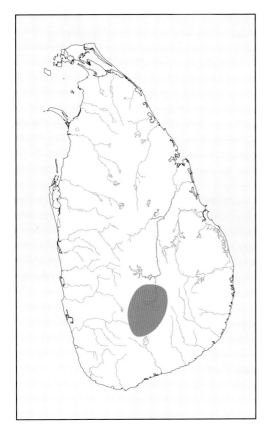

Ceylon Bush Warbler. Resident within breeding range.

MOVEMENTS Believed to be resident throughout the year. No seasonal or altitudinal movements have been reported.

DESCRIPTION
Plumage – Adult fresh Forehead to nape dark olive-brown. Supercilium pale buff and indistinct, from bill base to eye, merging with ear-coverts just behind eye. Lores dull brown, faintly tipped greyish white, forming a distinctly darker line between bill base and eye. Usually a small dark spot behind the eye, but no eye-line. Ear-coverts dull brown, narrowly but heavily streaked greyish white, rather paler than dark crown. No paler or contrasting eye-ring. Mantle, scapulars, rump and uppertail-coverts dark olive brown, concolorous with crown and nape. Tail dark olive-brown, as uppertail-coverts, crossed by numerous faintly darker cross-bars.

Chin and throat pale cream to bright yellowish buff. Sides of throat sharply demarcated from greyish brown malar region and lower ear-coverts. Upper breast pale creamy brown to yellowish buff with a greyish brown suffusion, most conspicuous towards the sides. Lower breast and belly washed pale primrose-yellow. Upper flanks greyish brown, darkening to deep umber on lower flanks and vent. Undertail-coverts deep umber, plain and unmarked. Lesser and median coverts dull olive-brown, lacking darker centres. Greater coverts dull olive-brown with slightly warmer, brighter brown fringes. Tertials dull olive-brown, similar to mantle, but indistinctly marked with slightly warmer, browner, narrow lines, creating a faintly hatched pattern. Primary coverts, alula, secondaries and primaries dark brown with dull olive-brown edges. Underwing-coverts dark olive-grey.
Juvenile Similar to adult, but dull olive-brown crown and upperparts slightly darker, more rufescent. Pale buff supercilium still less conspicuous. Olive-brown ear coverts less strongly streaked, contrasting little with crown. Underparts duller and browner than in adult, with chin and throat dull creamy white to sulphur-yellow, feathers heavily tipped olive-brown and merging with olive-brown cheeks and lower ear-coverts. Breast deep sulphur-yellow with dull greyish brown tips, these being darker on the sides of the breast, lower sides of neck and upper flanks.
Bare parts Upper mandible dark brown with slightly paler cutting edge. Lower mandible pale straw, sometimes with a dark shadow towards the tip. Tarsi and toes warm straw. Iris rich ruby red in male, white to pale creamy buff in female.

IN HAND CHARACTERS
Measurements

Sexes combined:

Wing	58–65 (61.3; 17)
Tail	58–69 (62.8; 18)
Bill	16.5–19 (18.1; 16)
Tarsus	24–27 (25.8; 18)

Tail/wing ratio: 98–107% (102%; 17)
Bill width: 3.6–4.2 (3.9; 11)
Hind claw: 7.0–8.0 (7.3; 12)
Tail graduation: 27–34 (31.2; 9)

Structure

Wing formula (n = 10):

p1/pc	p2	p3	p4	p5	p6	p7	p10
13–17	10–16	3–8	1–3	0–0.5	wp	0–0.5	3–5

Wing short and strongly rounded with large, broad, rounded p1 (*c.* 70% p2). Wing point p5–7; p2 < ss tips, p3 near ss tips; leading pp broad, with no emarginations.

Figure 22. Wing of Ceylon Bush Warbler.

Tail longish, strongly graduated; 12 narrow feathers.
Bill strong and broad-based, concave-sided with narrow tip.
Tarsi long and strong; toes and claws strong.

Weight *c.* 9–14g (del Hoyo *et al.* 2006).

GEOGRAPHIC VARIATION None recorded.

TAXONOMY AND SYSTEMATICS The affinities and origins of Ceylon Bush Warbler are uncertain and there have been no molecular studies to establish its phylogeny to date. It differs from *Bradypterus* in both appearance and structure and seems to have no close relatives in Asia. Although originally described as *Brachypteryx palliseri* by Blyth (1851), Legge (1880) included it in the monotypic genus *Elaphrornis; Brachypteryx* then being preoccupied. He gave it the English name Palliser's Ant-Thrush and suggested that it might be related to the wren-babblers. Although still included within *Bradypterus* by many authorities, this position is being increasingly questioned and Dickinson (2003) reinstated it in *Elaphrornis*. We have adopted this recommendation.

▲ ▶ Adult female, Horton Plains, Sri Lanka, March. The conspicuous pale iris identifies this as an adult female. Young birds may show a dark or dull greyish white iris (Gehan de Silva Wijeyeratne).

▲ Adult male, Horton Plains, Sri Lanka, March. Only the adult male shows the distinctive reddish iris (Uditha Hettige).

Genus *Locustella* Kaup, 1829

[Dim. from L. *locusta* grasshopper]

A genus of nine species that breed entirely within the Palearctic. Eight are long-distance migrants, some wintering in tropical Africa but most migrating to S or SE Asia. The ninth species, Japanese Swamp Warbler, is a resident or short-distance migrant.

These are small to rather large, slim-bodied warblers with an attenuated head shape and, typically, a slim fine-tipped bill. They have graduated, sometimes broad tails of 12 feathers, and long undertail-coverts that usually cover the outermost tail feathers. The migrants have long, bluntly pointed wings with a minute first primary. Most have rather slender legs, long slender toes and fine claws. A long central toe and short inner and outer toes of equal length represent adaptations to a walking gait and give relatively weak clinging ability (Leisler 1975: see Fig 23).

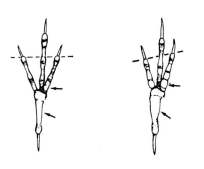

Figure 23. Comparison of foot structure of (a) a typical *Locustella* e.g. Savi's Warbler and (b) a typical *Acrocephalus* e.g. Sedge Warbler (after Leisler 1975).

Swinhoe (1863b) noted that the tibial tendons are hard and rigid, and blunted scissors during specimen preparation. The rictal bristles are vestigial. The plumage is subdued, greyish or olive to warm brown above, plain in some species, streaked in others. The breast is sometimes streaked or spotted, and the undertail-coverts are usually conspicuously marked, either with dark streaks or pale-tipped. Their head patterns are rather plain, the supercilium poorly marked.

These are generally secretive birds of low rank herbage and thicket, dense grass or reedbeds. They build bulky, cup-shaped nests, on or close to the ground. Four species breed in Europe as well as in Asia, and form a 'western group' characterised by distinctive reeling or pulsating songs and sharp ticking calls. A further four migrant species that breed entirely in central and/or eastern Asia form an 'eastern group'. Their songs consist of short, loud structured sequences, quite different from those of their western counterparts. The shorter-winged Japanese Swamp Warbler is resident in southern parts of its breeding range and its migratory northern populations winter well north of the tropics. This is an atypical *Locustella* with a unique wing claw, which was formerly included within the *Megalurus* grass warblers.

Relationships within the Locustellidae have recently been elucidated by DNA studies (Alström *et al.* in prep.). The western *Locustella* species fall within one major lineage together with the Asian *Bradypterus* warblers, while the eastern *Locustella* species make up a different lineage which includes the Japanese Swamp Warbler. This confirms earlier work by Drovetski *et al.* (2004) who demonstrated the separation of the western and eastern *Locustella* groups and placed Grasshopper Warbler closer to Chinese Bush and Chestnut-backed Bush Warblers than to Lanceolated Warbler. Extensive generic revision of this family is required. Both *Locustella* and *Bradypterus* as presently constituted are paraphyletic and will need to be redefined.

SAVI'S WARBLER
Locustella luscinioides   Plate 9

Sylvia Luscinioides Savi, 1824. *Nuovo Giornale de'Letterati*, 7(14): 341. Pisa.

A long-distance migrant that breeds commonly in wetlands and reedbeds from W Europe to C Asia and winters in N tropical Africa. Forms a species pair with River Warbler. Polytypic, with three races recognised, although the differences between them are slight and inconsistent; they comprise a cline of decreasing colour saturation progressing from west to east:

L. l. luscinioides (Savi, 1824). Continental Europe east to C Urals, Crimea and Balkans; also NW Africa.

L. l. fusca (Severtsov, 1873). C Asia to NW China and W Mongolia.

L. l. sarmatica Kazakov, 1973. E Ukraine (from Khark'ov and E shore of Sea of Azov) to S Urals, Volga River and N Caucasus; also Asia Minor and Levant.

IDENTIFICATION Length 13–14cm. Wing 66–77mm. Tail/wing 76–88%.

A medium-sized unstreaked warbler with rather dark, warm brown upperparts and a rounded tail. The most numerous and widespread *Locustella* of *Phragmites* reedbeds throughout much of its range. Its readily recognisable continuous reeling song is one of the characteristic wetland sounds from Europe to C Asia. Sexes alike.

Structure One of the larger *Locustella* species, exceeded in size within its breeding range only by River Warbler. It usually appears distinctly larger than Grasshopper Warbler, with which it overlaps widely, but they share a similar structure. A fairly flat forehead and crown and narrow fine-tipped bill give the head a neat, attenuated appearance. When singing from a reed head it adopts a more upright posture than Grasshopper Warbler, with the tail held vertically down and the head tilted back, giving it a hollow-backed appearance. The body can then appear quite stocky, almost pot-bellied, a feature exaggerated by the deep-based undertail-coverts that almost reach the tail tip. The tail is markedly graduated, the outer feathers falling short of the tips of the undertail-coverts, and can appear broad and rounded in flight. The wing is broad but pointed, with strongly curved outer primaries and with p2 similar in length to p3. These structural features separate it readily from the unstreaked *Acrocephalus* warblers with which it occurs.

Plumage and bare parts In Europe, adults and juveniles show uniform warm brown upperparts, rather darker in appearance than Eurasian Reed Warbler, especially on the uppertail-coverts and tail. The wing-coverts and flight feather edges match the upperparts but the whitish outer web of the second primary appears as a pale line along the outer edge of the wing. The head is marked by a narrow whitish to creamy supercilium of variable length, usually most conspicuous in front of the eye and narrowing over the ear-coverts and in some birds scarcely extending beyond the eye. It can become more obvious on a singing bird when the crown feathers are slightly raised. There is an indistinct eye-line, usually little more than a dark spot in front of the eye and another behind it. Below, a whitish chin and throat and whitish belly centre contrast with the breast and flanks, which are pale warm brown. In spring, some birds show a row of faint dark spots across the lower throat, but these are absent on freshly moulted adults in NW Europe. The undertail-coverts are warm brown, usually with narrow, paler tips, readily seen on a singing bird perched on a reed stem. The blackish bill shows a pale yellowish base below.

The upperpart colour of birds breeding around the northern shores of the Black Sea is slightly paler and less warmly toned than in W European birds and they tend to show more conspicuous and extensive throat spotting. These birds have been recognised as a distinct race *sarmatica* by some authorities. However, similar birds also occur in the Iberian Peninsula, while others breeding there are inseparable from the paler C Asian race *fusca* which appears pale olive-brown or even greyish brown above and often slightly paler and colder below.

During the breeding season, the bill is dark grey to blackish with a slightly paler base to the lower mandible. At other times, the lower mandible becomes largely pale pink to fleshy brown. The legs and feet are dull plumbeous-brown or purplish brown and appear darker than those of Grasshopper Warbler.

SIMILAR SPECIES The long undertail-coverts, strongly graduated tail and long, curved outer primary (p2) with pale outer web should preclude confusion of Savi's Warbler with any of the unstreaked *Acrocephalus* species. Within Europe, two *Locustella* species, the Grasshopper and River Warblers, occur within the range of Savi's Warbler and could present identification issues.

River Warbler is readily separated from Savi's by its olive-brown upperparts, often showing a distinct greenish tinge, a conspicuous band of dark brown striations across the upper breast quite different from the necklace of indistinct spots shown by some Savi's, and the usually broad, whitish and contrasting tips to its undertail-coverts. Many River Warblers have the head sides and underparts tinged yellow. When compared with Savi's of the C Asian race *fusca*, River Warbler tends to appear darker and often more greenish. It also

averages slightly larger than Savi's but there is considerable overlap in wing length.

Grasshopper Warbler shares a similar 'reeling' song with Savi's but its pitch and tone are quite different and the two should not be confused. The crown, mantle and wing-coverts usually show olive-brown fringes that contrast with dark centres to produce a patterning which is absent in Savi's. There is usually some fine streaking across the lower throat and upper breast. However, a small minority of Grasshopper Warblers are slightly warmer and browner above than 'typical' birds, less well marked above, and with little or no throat streaking. The wing formula of Grasshopper Warbler is different from Savi's, with emargination on p3, and p2 falling well short of p3.

VOICE The song of Savi's Warbler is a distinctive monotonous tuneless 'reel', sometimes restricted to intermittent bursts of only a few seconds but occasionally continuing uninterrupted for up to five minutes. Most sequences last for a minute or less and include several brief pauses. The reel is similar in structure to those of Grasshopper, Lanceolated and River Warblers, but distinctly harder and more penetrating than any of those and noticeably lower-pitched, in a frequency range between 3–5kHz. The paired elements forming the song are delivered much faster than in Grasshopper or Lanceolated Warbler, typically at 45–48 per second (cf. 25 per second in Grasshopper). The intervals between the elements are not registered by the human ear and so the reel lacks the tinkling or ringing quality of Grasshopper and sounds harder and more 'droning'. It has been likened to the stridulations of Roesel's Bush-cricket *Metrioptera roeselii*. Reeling is often preceded by the call, followed by a rapid chatter or an excited churring lasting up to two seconds. The song is not particularly loud when heard at close quarters but its penetrating quality makes it audible over distances up to 300m or more in calm conditions. As the bird turns its head, both the direction and volume of the song can appear to change.

Songs of the race *sarmatica* from the Black Sea and Armenia and *fusca* from E Kazakhstan and western Mongolia sound identical to that of nominate *luscinioides* from W Europe and birds of each form respond readily to each other's songs.

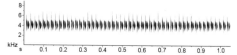

Part of song of Savi's Warbler recorded within breeding range of *L. l. luscinioides*, Poland, May. (Sample 2003)

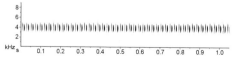

Part of song of Savi's Warbler recorded within the breeding range of *L. l. fusca*, Khar Us Nuur, western Mongolia, June. (Geoff Carey)

The call is a single, fairly loud and slightly metallic '*chit*' or '*whit*', sometimes repeated rapidly when excited.

MOULT The main moult is complex and its timing and strategy are extremely variable. In Europe most adults begin between mid July and late August, many finishing before migration but others suspending, usually with new body and head plumage but retaining a variable number of old wing feathers, usually inner primaries, and tail feathers. After breeding, adults in N France commence moult and by late August many are fully moulted (PP *in litt.*) but elsewhere birds begin moult at staging areas along the migration flyway, and some leave Europe unmoulted. Primary moult usually begins in the middle of the tract, between p8 and p6, and proceeds both outwards and inwards – termed eccentric moult by Thomas (1977). Some birds, however, follow the normal descendent sequence beginning at p10. The secondaries are moulted late and rapidly, the tail feathers rapidly, sometimes almost simultaneously. The estimated duration of moult in Germany and Austria is approximately six weeks (Steiner 1970; Müller 1981).

Young birds depart from breeding grounds in juvenile plumage, some still completing feather growth up to September or even October. A full moult occurs in Africa but the inner primaries p8–10 are commonly retained (and occasionally p1–3). There is little information on timing but it presumably occurs mainly between October and January (see data from Senegal below). Exceptionally, birds have shown growing primaries on spring arrival in Europe.

Data from tropical W Africa is limited and the age of most birds trapped there for ringing is unknown. Of 395 birds in N Senegal, the proportions in active primary moult were as follows: November 3 of 16, December 4 of 67 plus seven suspended, January 9 of 135 plus seven suspended, February 1 of 120 and March 0 of 57 but one suspended (SJRR *in litt.*). Of six birds trapped In N Nigeria, one in late November was completing primary moult after an earlier suspension, and one in early February was growing the two inner and the two outer primaries, with p3–8 new (Aidley & Wilkinson 1987). Three December birds and one in February had completed primary moult, one in December after an earlier suspension. Some European birds appear to have a partial pre-breeding moult in winter quarters, and reach the breeding grounds with fresh body, tail and tertial feathers, and flight feathers slightly older (Cramp 1992).

Eastern birds tend to delay autumn moult until after migration. Of 25 adults caught on the Sudan Red Sea coast between late August and mid October, one was fully moulted, nine suspended with five or more new primaries per wing, and the remainder unmoulted (GN pers. comm.). In Darfur, moult of wing, tail and body feathers (primaries starting at p10 or p8) begins about late September–early October, and appears to be rapid (Williamson 1963; Stresemann & Stresemann 1970). In Ethiopia, J. S. Ash (*in litt.*) caught moulting birds in November and January. An adult *fusca* caught in Kenya in late December had completed its moult apart from the three inner primaries and three outer secondaries (Pearson *et al.* 1988b).

HABITAT In Europe, shows a preference for extensive stands of Common Reed *Phragmites australis* growing over fresh or brackish water, but also breeds in wet fens with bulrush *Typha* sp. It tends to prefer reedbeds with substantial accumulations of old decayed reed. Also favours a mixed habitat with reed, sedge and early succession of alder carr and willow. Occasionally breeds in wet sedge *Carex* marshes that lack reeds, particularly in Poland and Belarus (Hagemeijer & Blair 1997), but probably elsewhere in Eastern Europe. In Central Asia, it breeds in a wider range of wetland habitats. In addition to the preferred *Phragmites* reedbeds, it frequents moist willow thickets, sedge marshes and wet meadows with tall grasses and bushes. Although most breed on lowland plains, it is frequently found in mountain wetlands up to 1,800m (Gavrilov & Gavrilov 2005).

On migration it generally avoids mountains but occurs in a wider range of lowland habitats than used for breeding. These include stands of tangled vegetation, bushy areas, crops such as alfalfa and corn, and swampy vegetation, as well as reedbeds. It is occasionally found in forest and tall weed thickets, but usually in damper areas or close to wetlands. In Eritrea, passage birds have been noted in dense thickets of *Salvadora persica* by permanent springs in acacia bush.

During winter, it occurs in reedbeds, *Typha*, rank grass, rice fields, sugar cane and occasionally in garden shrubbery. It also frequents a wide range of dense scrubby vegetation, usually near water, as well as marshes and swamps.

BEHAVIOUR Particularly elusive when silent. It walks on the ground among stems of *Phragmites* and other damp, rank vegetation and picks food from low stems, or from the mud or water surface.

Males sing immediately on arrival on the breeding grounds. They can be heard at most times of day, but mainly in the early morning and evening and often well into the hours of darkness. Prolonged and persistent song ceases once birds are paired, but there is often a resurgence prior to the second brood. The male typically sings from a reed stem, perched well down out of sight. However, in calm conditions it may slowly move up the stem and sit singing for long periods conspicuously near the top. It usually shuffles down out of view when song ceases. Birds with territories on the edges of reedbeds often sing from bushes. A reeling bird usually throws its head back with the bill raised between 30–45°, puffs out the throat feathers and also tends to raise the forecrown feathers, giving the head a ragged, untidy appearance. It has a distinctive habit of turning its head abruptly from side to side about once per second, enhancing the ventriloquial effect of the song. It occasionally flies a short distance low over the reed tops before dropping back into cover. On the ground it tends to hop more than other *Locustella* species (Leisler 1975).

Behaviour in winter quarters is poorly known. The reeling song has been heard in Senegal from December to February and once in Ghana in January (Walsh & Grimes 1981). It also reels on spring passage.

BREEDING HABITS Breeds in Europe between mid April and early August. It is solitary and territorial. Mean territory size estimates in Europe range from about 0.1–0.5ha (Cramp 1992), with singing birds usually spaced more than 40m apart, but sometimes closer where suitable habitat is limited. Nesting density in W European marshes can be high, e.g. 180 pairs/km² in Marne, France (Erard & Spitz 1964). The nest is placed low down in wet marshes, usually within 0.2m of the ground or water. It is a well-concealed but untidy construction of dead leaves and grass stems, the cup being lined with fine leaves and fibres. The clutch of 3–6 eggs is laid from mid April onwards in southern Europe, but later to the north and east. It is incubated for 10–12 days by both sexes, but mainly by the female. Double-brooded in southern Europe and often also further north and east in the range.

DISTRIBUTION A widespread summer visitor to temperate wetlands of the W and C Palearctic, wintering in Africa.

Breeding

L. l. luscinioides The nominate race breeds in small numbers in North Africa, in the coastal lowlands of N Morocco,

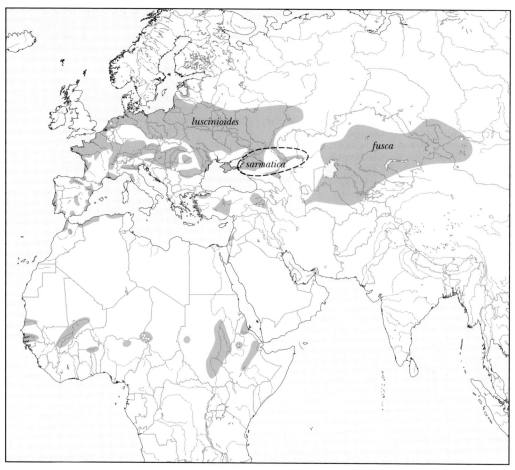

Map 30. Savi's Warbler. Breeding range and winter distribution.

N Algeria and N Tunisia, It also ranges across the lowlands of W Europe, from Portugal and Spain north to Denmark and the Baltic countries, although local and uncommon in Estonia. Much of the European breeding range lies between 36°N and 60°N. It only rarely breeds in S and E England (where formerly regular) and S Sweden. Also breeds sporadically in S Finland, where the range contracted in the1990s and it probably now depends on warm southeast winds to bring birds across Gulf of Finland. It is local and patchily distributed in W Europe, with many apparently suitable areas unoccupied. It is more widespread in C and E Europe, where locations such as Neusiedlersee in E Austria and the Danube delta in Romania hold large concentrations. It is generally widespread throughout Poland and south to Hungary but scarce and localised in the Balkan countries. Romania holds the bulk of the European breeding population, which (excluding Russia) was estimated in the 1990s at 200,000 pairs (Hagemeijer & Blair 1997), but these may not all belong to the nominate form (see below). The smaller western populations are subject to fluctuation, with the breeding range expanding and contracting over periods of several years. The small British population at the northwestern limit of the range became re-established during the

1970s and 1980s, but has almost disappeared as numbers have fallen in adjacent continental Europe.

L. l. sarmatica Breeds from the Black Sea coast in E Ukraine and into S Russia. To the west around the Danube delta in Romania, many birds lack the warm brown upperparts of those breeding in W Europe and tend to show characters associated with the race *sarmatica*. However, with apparent intergradation, it is difficult to define racial limits in this region. It is unclear which race breeds locally throughout the Middle East, including C and E Turkey, northern Israel and Armenia. Apparently absent from the wetlands of Iraq and Iran. Although duller than W European birds, those breeding in N Israel were considered by Shirihai (1996) not to be typical *fusca*, and probably fall within the variability associated with *sarmatica*. This race extends around the northern Caspian Sea to the Ural River in NW Kazakhstan (Gavrilov & Gavrilov 2005).

L. l. fusca Occupies the species' range east of the Caspian. It is widespread throughout much of Kazakhstan, where its distribution includes the Irgiz and Emba Rivers, the Naurzam Lakes, the Kurgaldzhino Reserve near Astana and the Zaysan Depression. In S Kazakhstan, it has been recorded in the Aksu-Dzhabagly Reserve in the Tien Shan mountains at 2,360m and may breed here.

Also occurs locally in wetland sites around Bukhara, Uzbekistan, including the Amu-Bukhara canal and Todakul Lake, but perhaps on passage only. Mapped as breeding in NW Afghanistan by Harrison (1982) but there are no confirmed breeding records and it is unclear whether it occurs other than on passage. Small numbers breed in W China in the Xinjiang Uygur Autonomous Region where singing birds have recently been reported in reedbeds at 600–1,000m. It is regularly reported in June from the Tarim Basin at Bosten (Boshteng) Hu, and also recorded recently at Ili River in the foothills of the Tien Shan, in a marsh in the Altai Mountains c. 25km east of Haba He, and at Buerjin (Lewthwaite et al. 1998; Hornskov 2001; GJC & PJL pers. comm.). Singing males at Khar Us Nuur, NW Mongolia, in June 2005 (GJC & PJL pers. comm.) represent a further extension of the range.

Non-breeding Winters in the northern tropics of Africa, in a fragmented band from Senegal to Ethiopia, but the distribution of each race remains unclear. Undoubtedly occurs more widely than indicated by existing records, many of these being birds trapped for ringing. It is still unrecorded from Gambia although known to winter to the north and south in Senegal along the lower Senegal and Casamance River valleys. Elsewhere in W Africa, recorded only from S Mali, N Ghana and N Nigeria. These birds accord with the nominate race and presumably originate from W and C Europe.

Its apparent absence across much of NC Africa probably reflects a lack of observers and ringing activity. To the east, Sudan and Ethiopia hold an appreciable wintering population, including birds referable to *fusca*, and there are old records from the Asmara–Massawa area, Eritrea. In Sudan, it is known from Darfur in the west and from the Nile valley in central and southern areas. In Ethiopia it has been found in and west of the Rift valley, south to Lake Abiata, with most records along the Awash River. There are just two records from Kenya; birds of race *fusca* trapped in December at Ngulia, Tsavo West National Park, and it appears that only stragglers occur that far south.

There are occasional winter reports north of the Sahara, from Algeria, Egypt and Israel, but it is unclear whether wintering occurs regularly.

MOVEMENTS W European breeders are believed to move south or southwest, while C and E European birds migrate to the southeast or south through the E Mediterranean and Middle East. Birds from C Asia migrate southwest across Middle East countries to enter Africa along the Red Sea coast from Israel southwards.

W European birds depart from breeding areas in August and all have left by mid September, although Moroccan birds may remain until October. Migrants move through Morocco between August and October although a paucity of records from North Africa suggests that many overfly this region. The earliest migrants are noted in Nigeria in September, but there are few records from Senegal and Mali before mid November.

E European birds leave the breeding grounds from mid August onwards, but some remain in southern areas into October. Similarly, in C Asia, most depart in August, but some remain in N Kazakhstan to mid September and near Tashkent, Uzbekistan, into October (Cramp 1992). Autumn passage through Cyprus is sparse, from August to October. In Israel, Shirihai (1996) noted passage of all three races, with nominate *luscinioides* being uncommon, *sarmatica* quite

common throughout and *fusca* common mainly in the east. Birds pass from late July and early August but mainly in two distinct peaks, from 25 August to 13 September and from 3 to 12 October, with stragglers to late November. The main passage on the Sudan Red Sea coast occurs from late August to mid October (GN pers. comm.). Moulting birds are present in Darfur by October (Lynes 1925).

All populations begin northward migration in February. Birds remain in Senegal into March with a few to mid April and are recorded until April in N Nigeria. In the east, birds remain in S Sudan to March and are still fairly common in Ethiopia to late March, the latest recorded date being 4 May (Ash 1980). Passage through North Africa is more noticeable in spring than autumn, occurring through Egypt mainly from late March to mid May. In Israel, where migration is concentrated through the eastern valleys, the pattern appears different. Shirihai (1996) recorded the first returning birds in late January, then two distinct passage waves, from 25 February to 10 March and from 17 to 28 March. Most have moved through by May but late stragglers occur into June. Passage occurs through Cyprus from mid March to April, spring numbers usually exceeding those of autumn. Near Antalya, S Turkey, where over 3,000 were ringed during spring migration, passage peaked in late March and early April (RV *in litt.*). Birds return to Moroccan breeding sites in March. European birds return about ten days earlier than Grasshopper Warbler. Breeding sites in W France, Belgium and W Germany are occupied from the first half of April, those in NW Europe from the third week onwards. It arrives in Ukraine from late March and Poland from mid April, with passage continuing to mid May. It reaches S Sweden and S Finland in mid May, with a secondary arrival in early June (Cramp 1992).

Birds returning to C Asia apparently cross the Arabian Peninsula north to Israel, but there are few records. Passage occurs through the Gulf States and singing birds are occasionally heard in Kuwait in March and April. Migrants pass through SW Iran from the second half of March and reach Turkmenistan, Uzbekistan and S Kazakhstan from early April onwards. Noted at Chokpak Pass in S Kazakhstan only in late April, these presumably being northern breeders. It reaches N Kazakhstan from late April, becoming widespread and numerous from mid May.

Vagrancy There are few reports of Savi's Warbler beyond its usual range. Most are from W Europe where it is a vagrant to countries fringing the breeding range. It has reached Ireland on seven occasions, and Scotland with just 11 records to 2008, all but one from Shetland.

DESCRIPTION *L. l. luscinioides*
Plumage – Adult fresh (Variable: late August onwards in NW Europe, January to May elsewhere) In fresh plumage, forehead to nape unmarked rich warm brown. Supercilium poorly defined, pale cream to buffy brown; most conspicuous from bill to rear of eye, narrowing behind eye and merging with sides of head. Lores creamy buff, merging with supercilium. A dark brown spot in front of eye sometimes forms an indistinct loral line, almost reaching bill base. Eye-lines dark-brown, narrow but distinct, extending to sides of nape. Ear-coverts warm brown, faint pale buffy brown tips giving mottled appearance towards upper edge, but lower coverts speckled rather than mottled, merging with malar region and sides of throat. Eye-ring dull buff, narrow and inconspicuous. Mantle and scapulars to uppertail-coverts uniform warm brown, similar to crown but with slight rufous wash. Tail similar to, or slightly darker and

browner than uppertail-coverts, often with a faint pattern of narrow, darker cross-barring.

Chin and throat white, washed buff towards lower edge and sides of throat. Breast, flanks and ventral region suffused warm brown, sometimes with pinkish or buffy tinge, less deeply coloured than upperparts and closed wing. Most birds in spring show small, indistinct brown spots on sides of throat, often also on the malar region and along the lower edge of the throat, but these are absent on fresh adults in autumn. Exceptionally, these may produce faint striations onto upper breast and sides of neck. Belly white, grading to buffy white towards sides. Undertail-coverts washed warm brown, without the rich tone of upperparts; sometimes with diffuse, usually narrow, paler brown to whitish tips. Undersurface of tail darker and greyer than undertail-coverts.

Lesser, median and greater coverts, tertials and alula warm brown with little or no contrast between centres and fringes. Primary coverts, primaries and secondaries dark greyish brown, edges warm brown with slight rufous wash; outer web of p2 greyish brown, slightly paler than edges to other primaries.

Adult worn (June to August) Similar to fresh adult, but head usually plainer, more featureless, with greyish tinge on sides and less mottling on ear-coverts; supercilium slightly duller and darker loral line reduced to a small brown spot in front of the eye. Upperparts and tail warm brown but slightly paler than in fresh adult, with rufous wash reduced or lost entirely. Outer web of p2 usually paler, greyer and more contrasting. Chin, throat and belly whiter, while breast and flanks faded to dull buffy brown with little or no spotting present. Undertail-coverts paler buffy brown.

Juvenile Closely resembles fresh adult, but upperparts, including tail and closed wing, slightly brighter warm russet-brown. Supercilium usually less conspicuous, appearing as an indistinct bulge above the eye. Loral line also inconspicuous, so that the head appears particularly plain. Underparts as fresh adult but wash on breast and flanks often slightly warmer and more extensive. Outer web of p2 usually less pale than in adult.

Bare Parts Upper mandible dark grey with pale pinkish horn cutting edge. During breeding season, lower mandible also dark except for slightly paler base. Outside breeding season lower mandible much with more extensive, pale pink to fleshy brown area in adult, yellowish in first autumn. Mouth brownish or greyish flesh. Tarsi and toes dull plumbeous brown, sometimes with slight purple cast. Iris dark brown to warm brown.

IN HAND CHARACTERS
Measurements *L. l. luscinioides*

	Male	Female
Wing	67–77 (71.3; 46)	66–71 (69.0; 20)
Tail	53–62 (57.5; 43)	50–58 (54.2; 17)
Bill	15–17 (16.0; 41)	14.5–16 (15.3; 15)
Tarsus	20–23 (21.6; 38)	20–22.5 (21.6; 19)

(Includes data from Cramp 1992)

Sexes combined:
Tail/wing ratio: 76–88% (80%; 25)
Bill width: 3.3–4.0 (3.6; 18)
Hind claw: 5.8–7.2 (6.5; 22)
Tail graduation: 13–18 (15.3; 26)

Juvenile wing averages 1.5mm shorter than in adult, tail 5.0mm shorter (Cramp 1992).
L. l. sarmatica (sexes combined): *wing* 67–74 (69.7; 17) (Kazakov 1973).
L. l. fusca (sexes combined): *wing* 66–73 (69.6; 25); *tail* 54–62 (57.6; 10); *bill* 15.5–17.0 (16.2; 12); *tarsus* 21–23 (21.7; 10) (includes data from Cramp 1992).

Structure *L. l. luscinioides*

Wing formula (Cramp 1992).

p1/pc	p2	p3	p4	p5	p6	p7	p10
1–3	wp	0.5–3	3–6	6–9	8–11	9-13	16–20

Wing rather broad; pointed, with minute p1. Wing point p2 (rarely also p3); p2 distinctly curved, with pointed tip and narrow outer web; primaries lack emarginations and notches.

Figure 24. Wing of Savi's Warbler.

Tail graduated; feathers rather broad and rounded.
Bill rather small; narrow and laterally compressed, with slightly finer tip than in River Warbler. Tarsi quite strong; toes rather long with fine claws.
L. l. fusca and **L. l. sarmatica** Structure as nominate race.
Recognition The combination of plain upperparts, rounded tail feathers and distinctive wing formula, with p2 forming the wing point, separates this from all other *Locustella* species except River Warbler. Smaller than River Warbler but wing length overlaps broadly above 67mm. Separation from River Warbler usually depends on plumage features: in Savi's markings on lower throat are absent or restricted to a necklace of small dark spots; contrasting whitish tips to the undertail-coverts are lacking, and the brown upperparts and flanks are warm-toned rather than olive (but see *fusca*).

Larger than Grasshopper Warbler; wing length overlaps extensively with it in Europe, although not in Asia. Lacks the emargination on p3 shown by Grasshopper Warbler.
Ageing Juveniles in early autumn have fresh unworn primaries and tail feathers of uniform age, usually still in good condition on arrival at staging and wintering areas. Fully moulted adults from late August onwards closely resemble juveniles but are readily separated by the colour of the gape flange: pink and indistinct in adults, yellowish and fleshy in juveniles. Adults partially moulted or unmoulted in autumn are readily distinguished by their old abraded primaries and tail feathers. Age will usually be indeterminate in winter, but first-year birds sometimes retain one or more juvenile primaries per wing. Spring or summer birds with old pale inner primaries are likely to be first year birds.
Weight Range 10.4–24.1g. Usual weight of lean birds 13–17g. Fattening migrants are often over 18g and have

been recorded at 23–24g in both spring and autumn in S Turkey (RV & WP *in litt.*).

GEOGRAPHIC VARIATION Three races are recognised but differences between them are slight and clinal and relate mainly to the intensity and tone of coloration of the upperparts and body sides. There are also minor differences in biometrics. There is a trend of decreasing colour saturation from west to east within the breeding range, W and C European birds of the nominate race usually being browner and more rufescent than those breeding to the east. Central Asian birds of race *fusca* are readily separable, being duller olive-brown above and paler below. Between these forms, the race *sarmatica* shows intermediate characters, although this subspecies is poorly defined and not universally recognised.

L. l. luscinioides (NW Africa; continental Europe east to C Urals and Crimea) Described above. E European birds are similar in wing length to the following two races but those of W Europe are distinctly smaller.

L. l. sarmatica (N Black Sea coast to S Ural and Volga Rivers and N Caucasus; possibly also Asia Minor and Levant) Closely resembles nominate race, but upperparts slightly less rufescent, sometimes with slight olive tinge

and olive-brown flanks marginally duller. Cramp *et al.* (1992) noted the underpart colour of Romanian breeders as slightly less saturated than in birds breeding further west, although they show similar warmly toned upperparts. They also show a greater tendency to throat spotting than W European birds. Birds breeding in the Danube delta and on W Black Sea coast may be *sarmatica* although most cannot be confidently assigned to either this race or the nominate form.

L. l. fusca (C Asia) Lacks warm plumage tones. It differs from the nominate race and *sarmatica* in having the upperparts dull olive-brown to greyish brown, the breast paler and with a colder wash and the flanks paler, buffy brown to pinkish buff. The undertail-coverts are slightly paler, buffy brown to pinkish buff, frequently with narrow whitish tips, more conspicuous and contrasting than in European birds. Often shows light spotting on throat and upper breast, sometimes forming indistinct striations. Birds resembling *fusca* occasionally breed in Europe, particularly Spain, but warmer-toned birds are not believed to occur in C Asia.

TAXONOMY AND SYSTEMATICS The race *sarmatica* is not universally recognised. Otherwise, no issues arise.

▲ Adult *L. l. luscinioides*, Poland, April. Usually sings from a reed stem or low bush within extensive *Phragmites* reedbeds. Singing male often adopts characteristic posture with head held slightly back, bill held open, and belly slightly bulging. Note uniform appearance and long, unmarked undertail-coverts (Mateusz Matysiak).

▲ Adult *L. l. luscinioides*, Poland, April. Adults in Europe usually lack spotting on lower throat but those from the Black and Caspian Sea region often show a band of small spots across the lower throat. Note dull greyish-pink base to the lower mandible, characteristic of adult birds (Mateusz Matysiak).

◄ Adult *L. l. luscinioides*, Normandy, France, August. An exceptionally drab adult in fresh plumage, just finishing complete moult. Lack of warmer tones is atypical for nominate race and this bird is probably not safely separable from *fusca* (James Kennerley).

▲ Juvenile *L. l. luscinioides*, Tuscany, Italy, September. Closely resembles freshly moulted adult in autumn, but differs by yellow base to lower mandible (Daniele Occhiato).

◄ Adult *L. l. fusca*, Kuwait, February. Differs from nominate race by overall duller and colder appearance. Often shows indistinct spotting on throat and upper breast. Undertail-coverts duller than in European birds and often with whitish tips (Abdul-Rahman Al-Sirhan).

◄ Juvenile *L. l. fusca*, Xinjiang, China, August. Even in warm sunlight, the olive-brown tone to the upperparts remains apparent. Unlike European birds, frequently shows narrow whitish tips to undertail-coverts (Paul Leader).

218

RIVER WARBLER
Locustella fluviatilis   **Plate 9**

Sylvia fluviatilis **Wolf, 1810**. In: Meyer & Wolf, *Taschenbuch Deutschen Vögelkunde* 1: 229. Danube, Austria.

A long-distance migrant that breeds widely in damp grassy or herbaceous vegetation from central Europe to W Siberia and winters in E and S Africa. It forms a species pair with Savi's Warbler. Monotypic.

IDENTIFICATION Length 14cm. Wing 69–80mm. Tail/wing 70–78%.

A fairly large, plain-backed, olive-brown *Locustella* with a broad rounded tail and dark striations on the lower throat and upper breast. It can occur alongside the similar Savi's Warbler both within its breeding range and during passage through the Middle East and northeast Africa and care may be necessary to distinguish these two. Its plumage, structure and characteristic jizz should, however, separate it readily from all other plain-backed migrant warblers in Europe and Africa. There is a possibility of confusion with some streak-throated resident African *Bradypterus* species but these are structurally quite different. It is secretive but often draws attention with its sharp '*chick*' calls or its distinctive throbbing insect-like song. Sexes alike.

Structure Shows some unusual features of shape and structure. A flat forehead and crown and narrow, rather fine-tipped bill produce an attenuated head shape, while the long, bulky undertail-coverts reach near the tail tip to produce a tapered looking rear. The wings are long and broad with pointed tips and a long primary projection equalling the full length of the exposed tertials. The wing formula itself is unusual, the second primary typically being slightly longer than the third and forming the wing point. The primaries are rather broad-based and the outer most are noticeably curved. The tail is strongly graduated and the feathers are broad. The pinkish brown legs are rather slender and the toes long. Many of these features, including the wing structure, are shared with Savi's Warbler but Savi's appears rather less full-tailed and has a still finer bill.

Plumage and bare parts Freshly moulted spring adults are uniformly dark olive-brown above with a variable greenish tinge. The wing-coverts match the upperparts, while the remiges and tail feathers are rather darker brown and the fresh tertials show narrow olive-brown fringes. The flight feathers are edged olive-brown but the long outer primary (p2) shows a pale brown outer web. The head pattern is subdued. A narrow buffy white stripe above dark lores merges with a narrow whitish eye-ring, but behind the eye the paler supercilium is scarcely noticeable between the olive-brown crown and the buff-streaked brown cheeks and ear-coverts. The underparts are typically buffy white, with the upper breast and flanks washed olive-brown. They show a gorget of diffuse dark brown striations from the lower throat which broaden onto the upper breast. Brown bases to the undertail-coverts usually show as broad dark bars, contrasting with greyish white tips. On some the broad tips obscure the underlying dark feather bases, so that the undertail-coverts appear entirely pale.

There is considerable variation in plumage. Some 10–20% of birds have the supercilium, chin, throat and underparts tinged yellow and these usually have more greenish upperparts. There is also variation in the intensity and extent of the dark throat streaking. Some have broad dark streaks extending from the lower throat to cover the upper breast and narrow streaks also on the chin and upper throat. Others have narrower fainter streaks, confined to the lower throat and upper breast border. Even these however have longer and more prominent streaks than ever shown by Savi's Warbler, which at best shows small diffuse spots across the lower throat and typically lacks throat marks altogether.

During the breeding season, the body plumage of adults becomes duller, the wing and tail feathers browner and the outer primary tips worn. Then, after partial moult in NE Africa, late autumn adults again have fresh rich olive-brown body and head plumage and darker newly moulted outer primaries that contrast with the older, browner inner primaries and secondaries. Juvenile River Warblers resemble fresh adults in plumage and vary in colour in a similar way. Yellow-tinged birds occur alongside the predominant olive-brown and buffy white type, but a few are more deeply yellow below and show a distinctly rufous-brown tone above.

The bill is dark horn-brown with a pale pinkish flesh base to the lower mandible, with slightly dusky sides towards the tip. The legs and feet vary from pinkish brown to flesh-pink.

SIMILAR SPECIES A silent, skulking River Warbler could be mistaken for a Savi's Warbler, although the two species occupy very different habitats and are unlikely to occur together except during migration. In a vagrant context in Europe, confusion with the larger Gray's Grasshopper Warbler is possible. Wintering birds in Africa bear a resemblance to Little Rush Warbler but are unlikely to occur in similar habitats. The separation of these species is discussed below.

Savi's Warbler is structurally similar to River Warbler but is never greenish above or yellowish below. Western birds (nominate race) are dark like River but tinged rufous-brown above, while eastern birds (race *fusca*) are paler than River but less olive. Savi's may show a gorget of dusky spots or short streaks on the lower throat but these never form the long, broad striations of River. The barring on the undertail-coverts of Savi's is usually much less pronounced. Savi's Warbler averages about 10% smaller than River but the two species overlap substantially in wing length.

Gray's Grasshopper Warbler is a distinctly larger, heavier bird than River Warbler, with a stronger bill, thicker legs and a longer tail, but there is some overlap in wing length. Its plain upperparts may suggest those of River but the throat shows only slight streaking and the warmly coloured undertail-coverts lack pale tips and appear plain. It is a vagrant to Europe, where it is extremely unlikely to overlap with River Warbler.

Little Rush Warbler shows the streaked throat, broad rounded tail and pinkish legs of River Warbler but is easily distinguished by its warm-toned upperparts, shorter undertail-coverts and short, rounded wings. It is mainly found in wetlands and swamps in Africa where River Warbler is unlikely to occur.

VOICE The song consists of high-pitched, penetrating pulses or stridulations, '*dzi-dzi-dzi-dzi-dzi-…*', in a frequency range between 3–8kHz. It is delivered at *c.* 12 to 16 pulses or elements per second, thus much more slowly than the elements in the songs of Savi's and Grasshopper Warblers. It may last from a few seconds to many minutes at a time and is audible at distances of up to 300m. It has a mechanical or insect-like quality and has been likened to the sound of a bush cricket or cicada, or in Africa to the display calls of certain *Euplectes* bishops. A slower delivery involves a succession of longer, more grinding '*dzuzz*' notes, given at *c.* 5–10 per second and sometimes paired, alternating with a shorter '*dzi*'. At close range, additional very high-pitched squeaks or clicks can be heard at irregular intervals The song is sometimes introduced by a series of quiet thin twittering notes. Song is often heard in African winter quarters but it is less powerful there than on the breeding grounds and bursts usually only last a few seconds.

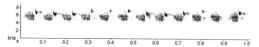

Part of song of River Warbler, Estonia, June. (Peter Kennerley)

The main contact and alarm call is a sharp '*tchick*', with a whiplash quality, which may be repeated continuously about twice per second. It has been noted more often in Africa than on the breeding grounds, but it is also given in Europe when disturbed. A soft '*churr*' is also given.

MOULT All birds, both adults and first years, have a complete moult in southeast Africa in late winter, prior to northward migration. There is apparently no moult in the breeding area and adults migrate to northeast Africa with old body, wing and tail feathers and worn outer primary tips. They then undergo an extensive moult in Ethiopia between September and November, replacing the body and head plumage, many of the wing-coverts, the tertials and up to six (usually just two to three) large outer primaries on each wing (Pearson & Backhurst 1983). Almost all adults replace these outer primaries, but retain the old secondaries and usually the tail. After onward migration to winter quarters south of the equator, they moult their entire plumage (including the outer primaries) in a typical passerine sequence between late January and early April. Individuals moult quite rapidly, often with 3–4 feathers growing in each wing and with all the tail feathers growing simultaneously. First-year birds appear to retain their juvenile plumage throughout the first autumn although some body feathers may be renewed in Ethiopia. They moult completely in winter quarters, apparently at the same time as adults.

HABITAT Breeds in moist, low vegetation, along streams and ditches, on meadows and river floodplains and near ponds and lakes; also away from water in deciduous forest clearings and orchards and on the margins of cultivation. Favours wooded swamps, Alder carr, sedge marshes, bogs and willow scrub, typically with a dense undergrowth of grasses or tangled herbage, such as nettles or meadowsweet, and a low bush layer.

It can occur on migration in any grassy, herbaceous or low bushy cover, typically in moist places. It winters in Africa at low to medium altitudes, in dense green bush and thicket, rank herbage and woodland undergrowth. In Kenya, it occurs below 1,700m in sites with tall grass and acacia scrub, or thickets of *Premna, Grewia* and *Combretum*; in northeast Botswana, among long grass and *Baphia* and *Bauhinia* scrub in more open parts of Rhodesian teak (*Baikiaea*) woodlands. On southward migration through Africa and in winter quarters it utilises the flush of new vegetation that follows the rains.

BEHAVIOUR A secretive species that skulks in low cover and is usually located by its song or calls. It creeps among twigs or runs on the ground among grassy vegetation with the tapered body held horizontal. It may emerge into view, calling frequently, when excited. It flies reluctantly, straight and low with the rounded tail spread, and usually drops back quickly into cover. Males sing strongly from their arrival on the breeding grounds until they have paired, mainly at night and especially during the two to three hours after dusk. Song periods and song bouts are much reduced during incubation and brooding but may increase again before the young fledge. Unpaired males continue to sing throughout mid summer until late July. A singing bird usually climbs to a perch about 2–3m high, such as the side branch of a bush or tree, a tall plant or a pile of twigs. It sings with its head thrown back and the bill raised to about 45° above horizontal and held wide open, turning its head vigorously from side to side. A singing bird can often be approached to within a few metres and may remain perched and visible for up to half a minute between song bouts. Birds are usually solitary outside the breeding season. In Africa, they occupy a winter territory and sing during the day, not only in the winter quarters but also during southward passage stopovers in Kenya.

BREEDING HABITS The breeding season in eastern Europe lasts from the end of May to about mid July. It is monogamous and strongly territorial but a succession of territories may form local concentrations in suitable habitat. The nest is placed on or close to ground, among thick vegetation or at the base of a bush. It is a loose cup of grass and leaves, lined with finer grass and hair, often with an entrance run. A clutch of 4–5 eggs is usual, occasionally up to seven or as few as three. These are incubated by both sexes, but mainly by the female, for about 12 days. The fledging period is about 14–16 days, the young being cared for and fed by both parents. The young remain dependent on their parents for at least two weeks after fledging. Single-brooded.

DISTRIBUTION

Breeding It occupies a wide breeding area in cool temperate C and E Europe, extending into W Siberia. In Europe, it ranges west to central and eastern Germany, northern and eastern Austria and northern Croatia. From here it breeds north through the Baltic countries to S Finland, north to *c.* 62°N, where numbers vary each year depending on favourable spring weather conditions. It breeds throughout much of temperate European Russia and into W Siberia east to at least the Irtysh River at *c.* 70°E. The southern limit extends from N Romania along the northern Black Sea coast to the Crimean Peninsula and Don River, north of the Caspian Sea along the lower Volga River and south to *c.* 46°N in western Kazakhstan along the Ural River valley south to Chapaevo. The distribution is local and patchy throughout the range, reflecting the availability of suitable habitat. Russia holds perhaps half the European population, the remainder breeding mostly in Belarus, Latvia, Poland and Hungary. Densities of up 160 pairs/km² have been reported in Poland, *c.* 40 pairs/km² in northwest Russia and 26 pairs/km² in Estonia, but not more than 10 pairs/km² in Germany. The overall population may be estimated at 400,000–1,500,000 breeding pairs (Hagemeijer & Blair 1997).

Its breeding range has expanded in N and W Europe since the mid twentieth century. Singing males have occurred with increasing frequency in S Sweden since 1980s. They are also regular in Denmark and W Germany, although breeding here is erratic and occasional. Recent increases have also been noted in Finland and Bulgaria.

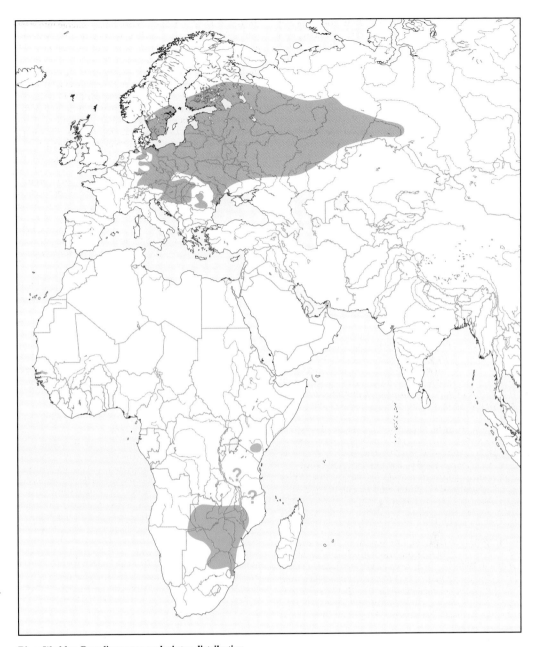

River Warbler. Breeding range and winter distribution.

Non-breeding The extent of the wintering area in SE Africa is still poorly established. It extends from SE Kenya to Malawi, C and S Zambia, C Mozambique, Zimbabwe, N and E Botswana and NE South Africa (south to Gauteng, Mpumalanga and KwaZulu-Natal midlands). There are very few records from Tanzania however, or from northern Mozambique. A large concentration of wintering River Warblers has been discovered in N Botswana (Herremans 1994).

MOVEMENTS Autumn migration is channelled through the Middle East and along narrow corridors through E

Africa. It is a two-stage process. The breeding grounds are vacated between late July and early September, C European birds moving southeast to the E Mediterranean and the Levant while eastern birds from Russia move southwest. Birds enter Africa east of 30°E and then follow a narrow route through NE Sudan, Ethiopia and C and SE Kenya. The first stage of migration is rapid, with the main passage across the Sudan coast from mid August to early October. There are surprisingly few records from Ethiopia, dated early September to mid November, but birds complete a substantial partial moult there and presumably occupy stopover sites for many weeks, probably west of the rift valley. The onward migration through Kenya occurs through areas at 500–1,500m, to the east of the central highlands and immediately east of Mount Kilimanjaro. The first Kenya records are in early November and the main passage through Tsavo occurs from mid November to early January. Here, hundreds are caught and ringed annually after being attracted to lights at Ngulia Safari Lodge. Away from the main Kenyan route there have been occasional November records from SE Somalia, W Kenya and (presumably a vagrant) W Uganda. Birds reach Zambia and Malawi from mid December and southward passage is still in progress through S Zambia during late December and into early January.

Wintering sites in S Africa remain occupied until late March and early April. Northward passage through Kenya is less conspicuous and more rapid than that in autumn and few birds linger in transit. It occurs during early to mid April and is again recorded from central and eastern areas. There are few other spring records from Africa, all from C and E Ethiopia in late April and early May. Passage through the Middle East is mainly between the end of April and mid May. Small numbers have occurred at Saudi Arabian ringing sites (GN pers. comm.) and there are a few records from the UAE and Kuwait. It is uncommon but regular at Eilat, Israel, and higher numbers occur here with southeasterly winds (Shirihai 1996), suggesting that the main passage occurs further east. There are records from the E Mediterranean and the Levant between late March and mid May, but the numbers involved are very small. It is considered a vagrant in Cyprus but over 40 were trapped for ringing in spring over a period of 15 years near Antalya in S Turkey (RV & WP *in litt.*). It is considered a rare migrant through Armenia. Singing males reach breeding territories from early May onwards. Most of the breeding range is occupied by the middle of the month, but birds reach Finland and N Russia during late May and early June.

Birds caught in Kenya in November–December have given ringing exchanges with Slovakia, Slovenia and with the Smolensk Oblast, southwest of Moscow, Russia.

Vagrancy Vagrants have reached most European countries to the west of the breeding range. There have been 35 records from Britain to the end of 2008, split between 21 in spring and summer, mostly singing adults, and 14 in autumn, the latter primarily from Fair Isle, Shetland. Elsewhere it has occurred north to Iceland and south to Spain. Six records in late March and early April in the 1960s in SE Morocco and NW Algeria (Arnould 1961; Depuy & Johnson 1967; Smith 1968) suggest the possibility of a small West African wintering population.

DESCRIPTION

Plumage Shows variation, with two basic colour types or morphs. The majority are 'brown morph' and lack any hint of yellow in the plumage but 10–20% are 'yellow morph', being lightly washed with yellow.

Adult fresh, brown morph (April to June) Forehead and crown rather dark olive-brown. Supercilium olive-buff, narrow in front of eye, broader behind it but poorly marked, merging into the olive-brown sides of the crown and upper ear-coverts; joins narrow buff eye-ring above eye, but this is absent on some individuals. A dusky brown triangular patch on lores is linked below eye with the dark ear-coverts, which are olive-brown streaked finely with buff. Cheeks olive-brown, mottled or diffusely streaked with buff. Mantle and scapulars to uppertail-coverts rather dark olive-brown,

or greyish olive-brown, usually with greenish tinge. Nape and sides of neck usually slightly greyer than mantle. Tail feathers dark olive-brown above, often with distinct narrow darker barring; dark greyish brown below. Chin and throat pale buff or off-white with variable short dark brown streaks except on upper chin. These may be narrow and grey-brown, or heavier and blackish, broadening on lower throat and extending diffusely onto breast. Upper breast brownish buff or olive-buff. Sides of breast and flanks greyish olive-brown. Centre of lower breast, belly and ventral region off-white. Undertail-coverts greyish brown with broad greyish white tips, the darker bases usually showing as widely spaced bars although sometimes almost hidden. Lesser, median and greater coverts olive-brown, tinged greenish, concolorous with upperparts. Primary coverts and alula dark grey-brown, the latter with narrow pale brown fringe. Tertials dark olive-brown with indistinct narrow and slightly paler olive-brown fringes. Remiges dark grey-brown with narrow, light olive-brown edges, although outer long primary (p2) has a wholly pale grey-brown outer web. Underwing-coverts dark grey-brown, fringed pale buff.

Adult fresh, yellow morph differs from brown morph in having the supercilium, chin and throat washed olive-yellow and the lower breast and belly usually with olive-yellow tinge. Upperparts slightly greener.

Adult worn (July to September) Upperparts, upperwing and tail duller, greyer brown, less olive. Supercilium, chin, throat and lower underparts whiter, streaking on throat and breast often sharper. White tips to undertail-coverts narrower. Tips of outer primaries abraded by August–September. These outer primaries, together with body plumage and upperwing-coverts are replaced during autumn by fresh adult plumage (see **Moult** and **Ageing**).

Juvenile Similar to adult but, when fresh, is suffused buffy yellow below and tinged greener above. Later in autumn, young birds resemble adults closely. They vary somewhat in colour but most fall within the same 'brown' or 'yellow' plumage types as adults. A small minority show more intense yellow on the face and underparts and have a strong rufous-brown wash above.

Bare Parts Upper mandible dark horn-brown with paler cutting edges. Lower mandible pale pinkish flesh, slightly duskier near tip. Mouth pale yellow to pinkish flesh; tongue of juvenile with two black spots at base and one at tip; these sometimes persist in adults over one year old. Tarsi and toes pinkish brown or flesh-pink to deep reddish brown; claws pale grey-brown, soles pinkish brown. Iris mid brown in adult with chestnut tinge, dark brown in juvenile.

IN HAND CHARACTERS
Measurements

	Male	Female
Wing	73–80 (76.6; 36)	69–77 (74.4; 16)
Tail	53–61 (57.8; 15)	49–57 (53.4; 11)
Bill	15.2–16.4 (15.8; 15)	14.6–15.7 (15.3; 13)
Tarsus	20.5–23 (21.7; 15)	20.8–22.8 (21.7; 12)

(from Cramp 1992)

Sexes combined:
Tail/wing: 70–78% (74%; 26)
Bill width: 3.6–4.3 (3.9; 24)
Hind claw: 5.7–7.2 (6.4; 22)
Tail graduation: 11–18 (14.3; 20)

Juvenile wing averages *c.* 1.5mm shorter than in adult, tail *c.* 2mm shorter.

Structure

Wing formula (Cramp 1992):

p1/pc	p2	p3	p4	p5	p6	p7	p10
(7)–0	wp	0–3	2–7	5–10	8–12	10–16	17–23

Wing rather broad but long and pointed; p1 minute. Wing point p2 (3); p2 strongly curved with pointed tip and narrow outer web; primaries lack emarginations and notches.

Figure 25. Wing of River Warbler.

Tail graduated; feathers rather broad with rounded tips (Fig. 39).

Bill rather small with concave sides and narrow tip; slightly decurved near tip.

Tarsi rather short but quite strong; toes long, claws fine.

Recognition Plain upperparts, rounded tail feathers and wing formula, with p2 forming the wing point, distinguish this from all other *Locustella* warblers except Savi's Warbler. Larger than Savi's, but wing length overlaps broadly in the range 67–76mm. Separation of smaller birds from Savi's relies on plumage features: broad dark streaks on lower throat to upper breast; contrasting broad whitish tips to undertail-coverts; upperparts olive-brown or greenish tinged (not warm brown as in Savi's); often a yellow tinge on face and breast (not seen in Savi's).

Ageing Ageing is possible until the main winter moult. In early autumn, adults with worn body plumage and abraded outer primary tips are easily separated from young birds whose plumage is entirely fresh. In late autumn, in E Africa, adults are distinguished by having fresh, darker grey-brown outer primaries, which contrast with the paler and browner inner primaries and secondaries. In young birds, the wing feathers are all remarkably unworn at this time and there is no contrast in the primary tract. A consistent chestnut tinge in the brown iris of adults is absent in young birds in late autumn. Tongue spots provide no assistance. They are lacking in some first autumn birds, but often still present in adults. Incomplete skull ossification separates first year birds until at least December.

Weight Range 12–31g. Usual weight of lean birds 14–18g. Fattening migrants are often over 20g and have been recorded at 22–27g in spring in E Ethiopia (HB unpublished data) and 30–31g in autumn in Crimea and S Turkey (GN & DJP unpublished data; RV & WP unpublished data).

GEOGRAPHIC VARIATION None reported.

TAXONOMY AND SYSTEMATICS No issues arising.

▲ Adult, Czech Republic, May. Singing males typically perch in the open, on top of or among the lower branches of a bush. Characteristic posture, with bill held open and slightly raised, accentuating the throat and breast striations (Jiri Bohdal).

▲ Adult, Finland, May. A poorly marked individual showing diffuse throat and breast streaking. Note the strongly curved primaries and pale outer web to longest outer primary (p2) (Antti Below).

◄ Adult, Poland, June. Typical adult with pronounced breast streaking and slight yellowish wash to ear-coverts. Note broad pale tips to undertail-coverts (Mateusz Matysiak).

◄ Adult, Ngulia, Kenya, December. Adults replace the outer primaries in autumn during a partial moult. Here the contrast between five older inner primaries and replaced darker outer primaries is apparent (David Pearson).

◄ Juvenile, Ngulia, Kenya, December. Separated from adults until the complete late winter moult by uniformly unworn primaries and lack of chestnut tone to brown iris (David Pearson).

GRASSHOPPER WARBLER
Locustella naevia   Plates 10 and 11

Motacilla naevia **Boddaert, 1783**. *Table Planches Enlum*, page 35. (Based upon Brisson, 1760, *Ornith.* 3: 389–390 and *La Fauvette tachetée* of Daubenton 1765–81, *Planches Enlum.*, plate 581, figure. 3). Bologna, Italy.

A long-distance migrant, breeding from the British Isles to W Siberia and C Asia and wintering in the northern tropics of Africa and the Indian subcontinent. Generally the most widespread and often the most numerous *Locustella* in the Western and Central Palearctic, Forms a species pair with Lanceolated Warbler (but see **Taxonomy and Systematics**). Polytypic, with three races recognised:

L. n. naevia (Boddaert, 1783). W, C and N Europe and east in Russia to about the Volga River.

L. n. obscurior Buturlin, 1929. The Caucasus.

L. n. straminea (Severtzov, 1873). Russia (from the Urals and across western Siberia), Kazakhstan (the Kirghiz steppes, east to the N Altai and Tien Shan), extreme NW China and W Mongolia.

IDENTIFICATION Length 12–13cm. Wing 55–68mm. Tail/wing 79–97%.

Grasshopper Warbler is a rather small olive-brown warbler with dark streaked upperparts and characteristic *Locustella* features, including a slender pointed bill, a fairly long, markedly graduated tail and long, deep undertail-coverts. Typically skulks on or close to the ground and usually detected and identified by its characteristic high-pitched reeling song. In W Europe, only Savi's Warbler has a similar song but it is slightly lower-pitched, harder, faster and less insect-like. Confusion is more likely with Lanceolated Warbler where the breeding ranges overlap from E Finland and across European Russia to W Siberia. Sexes alike.

Structure The smallest of the three *Locustella* species occurring regularly in W Europe, similar in size to Sedge Warbler but slightly larger than Lanceolated Warbler. It can appear slim and sleek as it creeps through vegetation, but sometimes looks quite stocky, thick-necked and pot-bellied, especially when singing and relaxed. The long, deep-based undertail-coverts reach almost to the tail tip and give the tail a thick base, often noticeable on singing birds. The primary projection is distinctly longer than that of Lanceolated Warbler in nominate birds, but more closely approaches Lanceolated in the smaller Asian form *straminea*. The tail is distinctly longer and less narrow than in Lanceolated Warbler.

Plumage and bare parts Somewhat nondescript but shows obvious dark mottling or streaks on the upperparts and usually some light spotting across the lower throat. There are some racial differences but a great deal of variation results from individual differences and wear and it can be difficult to base racial separation on plumage features alone. European and eastern birds are polymorphic, most being either 'brown morph' (brown above, white below) or 'yellow morph' (olive-brown above, yellowish below). The upperparts of fresh plumaged adults in western Africa and Europe in late winter and spring are olive-brown (tinged more olive or greenish in 'yellow morph' birds), with somewhat diffuse dark brown feather centres. An olive-brown fringe completely encircles each feather so the overall appearance is mottled (the dark lines on the mantle characteristic of Lanceolated Warbler are generally absent). The rump is olive-brown with diffuse darker brown

centres. The uppertail-coverts are similar in colour to the rump or marginally warmer but occasionally lack dark centres and show little contrast with the brown tail. By late summer, worn adults have narrower, faded buffy fringes to the upperpart feathering, enhancing the prominence of the dark centres, but only heavily abraded individuals lose the fringed tips to the mantle feathers to produce long dark streaks and such extremely worn individuals are rare. The wing-coverts and tertials show dark brown centres that merge into paler, broad, olive-brown fringes without the sharp demarcation shown by Lanceolated Warbler (Fig. 28). The rather featureless head lacks a contrasting eye-stripe but usually shows a small dark loral triangle and a smaller dark spot behind the eye. A faint narrow whitish or yellowish supercilium extends from the bill base to the rear of the ear-coverts, appearing most conspicuous above and behind the eye. This is sometimes almost absent, but even poorly marked birds usually show a trace just behind the eye. A pale narrow eye-ring sometimes appears conspicuous, the upper edge merging with and accentuating the supercilium.

Underpart colour varies, apparently randomly, throughout range, with some appearing brownish below (brown morph) while others are distinctly yellow below (yellow morph). In Europe, brown morph birds appear silvery white below but are usually strongly tinged buffy brown on the breast and flanks. Yellow morph birds show a distinct yellow wash to the entire underparts, strongest on throat and upper breast. Both morphs display a necklace of fine spotting across the lower throat, with broader more diffuse streaking along the flanks. More prominently marked birds show streaks on the middle and lower throat, extending as a bib onto the central upper breast, but these are unusual. The undertail-coverts are paler than the flanks, pale tan to pale buff, and each feather has a pointed dark centre, rather diffusely demarcated but extending to the feather base: these centres can be obvious on singing birds.

Juvenile plumage closely resembles that of fresh adults and both colour morphs occur at this age. The narrow gorget of fine spotting tends to be more conspicuous but is never as well marked as the pectoral band characteristic of Lanceolated Warbler.

The bill is dark brown or blackish with a pale yellowish pink to dull fleshy pink lower mandible, usually darkening slightly towards the tip. The legs and feet vary from pale pink to brownish pink.

Asian breeding birds of the race *straminea* differ in lacking the olive plumage tones and appearing rather greyer above and paler below than the nominate race. This race has slightly more heavily marked upperparts and a less well defined supercilium and eye-ring, giving it a closer resemblance to Lanceolated Warbler, which it also matches in size. However, it is generally paler and greyer than Lanceolated, with mottled rather than streaked upperparts, and the tertials show the broader, slightly diffusely demarcated fringes characteristic of Grasshopper Warbler.

SIMILAR SPECIES Within the breeding range, confusion is most likely to occur with Lanceolated Warbler. A poorly marked Grasshopper might occasionally be mistaken for Savi's Warbler while, exceptionally, Pallas's Grasshopper Warbler has been misidentified as Grasshopper.

Lanceolated Warbler resembles Grasshopper Warbler closely but shows several consistent plumage differences. The pale fringes to the dark-centred tertials are narrow but well-defined and sharply cut off from the brown centres;

the olive-brown fringes to the dark mantle feathers are broken at the tips to create well-defined striations on the upperparts; the gorget across the throat and upper breast is more extensive and well-marked, appearing as well defined, fine, lanceolate streaks; the spots or streaks on the undertail-coverts are narrower but more sharply defined and do not extend to the feather bases; there is no conspicuous eye-ring. Many of these distinctions are less apparent in *straminea* but the unstreaked underparts are common to all races of Grasshopper Warbler.

Savi's Warbler has uniform upperparts and lacks the streaking shown by Grasshopper. It also lacks streaking on the undertail-coverts and shows only indistinct mottling across the lower throat rather than a gorget of fine spotting. See under Savi's Warbler for further discussion.

Pallas's Grasshopper Warbler was considered to be a potential confusion species when its field characters were poorly understood but, given good views, confusion is unlikely. Many of the features useful in separating Lanceolated and Pallas's Grasshopper Warblers (*q.v.*) can also be applied when eliminating Grasshopper Warbler. It should be stressed that Grasshopper does occasionally show pale tips to the tail feathers, particularly in the races *obscurior* and *straminea*, but these are less well-defined than those typical of Pallas's Grasshopper. Conversely, pale tips are sometimes lacking in some Pallas's Grasshoppers due to damage or abrasion. Otherwise, separation is straightforward. Pallas's Grasshopper shows a long and conspicuous supercilium, obvious contrast on the mantle between rusty brown fringes and blackish feather centres, a bright rusty brown rump and uppertail-coverts contrasting with the darker mantle and tail, blackish tertials with thin, crisp brownish fringes, a pale indentation at the tip of the inner web of the two innermost tertials (although this feature varies depending upon age and race) and unmarked undertail-coverts.

VOICE The highly distinctive song is a continuous, evenly pitched, hard-reeling trill with a slight pulsing delivery that carries well over long distances, up to 400m on calm mornings and evenings. The sound often appears to drift, sometimes seeming louder, then becoming almost inaudible, as the bird turns its head from side to side. Locating a distant singing bird can be difficult, as the faint song, 'bounces' off surrounding vegetation, giving rise to the well known 'ventriloquial effect'. The song itself comprises a rapid series of elements delivered at about 25 per second, each consisting of a pair of notes, the first similar to the call, the second slightly lower in pitch (Sample 2003). This combination, delivered at high speed, produces a fast clicking sound with a metallic ringing quality, as the two components of each element are just separable by the human ear. It is slightly higher pitched than the song of Savi's Warbler, ranging from 4.5–8kHz, with a single energy peak at 5–5.5kHz where the pair of notes comprising each element overlap. This song has been likened to the stridulation of the bush-cricket *Tettigonia viridissima* and the wood-cricket *Nemobius sylvestris*.

Songs varies in length and lacks the introductory notes typical of Savi's Warbler. It usually starts quietly and increases in volume over a period of several seconds, then ceases abruptly. An initial burst may last only a few seconds before a pause. If undisturbed, a bird may sing for several minutes with barely discernible breaks, but more deliberate pauses of up to a few seconds are normal. Song can be heard at any hour, but is less frequent during daylight, when sequences

are typically shorter, often lasting ten seconds or less. The longest continuous sequences tend to be given during the hours of darkness. One recorded example lasted for 110 minutes (Cramp 1992). Unmated birds may sing for longer periods in daylight, particularly if several males are singing in close proximity,

While there is slight individual and regional variation in pitch, the song is readily recognisable throughout the range. Variants are occasional heard, including a harsh rattling which alternates with the reeling song. In addition Norris (1977) and Wilson (1985) likened it to the song of Corn Bunting. The song of *obscurior* in the Caucasus mountains and *straminea* in Central Asia is extremely similar to that of *naevia* in Europe, particularly when the extent of individual variation is considered.

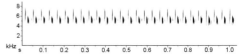

Part of song of Grasshopper Warbler recorded within breeding range of *L. n. naevia*, Suffolk, England, May. (Peter Kennerley)

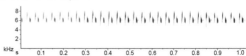

Part of song of Grasshopper Warbler recorded within breeding range of *L. n. obscurior*, near Syunik, Armenia, May. (Peter Kennerley)

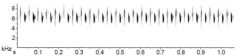

Part of song of Grasshopper Warbler recorded within breeding range of *L. n. straminea*, Astana, Kazakhstan, May. (Peter Kennerley)

Grasshopper Warbler shares a high-pitched reeling or pulsing song with three other *Locustella* species; Lanceolated, Savi's and River Warblers, all of which breed in Europe. The reel of Lanceolated Warbler bears the closest resemblance, but is slightly thinner and higher pitched, with a ringing quality lacking in nominate *naevia*. In Europe, a few male Lanceolated regularly establish territories in southeastern Finland and the Karelia region of W Russia, where confusion of songs is possible. From the Urals to W Siberia and N Central Asia, there is a real possibility of confusion where *straminea* and Lanceolated Warbler overlap and care is required to separate them on song alone throughout this region. Savi's Warbler has a reeling song which also consists of elements of paired notes, but these are delivered more rapidly, at about 50 per second, giving it a harder, buzzing quality, slightly lower in pitch than in Grasshopper. Confusion with River Warbler song is unlikely, this being much slower and lower-pitched, with a distinctive pulsing or stridulating rhythm, and a grating quality lacking in Grasshopper.

The most frequently heard call is a short, sharp, metallic, but quiet, '*pit*', '*chit*', '*chik*', '*plik*' or variation on this, presumably an alarm, often heard when birds are disturbed near the nest. This may be repeated or run together in a slurred series. Other calls heard occasionally include a short repeated '*churr*', sometimes extended into a rapid '*sisisi…*', along with other high-pitched squeaking and harsh scolding calls from agitated birds (Sample 2003).

MOULT In the nominate race, some adults have a partial post-breeding moult prior to migration, usually confined to the body and head feathers, but sometimes involving the tertials and central tail feathers. A few replace the inner primaries and Cramp (1992) cites an adult trapped on autumn migration that had undergone complete moult. The extent of any autumn moult in Iberia and North Africa has not been established, but the majority of birds moult completely in tropical Africa. Because the flight feathers of spring birds appear unworn, this moult has usually been thought to occur late, during February and March (Witherby *et al.* 1938; Williamson 1968), but it appears that it takes place between October and January, at a time when other Palearctic warblers are moulting in the northern tropics of Africa. This picture is supported by data from Djoudj National Park, Senegal, where birds were trapped for ringing in October (1), November (3), December (83), January (153), February (67), March (29) and April (8); the lack of captures before December being due to high water levels (SJRR *in litt.*). The October bird was in suspended moult with new inner primaries and tertials. One in early January was actively replacing primaries and secondaries. All other birds appeared to have finished moult, although two in January retained an inner primary and some secondaries respectively. December birds were noted to have fresh-looking plumage. Of four birds trapped in N Ghana in November, one had recently completed primary moult, while in the other three it was in the mid to late stages (Hedenström *et al.* 1990). There is no suggestion of a subsequent body moult prior to spring migration.

Young birds do not moult on the breeding grounds after fledging but retain their juvenile body plumage until after autumn migration. They then have a full moult, presumably at the same time as adults. This is usually complete but a minority, probably first-year birds, arrive back on the breeding grounds with a few faded, unmoulted, inner primaries and outer secondaries.

The timing and extent of moult in *straminea* is poorly understood. Dement'ev & Gladkov (1968) reported some adults as moulting from mid July to mid August, prior to migration (presumably the body plumage), while others had not yet started by mid September. Williamson (1968) mentioned a specimen from northern India that was already moulting the innermost primaries, tertials and greater coverts on 9 September. The majority of birds, both adults and first-years, appear to have a complete moult in India, probably between October and January. The wings and tails of spring birds returning to the breeding grounds are in pristine condition and it may be that *straminea* moults slightly later than *naevia*.

HABITAT Restricted throughout most of NW Europe to lowlands below 150m but a few breed regularly up to 300m (occasionally 350m) in Britain and to 500m in the Swiss Alps. In Europe, it occupies a wide range of both dry and damp habitats with thick low-lying vegetation. These include scrubby edges of open woodland, young conifer plantations with tussocky grass, field edges, nettle beds and bramble, damp grazing land and water meadows, upland moor with willow and birch scrub, fens and reedbeds with sedges and scattered bushes, and damp hollows in sand dune systems. Small numbers nest in disused, overgrown industrial sites. It appears able to respond rapidly to the temporary availability of habitats. In the Caucasus, *obscurior* breeds in

dense grass and wildflower meadows, damp scrub woodland, cereal fields, thickets around lake edges and marshes and meadows on hill slopes, mainly between 600m and 1,500m, but sometimes up to 1,800m in scrubby alpine pastures (AA *in litt.*). The breeding habitats of *straminea* appear not to differ substantially from those of the nominate form. It is found in meadows and marshes with tall grasses, bushes and reeds from the plains up to 1,700m.

In West Africa, wintering birds frequent grassy or herbaceous growth with bushes, including undergrowth in acacia and open deciduous woodland, often near water. In Senegal, it is most frequently encountered in *Phragmites* reedbeds and adjacent scrub and in Mali in *Mimosa pigra* on the margins of floodland. On Mount Nimba, Guinea, it has been recorded in clearings at 550m with shrubs and 2m-high *Andropogon* and *Hyparrenia* grasses (Brosset 1984), while in Ethiopia it has been found above 2,000m. The two Kenya records are both from montane altitudes; Loita Hills on 19 June 1977 at *c.* 2,000m in dense undergrowth by a swamp edge, and Mount Marsbit on 8 March 2000 at *c.* 1,500m in dense bush *c.* 70m from the shore of Lake Paradise. In the lowlands of the Indian subcontinent wintering birds occur in damp lakeside vegetation, marshes, thick grass and tamarisk scrub, rice fields and reedbeds. At higher elevations in the Western Ghats, they utilise grass-covered slopes with scattered bushes.

BEHAVIOUR Its skulking behaviour is legendary. It only flies reluctantly and typically remains close to or on the ground, walking or running through dense cover in a mouse-like manner. Feeds from low stems or among dead leaves and other ground debris.

Males return to the breeding territories about ten days before females and immediately begin to sing. The song can then be heard at any time of day, but most frequently and persistently at night and for up to an hour before sunset and after sunrise. It is usually delivered from concealment within low cover, but also from higher exposed perches on windless mornings and evenings. Males in scrub and bushes generally remain within 2m of the ground, moving within cover when silent, but becoming almost stationary when singing. A bird singing close to the edge of vegetation may creep gradually along its perch until fully exposed. Birds singing in *Phragmites* reedbeds often perch part-way up a stem, making viewing difficult. However, in most reedbed territories a small bush is selected as the preferred song post. Singing birds can often be approached and observed closely. They adopt an upright posture, with the tail pointing down, the head raised and the bill held open. During continuous song, the wings shiver rapidly, the tail vibrates and the throat pulsates, but this ceases immediately song stops.

Song is heard in Britain mainly from arrival in mid April to mid or late July, but occasionally also from migrants in autumn; once in Cornwall as late as 21 October (King 1968). In Russia, song lasts from mid May to early August. It becomes more intermittent when a female arrives and practically ceases between pairing and the fledging of the first brood. There is usually then a resumption before completion of the second nest and then finally more weak song after the second brood has fledged.

Singing males are highly territorial and respond vigorously to taped recordings of their song. They remain close to the song source, often oblivious to human presence, running rapidly along the ground, but using any available cover. They occasionally appear in the open, flicking their wings above back in an agitated manner and calling

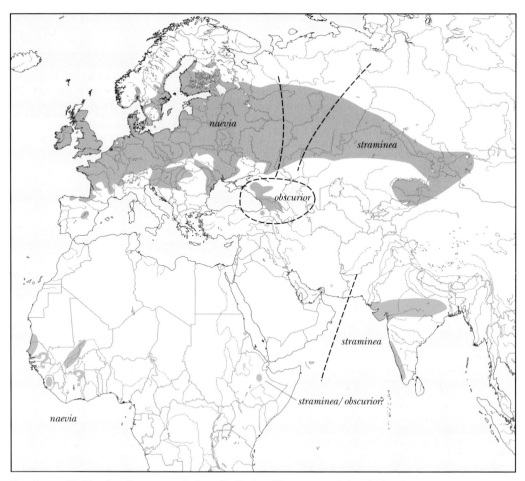

Grasshopper Warbler. Breeding range and winter distribution. Winter range of *obscurior* is unknown.

repeatedly. Birds may also begin to sing in response to sounds that resemble their songs. Dean (1993), for example, described a Grasshopper Warbler reeling in response to an electric drill.

BREEDING HABITS Breeds in W and C Europe between late April or early May and early August. It is solitary and territorial and apparently monogamous. A pair may require only 1ha but more typically occupies 3–4ha. In prime areas in the core of the breeding range, densities may reach 20–50 pairs/km², but in peripheral areas, such as Finland, 3–8 pairs/km² is more typical (Hagemeijer & Blair 1997). The nest, built by both sexes, is placed in a grass tussock or among thick vegetation such as sedge, rushes, heather or bramble, on or within 1m of the ground. It is a cup of grasses, leaves and plant stems, lined with finer grass and other material such as moss, feathers, hair and plant down. There is usually an entrance run leading to the nest.

A clutch of 5–6 eggs is laid. Incubation lasts 12–15 days and is carried out by both sexes. The fledging period is 10–12 days, both parents feeding and caring for the young. Typically double-brooded in W and C Europe and probably also in Siberia and C Asia.

DISTRIBUTION A widespread summer visitor throughout temperate regions of the W and C Palearctic, but its secretive and unobtrusive behaviour makes it difficult to assess the abundance and density of breeding birds. Populations appear to fluctuate for reasons that are not fully understood, although it is established that preferred habitats such as young conifer plantations fall into disuse as they age. Numbers fluctuate even in apparently ideal and unchanged habitats and numbers trapped at coastal and inland ringing stations can also show significant annual variation. It has been suggested that a partially nomadic breeding population may be strongly affected by weather conditions during spring migration. Drought on the wintering grounds may also have a significant effect on numbers breeding in Europe. It is uncertain whether Asian populations are also subject to such fluctuations.

***L. n. naevia* Breeding** Ranges from Ireland in the west, south to N Spain west of the Pyrenees and north and east through France to the Black Sea coast in Romania, but avoiding the Mediterranean basin. Breeds widely, albeit patchily, across C Europe to the shores of the Baltic Sea and Gulf of Bothnia, north to at least 65°N in Sweden and Finland, although the majority occur between 45°N and 60°N from Germany east through Poland and the Baltic States into Russia. In Russia, the extent of intergradation with *straminea* is poorly known. Vaurie (1959) includes birds breeding east to about 47°E in E Vologda within *naevia*. But Dement'ev & Gladkov (1968) note intergrading with *straminea* in the Oka and Tambov region, to the west of the Volga River, extending over approximately ten degrees of longitude.

Non-breeding The wintering range is still poorly understood and based largely on limited information from ringing studies. The majority of birds winter in sub-Saharan West Africa, from W Mauritania, through Senegal, Gambia, Mali, Guinea, Sierra Leone and Liberia, east to Ghana. It is said to be a scarce and irregular winterer in Morocco (Thévenot *et al.* 2003). In Senegal it is common in Djoudj National Park, records suggesting a mainly coastal distribution (Rodwell *et al.* 1996). However, most recent ringing in West Africa has concentrated along coasts and this undoubtedly biases understanding.

L. n. obscurior **Breeding** Apparently isolated from the nominate form and restricted to the Caucasus Mountains in Russia and Georgia and to the mountains forming the borders between Georgia, Armenia and NE Turkey. Patchily distributed between 600m and *c.* 1,500m and generally quite scarce, but more widespread and locally numerous in S Georgia, including the region along the border with Armenia, the southern slopes of eastern Trialeti Ridge, the Paravani River basin, the Gomareti mountain steppe, the Khrami River basin and the Kura (Mtkvari) valley, from the Turkish border to Borjomi Gorge (AA *in litt.*).

Non-breeding The winter quarters are unknown and the only documented record away from the breeding area concerns a presumed wintering bird in Zagros, SW Iran (Vaurie 1959). There are, however, two records of vagrant Grasshopper Warblers mist-netted in Kenya, one in the southwest in June (Fayad & Fayad 1977), the other in the north in March (Borghesio *et al.* 2004). Wing lengths of 65mm and 64mm respectively place these birds outside the range of Asian breeding forms and *obscurior* is perhaps more likely to occur here than nominate *naevia*. Any Grasshopper Warbler in eastern Africa or the Middle East merits critical examination.

L. n. straminea **Breeding** Breeds in Russia east of the Volga River, from about 55°E in the W Ural foothills, north to *c.* 61°N and across the West Siberia plain, east to Novosibirsk and Tomskat *c.* 55°N, and the northern foothills of the Altai Mountains. Breeds throughout much of central and northern Kazakhstan, from the northern Aral Sea region, east across the Kirgiz steppes to at least Lake Alakol and the Zaysan Depression, and south to the Tien Shan mountains, and in the region of the May Saz Pass and Karakol, Kyrgyzstan. Also reported from the Pamir Mountains in Tajikistan but breeding here is uncertain. The eastern limit extends to at least 91°E at Qing He, NW Xinjiang Uygur Autonomous Region, W China (GJC *in litt.*) and into W Mongolia. It apparently intergrades with *naevia* in the Oka and Tambov regions southeast of Moscow (Dement'ev & Gladkov 1968).

Non-breeding Reported to occur in winter from the southern Caspian Sea east through Iran and S Afghanistan to Baluchistan, Pakistan, but the very few records from this region may refer to passage birds. Most are believed to winter within the Indian subcontinent where it is probably overlooked. Generally widespread within India, ranging from the Punjab east across the Gangetic Plain to Bengal, Assam and Bangladesh and south to Tamil Nadu and Kerala (Ali & Ripley 1973). Apparently a vagrant to Nepal (Inskipp & Inskipp 1991). A small population winters in northeast Africa, where Ash (1978) netted a few in NW and C Ethiopia between mid September and early April, and Nikolaus (1984) caught passage birds on the Sudan coast on 18 August and 21 September 1983. There is an old record from Iraq and a more recent occurrence on the Red Sea coast of Yemen on 21 March 1995, presumably involving a returning migrant of this race (Al-Saghier & Porter 1997).

MOVEMENTS The departure of nominate *naevia* from the breeding grounds is difficult to detect and there are relatively few records from well-watched sites along known migration routes. It probably makes long, unbroken flights, for some juvenile birds carry sufficient fat reserves to reach North Africa with just a single stopover. In Britain, ringing in reedbeds along the English south coast has revealed three distinct pulses of southbound juvenile migration, with first arrivals in late July, a main passage in late August and a final movement in late September (Wernham *et al.* 2002). It is likely that some late birds are of continental origin. British migrants head south towards SW France, where there have been several ringing recoveries. Birds from further east head southwest towards the Iberian peninsula. There is a strong passage through the Alps, presumably of birds from the northern and eastern part of the range and this appears to be an important staging area. Most birds pass through S Iberia in September and early October, with only small numbers through S Italy and presumably into Tunisia. It is quite common along the Moroccan west coast and a frequent prey item of Eleonora's Falcons breeding on Essaouira Island (Cramp 1992). Recorded from S Mauritania from August and on wintering grounds in S Mali from September.

Northward migration begins early in Africa. Most birds leave Djoudj National Park by February (SJRR *in litt.*), but a few passage migrants occur in Senegal to May. Wetlands in NW Africa appear to provide an important stopover between February and May. The species is widespread in Algeria as well as Morocco, suggesting that many European birds use a more easterly route in spring. It arrives in Gibraltar and southern Spain from late March, with passage continuing into May. Birds reach Britain from the first week of April but the main influx occurs in late April, with most territories occupied by early to mid May. The vanguard reaches Germany about the third week in April and Sweden in early May, but first arrivals in the St. Petersburg and Moscow regions of Russia are not until mid May. This suggests these eastern birds also use the route through SW Europe. Some from southeastern parts of the breeding range may migrate to and from Africa more directly, but passage through the eastern Mediterranean is sparse, even in spring.

There have been just four trans-Saharan ringing recoveries involving British birds, all to/from Senegal. Birds ringed at Rye Bay (Sussex) and Titchfield, (Hampshire), were controlled at Djoudj National Park and two ringed at Djoudj were found in Cumbria and Dumfries & Galloway. Two others recovered in Senegal originated from Germany and Sweden and one ringed in Gambia was found in NW Germany (Wernham *et al.* 2002).

In Georgia, *obscurior* is recorded between mid April and late September or early October (AA *in litt.*). It vacates its breeding grounds mainly in late August and early September (Zhordania 1962, cited in Cramp 1992).

Nothing is known of this form on migration.

In the eastern part of the range, *straminea* begins to depart from breeding areas in July and peaks in the first half of August, with late birds remaining in the Tomsk region of Siberia to mid September. Passage is apparently limited through W Kazakhstan, but heavier through mountain passes to the east, such as Chokpak (W Tien Shan, Kazakhstan) and also through the Pamirs, suggesting that many follow this route. Around Tashkent, Uzbekistan, passage lasts from mid August to late September and the timing of arrivals indicates several waves of passage, perhaps from different parts of the breeding range. Birds appear in wintering areas from early September. In spring, migration begins in late March, but some birds remain in India to early May. First arrivals in S Kazakhstan are in early April but it only reaches N Kazakhstan in early to mid May, the Novosibirsk region in mid May and the western extremity of the range in W Siberia only in late May.

Vagrancy Vagrants have been recorded from Iceland in the west, the Kuril Islands in the Sea of Okhotsk (Nechaev 1969) and Sri Lanka.

DESCRIPTION *L. n. naevia*

Variable in plumage colour and extent of throat and breast spotting. Most birds (typical brown morph) are predominantly olive-brown above and whitish below, but 20–40% (yellow morph) are washed yellowish on the sides of the head and underparts, with a slightly greener tone above. A few are intermediate in appearance and a small minority in the east of the range are greyer brown than the typical brown morph.

Plumage – Adult fresh, brown morph (February to May) Forehead to nape feathers blackish, narrowly fringed olive-brown to warm brown, to give a spotted or streaked appearance. Supercilium narrow, variable in colour and extent; in some birds forming an indistinct dull olive-brown line above the lores only, in others more contrasting, pale brown to greyish white and extending to above ear-coverts. There is a small olive-brown loral spot in front of the eye and often a small dark spot behind it, but the eye-stripe is indistinct or absent. The pale creamy eye-ring is narrow, but usually conspicuous. Ear-coverts dull olive-brown to greyish brown with darker tips and paler shafts giving a faintly streaked appearance. Nape and sides of neck slightly plainer, less heavily streaked than crown. Mantle feathers and scapulars variable, the dark centres small, round and inconspicuous in some birds, larger and distinctly blackish in others; fringes olive-brown to warm brown, completely encircling the feather centres, including the tips, usually giving the upperparts a mottled appearance. Rump and uppertail-coverts similar to mantle, with broad fringes, but with longer, narrower blackish streaks along feather centres. Tail dark olive-brown, slightly darker than mantle and rump, regularly showing indistinct narrow cross-barring but absent on some individuals. Undersurface of tail grey and unmarked. Chin and throat white with faint greyish white to buffy white wash. Breast and upper flanks washed light brown to warm buffy brown, contrasting with white or greyish white belly. Some birds are completely unstreaked below but most have a small gorget of indistinct dark grey to dark brown spots along the sides and across the lower edge of the throat, very rarely appearing as a narrow band of crisp, dark brown or blackish streaks across the upper breast, widening towards the sides of the breast and lower sides of the neck, sometimes extending more diffusely to upper flanks. Lower flanks and vent buffy brown, occasionally with faint long, thin dark streaks. Undertail-coverts buffy brown, with narrow, pointed blackish centres reaching to feather bases, crisp and well-defined on shorter feathers, but with edges more diffuse on longer central feathers. Lesser and median coverts blackish, fringed olive-brown to dull cinnamon-brown. Greater coverts slightly browner, fringes broader, tending to merge more with centres. Tertials with dark grey-brown centres, merging with broad, olive-brown to dull russet-brown fringes, broadest at feather bases, narrower towards tips. Primaries, secondaries and primary coverts dark grey-brown, with narrow olive-brown to dull cinnamon-brown edges, matching wing-covert and tertial fringes closely. Alula dark brown or greyish brown, broadly fringed greyish brown to pale buff. Underwing-coverts pale buff.

Adult fresh, yellow morph As brown morph, but supercilium, eye-ring, malar region and shafts of ear-coverts tinged yellowish. Upperparts, wing-coverts and tertials fringed olive-brown. Edges of flight feathers usually slightly warmer with a marginally more distinct greenish tinge. Chin, throat and belly pale yellowish white to buffy yellow. Breast, flanks, vent and undertail-coverts dull yellowish olive-brown or olive-yellow; breast often slightly darker with a brownish wash over yellow feather tips. Extent of breast streaking and undertail-covert pattern as in brown morph.

Adult worn (June to November) Difference between colour morphs is largely obscured. Fringes to worn upperpart feathers narrower, sometimes entirely absent, enhancing blacker feather centres. Crown appears darker than in fresh plumage and mantle more prominently streaked. Supercilium and eye-ring usually whiter and more prominent. Underparts become whiter as brownish or yellowish feather tips are lost. Breast streaking variable, as in fresh adults; conspicuous in some birds, almost absent in others. Centres to greater coverts and tertials faded greyish brown, fringes paler and browner without olive tones. Undertail-coverts may show paler buff tips.

Juvenile Like fresh adult and inseparable on plumage colour. Equally variable as regards colour of underparts and extent of spotting on throat and breast. Incidence of different colour morphs as in adult.

Bare Parts Upper mandible dark brown or blackish with dull flesh-pink cutting edge. Lower mandible pale yellowish pink to dull fleshy pink, sometimes unmarked but usually with dark sides towards tip. In first autumn lower mandible more often lacks dusky tip, appearing entirely pale pinkish flesh. Mouth yellow or pale flesh in adult, yellowish flesh in first autumn; three tongue spots in juveniles are often retained until first spring, possibly longer. Tarsi and toes usually conspicuous pale pink or brownish pink, occasionally darker greyish pink, claws light horn or pinkish brown. Iris warm brown.

IN HAND CHARACTERS
Measurements
L. n. naevia

	Male	Female
Wing	61–68 (64.2; 33)	61–65 (63.3; 12)
Tail	51–59 (54.6; 32)	49–58 (52.2; 12)
Bill	13–15.5 (14.3; 32)	13.5–15 (14.2; 12)
Tarsus	19–21.5 (20.3; 44)	19–20.5 (20.0; 22)

(Includes data from Cramp 1992)

Sexes combined:
Tail/wing ratio: 80–92% (84%; 23)
Bill width: 3.0–3.5 (3.2; 18)
Hind claw: 5.3–6.7 (5.8; 18)
Tail graduation: 12–21 (16.2; 15)

Juvenile wing averages about the same as in adult, but tail *c.* 5mm shorter.

L. n. straminea

	Male	Female
Wing	58–61 (59.4; 25)	55–59 (57.3; 8)
Tail	46–56 (51.8; 21)	47–54 (50.5; 8)
Bill	13.5–15.5 (13.9; 23)	13–14 (13.4; 8)
Tarsus	17.5–19.5 (18.8; 19)	17.5–19.5 (18.5; 7)

Sexes combined:
Tail/wing ratio: 79–97% (87%; 30)
Bill width: 2.8–3.2 (3.1; 18)
Hind claw: 4.6–5.7 (5.1; 10)
Tail graduation: 15–25

All measurements thus smaller than in nominate race.

L. n. obscurior (♂♂ only): *wing* 60–68 (65; 10) (Vaurie 1959). Measurements similar to nominate race.

Structure

L . n. naevia

Wing formula (Cramp 1992):

p1/pc	p2	p3e	p4	p5	p6	p7	p10
(3)–3	0.5–3	wp	0.5–3	3–5	5–8	7–11	12–17

Wing pointed; p1 minute. Wing point p3; p2 = p3/4–4/5 (5); emargination on p3. Notch on p2 8.5–11mm from tip in adult, 7.5–10mm in juvenile; falls at p7–10.

Figure 26. Wing of Grasshopper Warbler.

Tail graduated; feathers rounded (Fig. 30).
Bill rather short, slender, concave-sided with very narrow tip.
Tarsi short, rather strong; toes long and slender; claws small, fine, rather straight.
L. n. straminea Wing typically blunter than in nominate *naevia*; p2 usually shorter than p4, p4 occasionally emarginated as well as p3. Tail typically more strongly graduated.
Recognition Distinguished from Lanceolated Warbler by diffuse blackish centres to undertail-coverts which reach base of feathers and by more mottled upperparts with feather fringes surrounding dark centres. Marking below typically confined to spots across upper breast. Most birds

(all races) also separable from Lanceolated by deeper notch on p2 (9mm or more from tip); and longer tail (usually > 48mm) with broader feathers (> 8mm) (see Fig. 30). Most nominate birds and *obscurior* have a wing length above range of Lanceolated (> 62mm).

Ageing Juveniles resemble fresh adults in plumage, with variation in colour and extent of throat spotting apparently similar. In late summer and early autumn, distinction should be easy when adults are heavily worn, with abraded primaries and tail feathers. The upperpart feather fringes are dull, more greyish buff, and any yellow tinge below is reduced or worn away. Juveniles have fresh wing feathers with, at most, only slight wear on the outer primaries and tail feathers typically with only slight castellations at the tips. They typically show brighter, olive-tinged upperpart fringes and many have a strong yellow suffusion below. Tongue spots are of limited use; they are sometimes lost quickly during first autumn, yet are retained by some adult birds.

Weight
L. n. naevia: range 9–20g, typically 11–14g. Commonly reaches pre-migratory weights of 15–17g.
L. n. straminea: typically 10–13g. In Kazakhstan, 9.2–16.0g (12.1; 122) (AG unpublished data).

GEOGRAPHIC VARIATION Three races recognised, forming two distinct groups based on measurements and distribution. The forms *naevia* and *obscurior,* breeding in the Western Palearctic, are larger, *naevia* generally olive-brown above, *obscurior* slightly colder, appearing greyish rather like *straminea*. Eastern *straminea*, breeding in the C Palearctic and wintering in India, is smaller and distinctly greyish above. Intergrades between *naevia* and *straminea* are subtle and poorly understood and appearance is likely to vary individually across the intergrade zone.

L. n. naevia (W Europe, east in Russia to the Volga River) Polymorphic, with brown and yellow morphs. Described above.

L. n. obscurior (Caucasus Mountains) Similar in size and structure to nominate *naevia*, but shows, on average, slightly larger, more contrasting blackish centres to the crown and upperpart feathers. Olive tone to brown upperparts less pronounced than on *naevia* or absent during breeding season, with some birds distinctly greyish in this respect like *straminea*. Underparts greyish white, the flanks warmer and browner, but pattern and extent of spotting on the lower throat generally resembles that of nominate *naevia*. It is unclear whether this race has a yellow morph.

L. n. straminea (Urals east through W Siberia to N Altai, the Tien Shan, extreme NW China and W Mongolia) Polymorphic, with brown, yellow and grey morphs. Spring birds are generally more heavily marked above than *naevia* with larger, darker, more rounded feather centres and narrower, paler and greyer fringes. Fringes and edges of the wing feathers also grey-brown, matching those of the upperparts. Many *straminea* show a tendency for the fore-supercilium to merge with the pale lores to give the head a plain-faced, bland and uniform appearance. In some individuals this appears as a well defined and contrasting 'arrowhead', pointing towards the bill base, with the supercilium and lower loral line separated by a dark spot immediately in front of the eye.

In the brown morph, the underparts are washed warm brown, strongest across breast, gradually becoming paler brown on the belly, appearing almost white on the palest individuals. Overall, *straminea* is less well marked on the underparts than *naevia*. Blackish spots are usually present on lower throat, typically smaller and less conspicuous than in *naevia*. A minority show round, crisp spots on the lower throat and upper breast, which may extend to form thin black streaks along the flanks; these are better defined than in *naevia* but such birds are rare. The undertail-coverts are pale greyish white to light creamy buff with diffuse darker centres that extend to the feather bases as in *naevia*.

Adults resembling the yellow morph appear to be rare in the breeding season, at least in the eastern part of the range (east of 70°E). This morph seems to be common among wintering birds, suggesting that yellow tones persist only for a few months after moult. Yellow morph wintering birds resemble *naevia*, with the entire underparts washed dull yellowish olive-brown, slightly darker on the breast and with an indistinct brownish wash over the feather tips. The yellow morph is less prone to show throat spotting which, if present, is less distinct than on brown morph birds. Freshly moulted birds in winter have the fringes of the upperparts and wing feathers browner, with a slight olive cast and more closely resembling nominate *naevia*, and underparts tinged pale yellow, with a warmer grey-buff wash on the breast and flanks.

In the east of the range, from E Kazakhstan to W China and W Mongolia, spring birds closely resemble *straminea* breeding to west, with fringes on the upperparts and wing feathers the same or just slightly greyer. The underparts, however, are typically paler, with only a light greyish wash across the breast and pale buffy grey flanks. Some have light, diffuse spotting on the lower throat but others lack throat markings entirely. These birds have been treated as race *mongolica*. However, they probably represent a clinal trend and some breeders from further west in Kazakhstan and S Siberia share this same pale appearance and lack of spotting. We therefore prefer to regard '*mongolica*' as a grey morph of *straminea* rather than a distinct race. Examination of specimens from the wintering range has shown that if *mongolica* exists as a distinct form it is not diagnosable from *straminea* at this season.

TAXONOMY AND SYSTEMATICS The race at the eastern extremity of the breeding range has often been recognised as *mongolica*. But it is poorly defined and we follow others (e.g. Stepanyan 2003) in treating it as a synonym of *straminea*. In fact, *mongolica* was described from E Kazakhstan where all closely examined birds have proved to be indistinguishable from *straminea*. Although these eastern birds tend to show a paler appearance, similar individuals occur within the recognised range of *straminea*. Apart from their paler underparts and slightly greyer upperparts, birds included within *mongolica* show no other distinctive structural or plumage characters.

The similarities of morphology, song and behaviour between Grasshopper and Lanceolated Warblers have suggested that they are closely related. However, DNA studies have shown that these are not each other's nearest relatives. Grasshopper Warbler is found in a clade which includes Chinese Bush Warbler and Brown Bush Warbler, and is more distantly related to the other 'western' *Locustella* species (Drovetski *et al.* 2004; Alström *et al.* in prep).

▲ Adult *L. n. naevia*, yellow morph, Cheshire, England, April. Yellow-morph birds show an olive tone in the upperparts and yellowish wash on the underparts. Note brown fringes to mantle feathers giving upperparts a mottled rather than streaked appearance (Steve Round).

▲ ▶ Adult *L. n. naevia*, brown morph, Merseyside, England, April. Singing males often emerge to sit fully exposed, when this characteristic upright posture is adopted. Many adults lack spotting on the lower throat (Richard Steel).

▲ ▶ Juvenile *L. n. naevia*, yellow morph, Suffolk, England, July. Aged as a juvenile by the fresh, unworn plumage. Shows slight olive tone to brown upperparts and conspicuous yellow wash on underparts. Faint, diffuse spots on lower throat is typical of European birds (James Kennerley).

▲ ▶ Juvenile *L. n. naevia*, brown morph, Suffolk, England, September. Darker than juvenile yellow morph, and lacks olive tone to upperparts and yellow wash to underparts. Note contrast between whitish throat and brown wash on breast, and lack of spotting on throat (James Kennerley).

▲ ▶ Adult *L. n. obscurior*, Armenia, May. Upperparts greyish brown and lack olive tone; some can resemble *straminea* but larger, and appears slightly longer-tailed than other races. Note slightly larger, more contrasting blackish centres to crown and upperpart feathers giving streaked appearance. Underparts greyish white with small diffuse spots on lower throat as nominate *naevia* (Peter Kennerley).

◀ Adult, race uncertain (possibly *obscurior*), Kuwait, August. This is an exceptionally dark bird. The abraded flight feathers establish it as an adult, but shows fresh, olive-tinged body feathers, inner greater-coverts and central tertial. Note the particularly broad fringes to the fresh tertial, as well as the mantle feathering and scapulars. Shows fine streaking on lower throat, particularly prominent flank-streaking and conspicuous long, dark centres to undertail-coverts, features usually associated with Lanceolated. Also note the deep pink legs, a colour not associated with any race (Michael Pope).

◀ ▲ Adult *L. n. straminea*, grey morph, Novosibirsk, Siberia, Russia, June. The smallest race. Breeding adults often show entirely pale lores and the bill is frequently entirely black during the breeding season, giving the head a distinctive appearance. Upperparts generally more contrasting than in nominate *naevia*, with larger, darker, rounded feather centres and narrower, paler and greyer fringes. Underparts show light greyish wash across breast and unmarked pale buffy grey flanks. Some show small, diffuse spotting on lower throat but most adults lack throat markings (Peter Kennerley).

◀ Juvenile *L. n. straminea*, Xinjiang, China, August. Closely resembles juvenile brown morph of nominate *naevia* but note entirely pale lores. Separation only possible by measurements and wing structure, *straminea* having a shorter wing with p2 usually shorter than p4, and the tail is often more strongly graduated (Paul Leader).

LANCEOLATED WARBLER
Locustella lanceolata   Plate 11

Sylvia lanceolata **Temminck, 1840**. *Man. Ornith.*, ed. 2(4): 614, 'Mayence,' error for Russia.

A long-distance migrant that breeds widely in moist habitats across cool temperate regions of the Eastern and Central Palearctic and winters from E India to SE Asia. Forms a species-pair with Grasshopper Warbler. Polytypic, with two races recognised:

L. l. lanceolata (Temminck, 1840). Russia (Perm and the W Ural Mountains, south to the N Altai Mountains and east through Siberia to *c.* 65°N along the lower Kolyma River, S Kamchatka and Sea of Okhotsk south to Amurland and Ussuriland) and NE China. Expanding west to Karelia, W Russia and S Finland.

L. l. hendersonii Cassin, 1858. NE Russia (Sakhalin and S Kuril Islands) and Japan (Hokkaido and N Honshu).

IDENTIFICATION Length 12cm. Wing 52–62mm. Tail/wing 71–82%.

The smallest and most heavily marked of the *Locustella* warblers. Separation from Grasshopper Warbler requires care, and both share a similar reeling song. When seen well, the dull olive-brown upperparts of Lanceolated Warbler show broad dark streaks, the breast has a distinctive gorget of thin streaks and the flanks have long, thin 'lanceolate' streaks. Unlike Grasshopper Warbler, it does not have a yellow morph. Sexes alike.

Structure Resembles Grasshopper Warbler with a strongly graduated tail and deep-based undertail-coverts that extend almost to the tail tip. Appears slightly more stocky, less rakish, however, especially when singing and the tail is both shorter and narrower. The bill appears both shorter and smaller, giving the head a more compact appearance than that of Grasshopper Warbler (Fig. 27). Slightly smaller than nominate Grasshopper Warbler and with a distinctly shorter primary projection, but these differences become unreliable when comparing with the smaller Asian race *straminea* of Grasshopper Warbler. The wing point is formed by p3, which is the only emarginated primary.

Figure 27. Head and bill shape of (a) Lanceolated Warbler and (b) Grasshopper Warbler.

Plumage and bare parts Fresh spring adults show heavy, dark upperpart streaking, often appearing as a series of fine parallel lines from the nape to the lower back. The crown and upperpart feathers have blackish centres and contrasting fringes, rather warm olive-brown to paler, more greyish brown. An important feature is that the dark centres to the mantle feathers reach the tips, so that they form a series of distinctive blackish and olive-brown lines of almost equal width that extend down the mantle. The rump and uppertail-coverts are quite heavily marked, with obvious dark feather centres but broader, browner fringes, the latter contrasting little with the upperside of the tail. The dark-centred tertials show narrow, sharply demarcated olive-brown fringes that form three distinct chevrons pointing

towards the tail. These are a striking feature, unlike the more diffusely marked tertials of Grasshopper Warbler (Fig. 28). The greater coverts also show dark brown centres and crisply defined, although wider, olive-brown fringes, and the fringes to the primaries and secondaries are slightly warmer and browner than the upperparts.

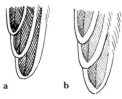

Figure 28. Comparison of tertial pattern of (a) Lanceolated Warbler and (b) Grasshopper Warbler.

The head pattern is rather plain and featureless. At best, there is a narrow whitish supercilium extending from the bill base to the rear of the ear-coverts, as in Grasshopper Warbler. This is often suffused with brown behind the eye, where it merges with the sides of the crown. Most birds show a pale, narrow line below the eye, meeting the supercilium at the bill to enclose a small triangle of dark loral feathering. A short dark line behind the eye is poorly defined, merging into the upper ear-coverts.

Lanceolated Warbler has streaked underparts, shown by all birds and conspicuous on most. Adults have a gorget of small, fine streaks across the lower throat and slightly longer streaks on the upper breast and upper flanks, where they tend to form distinctive lines converging towards the throat. Even a poorly marked Lanceolated shows a more extensive and better defined gorget than the best-marked Grasshopper Warbler. This streaking is only exceptionally lacking or inconspicuous, more often apparently in the race *hendersonii* than in mainland Asian breeders. The majority of birds show long, well-defined streaks running the entire length of the flanks, with thin lines extending towards the undertail-coverts. This flank streaking is occasionally subdued or absent or it may take the form of larger and broader, teardrop-shaped spots. Lanceolated is not dimorphic and adults rarely, if ever, show any hint of yellow below. Flank colour varies from warm buff to greyish white. Adults can show large, broad, drop-shaped spots on the ventral feathering. The undertail-coverts are pale buff to rusty brown, generally more richly coloured than the flanks. The shorter, outer feathers show a clear, small, dark brown central streak or spot that never extends to the feather base, while on the longest feathers this is either lacking or restricted to a neat dark line along the shaft. These may show whitish tips when fresh. Freshly moulted birds in late winter and spring sometimes show pale tips to the rectrices, which can be quite prominent, even whitish on the central pair, but never clearly cut off as in Pallas's Grasshopper Warbler.

Juvenile birds resemble adults closely in markings and coloration but some, particularly of the race *hendersonii*, show a faint yellow-ochre flush to the throat and upper breast.

Breeding birds become paler and somewhat bleached by late summer. Further wear and bleaching during winter, before the complete moult, transforms the appearance of both adults and juveniles, removing brown feather fringes and enhancing darker upperpart markings. In addition, the supercilium tends to become more apparent when worn, the dark back streaks are less blackish and appear broader, and the tertials become more uniformly blackish as fringes wear away. The breast becomes whiter and more uniform with the belly, and the underpart streaking becomes narrower and browner and generally restricted to a gorget across the throat and to the rear flanks.

The bill is dark brown to blackish with a pale pink base to the lower mandible. During the breeding season, the sides of the lower mandible darken slightly towards the tip. The legs and feet are conspicuously pale pink.

SIMILAR SPECIES Within its breeding range, it overlaps widely with Grasshopper Warbler in the west and Pallas's Grasshopper Warbler in the east. No other *Locustella* or *Bradypterus* species with streaked upperparts occur within its breeding or wintering ranges.

Grasshopper Warbler overlaps extensively with Lanceolated from SE Finland and parts of westernmost Russia to the Ural Mountains and S Siberia. Moreover, regular westward vagrancy in autumn regularly brings juvenile Lanceolated into W Europe, where they occur in areas where juvenile Grasshopper Warblers are frequent. Across W Siberian and northern parts of Central Asia, Lanceolated Warbler overlaps extensively with the smaller race *straminea* of Grasshopper Warbler.

Consistent plumage differences have established reliable means of separating Lanceolated and Grasshopper Warblers (e.g. Alström 1989; Riddiford & Harvey 1992; Svensson 1992; Votier & Moon 1995). The eye-ring of Grasshopper is variable but more conspicuous than shown by Lanceolated, at least in spring. The mantle feathers of the race *naevia* of Grasshopper have dark centres surrounded by broad and rather diffuse lighter brown fringes, producing a mottled appearance rather than the well-defined dark lines of Lanceolated. The mantle fringes in *straminea* are more sharply defined but extend around the feather tips, to produce the typical mottled pattern of Grasshopper. Moreover, the upperparts of *straminea* in spring should appear paler and greyer than Lanceolated would ever show. The tertials on all races of Grasshopper show paler and browner centres than in Lanceolated and broader, less sharply defined fringes. Flank streaks are usually lacking on Grasshopper and where present, they are long and diffuse and quite different from the short, narrow and crisp streaks typical of Lanceolated Warbler. Grasshopper Warbler usually shows a line of small spots across the lower throat, whereas lines of sharply defined streaks form a pectoral band in Lanceolated. In the most prominently marked Grasshopper, spots and small streaks are confined mainly to the middle and lower throat, extending only as a bib onto the upper breast. The risk of confusion with Grasshopper becomes greater in summer, when streaking on adult Lanceolated Warbler tends to be more subdued. Differences in undertail-covert pattern are useful; in Grasshopper the outer feathers show small, dark, rounded centres and the long inners feature broader more diffuse centres, but it is important to note that all of these extend to the base of the feathers. In Lanceolated, well-defined small spots or narrow streaks do not extend to the feather bases and the longest undertail-coverts are sometimes unmarked.

Pallas's Grasshopper Warbler seems unlikely to be mistaken for Lanceolated but this has occurred with autumn juveniles (Galsworthy 1991), although such confusion would only occur with *minor*, the smallest race of Pallas's Grasshopper. There is overlap in wing and tail measurements between the largest Lanceolated and the smallest Pallas's Grasshopper,

but Pallas's Grasshopper is a larger, stockier bird than Lanceolated, with a deeper-bellied profile, flatter head, longer bill and proportionately longer and broader tail. Regardless of age and time of year, all races of Pallas's Grasshopper should be separable from Lanceolated (and Grasshopper) Warblers on plumage features alone. In fact Pallas's Grasshopper more closely resembles Sedge Warbler than either of these two species. It shows a thin but usually conspicuous supercilium extending back to the rear ear-coverts; blackish-centred tertials with a crisp, rich brown fringe (in some races the inner two l pairs often feature a small white spot at the tip of the inner webs); and a rusty brown rump and uppertail-coverts that contrast with the darker brown to blackish uppertail. The overall effect is of darker, but more colourful and contrasting upperparts. The underparts of juvenile Pallas's Grasshopper are washed yellow and despite variation this alone should eliminate Lanceolated. Most juvenile Pallas's Grasshopper show a gorget of small spots, streaks or arrowheads across the lower throat, vaguely suggesting Lanceolated, but the latter rarely shows such restricted markings on the underparts and overlap in these markings with juvenile Grasshopper is more likely. The undertail-coverts of Pallas's Grasshopper are unmarked except for paler tips, and these are most conspicuous on the darker feathers of the race *rubescens*. Finally, the characteristic whitish tail-feather tips of Pallas's Grasshopper are generally considered diagnostic on any *Locustella* away from the Asia-Pacific seaboard. These do vary in prominence and are sometimes difficult to see, especially when worn. Conversely, a small percentage of Lanceolated (and Grasshopper) Warblers can show pale tail feather tips, but these tend to be narrow, pale creamy and diffuse gradually into the brown tail rather than being sharply cut off near the tip as in Pallas's Grasshopper.

In many encounters, a *Locustella* warbler flushes at an observer's feet and flies briefly, then drops into cover and is never seen again. In these circumstances, a distinctive rusty brown rump is sufficient to indicate Pallas's Grasshopper and eliminate Lanceolated. Also, Pallas's Grasshopper appears slow and ponderous in flight and lacks the fast, whirring bee-like action of Lanceolated. It typically rises further away and flies low and direct for several metres rather than dropping to cover immediately. Unlike Lanceolated, Pallas's Grasshopper Warbler can often be flushed repeatedly.

VOICE The song is a continuous reeling trill that carries well over distances of 300m or more in calm conditions. It resembles the reeling song of Grasshopper Warbler and has a similar 'ventriloquial' quality, the volume appearing to rise and fall as the bird rotates its head.

It consists of a rapidly delivered series of elements, each comprising a pair of notes, the first slightly lower in pitch than the second. These are delivered at about 15 to 20 per second, slightly more slowly than in Grasshopper Warbler, within a frequency range of 5–8kHz. Lanceolated song is slightly higher pitched, sounding thinner and rather more 'tinny' than that of Grasshopper as there is greater overlap in the frequency of the two notes within each element. With its slightly slower delivery the individual elements in the reel are readily detectable by the human ear, giving it a pulsing or stridulating quality not noticeable in Grasshopper Warbler. It does not, however, approach the slower, pulsating stridulations of River Warbler, which are also considerably lower pitched. Lanceolated Warbler song could be mistaken for the sound of certain crickets (Orthoptera) and bush-crickets (Tettigoniidae), although it is unclear whether any of these occur within the breeding range.

Song is most intense at night and for the first hour before sunset and after sunrise. It may continue for up to five minutes without a break, but the longer unbroken sequences reported for Grasshopper Warbler have not been noted. Song intensity declines as the day warms up and songs then usually last for only a few seconds.

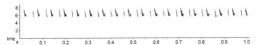

Part of song of Lanceolated Warbler of race *L. l. lanceolata*, Kemerovo region, Siberia, Russia, June. (Veprintsev 2007)

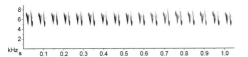

Part of song of Lanceolated Warbler of race *L. l. hendersonii*, Hokkaido, Japan, July. (Ueda 1998)

Lanceolated Warblers call regularly on migration and during winter. The most frequently heard call is a distinctive, rather explosive '*tchk....tchk....tchk....tchk...*', repeated continuously at an even rate of about one call per second. This is probably the normal contact call. One variation, a slightly lower pitched '*chek-chek-chek-chek...*' with a faster delivery, may be an alarm call. Other calls, a sharp metallic '*pit*' and a scolding, slightly excited shrieking, are heard less often and are similar to calls given by other *Locustella* species.

MOULT Adults have an extensive partial moult prior to autumn migration, which includes replacement of the head, mantle, scapular, breast and flank feathering. Some birds also replace either the outer or inner primaries and may even have a complete moult. A specimen from E China in early October shows completely new plumage (Cramp 1992), while adults examined in Hong Kong in autumn show suspended moult; typically having replaced the four outer primaries but retained six worn inner primaries and all the secondaries. It is not clear what proportion of adults moult their primaries in autumn, or whether this strategy is confined to particular, perhaps more southerly, breeding populations. No active flight feather moult was found between October and December in migrants in Malaya (Medway & Wells 1976). Cramp (1992) suggested that young birds from early broods replace some feathering prior to migration and noted September birds with first-winter body plumage together with juvenile remiges and rectrices. It is believed that the majority of young birds have little or no moult on the breeding ground and, like Grasshopper Warbler, migrate to winter quarters in juvenile plumage, which is retained to the end of the year and beyond (Loskot & Sokolov 1993).

The main moult takes place in adults and first-winter birds shortly before spring migration. Timing varies, the earliest beginning in late January, but with some from Burma still showing old, worn plumage in March (Cramp 1992). Most, however, begin in February and finish in April. Moult is usually complete, but some older outer or central primaries are sometimes retained (Svensson 1992). These

are presumably either retained juvenile feathers or feathers replaced in adults the previous autumn.

HABITAT Found in a wide diversity of open and semi-open habitats, but usually in thick, low, moist vegetation, often by water. Breeds in damp valleys, typically near a lake edge, marsh, stream or river; or in open meadows with a few scattered bushes. Also in drier situations, including forest edge and open glades and clearings in birch *Betula* and larch *Larix* forest with bushes and overgrown patches of scrub. Occurs mainly below 200m in Siberia, but recorded at 600m in the Kolyma Uplands, at the upper forest limit. Elsewhere in Russia, ranges to 800m in the northern Altai Mountains and 1,300m in the Sikhote-Alin Mountains in Japan and noted on Honshu at 1,660m (Loskot & Sokolov 1993).

On migration, tends to favour wet or damp ground. Migrants in coastal China occur in marshes, emergent vegetation along reservoir edges, drainage ditches and damp fields; also in dry overgrown scrub, long grass at the edge of woodland and the ground layer of poplar *Populus* plantations. In Hong Kong, recorded from wet grassland, scrub and bushes bordering *Phragmites* reedbeds and, less frequently, from the edge of woodland. A similar range of habitats is utilised during the winter months, when it can be common in almost any type of damp, overgrown scrub, or in tall, damp grassland and damp rice paddy stubble with bushes nearby.

BEHAVIOUR Behaviour closely mirrors that of Grass-hopper Warbler. A furtive and secretive species that typically keeps well hidden in low vegetation. Often located by its distinctive and frequently uttered call, which can reveal its true abundance on the wintering grounds. Rarely flies except when disturbed and difficult to flush. Walks furtively through the densest undergrowth continuously flicking its wings over the back. Tends to remain under available vegetation and at times seemingly vanishes into the slightest cover, never to re-emerge. However, if disturbed in the open, it may freeze and remain motionless for several minutes. It is not particularly shy and birds encountered on migration or the wintering grounds can be remarkably confiding, approaching observers to within a metre or less and occasionally walking between them or even over their boots! When flushed, it typically flies less than 10m before diving back into cover. Migrants passing through Beidaihe in Hebei Province, China, often fly on to lower tree branches when disturbed and perch motionless for several minutes in full view.

The reeling song can be heard from late May, when males return to territories. Many perch in low ground cover when singing but they are more inclined to sing from an exposed perch such as a branch or wire fence than is typical for Grasshopper Warbler. They may even sing in full view from a tree, up to 6m from ground. Favoured song perches are always close to thick cover, however. Song is most frequently heard between dawn and mid morning and again around dusk, and also throughout the night. Several birds will often sing simultaneously, others joining in as soon as one starts to sing. Singing Lanceolated adopt an upright posture, rotating the head from side to side, but unlike Grasshopper Warbler, they tend to hold the tail in the same plane as the back, rather than angled and lowered below the body. In full uninterrupted song the throat pulsates slightly and the wings lightly vibrate. Tjernberg (1991) noted that the lower mandible vibrated when singing, unlike in a singing Grasshopper Warbler. Song continues regularly throughout June and well into July, but usually ceases by the end of that month. It has also been heard in wintering areas, after arrival and shortly before departure (Sample 2003).

BREEDING HABITS Solitary and territorial but common or abundant in suitable habitat. The nest is apparently built by the female alone, on or near ground in thick vegetation; often in a shallow hollow beside a tussock, where it is concealed by nearby grasses and dry leaves. It is a deep, thick-walled cup, often placed on a collection of leaves and constructed from grass stems and leaves, bits of moss and other dry leaves and lined with finer grass stems. A clutch of 4–6, but usually five, eggs is laid in early to mid June. Incubation lasts 13–14 days, apparently carried out by the female alone; beginning in mid June in Transbaikalia. Believed to raise just a single brood. A density of 152 pairs/km² was estimated in favoured habitat in the northeastern Altai, but lower densities are more typical, with estimates of 20–50 pairs/km² in Russia and Hokkaido (Cramp 1992).

DISTRIBUTION The core breeding range is centred on temperate regions of Siberia from the Ural Mountains east to Hokkaido and Kamchatka, with a small but apparently expanding population in Karelia in European Russia.

L. l. lanceolata In E Siberia, the nominate form ranges from the shores of the Sea of Okhotsk, including the Shantar Islands and W Kamchatka, north to the region of Magadan and to the lower Kolyma and Indigirka river valleys at 66–69°N; the northern limit partly coinciding with that of larch *Larix* forest (Loskot & Sokolov 1993). To the south, it occurs widely throughout much of Ussuriland and Amurland, east to the Sea of Japan and in NE China, in the Da Hinggang Mountains, the northeastern parts of the Nei Mongol Autonomous Region and in the northern provinces of Heilongjiang, Jilin and Liaoning, south to the northern part of the Gulf of Bohai (Cheng 1987). It probably also breeds in the mountains of North Korea. Its range encompasses a vast area in C Siberia, north in Transbaikalia to about 65°N and south to S Baikal region, the Kentai Mountains in N Mongolia (where regularly recorded at Terelj) and the foothills of the N and NE Altai. It extends northwest to the Ob River in the region of Novosibirsk and Tomsk, then along the Ob valley to its confluence with the Irtysh River east of the Urals. Further west, it becomes rare and sporadic in the W Urals, with most of the European population confined to the Perm region (Hagemeijer & Blair 1997). Recent discoveries of singing males in S Finland and adjacent Karelia in W Russia suggest it to be more widespread in European Russia than previously suspected.

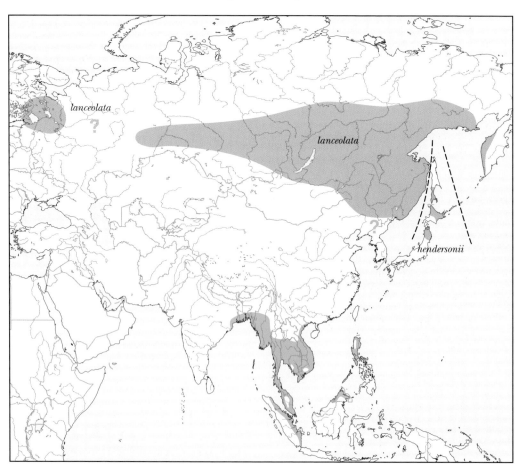

Lanceolated Warbler. Breeding range and winter distribution.

The European population has been reported as 5,500–6,000 breeding pairs (Hagemeijer & Blair 1997). Surveys centred on Lake Ladoga, East Karelia, located four singing males in 2000 (Loippo 2002). In adjacent southern Finland, the number of singing males increased steadily from just one prior to 1975 to a peak of 20 in 2000 (Luoto *et al.* 2002), but have subsequently fallen back, to just one singing male in 2006 (Lindblom 2008). Numbers reaching Finland in any year seem dependent on weather conditions along the migration route.

L. l. hendersonii The form *hendersonii* is restricted to islands fringing the Sea of Okhotsk. In Japan, it is locally common in E, NE and N Hokkaido, breeding in Rumoi, Soya, Abashiri, Numuro and Kushiro districts (Brazil 1991) and occasionally in N and C Honshu. Elsewhere, it breeds on Sakhalin and the S Kuril Islands, including Kunashir, Shikotan and Iturup (Loskot & Sokolov 1993). The northern limit is not known but breeding probably extends little further north than S Sakhalin.

Non-breeding Winters over much of mainland SE Asia, where it is particularly numerous in Thailand (PDR *in litt.*), but apparently scarce in W, C and N Burma. Occurs regularly in NE India, west to E Bengal and E Orissa (Baker 1924), but rare elsewhere on the sub-continent, with few reported west to Haryana and south to Karnataka (P. Holt *in litt.*). It is a vagrant to Nepal with just four recorded occurrences (Inskipp & Inskipp 1991; CI *in litt.*). Also thought to be a vagrant in Bangladesh, although possibly under-recorded there. It winters throughout the Malay Peninsula but is less numerous there than in continental SE Asia. It becomes scarcer further south, reaching Singapore only in small numbers, and is apparently scarce in Sumatra but may be overlooked. It is a vagrant to Borneo with just 13 records. These include four specimens from the Kelabit Uplands in Sarawak (Smythies 1957) and the remainder coming from Sabah, although again it is probably overlooked here. One of these reports referred to a singing male on Mount Kinabalu at an elevation of 1,380m on 10 April 1986, while another was reported at 1,200m in April 1996, (Smythies & Davison 1999; Speight *et al.* 1986), perhaps suggesting that it winters in the hills rather than the lowlands. More numerous and fairly widespread in the Philippines, from Luzon south to Palawan.

MOVEMENTS Leaves its breeding areas in the NE Altai from mid to late July. In Hokkaido, departure commences during August and continues into early September, with few birds remaining after the middle of September, but there is one late record on 30 October (Brazil 1991). Rare on migration through Japan, suggesting that most depart to the west and enter Russia before following the coastline of the Korean peninsula and E China to wintering areas in SE Asia. Occurs on migration throughout China and can be abundant in the coastal eastern and southern provinces. Passage at Beidaihe and Happy Island in Hebei Province occurs from late August to early October with most in the first half of September (JH *in litt.*). Occurs at Hong Kong from late September to late November, but in smaller numbers, suggesting that many birds follow an inland route and avoid coastal SE China. Recorded from the Andaman Islands, India, suggesting a regular overfly of the Bay of Bengal en-route to wintering areas in Sumatra or the Malay Peninsula. Passage through the Malay Peninsula is light, with the earliest record on 10 September. A small

but regular autumn movement occurs across Fraser's Hill, north of Kuala Lumpur, where ringing studies have shown it to be a nocturnal migrant in small numbers between early October and late December (Medway & Wells 1976). Migrants reach Singapore in November but records are few after early December, suggesting that most continue south into the Riau Islands or Sumatra.

Northward migration begins in April. Over 3,000 were ringed on Luzon, Philippines, between 1964 and 1967 (McClure & Leelavit 1972). Migrants were trapped regularly at 3,500m at Dalton Pass, north of Manila, in habitat unsuited to wintering birds and these presumably originated from wintering areas south of Luzon. Spring migrants are scarce and inconspicuous in Singapore and Malaysia, while to the north, the large numbers wintering in Thailand mask the smaller passage from the south. Migration through China largely bypasses the south coast and there are just a handful of spring records from Hong Kong, between early March and mid May. Further north in China, it is very common in the grasslands and wheat fields of the lower Yangtze and common at Beidaihe and Happy Island during the second half of May (JH *in litt.*). Most return to breeding territories in E Russia only from the third week in May, while further west, in central and western Siberia, the main arrival takes place during the second half of June. In Finland, at the western breeding limit, the earliest birds arrive during the last week in June and most during the first or second weeks in July (Luoto *et al.* 2002; Lindblom 2008). In Hokkaido, singing birds begin to return from late May, with the main arrival during the first week of June. Spring birds are scarce and inconspicuous elsewhere in Japan and on other islands in the Sea of Japan, suggesting that birds reach Hokkaido via the continental mainland (Brazil 1991). First arrivals on the southern Kuril Islands coincide with those on Hokkaido, but the earliest birds on Kamchatka are not usually until early June.

Vagrancy Despite the close proximity to the Russian breeding range, it is a vagrant to Kazakhstan, with one record of a singing male at the Nura River Valley near Astana, in June 2003 and just three autumn records.

Considered to be a vagrant to North America, although an exceptional influx occurred in 1984 on Attu Island in the western Aleutian Islands, Alaska, with up to 25 singing males noted between 4 June and 15 July (Tobish 1985). The first breeding record for North America occurred on Bulder in 2007, when a pair nested and at least three other singing males were present on the island. Away from Alaska, there is a single record of a bird trapped on Southeast Farallon Island, California, USA, on 11 September 1995 (Hickey *et al.* 1996).

In autumn, westward vagrancy brings small numbers annually to Western Europe between late August and late October. There are autumn records from most countries bordering the North and Baltic Seas, summarised by Verbelen & De Smit (2003) and Gantlett (2003, 2004). Most are from the British Isles (120 autumn records up to 2008 with the Shetland Islands and Fair Isle accounting for over 80%), but there are others from Iceland, Belgium, Denmark, Germany, Finland, France (including an extremely early bird on 15–16 August), Netherlands (including one in December), Norway, Sweden and the former Yugoslavia In Europe, autumn records away from the Shetland Islands largely relate to birds found in mist nets and not seen again after release. Away from southern Finland, there are just a handful of records of singing males, from southern Sweden (e.g. Cederroth 2000; Verbelen & De Smit 2003; Gantlett 2004), and two in Norway in July 2007.

One old December record from Halmahera, Indonesia and two subsequent reports on Sangihe Island, off northern Sulawesi (Wardhill & Riley 2000) are the only records from the Wallacean region.

DESCRIPTION *L. l. lanceolata*

Plumage – Adult fresh (April to July) Forehead dull olive-brown, feather centres with faint blackish spots. Crown olive-brown with blackish feather centres larger, better defined and extending to tips to create narrow well-defined streaks. Nape usually plainer, with smaller blackish feather centres and broader olive-brown fringes. Supercilium faint and narrow, on most birds extending from bill base to front of ear-coverts, but occasionally reaching rear of ear-coverts. A small dark loral spot, occasionally extends to the bill base to form narrow loral line. Typically, a line of pale feathers below eye meets the supercilium at the bill to form a triangle around the loral spot. Eye-stripe absent or indistinct, showing little contrast with ear-coverts. Eye-ring narrow and faint, pale yellowish buff to buffy white. Ear-coverts olive-brown with subdued darker mottling. Sides of neck rather plainer and greyer than ear-coverts and nape. Mantle, scapulars and back with prominent, sharply defined blackish feather centres, extending to tips to form a series of conspicuous black lines from base of nape to rump; feather fringes variable, usually dull olive-brown, but occasionally warm olive-tan or slightly paler sandy tan to greyish olive. Rump and uppertail-coverts similar to mantle, the latter often slightly warmer and browner; streaking variable, often less prominent than on mantle with blackish centres smaller and fringes broader. Tail brown above, similar in colour to uppertail-coverts, usually with indistinct narrow darker cross-barring; feathers occasionally with narrow, pale or even whitish tips. Underside of tail grey, usually unmarked, contrasting with warmer, paler undertail-coverts. Chin to breast white with a faint grey-buff wash. Chin sometimes with indistinct grey-brown streaks; throat with more distinct blackish streaks, forming conspicuous lines that extend as a pectoral band across the upper breast. Streaking slightly longer and more conspicuous towards sides of breast, extending to sides of neck and meeting nape streaking. Sides of breast with light olive-brown wash, appearing as a dull smudge adjacent to carpal bend. Flanks washed light greyish brown to pale olive-brown, usually with a warmer ochre tinge. Streaking usually extends along the upper flanks, still narrow and well defined; it is longer, wider and more conspicuous on the lower flanks. Belly white, unmarked, contrasting with darker flanks and vent. Undertail-coverts washed pale buff to warm tan, the longest usually with broad paler tips; shorter outer feathers with narrow, dull brown central streaks or teardrop-shaped spots, not reaching to feather bases or tips; the longest either plain and unmarked, or with a similar crisp, thin streak along the shaft, widening distally.

Lesser and median coverts blackish with narrow, well-defined pale buff to greyish brown fringes; greater coverts similar, but fringes broader. Tertials blackish or blackish brown, with narrow (0.6–1.0mm wide) but well demarcated pale to mid brown fringes around the entire feathers, similar to or slightly paler than mantle fringes. Primaries, secondaries and primary coverts dark greyish brown, with narrow olive-brown edges. Alula dark brown or greyish brown with broad pale buff to greyish brown fringe. Underwing-coverts pale buffy brown.

Adult worn (January to March) Fringes on upperparts and tertials narrower and paler, dark feather centres more pronounced. Supercilium slightly paler, usually more conspicuous. Breast whiter and underpart streaking significantly reduced, typically restricted to a gorget across the throat and rear flanks. In early autumn, renewed body plumage contrasts with old, worn wing and tail feathers, but becomes worn and faded by late winter.

Juvenile Resembles fresh adult, but supercilium and orbital ring poorly defined, sometimes completely lacking. Dark loral spot indistinct and eye-stripe often absent. Ear-coverts usually plainer, with fainter mottling. Underparts usually whiter, with streaking on throat, breast and flanks rather more diffuse and paler greyish brown. A minority show a faint yellowish tinge on chin, throat, breast and belly. Tertials with slightly narrower olive-brown fringes, often paler towards tips.

Bare parts Upper mandible dark brown or greyish black. Lower mandible pale pink to pinkish flesh, adults with dark tip, often less extensive or absent in first autumn birds. Mouth pale yellowish pink; juveniles have three tongue spots, often retained until their first spring. Tarsi, toes and claws conspicuous pale pink, occasionally slightly darker. Iris warm, dark brown in adults, slightly duller and greyer in first autumn birds.

IN HAND CHARACTERS
Measurements

Races combined, mainly nominate *lanceolata*

	Male	Female
Wing	55–62 (57.0; 41)	53–61 (56.3; 38)
Tail	41–47 (43.1; 13)	40–47 (43.4; 15)
Bill	12.5–14 (13.2; 13)	13–14 (13.3; 14)
Tarsus	18.5–20 (18.9; 14)	18–19.5 (18.6; 14)

(Includes wing data from Cramp 1992)

Sexes combined:
Tail/wing ratio: 71–82% (75.5%; 29)
Bill width: 3.2–3.8 (3.5; 24)
Hind claw: 5.4–7.0 (6.3; 22)
Tail graduation: 13–20 (15.7; 12)

Wing of juvenile averages *c.* 1.5mm shorter than in adult.

Data from Loskot & Sokolov (1993):
L. l. lanceolata (♂♂ only): *wing* 52–60 (55.6; 58); *tail* 42–49 (45.3; 58); *tarsus* 17–20 (18.1; 58).
L. l. hendersonii (♂♂ only): *wing* 56–61 (57.8; 24); *tail* 42–50 (46.4; 24); *tarsus* 18–20 (18.7; 24).

Race *hendersonii* apparently averages slightly larger than nominate race. Wing structure does not differ significantly.

Structure

Wing formula (Cramp 1992):

p1/pc	p2	p3e	p4	p5	p6	p7	p10
(3)–2	0.5–2	wp	1–3	2.5–4	4–7	6–9	10–13

Wing pointed; p1 minute. Wing point p3; p2 = p3/4–4 (4/5) [= 5]; emargination on p3. Notch on p2 6–8 from tip, falling between p6 and p10. Longest tertial usually extends to tip of p10, occasionally p8.

Figure 29. Wing of Lanceolated Warbler.

Tail graduated, rather short; feathers rounded, narrower than in Grasshopper Warbler (Fig. 30).

 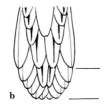

a　　　　　　　b

Figure 30. Comparison of tail shape and undertail-covert pattern of (a) Lanceolated Warbler and (b) Grasshopper Warbler.

Bill short and slender; sides slightly concave.

Tarsi rather strong, toes slender, claws small but hind claw longer than in Grasshopper Warbler.

Recognition Distinguished from Grasshopper Warbler by sharp blackish streaks or spots on undertail-coverts that do not reach feather bases. Also by crisp narrow pale fringes to very dark tertials and more distinctly streaked upperparts with dark feather centres extending to tips. Typically more extensively and completely streaked below, especially on flanks. Usually separable from Grasshopper by shallower notch on p2 (< 8mm from tip) and by size. Most have wing length < 60mm, below range for nominate Grasshopper. Tail length commonly below range for any Grasshopper (< 44mm), with narrower feathers (< 8mm wide) (see Fig. 30).

Ageing Depends on nature and extent of feather wear, combined with indications of moult. In early autumn, juveniles have fresh-looking primaries and tail feathers, the latter usually with small castellations at tips. Streaking on throat, breast and flanks is rather diffuse, greyish brown rather than blackish. Autumn adults have heavily worn primaries and tail feathers, but show fresh body plumage after a partial moult, with sharper and blacker streaks than in juveniles (but not distinguishable from young birds which have had a post-juvenile moult). Adults often replace some primaries (usually outermost) on the breeding grounds and show a contrast between fresh and worn feathers which should remain diagnostic until early winter. They may occasionally moult completely after breeding, but would then be distinguishable in early autumn by darker new flight and tail feathers, the latter with unworn tips. The

underparts of most juveniles match those of adults, but in young *hendersonii* a faint yellow flush sometimes provides a supporting character. There are no known ageing criteria after the winter moult.

Weight Range 9.0–13.3g (Cramp 1992). Thailand, 9.1–11.9g (10.3; 19). (PDR unpublished data)

GEOGRAPHIC VARIATION Two races recognised.

L. l. lanceolata (SE Finland and Russia east to Sea of Okhotsk and NE China) Described above.

L. l. hendersonii (Sakhalin, S Kuril Islands, Hokkaido and N Honshu) Closely resembles nominate form but, on average, is less well-marked. In fresh adult and juvenile plumages, upperpart feather fringes are slightly paler than in nominate race. Streaking on the crown, mantle and rump is less well-defined, due to slightly narrower dark feather centres and broader fringes. Underpart colour more variable. Adults lack yellow tones, but juveniles sometimes with faint ochre tinge on chin, throat and breast. In extreme cases the entire underparts are washed rich sulphur-yellow while the flanks are usually clear reddish ochre (less brownish), this sometimes extending as a wash across the breast. Underpart spotting and streaking tends to be less well developed; spots are usually absent on the chin and upper throat and those on the breast are usually smaller, paler and less conspicuous. Flank streaking is poorly developed and occasionally absent. Undertail-coverts usually paler, reddish ochre (less brown), with dark centres most obvious on shorter outer feathers and often diffuse or absent on longer feathers. On average, it is slightly larger than the nominate race (see **Measurements** above). Loskot & Sokolov (1993) concluded that assessment of underpart streaking was sufficient to establish the identity of most birds, with overlap only between the most well marked *hendersonii* and poorly marked *lanceolata*.

TAXONOMY AND SYSTEMATICS The nominate form shows remarkably little variation across its range, birds from Europe not differing significantly from those of eastern Siberia. Often treated as a monotypic species, but the larger size and less prominent streaking of birds breeding on islands fringing the Sea of Okhotsk justifies their separation as *hendersonii*. Cramp (1992) did not recognise *hendersonii* but discussed a form *gigantea*, described by Johansen (1954) from specimens taken on Shaweishan Island, E China. Comparing these with mainland specimens Cramp concluded that the longer wing and slight plumage difference attributed to *gigantea* could also be found in birds originating from the range of the nominate form, and so included *gigantea* within *lanceolata*. Loskot & Sokolov (1993), however, considered *gigantea* to be a synonym of *hendersonii*. They established that, despite limited overlap between *lanceolata* and *hendersonii*, a comparison of plumage features together with size could be used to separate these races in almost all instances. These authors have been followed by Dickinson (2003), who also recognises *hendersonii*. Birds resembling *hendersonii* do occur within the range of the nominate form, but it is emphasised that they are rare.

▲ ▼ Adult *L. l. hendersonii*, Hokkaido, Japan, June. Shows dark centres to mantle and scapulars extending to feather tip, giving distinctive streaked appearance to upperparts. Note long 'lanceolate' streaks on flanks and shorter, fine dark streaks on upper breast. Differs from Grasshopper Warbler by narrow brown fringes to tertials contrasting with darker centres (Pete Morris).

◀ ▲ Adult, Hong Kong, China, October. An extremely well-marked bird with large blotches, rather than fine streaks, along the flanks, and an extensive gorget of broad streaks on throat and breast. Aged as an adult by six worn inner primaries contrasting with the fresh outer primaries (James Kennerley).

◀ Juvenile, Shetland, Scotland, September. Unworn appearance of this bird ages it as a juvenile. Note that prominence and extent of breast- and flank-streaking is variable; this is a poorly marked individual (Rebecca Nason).

▲ Juvenile, Shetland, Scotland, September. Another poorly marked juvenile, but dark breast-streaking is more prominent and better defined than juvenile Grasshopper Warbler would show (Hugh Harrop).

▲ Juvenile, Shetland, Scotland, September. Juveniles reaching Western Europe in autumn are often found on windswept islands with little cover in which to hide, enabling them to be viewed for prolonged periods (Hugh Harrop).

◀ Juvenile, Hong Kong, October. Note lack of contrasting pale eye-ring (compare Grasshopper Warbler). A typical juvenile with largely white belly and a light creamy wash to the upper breast and throat. Compared with the adult overleaf (p. 242) the breast streaking is finer, slightly paler and less extensive (James Kennerley).

◀ Juvenile, Hong Kong, October. An atypical dark bird with an unusually rich creamy-buff wash on the supercilium, malar and underparts, suggesting *hendersonii*, and supported by reduced streaking restricted to upper breast (James Kennerley).

◀ Juvenile, Hong Kong, October. Note light pinkish ochre wash to underparts, usually but not exclusively associated with *hendersonii*, in which underpart colour is quite variable, ranging from white to sulphur-yellow or even reddish ochre (James Kennerley).

◀ Juvenile, Changhua, Taiwan, November. Shows characteristic black and brown 'tramlines' along mantle, narrow, pale tertial fringes contrasting with dark grey centres, gorget of fine streaks on the white upper breast, and conspicuous flank streaks extending to base of tail (Liao Pen-shing).

PALLAS'S GRASSHOPPER WARBLER
Locustella certhiola   **Plate 12**

Motacilla certhiola Pallas, 1811. *Zoographia Rosso-Asiat.* 1: 509, 'in regionem ultra Baicalem' [mountainous region between Onon and Borzya in eastern Transbaikalia], *fide* Meise, 1934, *Abh. Ber. Mus. Tierkunde Völkerkunde Dresden*, 18(2): 39.

A widespread *Locustella* warbler, restricted to Asia where it breeds across a wide range of habitats within the warm and dry, to cool and damp, temperate regions of the Central and Eastern Palearctic. Winters to the south of the breeding range from Sri Lanka and eastern India, east and south throughout much of Southeast Asia and into Sumatra and Borneo. Generally common and widespread wherever damp and overgrown habitats occur. Polytypic, with five races recognised:

L. c. certhiola (Pallas, 1811). SE Transbaikalia, E Mongolia and NC China south to Gansu and N Hebei Provinces.

L. c. rubescens Blyth, 1845. Siberia to north of other races, from the Yenisey River in C Siberia to the Sea of Okhotsk.

L. c. minor David & Oustalet, 1877. Amurland region of SE Siberia to NE China, east of *certhiola*.

L. c. centralasiae Sushkin, 1925. E Kazakhstan, C Mongolia and NW China.

L. c. sparsimstriata Meise, 1934. W Siberia from the Irtysh River east to at least the Ob River, to the south of *rubescens* and northwest of *centralasiae*.

IDENTIFICATION Length 12–14cm. Wing 57–72mm. Tail/wing 68–83%.

A highly variable species in both plumage and size. It occupies the ecological niche of Sedge Warbler across much of the temperate E Palearctic where that species is absent. It also shares many characters with Sedge Warbler, including size, a prominent supercilium and a contrasting warm brown rump. The brief, loud song is quite unlike the tuneless reeling or pulsating songs of the European breeding *Locustella* warblers. Sexes alike.

Structure Pallas's Grasshopper Warbler shows the characteristic *Locustella* structure, with a short neck, rounded body, deep-based and long undertail-coverts extending almost to the tail tip and a strongly graduated tail. Overall, it is similar in size and structure to Grasshopper Warbler but is slightly stockier with a distinctive thickset, pot-bellied appearance. The wing is long and pointed, with a short first primary (p1) falling below the primary coverts, the wing point formed by p3, and with p3 and sometimes p4 emarginated. The tail is heavily graduated and frequently held slightly open, which exaggerates its apparent size and width and reveals the graduated shape – something Grasshopper Warbler rarely does. In flight, the tail is also usually spread slightly, so that the broad base and graduated structure are often discernible. This feature, combined with the pot-bellied structure, gives it a distinctive appearance in flight that European *Locustella* species rarely exhibit.

Plumage and bare parts One of the most distinctive *Locustella* warblers and the easiest to identify. The combination of a conspicuous pale supercilium, distinctive rusty brown rump and uppertail-coverts, well-marked and contrasting mantle feathering and a whitish web to the second outermost primary (p2) is common to all races, making identification straightforward. The whitish tips to the tail feathers can be difficult to see in the field, even in flight, but are a characteristic feature of Pallas's if visible.

These tips can be inconspicuous on the upper surface of the tail and absent from the central pair on some adults, but they are more evident on the underside. They are usually quite conspicuous in spring, when the tail is fresh, but they become indistinct by late summer, even on the underside.

Adults in fresh plumage in spring show well-marked and contrasting upperparts. Although the races differ slightly, mainly in the extent of the contrast between the feather fringes and centres, all share certain features. These include a conspicuous pale supercilium extending from the bill base to the rear of the ear-coverts and contrasting with the finely streaked crown and darker ear-coverts, heavily streaked upperparts, and crisp, narrow pale fringes to the wing-coverts and tertials that contrast with conspicuous dark centres. The rump and uppertail-coverts are warm rusty brown and usually unmarked apart from large, blackish teardrop shaped centres to the longest uppertail-coverts, although some races can lack these while others show indistinct spotting on the rump. The tips to all the rectrices apart from the central pair are whitish, but this can often be difficult to see from above, even in flight, but is usually obvious from below. The underparts are rather variable, although all show a whitish chin and throat, sometimes with a row of indistinct spots across the lower throat. The breast and flank colour ranges from pale tan to darker rufous-brown, but the belly is paler, usually whitish. All races usually show a whitish fringe to the outer web of p2 and plain, unmarked undertail-coverts, which are highly variable in colour, even between birds of the same race. On most, these range from creamy white with indistinctly paler tips to warm sandy buff with large but diffuse whitish tips, but on darker individuals (usually of the race *rubescens*), they vary from tawny-brown to fulvous brown with more conspicuous broad, diffuse, pale buffy or creamy tips.

A feature frequently mentioned as being diagnostic of Pallas's Grasshopper, but not shown by all individuals, is a distinctive whitish spot on the tips of the inner webs of the two innermost tertials and sometimes also on the longest, adjacent to the feather shaft, each of which appears as a whitish notch or tooth. This feature, which contrasts with the darker feather centres and brownish fringes on the outer web is, however, also shared with some Middendorff's Grasshopper Warblers and occasionally with Styan's Grasshopper Warbler. Separation of these species from Pallas's Grasshopper is usually straightforward and their identification is discussed below. It should be remembered that some birds will lose these notches through abrasion, so that by late summer and mid winter they may be less apparent than on fresh adults in late spring.

The juvenile plumage closely resembles that of the adult but is generally darker and the patterning of feather fringes and centres is less clearly defined. Juveniles are, however, quite variable and can be particularly difficult to assign to a specific race away from the breeding areas, although *centralasiae* and *rubescens* can be racially identified with care and experience. Despite the extent of this variation, all juveniles share a number of common characteristics, including a supercilium that is usually less conspicuous than that of adults and variable in both extent and prominence. On some birds, it is restricted to a thin and indistinct creamy or yellowish line, barely visible in front of and behind the eye (e.g. Broyd 1983), while on other individuals, it remains broad and full but is duller and so lacks the contrast with the greyish crown. On juveniles, the crown tends to appear greyer than in adults and it contrasts with the browner mantle. The fringes to the mantle feathering, wing-coverts and tertials generally lack the crisp contrast and definition shown by adults, instead appearing slightly blurred or smudged. Like adults, the rump and uppertail-coverts are warm, rusty brown and contrast with the dark grey tail, but the rump is often finely spotted with darker brown centres and the uppertail-coverts show smaller and less distinct darker interiors. Juveniles share the contrasting pale tail tips with adults, but these are more variable in colour, ranging from greyish white to dull, buffy brown and on some individuals, the central rectrices are also tipped paler. Most juveniles show the characteristic pale notch on the inner webs of the two inner tertials.

Underpart colour is variable but juveniles always show a yellowish tone that is lacking in adults. This can appear a bright citrus-yellow or even primrose-yellow but, particularly in *rubescens*, may be closer to dull sulphurous yellow covered with an extensive brownish wash. Juveniles of all races show dark spotting, usually as a series of small arrowheads across the lower throat and extending towards the malar region, although this can be indistinct on some *rubescens*. On many birds, the upper breast is also marked with small but distinctive forward-pointing blackish arrowheads, forming an irregular gorget which may extend to the upper flanks, with thin blackish streaking sometimes reaching the lower flanks. The flanks are fairly pale in most races, but tend towards warm buffy brown in *rubescens*. The undertail-coverts vary from unmarked pale sandy buff with slightly paler tips to warm buff with dark shaft streaks and poorly defined pale buff tips in *rubescens*.

The bill is dark brown or blackish with a pink base to the lower mandible, which darkens at the sides towards the tip. The legs and feet vary from dull pink to pinkish brown.

SIMILAR SPECIES Pallas's Grasshopper is most likely to be mistaken for the rather similar Middendorff's Grasshopper or Styan's Grasshopper Warblers and their separation is discussed below. Confusion has occurred with Grasshopper Warbler in Europe and with Lanceolated Warbler in Asia. Their identification and separation from Pallas's Grasshopper should be straightforward except when not seen particularly well and is discussed further within the respective species accounts.

Middendorff's Grasshopper Warbler closely resembles Pallas's Grasshopper and their separation requires care, in particular because both are quite variable and share a similar shape and structure. In particular, the possibility of hybrids or intergrades needs to be considered where their ranges overlap along the lower Amur River and Primorskiy coastal region in southeast Siberia. Perhaps the greatest potential pitfall lies in the extent of variation in Middendorff's Grasshopper, which is largely undocumented. Although many authorities treat Middendorff's Grasshopper as a monotypic species (e.g. Williamson 1968; Kalyakin *et al.* 1993; Dickinson 2003; Stepanyan 2003), suggesting that it exhibits a stable suite of plumage characters, this is not the case. The extent of variation in Middendorff's Grasshopper is considerable, some birds showing diffuse mantle streaking and others varying in upperpart colour saturation.

Middendorff's Grasshopper is marginally larger than most Pallas's Grasshoppers but there is considerable overlap in measurements, so that shape, size and structure are of little assistance in their separation. Confusion is most

likely to arise between a boldly marked Middendorff's Grasshopper with diffuse mantle streaking, most frequent in the race *subcerthiola*, and a poorly marked Pallas's Grasshopper, perhaps a juvenile of the race *centralasiae* or *sparsimstriata*.

Middendorff's Grasshopper Warbler differs from Pallas's Grasshopper in having, at best, diffuse and obscure darker mottling on the mantle. The rump and uppertail-coverts appear slightly warmer and brighter than the mantle and lack the darker mottling or crisp feather centres which Pallas's Grasshopper displays. The crown and nape are marginally darker and greyer than the mantle, with indistinct and diffuse darker feather centres. There is a thin greyish white supercilium that extends from the bill base to the rear of the eye, gradually fading above the ear-coverts, but this is less obvious than on all but the most poorly marked Pallas's Grasshopper. In adults, apart from the white chin and throat, the underparts are dull creamy white with an olive-brown wash across the breast and onto the flanks, while juveniles are washed yellow below. The undertail-coverts are pale creamy buff, with diffuse white tips, paler than those of the race *rubescens* of Pallas's Grasshopper, but overlapping with other races. Middendorff's Grasshopper also shares with Pallas's Grasshopper the broad white tips to the rectrices, except for the central pair, and a pale greyish white or whitish brown outer web to p2.

Styan's Grasshopper Warbler has a similar shape and structure to Pallas's Grasshopper but has a proportionately longer, slightly more robust bill. In appearance, it is considerably different, resembling a faded and unmarked Pallas's Grasshopper, with only the pale tips to the rectrices in common. The upperparts, including the crown, mantle, rump, uppertail-coverts and tail are uniform dull grey-brown. In some lights, a faint hint of mottling may be discernible on the mantle, but even this is lacking on many birds. There is slight contrast between the centres and fringes of the wing-coverts and tertials but never as much as shown by Pallas's Grasshopper. Generally, Styan's Grasshopper Warbler is larger and heavier and appears more bulky than Pallas's Grasshopper, with a proportionately longer tail. However, there is overlap in wing length above 66mm, the shortest wing length recorded for Styan's Grasshopper, while some Pallas's Grasshoppers' of the race *sparsimstriata* can reach 73mm.

VOICE There are no documented differences in song throughout the breeding range and recordings of the songs of the five races demonstrate that they quite similar, with only the minor apparent differences in pace and volume that would be expected across such a vast region.

The song is quite different in structure from the distinctive 'reeling' songs of the four European breeding *Locustella* species. It is much slower and quite varied although retaining a consistent pattern with a frequency range spanning 3.5–8kHz. It invariably starts with two or three quiet but harsh '*schrip*' calls, similar to the typical call, followed by a variable, but thin and rather scratchy *Acrocephalus*-like series of harsh, inflected notes and ending in a terminal flourish of six or seven notes which run into each other. Each complete song sequence given by nominate *certhiola* can be transcribed as '*chit-chrit-werwerwerwer-tatatatatatatata-cherwee-cherwee-cherwee-chechechechechecheche*', while *centralasiae* gives a similar but slightly slower and subdued '*chip-chrip-chip-cheweechewee-churr-schur-chat-cher-chechechechechecheche*'.

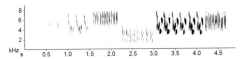

Song of Pallas's Grasshopper Warbler, recorded within breeding range of *L. c. certhiola*, Choibalsan, eastern Mongolia, June. (Geoff Carey)

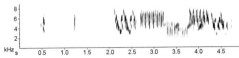

Song of Pallas's Grasshopper Warbler, recorded within breeding range of *L. c. centralasiae*, Khar Us Noor, western Mongolia, June. (Geoff Carey)

Song is heard during spring migration and immediately upon return to the breeding grounds, from late May until early July and occasionally later. A more subdued song is given by wintering birds from January onwards until late May when the last birds depart. Winter songs tend to be shorter, up to two seconds, and may lack the full complement of elements given during the breeding season.

Although song structure is similar to that of Middendorff's Grasshopper Warbler, the entire song of Pallas's Grasshopper is thinner and more scratchy than that of Middendorff's Grasshopper, which tends to sound richer, louder and more powerful. It is also delivered in a more hurried manner with shorter pauses between sequences. Each complete song sequence, including introductory calls and the terminal flourish, lasts 4–5 seconds or less, whereas in Middendorff's Grasshopper it generally lasts for five seconds or slightly longer.

The typical call is a quiet, hard and rather metallic '*pwit*', uttered repeatedly at intervals of one or two per second. This call can be heard throughout the year and is often the only indication of its presence during the winter months. It is quite similar to the contact call of Lanceolated Warbler and care is required in their separation, but identification by call alone is possible once the observer is familiar with it. There is also a rather quiet tinkling, rolling or rattling '*rit-tititit*' trill, similar to one element of the song that is given less frequently.

MOULT Adults replace body and head feathers prior to autumn migration. Some trapped for ringing in Hong Kong in September had also replaced the three outer primaries (p1–3), presumably before migration. Based upon birds trapped in Hong Kong, some juveniles of the southern breeding race *minor* also complete body moult before autumn migration, but many do not. Exceptionally, a juvenile *rubescens* trapped in Hong Kong in mid September was recaptured in mid November, having undergone a complete moult (PJL *in litt*). There follows a complete moult by both adults and juveniles, usually in late winter, although some birds appear to undergo extensive moult shortly after arrival in the wintering area. For example, Williamson (1968) noted that birds from Burma were replacing body feathers, wing-coverts and tertials between mid October and mid November and two specimens, dated 7 and 20 November, were in active primary moult with the remainder of their plumage new. In Malaysia, however, Nisbet (1967) did not find any moulting flight feathers among 63 autumn birds caught (presumed nominate *certhiola*).

Typically, a complete and rapid moult occurs on the wintering grounds in late winter. In Malaysia, Nisbet (1967) recorded active moult between late February and early May. There was a spread of four to five weeks in commencement date, but all birds were moulting primaries between 17 March and 26 April. Individual duration was approximately 50 to 60 days, with two to four primaries growing concurrently per wing in mid moult. Tail moult commenced when primary moult was well established, with all feathers being dropped simultaneously and replacements growing together.

Dement'ev & Gladkov (1954) commented that nominate *certhiola* has a partial post-juvenile moult shortly after fledging. This has not been substantiated for nominate *certhiola*, but some *minor*, which probably breeds earlier than other races, have replaced some body contour feathering and greater coverts by mid September in Hong Kong. Some birds may replace the juvenile primaries or tail feathers before arrival in wintering areas (note the *rubescens* in Hong Kong referred to above) but this is exceptional, and for the vast majority of birds of all races there is no suggestion of replacement prior to the late winter moult. Nisbet (1967) provided overwhelming evidence for a complete moult of juvenile plumage prior to spring migration, at the same time as the moult of adults.

HABITAT Occupies a wide range of moist lowland habitat, avoiding mountains except during the breeding season. Near its northern limits, in the taiga region, it breeds in almost any suitable damp area, including boggy woodland clearings, moist grassland with low scrub and scattered small trees, patches of thick birch *Betula* scrub, and tall rank grasses and reeds. Some breed in mountains In western areas, reaching the tree line, but only where there are damp grasses or small overgrown pools. In Yakutia, E Siberia, *rubescens* extends onto mountain tundra where damp grasses and sedges are available. In parts of eastern Russia, it has adapted to drier regions where it breeds in cereal fields and dry meadows fringed with dense herbage and shrubs, as well as in rank grasses and tussocks along rivers, boggy meadows with scattered trees and shrubs and near wet springs or flushes. In the south of the range, the race *centralasiae* breeds in the semi-desert and steppe region of Mongolia, where it is dependent on localised lakes and pools, damp grassland or *Phragmites* reedbeds. In Mongolia, it also breeds on *Artemisia*-covered slopes above rivers and streams.

In winter, it occurs in almost any wetland habitat, but generally below 100m, from overgrown damp grassland and sedge beds to reed fringes by large lakes and rivers, although small numbers regularly over-winter in Sri Lanka up to *c.* 1,800m and in Borneo to *c.* 1,300m. It has been trapped in Hong Kong in or near *Phragmites* reedbeds, a habitat apparently rarely used by autumn migrants although migrants can appear in any damp habitat with thick cover. In China, it prefers tall, damp grasses, usually with nearby shrubs and bushes; in Hong Kong, it frequents flooded grassland, typically up to 0.2m deep with emergent grasses up to 0.4m high. In regions of arid steppe, any available cover is used for shelter, including scrub and small bushes around farms and camel stations. Vagrants to Europe have occurred in crops and small damp ditches, and occasionally remain for several days in inhospitable, barren, open habitat such as sparsely vegetated shingle ridges.

BEHAVIOUR Behaviour resembles that of other small *Locustella* warblers. On the wintering grounds, its presence is usually revealed only by its distinctive call, but it is typically skulking and elusive outside the breeding season and is rarely seen except when flushed. It habitually adopts a horizontal posture and creeps or runs, mouse-like, through and under thick cover, rarely remaining stationary for more than a few seconds. Occasionally, a bird will appear briefly on bare ground or mud at the base of reeds, or on an exposed branch, nervously flicking its wings, before dashing back into cover. When disturbed, it has a rapid, whirring flight just above low vegetation, with the graduated tail fully spread and the rusty brown rump exposed. It usually flies further than Lanceolated Warbler, for 20m or more, and, unlike Lanceolated, it rarely runs far after landing and can often be flushed repeatedly.

Males are particularly conspicuous on arrival on the breeding territories and are often quite easy to see when singing, particularly in still, calm conditions. As with other *Locustella* species, the song is most frequently given before dawn and after dusk and in the first hour of daylight after sunrise and before sunset, but newly arrived males will sing throughout the day. Song can be delivered from deep within cover, but is more frequently given from the lower part of a bush, such as a scrubby willow *Salix*, or near the crown of a *Phragmites* reed stem. It seems more inclined to sing from an exposed perch than either Lanceolated or Grasshopper Warblers. Several birds may breed in close proximity and singing can then continue throughout the day and night, with males pursuing each other through low cover. They occasionally perform a brief song-flight, rising to about 10m then descending in a slanting glide back into cover. Song decreases in frequency once pairs are established, becoming more restricted to dawn and dusk. It continues, however, up to late July or early August. The song, or a more subdued version, is also heard on wintering grounds, from January up to late May, when the last birds depart.

BREEDING HABITS Very little data is available. It occupies a rather small territory, with several birds sometimes nesting in close proximity. The nest is built in thick grass and eggs are laid from mid June onwards in Ussuriland and late June in Transbaikalia. It is single-brooded, with the young leaving the nest from early August onwards (Dement'ev & Gladkov 1954).

DISTRIBUTION
Breeding The breeding range of Pallas's Grasshopper Warbler extends across a vast swathe of the C and E Palearctic, from the middle Irtysh River in W Siberia, south to E Kazakhstan and W China, and east through Transbaikalia and Amurland to the shores of the Sea of Okhotsk and northern part of the Sea of Japan. The northern limit is poorly known but certainly extends to at least 64°N in the region of Yakutsk. The southern limit extends through S Mongolia and N China, from the C Xinjiang Uygur Autonomous Region, east through NC China to NE China and the Primorskiy region of Russia and the Sea of Japan. It is common and widespread throughout much of its range, becoming abundant on migration in coastal China and in suitable wintering habitat in SE Asia. Dement'ev & Gladkov (1954) considered it locally common in the northern part of its range, but sporadic in the south. The variation in appearance of birds across this region is considerable and intergrades appear where the ranges of adjacent forms come into contact or overlap.

L. c. rubescens This northern form breeds across C and E Siberia to the north of the other races, although the ranges overlap in places, particularly along the southern edge of its range. From the southwestern limit close to Krasnoyarsk in S Siberia, it extends east through the Baikal region, where it breeds east to the Argun River. Intergrades with nominate *certhiola* on the Vitim Plateau to the east of Lake Baikal (Dement'ev & Gladkov 1954) and also towards the southern end of the lake. Breeding may also extend into N Mongolia, where it reportedly breeds in the Tola River valley and has been trapped at Hovsgol Nuur in late June (PJL *in litt.*). To the north, it reaches to at least 66°N in the Yenisey River valley to the north of the range of *sparsimstriata* and 64°N on the Nizhnyaya–Tunguska watershed. Vaurie (1959) considered it to occur west to the Ob River but generally to the north of the range of *sparsimstriata*, although intergrades with *sparsimstriata* occur from about 61°N to the region of Narym on the Ob. It breeds east across C Siberia, reaching 64°N along the Vitim River, Yakutia, then southeast towards the Maya River and the shores of the Sea of Okhotsk, north to Okhotsk (Dement'ev & Gladkov 1954). It is uncertain whether it extends north to the Magadan region, where intergrades with Middendorff's Grasshopper Warbler have been reported (Kalyakin *et al.* 1993). However, examination of birds from this region suggests they are not hybrids and appear to be well-marked Middendorff's Grasshopper Warblers of the northern form *subcerthiola*. A juvenile has been recorded from Kronoki Bay on eastern Kamchatka in September (Dement'ev & Gladkov 1954) but by that date it would probably have been a migrant.

L. c. sparsimstriata The western form, breeding in W Siberia, overlaps and intergrades with *rubescens* to the north, *certhiola* to the east and, possibly, with *centralasiae* to the south. The western limit reaches the Irtysh River at *c.* 70°E, then east to the Ob River, north to the region of Narym and south to Novosibirsk. From here, the range presumably extends to the east to include much of the West Siberian Plain to the region of Krasnoyarsk on the Yenisey River. Although the region between the Ob and Yenisey Rivers may be occupied by intergrades with *rubescens*, we have not seen any birds that could be considered intergrades. In the hills east of the Yenisey River, it may overlap with the more northerly breeding *rubescens*.

L. c. centralasiae Breeds across the arid steppe region of C Asia, centred on wetlands in grasslands and deserts of Mongolia and NW and NC China. The western limit lies in extreme NE and E Kazakhstan where it breeds from the Irtysh River valley and the Altai Mountains east of Öskemen, to the foothills of the southern Altai and south to the Alakol basin and the foothills of the Dzhungarskiy Alayau Mountains. To the east it breeds widely across the dry semi-desert regions of W and S Mongolia including the Tsagan Nor region and north to the Khanghai Mountains (Dement'ev & Gladkov 1954). In China, it breeds in the Xinjiang Uygur Autonomous Region of W China, adjacent to S Mongolia and including the lower slopes of the eastern Tien Shan Mountains, the western section of the Tarim Basin and regions near Kashi and the Hami Oasis. Although there are few records from NC China, range appears to extend through N China to NW Qinghai Province, where it breeds along the upper Huang Ho (Yellow River) and the Zaidam depression, and to the arid regions of NW Gansu Province and the Nei Mongol Autonomous Region (Cheng 1987), where it may overlap with nominate *certhiola*. The eastern limit is uncertain and it appears to intergrade with nominate *certhiola* in C and SE Mongolia and NC China. There is one record from E Kyrgyzstan (Roth & Jalilova 2004).

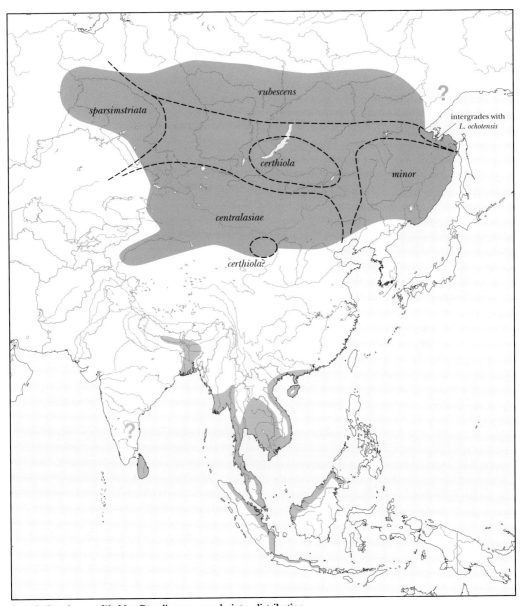

Pallas's Grasshopper Warbler. Breeding range and winter distribution.

L. c. certhiola The nominate form breeds in SC Siberia, in the Transbaikal region, to the south of *rubescens* and bounded to the west by *sparsimstriata* and to the east by *minor*. There appear to be no precise racial boundaries in this region and intermediate characters appear where forms meet, particularly between *certhiola* and *minor* to the east of Lake Baikal, between *certhiola* and *rubescens* in the Baikal region and northern Mongolia, and perhaps between *certhiola* and *centralasiae* in eastern Mongolia, although most here appear to be *certhiola*. The eastern limit of birds resembling *certhiola* lies close to the Onon and Argun Rivers, where it merges with *minor* in the Da Hinggan Ling Mountains in NE Nei Mongol Autonomous Region. The race breeding in N Mongolia

is considered to be nominate *certhiola* by Dement'ev & Gladkov (1954) and during recent studies only nominate *certhiola* has been found breeding in E Mongolia (PJL *in litt.*), where nominate *certhiola*, *centralasiae* and *rubescens* have all been reported to breed (Dement'ev & Gladkov 1954; Vaurie 1959). Birds resembling *certhiola* breed in Ningxia Province in NC China, within the range of *centralasiae* but occupy different habitats (PJL *in litt.*). It is uncertain whether the ranges of *sparsimstriata* and *certhiola* meet, or whether birds breeding in the region west of Lake Baikal are intergrades between these forms.

L. c. minor The range of *minor* lies to the east of the nominate form and south of *rubescens* in the Primorskiy region of SE Russia and NE China. In the Russian Far East, it breeds in the basins of the Amur and Ussuri Rivers, west to the confluence of the Shilka and Argun Rivers (Dement'ev & Gladkov 1954). To the south, its range in NE China includes the Da Hinggang Mountains in the northeastern part of the Nei Mongol Autonomous Region and northern Heilongjiang Province (Cheng 1987). Sushkin (1925) also includes the Ordos and Ala Shan regions of the Nei Mongol Autonomous Region within the range of *minor*. In NE China breeding probably occurs locally across much of Heilongjiang, Jilin and Liaoning Provinces, and the southern limit formerly extended south to the Chihli plain (now Hebei Province), where La Touche (1925–30) confirmed breeding, although Cheng (1987) omitted it from this region. Comments by Sushkin that it breeds as far south as Kiukiang (Jiujiang, Jiangxi Province), on the Yangtze River appear erroneous and presumably refer to migrants returning to the breeding areas.

Non-breeding Pallas's Grasshopper Warbler occupies an extensive wintering range across much of SE Asia, west to NE India and south to Sri Lanka. Its skulking nature and the lack of observers throughout much of this range suggest that it is more widespread and numerous than records would suggest. It winters regularly in Sri Lanka and SC India and from NE India into Burma, Thailand and the Malay Peninsula south to Singapore. There are occasional records of wintering birds from Nepal, SE China, Vietnam, Laos, Sumatra and Java and it may be regular here but it is likely that many are overlooked in regions outside the core wintering range.

As the plumage of worn adults and juveniles on the wintering grounds differs from that of adults on the breeding grounds, the non-breeding ranges of the various races are uncertain. There are no ringing recoveries to indicate where these may lie.

It is a common winter visitor to SE Asia south to Singapore. Birds wintering south of Thailand resemble nominate *certhiola*, but as separation from *minor* is difficult at this season, it is safer to refer to these as *certhiola/minor*. The winter distribution of *certhiola/minor* appears to include much of continental Thailand and the Malay Peninsula south to Singapore. The birds wintering throughout the lowlands of the Malay Peninsula were attributed to *certhiola* by Medway & Wells (1976) but it seems likely that some *minor* were involved. Five winter occurrences in Hong Kong since the late 1980s, between 26 February and 21 March, are well outside the known wintering range and are too early to relate to returning migrants (Carey *et al.* 2001). These birds were quite dark, slightly darker than birds regularly trapped in the Malay Peninsula and Singapore and were probably *minor*.

Birds attributed to nominate *certhiola* occur in small numbers throughout Sumatra in winter, from Banda Aceh and Sumatra Utara, south to Lampung and the Straits of Malacca (Marle & Voous 1988). Birds wintering elsewhere in the Greater Sundas, including Java and Bali, and on Borneo from sea level to 1,300m are also probably *certhiola*, but could be *minor* or intergrades. Smythies (1968) included Burma within the wintering range of *minor*, but did not differentiate between records of *minor* and *rubescens*.

Birds showing the characters of *rubescens*, the most readily recognised race and described from a bird collected at Calcutta, winter mainly in S Asia, where they are locally common in lower Bengal, Assam, Bangladesh and central India (Ali & Ripley 1973) and vagrants to Nepal and Kerala in SW India. This race is widespread throughout wetlands

in Sri Lanka, although apparently not common anywhere and it was presumably this which Legge (1880) observed and collected in the Mutturajawella swamps. Smythies (1968) considered *rubescens* (as well as *minor*) to be locally common in C and S Burma and the Shan States. It occurs regularly in C and N Thailand (PDR *in litt.*) but is unknown from the Malay Peninsula. A February bird reported from Sulawesi was attributed to this race (White & Bruce 1986) but may have been a hybrid between Pallas's Grasshopper and Middendorff's Grasshopper Warblers (Coates *et al.* 1997)

To-date, there are no published records of unequivocal *sparsimstriata* away from the breeding grounds and the wintering range remains unknown. Two birds trapped for ringing in Thailand on 7 October 2000 were tentatively ascribed to this race, based upon their large size and resemblance to the available descriptions (PDR *in litt.*). The westerly bias to the breeding range suggests that it may winter in the Indian subcontinent, although there are no substantiated records to support this. However, returning breeding birds do not reach territories in western Siberia until mid to late June. This late arrival, combined with the long wing length, suggests these birds may undertake a long migration, so some of the late-departing birds which winter in Thailand may be of this race.

The winter range of *centralasiae* is poorly known. Sushkin (1925) included Fuzhou (Foochow) Fujian Province in E China, but since there are few winter records of Pallas's Grasshopper from SE China, this is probably erroneous. It may be based on La Touche (1925–30) who discovered a migrant at Fuzhou on 7 October 1896 which he believed to be *centralasiae*. Other wintering locations mentioned by Sushkin (1925) include lower Pegu, Burma, and the Andaman Islands in the Bay of Bengal, while Ali and Ripley (1973) also include the Nicobar Islands.

MOVEMENTS Due to the similarity between nominate *certhiola* and *minor* and the presence of intergrades, the passage status of these two races in E China and SE Asia is uncertain. These races are treated together here except where data specifically relating to one race is available. The movements of *sparsimstriata* and *centralasiae* are unknown and not discussed further.

L. c. certhiola/minor Dement'ev & Gladkov (1954) stated that nominate *certhiola* begins to vacate the breeding grounds in early August, the latest birds being recorded up to 15 September. In the Russian Far East, they documented migrant *minor* at Sudzukhe, outside the breeding range, from 10 August onwards, with a heavy passage during the first two weeks of September. As a migrant, *minor* remains common in the Primorskiy Region until mid September. In China, Cheng (1987) considered *certhiola* to be a vagrant, citing just one autumn record relating to a bird mentioned by La Touche (1925–30), procured at Qinhuangdao (Chinwangtao), Hebei Province. However, *certhiola* must pass through China to reach its wintering grounds and some must be mistaken for *minor*, which occurs widely throughout the coastal provinces from Liaoning to Guangxi, although there are very few records from inland provinces. La Touche (1925–30) considered *minor* to be abundant on passage at Qinhuangdao from the last week of August to middle of September. This is still largely correct and it remains common and at times abundant, on passage at Beidaihe and Happy Island, Hebei Province (JH *in litt.*). In Hong Kong, *certhiola* and/or *minor* predominate on passage, where numbers reach a distinct peak in the last three weeks in September (Carey *et al.* 2001). Like *rubescens*, which occurs here at the same time, the numbers recorded vary annually, dependent on whether adverse weather conditions ground migrants. Despite this, the numbers passing through Hong Kong are invariably much smaller than those occurring in coastal northeast China, suggesting that many birds follow an inland route to wintering areas in SE Asia.

Migrants reach the Malay Peninsula from mid September onwards and most follow the coasts and lowlands. Passage through the hills is negligible, with just 36 birds trapped for ringing at Fraser's Hill (at 1,300m) between 1966–69. Records here, and casualties at coastal lighthouses confirm passage dates between 18 September and 25 November. The earliest record from Sumatra is 29 September (Marle & Voous 1988), and from 12 September, Borneo.

Departure from the wintering grounds is poorly documented and few birds are then trapped for ringing or become lighthouse casualties. Nisbet (1967) noted departure within two weeks of completion of moult. They certainly stay on the wintering grounds in Malaysia until early May and it remains fairly numerous in Thailand until the middle of May. The latest recorded dates from known wintering areas include 2 May in Sabah, Malaysia, 8 May in Sumatra and 21 May in peninsula Malaysia.

Migrants avoid SE China in spring, where there are just three records from Hong Kong, all between 15–17 May (Carey *et al.* 2001). La Touche (1925–30) considered it to be scarce at Fuzhou, but quoted Styan as saying it was 'abundant at Kiukiang on the grassy plains in May…'. Returning migrants presumably, therefore, follow a direct overland route to reach the northeast coastal provinces north of Shanghai. The earliest migrants appear in Hebei Province in the second half of May, where La Touche (1925–30) considered *minor* to be abundant on passage at Qinhuangdao between late May and 10 June. Birds reach the Primorskiy region of the Russian Far East in the last few days of May (Dement'ev & Gladkov 1954). Within days, it becomes abundant there as returning migrants surge northwards to occupy breeding territories that only become habitable in early June. The earliest birds in the Baikal region, presumably nominate *certhiola* or intergrades, are also in late May, but the main arrival occurs in early June (Dement'ev & Gladkov 1954), slightly later than *minor* returns to breeding areas in the Russian Far East.

L. c. rubescens Departure from the breeding range begins in early August and reaches a peak in late August and early September. Dement'ev & Gladkov (1954) considered that all birds had left the Lake Baikal region by mid September. Passage through eastern Mongolia occurs during the first three weeks of September. Migrants move through the coastal provinces of China from late August onwards, and La Touche (1925–30) reported *rubescens* as being by no means uncommon at Qinhuangdao (Chinwangtao), Hebei Province, from late August to first half of September. This statement holds true today, although *rubescens* is usually is less numerous than *certhiola/ minor*. Autumn passage through Hong Kong commences slightly later, in early September, and peaks in the last three weeks of the month (Carey *et al.* 2001). Numbers of both *rubescens* and *certhiola/minor* are then quite variable and although

rubescens is usually less numerous, this situation can be temporarily reversed. September accounts for almost 90% of all records of Pallas's Grasshopper Warbler (Carey *et al.* 2001) and there is no obvious difference in migration timing between the two racial groups. Numbers decline rapidly in early October and passage ceases by the end of the month.

Return passage in spring is presumably quite rapid, as birds are still in wintering areas in mid May. There are few documented passage records of *rubescens* although La Touche (1925–30) reported it from Qinhuangdao from the end of May to mid June. It arrives on the breeding grounds from the first week of June onwards, but the majority do not reappear in Transbaikalia until the middle of the month, and breeding birds have established territories by the third week of June (Dement'ev & Gladkov 1954). Towards the western range limit, birds reach Minusinsk during early June (Dement'ev & Gladkov 1954) and Krasnoyarsk just a few days later, with passage continuing until late June.

Vagrancy Westward vagrancy by Pallas's Grasshopper Warbler into NW Europe has increased and it is being recorded almost annually, in part due to increasing numbers of observers. All European occurrences have been in countries bordering the Baltic and North Seas and all have been between mid September and late October, apart from the first record on Helgoland, Germany, on the exceptionally early date of 13 August 1858. As with many vagrants originating in Siberia and C Asia, the British Isles, with the Shetland Islands and Fair Isle in particular, account for the majority of records, where a total of 41 birds had occurred in Britain up to 2008. Elsewhere in Europe, vagrants have reached Ireland, Norway, Sweden, Latvia, Germany, Netherlands, Belgium, France and Poland. It also occurred at Eilat, Israel, on 25 February 1983 (Shirihai 1996); a date suggesting this would be a wintering bird rather than a migrant.

No European records have yet been attributed to a specific race. Many show characters associated with *rubescens* and as this is the form breeding at the northwestern extremity of the range in W Siberia, it seems the most likely to occur.

It is a vagrant to Nepal with just three records, the most recent being at Koshi Tappu Wildlife Reserve on 5 May 2001. In the eastern part of its range, Pallas's Grasshopper Warbler is an accidental visitor to Japan, where it was first recorded on 29 September 1985 at Hamatonbetsu Bird Banding Station, Esashi-gun, Hokkaido (Kawaji & Abe 1988). It remains extremely rare there, with just two further occurrences, in May and November. All records are believed to relate to *rubescens* (Eguchi *et al.* 2000), although Kawaji & Abe (1988) recognise that *minor* is equally likely to occur.

DESCRIPTION *L. c. certhiola*
Plumage – Adult fresh (April to July) Forehead warm brown, streaking lacking or indistinct. Crown blackish, feathers with dull ash-grey fringes giving grey/black-streaked appearance. Nape warm tan to rusty brown with small black feather centres, almost uniform and unmarked towards sides of neck. Supercilium whitish or pale sandy grey, long and broad, from bill base to rear of ear-coverts. Narrow black loral spot, most conspicuous in front of eye, not usually reaching bill base. A warm to dark brown eye-stripe behind the eye broadens and diffuses into nape. Eye-ring narrow, faint and inconspicuous. Ear-coverts greyish brown

with fine whitish shafts giving faint streaking. Mantle and scapulars with black feather centres extending to feather tips, and broad rusty brown fringes, giving dark heavy streaking. Rump rich chestnut-brown, usually unmarked but sometimes with small, indistinct, blackish feather centres on lower rump. Uppertail-coverts as rump but with large black teardrop shaped spots close to tips. Rectrices dark grey-brown with indistinct and diffuse cross-barring and broad rusty brown fringes to the outer webs, central pair with rusty brown fringes to both webs, broadest at tip and tapering along shafts for distal halves; all feathers except central pair with white outer tail-feather grey. Underside of tail dark grey, with whitish tips to all feathers, widest and most obvious on three outer pairs (t4–6), narrower on next two pairs (t2–3), barely visible on central pair. Chin, throat and belly white or faintly washed creamy white. Upper breast creamy white, lightly washed pale tan, sometimes darkening across lower breast to form an indistinct band. Throat unmarked or with small, indistinct spots on lower throat extending to centre of upper breast. Sides of breast dark sandy brown or pale rusty buff, this extending to sides of neck, along flanks and across ventral region. Undertail-coverts pale sandy buff to creamy white with large diffuse whitish tips.

Upperwing-coverts and alula with blackish centres and narrow, pale buff to whitish fringes and tips, contrasting in colour with mantle fringes. Tertials blackish with narrow, crisp, warm brown to pale greyish white fringes of uniform width, usually becoming white at tips of inner webs adjacent to feather shafts, forming whitish notches or indentations. Remiges grey-brown, narrowly edged warm sandy brown, long outer primary (p2) with paler sandy buff to greyish white outer edge. Primaries with narrow buffy brown tips. Underwing-coverts pale creamy buff to pale greyish cream, considerably paler than flanks.

Adult worn (December to March) Does not differ significantly from fresh adult. Fringes to upperpart feathers narrower, streaking more prominent.

Juvenile Feathers of forehead and crown dark grey, with pale sandy buff fringes forming distinct streaking. Nape warmer than crown and mantle, poorly marked with small dark feather centres. Supercilium pale buffy yellow, most conspicuous in front of eye, flecked light brown behind eye; less broad and contrasting than in adult. Loral spot as adult but stripe behind eye shorter, narrower and rather diffuse. Eye-ring inconspicuous. Ear-coverts washed pale yellowish buff with darker tips and paler shafts, appearing distinctly mottled. Mantle and scapulars with large blackish feather centres and broad dull brown to rufous-brown fringes, giving heavy streaking. Rump as adult but darker feather centres slightly more conspicuous. Uppertail-coverts slightly duller than in adult, with large dark spots near tips less crisply defined. Tail as adult, but often with conspicuous pale tips to central feathers.

Chin, throat and belly washed pale yellow. Breast and flanks washed yellowish buff. Lower throat with a row of small distinct spots, often extending along the sides below the malar region. Upper breast with small, forward-pointing blackish arrowheads, forming a band widening towards the sides and extending onto the upper flanks. Lower flanks sometimes with thin blackish streaks. Undertail-coverts pale sandy buff with slightly paler tips.

Upperwing-coverts and tertials similar to fresh adult but fringes more closely match those of mantle. Usually a small white or pale buff notch on inner web of the two inner tertials.

Bare parts Upper mandible dark brown or black with narrow pink cutting edge. Lower mandible pink at base, darker at sides towards tip. Tarsi and toes dull pink or yellowish pink to pinkish brown; claws horn brown, slightly darker than toes. Iris rich dark brown in both adults and young birds.

IN HAND CHARACTERS
Measurements

Races combined:

	Male	Female
Wing	57–72 (65.1; 43)	60–72 (64.0; 24)
Tail	44–55 (48.8; 42)	43–53 (48.2; 24)
Bill	14–16 (15.1; 42)	14–16 (15.0; 22)
Tarsus	19.5–23 (21.4; 41)	19.5–23 (21.5; 23)

Sexes combined:
Tail/wing ratio: 68–83% (75%; 83)
Bill width: 3.0–4.2 (3.4; 50)
Hind claw: 6.0–8.0 (7.3; 48)
Tail graduation: 11–20 (14.8; 41)
 Wing and tail of juvenile *c.* 1mm shorter than in adult.

Individual races (Sexes combined):
L. c. certhiola: *wing* 60–71 (65.0; 17); *tail* 46–53 (49.1; 17); *bill* 14–16 (15.1; 17); *tarsus* 20–23 (21.3; 18).
L. c. minor: *wing* 57–67 (61.6; 21); *tail* 43–49 (46.3; 20); *bill* 13.5–15.5 (14.7; 21); *tarsus* 19.5–22 (20.8; 18). The smallest race.
L. c. rubescens: *wing* 61–66 (63.7; 17); *tail* 45–55 (49.5; 17); *bill* 14.5–16 (15.3; 16); *tarsus* 19.5–23 (21.6; 17).
L. c. sparsimstriata: *wing* 65–72 (69.1; 8); *tail* 50–54 (52.1; 8); *bill* 15–16 (15.5; 8); *tarsus* 21.5–23 (22.6; 7). The largest race.
L. c. centralasiae: *wing* 60–71 (64.8; 21); *tail* 43–51 (48.0; 21); *bill* 14–16 (14.8; 21); *tarsus* 19.5–23 (21.4; 21).

Structure *L. c. certhiola*

Wing formula (n = 20):

p1/pc	p2	p3e	p4(e)	p5	p6	p7	p10
(2)–3	3–5	wp	1.5–3	3–6	5–8	7–11	13–18

Wing pointed; p1 minute. Wing point p3; p2 = p4–5 (5/6); emargination on p3, sometimes slightly on p4. Notch on p2 8–11 from tip; falls at p7/8–p9.

Figure 31. Wing of Pallas's Grasshopper Warbler.

Tail rather short, graduated; feathers broad, tapering to a blunt point at tip.
Bill medium, concave-sided with very narrow tip. Less

strong than in Middendorff's Grasshopper Warbler, but deeper and broader-based than in Grasshopper Warbler.

Tarsi strong; toes long and slender; claws fine.

Other races. Similar to nominate race, but *minor* tends to show a shorter p2 (more often = p5 or = p5/6).

Recognition Distinguished from Grasshopper and Lanceolated Warblers by dark or blackish distal part of tail feathers with whitish tips to all except t1. Also by rufous-brown rump and uppertail-coverts, the latter usually with black markings; by whitish spots or indentations (if present) at tips of inner webs of tertials; and by typically unmarked buff or rufous-buff undertail-coverts. May show a gorget of dark breast spots (especially young birds) but lacks the distinct streaking shown particularly by Lanceolated. Wing formula similar to that of Grasshopper and Lanceolated Warblers. Measurements overlap those of the former, but are larger than those of the latter.

Separated from Middendorff's Grasshopper Warbler by crisp blackish mantle streaking and contrasting rufescent rump (rusty brown to olive-brown rump in Middendorff's Grasshopper contrasting less with mantle). Also usually by smaller size, birds with wing < 65mm, tail < 50mm or bill < 16mm being below the range for Middendorff's Grasshopper Warbler.

Ageing Juveniles in early autumn show fresh primaries, whereas in adults these are slightly worn. Juveniles are yellowish buff on the throat and belly centre and have dark brown spotting on the upper breast, while adults are whitish on throat and belly, with no yellow tinge and with any breast spots very small. Young birds retain juvenile plumage up to the main moult and are thus usually separable from adults until mid winter.

Weight Thailand, 11.6–19.0g (15.1; 68) (PDR unpublished data); Hong Kong, September–November, 10.3–19.4g (14.7; 14) (HKRG unpublished data).

GEOGRAPHIC VARIATION Five races are recognised, but there are areas of extensive intergradation away from the respective core ranges. Many birds, particularly young birds away from the breeding areas, show intermediate characters and cannot be assigned to a specific race. Criteria for their separation are under investigation and will be published in the near future (Leader & Kennerley in prep.). The western taxa, *sparsimstriata* and *centralasiae*, tend to be paler than *certhiola*, and *sparsimstriata* is distinctly larger than all other races, averaging even larger than Middendorff's Grasshopper and equalling most Styan's Grasshopper Warblers in wing and tail lengths. In the east of the range, birds referable to *minor* are darker and generally warmer-toned and more richly coloured than *certhiola*, but many intermediates occur. The breeding range of *rubescens* is the most extensive of all the races, extending across the entire range of the species in Siberia and bounded by *sparsimstriata*, *centralasiae*, *certhiola* and *minor* to the south. It shows little variation, however, and intergrades with neighbouring races are poorly represented in collections, although they would be easily overlooked.

L. c. certhiola (SE Transbaikalia, E Mongolia and NC China) Described above.

L. c. rubescens (Siberia north of other races from the Yenisey River to the Sea of Okhotsk) A distinctive race, the adult appearing darker and browner than other forms, but lacking the warmer, richer tones of nominate *certhiola* and *minor*. Has a well-marked supercilium and the crown shows the blackish feather centres with contrasting mid

grey fringes, also characteristic of *certhiola* and *minor*. The mantle and scapulars differ from other races in having fairly small blackish centres extending to the tip and quite broad cold straw-brown fringes. The pale, rufous-brown rump shows diffuse darker centres towards the tail base, while the darker, rufous-brown uppertail-coverts always show dark centres. On the most well-marked birds, (which perhaps are intergrades with *certhiola*) these centres appear large, black and well defined, reaching the feather tip and forming two broad converging black lines when the feathers are correctly positioned. Less well-marked birds, perhaps typical *rubescens*, show smaller, diffuse dark centres to the uppertail-coverts.

The chin, throat, lower breast and belly are white, lightly washed pale grey, while the upper breast is usually lightly washed light buff to warm brown. Some adults lack throat spotting but most show at least a scattering of small, dark spots across the lower breast, extending as far as the chin on some. The flanks are greyish white but the sides of the rump and undertail-coverts are heavily washed warm rufous-cinnamon, the undertail-coverts also being conspicuously and broadly tipped buffy white.

Compared with the adult, the upperpart streaking of juvenile birds in autumn is less prominent, with the blackish feather centres being smaller and with slightly warmer but broader tawny-brown fringes that usually extend across the tips, so the streaked effect on the mantle may be lacking. The underparts are a dull sulphurous yellow, becoming sulphurous buff across the breast, with a band of brown arrowheads across the lower throat and upper breast. Juveniles are generally darker than in other races and show darker undertail-coverts with contrasting paler tips.

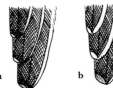

Figure 32. Comparison of tertial pattern of Pallas's Grasshopper Warbler of races (a) *certhiola* **and (b)** *rubescens.*

Figure 33. Comparison of tail and uppertail-covert pattern of Pallas's Grasshopper Warbler of races (a) *certhiola,* *minor* **and** *rubescens,* **and (b)** *sparsimstriata* **and** *centralasiae.* **Some** *sparsimstriata* **and** *centralasiae* **can lack spots on the uppertail-coverts.**

L. c. sparsimstriata (W Siberia from the Irtysh River east to at least the Ob River) The largest race. In the western part of its range it appears paler and greyer than *certhiola* and bears a closer resemblance to some *centralasiae*. It is not yet clear just how far to the east of the Ob River the characters of *sparsimstriata* are maintained.

However, *sparsimstriata* appears to intergrade with nominate *certhiola* east of the Yenisey River, making racial recognition difficult. These paler intermediate birds are usually included within *sparsimstriata*, particularly if the identification is supported by measurements.

The crown is pale ash-grey, streaked blackish, similar to that of nominate *certhiola* and not as dark as in *rubescens*, nor pale brown as in *centralasiae*. A distinctive, long, pale buffy white supercilium extends from the bill base to the rear ear-coverts. The mantle and scapulars are warm sandy brown, similar in colour to the nape but show ill-defined blackish centres, giving the upperparts a diffusely mottled appearance, not as heavily marked and contrasting as *certhiola* typically appears, with feather fringes generally slightly paler and lacking rufous tones. Some birds can approach the upperpart appearance of *centralasiae* but are not usually quite so pale. The rump and uppertail-coverts are buffy brown and cinnamon-brown, the rump without darker centres. Unlike *certhiola*, the longer uppertail-coverts show, at best, a poorly defined, blurred darker streak along the shafts and some birds lack these completely. The upper surface of the tail is warm sepia-brown with whitish tips, and the warm brown central feathers lack the darker brown wedge along the shaft typical of *certhiola*. The closed wing appears much paler than in *certhiola*, with mid brown feather centres and slightly paler ashy buff fringes to the wing-coverts. The tertials are buffy brown, similar to the mantle fringe colour and paler than in *certhiola*. The outer webs of the remiges are narrowly edged tawny-brown, slightly duller and less contrasting than the inner wing, although the outer primary (p2) shows a greyish white outer web. The chin, throat and belly are white and contrast with a pale sandy buff wash across the breast and along the flanks. This darkens slightly on the lower flanks and ventral region but remains paler than in *certhiola*. The undertail-coverts are washed light creamy buff with large but ill-defined creamy or whitish tips. Some adults show scattered faint, indistinct spots across the lower throat.

Juveniles resemble *centralasiae* and criteria for their separation have yet to be established. Although some specimens labelled as being of this form do exist in specimen collections, none that we have examined have come from within the breeding range of *sparsimstriata*. Larger birds may be separable from other races on wing and tail length.

L. c. centralasiae (E Kazakhstan to C Mongolia and NW China) This race, restricted to wetlands in the arid regions of central Asia, is the palest and least contrasting form. Compared with other races, the upperparts are poorly streaked. It is, on average, slightly paler than *sparsimstriata* and always significantly paler and greyer than *certhiola*. On adults, the crown shows dark, narrow feather centres with pale sandy brown (rather than greyish) fringes. The nape is edged grey-brown and appears paler and colder than both the crown and mantle, while the mantle and scapulars show relatively small and diffuse blackish centres and broad, dull tan fringes, sometimes washed light grey. The rump is warm cinnamon-brown and unmarked, while the uppertail-coverts are similar in colour but show a diffuse brown spot towards the feather tips as in *sparsimstriata*. The outer fringes to the outer rectrices are warm cinnamon-brown, contrasting with the darker grey webs, while the central pair are lightly washed cinnamon-brown

throughout. As in other races, the rectrices are broadly tipped greyish white although on the central pair these tips are narrower and less conspicuous. The underside of the tail is both paler and browner than in *certhiola* and the whitish tips are rounded and hook into the shaft, unlike *certhiola* where the division between tip and darker feather base forms a straight line, but it is not known whether this feature is diagnostic. The closed wing is paler than in other races, the mid brown coverts showing distinctive narrow, light sandy buff fringes, which contrast little with the centres. The tertials are mid brown with narrow, crisp, whitish fringes. Adults usually lack the whitish notch by the feather shaft on the inner two tertials. The remiges are edged warm tawny-brown to bright buff, except for the long outer primary, which is narrowly edged pale greyish white. On adults, the chin, throat and belly are white and unmarked, while a pale rusty buff wash forms a narrow band across the breast, broadening to become richer, warmer buff towards the sides of the breast and onto the sides of the neck. The flanks are white, washed pale buff but becoming darker rusty buff towards the lower flanks and the ventral region. The undertail-coverts are pale creamy buff to pale rusty buff; those with darker bases show paler tips that can appear almost white in some birds.

Juveniles are quite distinctive and readily separable from juvenile *certhiola*, *minor* and *rubescens*. Compared with these races, the brown fringes to the upperparts are paler and lack rich chestnut tones, and the rump and uppertail-coverts are uniform, lacking the prominent dark centres. There is variation in the prominence of the streaking on the upperparts, the strength of the yellow wash to the underparts and the extent of spotting across the breast. It is uncertain whether juvenile *sparsimstriata* and *centralasiae* can be separated using plumage characters.

L. c. minor (SE Siberia and NE China, to east of *certhiola*) Similar to nominate *certhiola* and intergrades with it in SE Transbaikalia and NC China. The most richly coloured race. Differences relate primarily to the warmth of the fringes to the upperpart feathering and the increased contrast with the blackish feather centres. The fringes to the mantle and scapulars of adult *minor* vary from warm tan to warm rufous-brown and appear generally warm, bright and contrasting, more so than in *certhiola*. The rump tends to be slightly paler, warm straw or warm tan, not quite as dark and rufous as that of *certhiola*. The uppertail-coverts are rich rufous-brown, slightly darker than the rump with conspicuous black centres, a feature shared with nominate *certhiola*. The fringes to the wing-coverts and tertials are slightly warmer and more richly coloured, but narrower than in *certhiola*, so that the greater coverts tend to form a contrasting dark panel in the closed wing. Dark-centred tertials show narrow, crisp, rusty brown fringes, becoming paler and greyer towards the tip. Like adult *certhiola*, adult *minor* appears to lack the white notch against the shaft tip on the inner tertials. The primaries and secondaries are narrowly edged rufous-brown, most broadly towards the feather bases, so that the closed wing appears similar to, or marginally brighter than in *certhiola*. Like *certhiola*, the long outer primary (p2) shows a greyish white edge. Tail and underparts match those of *certhiola* in colour and pattern.

TAXONOMY AND SYSTEMATICS There is divergence of opinion regarding which races of Pallas's Grasshopper

Warbler are recognised. Most authorities consider *L. c. certhiola*, *L. c. rubescens* and *L. c. centralasiae* to be well-defined and valid taxa showing a distinctive suite of characters (e.g. Williamson 1968; Cramp 1992; Dickinson 2003; Stepanyan 2003). The race *L. c. minor*, which breeds in southeast Siberia and northeast China, is not widely recognised, and Cramp (1992), Stepanyan (2003) and Dickinson (2003) treat it as a junior synonym of nominate *certhiola*, while Williamson (1968) considered that the extent of intergradation and overlap with *certhiola* precluded safe recognition. It was strongly supported by La Touche (1925–30), based upon plumage differences, and also recognised by Dement'ev & Gladkov (1954) and Cheng (1988). Furthermore, its validity was been supported by a recent mtDNA study (Drovetski *et al.* 2004). The westernmost race *sparsimstriata* was not described until 1934 and was not recognised by either Williamson (1968) or Dement'ev & Gladkov (1954), but its validity is now accepted by most authorities including Stepanyan

(2003). However, *sparsimstriata* presents interesting challenges and it is far from certain to which race(s) it is most closely related. As well as being a pale and relatively poorly marked form, it is also the largest of all the races and a near relationship with nominate *certhiola* and *rubescens* is uncertain. In the west of its range it possesses a stable suite of characters, but it appears to merge and intergrade with *rubescens* to the east and possibly *centralasiae* to the south.

At the species level, Pallas's Grasshopper Warbler is closely related to Middendorff's Grasshopper and Styan's Grasshopper Warblers and hybridisation with Middendorff's Grasshopper Warbler has been reported where their respective ranges overlap. Studies of plumage and measurements by Kalyakin *et al.* (1993) in the Lower Amur River area of the Primorskiy Maritime Territory and on Sakhalin suggest that hybridisation here is widespread, and that birds showing mixed characters form a self-sustaining intergrade population. See also under Middendorff's Grasshopper Warbler.

◄ Adult *L. c. certhiola*, Mongolia, June. Typical adult showing dull ash-grey fringes to crown, broad rusty brown fringes to mantle and scapulars, and black centres extending to feather tips so upperparts appear heavily streaked. Rump and uppertail-coverts rich chestnut-brown, the latter with large black teardrop-shaped spots (Paul Leader).

◄ Adult *L. c. certhiola*, Lake Baikal, Siberia, June. A 'colder' bird with straw-buff rather than rich buff fringes and paler, more contrasting edges to wing-coverts and tertials. Note rusty brown uppertail-coverts with conspicuous black centres and unusually extensive dark spotting on lower throat and upper breast (Peter Kennerley).

▲ Adult *L. c. rubescens*, northern Mongolia, June. The darkest, drabbest race. Rufous-brown uppertail-coverts always show dark centres. Underparts darker than other races, approaching upperpart colour, so contrast with upperparts less apparent. Unlike other races, undertail-coverts washed dull brown to drab cinnamon-brown and broadly tipped buffy white (Paul Leader).

▲ Adult *L. c. sparsimstriata*, Novosibirsk, Siberia, June. Some show grey-brown fringes and approach the upperpart appearance of *centralasiae* but slightly darker. Note blackish-streaked, pale ash-grey crown, distinctive long, pale buffy white supercilium, and warm sandy brown mantle and scapulars bleeding into blackish centres, lacking crisp appearance of *certhiola* (Peter Kennerley).

▲ Adult *L. c. sparsimstriata*, Novosibirsk, Siberia, Russia, June. The largest race, wing length overlapping with some Styan's Grasshopper Warblers. Warmer, browner and lacking obviously darker centres to wing-coverts and tertials, so appears less boldly marked than *certhiola*. Rump and uppertail-coverts cinnamon-brown, often unmarked or, as on this bird, showing a poorly defined, blurred darker spot near tip (Peter Kennerley).

▲ Adult *L. c. centralasiae*, central Mongolia, June. Always significantly paler and greyer than *certhiola* and generally slightly paler than *sparsimstriata* with weakly streaked upperparts. Note the relatively small and diffuse blackish centres and broad, dull tan fringes to the mantle and warm cinnamon-brown rump and uppertail-coverts, the latter either unmarked or with a diffuse brown spot towards the feather tips as in *sparsimstriata* (Paul Leader).

▲ Adult *L. c. minor*, Hong Kong, September. Smallest and most richly coloured race, differing from *certhiola* by warmer, richer fringes to upperpart feathering and increased contrast with blackish feather centres (Peter Kennerley).

▲ Juvenile *L. c. minor*, Hong Kong, September. Richly toned fringes and black centres to crown and mantle are typical of adult and juvenile *minor*. Unworn flight feathers and ochre-buff wash to supercilium, side of head and breast establish this as a juvenile (Paul Leader).

▲ Juvenile, Shetland, Scotland, October. Juveniles reaching Europe show dull brown and black mantle streaking and prominent black spots on the rump and uppertail-coverts. Although not proven, these birds are closest in appearance to *rubescens* (Ashley Banwell).

▲ Juvenile, Shetland, Scotland, October. Note band of dark spots on lower throat, fine flank streaks and conspicuous white notches on inner web of the two inner pairs of tertials. Some juveniles have the yellow wash restricted to the chin and throat (Mark Breaks).

▲ Adult, probably *L. c. minor*, Hebei, China, May. Bold black centres to mantle and crown, and large black spots on uppertail-coverts are typical of adult *minor*, but feather fringes are less richly toned than typical *minor* would show and possibly an intergrade with nominate *certhiola* (Peter Kennerley).

▲ Juvenile, probably *L. c. rubescens*, Hong Kong, China, September. Drabber and browner than adult. Generally darker than juveniles of other races, and upperparts often less well-marked with smaller dark feather centres, occasionally obscured. Underparts dull sulphur-yellow to sulphurous buff, with band of brown spots or arrowheads across lower throat and upper breast. Note darker undertail-coverts with contrasting paler tips (Peter Kennerley).

MIDDENDORFF'S GRASSHOPPER WARBLER
Locustella ochotensis   Plate 13

Sylvia (*Locustella*) *Ochotensis* **Middendorff, 1853**. *Reise Sibiriens* 2(2): 185–186, plate 16, figures 7–8. Udskoe Ostrog, lower Uda River, Udskaya Gulf, Okhotsk Sea.

A long-distance migrant, breeding on coasts and islands fringing the Sea of Okhotsk in northeast Asia. Winters primarily in the Philippines and N Borneo, with few records elsewhere. It forms a superspecies with Pallas's Grasshopper and Styan's Grasshopper Warblers. Polytypic, with two races recognised, but morphological variation is complex (see **Geographic Variation**) and an apparently stable hybrid population is maintained where it meets Pallas's Grasshopper along the lower Amur River in the Lower Primorskiy region of the Russian Far East and N Sakhalin.

L. o. ochotensis (Middendorff, 1853). NE Russia (S Kuril Islands, S Sakhalin) and Japan (N Hokkaido).

L. o. subcerthiola Swinhoe, 1874. NE Russia (Northern regions of the Sea of Okhotsk including Kamchatka and the N Kuril Islands).

IDENTIFICATION Length 14–15cm. Wing 66–77mm. Tail/wing 71–84%.

A medium-sized *Locustella* that resembles Pallas's Grasshopper Warbler and shares the characteristic whitish tips to the tail feathers, but shows indistinct and diffuse mantle streaking. Also overlaps with the similar Styan's Grasshopper Warbler on migration through coastal China, although the two have different wintering areas. For a useful introduction to identification and separation from these related taxa see Kennerley & Leader (1993). Sexes alike.

Structure Smaller birds overlap in size with Pallas's Grasshopper Warbler, while larger birds are comparable with Styan's Grasshopper. It shows the rounded body and long, deep-based undertail-coverts characteristic of the genus and resembles Pallas's Grasshopper closely in structure. The wing is long and pointed, with a short first primary (p1), the wing point formed by p3, and with p3 and sometimes p4 emarginated. The tail is broad-based and strongly graduated, but shorter than in Styan's Grasshopper.

Plumage and bare parts The adult resembles a pale and poorly marked Pallas's Grasshopper Warbler. The crown is fairly uniform greyish brown. The mantle is slightly browner, often shows a hint of darker feather centres and can appear faintly mottled, especially in worn birds in late summer and again in late winter (see **Moult**). The unmarked rump and uppertail-coverts lack the darker feather centres typical of Pallas's Grasshopper Warbler and are warm tawny-brown, slightly brighter than the mantle. The centres to the tertials and the greater and median coverts are dark brown (not blackish as in most fresh Pallas's Grasshopper), with narrow warm brown fringes matching the mantle, although the inner webs of the tertials adjacent to the feather shafts appear slightly paler than the outer webs. Warm brown flight feather edges match the mantle, but the second primary, like that of Pallas's Grasshopper, has a conspicuous whitish outer web. The fresh primaries show narrow whitish tips.

The head appears rather plain. A whitish supercilium extends from the bill base to the rear of the ear-coverts, but this is rather narrow and diffuse and usually less conspicuous than in Pallas's Grasshopper. This combination of subdued supercilium, together with a poorly defined loral spot

and lack of eye-stripe and eye-ring creates a bland facial expression. The underparts are whitish and unmarked, with a faint warm brown wash across the upper breast, darkening towards the lower flanks. The undertail-coverts are creamy buff but lack well-defined paler tips, unlike those of some Pallas's Grasshopper Warblers. Adults rarely retain any hint of juvenile spotting on the lower throat.

The upper tail is warm tawny-brown, similar in tone to the uppertail-coverts. Seen from behind in flight, the rump, uppertail-coverts and tail appear warmer and brighter than the mantle, but lack the contrasting appearance of most Pallas's Grasshoppers. When fresh, all the tail feathers show narrow and indistinctly darker cross-bars and white or greyish white tips. These tips are most conspicuous on the outer feathers but are narrow and indistinct on the central pair, from which they are readily lost by abrasion. The underside of the tail is duller and greyer, so the pale feather tips are often more contrasting and easily seen when a perched bird faces the observer.

Juveniles resemble adults but sometimes show slightly darker striations down the mantle. The supercilium is generally less prominent, typically appearing as a narrow yellowish line from the bill base to the eye, flaring behind the eye then diffusing abruptly into the crown and ear-coverts. The underparts are washed with yellow and a gorget of small oily brown spots typically separates the brighter, paler throat from the duller breast. These spots often merge to form a distinct border and extend as diffuse mottling or streaking onto the upper breast and flanks. The yellow wash fades to white or creamy white on the belly, while browner tones predominate along the flanks towards the undertail-coverts. The stronger yellow tends to fade as juveniles wear and bleach during the winter months.

The bill is dark grey with a greyish pink base to the lower mandible and with darker shading along sides towards the tip. The legs and feet are dull reddish brown to plumbeous-pink.

SIMILAR SPECIES Only Styan's Grasshopper and Pallas's Grasshopper Warblers are likely to be mistaken for Middendorff's Grasshopper Warbler.

Styan's Grasshopper Warbler has an insular breeding range mostly to the south of Middendorff's Grasshopper, centred on islands off the coasts of southern Japan and South Korea. It averages slightly larger and has a proportionately longer tail and noticeably longer bill. Both species have fairly uniform upperparts and whitish tips to the tail feathers, but the upperparts of Styan's Grasshopper are colder and greyer and almost invariably lack the diffuse mottling usually visible on Middendorff's Grasshoppers. It typically shows a still narrower and less distinct supercilium than Middendorff's Grasshopper, but has a better marked eye-ring. In flight, the rump and tail appear uniform grey-brown rather than warm tawny-brown as in Middendorff's Grasshopper.

Pallas's Grasshopper Warbler is quite variable in appearance with five races recognised plus a range of variable intergrades, but all show moderately to strongly patterned upperparts. If seen well Pallas's Grasshopper always shows well-marked blackish centres to the crown, mantle feathers, wing-coverts and tertials, with the rump and uppertail-coverts appearing rich rufous-brown or rusty brown. In most Pallas's Grasshopper the longest uppertail-coverts show conspicuous dark centres. However, the westernmost race *sparsimstriata* often lacks these darker centres and the mantle streaking of adults and first-winter birds can be subdued, particularly in the wintering areas. The separation of Pallas's Grasshopper and Middendorff's Grasshopper Warblers is discussed under Pallas's Grasshopper Warbler. The appearance of an apparently stable hybrid population of Middendorff's Grasshopper x Pallas's Grasshopper Warbler along the lower reaches of the Amur River and in northern Sakhalin is more problematic (see **Geographic Variation**).

VOICE The song contains fairly harsh *Acrocephalus*-like churs, rasps and chacks and is quite distinct from the 'reeling' songs of European *Locustella* species. It closely resembles that of Pallas's Grasshopper Warbler in structure and shares similar phrasing and timing, but spans a slightly wider frequency range of 2.5–8kHz. It comes across as being clearer, louder and more strident, with individual sequences more distinct and definable. The first few notes, usually slurred upwards, are followed by a musical flourish, more drawn-out than in Pallas's Grasshopper. The full song lasts approximately three seconds, commencing with two or three clear '*chit*' notes followed by a hurried but clear repeated warble that can be divided into several well-defined elements. The entire song sequence can be transcribed as '*chrit-chrit-chut-witwit-cherwee-cherwee-cherwee*', sometimes followed by a quiet but almost grinding '*wutwutwut*' and a rather slurred '*wer-wer-wer-wer*'.

This song appears consistent throughout the range, those recorded on Hokkaido, Japan, not differing noticeably from those breeding near the northern limit on Talan Island in the Sea of Okhotsk, Russia.

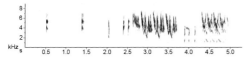

Song of Middendorff's Grasshopper Warbler, recorded within breeding range of *L. o. ochotensis*, Hokkaido, Japan, June. (Ueda 1998)

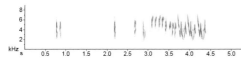

Song of Middendorff's Grasshopper Warbler, recorded within breeding range of *L. o. subcerthiola*, Talan Island, northern Sea of Okhotsk, near Magadan, Russia, July. (T. Mano)

The call is a quiet '*kit*' or '*chrit*', similar to the '*pwit*' call of Pallas's Grasshopper Warbler, but slightly harder. It closely resembles the '*chrit*' notes that precede the main song sequence. This call can be heard throughout the year and is often the only indication of presence away from the breeding areas.

MOULT Little known, with only limited data from live birds or specimens and no published studies. Dement'ev & Gladkov (1954) considered adults to have a complete moult on the breeding grounds, finishing by mid August. Williamson (1968) also speculated that a full post-breeding moult might occur in early autumn, citing a heavily worn but unmoulted male from Sakhalin on 23 July and a second Sakhalin bird, replacing the four outer long primaries on 15 August. Some birds certainly do moult the outer primaries before migration, but it is likely that adults adopt a similar strategy to Pallas's Grasshopper Warbler, replacing the head and body feathers before autumn migration.

Some also moult the outer primaries and rectrices. Four individuals examined in the hand at Candaba Marsh, Luzon, Philippines, in early February (PRK) had all primaries and tail feathers moderately to extremely worn, suggesting that none had been replaced in autumn.

There is a complete moult in late winter and early spring, starting in March and finished shortly before northward migration in May. Four birds examined in February in the Philippines showed no sign of moult, but seven out of nine examined in mid March were in active moult, while the other two had not yet started (PDR *in litt.*). Two of three birds caught there in late April were still in active moult and one had completed moult. Two birds from Davao, Philippines, in the NHM, Tring, collected in April on an unspecified date, had also finished moult and were in fresh plumage. Twenty specimens from coastal China, held at the NHM, Tring, and collected between 25 May and 4 June, are in fresh plumage.

Examination of specimens held in the NHM, Tring, reveals no evidence of an autumn post-juvenile body moult. Young birds from coastal China collected on migration show fresh or slightly worn primaries and tail feathers and yellow-tinged underparts. Full juvenile plumage appears to be retained until a complete moult in late winter, like that of adults.

HABITAT Usually closely associated with water and damp regions and typically inhabits similar habitats to those used by Pallas's Grasshopper Warbler. When breeding, it frequents patches of tall rank grasses in clearings with scattered bushes, small trees (especially birch *Betula* and willow *Salix*) and scrub. Usually found close to a lake edge, marsh, damp hollow or slow-moving stream, but sometimes occurs in drier habitats including the slopes of shallow valleys. In coastal regions, it can be common in dwarf bamboo (sassa) on exposed, windswept headlands and offshore islands. On Sakhalin and Kamchatka, it prefers brushy willows *Salix, Eupatorium, Solidago* and other tall, rank and broad-leaved deciduous shrubby vegetation. On Sakhalin, it often occurs together with Black-browed Reed Warbler and Japanese Bush Warbler (Scott Atkinson *in litt.*).

In the wintering areas it remains closely associated with freshwater marshes, but bushes are not a requirement at this season. It is likely to be found in any moist habitat within its range, including damp scrub, wet grassland, water-filled ditches, the edges of rice fields and reed swamps. On migration, it is less restricted to damp locations and uses habitats similar to those favoured by Pallas's Grasshopper; often in reedbeds and along riverbanks, but not typically found in mangrove forest.

BEHAVIOUR Not known to differ from Pallas's Grasshopper Warbler. Males begin singing when they arrive on the breeding territories in late May. Song continues with decreasing frequency throughout June and the first half of July, but has been heard on Kamchatka up to late August (Dement'ev & Gladkov 1954). The song can be heard through the hours of darkness as well as during the day, but is most frequent in the evening until well after sunset and from 1–2 hours before sunrise until mid morning. At northern latitudes, where nights are short, it often continues from dusk to dawn without an obvious pause. Males frequently perform a short song-flight. Song is occasionally heard on the wintering grounds from at least February onwards.

BREEDING HABITS Arrives late on the breeding grounds, usually from the first week in June onwards. Dement'ev & Gladkov (1954) commented that nest building cannot commence until vegetation is sufficiently tall and early arrivals may not be able to commence breeding. A nest is constructed from woven leaves and grass stems in thick grass or on the ground. The cup is lined with fine stalks and small feathers. A clutch of 5–6 eggs is laid from early June onwards in Hokkaido, but up to three weeks or more later in the northern part of its range. Incubation lasts 12–15 days and the first juveniles may be away from the nest by the end of the first week in July, while others may fledge as late as 10 August. Believed to be single-brooded.

DISTRIBUTION Prior to 1990, the criteria for separating Middendorff's Grasshopper and Styan's Grasshopper Warblers were poorly understood and reports rarely distinguished between the two taxa, which were generally treated as races of a single species. Most pre-1990 reports therefore lack sufficient detail to establish the separate distributions of the two, although Middendorff's Grasshopper was undoubtedly the taxon concerned in most cases, being by far the more numerous and with a greater geographical range. To add to confusion, the extent of morphological variation within Middendorff's Grasshopper was not appreciated and the overlap of plumage characters with those of Pallas's Grasshopper Warbler and the appearance of intergrades was poorly understood and largely ignored.

Breeding

L. o. ochotensis The nominate race breeds from about 43°N on N and E Hokkaido, S Sakhalin and the S Kuril Islands. Kalyakin *et al.* (1993), considered that

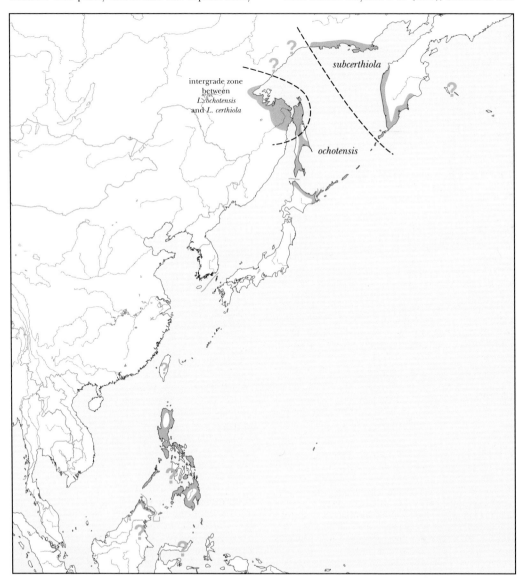

Middendorff's Grasshopper Warbler. Breeding range and winter distribution.

birds from N Sakhalin and the lower Amur region represented intergrades with Pallas's Grasshopper Warbler (see **Geographic Variation**). The suggested intergradation zone extends from the River Uda and along the lower Amur River to the region of Amursk and across N Sakhalin. Middendorff's Grasshopper also breeds on many of the small offshore islands fringing the Primorskiy and Khabarovsk coastline of the Russian Far East including the Shantar Islands, Moneron and Korovii (Dement'ev & Gladkov 1954), but it is unclear whether these represent intergrades with *L. certhiola*. In coastal S Sakhalin, it is locally abundant and Kalyakin *et al.* (1993) give densities of 12–15 singing males/km² in the south, 5–6 males/km² in central areas and 3–5 males/km² in the north. Locally very common in N and E Hokkaido.

L. c. subcerthiola The exact distribution is uncertain as the validity of *subcerthiola* has not been widely recognised. Originally described from a specimen collected on Kamchatka and believed to occupy the northern part of the species breeding range centred on the northern and eastern coasts of the Sea of Okhotsk. Dement'ev & Gladkov (1954) included the coastline of the Russian Far East north to approximately 60°N near Magadan within the range of the species, and birds that resemble *subcerthiola* breed on Talan Island, near Magadan (PRK pers. obs.). Probably numerous on many islands and headlands in the Sea of Okhotsk and reported to be locally abundant along both coasts of S Kamchatka, north to *c.* 56°N.

Non-breeding The non-breeding range is equally restricted and the distribution of the two races presumably overlaps. Small numbers probably winter regularly in S Taiwan but the main wintering area extends from the N Philippines south to N Borneo. In the Philippines, reported from the islands of Basilan, Bohol, Calayan, Catanduanes, Fuga, Luzon, Marinduque, Mindanao, Mindoro, Negros, Palawan, Romblon, Samar and Siargao (Dickinson *et al.* 1991). Locally numerous in damp habitats in Luzon where its skulking behaviour obscures its true abundance (PRK pers. obs.). In Borneo, it is common in the coastal wetlands of Sabah, Malaysia, but becomes progressively less numerous to the south in Brunei and through Sarawak. It has not been recorded with certainty from Kalimantan, Indonesia, but is likely to have been overlooked. There are few reports elsewhere during the winter months, although a bird on Iriomote-jima, Japan, on 13 February 1982 was probably wintering (Brazil 1991).

MOVEMENTS Departure from the breeding grounds begins in the second half of August. Ozawa (1964) noted a migrant on a ship in the Sea of Japan on 22 August, along with 20–30 Lanceolated Warblers. Most leave Kamchatka in late August and Scott Atkinson (*in litt.*) noted its absence around Petropavlovsk after mid August. Migration takes place on Sakhalin from early September and most birds have departed by the end of that month (Dement'ev & Gladkov 1954). A bird at Ozerskii, SE Sakhalin, on 8 October (Scott Atkinson, *in litt.*) was late, but Dement'ev & Gladkov (1954) noted birds in the southern Kuril Islands throughout October and into early November. Brazil (1991) recorded departure from Hokkaido in August and September, with occasional migrants up to early November. Migration through Japan appears to follow the coastline of the Sea of Japan rather than the Pacific coastline. There are a few September and October records from the Chinese coastal

provinces (La Touche 1925–30; Cheng 1987) and many birds must travel along a direct route to the wintering areas, via Taiwan. Records from Okinawa on 19 and 22 September would indicate passage through the Nansei-shoto. There is an early record from Luzon on 8 August (Dickinson *et al.* 1991) but the main arrival in the Philippines occurs in late September and October.

Return passage begins late, with birds remaining in the Philippines until early May, occasionally to the end of May (Dickinson *et al.* 1991). Within the Philippines, migrants avoid the mountains and largely avoid Dalton Pass, Luzon, where only small numbers were trapped during the MAPS project (McClure & Leelavit 1972), and ringing has yet to reveal the precise routing of passage through eastern Asia. After leaving the Philippines, they appear to follow a north to northeast heading, although small numbers cross the South China Sea. La Touche (1925–30) and Cheng (1987) included Guangdong within the range of passage birds, but it is rare there. There are no spring records from Hong Kong and very few from mainland China south of the Yangtze River. On the island of Shaweishan, east of Shanghai (along a bearing almost due north of Luzon and Taiwan), La Touche considered it to be a common migrant in late May and early June and specimens from there show features associated with the race *subcerthiola*. It apparently avoids the mainland coastline of northeast China and the Gulf of Bohai. Migrants occur regularly on passage throughout Taiwan and in Japan south of Hokkaido, where its apparent scarcity is doubtless due to its unobtrusive behaviour. The late departure suggests a rapid northward migration with a limited number of stopover points.

Migrants occasionally overshoot the breeding range and have appeared on islands in the Bering Sea. Close to Kamchatka, it has been recorded from the Komandorskiy Islands as a rare straggler in June and July. One was collected on Nunivak Island, close to the Alaskan mainland on 15 September 1927 (Swarth 1934), and at least six arrived on Attu Island between 18 and 25 September 1979. It has subsequently occurred on Attu and Buldir in the western Aleutians, at Gambell, St Lawrence Island and at Saint Paul, Pribilof Islands, with records spanning 10 June to 11 July and 30 August to 25 September.

Vagrancy Outside the recognised range it is a vagrant to Hong Kong with just two records: a single bird resembling the nominate form on 26–27 February 1993 (Leader 1994), and a juvenile, probably *subcerthiola*, trapped on 29 October 2009. In the Wallacean region of Indonesia, there are three records from Sulawesi and one from Luang in the Lesser Sundas (White & Bruce 1986). Elsewhere, a juvenile photographed on Ashmore Reef, off the northern coast of Western Australia, in October 2005 was the first record for Australia (Clarke 2006). This was followed by a second bird there on 27–28 October 2007. As Ashmore Reef lies approximately 170km to the south of the Indonesian island of Roti, it is possible that Middendorff's Grasshopper Warbler occurs more frequently in the Lesser Sundas than records suggest.

DESCRIPTION Middendorff's Grasshopper Warbler shows a surprising degree of morphological variation for a species that is often treated as monotypic. Within this variation, the tawny-rumped nominate form and the duller and less contrasting but slightly better marked race *L. o. subcerthiola* predominate. However, other plumages occur between and beyond these two races, some of which are probably a consequence of hybridisation with

Pallas's Grasshopper. Others may be due to clines within races occurring in poorly known parts of its range in the northern Sea of Okhotsk.

L. o. ochotensis

Plumage – Adult fresh (April to July) Forehead and crown dull greyish brown with small, slightly darker, feather centres creating faint diffuse streaking. Supercilium pale grey-buff, extending from the bill base to the rear of the ear-coverts and contrasting well with sides of head; usually most prominent in front of the eye and less distinct towards the nape. An olive-brown spot in front of the eye, often extends to the bill base to form a thin loral line. Behind the eye, a narrow, poorly defined olive-brown eye-line extends to the rear of the supercilium. Ear-coverts and cheeks dull olive-brown with pale shafts forming fine streaking or flecking. Eye-ring narrow, dull creamy white, merging above eye with supercilium, contrasting slightly with darker cheeks, but never prominent. Nape, mantle and scapulars warm olive-brown to dull tawny-brown, slightly warmer than crown, with dull feather centres appearing as indistinct lines of mottling or diffuse streaking. Rump and uppertail-coverts dull tawny-brown, similar to, or slightly warmer than mantle, but uniform and unmarked. Central tail feathers tawny-brown on both webs from base to tip with only a narrow area adjacent to the shaft appearing darker. Remainder of tail-feathers dark greyish brown, outer webs with broad tawny-brown edges. All tail feathers with indistinct narrow cross-barring and conspicuous, broad whitish tips, these being rather narrower on central pair. Chin and throat whitish and unmarked. Breast white, washed pale olive-buff to light olive-brown, sometimes with greyish tinge, forming a diffuse breast-band that often extends to sides of neck below ear-coverts, where it darkens slightly, shows faint mottling and merges with sides of nape. Upper flanks pale olive-brown, becoming pale buff towards lower flanks and across ventral region. Belly whitish and unmarked. Undertail-coverts pale creamy buff to warm olive-buff, usually with broad white tips that merge into darker bases. Lesser, median and primary coverts dark brown with narrow warm brown fringes. Greater coverts and tertials with large olive-brown centres and wide, contrastingly warm brown fringes, similar in colour to mantle. Tips of tertials pale sandy brown or whitish, especially on inner web. Primaries and secondaries dull greyish brown with warm brown edges. Primaries with conspicuous, narrow whitish tips, second primary (p2) with whitish outer web. Alula dark brown, finely edged silvery grey. Underwing-coverts drab greyish white, paler than flanks.

Adult worn (December to March) Fringes of mantle feathers and scapulars are dull olive-brown when worn, often lacking the warmer tones of fresh plumage and contrasting less with crown. Striations on upperparts remain light, diffuse and indistinct (cf. *L. certhiola*). Breast, flanks and undertail-coverts often paler, more sandy buff. Fringes of wing-coverts and tertials narrower, barely contrasting with olive-brown centres. Edges to primaries and secondaries duller, but whitish edge to second primary (p2) remains. Shorter outer tail feathers retain tawny-brown fringes and usually the whitish tips.

Juvenile When fresh, top of head to mantle and scapulars is dull olive-brown with dark brown or greyish brown feather centres, these contrasting with fringes to produce diffuse striations, usually better marked than in fresh adult. Supercilium and lores primrose-buff to dull ochre-

yellow. A dark olive-brown loral spot immediately in front of the eye does not usually extend to the bill base. Ear-coverts and cheeks dull olive-brown with conspicuous fine ochre-buff shaft streaks. Eye-ring dull ochre, narrow and inconspicuous. Rump and uppertail-coverts plain warm olive-brown to tawny-brown, slightly brighter than mantle. Chin and throat creamy white to pale primrose-buff. Upper breast darker, with olive-yellow wash. Lower edge of throat usually with diffuse sandy brown spots, sometimes small and indistinct, forming faint gorget, but often larger, darker and more conspicuous, forming light striations which extend onto flanks. Flanks dull olive-yellow, the yellow tones more prominent towards carpal bend. Belly and vent white, sometimes with faint creamy or yellowish wash. Undertail-coverts warm olive-buff. Closed wing pattern as in adult, but fringes to wing-coverts and tertials pale olive-brown, slightly paler than mantle. Edges to primaries and secondaries warm brown, often duller than in adult, with outer web of second primary (p2) whitish, but pale primary tips olive-brown, less contrasting than in adult. Tail feathers with broad warm brown fringes that extend across both webs basally, leaving dark brown centres conspicuous only towards tips; all feathers with buffy white to light sandy buff tips, broadest on outer tail feathers, narrow on central pair.

Bare parts Upper mandible dark grey with narrow flesh-pink cutting edge. Lower mandible greyish pink with darker shading along sides towards tip. Mouth yellow to pale pink; tongue spots absent or very faint in presumed adults trapped in Philippines in February, but obvious on two breeding birds trapped on Talan Island in June. Tarsi and toes dull reddish brown to greyish pink; claws similarly coloured. Iris light brown to dark, rich chocolate brown, the difference perhaps age-related.

IN HAND CHARACTERS
Measurements

Races combined:

	Male	Female
Wing	66–77 (71.6; 39)	67–71 (69.0; 11)
Tail	51–58 (54.3; 20)	49–56 (52.6; 9)
Bill	16–18.5 (17.2; 19)	16.5–17.5 (17.1; 11)
Tarsus	23–25.5 (23.8; 21)	22–24.5 (23.3; 8)

Sexes combined:
Tail/wing ratio: 71–84% (78%; 36)
Bill width: 3.6–4.2 (3.9; 15)
Hind claw: 6.0–8.8 (7.7; 15)
Tail graduation: 15–23 (16.1; 15)
Also, breeding season data from Kalyakin *et al.* 1993 (sexes combined):
L. o. ochotensis, S Kuril Islands: *wing* 67–74 (70.3; 95); *tail* 52–59 (55.9; 16); *tarsus* 21.1–25.0 (23.1; 15).
Intergrades with L. certhiola, Lower Primorskiy & N Sakhalin: *wing* 67–73 (69.7; 23): *tail* 52–59 (54.7; 23); *tarsus* 21.2–24.3 (22.8; 25).

Live measurements:
L. o. subcerthiola, two birds, probably from same breeding pair, Talan Island, Magadan, Russia, July (PRK): *wing*, ♂ 74, ♀ 72; *tail*, ♂ 60, ♀ 56; *bill*, ♂ 18.3, ♀ 18.2; *tarsus*, ♂ 21.5, ♀ 22.6. Both at upper end of known range of wing, tail and bill measurements.

Structure

Wing formula:

p1/pc	p2	p3e	p4(e)	p5	p6e	p7	p10
(2)–3	2–5	wp	2–3	5–7	8–10	11–14	15–19

Wing pointed with minute p1. Wing point p3; p2 = p4–4/5; emargination on p3 sometimes slightly on p4. Notch on p2 8.5–10mm from tip, falling at p6–8. Longest tertial reaches only to tips of secondaries (to p10 tip in Pallas's Grasshopper Warbler).

Figure 34. Wing of Middendorff's Grasshopper Warbler.

Tail strongly graduated; feathers broad but tapering to a point at tip.

Bill strong, but less deep and shorter than in Styan's Grasshopper Warbler; concave-sided with very narrow tip.

Tarsi strong; toes long, claws fine.

Recognition Distinguished from larger Styan's Grasshopper Warbler by warmer tawny-brown (rather than greyish) upperparts, usually with faint mottling on mantle and by whitish outer web to p2. Also separable by shorter bill (< 18.5mm) and usually by shorter tail (55mm or above in Styan's Grasshopper). Wing lengths overlap, but Middendorff's Grasshopper tends to have longer p2 (equalling p3–5; usually = p5–6 in Styan's Grasshopper), with notch falling at p6–8 (usually above p9 in Styan's Grasshopper).

Lacks the strongly patterned upperparts or rich rusty brown rump of Pallas's Grasshopper Warbler. Measurements overlap those of large Pallas's Grasshopper Warblers, but birds with wing > 74mm, tail > 55mm, bill > 16.5mm and tarsus > 23.5mm should be identifiable as Middendorff's Grasshopper.

Ageing As with Pallas's Grasshopper, wing and tail feathers of adults are usually more heavily worn in autumn than those of juveniles. Some adults replace outer primaries and tail feathers in late summer and contrast between older and newer feathers should then be sufficient to establish age. Autumn juveniles show a variable yellow wash below, most conspicuous across the upper breast. They usually have a necklace of diffuse spots or arrowheads across the lower throat and upper breast and sometimes faint striations on the flanks. Adults lack the yellow wash and usually lack throat spots. Birds cannot be aged reliably after the winter moult.

Weight *L. o. ochotensis*: Hokkaido, 15.2–20.9g (17.6; 25) (TM unpublished data). 16–24g (18.5; 19) (Deng & Zhang 1990).

GEOGRAPHIC VARIATION Shows marked variation in plumage and biometrics for a species often treated as monotypic. Within this, the tawny-rumped nominate form and the duller but slightly more distinctly marked race *subcerthiola* predominate. Northern populations are particularly variable and some individuals cannot be assigned to either race. Kalyakin *et al.* (1993) commented upon the variation on northern Sakhalin and the adjacent mainland coast, which he considered was a result of hybridisation with Pallas's Grasshopper Warbler (see below). A few birds show characters that cannot be reconciled by reference to either Middendorff's Grasshopper or Pallas's Grasshopper Warblers.

From examination of specimens at the NHM, Tring, and comparison with two of Swinhoe's *subcerthiola* syntypes (see **Taxonomy and Systematics** below), it is clear that many of the spring migrants collected in coastal China show characters associated with *subcerthiola*. The winter range of this race remains unknown. There are certainly no conclusive reports away from coastal China and the breeding areas.

L. o. ochotensis (S Kuril Islands, S Sakhalin Russia and N Hokkaido, Japan) Described above.

L. o. subcerthiola (Northern regions of Sea of Okhotsk, including Kamchatka and the N Kuril Islands) A poorly known taxon described from Kamchatka, but also found on offshore islands and headlands fringing the northern Sea of Okhotsk. Resembles the nominate form, but adults differ in the slightly duller greyish brown upperparts which, in spring at least, show an indistinct olive or yellowish tone, together with marginally more conspicuous darker mantle feather centres, creating the effect of indistinct, diffuse mottling and, in some cases, ill-defined streaks on the crown. The rump and uppertail-coverts are completely unmarked and tend to be dull olive-brown rather than the tawny-brown of typical *ochotensis*. Consequently, adult *subcerthiola* shows little or no contrast between the mantle, rump, uppertail-coverts and upper surface of the tail. Juveniles resemble adults but the olive tone to the upperparts is more pronounced and these is a necklace of diffuse streaks across the lower throat.

Birds breeding on Talan Island, close to the Russian mainland at the northwest limit of the breeding range, have been studied in detail. Compared with typical *subcerthiola*, these birds are slightly greyer and colder above, with diffuse, dark crown streaks and more conspicuous but still diffuse mottling on mantle and scapulars. The rump and uppertail-coverts are unmarked dull ash-brown, slightly browner than the mantle and contrasting with the darker, greyer tail, The supercilium is paler, more conspicuous than in typical *ochotensis* and *subcerthiola*, the ear-coverts dark greyish brown with fine whitish streaks. The underparts are particularly pale, greyish white with a dull greyish olive wash on the flanks, and lack warmer or browner tones. The undertail-coverts are sandy brown with broad whitish tips, particularly prominent on the longest central pair. On the closed wing, the median and outer greater coverts and the two inner tertials have pale sandy buff edges, and the tips to the inner web of the two inner tertials show a broad white notch, similar to that of some adult Pallas's Grasshopper Warblers (but usually absent in *ochotensis*). The longest tertial is fringed warmer buffy brown and lacks the pale notch. Dark greyish primaries and secondaries are edged dull tawny-brown, p2 with a greyish white outer web. The primary coverts and alula are dark greyish brown with narrow greyish white fringes and appear as a small dark patch on the closed wing. The tail feathers all show white tips, broadest on the outer feathers. The upper mandible is entirely black, the lower mandible black apart from an inconspicuous paler basal spot on the underside (cf. *ochotensis*). The legs, feet and claws are dull plumbeous-flesh, distinctly darker than in *ochotensis*.

These northern breeding *subcerthiola* are distinctly larger than the more southerly birds of the nominate form, with wing lengths matching the largest Styan's Grasshopper Warblers. Two birds from Talan Island were exceptionally large, with wing lengths 72mm (female) and 74mm (male), placing them at the upper end of the *L. ochotensis* range and equalled within Pallas's Grasshopper only in the western race *sparsimstriata* from WC Siberia. Bill lengths of 18.2mm and 18.3mm also exceed the largest *certhiola* and nominate *ochotensis*. The song of the Talan Island birds was not discernibly different from that of typical *ochotensis* and they responded strongly to recordings of *ochotensis* from Hokkaido.

The problem of hybrids The breeding ranges of Middendorff's Grasshopper and Pallas's Grasshopper Warblers are largely allopatric, but apparently come together on the coastal plain of the lower Primorskiy region, in particular along the lower Amur River. Here, and in northern Sakhalin, up to 70% of breeding birds are reported to represent a hybrid population between *ochotensis* and *certhiola* (Kalyakin *et al.* 1993), varying from almost 'pure *ochotensis*' to almost 'pure *certhiola*'. Birds with characters of *certhiola* (*certhiola>ochotensis*) predominate towards the north and west of this region, those with characters of *ochotensis* (*ochotensis>certhiola*) towards the south and east. On Sakhalin, birds breeding in the north of the island are mainly *ochotensis>certhiola* intergrades, with *ochotensis=certhiola* scarce and *certhiola>ochotensis* rare. Progressing towards the south of the island, birds gradually take on the characters of *ochotensis>certhiola*, then 'pure *ochotensis*', appearing indistinguishable from those breeding in Hokkaido and the southern Kuril Islands. These intergrades apparently form a self-sustaining population that no longer requires the presence of pure *ochotensis* or *certhiola* to maintain their mixed characters. Apparent intergrades have been encountered on the wintering grounds and on migration.

Across the range of Pallas's Grasshopper Warbler, there is a west–east cline of increasing richness, warmth and contrast in plumage tones, with *L. c. minor* being the most richly coloured and contrasting of the five races. Consequently, if Middendorff's Grasshopper is a race of Pallas's Grasshopper, this cline of increasing contrast and strengthening colour would be expected to continue into the Kuril Islands and Kamchatka. This is not the case, however, as *ochotensis* exhibits paler upperparts with subdued dark feather centres, quite unlike the rich and contrasting appearance of *minor*, the race of Pallas's Grasshopper reaching the Pacific coastline along the lower Amur River and near Sakhalin. A more likely scenario is that Pallas's Grasshopper and Middendorff's Grasshopper shared a common ancestor but became separated, with Middendorff's Grasshopper evolving in isolation on the islands of northeast Asia, while Pallas's Grasshopper did likewise on the continental mainland. Variation has probably arisen due to secondary contact in the relatively recent past.

The large greyish brown *Locustella* breeding on Talan Island in Tauyskaya Bay in the northern Sea of Okhotsk was regarded by Kalyakin *et al.* (1993) as an *ochotensis/certhiola* intergrade. We consider this unlikely as these birds lack features associated with Pallas's Grasshopper and believe they represent the extreme end of a cline of increasing size within Middendorff's Grasshopper of race *subcerthiola*, or an undescribed taxon.

TAXONOMY AND SYSTEMATICS Middendorff's Grasshopper Warbler is closely related to both Styan's Grasshopper and Pallas's Grasshopper Warblers. These taxa were each originally described as distinct species, but this position was eroded, particularly by Meise (1938) who examined apparent intergrades between Middendorff's Grasshopper and Pallas's Grasshopper Warblers from Sulawesi. By the 1950s the three taxa were usually treated as races of a single species, Pallas's Grasshopper Warbler, e.g. by Vaurie (1959) and Williamson (1968). However, Dement'ev & Gladkov (1954) and others treated Middendorff's Grasshopper and Pallas's Grasshopper Warblers as distinct species, although they retained Styan's Grasshopper as a race of Middendorff's Grasshopper and this arrangement became widely adopted up to the 1980s. Recent morphological comparisons, together with studies of migration timing and routes, and of vocalisations, have established that Middendorff's Grasshopper and Styan's Grasshopper are readily diagnosable and better treated as distinct species (e.g. Kennerley & Leader 1993), an approach followed by Eguchi *et al.* (2000), Dickinson (2003) and Stepanyan (2003).

Birds from Kamchatka and the northern Kuril Islands are the slightly longer-winged form *L. o. subcerthiola*. This northern form was originally described by Swinhoe (1874) as the Kamtschatkan Grasshopper-Lark *Locustella subcerthiola* and although accepted as a valid race of *ochotensis* by Kalyakin *et al.* (1993), it is not recognised by most other modern authorities (e.g. Eguchi *et al.* 2000; Dickinson 2003; Stepanyan 2003) who treat even the distinctive birds breeding in the northern Sea of Okhotsk as representatives of an exceptionally well-marked cline.

Historical context Middendorff's Grasshopper Warbler has a long and confused history. When selecting a specimen from the type series to represent *L. ochotensis*, Middendorff inadvertently chose a poorly marked juvenile *L. certhiola*, or possibly an intergrade between *ochotensis* and *certhiola* (*certhiola>ochotensis*). Although it came from the type series which included many typical *ochotensis*, it did not resemble birds from southern Sakhalin, the southern Kuril Islands or Hokkaido, which are generally accepted as resembling 'nominate *ochotensis*'. After studying the three remaining syntypes in the Zoological Institute of the Russian Academy of Sciences in St Petersburg, Loskot (2002) concluded that Middendorff had correctly identified the characters associated with *ochotensis*, but had selected a juvenile *L. certhiola*, in which the characters associated with *certhiola* were well pronounced, as the type. In order to rectify this discrepancy Loskot selected an alternative syntype (100397 from Middendorff's series) as the lectotype of *L. ochotensis*.

The name *subcerthiola* has been used to describe those larger and paler individuals within *L. ochotensis*. This form was originally described as *L. subcerthiola* by Swinhoe in 1874 based on a specimen collected by I. G. Voznesenskiy in about 1843, with the type locality being Hakodadi, (Hakodate), Japan. Dickinson *et al.* (2001) established that there were, in fact, three syntypes, one of which formed a part of a collection that was lost at sea when the shop carrying it, the 'Ariel', sank off Hakodadi. This led to the misunderstanding that Hakodadi was the type locality. Their investigations also revealed that the remaining two syntypes were sent by von Schrenck to Swinhoe, who named them the 'Kamtschatkan Grasshopper-lark', testifying to their origin. Dickinson *et al.* (2001) discovered these specimens in the NHM, Tring. One, (BMNH 1898.9.1.1323), came from the Seebohm collection, while the other (BMNH 1886.7.8.1750) appears to have been sent by Swinhoe to Hume and formed a part of his collection which was also deposited in the NHM, Tring. In fact, all three syntypes of *subcerthiola* originated from Kamchatka and Dickinson *et al.* (2001) revised the type locality to Kamchatka.

▲ ▶ Adult *L. o. ochotensis*, Hokkaido, Japan, June. Lacks bold and contrasting appearance of Pallas's Grasshopper Warbler. Shares similar whitish notches to inner webs of the two inner pairs of tertials. Note contrast between brownish upperparts and greyer nape and crown, typical of most adults. Often sings from a prominent perch above low luxuriant vegetation (Pete Morris).

▲ ▶ Adult *L. o. ochotensis*, Hokkaido, Japan, July. A slightly paler bird with a less prominent supercilium. Shows faint darker centres to mantle and wing-coverts giving characteristic diffusely mottled appearance to mantle, usually better marked than Styan's Grasshopper Warbler (Akiko Hidaka).

▲ Adult *L. o. ochotensis*, Taiwan. May. Seen from the front, the prominent pale supercilium, diffuse mantle mottling, tawny-brown uppertail-coverts and tail, and white tips to all but the central pair of rectrices show particularly well (Pei-Wen Chang).

▲ Adult, *L. o. ochotensis*, Tainan County, Taiwan, May. Resembles a Pallas's Grasshopper Warbler with subdued plumage contrast, even when fresh in spring. Note white outer web to long outer primary (p2) (Lin Ben Chu).

▲ Adult *L. o. subcerthiola*, Talan Island, Magadan, Russia, July. Differs from nominate by duller upperparts with marginally more conspicuous mantle mottling (Peter Kennerley).

▲ Adult, Tainan County, Taiwan, June. An extremely well-marked bird showing mixed characters with Pallas's Grasshopper Warbler, which is unknown from Taiwan. Possibly a hybrid (Lin Ben Chu).

▲ ▶ Juvenile *L. o. subcerthiola*, Hong Kong, October. The olive wash to the upperparts and lack of contrast between rump/uppertail-coverts and mantle is quite different to the browner appearance of the nominate race. Note the creamy brown wash to the throat and breast, and indistinct lines across lower throat that are much less conspicuous than in Pallas's Grasshopper (left Paul Leader, right James Kennerley).

STYAN'S GRASSHOPPER WARBLER
Locustella pleskei
Plate 13

Locustella pleskei **Taczanowski, 1889**. *Proc. Zool. Soc. London,* page 620. Tchimulpa, Korea.

A highly range-restricted migrant, breeding on small, offshore islands fringing the Pacific coast of Japan, the Sea of Japan and the Yellow Sea. Known in winter only from the Deep Bay region of Hong Kong and the Red River delta region of northern Vietnam. Forms a super-species with Middendorff's Grasshopper and Pallas's Grasshopper Warblers. Considered VULNERABLE by BirdLife International due to its small and declining population. Monotypic.

IDENTIFICATION Length 15–16cm. Wing 65–75mm. Tail/wing 81–94%.

A fairly large greyish brown warbler that resembles Middendorff's Grasshopper Warbler but is duller and drabber and with entirely unmarked upperparts. The long, broad and heavily graduated tail also shows whitish tail feather tips as in Middendorff's Grasshopper and Pallas's Grasshopper Warblers. In low flight, the tail appears longer and broader than in other *Locustella* warblers, giving the impression of a heavy and substantial bird. The uniform appearance of the upperparts is distinct from the smaller, more warmly toned and contrasting Middendorff's Grasshopper and Pallas's Grasshopper Warblers. The song resembles that of those species and is quite unlike the tuneless reeling of European-breeding *Locustella* warblers. Sexes alike.

Structure A large *Locustella* that averages larger than most Middendorff's Grasshopper and Pallas's Grasshopper Warblers, although there is limited overlap in wing length with both species, and the tail is proportionately longer. It also has a distinctly larger bill that is readily apparent when seen well in the field (Fig. 35). The primary projection is rather short, a third to a half the exposed tertial length, while the wing point is formed by p3, which is also the only emarginated primary. Like other *Locustella* warblers, Styan's Grasshopper has long, deep-based undertail-coverts extending almost to the tail tip.

Plumage and bare parts The fresh spring adult has grey-brown upperparts that appear rather colder and greyer than in Middendorff's Grasshopper Warbler and the mantle invariably lacks the slightly darker, diffuse and ill-defined feather centres typically visible in that species. The rump and uppertail-coverts are also grey-brown, usually showing no contrast with either mantle or upper tail. They are marginally paler on a minority of birds but are never the rich rusty brown of Pallas's Grasshopper, or tawny-brown as in Middendorff's Grasshopper. There is a well-marked pale buff supercilium, slightly less prominent than in Middendorff's, that is most obvious in front of the eye,

extending to the bill base, but more variable and sometimes inconspicuous behind the eye. The lores can be dark to the bill or appear as a restricted dark spot in front of the eye, but there is only a hint of a dark line behind the eye, and the plain grey-brown ear-coverts are concolorous with the crown so the sides of the head shows little contrast. It shows a conspicuous pale eye-ring, unlike Middendorff's Grasshopper. The chin, throat and belly are whitish, with a pale grey-brown wash across the breast and a stronger suffusion on the flanks. The undertail-coverts are typically unmarked, pale creamy buff, but are sometimes more strongly coloured, some approaching rich buff and with dark shaft streaks on the outer feathers, and tipped dull creamy white.

The closed wing shows indistinct contrast with the upperparts and the grey-brown edges to the primaries and secondaries closely match the mantle. Fresh spring birds may show paler primary tips, but these are inconspicuous and are soon lost on the breeding grounds. The outermost long primary (p2) lacks the obvious pale outer web seen in Middendorff's Grasshopper. The tertials and greater coverts show limited contrast, with grey-brown fringes and marginally darker centres, while the fringes on the median and lesser coverts and alula appear rather paler, more silvery brown or silvery grey. There is sometimes a poorly defined greyish white fringe at the tip of the inner web of the two inner tertials but this is never as obvious as the whitish indentations found on some Pallas's Grasshopper Warblers. The grey-brown upper tail shows narrow, slightly darker and poorly defined cross bars, and creamy white or pale buff feather tips, but in contrast to Pallas's Grasshopper and Middendorff's Grasshopper, these are restricted to the four outer pairs and they tend to be lost as the tail wears.

Juvenile plumage resembles that of the adult, but the chin, throat, upper breast and supercilium are washed yellow and there is ill-defined spotting across the lower throat. In some birds this wash is quite pale, while in others it is a richer ochre-yellow. Apparently unmoulted juveniles trapped in Hong Kong in November and December differed from known adults in showing a creamy or pale yellowish olive wash to the throat and belly and faint grey-brown spotting across the lower throat, sometimes just reaching the upper breast, but these characters are not as conspicuous as shown by fresh juveniles on the breeding grounds.

The bill is dark grey or blackish with a paler greyish pink to yellowish pink base to the lower mandible, which is usually unmarked but sometimes shows darker shading along sides towards tip. The legs and feet are warm reddish brown to fleshy pink with a slight grey or brown cast.

SIMILAR SPECIES Resembles Middendorff's Grasshopper Warbler but the two species have allopatric breeding and wintering ranges. Confusion with the more contrastingly patterned Pallas's Grasshopper Warbler is most unlikely and their separation is discussed under that species. To

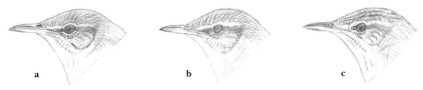

Figure 35. Comparison of head and bill shape of (a) Styan's Grasshopper Warbler (b) Middendorff's Grasshopper Warbler and (c) Pallas's Grasshopper Warbler.

the north of the breeding range of Styan's Grasshopper, the unstreaked Gray's Grasshopper Warbler is still larger with only limited overlap in bill and wing length, the largest Styan's Grasshopper only overlapping with the smallest Gray's Grasshopper Warbler. Size and the graduated tail structure separate it readily from Oriental Reed Warbler, the most abundant large warbler occurring within its range. Their separation is discussed below.

Middendorff's Grasshopper Warbler breeds to the north of Styan's Grasshopper and the two species do not overlap during the breeding season. Middendorff's Grasshopper is slightly smaller with a shorter tail and bill, and slightly more contrasting appearance. The upperparts appear fairly drab and nondescript, but there is usually slight, diffuse streaking on the mantle, distinct contrast between the darker centres and paler fringes to the wing-coverts and tertials. The tawny-brown rump, uppertail-coverts and tail contrast with the mantle, but appear uniform in Styan's Grasshopper. Separation is discussed in greater detail above and under Middendorff's Grasshopper Warbler.

Gray's Grasshopper Warbler is larger and darker than Styan's Grasshopper and their separation is relatively straightforward. Size alone is a useful indication, with Gray's Grasshopper approaching that of Oriental Reed Warbler. The entire upperparts are olive-brown, darker and warmer toned than Styan's Grasshopper, and the tail feathers lack pale tips. The greyish underparts are darker, with diffuse dusky spotting on the throat and upper breast and the undertail-coverts are warm orange-brown. The insular form *L. f. amnicola* has dull brown rather than grey underparts, but invariably darker than in Styan's Grasshopper. Juvenile Gray's Grasshopper Warbler is equally distinctive, the upperparts appearing slightly warmer than in the adult but darker and more richly toned than in the darkest Styan's Grasshopper. In juvenile Gray's Grasshopper the supercilium and eye-ring are distinctly ochre-yellow and the entire underparts washed dull yellow.

Oriental Reed Warbler is bold and noisy, frequently drawing attention with its loud, guttural churring calls and raucous song. It is a much larger and robust warbler with a heavier and deeper bill, a rounded rather than a graduated tail and much shorter undertail-coverts. Plumage differences are fairly evident, Oriental Reed appearing much warmer olive-brown than the greyer Styan's Grasshopper. Care is required as freshly moulted Oriental Reed Warbler can show pale tips to the rectrices. The global rarity and restricted range of Styan's Grasshopper Warbler were not widely appreciated until recently and it is unlikely that it will be encountered in winter away from the two known wintering areas.

VOICE The short song is similar to that of Middendorff's Grasshopper Warbler but is slightly deeper and differs in both the quality and speed of delivery, within a frequency range of 2–7kHz. It is rather slower paced, less hurried and pauses between song sequences are slightly longer. It lasts approximately four to five seconds (three to four seconds in Middendorff's Grasshopper) and consists of a series of thin reedy introductory notes (usually five or six compared with three or four in Middendorff's Grasshopper) leading into a louder terminal flourish, again more reedy, less rich and musical than in Middendorff's Grasshopper. Occasionally, as in Middendorff's Grasshopper, there is a final burst of three or four rather nasal notes that run into each other. The full song can be transcribed as '*chip-chit-chip-titit-chtrrrr-schwee-schwee-schwee*', sometimes followed by a tinkling '*tsweeetsweeetsweee*'.

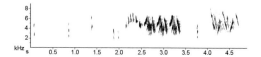

Song of Styan's Grasshopper Warbler, Miyake-jima, Izu Islands, Japan, June. (Ueda 1998)

The call is a short, clipped, '*chip*', '*chit*', or '*chir*', usually given when agitated. These resemble the introductory notes of the song and can be heard at any time of the year.

MOULT Information is limited and slightly confused. Data from Japan has established that adults replace the body plumage, including the wing-coverts and some or all of the primaries after the breeding season, commencing in July prior to autumn migration (YS *in litt.*). Unlike most *Locustella* species, it seems to replace inner primaries at this time, some birds starting at p10, others from the centre of the tract, usually at p6–7, moulting both inwards and outwards from that point. It is unclear, however, whether all adults replace all their primaries at that time. Contradictory data from adults arriving in Hong Kong in early winter suggests an alternative moult regime, in which only the outer primaries are replaced, the replacements then contrasting with the old and heavily abraded inner primaries and secondaries. By November, the body plumage shows slight to moderate wear following replacement in July. This latter moult strategy is comparable with that of Middendorff's Grasshopper Warbler (and see also River Warbler).

Other autumn birds in Hong Kong have fresh flight feathers and show no signs of suspended or arrested moult. These may be fully moulted adults or first-year birds (see below). During the winter months, the plumage does not abrade as severely as in Middendorff's Grasshopper and Pallas's Grasshopper Warblers, perhaps because the more open mangrove woodland and reedbed wintering habitat causes less wear than the wet grassland favoured by the other two species. The main moult, involving complete replacement of body, wing and tail feathers, usually commences in late February or early March and is complete by mid April, immediately prior to migration. Thus, birds newly arrived on the breeding grounds are in fresh plumage.

Circumstantial evidence suggests that, like other *Locustella*, juveniles do not moult prior to departure from the breeding grounds. Juveniles in Japan in June show a slight to moderate yellowish wash on the chin, throat, supercilium and upper breast, together with small but usually conspicuous spots on the throat and sometimes larger streaks on the breast. From November onwards, presumed juveniles trapped in Hong Kong show a faint yellow wash to the underparts and light spotting around the lower throat. Young birds are believed to have a complete moult at the same time as the adults, between February and April, after which they would be inseparable on plumage alone.

HABITAT Confined to small offshore islands with a mix of low evergreen trees, shrubs, tall grasses and coastal bamboo. There are no breeding records from mainland sites or from the main Japanese islands. N. Moores (*in litt.*) noted that one Japanese breeding site on a small islet near Fukuoka, Kyushu, was accessible on foot at low tide. In Russia, it breeds only on smaller islands, those 1km in length or less being preferred (Nazarov & Shibnev 1983). It favours rather open areas where forest cover has been replaced by dense scrubby secondary growth. On Miyake-jima, it breeds from sea level on low, windswept headlands with dense bamboo grass *Phyllostachys* and stunted *Camelia* trees up to at least 350m on the upper slopes of the active volcano. The highest numbers occur in dry grassland and small abandoned fields surrounded by thick evergreen cover and bamboo thickets, but it also inhabits open pine forest with a bamboo understorey. The breeding islands in Russia, with a cooler, temperate climate, are covered in grass and dwarf bamboo, a habitat closer to that favoured by Middendorff's Grasshopper Warbler. The habitat on Dagongdao, off the coast of the Shandong peninsula in eastern China, comprises stunted trees, scrub, grasses and low plants.

On migration and during the winter months Styan's Grasshopper uses a wide range of coastal wetland habitat, but it appears to avoid the open wet grasslands and marshes preferred by Middendorff's Grasshopper. In Hong Kong, most sight records are from mangrove forest in which *Kandelia candel* and *Aegiceras corniculatum* predominate (Leader 1998a), but it is undoubtedly easier to detect in this more open habitat. Most birds trapped for ringing In the Mai Po Marshes Nature Reserve have come from *Phragmites* reed and adjacent scrub, where there have been few other sightings.

BEHAVIOUR Poorly known, but similar to that of Midden-dorff's Grasshopper and Pallas's Grasshopper Warblers. A skulking species, but often conspicuous during the breeding season when it typically sings from prominent exposed perches. On Miyake-jima, territorial males often sing from an exposed perch such as a dead branch, within 3m of the ground and unconcerned by the presence of observers. As in Middendorff's Grasshopper Warbler, males often perform a short song-flight, keeping low and singing in flight over tall grassland and while dashing and twisting between bushes. On the breeding islands, the song lasts from late April to late June and occasionally up to mid July. Males can be heard throughout the day, even during wet and windy weather. Unlike Middendorff's Grasshopper and Pallas's Grasshopper Warblers, which favour denser vegetation and disappear into this deep cover when singing ceases, Styan's Grasshopper often remains in view after singing ceases and can be followed moving through fairly light cover. It sometimes appears on or close to the ground, when its distinctive *Locustella* structure, horizontal attitude and nervous wing flicking can be observed. It has been noted feeding on sandhoppers on sandy beaches and amongst rocks, a more open habitat than Middendorff's tends to use (N. Moores *in litt.*).

It appears to establish a territory during the winter months and remains within a relatively small area of suitable habitat. It is then always skulking and usually remains well hidden within undergrowth, but was once observed foraging in Hong Kong among the leaves of Water Hyacinth *Eichhornia crassipes*. In the wintering areas, males commence singing from late January onwards, invariably from within deep cover in mangrove woodland.

BREEDING HABITS Breeds during May and June on the Izu Islands. Lays a clutch of 3–6 eggs. Fledged juveniles have been noted by mid June in Wakayama Prefecture, S Japan (H. Kuroda *per* TM *in litt.*), and by the third week of June on Tate island, Minami-cho, Tokushima Prefecture, Shikoku (H. Nagata *per* YS *in litt.*). Singing males are regularly heard on Mikaye-jima in early July, suggesting that some birds there may be double brooded. No further information available.

DISTRIBUTION
Breeding The breeding range is highly localised within the warm, temperate zone of the Eastern Palearctic and is known from just four countries: Japan, South Korea, Russia and China. It is centred on the Sea of Japan and adjacent regions of the Yellow Sea and Pacific coast of southern Japan.

In Japan, it occurs on several islands in the Izu Archipelago, south of Tokyo, including To-shima, Nii-jima, Miyake-jima, Mikura-jima, Hachijo-jima and Aoga-shima. To the southwest, it breeds on unnamed islets off Honshu in Mie and Wakayama Prefectures and on Hashira-jima, Yamaguchi Prefecture. Around Kyushu, it probably breeds regularly on many small islands, including Okino-shima, Shikano-shima, Tsumura-jima and Tsukue-jima in Fukuoka Prefecture and Biro-jima in Miyazaki Prefecture. In South Korea, it breeds on many of the small islands and islets fringing the southern coastline of the peninsula. Reported sites include islets off the west coast near Inchon, Kyonggi Province; Hong Islet, South Kyongsang Province; Chilbal Island, South Cholla Province; and the islets of Taenap, Huksan, Taech'ilgi, Sosam, Taesam, Bakekarimen, Haenggum, Wando-gun, Taegukhul-to and the Chuja islands, in Cheju Province. It has also recently been found breeding on Ulleung Island in the Sea of Japan. In Russia, it is known only from islets in Peter the Great Bay in the Primorskiy region. It was found breeding on Klykov Island in July 1969 (Nazarov & Shibnev 1983) and has since occurred on several islands nearby, including Naumov, Kozlov, Sergeyeva, Tsivil'ka, Krotov, De-Livrona, Gil'debrandt, Durnovo, Moresa and the Pakhtusova Islands (BirdLife International 2001). In July 2006, the first breeding record for China came from the island of Dagongdao, near Qingdao, off the coast of Shandong Province (Qiao *et al.* 2006). Several adults and dependent young were discovered there and adults were also recorded on two neighbouring islands.

No overall population estimates are available, but the total population in Japan is very small (Brazil 1991). It was formerly common to abundant on Miyake-jima, with one report suggesting eight singing birds within 20m of the observer. However, this important site experienced major volcanic eruptions during August 2000 when the entire island was blanketed in fine ash. About 50% of the suitable breeding habitat was lost and it seems likely that the population was seriously affected. Russian data give estimates of 30 pairs on De-Livrona Island, 16 pairs on Durnovo and Pakhtusova Islands and 5–10 pairs on most other breeding islands (Nazarov & Shibnev 1983). There are hundreds of apparently suitable small islands within the breeding range, many of which have not been surveyed, so numbers are perhaps higher than current estimates suggest.

Non-breeding Only known in winter from two locations; the Mai Po Marshes Nature Reserve in Hong Kong (Leader 1998a; Carey *et al.* 2001), and the Red River delta in northern Vietnam. It probably winters in other suitable areas of marsh and mangrove along the coast of southern China. In Hong Kong, small numbers formerly occurred regularly in mangrove forest in the inner Deep Bay area where there were 35 records between 1984 and 1996, of which 28 were trapped. Since 2000, it has become increasingly rare, with no birds trapped since 2005 (P. J. Leader pers. comm.). In Vietnam, small numbers winter in Ha Nam Ninh Province at the Xuan Thuy Reserve, Red River delta. It was first recorded here in December 1993 when three birds were trapped for ringing. Subsequent

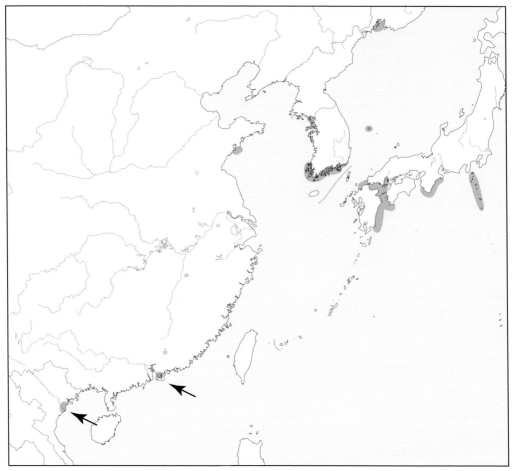

Styan's Grasshopper Warbler. Breeding range and winter distribution. Restricted to small offshore islands during the breeding season.

captures in March 1995 and December 1996 (K. Ozaki *in litt.*) and sight records in 1999 and 2003 (C. Robson *in litt.*) confirm its continued presence.

MOVEMENTS Departure from the breeding areas begins in September and all birds have left by October. A bird near Chipezan, Sakhalin, on 2 September (Dement'ev & Gladkov 1954) was presumably an early migrant, possibly from the Russia population. Southward passage through China is virtually unknown. The earliest autumn records from Hong Kong are 17 October and 27 October (Carey *et al.* 2001), but these probably relate to migrants, as the small wintering population appears to arrive from mid November onwards. There is often an upsurge in occurrences in April, suggesting birds pass through Hong Kong on their return migration, although these could be wintering birds dispersing prior to migration (Leader 1998a). The latest date recorded for Hong Kong is 12 May (Carey *et al.* 2001).

Spring records from China are very few. La Touche (1925–30) recorded it on migration at Swatow (Shantou, Guangdong Province) in May, but failed to find it at Shaweishan near Shanghai, or from elsewhere in NE China, suggesting that birds leave the Chinese coast to the south of Shanghai en-route to southern Japan. They presumably reach breeding grounds in South Korea and Russia via the Japanese coastline of the Sea of Japan. The first birds arrive in Japan in late April but most in early May (Nagata 1986; Brazil 1991), although Nagata noted that adult males continued to arrive until mid June and young males up to late June. There is one record from North Korea, in North Pyongan in May, but it probably occurs here more frequently, at least on migration.

There are no reports of vagrancy outside the established range.

DESCRIPTION The description below applies to typical birds, i.e. those breeding on islands off the coast of Japan and South Korea and wintering in SE China and N Vietnam. See **Geographic Variation** below for extent of variation.
Plumage – Adult fresh (April to July) Forehead and crown dull olivaceous grey, slightly darker feather tips creating indistinct mottling. Supercilium dull greyish brown, rather inconspicuous, showing limited contrast with sides of crown and sides of head; usually broadest in front of and over the eye, variable behind eye, tapering but usually extending to above rear of ear-coverts. A well defined dark greyish brown loral line extends from the bill base to the front edge of the eye. There is usually a slightly darker

spot immediately behind eye, but no distinct eye-line. Ear-coverts dull greyish brown, usually slightly darker towards rear edge, the whitish feather shafts giving a finely streaked appearance. Eye-ring narrow, dull greyish buff, the upper edge merging with supercilium, the lower edge usually slightly paler, contrasting with the darker grey-brown cheeks. Nape, mantle and scapulars uniform grey-brown, sometimes with a faint olivaceous wash. Mantle feathers usually unmarked, occasionally with slightly darker, diffuse centres, producing very faint striated effect. Rump and uppertail-coverts unmarked, dull olive-brown, slightly paler, less greyish, than mantle. Chin and throat whitish or pale greyish brown. Breast pale greyish brown, becoming darker greyish brown on sides of upper breast and sides of neck below ear-coverts. Lower throat and upper breast often with faint, diffuse greyish brown spotting. Flanks light creamy buff, darkening slightly towards the ventral region. Belly white or pale greyish white. Undertail-coverts typically creamy brown, but sometimes rich buff with paler tips and contrasting dark brown shaft streaks. Wing feathers dark grey-brown, lesser and median coverts and alula with narrow, crisp, silvery brown fringes. Greater and primary coverts and tertials with narrow, sharply defined olivaceous-brown fringes similar to mantle colour or slightly warmer. Flight feathers edged olive-brown, primaries with fine whitish tips, outer web of p2 dark. Tail feathers grey-brown with broad, diffuse olive-brown fringes and often with indistinct, narrow, darker cross-barring; shafts similar in colour to the webs. The outer four tail feather pairs with narrow creamy white or pale buff tips, the inner two pairs without pale tips or with narrow whitish fringes confined to the tips of the inner webs. Underwing-coverts drab greyish white, considerably paler than flanks.
Adult worn (July to December) Does not differ substantially from the fresh adult.
Juvenile Upperparts similar to adult when fresh, but slightly paler and browner (less greyish). Top of head and upperparts plain dark sandy brown, slightly paler on rump and uppertail-coverts. Supercilium pale yellow in June, wearing to pale sandy buff by November, contrasting little with sides of crown and sides of head. Loral line poorly defined, usually restricted to a small dark brown spot in front of the eye. Eye-line typically absent or forming an indistinct shadow below the supercilium. Ear-coverts dark sandy brown with indistinct whitish shafts. Eye-ring narrow, but quite conspicuous pale buffy white, merging above the eye with the supercilium. Chin and throat pale yellow to ochre yellow in June, wearing to creamy white or pale sandy buff by November. Upper breast pale to ochre yellow in June, wearing to pale sandy brown by November and becoming slightly darker and warmer on sides, and with a creamy or pale yellowish olive wash to throat and belly. There is a distinct row of small grey-brown spots across lower throat, sometimes just reaching upper breast, but this becomes less conspicuous or entirely absent by November. Upper flanks warm sandy brown, fading to pale sandy buff on lower flanks and ventral region. Undertail-coverts dull sandy brown to greyish brown. Upperwing as in fresh adult, but centres to wing-coverts, tertials and alula paler and warmer brown, fringes warm sandy brown, closely matching upperpart colour. Edges to secondaries and primaries warm brown with olivaceous tinge. Tail feathers with broad, diffuse, sandy brown fringes and slightly darker brown webs, tips of outer four pairs narrowly tipped whitish or pale buff.
Bare parts Upper mandible dark grey or blackish with narrow pinkish grey cutting edge. Lower mandible greyish pink to yellowish pink, usually unmarked but sometimes with darker shading along sides towards tip. Juvenile has upper mandible dark grey to blackish with bright yellow cutting edge and tip, lower mandible unmarked bright yellow. Mouth pale pink to pale yellowish pink; two tongue spots shown faintly by most birds during winter, regardless of age. Tarsi and toes warm reddish brown to fleshy pink with grey or brown cast; claws slightly paler pinkish. Iris dark brown to grey-brown, occasionally orange-brown in adult.

IN HAND CHARACTERS
Measurements

	Male	Female
Wing	72, 75 (n = 2)	68, 69 (n = 2)
Tail	62, 65 (n = 2)	56, 59 (n = 2)
Bill	19, 19.5 (n = 2)	18.5, 19.5 (n = 2)
Tarsus	24.5, 25 (n = 2)	23.5, 24 (n = 2)

Sexes combined:
Tail/wing ratio: 81–94% (87%; 20)
Bill width: 3.9–4.4 (4.1; 5)
Hind claw: 6.8–8.5 (7.7; 5)
Tail graduation: 18–22 (20; 4)
Juvenile ♀: *wing* 65; *tail* 54; *bill* 19.3; *tarsus* 22.4.
Live birds, Hong Kong (sexes and ages combined): *wing* 65–75 (68.6; 24); *tail* 54–68 (60.8; 20); *bill* 18.3–21.1 (19.7; 19) (HKRG unpublished data).

Structure

Wing formula (n = 4):

p1/pc	p2	p3e	p4	p5	p6	p7	p10
(2)–2.5	4–6	wp	1–2	3.5–5	6–7	9–12	14–17

Wing pointed with minute p1. Wing point p3; p2 = p(4/5) 5/6; emargination on p3. Notch on p2 8.5–10mm from tip, falling below p9.

Figure 36. Wing of Styan's Grasshopper Warbler.

Tail longish, strongly graduated; feathers rounded, broader than in Middendorff's Grasshopper Warbler.
Bill longish, strong, concave-sided with long narrow tip.
Tarsi strong; toes long, claws fine.
Recognition Distinguished from Middendorff's Grasshopper Warbler by colder, greyer brown upperparts without obvious dark feather centres, by shorter p2 which lacks conspicuous whitish outer web, and by restriction of whitish tail feather tips to outer four pairs. Averages larger than most Middendorff's Grasshopper and Pallas's Grasshopper

Warblers, but wing lengths overlap above 65mm. Bill length is diagnostic, always > 18.5mm in Styan's (< 18.5mm in Middendorff's, < 17.5mm in Pallas's).

Ageing More difficult in late autumn and winter than in Pallas's Grasshopper and Middendorff's Grasshopper Warblers. Presumed juveniles occasionally retain traces of a yellowish wash below and light spotting across the lower throat. Separation from adults becomes difficult from November onwards and young birds are moderately worn by mid winter. Tongue spots are unhelpful as known adults sometimes retain these. Tail fault-bars should be looked for as an indicator of juvenile feathers and the primaries checked for two generations of feathers, diagnostic of adults if present.

Weight Hong Kong: 17.2–23.2g (20.0g; 25). (HKRG unpublished data)

GEOGRAPHIC VARIATION Currently treated as a monotypic species. Birds breeding around the coasts of southern Japan and South Korea and wintering in Hong Kong and northern Vietnam share the suite of characters described above, with only limited individual variation. Differences noted elsewhere suggest that Styan's Grasshopper Warbler may comprise two or more taxa, but the validity of these has yet to be established.

For example, Berlijn (1995) reported the rump and uppertail-coverts of Russian birds breeding in Peter the Great Bay varied from tawny-brown to reddish brown and were not concolorous with the olive-grey mantle. None of the birds handled for ringing in Hong Kong between October and May have shown these warmer tones. Neither have breeding birds studied on Miyake-jima, Izu Islands, Japan, or observed near Fukuoka, Kyushu, Japan, and in South Korea (N. Moores *in litt.*). Whether these represent an undescribed taxon is not yet certain.

Kim & Isao (2004) published details of an unusual *Locustella* from Ulleung-do in the Sea of Japan off the eastern coast of South Korea, which they described as a new species. It was said to be 'much warmer in tone than the greyer *L. pleskei* nesting on Wan-do, South Korea and in the Izu Islands, Japan', the overall plumage 'bright brown, similar to *L. ochotensis*'. Although the techniques used to obtain the bill length and wing formula are not stated, details reported by Kim & Isao suggest that the Ulleung-do birds fell between Middendorff's Grasshopper and Styan's Grasshopper. However, DNA studies placed them closer to Styan's Grasshopper from Wan-do, than to Middendorff's Grasshopper from Kamchatka. Until more information becomes available, it is preferable to include the Ulleung-do *Locustella* within Styan's Grasshopper Warbler.

Since 1993, several distinctive Styan's-like *Locustella* warblers have been trapped in Hong Kong on dates from late September to mid October, the latest being 17 days earlier than the first arrival date of typical Styan's Grasshopper Warbler. These birds are similar in size and structure, and show largely unmarked upperparts typical of Styan's Grasshopper, but are distinctly darker and browner, which increases their resemblance to Middendorff's Grasshopper Warbler. Biometrics place them towards the upper end of the range of Styan's Grasshopper. Their identity and origin remain a mystery.

TAXONOMY AND SYSTEMATICS Since being described by Taczanowski in 1889 as *Locustella pleskei*, taxonomic uncertainty has surrounded Styan's Grasshopper Warbler. In the early years of the twentieth century, it was widely regarded as a distinct species (e.g. La Touche 1925–30). Meise (1938), in a review of the *certhiola/ochotensis/pleskei* complex, concluded that some specimens from Sulawesi were hybrids between Pallas's Grasshopper and Middendorff's Grasshopper Warblers and he used these to argue that they should be treated as races of the same species; Pallas's Grasshopper Warbler. He included *pleskei* as a race of *L. ochotensis* so that, by default, he subsumed it within Pallas's Grasshopper Warbler, despite the obvious differences. Vaurie (1959) supported this treatment, again including *pleskei* and *ochotensis* as subspecies of a wide-ranging *L. certhiola*. Subsequently, many authorities, including Williamson (1968), Cheng (1987) and Brazil (1991), have concluded that Pallas's Grasshopper Warbler and Middendorff's Grasshopper Warbler are better treated as distinct species, but with *pleskei* retained as a race of Middendorff's Grasshopper. Since the early 1990s, as a better understanding of the plumage, vocalisations, migration and behaviour of these forms has emerged, the argument has gone full circle. It is now widely accepted that Styan's Grasshopper merits recognition as a full species (e.g. Nazarov & Shibaev 1983; Kennerley & Leader 1993; Eguchi *et al.* 2000; BirdLife International 2001; Dickinson 2003; Stepanyan 2003).

In 2004, Drovetski *et al.* published findings of a molecular study of the phylogenetic relationships of various *Locustella* species. They found that the divergence in mtDNA between *ochotensis* and *pleskei* was barely greater than the variation within *ochotensis,* suggesting that the two forms have not yet reached the point where they can be treated as distinct species. Other unpublished DNA studies support these findings (PJL *in litt.*), which are at odds with the observed differences in morphology, migration and behaviour.

▲ ▶ Adult, Miyake-jima, Izu Islands, Japan, June. Resembles Middendorff's Grasshopper Warbler but has larger, heavier bill and more robust structure. Some, like this adult, show diffuse mantle mottling, although rarely as noticeable as in Middendorff's (Pete Morris).

▲ Adult, Izu Islands, Japan, June. Worn adult showing uniform grey-brown upperparts, but note pale wing-covert fringes contrasting with darker centres (Paul Leader).

▲ First-winter, Hong Kong, February. Young birds are often slightly darker brown than adults but differences are lost after the pre-breeding moult (Peter Kennerley).

▲ ▶ Probable juvenile, Hong Kong, January. An exceptionally dark individual showing unusually conspicuous mantle mottling and atypical dark centres to the undertail-coverts (Peter Kennerley).

GRAY'S GRASSHOPPER WARBLER
Locustella fasciolata   Plate 14

Acrocephalus fasciolatus **Gray, 1860**. *Proc. Zool. Soc. London*, page 349. Batchian, Moluccas.

A long-distance migrant that breeds in the cool, temperate forest zone of the Eastern Palearctic from C Siberia to N Japan and winters in the S Philippines, Wallacea and New Guinea. Polytypic, with two races recognised:
L. f. fasciolata (Gray, 1860). SC Siberia to SE Russia and NE China.
L. f. amnicola Stepanyan, 1972. Sakhalin, S Kuril Islands and N Japan.

IDENTIFICATION Length 16–17cm. Wing 74–86mm. Tail/wing 80–86%.
A large, drab and nondescript *Locustella* with rich brown upperparts and a rather long and strongly rounded tail. Although very elusive it has a loud and distinctive bulbul-like song. Sexes alike.
Structure The largest *Locustella*, somewhat larger than Styan's Grasshopper and River Warblers. Shows the strongly graduated tail, long deep-based undertail-coverts and flat attenuated head profile typical of the genus. The bill is straight and relatively strong and heavy (Fig. 37) and the dull plumbeous-pink legs appear stout and robust. The wings are quite long, showing a primary projection more than two-thirds the exposed tertial length and with the wing point formed by p3, which is often but not always emarginated. The tail is also quite long and although the undertail-coverts extend beyond the longest primary, they fall well short of the tail tip.

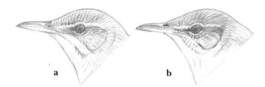

Figure 37. Comparison of head and bill shapes of (a) Gray's Grasshopper Warbler and (b) Styan's Grasshopper Warbler.

Plumage and bare parts Adults have rich warm brown to olive-brown upperparts and paler unmarked underparts. The upperparts are plain, but there is often slight contrast between the crown, mantle and wing-coverts and the marginally more rufescent rump, uppertail-coverts, and edges to the tail and flight feathers. The head is well-marked with a thin greyish white supercilium that extends from the bill to the rear of the ear-coverts. This varies individually but is usually most distinct over and just behind the eye, where it bulges slightly. There is little sign of a darker eye-stripe, but a small darker triangle usually shows immediately in front of the eye. The ear-coverts are rather greyer than the crown and may show fine greyish white streaks. The tail feathers lack the contrasting pale tips shown by Styan's Grasshopper, Middendorff's Grasshopper and Pallas's Grasshopper Warblers, but the outermost long primary (p2) usually shows a pale creamy brown outer web.
The underparts are dull and nondescript, with only the greyish white chin, throat and belly appearing conspicuously paler. The breast and upper flanks are dull greyish, although distinctly browner in birds from the east of the range. It

sometimes shows indistinct mottled striations on the sides of the upper breast. The pale brown lower flanks merge with the undertail-coverts, which vary from rich, warm buff to light rufous-brown. The dark grey bill shows a fleshy pink base.
In juveniles, the upperparts resemble those of adults, but may show faint diffuse striations running the length of the mantle. The supercilium is narrower and less conspicuous and washed buffy yellow and the ear-coverts are warm olive-brown with narrow yellowish buff streaks. The entire underparts are washed with yellow and lack the greyer tones of the adult. The chin and throat are clean, dull ochre-yellow, merging with the lightly mottled olive-brown to ochre-yellow breast. On some birds the breast is suffused with a broad band of olive-brown. The upper flanks are dull olive-brown, becoming pale buff to yellowish buff on the lower flanks and belly, and the unmarked undertail-coverts are warmer yellowish or peachy buff.
In adults, the bill is dark grey to blackish with a yellow or fleshy pink base to the lower mandible, which darkens at the sides towards the tip. The legs and feet vary from dull flesh to dull plumbeous-pink.

SIMILAR SPECIES The distinctly smaller, unstreaked Styan's Grasshopper Warbler may overlap with Gray's Grasshopper on migration in eastern China and any putative vagrant to Western Europe must be distinguished from the also slightly smaller, plain-backed River Warbler.
Styan's Grasshopper Warbler is similar in structure and proportions to Gray's Grasshopper but smaller, appearing as a mid sized, slim and attenuated warbler with finer bill and leg proportions, and less ponderous than Gray's Grasshopper. It has paler grey-brown upperparts and paler underparts, lacking the dark grey or brown tones to the breast, and it shows whitish tips to at least the three outermost pairs of rectrices. Their separation is discussed further under Styan's Grasshopper Warbler.
River Warbler does not overlap with Gray's Grasshopper Warbler, although vagrant Gray's Grasshopper Warblers have occurred twice in Western Europe and may do so again. River Warbler appears uniform olive-brown above, often with a slight greenish tinge and lacks any warmth on the lower underparts. Many River Warblers are tinged with yellow below and may resemble juvenile Gray's Grasshopper, but at all ages and all seasons River Warbler invariably shows dark striated mottling across lower throat and upper breast, forming a conspicuous band never found on Gray's Grasshopper. An additional diagnostic feature of River Warbler is the dark undertail-coverts with conspicuous buffy white tips. Separation of River Warbler from a vagrant Gray's Grasshopper should be straightforward using a combination of its smaller size, finer legs and slimmer bill. River Warbler also has a proportionately shorter tail so that the undertail-coverts appear longer, falling just short of the tip.

VOICE The song is loud, fluid, mellow and musical and reminiscent in quality and delivery of the song of a bulbul *Pycnonotus*. It differs markedly from the monotonous tuneless reeling buzz or tuneless scratchy warble of the smaller *Locustella* species. It can carry for up to 400m in calm conditions.
Each song sequence of nominate *fasciolata* lasts approximately three seconds and comprises up to three short, rather stuttering but distinct '*tryt*' notes, followed by a descending rich, fluty sequence formed by six repeated phrases, rising and falling in pitch from 1–5kHz. The

sequence is repeated after a pause of about two seconds and the song can be repeated continuously for 20 minutes or more without any noticeable pause. There is individual variation within the song, but each sequence follows a similar progression, transcribed as '*tryt-to-tryt-whut-trytortytortyt*', or '*chut-cheet-chut-cheet-chut-cheterrrrrrrrooot*'.

Song of Gray's Grasshopper Warbler, recorded within breeding range of *L. f. fasciolata*, Chita region, Siberia, Russia, July. (Veprintsev 2007)

The song of the race *amnicola* has the same loud and explosive quality as in the nominate form, but differs in having a slightly slower, more mellow and relaxed delivery. Each song sequence can last for up to four seconds, slightly longer than that of nominate *fasciolata* and includes up to four introductory '*chep*' or '*chuup*' notes, followed by three rather faster and slurred notes that form the bulbul-like '*chep-chuup-chep-chuup-chewp-chewp-chweeweep*' sequence. The difference in speed of delivery between the introductory and terminal phrases is not as well differentiated as in nominate *fasciolata*, so that they tend to run into each other.

Song of Gray's Grasshopper Warbler, recorded within breeding range of *L. f. amnicola*, Hokkaido, Japan, June. (Ueda 1998)

A variety of calls are given. These include a quiet guttural churring on the breeding grounds, possibly in alarm, while a distinct '*tek-tek*', a loud '*tek- tk- tk*' and a sharp '*chuck*' have been noted in the wintering area. It is not known whether calls of nominate *fasciolata* and *amnicola* differ.

MOULT Little studied and the information here is derived mainly from examination of specimens collected within the winter range. Adults have a partial post-breeding moult on the breeding grounds in July and August. This involves replacement of the head and body feathering and occasionally some or all of the rectrices. Some birds also replace up to four outer primaries (Cramp 1992), a strategy shared with some other *Locustella* species. However, heavily worn adults are encountered during winter with all the old flight feathers retained, so not all birds replace the outer primaries twice per year. The main moult occurs in the winter quarters and involves replacement of all feathers, including the flight feathers and rectrices. It begins between mid January and late February. Individuals take approximately 60 days to complete, so that all birds are in fresh plumage by late April, prior to spring migration.

The young of nominate *fasciolata* retain juvenile plumage throughout autumn and early winter, after which they have a complete moult, like adults, from late January onwards.

It is uncertain whether juvenile *amnicola* moults on the breeding grounds prior to autumn migration. There is no direct evidence for this but it would explain the lack of a yellow tone on the underparts of young *amnicola*, described by Stepanyan (1972, 1973) as a consistent difference between the two races.

HABITAT Typically breeds in damp localities including moist woodland around lakes, river valley bottoms, stream edges and ditches and on the fringes of woodland, especially among dense alder and willow thickets, or in clearings with regrowth of aspen and grasses. Favours lower levels with a luxuriant growth of vegetation such as nettles, tall grasses, tangled herbage and overgrown bushes. Occasionally found in more open situations such as orchards, but then seeks out the most overgrown corners. Avoids open areas, including reedbeds and woodland with little undergrowth.

In winter, it appears numerous in dense undergrowth along secondary forest edge, mixed grassland and the thick tangled growth recolonising cleared areas. Occasionally occurs in reedbeds but damp conditions do not appear to be essential. In Papua New Guinea, recorded from the edge of tall secondary forest and in secondary growth, thickets and rank grassland. Much of this region was formerly covered in rainforest, a habitat typically lacking a dense understorey. Forest clearance during the twentieth century led to an increase in luxuriant secondary regrowth and it seems likely that this abundance of suitable habitat has encouraged expansion of the wintering range.

BEHAVIOUR An extreme skulker, easily overlooked due to its retiring nature. Typically keeps close to the ground and rarely higher up than two metres. It avoids open habitats such as wet grassland and rarely gives a prolonged view in flight. Occasionally, it may dart across a short open space between bushes, giving a glimpse of rich, dark brown upperparts and a broad, graduated tail. More typical, however, are brief glimpses of a bird within the deepest shade of thick, low cover, rarely remaining stationary for more than a few seconds. Establishing identification under these conditions can be difficult. The fluty bulbul-like song provides the best means of location and identification on the breeding grounds, but it has a relatively short song period. Birds arrive only in early June and singing all but ceases by the end of June. It is thus easy to overlook and its true abundance can be difficult to establish. It is usually silent outside the breeding season.

Singing males tend to remain within the thickest cover and are most frequently heard at dawn and dusk, and often throughout the night. In locations where it occurs at high densities, it is not unusual to be within earshot of several singing Gray's Grasshopper Warblers, often together with singing Middendorff's Grasshopper and Lanceolated Warblers; a unique and memorable experience.

BREEDING HABITS Poorly known. Dement'ev & Gladkov (1954) stated that the nest is built on damp leaf- and twig-covered soil, not far from water. One of the two nests they describe was under a small bush, the other on the side of a hummock. The nest is a large construction of fallen leaves and dry grass stems, lined with finer grasses and stems. Four eggs are laid from mid June onwards. Believed to be single-brooded.

DISTRIBUTION Breeds in lowland areas in temperate mid latitudes of the E Palearctic, north to the southern edge of the taiga. Generally common and widespread but there are no population estimates available, either from the Russian range or from Hokkaido. Dement'ev & Gladkov (1954) considered it common almost everywhere within its range, and abundant in the Primorskiy region in the Russian Far East, but apparently rarer in the lower Amur River region and quite numerous on Sakhalin and northern Hokkaido.

Breeding

L. f. fasciolata The nominate race breeds in a narrow belt within the temperate forest region of the Eastern Palearctic, ranging between 54°N and 60°N. The western limit reaches the Ob River north of Novosibirsk, Russia. From here, breeding occurs east to the Sayan Mountains and the Lake Baikal region north to *c.* 60°N, and southeast through southern Transbaikalia to the lower Amur River basin. The northern limits in this region are poorly defined and it appears to be absent from large areas of suitable habitat. In NE China, it breeds in the Da Hinggang Mountains in NE Nei Mongol Autonomous Region and the Xiao Hinggang Mountains in Heilongjiang Province. Also reported to breed in North Korea but this requires confirmation.

L. f. amnicola The breeding range of *amnicola* is restricted to islands fringing the southern periphery of the Sea of Okhotsk. These include Hokkaido in N Japan, where it is locally common in lowland plains in the north and east (Brazil 1991; Eguchi *et al.* 2000), less numerous in southern lowlands and rare in the west. Within Russia, it breeds on Sakhalin and the S Kuril Islands north to Ostrov Urup (Dement'ev & Gladkov 1954).

Non-breeding The wintering range includes the S Philippines, Sulawesi, the Molucca islands and New Guinea. It appears to be genuinely rare in the Philippines, where Dickinson *et al.* (1991) mention only a handful of records. To the south, it is scarce in Sulawesi but on the small islands to the northeast it has been recorded from Talaud and Siau and is reported to be common on Sangihe. It also occurs on Tukangbesi to the southeast. In the Moluccas, it probably occurs on most islands with suitable habitat, and there are records from Sulu, Buru, Ambon, Haruku, Seram, Seram Laut (Maar), Watubela, Obi, Bacan, Halmahera, Mare, Moti, Kayoa, Ternate, Tidore and Morotai. Winters in Irian Jaya, ranging up to 1,800m in the west, but seems most numerous on smaller outlying islands, including Misol, Salawati, Waigeu, Gebe, Biak and Japen and in the Wissel Lakes region. Some birds reach Papua New Guinea, where it is regularly reported in December and January at Kiunga on the Fly River, but is rare further east, although it has been recorded from Waigani Swamp near Port Moresby. There is also a single record from New Ireland in the Bismarck Archipelago. Brazil (1991) mentioned an unusual record of a singing bird on Miyako-jima, Nansei Shoto, Japan, on 24 January 1986. This presumably refers to a bird that failed

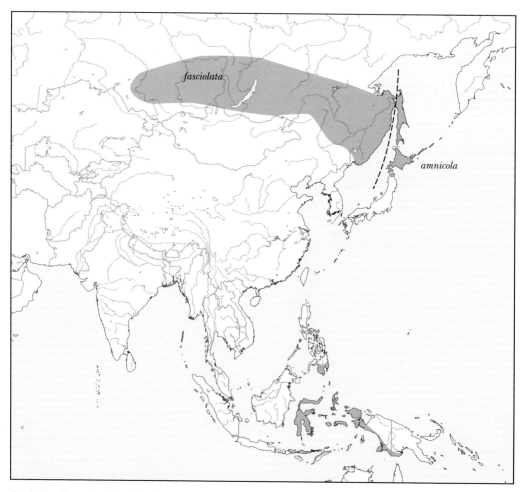

Gray's Grasshopper Warbler. Breeding range and winter distribution.

to migrate, but it is possible some winter undetected to the north of the usual range.

The wintering range of *amnicola* is presumed to lie in the Wallacean region and to overlap with that of the nominate form. A specimen in the NHM, Tring, showing the characters of *amnicola* was taken on Siau, in the Sangihe Islands between the Philippines and Sulawesi, in February 1866. In addition, there is a sight record from Lore Lindu in C Sulawesi in January (Watling 1983).

MOVEMENTS Its precise migration routes remain a mystery, but a lack of reports from SE China, mainland SE Asia, Java and Sumatra would indicate that this region is avoided in both autumn and spring. A direct route between the wintering areas and central and western parts of the breeding range would take birds across S China, and Guangdong Province in particular, yet there are no records from Hong Kong despite intensive observer coverage. Birds travelling to and from Wallacea presumably leave and enter continental Asia through SE Siberia or NE China.

The dates of post-breeding dispersal and departure are largely unrecorded. Dement'ev & Gladkov (1954) noted autumn migrants at Khalkhin, Mongolia, on 7 September and La Touche (1925–30) commented that Styan found birds on the island of Shaweishan near Shanghai in September 1910. It is considered to be a scarce migrant in the Philippines, but most of the population must pass through the archipelago in both autumn and spring. The earliest arrivals here take place in late August, with further occurrences in September, October and December, but its rarity suggests that most birds continue into Indonesia.

Gray's Grasshopper Warbler is one of the latest migrants to return to the breeding grounds. Departure from wintering areas begins in late April or early May, with passage through the Philippines occurring mainly during May, where lingering individuals have been recorded up to 29 May. Occasionally reported in spring from Taiwan but extremely rare in coastal E China, where its appearance may depend on displacement by adverse weather conditions. La Touche (1912) noted birds daily on Shaweishan from 5 to 15 June 1908, but failed to record any in 1907 and 1911. Cheng (1987) provides only a handful of migration records and intensive coverage since 1985 at Beidaihe in coastal Hebei Province has produced few reports. Spring migrants reach breeding grounds in NE China from the last week in May, with the main arrival occurring during the first week in June. In Russia, birds reach the Primorskiy region in SE Siberia from 25 May onwards, but arrive much later further west, from mid June near Krasnoyarsk with a 'conspicuous passage' as late as 23–25 June. (Dement'ev & Gladkov 1954). They reach the Ob River between 5 and 25 June. There are no records of the nominate form from Japan (YS *in litt.*).

The arrival dates of *amnicola* are better documented. Brazil (1991) considered it to be an uncommon migrant through Japan. He noted that in spring it passes through the Nansei Shoto, presumably arriving from Taiwan, and north through the islands of Kyushu, Shikoku and Honshu. Passage through Honshu lasts from late May to mid June, with early arrivals reaching Hokkaido in the last week in May, coinciding with the first appearance of lush nesting vegetation. Many remain in Hokkaido but others pass through to Sakhalin and the S Kuril Islands, where they arrive from early June. Specimens held at the Yamashina Institute in Japan show that migrant *amnicola* pass through S Japan, with five collected from Mizunoko island, Oita

Prefecture, one from Amami-ohshima, Kagoshima Prefecture and one from Okinawa.

Vagrancy Vagrants have twice reached W Europe; a juvenile was killed at the lighthouse at Ile d'Ouessant, Finistère, France, on 26 September 1913 (Ingram 1926) and another killed at the lighthouse at Lodbjerg, Denmark on 25 September 1955 (Dybbro 1976). A third record, of a bird claimed to have been found below the Ile d'Ouessant lighthouse on 17 September 1933 (Meinertzhagen 1948) is now believed to be a forgery (Kennerley & Prŷs-Jones 2006). Elsewhere, McKean (1984) documented two claims from Northern Territory, Australia, in 1979 and 1982, but both were subsequently considered inconclusive (Patterson 1991). A further claim in November 2001 also lacked adequate documentation and Gray's Grasshopper Warbler is not currently on the Australian list.

DESCRIPTION Although two races are recognised, Gray's Grasshopper Warbler shows greater variation than this suggests. The nominate form, breeding in eastern Siberia and northeast China, shows increasing colour saturation, with grey-breasted birds breeding in the western part of the range and birds with browner underparts breeding in the east, particularly in NE China. Most still retain some grey in the underparts tones but others may approach the underpart colour of the race *amnicola*, in which the grey tones are replaced with brown. There are no confirmed records of *amnicola* anywhere away from the breeding grounds and it is possible that the two races are inseparable after the post-breeding moult.

L. f. fasciolata

Plumage – Adult fresh (March to June) Forehead and crown dull olive-grey to olive-brown, slightly darker feather tips creating indistinct striations. Nape browner, sometimes warmer with a rufescent wash. Supercilium well-defined, ash-grey, narrowest over the lores, broadest just behind the eye and tapering over the ear-coverts to reach the sides of the nape; often flecked olive-brown above lores, but contrasting with the darker crown and eye-stripe. A broad olive-grey loral line extends from the eye to the bill base, usually appearing as small triangle of darker feathers. An olive-grey eye-line behind the eye gradually widens to merge with the nape sides, the lower edge diffusing into the ear-coverts. Upper ear-coverts dull olive-brown with fine flecking produced by whitish shaft streaks. Lower ear-coverts greyer with larger streaking, merging with the faintly mottled or barred malar region. Eye-ring narrow, dull greyish buff, contrasting little with the supercilium or cheeks. Mantle and scapulars unmarked, dull olive-brown to rich brown, sometimes with a warmer, rufescent wash. Rump and uppertail-coverts slightly warmer and brighter than mantle. Tail, including feather shafts, similar in colour to rump and uppertail-coverts, slightly warmer brown than mantle.

Chin and throat white. Sides of lower throat with pale ash-grey feather tips, forming faint barring. Breast dull ash-grey, feathers tips with narrow, slightly darker fringes; on paler individuals, these can appear as faint diffuse barring or striations, extending to the belly. Flanks variable; often dull greyish brown, fading posteriorly to dull fulvous-brown, but pale tawny-brown fading posteriorly to warm fulvous-brown on warmer-toned birds. Belly creamy white to greyish white, area small and restricted or larger and extending to sides of flanks and vent. Undertail-coverts unmarked, rich warm buff to paler creamy buff. Lesser and median coverts dull olive-brown. Primary and greater coverts and tertials with broad, diffuse olive-brown fringes and slightly darker centres. Primaries and secondaries dark grey-brown with olive-brown edges, slightly warmer and brighter than upperparts. Outer web of p2 greyish brown or greyish white. Alula dark brown with narrow olive-brown fringe. Underwing-coverts pale greyish olive-brown to drab yellowish brown, paler than flanks.

Adult worn (August to December) Upperparts duller brown or olive-brown with a warmer wash confined to rump and uppertail-coverts. Supercilium pale greyish white, showing enhanced contrast with sides of head and crown. Chin pale greyish white. Throat, breast and upper flanks dull ash-grey with diffuse barring confined to centre of upper breast. Undertail-coverts usually paler, creamy buff.

Juvenile When fresh in early autumn, forehead and crown are warm olive-brown to ochre-brown, with faint, darker brown tips forming diffuse narrow striations. Supercilium bright ochre to buffy yellow, rather less conspicuous than in adult. Loral line dark olive-brown and conspicuous; eye-line narrower and less apparent. Ear-coverts warm olive-brown, with narrow yellowish buff shaft-streaks towards upper edge, becoming brighter ochre-yellow below with diffuse dull brown spotting. Narrow eye-ring dull buffy yellow. Mantle and scapulars warm olive-brown with diffuse dull brown centres forming indistinct striations. Rump, uppertail-coverts and tail warm olive-brown, slightly brighter than mantle.

Chin and throat dull ochre; the latter narrowly tipped olive-brown, usually appearing finely barred, with barring at sides extending across malar region to merge with spotting on cheeks. Sides of neck dull ochre with faint olive-brown barring. Breast ochre-yellow with dull olive-brown fringes; some birds with barring across centre darkening and merging with solid smudge on sides, others with broader fringes and entire upper breast washed olive-brown with only slight mottling. Upper flanks dull olive-brown, fading to dull ochre or yellowish buff on lower flanks and belly. Undertail-coverts warm yellowish buff to peachy buff.

Closed wing as in adult but often slightly brighter, contrasting more with upperparts. Lesser and median coverts warm brown. Primary and greater coverts and tertials, dark brown with broad, warm brown fringes. Primaries and secondaries with warm brown edges, slightly brighter than tertial fringes; outer web of p2 pale greyish brown or greyish white.

Bare parts Upper mandible dark grey with narrow, dull fleshy pink cutting edge. Lower mandible yellow or fleshy pink at base, darkening towards black or dark grey-brown tip. In juveniles of the nominate race the entire lower mandible is yellow. Tarsi and toes dull flesh to dull plumbeous-pink. Iris dark brown or grey-brown.

IN HAND CHARACTERS
Measurements

L. f. fasciolata

	Male	Female
Wing	78–86 (82.1; 20)	74–82 (79.1; 16)
Tail	64–73 (68.3; 18)	64–72 (67.4; 11)
Bill	20–22 (20.9; 28)	19.5–22 (20.7; 22)
Tarsus	26.5–29 (27.8; 27)	26–28.5 (27.6; 21)

(Includes data from Cramp 1992)

Sexes combined:
Tail/wing ratio: 80–86% (83%; 13)
Bill width: 4.3–5.2 (4.7; 14)
Hind claw: 7.4–9.2 (8.5; 14)
Tail graduation: 19–27 (23.5; 13)

Wing and tail of juvenile average close to those of adult.

L. f. amnicola: wing (77–84) and tail (66–70) average shorter than in nominate *fasciolata* but there is extensive overlap.

Structure *L. f. fasciolata*

Wing formula (Cramp 1992):

p1/pc	p2	p3(e)	p4	p5	p6	p7	p10
(2)–7	0–3	wp	1–5	5–9	7–12	9–14	16–23

Wing rather long and broad; pointed with minute p1. Wing point p3; p2 = (p3) 3/4 (4); p3 often emarginated. Longest tertial reaches tip of ss. Notch on p2 (often faint) falls at p6–8.

Figure 38. Wing of Gray's Grasshopper Warbler.

Tail rather long, strongly graduated; feathers with pointed tips (Fig. 39).

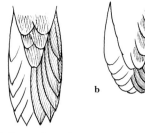

Figure 39. Comparison of tail shape of (a) Gray's Grasshopper Warbler and (b) River Warbler.

Bill deep and strong; broad-based but concave-sided with narrow tip; culmen decurved towards tip.

Tarsus thick and strong, but toes long and slender; middle and hind claws strong, inner and outer claw small and weak.

L. f. amnicola. Wing structure differs slightly: p2 = p3/4–4/5 whereas it is rarely if ever shorter than p4 in nominate *fasciolata*. Few individual *amnicola* could be identified from measurements and wing formula alone.

Recognition Plain-backed and larger than either Styan's Grasshopper or Middendorff's Grasshopper Warblers. Most have wing > 77mm and tarsus > 26mm, above the ranges for either of these species. Darker, more olive above than these two and greyer below, with contrasting warmly tinged undertail-coverts. Distinguished from River Warbler by longer tail (> 62mm) with pointed feather tips, and by much longer and stouter bill and longer tarsus. Also by plain throat (although yellow-tinged juveniles can show diffuse olive mottling) and plain undertail-coverts.

Ageing Adults lack any yellow on the underparts and an individual showing yellow tones must be a juvenile. However, a bird without yellow cannot be assumed to be an adult, even in early autumn, for *amnicola* also lacks yellow during first autumn. Ageing such birds requires careful assessment of feather wear, and replacement and growth patterns. The primaries and tail feathers of young birds are fresh and unworn and usually in good condition until at least November. They are all of the same age unless lost accidentally. In adults, these feathers show wear in autumn, often heavy. But some replace outer primaries and tail feathers prior to autumn migration. The presence of two generations of outer primaries and/or tail feathers in autumn or early winter following symmetrical replacement strongly indicates an adult bird.

There are no reliable ageing distinctions after the late winter moult. Y. Shigeta (*in litt.*) noted that some first-summer birds on the breeding grounds still retain two faint tongue spots.

Weight

L. f. fasciolata: ♂ 24–31g (27.6; 24), ♀ 26–28g (26.7; 4).
L. f. amnicola: ♂ 28–33g (30.1; 13), 2 ♀♀, 26g, 31g (Neufeldt & Netschajew 1977); Hokkaido, 23.9–29.6g (26.1; 18). (TM unpublished data).

GEOGRAPHIC VARIATION Coloration varies across the species' range and there are also small differences in wing formula. There is a cline of increasing warmth in the plumage from west to east. Birds breeding in C Siberia have a distinctly ash-grey wash across the breast but those in NE China and extreme SE Siberia, still recognised as the nominate form, often have a brownish tinge to the grey wash. In the insular race *amnicola* of Sakhalin and Hokkaido, grey breast tones are subdued and replaced with brown, and the upperparts are also browner and richer (less olive and greyish). In addition, *amnicola* tends to show a slightly shorter second primary.

L. f. fasciolata (SC Siberia to SE Russia and NE China) Described above.

L. f. amnicola (Sakhalin, S Kuril Islands and N Japan) In fairly fresh plumage in early June, the upperparts are warmer and browner than in nominate *fasciolata*, with reduced olive tones (though close to the colour of freshly moulted nominate race in the winter quarters). The supercilium is dull greyish brown, typically narrower and less contrasting than in nominate race, but still extending to the rear of the ear-coverts. The ear-coverts are slightly warmer and browner, with whitish shaft streaking restricted to the lower edge. The underparts differ more appreciably. The chin and throat are whitish or pale buffy white, with faint barring on the lower throat and sides of the throat, merging across the malar region with the streaked cheeks, while the sides of the neck are grey-buff. The breast lacks the greyish wash and faint striations typical of nominate *fasciolata* and appears dull olive-buff, sometimes faintly mottled, and darkening to buffy brown or greyish brown on the sides. The flanks and vent are washed warm fulvous-

brown. The undertail-coverts are warm peachy buff or cinnamon-buff, slightly brighter than in the nominate form and usually unmarked. The lower mandible is dull pink gradually darkening towards the tip.

In the first autumn, it is uncertain whether *amnicola* has a post-juvenile moult prior to migration. Unlike juvenile *fasciolata*, juvenile *amnicola* appears to lack a yellowish wash on the underparts, but this may be due to an earlier post-juvenile moult resulting in the yellow tones being lost before migration. The lower throat and upper breast vary between olive-brown and buffy brown, with indistinct contrast on the feather tips forming subdued mottling, which extends to the side of the breast and upper flanks. The lower breast and flanks are washed dull tawny-brown. The supercilium and sides of the head also lack the yellowish tones. In addition, first autumn *amnicola* shows warmer and browner fringes to the wing-coverts than in nominate *fasciolata*. Assignation of individuals to either race becomes problematic from late autumn onwards, as plumage wears.

TAXONOMY AND SYSTEMATICS Stepanyan (1972) described *Locustella amnicola* from two birds collected on Sakhalin in June 1972 and named it as a distinct species. He based separation from *fasciolata* on the darker, browner upperparts, lack of grey on the underparts (replaced with brown), shorter wing length and different wing structure, with p2 equalling or falling below p4. Neufeldt & Netschajew (1977) subsequently concluded that many of these proposed distinctions were minor and inconsistent and showed extensive overlap with *fasciolata*. Freshly moulted *amnicola* has not been discovered or described from the wintering grounds so distinctions, if any, from fresh nominate *fasciolata* have yet to be understood. Some of the birds breeding in NE China towards the eastern limit of nominate *fasciolata* show a tendency towards plumage characters associated with *amnicola*, including a warmer, browner breast. Establishing the racial identity of a putative *amnicola* away from the breeding grounds will be difficult. While recognition of *amnicola* as a distinct taxon is fully justified, many authorities, including Cramp (1992), Eguchi *et al.* (2000) and Dickinson (2003) prefer to retain it as a race of *L. fasciolata*. Stepanyan (2003), however, maintained its species status and this view received support from the molecular studies of Drovetski *et al.* (2004). They showed that Gray's Grasshopper Warbler belongs firmly within *Locustella*, forming a grouping with the other E Asian *Locustella*: Pallas's Grasshopper, Middendorff's Grasshopper, Styan's Grasshopper and Japanese Swamp Warbler. Within Gray's Grasshopper Warbler, they found a mtDNA sequence difference of almost 6% between *amnicola* and nominate *fasciolata*, suggesting these taxa had diverged sufficiently to form two distinct species.

Given their morphological and behavioural similarities, these two taxa are difficult to separate. And with presumed nominate *fasciolata* in NE China showing some characters associated with *amnicola*, it is not clear that breeding *amnicola* can always be identified with confidence. It may be premature to treat *amnicola* as a full species and, while acknowledging the molecular distinctions, we feel it prudent to await further studies before adopting this arrangement. We retain *amnicola* as a race of Gray's Grasshopper Warbler within a cline of increasing colour saturation, but recognise that this position may change.

▲ ▶ Adult *L. f. fasciolata*, Amurland, Siberia, June. The largest *Locustella*, extremely skulking and rarely seen away from dense cover. Nominate form shows grey wash to breast and drab brown upperparts, gradually become warmer towards wings and tail. Both races lack white tips to tail (Paul Leader).

▲ ▶ Adult *L. f. fasciolata*, Tainan County, Taiwan, May. Nominate race is recognised by grey supercilium, ear-coverts, throat and breast, olive-brown upperparts and bright yellowish base to lower mandible (Lin Wen-chong).

▲ Adult *L. f. fasciolata*, Tainan County, Taiwan, June. Overall appearance duller than *amnicola* with drab brown upperparts and ear-coverts, becoming brighter towards the uppertail-coverts, sullied grey-brown flanks and dull yellow base to lower mandible (Lin Ben Chu).

▲ Adult *L. f. amnicola*, Tainan County, Taiwan, May. Differs from nominate race by overall warmer and more richly toned upperparts, brown wash to breast and flanks, conspicuous whitish supercilium, pale ear-coverts that contrast with darker eye-stripe, and pink base to lower mandible (Lin Ben Chu).

▲ Adult *L. f. amnicola*, Hokkaido, Japan, June. Shows unusually rich brown upperparts, and warm buff supercilium and ear-coverts. Note wing structure with p2 shorter than p4; p2 is rarely shorter than p4 on nominate *fasciolata* (Akiko Hidaka).

▲ Adult *L. f. amnicola*, Hokkaido, Japan, June. Shows slightly warmer brown upperparts than nominate *fasciolata*, with olive tone reduced or absent. Unusually for *amnicola*, shows pale grey breast and ear-coverts, features usually associated with the nominate race, and a whitish supercilium. The dull greyish pink lower mandible is typical of *amnicola* (Pete Morris).

▲ Juvenile *L. f. fasciolata*, Angarsk, Siberia, July. Fresh juvenile shows dull ochre supercilium, throat and upper breast, narrowly tipped olive-brown, becoming ochre-yellow on lower breast, belly and rear flanks. Note unmarked yellow-orange lower mandible (Dasha Kuznetsova and Viktor Salovarov).

▲ Juvenile *L. f. fasciolata*, Yehliu, Taiwan, October. Note drab olive-ochre wash to underparts, ear-coverts and supercilium, placing it in the nominate form, and unworn primaries. Dull pink base to lower mandible tends to be associated with *amnicola* but it is uncertain how much this feature overlaps between races (Chang Pei-wen).

▲▶ Juvenile *L. f. amnicola*, Yehliu, Taiwan, October. Unlike juvenile of nominate race, upperparts (including edges to tertials) and flight feathers are warm brown and lack olive tone. Supercilium and underparts dull, drab olive-brown, lacking yellow tone, slightly paler than upperparts but becoming darker on rear flanks (Liao Pen-shing).

JAPANESE SWAMP WARBLER
Locustella pryeri   **Plate 15**

Megalurus pryeri Seebohm, 1884. *Ibis*, page 40. Tokio, not very far from Yokohama.

A poorly known *Locustella* of the E Palearctic, restricted to a few small colonies in C and N Japan and E and NE China. It is believed to be rare, declining and threatened and particularly susceptible to destruction of both its breeding and wintering habitats. Northern populations are short-distance migrants, while those breeding near Tokyo and Shanghai appear to be resident. Considered VULNERABLE by BirdLife International. Polytypic, with two races recognised:

L. p. pryeri (Seebohm, 1884). N and C Honshu, Japan.
L. p. sinensis (Witherby, 1912). NE China and the Yangtze Valley.

IDENTIFICATION Length 13–14cm. Wing 50–62mm. Tail/wing, *L. p. pryeri* c. 95%, *L. p. sinensis* c. 115%.

This small, heavily streaked and poorly known warbler was formerly included in *Megalurus*. It shares many characteristics associated with that genus but differs in its much smaller size, migratory behaviour and in being the only putative representative absent from the Southern Hemisphere. Many structural, plumage and behavioural characters resemble those of other *Locustella* species. Sexes similar, but male distinctly larger than female.

Structure Similar in size to Pallas's Grasshopper Warbler. It is unique among Old World warblers in retaining a vestigial wing claw, present in both adults and nestlings. It shows several other structural characters unlike those of typical *Locustella* warblers and which make it an uneasy fit within this genus.

These include a relatively long tail, approximately equal in length to the body and proportionately longer than shown by other *Locustella*, an appearance that is further enhanced by the relatively short wings. Furthermore, each rectrix is quite thin, giving the tail an essentially narrow appearance. The undertail-coverts are rather short, reaching only about one-third the way down the underside of the tail and falling level with the tips of the uppertail-coverts. Other distinctions from typical *Locustella* species include a relatively short, deep-based bill and a domed crown, and also the sexual dimorphism.

Wing structure also differs from that of the other *Locustella* species, which are all long-distance migrants. It shows a short primary projection, and has a relatively long, broad and rounded first primary (p1) while p2 is rather short. The wing is quite rounded, with the wing point formed by p4, and p4 and p5 are always emarginated.

The continental form *sinensis* undertakes longer migrations than the nominate form does within Japan, but there are no appreciable differences in wing structure between them. This race, however, has a significantly longer tail than nominate *pryeri*, giving it a different appearance in flight.

Plumage and bare parts A small, heavily streaked warbler, characterised by strong contrast between the blackish centres to the upperpart feathers and their broad brown fringes. In nominate *pryeri*, these fringes are rich, warm chestnut-brown. The sides of the head of are plain and unmarked, with a hint of a greyish supercilium from the bill base to above the ear-coverts. The lack of an eye-stripe results in minimal contrast between the supercilium, ear-coverts, cheeks and

lores. However, chestnut-brown fringes on the crown do contrast with the greyer sides to the head and nape.

The entire upperparts present a distinctive, contrasting appearance, particularly the tertials which show extensive black centres and rich chestnut-brown fringes. The entire mantle appears streaked, with parallel lines formed by the black feather centres and chestnut fringes, which narrow towards the tips. The greater coverts show this same patterning. As the wings are quite short, the fine, dark rump streaking can be obvious, although it is absent on some birds. The tail is warm brown, slightly duller than the upperparts, and there is usually contrast between the warm brown feather webs and darker brown shafts.

The chin and throat are white, with a slight greyish wash and the breast is slightly darker and browner than the throat while the belly is slightly paler. The flanks are rich dark brown but appear slightly paler than the upperparts. The vent and undertail-coverts are unmarked pale peachy brown, slightly warmer than the flanks. The continental race *sinensis* appears conspicuously paler and more contrasting than nominate *pryeri*. Juveniles resemble adults but show a slight yellowish wash to the underparts and supercilium.

The bill is blackish with a pink basal half to the lower mandible, darkening along the sides towards the tip, although the lower mandible may be entirely yellow in young birds. The entire bill tends to become blackish during the breeding season. The legs and feet vary from bright reddish pink to a paler yellowish pink.

SIMILAR SPECIES Several of the smaller, streaked *Acrocephalus* and *Locustella* warblers could be confused with Japanese Swamp Warbler although most are readily separable. The two species most likely to present an identification concern are Pallas's Grasshopper Warbler and Zitting Cisticola. The latter overlaps with it throughout the year, but Pallas's Grasshopper is only likely to do so on migration and, perhaps locally, during the breeding season.

Zitting Cisticola really should not present a problem, as there are significant differences in appearance, structure, behaviour and vocalisations between the two. It shares the heavily streaked appearance of Japanese Swamp Warbler and, at times, inhabits similar habitats including stands of rush and sedge over shallow water, as well as dry grasslands. It is smaller than Japanese Swamp Warbler and has a proportionately much shorter tail with conspicuous black-and-white tips to the underside of each feather, lacking in Japanese Swamp Warbler. The streaked upperparts are much paler than in either race of Japanese Swamp Warbler giving enhanced contrast with the black feather centres. Often perches conspicuously in the open on top on a grass or sedge tuft, a behaviour quite different to that of the skulking Japanese Swamp Warbler. It also has a distinctive undulating song-flight, giving single '*tzit*' calls as it flies overhead in large circles.

Pallas's Grasshopper Warbler shows streaked upperparts and reclusive behaviour, but there are diagnostic differences that separate it from Japanese Swamp Warbler. It shows a conspicuous supercilium extending well beyond the eye, crisp narrow pale fringes to the dark tertials, a bright rufous or cinnamon unstreaked rump, and conspicuous whitish tips to the rectrices. Spotting is often present across the lower throat of Pallas's Grasshopper but is absent on Japanese Swamp. The two species are similar in size but the tail of Pallas's Grasshopper is broader and heavier, and strongly graduated towards the tip. A flushed Japanese

Swamp Warbler appears long- and thin-tailed and lacks the contrast between a rufous or cinnamon rump and darker mantle that Pallas's Grasshopper shows.

VOICE The song of the nominate form is given while perched on a reed stem or in a short song-flight over the breeding territory, typically a *Phragmites* reedbed. It begins with repetition of a rising and falling '*chik-chok*' element given about 10–12 times in quick succession, each pair of notes lasting about 0.2 seconds, within a frequency range of 2–5kHz. This leads into the second, louder part of the song, a discordant chittering '*chitit-chitit-chitit-chitit-chitit-chitit-chitit-chitit-chitit*' with approximately eight elements per second and within a frequency range of 2–9kHz. This has an undulating structure, increases in speed, volume and frequency, and lasts about three seconds. The entire song sequence; '*chik-chok-chik-chok-chik-chok-chik-chok-chik-chok-chik-chok-chik-chok-chik-chok-chik-chok-chik-chok-chik-chok-chitit-chitit-chitit-chitit-chitit-chitit-chitit-chitit-chitit*', lasts for approximately eight seconds, after which the introductory '*chik-chok*' elements begin again, initially slowly then increasing in volume and leading into the main song, which is often repeated within ten seconds.

Song of Japanese Swamp Warbler, recorded within breeding range of *L. p. pryeri*, Aomori, Honshu, Japan, June. (Ueda 1998)

The song of the race *sinensis* is very similar in both structure and frequency range. It differs only in having fewer or no introductory elements, while the chittering, undulating section lasts longer, up to six seconds.

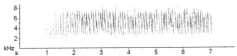

Song of Japanese Swamp Warbler, recorded within breeding range of *L. p. sinensis*, Zhalong, Qiqihar, Heilongjiang Province, China, June. (Per Alström)

The call is a rather distinctive flat, dry rattle lasting for two to three seconds.

MOULT Poorly understood. In Japan, adults have a complete moult after the breeding season, from late July to September. Juveniles also have a complete moult which occurs slightly later than that of the adults, in September and October, before departure from the breeding sites. Adults and young birds have a spring moult from mid March to early April, which includes replacement of body feathering and the outer three to five primaries (Morioka & Shigeta 1993; YS *in litt.*).

Resident populations in Ibaraki and Chiba Prefectures in the Kanto Plain have the same moult strategy as the northerly breeding migrant populations (YS *in litt.*).

HABITAT Closely associated with wetlands and marshes and the presence of *Phragmites* reed appears essential in the breeding habitat. In Japan some breed in abandoned rice-fields or similar low-lying damp grasslands, but most localities still retain extensive *Phragmites* reedbeds. Displaying birds watched in mid May near Shanghai favoured damp grasslands with large tussocks and nearby stands of *Phragmites* reeds up to 3m tall.

It occurs in a wider range of habitats in winter but is still closely associated with wetlands and *Phragmites* reedbeds remain important. In coastal Japan small numbers winter in reeds along slow-moving rivers (Brazil 1991). Wintering birds at Poyang Lake in Jiangxi Province, China, where there is little *Phragmites* present, favour the edges of tall, damp grassland away from the water's edge.

Migrants at Beidaihe in Hebei Province in E China, are often flushed from short, damp grass, above or close to standing water. Whether this is the habitat that migrants prefer is uncertain, and the ease of detecting birds using open habitats, compared to those in denser wetland vegetation distorts any attempt to quantify habitat preferences.

BEHAVIOUR Poorly known. Its behaviour and actions closely resemble those of all *Locustella* warblers, keeping on or close to the ground and rarely remaining in the open for more than a few seconds. When flushed it typically makes a short flight before dropping into a patch of reed or grass tuft. It will sit close and only flush again if closely approached. This can be repeated several times with most birds and occasionally they will sit in the open for several seconds to investigate the intruder before descending into the grass. On being flushed for a second or third time, birds will sometimes fly up to 100m to avoid further disturbance.

During the breeding season, males sing from within reedbeds, often clinging to two reeds, with legs splayed. They frequently perform an aerial song-flight which is typically preceded by song from within the reedbed, often out of sight. The bird gradually climbs to the top of a stem and then rises, still singing, to a height of 5–10m above the reeds before descending back to one of its favoured song perches. Song usually ceases when the bird returns to the reedbed, but if several males are singing this performance can be repeated, with song given while perched and in flight.

Japanese Swamp Warbler is rarely seen in winter as it usually remains on or close to the ground. In Japan, wintering birds in *Phragmites* reedbeds can be attracted to the edge of a reedbed if investigating an interesting or unfamiliar sound. In China, they winter in grasses, up to 0.5m tall and appear to avoid reedbeds. Despite their skulking nature, observations of wintering birds at Poyang Lake in fine rain and drizzle revealed a very different behaviour, where several birds were observed to sit out on the tops of grasses preening regularly, calling and occasionally singing and showed a reluctance to return into cover (PRK pers. obs.). This was presumably to avoid contact with the wet grasses, but may have been an opportunity to bathe. Subsequent observations during dry weather showed a return to their typical skulking behaviour.

BREEDING HABITS In Japan, the breeding season extends from June to August. The nest is placed in reeds or grasses, usually close to the edge of *Phragmites* reedbeds and up to 0.5m above the ground. The typical clutch size is 5–6 eggs with incubation taking 11–12 days and fledging a further 13–14 days. Believed to be double-brooded in Japan (Brazil 1991).

Nothing is known of the breeding biology of the race *sinensis*. However, as migrants are still passing through Beidaihe in late May, this race may only raise a single brood.

DISTRIBUTION
Breeding

L. p. pryeri Breeds at just six locations on Honshu, Japan, with a resident population near Tokyo and a migrant population breeding in N Honshu. It has always been centred on the extensive *Phragmites* reedbeds of the Kanto plain near Tokyo and Yokohama, Although formerly widespread here, the breeding range contracted and fragmented during the twentieth century due to destruction of wetlands and urban expansion. It is believed that this population is now restricted to Ibaraki and Chiba Prefectures close to Tokyo, with the most important site being Kamisu-machi, with 111 birds in 1993. It also breeds at Ukishima wetland at Kasumigaura Lake in Ibaraki Prefecture and at wetlands along the Tonegawa in adjacent Chiba Prefecture.

In N Honshu a migrant population breeds at three sites in Aomori Prefecture; the Iwaki-gawa river mouth (with *c.* 90 singing males), Takase-gawa river mouth where a small population breeds and Hotoke-numa wetland where 172 birds were counted in 1992 and 214 singing males in 1993. In Akita Prefecture it breeds at Hachiro-gata where 122 singing males were recorded in 1977, but the population here declined to just 2–3 males in the late 1990s (BirdLife International).

The population in Japan is estimated to be *c.* 2,500 birds (BirdLife International).

L. p. sinensis Until recently, believed to be restricted to Liaoning and Heilongjiang Provinces in NE China where it was recorded during the breeding season from the Shuangtai Hekou National Nature Reserve in Liaoning Province (Brazil 1992). Birds have also been reported during the breeding season from the Zhalong National Nature Reserve in Heilongjiang Province.

A second population has recently been discovered along the lower Yangtze River. Several singing males, including some performing display flights, were seen at Fengxian on Wangpan Bay, Zhejiang Province, south of Shanghai, in May 1989 (PRK pers. obs.), suggesting that breeding was occurring here. Subsequently, in 2005, several singing males were discovered at Chongming Dongtan Nature Reserve at the mouth of the Yangtze River at Shanghai (Gan *et al.* 2006) and juveniles were reported there later in the year. Based on subsequent surveys, it appears that the population there may number several thousand pairs. In 2007, a survey at Poyang Lake in Jiangxi Province revealed a large breeding population, estimated to be up to 5,000 pairs, of which 1,500 were within Nanjishan National Nature Reserve (BirdLife International). Prior to this, it was known only as a winter visitor to this region.

A singing male was recorded from the eastern shore of Lake Khanka in the Russian Far East on 25 July 1975 Gluschenko (1981). This individual was in suitable breeding habitat, singing from reed stems and performing a song-flight and may have been an unmated male outside the normal breeding range. To-date, this is the only published record from Russia. As Lake Khanka forms the border between Russia and China's Heilongjiang Province it seems possible that breeding will occur here.

In Mongolia, there are reports of birds recorded during the breeding season from the Numrug Strictly Protected Area in the extreme east of the country (BirdLife International).

Non-breeding In winter, the race *sinensis* occurs along the Yangtze River valley and adjacent flood plains. It was first recorded from Hankow, Hupeh Province (Wuhan, Hubei Province) in March 1912 by Rear Admiral Hubert Lynes (La Touche 1925–30), but most recent records are now centred on the Poyang Lake region of Jiangxi Province and East Dongting Lake in Hunan Province. It is presumed to occur between these two major wetland locations where suitable habitat remains, although there are no recent reports. As there is no evidence of birds wintering south of the Yangtze River, it is believed the breeding population at Chongming Dongtan is either resident or disperses along the Yangtze River, from East Dongting Lake to the coast.

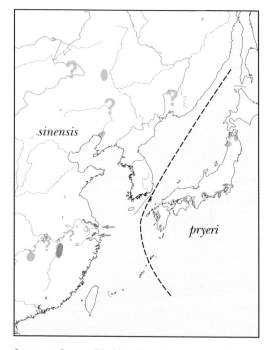

Japanese Swamp Warbler. Breeding range and winter distribution.

MOVEMENTS The skulking nature of this species makes it difficult to detect so establishing the true extent of movements will always prove problematic. Birds of the nominate form breeding in the low-lying reedbeds in C Honshu near Tokyo are believed to be resident there all year round, although Y. Shigeta (*in litt.*) has commented that some birds from the Kanto Plain population winter in Shizuoka and Aichi Prefectures.

Those breeding further to the north to Aomori prefecture in N Honshu vacate the breeding areas and ringing recoveries have established that they move to coastal reedbeds in Chiba and Ibaraki Prefectures along the Pacific coastline, where the climate is milder (Brazil 1991; YS *in litt*). Here they presumably mix with the resident population. A number of winter records from several additional sites in C and SW Honshu and Shikoku show that they sometimes occur elsewhere in Japan. However, there is no indication that this occurs sufficiently regularly to indicate an extension to the known regular wintering area. These wandering birds have been recorded from Saitama, Tokyo, Kanagawa, Niigata, Shizuoka, Aichi and Wakayama and Okayama Prefectures in SW Honshu and Tokushima Prefecture in Shikoku. (Brazil 1991; Eguchi *et al.* 2000).

The Chinese race *L. p. sinensis* is a migrant through the coastal regions of Hebei Province where it occurs regularly in small numbers at Beidaihe between late April and mid May and again in mid to late October. La Touche (1925–30) also recorded it in both spring and autumn at Chinwangtao (Qinhuangdao). It appears to have been more numerous in the early years of the twentieth century when La Touche (1925–30) remarked that a great many were seen on 18 October 1914 at Qinhuangdao. There are no other records of this skulking warbler on migration in China.

Elsewhere, Japanese Swamp Warbler, presumably *sinensis* is a vagrant to the Korean peninsula with records from the Seoul area and Cheju Island. In Hong Kong, *sinensis* was trapped at the Mai Po Marshes Nature Reserve on 11 November 2007 (PJL *in litt.*).

DESCRIPTION *L. p. pryeri*

Plumage – Adult fresh (April to June) Forehead and sides of crown warm brown, with indistinct dark feather tips. Central crown feathers with small blackish centres and broad warm brown fringes. Nape greyer-brown, with inconspicuous narrow blackish central streaks. Supercilium pale brown, extending from the bill base to the rear of the ear-coverts; palest, most clearly defined behind the eye, diffuse and ill-defined in front of eye, converging with the pale brown lores. There is a narrow, dark brown eye-line below the supercilium, above the ear-coverts. Ear-coverts greyish buff with indistinct white shaft streaks, merging with the greyish brown sides of the neck. Eye-ring inconspicuous. A short, dark brown moustachial line runs from the bill base to a point below front of eye. Mantle feathers with large, conspicuous blackish feather centres and broad, bright, warm-brown fringes, narrowing towards tips. Scapulars similar but with smaller black centres. Rump and uppertail-coverts bright brownish buff with narrow black shaft streaks. Tail feathers warm brown with slightly darker shafts.

Chin, throat and belly white with faint grey wash. Breast slightly darker greyish white, sometimes with faint brown wash. Flanks and sides of breast washed warm brown, slightly paler than upperparts. Vent and undertail-coverts pale peachy brown, slightly warmer than flanks and unmarked.

Lesser coverts uniform bright warm brown. Median and greater coverts bright warm brown with small blackish centres. Tertials blackish on outer webs with narrow, sharply-defined, bright, warm brown fringes, uniform bright warm brown on inner webs, darkening towards feather shafts. Alula dark brown with narrow warm brown fringe. Primary coverts warm brown, unmarked. Flight feathers blackish brown, broadly edged bright warm brown, primaries with narrow whitish tips, p1 usually with conspicuous pale outer edge. Underwing-coverts creamy white with traces of buff, much paler than flanks.

Adult worn (July to October) Upperparts become increasingly dark as feather fringes are lost to abrasion and blackish centres become more prominent, particularly on the crown, mantle and tertials. The whitish primary tips are lost by July.

Juvenile Closely resembles fresh adult but markings less well defined. Forehead and sides of crown uniform warm brown, lacking dark feather tips. Central crown feathers with small blackish centres and broad warm brown fringes creating a finely streaked appearance. Nape unmarked, slightly paler grey-brown than crown and mantle. Supercilium either absent or washed pale creamy yellow, extending from bill base to just behind eye. Lores unmarked warm brown merging with forehead. Ear-coverts and cheeks greyish buff. Eye-ring broad but inconspicuous, forming a large 'spectacle' around the eye. Mantle feathers as adult with large, conspicuous, blackish feather centres and broad, bright, warm-brown fringes, narrowing towards tip. Scapulars unmarked bright, warm-brown. Rump and uppertail-coverts bright brownish buff with narrow black shaft streaks. Tail feathers warm brown with slightly darker shafts.

Chin, throat and belly pale creamy yellow and unmarked. Breast slightly greyer but usually with cream wash. Flanks and sides of breast with brown wash, distinctly paler than upperparts. Vent and undertail-coverts pale greyish white.

Lesser coverts uniform bright warm brown. Median and greater coverts bright warm brown with small blackish centres. Tertials blackish on outer webs with fairly wide, sharply defined bright warm brown fringes, uniform bright warm brown on inner webs. Alula dark brown with narrow warm brown fringe. Primary coverts with blackish centres and warm brown fringes. Flight feathers uniform pale brown, p1 usually with conspicuous pale outer edges. Underwing-coverts creamy white with a trace of buff, much paler than flanks.

Bare Parts Upper mandible entirely blackish during the breeding season. Lower mandible dull brownish pink at base, black at tip. Outside the breeding season the upper mandible is blackish with a narrow pink cutting edge towards base, tip usually entirely black, lower mandible with pink basal half, distal half darkening towards blackish tip. In juvenile, upper mandible pale brown with conspicuous pale yellow-straw cutting edge extending from base to tip. Lower mandible entirely yellow. Bill darkens and resembles that of adult by November, but with pale areas still distinctly yellow. Juvenile shows three dark tongue spots in first autumn, two often retained until first summer. Tarsi and toes bright reddish pink in adult of nominate race, paler yellowish pink in race *sinensis*; soles pale greyish brown; claws slightly darker than toes. Tarsi, toes, claws and soles of first-winter birds similar to those of adult. Iris warm sepia brown in at least some adults in spring, dark greyish brown in first autumn.

IN HAND CHARACTERS
Measurements

L. p. pryeri

	Male	Female
Wing	55–59 (57.1; 16)	51–56 (52.8; 8)
Tail	46.5–55 (51.3; 15)	41.5–54 (48.1; 16)
Bill	11–12.8 (11.3; 17)	10.6–12.1 (11.2; 6)
Tarsus	18.8–21.1 (20.1; 15)	17.9–19.6 (18.9; 17)

(Data supplied by Y. Shigeta from specimens at YIO)

Males (n = 2):
Bill width: 3.0, 3.1
Hind claw: 7.0, 7.8
Tail graduation: 17, 22

L. p. sinensis
Live data: *wing* ♂ 55–61.5, ♀ 50–56; *tail* ♂ 61.5–63, ♀ 53–59; *tarsus* ♂ 19–20, ♀ 18–19. (La Touche 1925–30).

Sexes combined (n = 5):
Bill length: 11–12.5 (12.0)
Bill width: 2.6–3.1 (2.9)
Tail graduation: 17–27 (20.2)

Structure

L. p. pryeri

Wing formula (n = 2):

p1/pc	p2	p3e	p4e	p5e	p6	p7	p10
6–9	8	1–1.5	wp	0–1	2.5–3	4–4.5	6.5–7.5

Wing rounded with fairly small p1. Wing point p4(5); p2 = p10/ss tips; emargination on p3–5.

Figure 40. Wing of Japanese Swamp Warbler.

Tail longish, strongly graduated, feathers rather narrow.

Bill small, concave-sided with fine tip.

Tarsi slender, toes long; claws fine, the front ones small.

L. p. sinensis appears to have a considerably longer tail

Recognition Small and warmly toned, upperparts including rump and uppertail-coverts with bold blackish streaks, tail feathers plain. Distinguished from other *Locustella* warblers by the short wing with point at p4–5 and by the unique carpal claw.

Ageing Juvenile distinguished by unmarked greyish brown nape and yellowish wash to the underparts and supercilium; also by pale yellow lower mandible, yellow mouth lining and the presence of three tongue spots.

Weight

L. p. pryeri: ♂ 13.6–15.6g (14.5; 15), ♀ 11.1–17.2g (12.6; 17). (Shigeta 1988)

L. p. sinensis: n = 1, Hong Kong, 10.4g. (HKRG unpublished data)

GEOGRAPHIC VARIATION Two well defined races show distinct structural as well as morphological differences and their separation is relatively straightforward.

L. p. pryeri (N Japan) Described above.

L. p. sinensis (NE and E China) Shares a similar plumage pattern with nominate *pryeri*, but distinctly paler. The fringes to the upperpart feathering are paler, warm sandy brown to greyish brown, lacking the darker and richer tones of nominate *pryeri*. The blackish feather centres appear larger and more contrasting, and streaking extends up the nape to join with that on the crown. Streaking on the rump and uppertail-coverts is also broader and more conspicuous. The rectrices darken towards the feather shafts, giving a contrasting appearance to the tail lacking in nominate *pryeri*. The head is even plainer than in the nominate form. The supercilium is restricted to a greyish smudge in front of the eye, and the ear-coverts merge with the side of the crown and with the pale unmarked lores. The underparts of *sinensis* are also paler, with the white chin and

throat showing little contrast with the silky grey breast and belly, and the flanks and undertail-coverts are washed uniform bright buff, paler but warmer than in nominate *pryeri*.

The tail of *sinensis* is up to 10mm longer than that of nominate *pryeri*, giving it an attenuated appearance, particularly in low flight when flushed.

TAXONOMY AND SYSTEMATICS Japanese Swamp Warbler was placed within *Megalurus* by Seebohm (1884) on the basis of its upperpart pattern and coloration, although he recognised that it was structurally closer to Spotted Bush Warbler. He later revised his opinion and placed it in a monotypic genus *Lusciniola*. Subsequent authors then wavered in their treatment, some retaining it in *Lusciniola* and others placing it in *Tribura* or *Bradypterus*. Delacour (1942) restored it to *Megalurus*, commenting that it showed all the characters of this genus, differing from other species only in its extremely small size. But while the general wing shape is similar to that of *Megalurus*, the first primary is actually proportionately shorter. Delacour was presumably also unaware of the unique wing claw. Morioka & Shigeta (1993) reviewed this unusual warbler, examining a range of characters to determine which species were its closest relatives. Considering its structure, behaviour and geographical distribution they recommended that it should be provisionally included within *Locustella*. Support for this has come from DNA studies (Drovetski *et al.* 2004; Alström *et al.*, in prep.) which now place it firmly within the eastern lineage of *Locustella* warblers.

The two races of Japanese Swamp warbler are quite different in appearance, occupy mutually exclusive breeding and wintering ranges and are not known to come into contact. However, the suggestion that they might constitute two distinct species is not supported by molecular data (Alström *et al.*, in prep.).

▲ Adult *L. p. pryeri*, Chiba, Japan, June. Singing males often sit in the open on a *Phragmites* reed stem before performing a short song-flight (Kazuyasu Kisaichi).

▲ Adult *L. p. pryeri*, Chiba, Japan, July. Characterised by dull chestnut-brown appearance to upperparts and flight feathers. Shows chestnut-brown fringes to mantle and tertials that contrast with black centres, a largely unmarked nape and reduced blackish spotting on crown (Akiko Hidaka).

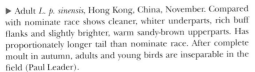

▲ Adult *L. p. pryeri*, Chiba, Japan, May. Flanks and sides of breast washed warm brown, contrasting with the dingy white breast and belly and pale peach-brown undertail-coverts. Note short undertail-coverts and strongly graduated tail; the nominate race is shorter-tailed than *sinensis* (Pete Morris).

▶ Adult *L. p. sinensis*, Hong Kong, China, November. Compared with nominate race shows cleaner, whiter underparts, rich buff flanks and slightly brighter, warm sandy-brown upperparts. Has proportionately longer tail than nominate race. After complete moult in autumn, adults and young birds are inseparable in the field (Paul Leader).

▲ ▶ Adult *L. p. sinensis*, Jiangxi, China, November. Overall appearance of *sinensis* is warmer and brighter than the nominate form. Lacks dull chestnut-brown fringes to upperparts and greyer tone to nape, side of head and underparts. Note larger black centres to crown, mantle, tertials and uppertail-coverts, giving this race a bold and contrasting appearance (Martin Hale).

Genus *Acrocephalus* Naumann & Naumann, 1811

[Gr. *akros* topmost, highest; *kephale* head]

A large genus of reed warblers within which we recognise 37 species. Of these, 16 are mostly long-distance migrants that breed in Eurasia, seven are resident or short-distance migrants that breed in Africa or on nearby islands, one is a short-distance migrant that breeds in Australia, and 13 species are resident on Pacific Ocean islands. The species are diverse in size but include some of the largest of the warblers. The smaller migrants of Europe and Asia differ markedly in structure from some of the large African or Pacific island residents but the genus is characterised by an attenuated head shape, a typically long, rather strong and broad-based bill, a rounded to moderately graduated tail of 12 feathers and strong tarsi, toes and claws. Their foot structure, with a relatively long outer toe, shorter inner toe and large hind toe pad, is adapted to clinging, and locomotion on the ground is usually by hopping (See Fig. 23 for comparison of *Acrocephalus* and *Locustella* foot structure). The rictal bristles are well developed.

Most species are olive-brown to rufous-brown above and rather pale below, a few with streaked upperparts. However, some of the Pacific taxa exhibit complex patterning and colourful plumage.

Typically, *Acrocephalus* warblers tend to be less secretive than the skulking *Locustella* and *Bradypterus* species, and are more inclined to emerge from thick cover. They often occur close to water, where they inhabit reedbeds, marshes, swamps, leafy thickets, herbaceous undergrowth and, sometimes, the low tree canopy. Most are exceptionally vocal, producing loud chattering or chuckling songs and many harsh charring or chacking call notes. They build characteristic open cup-shaped nests, usually suspended on upright plant stems and often over water. Most island forms occupy drier habitat and some are found in woodland and forest at all levels.

The Palearctic *Acrocephalus* are typically long-distance migrants but some have less migratory races. Thus, the wide-ranging Eurasian Reed Warbler has largely resident breeding populations in Morocco, Arabia and NE Africa, the Moustached Warbler has resident populations in S Europe, and the Clamorous Reed Warbler has a series of sedentary races extending from Egypt and the Middle East through southern Asia to the Wallacean subregion and east to the Solomon Islands. All these largely resident taxa have a small to minute first primary but slightly rounded wing structure. In contrast, most migratory species have a minute first primary and a distinctly long, pointed wing shape. The plumage of the Palearctic species ranges from ochreous or olive-brown to bright cinnamon or rufous-brown above, boldly patterned in some, with much paler, usually unmarked underparts. Head patterns tend to be bold, with dark lores and well-marked supercilia. The smaller species have vigorous chattering songs, often rhythmic or mimetic, while those of the larger species are loud, harsher and more grating. Based on morphology, four groupings or subgenera can be recognised. These are (1) the small striped species of the sub-genus *Calamodus*, typified by Sedge Warbler, and including Black-browed Reed Warbler, whose affinities have been much debated, and Moustached Warbler which has sometimes been placed within its own genus *Lusciniola*; (2) the small eastern plain-backed species typified by Paddyfield Warbler; (3) the longer-winged western plain-backed species typified by Eurasian Reed Warbler; and (4) the large plain-backed group including Great Reed Warbler, Oriental Reed Warbler and Clamorous Reed Warbler. These groups correspond to four clades revealed by DNA analysis (e.g. Leisler *et al.* 1997; Parkin *et al.* 2004; Fregin *et al.* 2009).

The two resident African swamp warblers, sometimes included in the sub-genus *Calamocichla*, are characterised by short and rounded wings with a well developed first primary, fairly long and rounded tails and very strong legs and claws. Their plumage is drab, with rather dark brown upperparts and a poorly defined head pattern. Two further species restricted to islands off the coast of Africa also share characters associated with the sub-genus *Calamocichla* including the rounded wing structure and large first primary; they are Cape Verde Warbler and the streak-breasted Madagascar Swamp Warbler. In addition, two smaller species that feature distinctly yellowish underparts, Seychelles Warbler and Rodrigues Warbler, were until recently placed in the genus *Bebrornis*, but this has now been subsumed within *Acrocephalus*. Molecular studies have indicated that all six of these African species belong within a single clade, quite closely related to the larger, plain-backed Great Reed Warbler group of Eurasian warblers (Leisler *et al.* 1997).

Australian Reed Warbler was, until recently, considered to be a race of the wide-ranging and highly variable Clamorous Reed Warbler, from which it has now been split. It is uncertain whether some of the small, resident taxa that inhabit islands from the Moluccas and Lesser Sundas in E Indonesia, east through the Bismarck Archipelago to the Solomon Islands, should remain with Clamorous Reed, become races of Australian Reed or be treated as one or more distinct species. We have adopted a conservative approach and retained all within Clamorous Reed Warbler, but this seems certain to change in the future. Thirteen resident *Acrocephalus* occur across the W and C Pacific, each endemic to a single archipelago, some to a single island. These are mostly large, and show a rounded wing tip combined with a very small first primary as in Australian Reed and Clamorous Reed Warblers. They have relatively short tails, strong legs and feet, and long strong bills. Three plain brown-backed species of the W Pacific: Nightingale Warbler of the Mariana Islands, Cook Islands Warbler and Nauru Warbler, resemble Australian Reed Warbler in plumage but have a longer bill, that of Nightingale Warbler reaching exaggerated proportions.

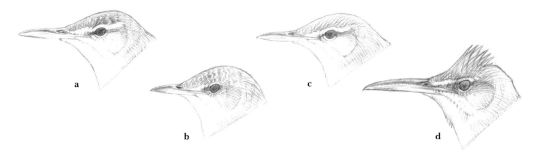

Figure 41. Comparison of head and bill shape of some Pacific Ocean *Acrocephalus* **(a) Northern Marquesan Warbler (b) Pitcairn Island Warbler (c) Caroline Islands Warbler and (d) Nightingale Warbler.**

Eight species in Polynesia show more varied plumage, greyish brown to dark olive above and whitish or yellow below, with prominent pale edges and tips to the wing and tail feathers. Some of these also show extensive random white feathering on the body, wings and tail. The largely olive-and-yellow plumaged Tahiti Warbler and the two Marquesan Warblers are particularly large with broad primaries and long, heavy bills. The Pitcairn Island Warbler has been found to be positioned genetically within the Great Reed Warbler complex (Leisler *et al.* 1997).

MOUSTACHED WARBLER
Acrocephalus melanopogon   Plates 15 and 16

Sylvia melanopogon **Temminck, 1823**. In: Temminck & Laugier, *Planches Color*, livr. 41, plate 245, figure. 2. 'campagnes prés de Rome'.

A resident or short distance migrant in Europe with a fragmented distribution in marshes and reedbeds in NW Africa and S Europe, while Asian breeders are strongly migratory, wintering from the Middle East to NW India. Polytypic, with three races recognised:

A. m. melanopogon (Temminck 1823). S Europe from Spain, S France, Italy, E Austria and Hungary to the Balkans, Crete and W Turkey and to the Lower Danube and S Ukraine east to about Khark'ov; also N Morocco and N Tunisia.

A. m. mimicus (Madarász 1903). S and E Turkey and from the Caucasus and the Caspian Sea east to *c.* 80°E in S Kazakhstan.

A. m. albiventris (Kazakov 1974). E Black Sea region of S Russia from Lower Don River and the Sea of Azov east to Krasnodar.

IDENTIFICATION Length 12–13cm. Wing 53–67mm. Tail/wing 78–90%.

A small warmly toned warbler with conspicuously streaked upperparts. A broad whitish supercilium and dark crown give it a striking face pattern. Sexes alike.

Structure A small *Acrocephalus*, European birds being approximately 10% smaller than Sedge Warbler while migratory birds breeding in C Asia are similar in size. It shares with Sedge Warbler a similar low-crowned profile, but appears rather more compact and the undertail-coverts are rather short for an *Acrocephalus*. The tail is slightly longer and fuller than that of Sedge and has a more graduated tip. Often the tail is characteristically cocked above the back, but at other times it is held along the body line. The tarsi are slightly longer and the toes and claws longer and stronger than in Sedge. The bill is weak and narrow with a very fine tip. The wing is rather short and rounded, with a relatively long first primary (p1), more than one-third the

length of p2. The closed primaries project no more than about 50% of exposed tertial length, with a maximum of six feather tips visible and with emarginations on p3–5, which also form the wing point.

Plumage and bare parts In Europe, adults of the nominate race are generally darker and more warmly coloured than Sedge Warbler, with a bolder, more sharply defined head pattern. In fresh plumage in autumn the crown appears almost entirely black, with pale feather tips in the centre barely visible and is sharply 'cut-off' by the contrasting and prominent broad chalky white or greyish white supercilium. This extends from the bill base to the rear of the ear-coverts, widening above and flaring behind the eye before terminating rather squarely and abruptly at the nape side. A well-marked blackish stripe extends through the lores and behind the eye above paler mottled greyish ear-coverts which, in turn, are bordered below by a narrow but clear dusky moustachial line. This gives the sides of the head a more contrasting appearance than that of Sedge. The upperparts are rich rufous-brown, with blackish streaks on the mantle and scapulars, while the rump and uppertail-coverts are similar in colour but plain. The rear and sides of the neck are unmarked, slightly paler than the mantle and form a perceptible warmly coloured 'shawl' separating the crown from the back. The tail feathers are dark but with broad rufous-brown to tawny-brown edges and show little contrast with the rump.

The chin, throat and central underparts are chalky white, with a contrasting tawny-buff wash on the breast and undertail-coverts and more deeply tawny-brown to pinkish brown sides and flanks. Some individuals show weak and faintly marked brown streaking across the upper breast. There are broad tawny-brown fringes to the greater coverts and tertials and also to the outer edges of the secondaries, which are warmer than in Sedge, but less sharply demarcated, so that the upperwing appears generally duller. In spring, after the pre-breeding moult, the body plumage, wing-coverts and tertials again appear fresh but the flight feathers are then slightly worn. The entire plumage becomes worn during the summer, so that the crown appears blacker, the upperparts duller tawny-brown and the central underparts whiter and contrasting more with the brown flanks.

Juveniles closely resemble spring adults, with almost uniform black crown, white supercilium and generally tawny-brown plumage. The fresh wing feather edgings are rather more buff than in the adult and the warm buff-washed breast may show faint greyish spots.

The eastern races *mimicus* and *albiventris* are conspicuously paler and less richly coloured than the nominate form in Europe and show a greater resemblance to Sedge Warbler. The upperparts are olive-brown rather than rufous-brown and the crown is brown rather than blackish and distinctly streaked.

All races at all ages show a blackish bill with a restricted and inconspicuous pale base to the lower mandible. The legs and feet are dark, dirty bluish grey to dark horn.

SIMILAR SPECIES Only likely to be mistaken for Sedge Warbler. Separation is usually straightforward but worn and faded birds and, in particular, C Asian breeders can sometimes be surprisingly difficult to separate in the field.

Sedge Warbler breeds to the north of Moustached Warbler and their ranges overlap only in SE Europe and around the N Caspian Sea. On migration, however, Sedge occurs throughout much of the range of Moustached. Although similar in overall appearance, subtle plumage differences are usually reliable, supported by structural and bare part differences. Sedge has a sleeker appearance than Moustached with a longer primary projection and a shorter, less rounded tail, which is never held cocked in the manner of an agitated Moustached. Sedge also has very different wing structure from Moustached, with a minute first primary and wing point formed by p3, the only emarginated primary.

The plumage of freshly moulted Sedge is conspicuously paler buffy olive than that of Moustached and the more warmly tinged rump and uppertail-coverts contrast distinctly with the mantle. It shows more strongly patterned wings with sharply defined buffy olive fringes to the tertials and coverts. Its dark streaked olive-brown crown and tapering buff supercilium differ from the blackish crown and square-cut whitish supercilium of nominate Moustached. Worn adult Sedge in late summer show more uniform-looking wings and whiter supercilium and underparts but lack the rufous-brown tone which the upperparts of Moustached would still show.

Sedge Warbler more closely resembles the paler eastern races *albiventris* and *mimicus* of Moustached. These have a brownish rather than blackish crown but their whiter, broader and square-ended supercilium still serves to separate them from Sedge. They are also slightly darker and more warmly toned than Sedge and lack contrast between the mantle and rump, show duller, less contrastingly patterned wings and are darker, warmer buff on the flanks and undertail-coverts. The rather pale greyish brown to yellowish brown legs of Sedge are very different from the darker brown to blackish legs of Moustached.

VOICE The song is a vigorous and typically Acrocephalid medley, with a steady tempo and repetition of phrases recalling that of Eurasian Reed Warbler. The song phrase is often introduced by a diagnostic series of whistles which increase slightly in pitch and volume, from 2–3 kHz, '*du-du-du-du-du-du...*', delivered at approximately four per second. These whistles have been likened to part of the song of Wood Lark or the crescendo of Common Nightingale but are less powerful. Just three or four may be given and

typically fewer than 20, but the song occasionally consists entirely of an extended whistle sequence.

The main song is slightly faster than that of Eurasian Reed Warbler with more high sweet notes and melodic passages given between 2–7 kHz. It lacks many of the buzzing and grating notes and the extended chattering of Sedge Warbler. The song often incorporates mimicry, including recognisable calls of shorebirds and songs of other warblers. Song phrases last from just a few seconds to half a minute or more and are separated by short pauses. Songs of western and eastern races are very similar although in *mimicus* in C Asia the introductory whistles are less frequent and for shorter duration. A quieter subsong is heard in Europe in autumn during fine weather.

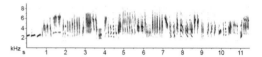

Song of Moustached Warbler recorded within breeding range of *A. m. melanopogon*, Spain, April. (Sample 2003)

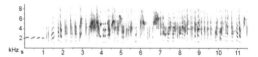

Song of Moustached Warbler recorded within breeding range of *A. m. mimicus*, eastern Turkey, May. (Peter Kennerley)

Calls include a short rolled '*trrk*' or '*ch-t-r*' and a sharp *tick* or low soft '*chak*', less hard than that of Sedge Warbler and recalling a Common Stonechat. When agitated, these calls may be repeated two or three times. A grating alarm-call '*tsrrr*' and a longer rattling '*trrrrrrr*' have also been recorded.

MOULT In the nominate race, adults have a complete, rather rapid moult in the breeding area before autumn dispersal. At Neusiedlersee, Austria, moult commences from late July onwards and finishes in September and October, taking approximately 50 days (Leisler 1972a). This is followed by a partial pre-breeding moult between December and February, during which the body and head plumage are replaced, together with the tertials, most wing-coverts and occasionally some tail feathers. Young birds have a complete post-juvenile moult on or near the breeding grounds at the same time as adults, those in Austria taking 39–53 days. They later have a pre-breeding moult as in adults.

Migratory populations of *mimicus* breeding in Kazakhstan adopt a different moult strategy. Adults migrate in autumn in old plumage. On arrival in the wintering area they have a complete moult between September and early November. A partial pre-breeding moult follows during February and March. Young birds retain their juvenile plumage until after migration. They also appear to have a complete moult in late autumn, followed by a late winter partial moult. Southern populations of *mimicus* breeding in more equable conditions around the S Caspian Sea and eastern Mediterranean, some of them resident, moult completely in late summer like nominate European birds.

HABITAT Breeds in Europe in flooded lowland reedbeds, especially where *Phragmites* is mixed with *Typha*, club-rush *Scirpus* and fen-sedge *Cladium*. It is well adapted for exploiting thick-stemmed, vertical emergent vegetation.

Its habitat overlaps that of Eurasian Reed Warbler but it requires a thick layer of old broken stems for nesting and is thus restricted to older and denser stands. The main strongholds are in the extensive reedbeds of larger river deltas and shallow lakes. In Asia, *mimicus* occupies a wider range of habitats. In Armenia and Georgia, it breeds at lakes and bogs and in sedge beds in the valleys of mountain streams, some reaching 1,950m in the Caucasus. In Turkmenistan, it is found in small bushes and sedgy tangles along stream banks. Outside the breeding season, wintering *mimicus* in NW India frequent various habitats including reedbeds, flooded rushes and thickets of tamarisk and range from the lowlands of the Gangetic plain up to 1,400m.

BEHAVIOUR Mainly solitary but may congregate at food sources. It tends to skulk low down in *Phragmites* or *Typha* beds, close to the water surface or on bare mud. Less actively than Sedge Warbler. It is an agile climber, however, moving easily up and down thick vertical stems of aquatic plants. It feeds mainly by picking and probing among reed bases, taking small beetles and caterpillars and tiny snails from leaves and stems, from wet ground or from below the water surface. It often cocks the tail above the back, especially when giving alarm calls, but when relaxed or feeding the tail is held straight in line with body. In flight, it is more flitting than Sedge Warbler, with the tail held straight, not depressed. On landing it usually perches briefly with the tail cocked before slipping down the reed stem.

It often sings from low within reeds, but sometimes uses an exposed perch. Unlike Sedge Warbler, it does not engage in song-flight. Males sing throughout much of the year, including the winter months, with a peak in activity in early spring and again after moult in October and November.

BREEDING HABITS Monogamous, although males seem to pair with different females from one year to the next. Territorial, a typical territory used for display and nesting extending to about 300–350m². The nest, built by the female, is placed 30–60cm above water in dense stands of reed, usually where mixed with reedmace, rushes and low shrubs. It is a loosely woven cup of leaves and stems of aquatic plants, but with a denser lining which may include reed flowers, *Typha* wool, feathers, algae and small roots. It is suspended by loops from several vertical stems and often has at least a partial roof.

In Europe, the typical clutch size is 3–4, but occasionally five or six, while in Kazakhstan 4–6 eggs is usual. Incubation is carried out by both sexes and lasts 14–15 days followed by a fledging period of approximately 12 days. Both sexes care for the young, bringing food from within the territory or not far away. The young remain dependent for 2–3 weeks after fledging. Breeding in Europe is early, with egg laying mainly during April and early May. In Asia, *mimicus* breeding around the S Caspian Sea may already be on eggs by late March, while more easterly birds in Kazakhstan lay in late April and early May. Single-brooded.

DISTRIBUTION Breeds widely but locally in the warm temperate region from NW Africa and the Iberian Peninsula east to Kazakhstan. European populations are largely resident, those of Asia mainly migratory.

A. m. melanopogon **Breeding** Breeds in NW Africa and through S Europe east to W Turkey and the western shores of the Black Sea and from the Mediterranean coasts north to Austria, Hungary, Romania and S Ukraine, with outlying populations in Switzerland and Slovakia. The main breeding areas are in S and E Spain

(including the Balearic Islands), SE France, W Italy, E Austria, Hungary, Croatia and Romania.

Distribution is patchy but the large reedbeds of Lake Neusiedlersee in Austria and the Danube delta in Romania hold major populations. The European population probably exceeds 30,000 pairs (Hagemeijer & Blair 1997) and densities of 2–5 pairs/hectare have been noted in optimal habitat. Small numbers breed in N Greece, Bulgaria, Crete and W and C Turkey (east to Sultan marshes) and possibly in Sicily. In NW Africa, a few breed in NW Morocco in the Bas-Loukkos marshes and in N Tunisia at Lake Ichkeul. A small population was discovered at a site in Germany in 1981 and breeding was proved here in 1984, but this has since been extirpated.

Non-breeding This race winters mainly on coasts and estuaries in the Mediterranean region. The birds of SW Europe are mostly sedentary, but those of Austria and the N Balkans vacate their breeding areas entirely. Many winter on the Adriatic and Aegean Sea coasts and some reach S Turkey, Crete, Cyprus and Israel. There is a winter influx to Corsica, Sardinia and Catalonia (NE Spain) and birds appear in non-breeding areas in N Morocco and occasionally coastal Algeria.

A. m. albiventris Range poorly known but it appears to be restricted to S Russia where it breeds in the large reedbeds of the River Don delta and the eastern shore of the Sea of Azov and east to the Krasnodar region near the border with Georgia. The wintering range is unknown, but is probably in the Middle East where *albiventris* would be overlooked among larger numbers of *mimicus*.

A. m. mimicus **Breeding** This eastern race has a more extensive range than the other two forms. The western limit lies in Turkey from Anatolia and the E Mediterranean coast and the Kizilirmak delta on the Black Sea coast (Kirwan *et al.* 2008), although its distribution through the east of the country is somewhat fragmented. It is a scarce and localised breeder at lower elevations in the Caucasus, including the region of Tbilisi and the Khrami River in Georgia and near Lake Sevan and Armash Fishponds in Armenia. It is common In Azerbaijan in the Shirvan National Park and probably along the lower Kura River and breeds in Russia in the Dagestan region along the Terek River. Proximity to Turkish breeding *mimicus* suggests that it is this race rather than *albiventris* that breeds in the Caucasus.

The main range lies north and east of the Caspian Sea. Large numbers breed in the extensive reedbeds of the lower Volga and Ural Rivers and along the Atrek River in Turkmenistan. Across C Asia it occurs mainly along the major rivers and their associated wetlands, from the N Aral Sea coast to the Ili River delta at Lake Balkash. Its range may have expanded here in the twentieth century due to extensive irrigation schemes. In Kazakhstan it is most numerous in the south between Shymkent and Taraz and south to Chinaz and the upper Amu Darya in Uzbekistan. Small numbers do, however, breed north to *c.* 50°N in the wetlands of the Kurgaldzlinskiy Reserve near Astana. To the south it breeds along the Murgab and Tedzhen Rivers in Turkmenistan and N Afghanistan. Breeding was reported from Baluchistan, Pakistan, in 1914 by Meinertzhagen. Outlying populations attributed to *mimicus* breed in N Syria, Israel, Jordon, NE Arabia, along the lower Tigris and Euphrates Rivers in S Iraq and in SW and E Iran.

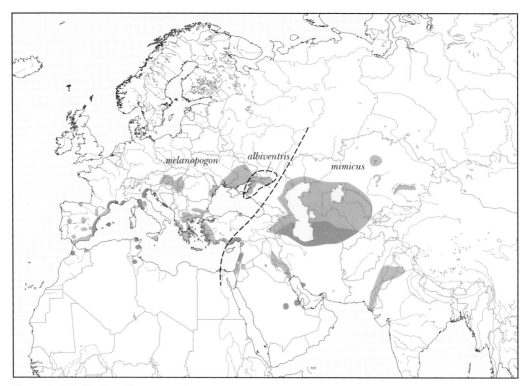

Moustached Warbler. Breeding range and winter distribution. Mostly resident or dispersive in S Europe.

Non-breeding Some birds winter within the southern margins of the breeding range, in particular around the S Caspian Sea and the lower hills of the Kopet Dag in Iran, at many breeding sites in Turkmenistan and in the foothills of the Pamiro-Alayai range near Samarkand in Uzbekistan. But most *mimicus* are strongly migratory and winter in the Middle East, Lower Iraq, Pakistan and NW India (south to Madhya Pradesh and east to Bihar). The species is scarce but regular in winter in Egypt (mostly Sinai and Suez south to Lake Qarun, although these are supposedly of the nominate form). It also reaches C Arabia south to Riyadh and is accidental in N Oman.

MOVEMENTS In Europe, birds leave Austrian breeding grounds between late September and early November. Migrants of unknown breeding origin pass through the Danube delta during September and October. Other birds reach the Spanish coast from early to mid September, but passage and arrival elsewhere in the Mediterranean area is mainly during October and November. In spring, movement begins early, wintering birds departing from Catalonia during February and Cyprus in late February or early March. Some, however, remain along the Dalmatian coast and in Crete until mid April. Birds arrive back at Neusiedlersee from early March onwards, but return to C Turkey only from early April. Most European records of vagrants from north of the breeding range have been in spring, presumably relating to overshooting migrants.

In Asia, autumn departure tends to be earlier than in Europe and the spring return later. Most adults have left Kazakhstan by early August, but the passage and departure of young birds continues through August and September. Movement through Turkmenistan is noted mainly during

October and early November but passage through W Pakistan occurs during late August and September, with arrival at wintering sites in Sind mainly in October. Birds continuing on to India arrive between August and October. Wintering birds are present in Israel from September to March and in Arabia from October to April.

Spring departure from India is mainly during March and early April, but a few birds linger to May. Passage through Afghanistan occurs from late February to late April and a strong movement through Iraq lasts well into May. Many migrants are back in Turkmenistan by early April and returning birds reach the Volga delta and Lake Balkhash by mid April. First arrivals reach Armenia and the Caucasus in early to mid March, but the main passage occurs from early April onwards, presumably of birds en-route to Caspian Sea breeding sites.

Vagrancy There are very few records of Moustached Warbler outside its known range. It is a vagrant to Portugal despite breeding in Spain. There are two records from Denmark; at Kongelunden on 10 May 1963 and at Hanstholm on 12 May 1967. Elsewhere in Europe, vagrants have reached Poland and Lithuania. In the east of the range, there is a single record from Nepal in December 2002 (Baral *et al.* 2004). The long-standing but controversial breeding record from Cambridgeshire, England, in 1946 (Hinde & Thom 1947) has now been discredited (Melling 2006) and the species is no longer on the British List.

DESCRIPTION *A. m. melanopogon*
Plumage – Adult fresh (September to December) Forehead and crown black, central crown feathers with narrow dark brown fringes. Supercilium long and broad, white; from just short of bill base, widening behind eye where tinged warm

buff, ending squarely and abruptly above rear of ear-coverts. A broad blackish band through lores and upper ear-coverts. Narrow broken eye-ring off-white. Rest of ear-coverts grey, mottled whitish, usually bordered below by a broken, dark grey, moustachial stripe. Nape and upper side of neck cinnamon-brown. Upperparts brighter rufous-brown, mantle and scapulars with narrow dull black streaks; rump and uppertail-coverts similar but unmarked. Tail feathers dark grey-brown, borders of t1 and outer edges of t2–6 broadly suffused dull cinnamon-brown.

Chin, throat and central underparts creamy white. Upper breast and undertail-coverts washed buff or pinkish buff. Sides of breast, flanks and tarsal feathering tawny-brown. Lesser and median coverts grey-brown with broad, dull, cinnamon-brown fringes. Rest of upperwing feathers blackish. Primary coverts and alula with fine brown fringes, greater coverts and tertials with broad tawny-brown fringes. Secondaries and bases of primaries narrowly edged tawny-brown, the primary tips with grey-buff fringes. Underwing-coverts white.

Adult worn (May to July) Crown blacker, with traces of brown streaking reduced. Mantle and scapulars duller tawny-brown (less rufous). Supercilium and throat whiter. Central underparts whiter, contrasting more sharply with brown breast sides and flanks. Brown fringes of greater coverts and tertials duller and narrower. Tail and flight feathers dark grey-brown, with brown edges largely worn away.

Juvenile Similar to fresh adult, but crown almost wholly black. Supercilium white and prominent, but dark stripe through lores and upper ear-coverts less blackish and contrasting. Upperparts cinnamon-buff, rather paler than in adult, with slightly broader dark streaking. Underparts white, upper breast washed warm buff and with faint large greyish spots. Flanks warm buff, paler than in adult. Undertail-coverts washed buff. Fringes of wing-coverts and tertials tawny-buff, narrower than in adult and contrasting more with blackish centres. Edges of secondaries tawny-buff.

Bare Parts Upper mandible dark horn-brown to blackish brown. Base of lower mandible paler, sometimes with fleshy tinge. Mouth orange in adult; yellow to orange-yellow in juvenile, with two black tongue spots which usually fade during autumn. Tarsi and toes plumbeous or dull bluish grey to dark horn-brown, purplish brown or olive-brown; soles dull yellow; claws dark grey-brown. Iris dark rich brown to olive-brown in adult, dark brown in juvenile.

IN HAND CHARACTERS
Measurements

A. m. melanopogon

Birds from Italy, Greece and E Mediterranean:

	Male	Female
Wing	55–63 (59.3; 25)	54–60 (57.6; 19)
Tail	48–53 (50.2; 23)	44–51 (48.5; 18)
Bill	14.8–16.5 (15.4; 25)	14.0–16.3 (15.1; 18)
Tarsus	20.2–21.9 (21.1; 22))	19.9–21.6 (20.7; 18)

(Includes data from Cramp 1992)

Sexes combined:
Tail/wing ratio: 78–90% (84%; 20)
Bill width: 2.6–3.3 (3.0; 20)

Hind claw: 5.2–7.4 (6.4; 20)
Tail graduation: 7–10 (8.3; 20)
Juvenile wing averages *c.* 2.5mm shorter than adult (Leisler 1972).
Birds from Iberia and S France are smaller: (sexes combined) *wing* 53–58 (55.1; 11), *tail* 44–50 (46.5; 11), *bill* 13.3–15.5 (14.5; 10), *tarsus* 19.5–20.6 (19.9; 11).

A. m. mimicus

	Male	Female
Wing	60–67 (63.2; 37)	57–66 (61.8; 21)
Tail	48–58 (52.9; 37)	50–56 (52.6; 21)
Bill	14.8–16.5 (15.6; 34)	14.3–16.3 (15.5; 19)
Tarsus	20–23 (21.3; 30)	20–22.5 (21.3; 18)

Tail/wing ratio (sexes combined): 78–89% (85%; 58)
Larger than nominate race throughout whole range.
A. m. albiventris: close to *mimicus*, *wing*, ♂ 59–64 (61.9; 16), ♀ 58–62 (59.7; 4); *tarsus*, ♂ 20–22 (20.9; 10), ♀ 19–23.5 (19.9; 4) (from Kazakov 1974).

Structure
A. m. melanopogon

Wing formula (Cramp 1992):

p1/pc	p2	p3e	p4e	p5e	p6(e)	p7	p10
5–9	5–9	0–2	wp	wp	1–3	3–4	7–10

Wing rounded, with small p1. Wing point p(3) 4–5; p2 = p7/8–8/9 (sometimes = p9 in Iberian birds); emargination on p3–5, sometimes slightly on tip of p6. Notch on p2 inner web slight, falling well below ss tips.

Figure 42. Wing of Moustached Warbler *A. m. melanopogon.*

Tail rounded; feathers with rounded tips in adults, narrower in juveniles.
Bill slim and straight; narrower at base than in Sedge Warbler, more laterally compressed, with fine tip to upper mandible distinctly decurved.
Tarsi slender; toes and claws rather longer than in Sedge Warbler.

A. m. mimicus

p1/pc	p2	p3e	p4e	p5e	p6	p7	p10
5–10	4.5–7	0–1	wp	wp	1.5–3	3.5–6	9.5–12

Wing as nominate race, but slightly less rounded: p2 = p(6/7)7–7/8 (8); p3–5 emarginated.

Figure 43. Wing of Moustached Warbler *A. m. mimicus.*

Recognition A bold whitish supercilium, broadening behind eye and ending rather squarely, contrasts with dark crown and dark side of head. Shows rufous-brown or warm brown upperparts and flanks, streaked mantle, plain rump and plain warm brown nape and neck side. Separated from Sedge Warbler by wing formula, with p2 shorter than p7 and p1 much longer than pc; and by tail shape, with t6 at least 7mm shorter than t1 (Fig. 44). Also by darker legs.

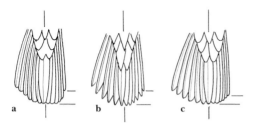

Figure 44. Comparison of tail structure and uppertail-covert shape of (a) Moustached Warbler (b) Aquatic Warbler and (c) Sedge Warbler.

Ageing In late summer, juveniles are distinguishable from worn adults by their unabraded wing and tail feathers, with fresh cinnamon-buff or tawny-buff edgings. The first primary is broader, less pointed than in adults and the tail feathers are narrower. In Europe, ageing in autumn may not be possible after moulting birds have shed their outer primaries. Some young birds, however, retain faint tongue spots to September–October or later.

Weight

A. m melanogogon: Neusiedlersee, Austria, 9.5–14.3g (11.4; 115) (Cramp 1992).

A. m. mimicus: Lake Alakol (SE Kazakhstan), Jul–Sep, 7.9–14.6g (10.7; 600) (AG unpublished data); Pakistan, winter, 8.5–13g (11.0; 12).

GEOGRAPHIC VARIATION Considerable, involving both size and coloration and a slight difference in wing structure. Size increases across S and central Europe, from the smallest birds in Iberia and France, becoming slightly larger in Greece, Turkey and the Levant. Russian and Asian birds are larger still, although with little size variation within this eastern part of the range. These more migratory eastern birds show a slightly less rounded wing. There is an abrupt colour change, birds from W Turkey and Ukraine westwards being darker and more rufous, with a blacker crown, than paler and more greyish olive birds breeding to the east. We recognise *albiventris* of S Russia as a valid form, although this is close to Asian *mimicus* in both size and colour. The breeding birds of S Turkey and the Levant are intermediate in colour, but closer to *mimicus* in size and overall appearance and are best placed with this race.

A. m. melanopogon (S Europe and NW Africa to W Turkey) Described above.

A. m. albiventris (Black Sea from Lower Don River and Sea of Azov east to Krasnodar) Closely resembles *mimicus* in size and colour, but the upperparts are slightly darker and greyer, the flanks slightly deeper ochre-brown, and the undertail-coverts paler, sometimes white. Tarsus longer (Kazakov 1974).

A. m. mimicus (E and S Turkey, Caucasus and Caspian Sea to S Kazakhstan, south locally to Middle East and Afghanistan) Differs from nominate *melanopogon* in having the forehead and crown olive-brown with narrow blackish streaks, often concentrated to form a distinct lateral band above the supercilium. Head pattern resembles *melanopogon* with a long, broad and whitish supercilium terminating squarely at the rear of the ear-coverts, but the band through the lores and upper ear-coverts is blackish brown. The nape, upper side of the neck and upperparts are warm olive-brown, with narrow blackish streaks confined to the mantle. The underparts are whitish, with warm brown on the breast sides and flanks less extensive than in *melanopogon*. The fringes of the upperwing-coverts and tertials and edges of the flight feathers are warm olive-brown. Marginally larger than *melanopogon* with a slightly less rounded wing.

TAXONOMY AND SYSTEMATICS Has previously been placed in a monotypic genus *Lusciniola* because of its rounded wing and long first primary. But these characters overlap with many other species now placed in *Acrocephalus* and it was returned to *Acrocephalus* by Parker & Harrison (1963). No other issues arising.

▲ Adult *A. m. melanopogon*, Italy, September. European birds are darker and more richly coloured than Sedge Warbler, particularly on mantle and underparts, and show a conspicuous white supercilium that flares behind the eye. This bird has adopted a characteristic pose with the tail held cocked above the back (Daniele Occhiato).

▲ Juvenile *A. m. melanopogon*, Italy, September. Drabber and lacking richer plumage tones of fresh adult. Paler and greyer iris and worn tail point to this being a young bird (Daniele Occhiato).

◀ Adult *A. m. mimicus*, Kuwait, October. This slightly warmer-toned bird shows greyish white underparts and a cold brown wash to the flanks, but remains noticeably duller than the nominate form. Note dark legs, short primary projection and emargination on p3–5 (Pekka Fagel).

▲ Adult *A. m. mimicus*, Kuwait, November. Eastern birds differ from the nominate race by their overall duller, less saturated appearance. Note brown crown with narrow blackish streaks. Greyish brown iris suggests this is a first-year bird (Rashed Al-Hajji).

▲ Adult *A. m. mimicus*, Kuwait, December. Although paler and duller than nominate form, upperpart tones may appear warmer in low sunlight and can approach the nominate (Michael Pope).

SEDGE WARBLER
Acrocephalus schoenobaenus   **Plate 16**

Motacilla Schoenobaenus **Linnaeus, 1758**. *Syst. Nat., ed.* 10: 184. Southern Sweden.

A long-distance migrant which breeds commonly in marsh and waterside habitats across temperate Europe from Ireland to C Siberia and E Kazakhstan. It winters widely throughout Africa, from the Sahelian wetlands to South Africa. Monotypic.

IDENTIFICATION Length 13cm. Wing 62–71mm. Tail/wing 66–76%.

A small *Acrocephalus* with streaked upperparts, a prominent pale supercilium and a plain, warmly coloured rump. In much of Europe it shares damp reedy breeding areas with the plain-backed Eurasian Reed Warbler. These two are quite easily separated by their songs, that of Sedge Warbler being hurried and chattering, less steady and rhythmic than in Reed Warbler. In the Western Palearctic, Sedge can occur alongside two similar streaked *Acrocephalus* warblers, Aquatic Warbler and Moustached Warbler, but is distinguishable in the field by features of plumage and structure and by its song. Sexes alike.

Structure A small and rather slim warbler similar in size to Eurasian Reed Warbler, but with a shorter tail and a shorter, more narrow-tipped bill. It has a low crown but the head lacks the attenuated appearance and longer, flat, forehead of Reed Warbler. The wing is long, the primaries projecting to about 80% of the length of the exposed tertials and reaching the longest uppertail-coverts. Eight evenly spaced primary tips are visible in the closed wing and the third primary, which is emarginated, forms the wing point. The undertail-coverts are long, extending well beyond the wing-tip, but are shorter and less bulky than those of a *Locustella* warbler. The tail is distinctly rounded and the individual feathers are relatively broad, unlike those of Aquatic Warbler.

Plumage and bare parts The fresh adult has a striking face pattern. A bold creamy white supercilium, broadest above and behind the eye, extends back and tapers away above the rear of the ear-coverts. This is accentuated by black crown sides and by dark lores and a dark stripe through the upper ear-coverts. The central crown is pale olive-brown, flecked with sharp, heavy, black streaks. The mantle and scapulars are light olive-brown with dark streaking, duller and less sharp than on the crown. The rump and uppertail-coverts are tawny-brown and almost unstreaked, thus tending to contrast with rest of the upperparts and also with the blackish brown tail. The underparts are pale buff, becoming whiter on the chin and throat and on the belly centre, with a warm brownish buff suffusion on the rear flanks. Adult Sedge Warbler never shows any breast streaking. The closed wing is contrastingly patterned with black and warm buff, similar in tone to the upperparts. The blackish feather centres are large and conspicuous, however, enhancing contrast with warm buff fringes to the greater and median coverts, tertials and flight feathers.

During the breeding season, olive tones to the feather fringes are lost. They become narrower and appear paler and greyer, while the darker feather centres are accentuated. The fringes to the upperparts become paler and colder greyish buff, the crown centre becomes blacker and the supercilium and underparts appear whiter as buff feather tips are lost.

Juveniles are more yellowish buff on the supercilium and underparts than fresh adults and most show a gorget of small, dark brown spots across the lower throat. They appear rather buffier above, with sharper mantle streaks, but again show the contrasting tawny-brown rump. Some have a distinct pale central crown stripe, formed by broader overlapping buff feather edges, but this is less sharply defined and contrasting and less yellowish than the crown stripe of Aquatic Warbler.

At all ages, the legs are brownish grey to yellowish grey or flesh-grey.

SIMILAR SPECIES Within its range, likely to occur sympatrically with Aquatic Warbler and Moustached Warbler, which both show a bold supercilium and streaked upperparts like Sedge Warbler and have a rather similar song. Sedge occurs throughout the range of Aquatic, but breeds north of Moustached and, except on passage, is likely to overlap with it only in SE Europe, around the Caspian Sea and in W Kazakhstan.

Aquatic Warbler generally has more yellowish plumage than Sedge, a bolder central crown stripe and heavier blacker upperpart streaking which continues narrowly across the rump. It also shows fine streaks on the upper breast, flanks and undertail-coverts where they are lacking in Sedge. It is structurally similar to Sedge, but has narrower, more pointed tail feathers. The legs are pinkish.

Moustached Warbler in Europe shows a blackish crown, a wide blunt-ended whitish supercilium and a bold black eye-stripe. It is generally more rufous tinged above than Sedge Warbler, with a distinct rusty shawl on the neck side. The underparts are more warmly toned and intensely washed and those of Sedge never approach even the dullest Moustached.

In Asia, the race *mimicus* is paler, less intensely coloured than its European counterpart and more closely resembles Sedge, but retains the classic, slightly flared and blunt-ended supercilium. The crown is olive-brown, less blackish than in nominate Moustached, thus again more like that of Sedge. Overall, however, *mimicus* appears rather darker and browner than Sedge (less buffy olivaceous), with a warm buff wash on the flanks and undertail-coverts. It also shows less strongly patterned wings and little contrast between rump and mantle.

All Moustached have a longer, fuller, more graduated tail than Sedge and a much shorter primary projection. The first primary is relatively large and the third, fourth and fifth are all emarginated. All Moustached show blackish legs, unlike the paler legs of Sedge.

VOICE The song is a sustained, vigorous and complex medley, varying in speed and rhythm, in which grating or buzzing churrs and more hurried chattering passages are interspersed with sweet clear whistles. A typical sequence might be rendered as '...–*tzurrr-tzurrr-tzurrr-chit-it-tzurrr-tzurrr-chi-it-it-tzerr-tzerr-twi-wi-wi-wi-wi-chit- chit-chwee-chwee-chit-it-it-chwee-churrrrrrr-...*'. It is more varied and mimetic and more buzzy than the song of Reed Warbler, with more rapidly delivered passages and without that species' steady repetition of units. It is much more complex than the similar but shorter repetitive song of Aquatic Warbler and it lacks the repeated penetrating crescendo characteristic of Moustached Warbler song. Sequences typically last 20–40 seconds, but sometimes over a minute, usually followed by a pause for only a second or two before the next begins.

8
6
4
2
kHz
s 1 2 3 4 5 6 7 8 9 10 11 12

Part of song of Sedge Warbler, Suffolk, England, May. (Peter Kennerley)

The most common calls are a short scolding *'tucc'* and a grating *'churr'* or *'tzrrr'*, more buzzy and rather higher than the similar call of Eurasian Reed Warbler. In alarm it gives a longer *'tucc-tucc-tuttuttuc'*.

MOULT Some adults moult part of the body and head plumage on the breeding grounds, but many begin autumn migration with entirely worn plumage. A complete moult takes place in Africa, but timing there varies greatly between different populations. Most birds moult in the northern tropics between September and December. Many then continue with fresh plumage in December and January to reach the final winter quarters in equatorial Africa. Others, especially birds heading south of the equator, start moult in the northern tropics, suspend during onward migration, then complete in winter quarters. Some N Nigerian wintering birds showed similar timing, beginning in October–November, suspending, then completing between February and early April (Aidley & Wilkinson 1987a). A few birds wintering near the equator and most of those wintering south of about 10°S (apparently all those reaching Botswana and South Africa), delay their entire moult until after migration, then complete it in *c.* 60–70 days between January and early April (Hanmer 1979; Ginn & Melville 1983). Birds which finish the full moult in autumn have a partial moult between February and early April involving many body and head feathers and occasionally tertials and tail feathers (Pearson 1973).

Young birds have no body moult on the breeding ground and retain their juvenile plumage until arrival in Africa. The timing of the full moult there appears to be much the same as in adults. Most young birds wintering in north tropical and equatorial latitudes moult in autumn while most reaching southern latitudes moult in late winter. In southern wintering populations with mixed early and late moulting birds, adults may well contribute to the former category more than young birds, but this remains to be established.

Birds returning to W and C Europe in spring generally have fresh body plumage but moderately worn primaries, indicating an autumn full moult followed by a late winter partial moult. However, a third of Kenya spring migrants (Pearson *et al.* 1979) and a substantial proportion of Middle East passage birds have fresh flight feathers and tail feathers. These are presumably the late-moulting birds from S Africa *en route* to Siberia, where the majority of breeders arrive in fully fresh plumage (specimens at NHM, Tring).

HABITAT Breeds mainly in lowlands and valleys in cool moist areas. It prefers marsh and waterside situations, nesting in the drier edges of reeds and among sedges *Carex*, horsetails *Equisetum* and other rank vegetation, especially where mixed with osiers and other low leafy bushes. It is often attracted to ponds, gravel pits and other moist depressions. Northern populations also utilise low alder woods near rivers. It is less closely linked to lake edges and wetlands than breeding Eurasian Reed Warbler and less partial to wetter reedbed areas in standing water. It can occur well away from water, for example in hedgerows, nettle beds, old orchards, young conifers and arable crops, but tends to avoid trees and tall bushes. A less specialised breeder than most of its congeners, it is consequently more widespread.

On passage and in winter quarters, it is more confined than Eurasian Reed Warbler to waterside situations and emergent vegetation in open wetlands, a reversal of the situation when breeding. In Africa, it occurs in reeds, sedges, reedmace, *Typha* and occasionally papyrus, around lakes, dams and sewage ponds and along rivers; and in seasonal swamps, inundated grassland and rice fields. It is also found in rank herbage, bushes and small trees growing beside or over water and in small acacias and scrub along ditches. It tends to use ephemeral or seasonal habitat not occupied by resident species. Passage birds may also occur in cultivation margins, drier bush and thicket and even desert scrub. In E Africa it favours medium to quite high elevations, wintering up to about 2,500m in Kenya and Ethiopia.

BEHAVIOUR Often easy to observe when feeding in the open or singing from an exposed perch, but usually forages within low vegetation or close above water. It feeds largely on slow-moving, soft-bodied prey such as emergent insects, gleaned from aquatic plants, the twigs of bushes or low trees, or from the mud surface. Carriage is typically horizontal when hopping through vegetation, flicking the tail frequently, but more upright when sidling up a reed stem. Flight is light and fluent, usually low and over short distances with the tail spread (Cramp 1992).

On the breeding ground, full song serves mainly to advertise for a mate. It is typically given from the top of a reed stem or bush, but sometimes from dense cover. It is often completed in a short song-flight in which the bird climbs steeply to 2–5m and performs a brief circular flight before gliding down on spread wings and with the tail held slightly cocked, to the original or a nearby perch. Song can be maintained from before sunrise until after sunset, with just a few quieter hours during the afternoon. It is sometimes heard at intervals throughout the night. The main vocal period lasts about 2–3 weeks before most males are paired and revert to a short low-intensity song. But a few unpaired birds, late arrivals or nesting failures, sing loudly throughout the breeding season.

Typically solitary outside the breeding season, but often forms small groups on migration. Impressive local concentrations may form in reedbeds on passage and large falls of migrants are sometimes seen. Scores per day have been caught for ringing at passage sites in Europe, Nigeria and Kenya. The species tends to gather readily at temporarily abundant food sources. In Europe in autumn it exploits concentrations of plum reed aphids *Hyalophorus pruni*. Wintering birds in Africa are less sedentary than other *Acrocephalus* species. They tend to move readily in response to changing water levels and are attracted to lakefly swarms. Many do however remain attached to a territory for several weeks and can show strong site fidelity. About 50% were estimated to have returned to the same Uganda wintering site in successive years (Pearson 1972). A sustained varied song is heard in winter quarters from November to April, mainly from January or February onwards.

BREEDING HABITS Males reach the breeding grounds 1–2 weeks before females. They immediately select territories, typically of 0.1–0.2ha (much larger than in Eurasian Reed Warbler) in which pairing and nesting take place. They advertise these with vigorous sustained song, which ceases once pairing has occurred. They are typically monogamous, but sometimes pair with different females, simultaneously or successively.

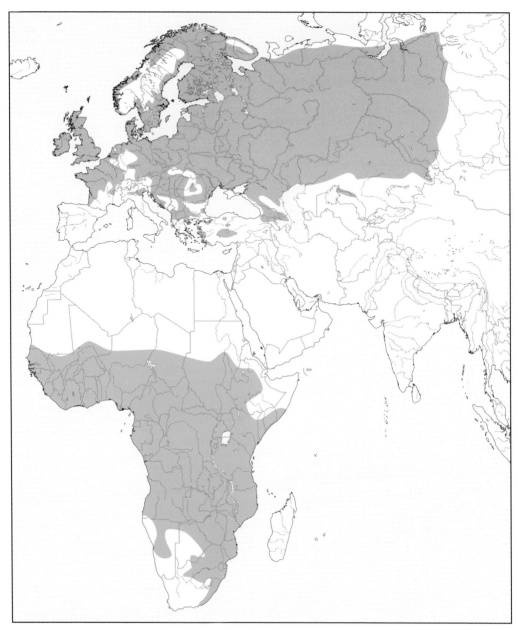

Sedge Warbler. Breeding range and winter distribution.

The nest is built by the female and placed on or within 0.5m of the ground. It is a rounded or cylindrical cup of loosely woven grasses, sedges, plant stems, moss and spiders' web, thickly lined with finer plant material and hair. The outer part is usually woven around vertical plant stems (Cramp 1992). The clutch is typically 5–6 eggs (occasionally 3–8). Incubation is carried out mainly by the female, with limited help from the male and lasts 13–15 days. Both sexes share the feeding and care of the young, collecting most food well outside the territory. The young leave the nest after 13–14 days, but continue to beg food from the parents for up to another two weeks. In NW Europe, egg laying takes place mainly between early May and mid-June; in Russia throughout June. Usually single-brooded, but a second brood is sometimes raised in the west of the range.

DISTRIBUTION

Breeding Breeds widely throughout the boreal and temperate regions of the Western Palearctic and east to C Siberia and C Asia. In the west, it ranges from W Ireland, south along the Atlantic seaboard of France to northernmost Spain (west of the Pyrenees) and north to 70°N in N Norway. It breeds extensively throughout much of C and N Europe to the Ukrainian Black Sea coast, but is absent from the

Mediterranean basin except in parts of S Greece. In Asia, it breeds locally across Turkey, through the lower Caucasus Mountains and along the lower Volga and Ural Rivers. To the east, it has a patchy distribution across the steppe region of Kazakhstan to the north of Lake Balkash and also breeds along the lower Syr Darya from Baygakum to the Aral Sea. It breeds widely across W Siberia east to the Yenisey River watershed between the Ob and Yenisey valleys and north to *c.* 70°N along the Yenisey. Breeding occurs south to the Altai Mountains and the Zaisan Depression in NE Kazakhstan.

It is largely common and widespread in Europe, with densities between 200 and 600 pairs/km² in favourable habitat. The population has been estimated at 2–2.5 million pairs in Europe, with probably at least as many again within the extensive Russian breeding range (Hagemeijer & Blair 1997).

Non-breeding Winters in sub-Saharan Africa, from the Sahel belt (SW Mauritania, Senegal and S Mali to C Sudan) and W and C Ethiopia south to C Namibia, Botswana and NE and E South Africa (to Free State, KwaZulu–Natal and Eastern Cape, with vagrants to Western Cape). Largest numbers winter in the W African wetlands north of about 9°N, from Senegal and the Upper Niger delta to N Nigeria and S Chad; also from C and E African lake areas south to waterside localities in Zambia, Malawi, Zimbabwe, N Botswana and NE South Africa.

MOVEMENTS Most British and NW European birds initially head south to SSW in autumn, but some from Finland move SSE. Russian birds migrate via the E Mediterranean, but some through the Middle East. Ringing recoveries indicate that most birds wintering from Senegal to Ghana are from NW Europe, while those wintering further east and in southern Africa are from populations east of the Baltic. Most winter recoveries from NW Europe have been in Senegal and Mali; others from Britain in Sierra Leone, Liberia and Ghana and from France in Ivory Coast. Finnish birds on the other hand have been recovered in the Congo basin and Zambia. A spring passage bird from Lake Chad was recovered in Russia at 43°E and a spring bird from Kenya also in Russia, at 48°E.

Ring recovery patterns and high pre-migratory weights would indicate that this species commonly makes long unbroken flights between widely separated wetland staging areas. Most adults leave European breeding sites in mid to late July, while most juveniles disperse between late July and mid August and move to pre-migratory fattening areas. Passage through Europe lasts chiefly from late July to mid September, with stragglers to early October. There is a conspicuous passage in August and September through the N and E Mediterranean, the Balkans and Crimea, but limited migration through the Middle East. It is scarce in N Africa in autumn, suggesting that most European birds fly direct to the tropics. Most British birds apparently begin long distance flights from fattening sites north of 45°N, near the English south coast or in N France. In S Siberia, passage takes place from mid July to mid August, with the last birds in late September. In autumn, it is scarce on the S Caspian Sea coast and in C Asia, but some are still present in September east to the western Xinjiang Uygur Autonomous Region in NW China.

The first birds reach Senegal in August and autumn movement through Africa is widespread and protracted. Passage lasts from September to November in Morocco and from September to December in Chad. Birds reach N Nigeria and N Ghana from September and mainly in October, but appear further south in W Africa only from November.

Migration through Egypt and through N and central Sudan lasts from mid August to mid October and birds occur in Ethiopia from September. The first birds reach Zambia from mid October, but the main arrival in S Africa, involving mainly unmoulted birds, is during November–December. In E Africa, unmoulted birds occur from October to December, but autumn passage is sparse, suggesting that most migrants overfly equatorial latitudes. The majority of birds which winter in Kenya and Uganda arrive there in December and January with moult completed.

Most birds leave W African wintering sites during March. In Senegal, northward passage lasts through March and April; at Lake Chad, it occurs from late March to early May. Many more birds make a landfall in N Africa in spring than in autumn, mainly between late March and late April (up to early May in Egypt). In S and E Africa, most birds remain in wintering sites almost a month longer, departing between late March and mid April. The migration of these populations follows a more easterly route through Africa in spring than in autumn. There is heavy passage through Kenya, Ethiopia and N Somalia between mid April and early to mid May, when many birds stop off and fatten extensively.

Returning breeders reach France from late March but mostly in early April; the British Isles mainly between mid April and early May; and most of N Europe between late April and mid May, although not until early June in arctic Norway. Eastern breeders return to W Kazakhstan from late April, SW Siberia from mid May and the Yamal peninsula in mid June.

DESCRIPTION
Plumage – Adult fresh (usually December to May, but dependent on variable moult timing) Forehead and centre of crown blackish with narrow, light olive-brown feather fringes forming distinct streaks; side of crown almost uniformly black, very narrowly tipped pale buff. Supercilium pale olive-buff, broad above and behind eye, narrowing above rear of ear-coverts. A creamy white eye-ring, broken in front and behind. A dark greyish stripe through lores and a dark brown stripe behind eye, bordering supercilium. Rest of ear-coverts and upper cheeks buffy brown, with fine blackish streaks. Nape and upper side of neck olive-brown with poorly defined darker feather centres. Mantle and scapulars with broad, rather diffuse, dark grey-brown centres and pale olive-brown fringes, forming distinct streaks down the mantle and scapulars; rump and uppertail-coverts warm olive-brown or tawny brown, usually with a few indistinct narrow greyish streaks. Tail feathers dark grey-brown, narrowly edged buffy-brown. Chin and throat white, tinged buff. Lower side of neck, upper breast, sides of breast and flanks pale warm buff, becoming more tawny brown on rear of flanks; a few greyish streaks on side of neck and side of breast. Lower breast and belly buffy white. Undertail-coverts pale warm buff. Lesser, median and greater coverts dark brown, broadly fringed light olive-brown. Tertials blackish brown, tips and outer edges broadly fringed buff; primary coverts, primaries and secondaries blackish brown, narrowly edged buff, primary tips with fine buff fringes. Alula blackish with fine buff fringe. Underwing-coverts creamy white.

Adult worn (June to August in Europe) Crown blacker due to loss of feather tips, olive-grey streaking confined to centre; supercilium whiter. Mantle and scapulars cold greyish straw, more closely streaked with dark grey-brown; rump and uppertail-coverts buffier brown. Underparts whiter, with buff wash more restricted to upper breast and flanks. Tertials and upperwing-coverts greyer brown, with pale fringes narrower and whiter. Primaries grey-brown, tips abraded.

Juvenile Similar to fresh adult, but pale edges to head feathers broader so that central crown brighter, buffy brown, often with variable black spotting rather than streaking; side of crown less uniformly black. Supercilium warm buff. Upperparts brighter, warm buff-brown (less olive) than in adult, dark streaking often more sharply defined, rump and uppertail-coverts tending to tawny-buff. Underparts washed more strongly with buff than in adult, with only throat and centre of belly whitish; sides of breast and lower throat/upper breast of most birds with small blackish spots, which sometimes extend to sides of neck and flanks, occasionally with larger blackish spots forming a distinct gorget across the lower throat. Pale fringes to wing and tail feathers typically slightly broader and brighter buff than in adult.

Bare parts Upper mandible dark horn or blackish with yellowish cutting edge. Lower mandible yellowish flesh at base, dark horn or blackish towards tip. Mouth orange or yellow-orange; variably marked grey tongue spots present throughout first autumn, sometimes retained in adults. Tarsi and toes brownish grey, slate-grey, yellowish or flesh-grey in adult, grey-brown to yellowish brown in juvenile; soles dull yellow; claws grey-brown. Iris in adult dark brown, mid brown or reddish brown, and dark brown or grey-brown in juvenile.

IN HAND CHARACTERS
Measurements

	Male	Female
Wing	65–71 (67.2; 72)	62–67 (64.7; 37)
Tail	44–51 (47.3; 35)	44–48 (46.7; 14)
Bill	14.1–15.5 (14.8; 63)	13.8–15.4 (14.6; 36)
Tarsus	20–22.5 (21.4; 38)	20.1–21.7 (20.8; 23)

(Adults, Netherlands, Cramp 1992)

Sexes combined:
Tail/wing: 66–76% (71%; 86)
Bill width: 3.4–3.9 (3.6; 20)
Hind claw: 6.2–7.2 (6.8; 20)
Tail graduation: 3–7 (4.6; 30)
Wing and tail of juveniles average *c.* 1mm shorter than in adult.
Birds breeding in continental Europe average slightly longer in the wing than those of Britain. Siberian birds and wintering/passage birds from E Africa (see **Appendix 2**) average still larger (Table 5).

Table 5. Variation in wing length of adult male Sedge Warbler across the geographic range.

Region	Wing length
British Isles	63–69 (66.0; 32)
W and C Europe	65–69 (67.1; 27)
W Siberia	67–71 (68.8; 16)

Structure

Wing formula (Cramp 1992):

p1/pc	p2	p3(e)	p4	p5	p6	p7	p10
(7)–(1)	0–2	wp	1–4	3.5–7	6.5–8.5	8.5–11	14–19

Wing pointed; p1 minute, always < pc. Wing point p(2) 3; p2 = (p3) 3/4 or 4 (sometimes p4/5 in eastern birds); emargination on p3. Notch on inner web of p2 10–13mm from tip in adults, falling at about p8; 8–10mm from tip in juveniles.

Figure 45. Wing of Sedge Warbler.

Tail rather short, slightly rounded; feather tips rounded (Fig. 47)
Bill slim, shorter than in Eurasian Reed Warbler, concave sided with fine tip.
Tarsi shorter than in Eurasian Reed; claws rather strong.

Recognition Separated from Aquatic Warbler by poorly defined central crown stripe (if present), diffuse and dull grey-buff to olive-brown, not sharp and yellowish; rump unstreaked or almost so. Also by less strongly rounded tail with slightly broader, more rounded feathers (Fig. 47) and pale greyish to mid brown legs. Aquatic Warbler has similar wing structure.

Generally paler, less richly coloured than Moustached Warbler, particularly on flanks and head pattern less striking (supercilium less whitish, crown less uniformly dark). Legs never blackish as in Moustached. Differences in wing structure are diagnostic, Sedge having p2 > p5, p1 shorter than primary coverts and only p3 emarginated. (Moustached has p2 < p7, p1 5–8 > pc and emargination on p3–5). See also different tail structures (Fig. 44).

Ageing In early autumn, adults have worn greyish brown upperparts, whitish supercilium and abraded wing and tail feathers, with worn whitish edges to the tertials. They are readily separated from juveniles which have fresh, buffy body plumage and supercilium and fresh wing and tail feathers, broad buff edges to the tertials and unworn primary tips. Most juveniles, but not adults, have the upper breast speckled dark brown. By late autumn, juveniles are rather bleached and moderately worn and unmoulted birds are much more difficult to age. But many young birds retain traces of breast speckling and/or relatively unworn primary tips up to December, when most adults are heavily abraded.

Weight Range 8–23g. Typical weight of lean birds 9–11g. Migrants commonly reach 14–18g and are noted for a tendency to accumulate very large fat loads. Weights of 19–23g are recorded in NW and E Europe in autumn and from W and E Africa in spring.

GEOGRAPHIC VARIATION Variation involves mainly size and moult strategy. The smallest birds breed in the British Isles, the largest in northernmost Scandinavia and N Russia. Unlike those of Europe, Siberian breeding birds tend to moult late in winter and appear on the breeding grounds with fresh flight feathers. In the east of the range, juveniles in September appear colder and duller than their European counterparts.

TAXONOMY AND SYSTEMATICS No issues arising.

▲ Adult, Merseyside, England, May. Adults have a winter body moult, so birds returning to the breeding grounds appear warmer and brighter than worn adults in autumn (Richard Steel).

▲ Adult, Kuwait, March. Asian breeders, particularly those from Siberia, moult later in Africa than European birds, and appear less worn in spring (AbdulRahman Al-Sirhan).

▲ Adult, Poland, May. Fresh appearance is soon lost due to plumage abrasion, enhancing contrast between the greyish brown mantle and warmer unstreaked rump and uppertail-coverts (Mateusz Matysiak).

▲ Adult, Suffolk, England, July. By late summer, adults are heavily worn and appear much darker and colder than juveniles (James Kennerley).

▲ Juvenile, Tuscany, Italy, September. Shows little contrast between the upperparts and underparts, making separation from worn adult in autumn straightforward (Daniele Occhiato).

▲ Juvenile, Tuscany, Italy, September. In autumn, juveniles are readily separated from adults by their fresh plumage and show a band of small, dark spots across the lower throat (Daniele Occhiato).

AQUATIC WARBLER
Acrocephalus paludicola   **Plate 16**

Sylvia paludicola Vieillot, 1817. *Nouv. Dict. d'Hist. Nat., nouv. éd.*, 11: 202. Lorraine and Picardy.

Europe's rarest migrant passerine, with a localised and patchy distribution extending from C and E Europe to the S Ural Mountains, and possibly east to Ob River in W Siberia. A long-distance migrant wintering in W African wetlands where its range is poorly known. Monotypic.

IDENTIFICATION Length 13cm. Wing 60–66mm. Tail/wing 71–80%.

A small, yellowish buff warbler with a boldly striped head and heavily streaked upperparts. On its breeding grounds, on passage and in winter it is likely to occur alongside the similar Sedge Warbler, but it differs in details of plumage and, with good views, field identification should not be a problem. Its song, with grating and whistled notes recalls that of Sedge, but is much shorter, slower and less complex. Sexes alike.

Structure Although slim and flat-crowned like Sedge Warbler, Aquatic Warbler has a subtly different, more compact-bodied jizz. The head appears longer, the bill slightly shorter and the tail is narrower and more graduated, with unusually narrow and pointed feathers. Wing structure is similar to that of Sedge, with wing point at p3 and only p3 emarginated, but it is slightly shorter with a primary projection of 60–70% and shows 7–8 visible primary tips.

Plumage and bare parts A strikingly marked *Acrocephalus* with a boldly marked head and upperpart pattern. In spring, adults have a broad, yellowish buff supercilium and a narrower but clearly defined buff stripe down the centre of the crown, both extending from the bill to the hind crown and separated by broad, blackish, lateral crown stripes. Unlike Sedge, the lores are pale (almost lacking the dark loral stripe of Sedge Warbler), but there is a well-marked dark stripe behind the eye. Pale buffish cheeks are crossed by a narrow dark moustachial stripe and there is usually a distinct fine blackish malar streak visible. The tawny-buff upperparts are heavily streaked to produce long, broad, buff and black stripes that extend down the mantle and scapulars, become finer and narrower across the rump and uppertail-coverts. It has yellowish buff underparts that are palest on throat and belly and usually show fine blackish streaks on the breast side and flanks and sometimes across the upper breast. The dark wing feathers are slightly worn in spring, with contrasting buff fringes to the median and greater coverts and tertials and buff edges to the flight feathers, those on the secondaries forming a pale panel on the closed wing. The dark tail feathers are also edged pale buff.

By August, the scapulars, wing-coverts and edges to the flight feathers on heavily worn adults become abraded, appearing greyish buff or even greyish, while the distinctive streaking on the breast and flanks tends to become more prominent. Adults may moult some worn body and head feathering during July and August but many retain worn plumage until their complete moult in the wintering area.

Juveniles are similar to freshly moulted adults, with broad pale buff fringes to the tertials and wing-coverts that contrast sharply with blackish centres. The lores and cheeks are pale (unlike those of juvenile Sedge). The head stripes and the edges to the upperpart feathers tend to be paler,

more golden buff than in fresh adults, contrasting strongly with blackish markings, but the streaked uppertail-coverts and broad buff edges to the tail feathers are distinctly more tawny. In young birds, the breast sides are usually marked with a few dusky spots rather than longer sharp streaks.

The bill is dark blackish brown with a yellowish or pinkish flesh lower mandible and the legs and feet are pale pinkish brown or yellowish flesh at all ages.

SIMILAR SPECIES Within Europe, it is only likely to be confused with Sedge Warbler, with which it occurs sympatrically throughout much of its range.

Sedge Warbler resembles Aquatic in overall size and shares a pale supercilium and streaked upperparts. It differs in appearing generally more olive, less yellow-toned than Aquatic, with the upperparts less heavily and completely streaked and it shows a discrete warm rump. The supercilium is shorter and less prominent than Aquatic shows and it has a poorly defined and usually fairly inconspicuous pale crown stripe, although this tends to appear more conspicuous on juveniles. It also shows a dark stripe through the lores which Aquatic lacks. Streaking on the upperparts is less heavy and more diffuse than in Aquatic and the almost completely unmarked tawny-brown rump and uppertail-coverts contrast distinctly with the mantle. Adult Sedge lacks the distinct fine streaks on the breast and flanks, but juveniles do show diffuse spots at the sides of the upper breast, which on some individuals form an indistinct gorget across the upper breast, but these spots are never as contrasting and well defined as the fine streaking which Aquatic shows. The tail is less graduated and shows broader, more rounded feathers. The legs are duller and greyer (less pinkish) than in Aquatic.

VOICE Although reminiscent of Sedge Warbler, the song of Aquatic is less varied and complex and rather more slowly delivered. It consists of a repetition of a rather simple sequence lasting no more than a few seconds. One or more emphatic, grating '*terrr*' calls (harder and lower pitched than the similar sound in Sedge Warbler song and descending slightly in pitch) are followed immediately by a series of quicker, higher pitched and more melodious notes or soft whistles. Several such sequences may be run together '*terrr-du-du-du-du-, tsrr-di-di-di, terrr-err-err-wi-wi-wi-wi-wi-*'.

The repertoire is rather limited but would seem to include mimicked sounds such as wader calls within a frequency range of 2–6kHz. Song may be heard almost continuously, but bursts of 1–8 seconds are usually separated by pauses of a few seconds. The longest, most complex songs are often given in song-flight. Individual males tend to sing a constant song.

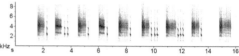

Part of song of Aquatic Warbler, Poland, May. (Sample 2003)

The contact-alarm calls include a hard *tack* or '*tseck*' and a soft '*tucc-tucc*' or '*chut*', very like the calls of Sedge Warbler. A grating or rattling '*trrerr*' or '*trrtrrtrr*', is similar to the rattles in the song.

MOULT Adults may moult part of the head and body plumage in Europe between July and September, although the extent of this varies between individuals and many replace little or no feathering before they reach the tropics.

A full wing and tail moult takes place soon after arrival in winter quarters, probably between October and December. Body and head moult is then completed, but whether or not plumage renewed before migration is replaced again is unknown. Another variable partial moult follows during February–March, before spring migration, during which some birds replace all the head and body feathers, tertials and some inner wing-coverts, but others the head, breast and some upperpart feathers only. Young birds have no body moult in the breeding area and retain full juvenile plumage during autumn migration. They apparently have a complete moult shortly after reaching winter quarters, followed by a partial late winter moult as in adults.

Thus birds returning to the breeding grounds in spring have fresh head and body plumage and often some fresh tertials and inner wing-coverts, which contrast with the distinctly worn tail and flight feathers.

HABITAT Aquatic Warbler breeds in low, open marshy tracts, favouring communities dominated by sedge *Carex* rather than reedbeds. It is found over or close to shallow water, around lake edges, on flooded meadows, by slow flowing river tributaries and along ditches. In Poland, it breeds on swampy meadows with low tussocky sedge growing on peat beds. It typically prefers clumps of sedge up to 80cm high, growing with mosses, or with iris, horsetails and grasses and tolerates the presence of scattered willow bushes or a few short reeds. It also breeds on partially drained hay meadows; in calcareous marshes dominated by great fen-sedge *Cladium mariscus*; and in some Baltic Sea coastal sites and estuaries in seasonally flooded saltmarsh with weak, low, reed stands (Aquatic Warbler Conservation Team 1999). Densities of up to one male per hectare have been recorded in suitable *Carex* marshes, but breeding is now mainly restricted to local pockets.

On passage, it occurs in a wider variety of habitats, although it favours low stands of sedges and reeds near open water, usually along rivers, estuaries and coastal lagoons (De By 1990). It is also found in willows by ponds and along river banks, reedy ditches, low scrub and bushes and crop fields. Wintering birds in W Africa have been found in extensive areas of flooded grassland and reed.

BEHAVIOUR Usually seen singly on migration. It is more secretive than Sedge Warbler, usually feeding just above the ground or water, often taking relatively large arthropods. When scurrying and climbing through dense low vegetation its movements suggest a *Locustella* warbler. When alert, or climbing within sedge, it can adopt a slim upright posture with the neck outstretched. In autumn, it sometimes feeds higher up in willow bushes. Flight is usually low and for short distances, with the tail slightly depressed, but is lighter, more darting, than in Sedge Warbler and the rump and tail appear less broad.

On the breeding grounds, males move about quite widely and may sing from a number of perches within a home range. They often sing from within cover, but may allow close approach. They adopt an upright posture with head and bill pointing up, head and throat feathers ruffled and tail held down. They often perform a song-flight (although less frequently than Sedge Warbler), rising steeply with fluttering wing beats, commencing song during the last phase of ascent or at the summit, then continuing during a steep or gliding descent into vegetation, often some distance from take-off (Cramp 1992). They may also sing in low undulating flights between song-posts. Song peaks around dawn and dusk. It continues through the breeding

season, in central Europe from late April until July or even August. Breeding females are very secretive and reluctant to fly, preferring to run rodent-like between clumps of vegetation (Cramp 1992).

BREEDING HABITS The breeding system is unusual, being either polygynous or promiscuous (Schulze-Hagen *et al.* 1989, 1999; Dyrcz & Zdunek 1993a). Territorial behaviour is poorly understood as there is no real pair bonding and the female raises young without help from the male.

Males and females appear to arrive on the breeding ground together and egg laying begins about a week later. Nest aggregations may be found at sites with high food productivity. Each male adopts a large home range or singing area (up to 8ha.) within which he makes long excursions, crossing the home ranges of other males, showing no antagonism to them or obvious territory limits. Song perches may be used by different males in quick succession. Males sing and attempt to attract as many females as possible throughout the breeding season, while females mate with more than one male. Each female has a territory (0.6–1.5ha.) in which she nests and collects food for the young, although there is some overlap between these territories.

The nest is built by the female. It is placed 3–30cm above swampy ground or water, usually in an old sedge clump, tucked amongst stems but not woven to them. It is a loosely constructed cup of grass, plant stems, down and spiders' webs, lined with finer material, sometimes with feathers. It is slightly smaller than the nest of Sedge Warbler. The clutch size is 4–6 (3–8). The eggs are incubated by the female for 12–15 days. The young are brooded and fed in the nest for 13–15 days by the female alone. She brings large arthropod prey, mostly collected close to the nest. After fledging, the young are accompanied by the female for a further 5–8 days. Egg laying in Europe takes place from early May to mid July. Most females are double-brooded.

The rapid start to laying, large clutch size and high frequency of second broods are apparently associated with the unusual mating system, itself made possible by the exploitation of a specialised habitat with a rich source of large food items (Schulze-Hagen *et al.* 1989.).

DISTRIBUTION
Breeding Breeds in C and E Europe between about 47°N and 59°N but within this range, its distribution is highly fragmented and severely limited by availability of habitat and the current distribution probably represents a relict of a formerly more continuous range. Since the late nineteenth century it has been lost as a breeding species from France, Belgium, Netherlands, former West Germany, Latvia, former Czechoslovakia, former Yugoslavia, Austria and Italy (Glutz von Blotzheim & Bauer 1991; Cramp 1992). It has also contracted within its remaining breeding areas following habitat loss from drainage and changing agriculture. It is now thought to breed in less than 50 regular sites in just seven countries, from extreme NE Germany to the S Ural Mountains in European Russia, with an isolated population in Hungary and possibly a few remaining birds in W Siberia. The total population is estimated at 22,000–30,000 and it is considered the rarest migratory passerine in Europe (BirdLife 2008).

Fewer than 50 males remain in two sites in NE Germany, 150–300 at a few sites in W Lithuania and perhaps fewer than 100 in the Hortobagy marshes in Hungary, where numbers have recently collapsed. Largest numbers breed in N and E Poland (2,900–3,400 males), W and S Belarus

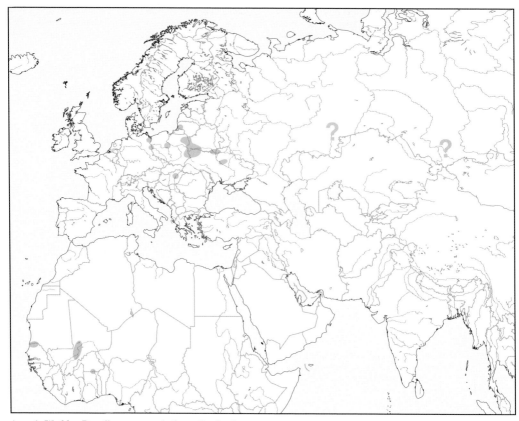

Aquatic Warbler. Breeding range and winter distribution.

(4,800–6,300 males) and N Ukraine (1,400–4,000 males) (BirdLife 2008). The core population is centred on the Biebrza Marshes (NE Poland) and the upper Pripyat and Yaselda River systems, which are now believed to hold 75% of the world population. It formerly bred across European Russia to Yekaterinburg and Chelyabinsk, but its current status here is uncertain. There still appear to be some irregular and small breeding populations in the South Ural area (Aquatic Warbler Conservation Team 1999). In W Siberia, it was formerly reported to breed east to the Ob River but recent searches found only a few birds in N Omsk region (Kalyakin 1996; Flade 1999; Kalyakin *et al.* 2000). This tiny, scattered and fluctuating population is perhaps at the brink of extinction and the total Russian breeding population is thought to number fewer than 500 males.

Non-breeding The wintering grounds are poorly known but are believed to lie within the Sahelian wetlands in W Africa. A major site was discovered in 2007 on the Lower Senegal River, in and adjacent to Djoudj National Park in Senegal. It is estimated that this region holds at least 5,000–10,000 birds. Wintering birds have also been recorded from the Inner Niger delta in Mali and from N Ghana. There is no convincing evidence to support over-wintering in the Mediterranean region.

MOVEMENTS Early autumn movements of birds from Poland and Belarus have been clarified by mist-netting in reedbeds. These populations move west to southwest through the Low Countries to NW France, with some appearing regularly on the coasts of S England. The main route is then through SW France, Iberia (where it occurs regularly in Portugal) and N Morocco. Autumn migrants have been recorded in coastal Mauritania and the Canary Islands. Some birds would appear to perform a loop migration, returning from Africa by a more direct route. Thus, the species is rare in spring in NW Europe, but more regular in NE Morocco, N Algeria, E Spain and E France. Whether Russian birds follow the same routes is unknown. A regular passage occurs through Bulgaria in both autumn and spring, suggesting undiscovered wintering sites exist in C or NE Africa. In addition there are three recent spring records from Turkey including single birds at the Kizilirmak River delta on the north coast on 1 May 1992 and another trapped and ringed there on 28 March 2006. It has also been reported on the Mediterranean Sea coast on 5 September 1991 (Kirwan 2008).

Both sexes leave the breeding grounds from late June, but some females with late broods remain to mid or late August. Juveniles depart soon after fledging. Passage in Belgium and N France extends from late July to early September, with British records peaking in mid August. In C Europe passage occurs from mid July to early October with stragglers into mid or late October. Most records from S France are in September, those from Morocco in September or early October. Some birds remain in Russia and Ukraine up to early or mid September. Northward movement begins early, with birds in Morocco and N Algeria from February to mid-April. Spring records from Spain and the Camargue, France, are in late April and from Switzerland between mid

April and mid May. Birds return to breeding grounds in Germany, Poland and Belarus between late April and mid May.

Autumn ringing recoveries include birds from Polish breeding grounds to Belgium and SW England, and from Belarus to SE England, S and SW France and N Spain. Autumn passage birds ringed in Belgium have been found in England, France, Spain and Portugal, and one ringed in September in NW France was relocated on the breeding grounds in Belarus the following July.

DESCRIPTION

Plumage – Adult fresh (December to March) Forehead to hind crown with yellowish buff central stripe, bordered on each side by a broader black stripe, this sometimes with narrow tawny-buff feather fringes. Supercilium long and broad, yellowish buff, often paler towards rear. Eye-ring narrow, buffy white. Lores pale buff, usually crossed by a dusky mottled streak. A narrow, blackish brown streak across the upper ear-coverts below rear of supercilium; lower ear-coverts, upper cheek and side of neck yellowish buff, finely mottled dark brown. Usually a short, dark brown, moustachial stripe and a fine, blackish, malar streak. Nape yellowish buff with diffuse dusky streaks or spots. Mantle and scapulars tawny-buff with black feather centres forming broad, sharply defined streaks. Rump and uppertail-coverts slightly warmer tawny-buff, with fainter, narrow, dark grey streaks. Tail feathers dark grey-brown with broad tawny-buff edges, tips narrowly fringed pale buff; outermost feathers grey-buff, becoming paler on outer edge. Underparts yellowish buff, paler and whiter on chin and throat and on centre of belly; warmer, pale tawny buff on rear flanks and undertail-coverts. Flanks usually with short, dark grey or blackish streaks, these often also present across upper breast. Undertail-coverts sometimes with fine dusky streaks. Wing feathers blackish; lesser, median and greater coverts and tertials, broadly fringed tawny-buff; primary coverts and alula narrowly fringed pale buff; flight feathers edged buff, quite broadly on bases of secondaries; primary tips narrowly fringed greyish white. Underwing-coverts white.

Adult worn (June to August) Resembles fresh adult but colder and greyer in overall appearance. Lateral crown stripes dark grey-brown, contrasting sharply with yellowish buff supercilium and central crown stripe. Mantle with large blackish feather centres and narrow warm buff fringes. Ear-coverts and sides of neck yellowish buff. Lores, cheeks and eye line blackish, diffuse and ill-defined but more prominent than in fresh adult. Scapulars dark grey-brown with paler ash-grey fringes. Rump and uppertail-coverts tawny-brown with narrow blackish shaft streaks. Breast and belly off-white, with yellowish buff tones confined to chin, throat and flanks. Dark streaks on breast and flanks variable in length and prominence, but typically more conspicuous than on fresh adult, particularly on lower flanks. Wing-coverts dark grey-brown with paler ash-grey fringes. Tertials dark grey-brown with pale greyish white fringe, broadest on inner web. Secondaries dark grey-brown with greyish white fringes forming an indistinct pale panel in closed wing. Primaries uniform dark grey-brown except p2 which has a narrow whitish outer web. Buff fringes to grey-brown tail feathers worn and narrow, shafts usually paler than webs, particularly on central rectrices.

Juvenile Similar to fresh adult, but yellowish buff head stripes slightly paler; lores and cheeks pale buff with loral and moustachial stripes indistinct. Golden-yellow to yellowish buff edges to mantle feathers and scapulars

paler, contrasting sharply with broad brownish black streaks; rump, uppertail-coverts and broad outer borders of tail-feathers more tawny-buff. Underparts occasionally unmarked but usually with some small dark blackish spots on lower sides of neck. Flanks usually with short dark grey or blackish streaks as in adult. Fringes to wing feathers paler buff, less tawny than in adult, those on primary coverts, alula and secondaries slightly broader.

Bare Parts Upper mandible dark horn to blackish brown, often with small pale tip, and yellowish or pinkish flesh cutting edges. Lower mandible yellowish or pinkish flesh, tip of lower mandible dusky brown. Mouth yellow (less orange than Sedge Warbler). Tarsi and toes pale pinkish brown or yellowish flesh; claws pale grey-brown. Iris brown or dark brown.

IN HAND CHARACTERS
Measurements

	Male	Female
Wing	60–66 (63.1; 120)	60–66 (62.7; 80)
Tail	43–50 (46.0; 28)	45–50 (46.6; 22)
Bill	12.5–14.6 (13.6; 26)	12.9–14.5 (13.7; 22)
Tarsus	19.9–21.7 (20.7; 27)	19.7–21.5 (20.5; 21)

(Cramp 1992; adults and juveniles, mainly Netherlands, autumn)

Juvenile measurements not significantly different from those of adults (Cramp 1992).

Sexes combined:
Tail/wing ratio: 71–80% (75%; 20)
Bill width: 3.3–3.9 (3.6; 20)
Hind claw: 5.4–6.5 (6.0; 20)
Tail graduation: 8–11 (9.1; 20)

Structure

Wing formula (Cramp 1992):

p1/pc	p2	p3e	p4	p5	p6	p7	p10
(5)–0	0–2	wp	1.5–3	4.5–6	7–9	9–11	13–17

Wing pointed; p1 minute. Wing point p(2) 3; p2 = (3) 3/4 or 4 (4/5); emargination on p3. Notch on inner web of p2 9–12mm from tip, falling at about p8.

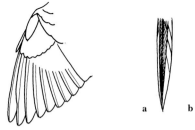

Figure 46. Wing of Aquatic Warbler.

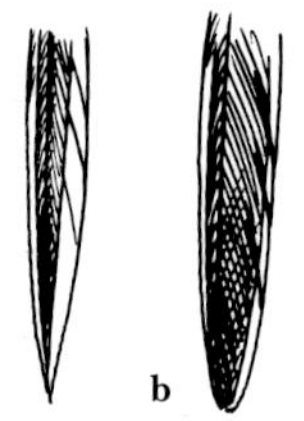

Figure 47. Comparison of central tail feather of (a) Aquatic Warbler and (b) Sedge Warbler.

Tail strongly rounded; feathers narrow with pointed tips.

Bill rather short; slightly less concave-sided and less fine at tip than in Sedge Warbler

Tarsi as Sedge Warbler, but foot structure differs, with inner and outer toes almost equal as in *Locustella* species; claws smaller than in Sedge Warbler.

Recognition Separated from Sedge Warbler by conspicuous pale yellowish buff central crown stripe, heavily streaked mantle and scapulars and distinctly streaked rump; also (if present) by streaks on breast sides and flanks. Note also the more rounded tail with narrower feathers (Fig. 44) and bright flesh or pinkish legs.

Ageing Ageing is straightforward in early autumn. Juveniles have fresh wing and tail feathers and fresh, yellowish tinged head and body plumage, with pale lores and unstreaked underparts. Adults have very worn wing and tail feathers. Some retain worn greyish buff body plumage, but in others this is largely replaced by fresh tawny-buff feathers. The breast and flanks are usually finely streaked and there is often a dark loral stripe. Young birds are not normally distinguishable from adults after the main moult.

Weight In Europe, 10–14.5g in 101 breeding birds, 9–15g in 61 autumn migrants (Cramp 1992). Passage birds Belgium, Jul–Sep, 9.1–13.9g (11.2, 584) (NR unpublished data). One trapped Djoudj (Senegal) weighed 10g on 2 March and 16g when retrapped on 17 March (Cramp 1992).

TAXONOMY AND SYSTEMATICS No issues arising.

▲ Adult, Normandy, France. August. Adults commence body moult while on migration in Europe. Note contrast between the fresh head and mantle feathers and the worn and retained grey-toned scapulars, wing-coverts and flight feathers (James Kennerley).

▲ ▼ Adult, Biebrza Marshes, Poland, June. Adults show streaking on lower throat, breast and flanks, which adult Sedge Warbler lacks (Mateusz Matysiak).

▼ ▶ Juvenile, Normandy, France, August. Differs from juvenile Sedge Warbler by broad blackish lateral crown stripes contrasting with narrow paler central crown stripe, greater contrast between pale fringes and dark centres in upperparts, dark streaks on uppertail-coverts and fine, dark streaks on breast and flanks (James Kennerley).

STREAKED REED WARBLER
Acrocephalus sorghophilus   **Plate 17**

Calamodyta sorghophila **Swinhoe, 1863**. *Proc. Zool. Soc. London*. p. 92. Amoy, Fohkien, China.

The rarest and least known *Acrocephalus* occurring in the E Palearctic. The breeding area remains unknown but a singing male was recently discovered in reedbeds along the Amur River in the Russian Far East and it probably breeds here and in adjacent regions of NE China. Only known to winter in the Philippines. Considered to be VULNERABLE by BirdLife International. Monotypic.

IDENTIFICATION Length 12cm. Wing 55–59mm. Tail/wing 79–83%.

The combination of a conspicuous pale supercilium and fine brown streaking on the crown and mantle, with generally warm straw to sandy brown plumage gives Streaked Reed Warbler a unique appearance among the small E Asian *Acrocephalus*. Only Black-browed Reed Warbler occurs commonly within its range and the identification and separation should be straightforward. Sexes alike.

Structure A small and slim *Acrocephalus*, similar in size to Black-browed Reed Warbler. with an attenuated structure and small, delicate and fine-tipped bill. The wing appears proportionally longer than in most small E Asian *Acrocephalus*, showing a primary projection equal to about half the tertial length. Five or occasionally six evenly spaced primary tips are visible, with a short first primary extending to, or just beyond the primary coverts. The wing point is formed by p3–4 and p3–5 are emarginated. The tail is rather short as in Black-browed Reed, but the individual rectrices are narrower.

Plumage and bare parts A small, pale and lightly streaked *Acrocephalus* and the only species likely to show streaked upperparts in E Asia. The crown and mantle vary from warm straw to light sandy brown, while the side of the crown is bordered by a narrow but usually conspicuous dark brown to blackish band that extends above the supercilium but stops short of the bill, although pale feather tips may break up the outline on fresh birds. The long, pale, sandy brown supercilium is always conspicuous and contrasts with the dark side of the crown. It is similar to that of Black-browed Reed Warbler but slightly more diffuse and lacks the crisp, square-cut appearance that most Black-browed Reed exhibit. The eye-stripe is not particularly obvious or contrasting. There is a small dark spot immediately in front of the eye. Behind the eye the eye-stripe is little more than a pale brown line that widens slightly towards the rear of the ear-coverts and merges with the side of the nape.

The crown and mantle vary in colour between warm straw and light sandy brown and show narrow, dark brown feather centres that give it the characteristic finely streaked appearance. On juveniles, however, pale fringes may obscure the darker streaks so the mantle may appear uniform. On adults in autumn the streaking can also be faint and subdued. Typically, the nape is sandy buff, slightly greyer and colder than the mantle and lacks the fine streaking. Contrasting with the mantle, the rump and uppertail-coverts are unstreaked warm rufous-brown to fulvous-brown, while the tail is similar in colour to the uppertail-coverts and when fresh shows narrow paler tips.

The closed wing is variable in appearance. Some individuals, probably first-winter birds in fairly fresh plumage, show dark-brown or even blackish centres to the tertials,

greater coverts and, in particular, the median coverts and also the alula. There is often a conspicuous pale panel formed in the closed wing by straw-coloured edges to the tertials and secondaries that contrast with the darker edges to the primaries. In combination, these features give Streaked Reed Warbler a contrasting appearance not seen in other E Asian *Acrocephalus*. Some individuals, particularly worn and faded adults, show paler feather centres and as the fringes lose their contrast the closed wing appears fairly uniform.

The bill is dark grey with an unmarked yellowish pink lower mandible. The legs are pale grey with a slight greenish tinge.

SIMILAR SPECIES All of the smaller *Acrocephalus* known to occur within the range of Streaked Reed Warbler show unstreaked upperparts so confusion is unlikely. However, Black-browed Reed Warbler shows prominent dark bands bordering the sides of the crown above the supercilium and its separation is briefly discussed below. Manchurian Reed and Paddyfield Warblers show less conspicuous dark bands above the supercilium. Sedge Warbler is unrecorded in E Asia but breeds in W China and presents a potentially greater source of confusion.

Black-browed Reed Warbler always lacks streaking on the crown and mantle and never shows such obvious contrast between the darker centres and paler fringes to the wing-coverts and tertials, or the contrast between the pale mantle and the warm rufous-brown rump and uppertail-coverts. Some Streaked Reed Warblers, particularly fresh first-winter birds, can show less prominent streaking. However, Black-browed Reed always appears darker, browner and, in particular, more uniform above than Streaked Reed, with an olive tone to the upperparts; quite unlike the rather pale sandy brown appearance of Streaked Reed. Although both species exhibit dark sides to the crown, these are usually broader and more conspicuous in Black-browed Reed. It also has a slightly longer primary projection, 60–70% of the tertial length and six or even seven primary tips are visible.

Sedge Warbler is unrecorded in E Asia so may be thought to be an unlikely confusion species. However, it breeds east to W China and within the range of other small *Acrocephalus* which have reached E China, including Paddyfield Warbler and Blyth's Reed Warblers. Furthermore, Streaked Reed is now so rarely seen that Sedge Warbler should be considered if a potential Streaked Reed Warbler is encountered. The two species share many plumage features and closely resemble each other. Sedge Warbler is significantly larger and slightly warmer and darker above and has wider but diffuse, less contrasting and less conspicuous streaking on the mantle, but better-defined crown streaking. In adults, the dark sides to the crown are broader than Streaked Reed shows, but on young birds they are narrowly tipped bright buff and appear less obvious. Despite this, the streaking in the centre of the crown should be more conspicuous than that on a Streaked Reed of a similar age.

Sedge Warbler is readily separated using measurements and wing structure. It is a significantly larger bird than Streaked Reed, with wing length ranging from 62–71mm, longer than the largest Streaked Reed (52–59mm), while the tail/wing ratio of Sedge (67–75%), is much lower than that of Streaked Reed (79–83%). Sedge Warbler also shows a conspicuously longer primary projection, at *c.* 80% of the tertial length, with eight evenly spaced primary tips visible and with only the third primary emarginated.

VOICE The song is undescribed and no recordings are available for comparison with similar species. However, the song of a migrant heard at the Summer Palace near Beijing, China, in June had a recognisably *Acrocephalus*-like structure. Compared with the numerous Blunt-winged Warblers present, the song was more varied, higher pitched and thinner (PRK pers. obs.). The call from the wintering area in the Philippines is a short and slightly slurred '*thrrrr*', typically given at intervals of two or three seconds. Occasionally given more rapidly in a short burst where several calls run into one another, some given at slightly differing pitch, to form a sequence which becomes almost a sub-song.

MOULT Uncertain whether adults and juveniles have a body moult before leaving the breeding grounds, but as they are early migrants this appears unlikely. Birds trapped in the Philippines in early February showed moderate wear to the primaries and tail but had not yet started to moult. The only report of a bird moulting its primaries comes from Candaba Marsh on Luzon, Philippines, where a heavily worn bird was trapped on 9 March (PDR *in litt.*). Specimens collected in spring in N China show fresh primaries and fresh or slightly worn rectrices. These data strongly suggest there is a complete late winter moult before spring migration. No other details known.

It is interesting to speculate that the lack of records at Dalton Pass on Luzon between mid March and mid May (see **Movements** below) suggests that birds are moulting in this period.

HABITAT Breeding habitat uncertain. A singing male observed at the Muraviovka Park in the Amur region of the Russian Far East was singing in willow scrub, not far from two small ponds within a *Phragmites* reedbed (F. & S. Pékus *in litt.*) and this may be the preferred habitat elsewhere. A singing male at the Summer Palace, Beijing, in early June, presumably a migrant, was singing from reed stems in a *Phragmites* reedbed (PRK pers. obs.).

In winter, shows a preference for reedbeds and tall rank grassland near water. Also occurs in adjacent areas of tall grass and scattered rank vegetation up to 1m in height over shallow standing water.

La Touche (1925–30), found it to be very common on autumn passage in small millet fields at Chinwangdao in Chihli (Qinhuangdao, Hebei Province, China).

BEHAVIOUR Poorly known. Casual observations suggest its behaviour does not differ significantly from that of other small *Acrocephalus* warblers such as Black-browed Reed Warbler. The singing male observed at Muraviovka Park on 21 June 2004 was reported to be very active and animated, frequently flying between bushes and occasionally performing a short song flight.

BREEDING HABITS Unknown.

DISTRIBUTION

Breeding The breeding range is unknown but has been widely assumed to lie somewhere in NE China. The late occurrence of spring migrants in coastal E China suggests that breeding occurs in wetlands in Hebei, Liaoning, Jilin and Heilongjiang Provinces. Singing males at Beidaihe and at the Summer Palace in Beijing in early June were probably on passage, but these locations may lie within the breeding range.

In 2004 a singing male was discovered in the Muraviovka Nature Park in the Amur Region of the Russian Far East, bordering the northern shore of the Amur River. It is assumed that breeding takes place here. However, a subsequent search of the area in July 2007 failed to locate any birds, although breeding may have finished by that time (PJL *in litt.*).

Non-breeding The entire population is believed to winter in the Philippines. Almost all records are from Luzon, where it is both a passage migrant and winter visitor. Recorded from a number of Luzon localities, but the only known regular wintering site in recent years has been Candaba Marsh in Pampanga Province. Even here it is declining due to drainage and habitat loss and is now rare and often difficult to find. It doubtless winters elsewhere in Luzon, for example at Lake Baao near Naga city (Clarke 1983) and Laguna de Bay (BirdLife International, 2000), while other possible sites have not been thoroughly explored. Elsewhere in the Philippines there are records from Negros and Bohol.

The population decreased during the twentieth century and is now estimated at fewer than 10,000 individuals. The species is considered Vulnerable by BirdLife International (2000), mainly because of the destruction of wetlands on the Philippines wintering grounds. Conversion of wetlands to agricultural use in NE China may also have contributed to its decline.

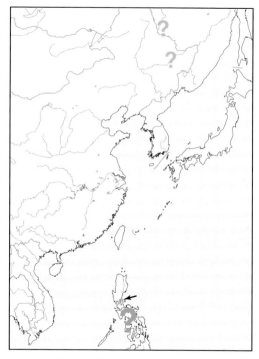

Streaked Reed Warbler, breeding range and winter distribution.

MOVEMENTS One of the latest spring migrants to pass along the coast of China and one of the earliest to return. It is a rare migrant along the coast of the Gulf of Bohai and East China Sea south to Xiamen in Fujian Province and is most frequently encountered in spring. It was always uncommon, even in the late nineteenth and early twentieth centuries, when spring migrants were collected from Shaweishan off the mouth of the Yangtze River and at Chinwangtao, Chihli (Qinhuangdao, Hebei Province) where La Touche (1925–30) regularly encountered it in late May and early June. One or two birds still occurred annually in the Beidaihe region of Hebei Province during the 1980s, but spring occurrences have since became infrequent and it is now recorded here less than annually.

Autumn passage occurs almost unnoticed and there have been no recent documented records from E China. In the early years of the twentieth century, however, it was said to be common at Chinwangtao in late August and early September (La Touche 1925–30).

Elsewhere in China, a presumed migrant was singing in the reedbed at the Summer Palace in Beijing on 2 June 1985 (PRK pers. obs.). Away from the coast, there are no other confirmed reports in China since the early twentieth century.

The most valuable set of occurrences away from the wintering sites was collected in the Philippines during the MAPS project, when 351 migrants attracted to lights were trapped for ringing at Dalton Pass in Nueva Vizcaya Province on Luzon, between 1965 and 1970 (McClure & Leelavit 1972). The earliest arrival occurred on 15 September. This, however, was exceptionally early and passage usually began in the second week of October. Thereafter, numbers increased rapidly to peak in the middle ten days of October when 78 were trapped. Numbers then declined but passage continued throughout November and December, with secondary peaks in the third ten-day period of November (27 trapped) and the middle ten-day period of December (36 trapped). Small numbers occurred throughout January, February and up to the middle of March, but there were no further records until the middle of May, when a small return passage was noted, peaking at 31 birds in the last ten days of the month. It was unrecorded at Dalton Pass between 16 June and 6 October, with the exception of the 15 September capture noted above.

As a vagrant, it has occurred at least three times in Taiwan but it must surely occur here more frequently. It has also been recorded once from Japan, on Yonaguni Island in the S Ryukyu archipelago, east of Taiwan, on 11 October 2002.

DESCRIPTION

Plumage – Adult fresh Forehead warm tan with sparse small blackish streaks. Crown warm tan with slightly larger, more distinct blackish streaks. Supercilium broad, creamy buff, reaching to base of bill, widening slightly behind eye and tapering onto side of nape, bordered above by ill-defined blackish band, flecked sandy-brown, extending along side of the crown from front of eye to rear of ear-coverts. Lores pale buff, usually with black spot immediately in front of eye, or sometimes diffuse dark line extending to bill base. Behind eye, a fairly large blackish spot and a poorly defined blackish eye-line extending to rear of ear-coverts. Ear-coverts pale ochreous-buff with a few darker streaks, darkening around rear edge. Usually a narrow, dark brown moustachial line below eye. Pale eye-ring indistinct.

Nape sandy brown with faint greyish wash and indistinct darker mottling. Mantle and scapulars light fulvous-brown, with narrow, dark brown feather centres creating diffuse streaking. Rump and uppertail-coverts slightly warmer and richer brown than mantle, unstreaked. Tail warm brown, closely matching uppertail-coverts, feather tips slightly paler. Chin and throat creamy white, merging with creamy buff centre of breast. Side of breast and side of neck ochreous-buff with greyish wash. Flanks warm buff, fading to pale creamy buff on belly. Undertail-coverts washed creamy white, slightly paler than lower belly.

Lesser coverts sandy brown with faint greyish tinge. Median coverts blackish with broad buff fringes. Greater coverts grey-brown with broad, pale buff fringes. Tertials dark brown with broad, crisp, sandy straw fringes. Primary coverts, secondaries and primaries dark grey-brown, edged

pale buff. Primaries edged and tipped pale straw. Alula black centred with crisp, narrow, sandy straw fringe. Underwing-coverts pale creamy buff.

Adult worn Overall appearance paler than fresh adult. Dark side to crown more conspicuous and contrasting, supercilium paler and overall head pattern bolder and pronounced. Mantle and scapulars paler sandy brown with dark brown streaking more conspicuous. Underparts typically paler and colder, with sandy buff wash confined to flanks. Closed wing faded and more uniform with contrasting fringes worn away. Centres to median coverts and alula less dark.

Juvenile/first-winter When fresh, brighter and more striking than fresh adult. Crown and nape bright sandy buff with darker streaking on crown centre largely obscured and only the black border above supercilium prominent. Mantle bright sandy buff to orange-fulvous, with streaking largely obscured. Rump and uppertail-coverts warm orange-fulvous, more uniform with mantle colour than in adult. Entire underparts washed ochreous-buff, rather yellower than in adult, this wash fading to creamy buff on chin and throat and darkening slightly on flanks. Median coverts and alula with narrow, warm sandy buff fringes and contrasting blackish centres which are conspicuous on closed wing. Greater coverts, secondaries and primaries with broad, bright sandy buff to orange-fulvous fringes, the darker centres largely obscured.

Bare parts Upper mandible dark grey, narrowly edged yellowish pink. Lower mandible yellowish pink, unmarked. Mouth yellow. Tarsi, toes and claws pale grey with a slight greenish tinge; soles greenish yellow. Iris of first-winter birds dull greyish brown, becoming dark brown in adults.

IN HAND CHARACTERS
Measurements

Sexes combined (n = 3): *wing* 57–59 (57.7); *tail* 45–58 (46.7); *bill* 13.5–15 (14.3); *tarsus* 20–21 (20.5); bill width 3.4–3.8; hind claw 6.5–6.8; tail graduation 7–9.
Live wing length: Philippines, 55–59 (56.6; 13) (MAPS data, per PDR).

Structure

Wing formula (n = 3):

p1/pc	p2	p3e	p4e	p5e	p6	p7	p10
0–1.5	4–5	0–0.5	wp	1–1.5	3–4.5	5.5–8	11–12

Wing rounded, p1 minute. Wing point p(3) 4; p2 = p6–6/7; emargination on p3–5.

Figure 48. Wing of Streaked Reed Warbler.

Tail rounded; feathers narrow and rather pointed.
Bill small and slender; slightly concave sided with narrow tip.
Tarsi and toes very slender, claws fine.

Recognition Distinguished from Black-browed Reed Warbler by paler sandy brown upperparts with contrasting warmer rump and by finely streaked mantle and crown; shows more prominent pale fringes to wing-coverts and tertials. Tail feathers narrower, more pointed than in Black-browed Reed and p1 smaller (usually over 4mm > pc in Black-browed Reed). In similar but larger Sedge Warbler, wing point is formed by p3; p2 = p3/4–4 (4/5), and only p3 is emarginated.

Weight Philippines, January 7.2–9.1g (8.1; 9) (MAPS data, per PDR).

GEOGRAPHIC VARIATION None recorded.

TAXONOMY AND SYSTEMATICS No issues arising.

◀ ▶ Adult, Amur River, Russia, June. The only small streaked *Acrocephalus* in eastern Asia. Note narrow streaks on mantle and crown, an unmarked greyish straw wash on nape, warmer rump, dark sides to crown and creamy wash to the supercilium. This bird, photographed at Muraviovka on the northern bank of the Amur River in the Russian Far East, represents the only known sighting from a possible breeding area (Fabien and Sophie Pékus).

▼ ▶ Probable juvenile, Luzon, Philippines, February. By late winter adults and young birds are heavily worn, making ageing difficult, but the grey-brown iris suggests this is a young bird. Uniquely among the small Asian *Acrocephalus*, this species has a complete moult in late winter, so in spring all birds are in fresh plumage (Peter Kennerley).

▲ Juvenile, Luzon, Philippines, November. An early autumn migrant, moving through N China in early August, so unlikely to have a post-juvenile moult. The warm, bright appearance points to this being a young bird, presumably a juvenile rather than first-winter (Urban Olsson).

BLACK-BROWED REED WARBLER
Acrocephalus bistrigiceps   Plates 17 and 25

Acrocephalus bistrigiceps **Swinhoe, 1860.** *Ibis* p. 51. Amoy, Fohkien, China.

The most numerous and widespread of the small E Asian *Acrocephalus*, breeding extensively in wetlands from E Mongolia and SE Siberia to NE China, the Korean peninsula and Japan and wintering in SE Asia. Monotypic.

IDENTIFICATION Length 12cm. Wing 51–60mm. Tail/wing 74–91%.

A small, unstreaked *Acrocephalus* with a conspicuous pale supercilium and bold blackish stripes bordering the crown sides. It is quite variable in appearance, this perhaps being age- and wear-related, but it always shows uniform upperparts. Some birds are quite pale and sandy, others much darker with a faint cinnamon tone to the upperparts. Most, however, are dull olive-brown above and paler drab buff below. Within its range, only likely to be mistaken for the much rarer Manchurian Reed Warbler. Sexes alike.

Structure A small and relatively short-tailed warbler with a compact body, rounded crown and relatively long undertail-coverts, giving it a neatly proportioned and dainty structure. It shows a long primary projection, extending to 60–70% of the tertial length, with six or sometimes seven primary tips visible in the closed wing and emarginations on p3–5. The bill is quite small and fine and the upper mandible is slightly decurved towards the tip. When singing or agitated, it raises the feathers on the rear crown in a manner similar to that of Sedge Warbler; and unlike most unstreaked *Acrocephalus,* including Manchurian Reed Warbler, in which the fore-crown feathering is raised.

Figure 49. Variation in head pattern of Black-browed Reed Warbler depending on position of crown feathering.

Plumage and bare parts The head provides the only distinctive features in the otherwise drab and uniform appearance of Black-browed Reed Warbler, with the crown being bordered on each side by a broad black band extending from just in front of the eye to the rear of the supercilium. Below this, the long, broad supercilium extends from the bill base, flaring slightly behind the eye and terminating cleanly and abruptly towards the rear of the ear-coverts. This is pale creamy-buff when fresh, but becomes whiter when worn, enhancing the contrast with the black 'brows'. There is a narrow, dark line along the lores, but the narrow diffuse eye-stripe shows little contrast behind the eye with the plain ear-coverts. Apart from this distinctive head pattern, the plumage is drab and nondescript. The crown centre and upperparts, including the wing-coverts, are typically mid brown, some with a slight greyish tinge, others with a faint olive cast; but some appear warmer and richer brown above, occasionally with a slight cinnamon tinge when freshly moulted. The rump and uppertail-coverts are unmarked and tend to be slightly warmer and richer than the mantle and can appear contrastingly bright in flight.

The mid brown to greyish brown tail shows conspicuous pale feather tips when fresh.

When fresh, the closed wing appears warmer and brighter than the mantle, with broad, warm brown wing-covert and tertial fringes and edges to the flight feathers. Additionally, there are conspicuous narrow whitish tips to the primaries. As the plumage wears and fades these tips are lost and the wing becomes increasingly uniform, more closely matching the upperpart colour. The underparts tend to look contrastingly pale, with the chin, throat and undertail-coverts being off-white to creamy white, the breast and belly slightly darker and washed pale buff. The breast sides and flanks show a stronger and brighter wash than the breast, occasionally appearing deep orange-buff, but more typically most are drab, warm creamy brown.

Juvenile plumage closely resembles that of the adult but may appear slightly warmer and with less well-defined black stripes along the sides of the crown. Usually replaced by late August, after which young birds appear identical to adults in the field.

The bill is dark grey with an unmarked pink lower mandible. The legs and feet are dull grey.

SIMILAR SPECIES Within its range, Black-browed Reed Warbler is the most numerous of the smaller *Acrocephalus* and any *Acrocephalus* in E Asia showing a conspicuous supercilium and blackish sides to the crown is most likely to be this species. However, Manchurian Reed Warbler also shares similar characters and their separation is discussed below. Streaked Reed Warbler also shares a similar head pattern but has streaked upperparts and these should not be mistaken. A mixed pairing of Eurasian Reed Warbler x Sedge Warbler has been documented in Europe and the appearance of such hybrids is an unexpected, albeit unlikely, source of confusion,

Manchurian Reed Warbler shares a similar head pattern with Black-browed Reed Warbler but has very different structure and plumage tones. The upperparts tend to be warmer, particularly when fresh, and the peachy buff underparts are brighter than ever shown by Black-browed Reed. As the plumage abrades and fades, the appearance of the two species converges, but greyer tones are usually absent in Manchurian Reed. The head pattern is invariably less bold than in Black-browed Reed, with the bands on the crown sides narrower and less well defined and dark brown rather than black. The supercilium is often broadest in front of the eye on Manchurian Reed, dropping into the loral region, leaving just a small dark spot in front of the eye rather than the dark loral line typical of Black-browed Reed.

Structural differences provide further pointers to their separation. Manchurian Reed is a slightly larger and proportionately longer tailed bird with narrower rectrices. The bill is also longer, deeper and broader towards the base, which gives the head a heavier and more powerful character than Black-browed Reed Warbler.

Streaked Reed Warbler also shares a prominent supercilium and dark borders to the crown sides with Black-browed Reed, but the overall appearance of the two is quite different and their separation straightforward. Streaked Reed is always paler than Black-browed Reed and usually appears both brighter and sandier. The crown and mantle show obvious narrow blackish streaks which Black-browed Reed lacks, and the rump and uppertail-coverts are warm fulvous-brown, producing greater contrast with the mantle. Equally contrasting are the pale sandy brown fringes to the dark-centred tertials and wing-coverts. The underparts are similar to those of Black-browed Reed, although typically washed brighter buff in young birds.

Sedge Warbler and **Eurasian Reed Warbler** have formed mixed pairings in Europe, resulting in offspring that resemble Black-browed Reed Warbler (Sharrock 1985; van Eerde 1999). Thus, a hybrid origin must always be considered if a potential extralimital Black-browed Reed Warbler is encountered in Europe. Documented hybrids have shown a combination of plain brown upperparts, contrastingly patterned tertials and upperwing-coverts and a striking head pattern with a conspicuous supercilium extending well behind the eye and dark brown bands along the sides of the crown. Photographs show that the dark crown borders are less distinct and contrasting than in Black-browed Reed, but plumage differences are slight.

A potential vagrant Black-browed Reed in Europe should be readily separable from a hybrid Sedge x Eurasian Reed Warbler using a combination of biometrics and wing structure. Black-browed Reed is conspicuously smaller than both Sedge and Eurasian Reed Warblers with a maximum wing length of 61mm, well below the 64–67mm quoted for hybrids by van Eerde (1999). Moreover, it shows emargination on the outer webs on p3–5 and a wing point formed by p3–4 and sometimes p5. In hybrids, as in both parent species, emargination is restricted to p3 and sometimes p4 and the wing point formed by p3 only.

VOICE The song is a rapid mix of '*chirps*', '*churrs*' and whistles typical of many of the smaller *Acrocephalus* but appears not to include mimicry. It consists of a series of short, harsh, unmusical phrases ranging in frequency from 2–7kHz, each phrase being repeated up to 12 times before a different phrase is started and repeated. There can be upwards of 14 repeated phrases within any 60-second continuous song sequence. Typically, song sequences last 8–25 seconds followed by a pause of up to 15 seconds before recommencing. Songs from Mongolia and Japan, at opposite ends of the breeding range, sound rather different, that from Mongolia being slightly more rapid and the repeated sequences shorter than those given in Japan, but the repetitive structure is the same. Whether this is due to regional or individual variation is unknown.

Part of song of Black-browed Reed Warbler, Hokkaido, Japan, June. (Ueda 1998)

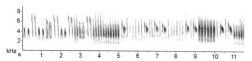

Part of song of Black-browed Reed Warbler, Durur, eastern Mongolia, June. (Geoff Carey)

The call is a relatively soft, rich '*thack*', which may be uttered two to three times per second to form a sequence lasting several seconds.

MOULT Adults and juveniles have a complete moult prior to departure from the breeding grounds. This commences after breeding, typically from mid July, and is completed by early September. Migrants reach Hong Kong from early September but, unlike Oriental Reed Warblers in which a minority are still growing the primaries when they reach Hong Kong, moult is completed before arrival there, by when all birds are in fresh plumage. There are no instances of migrant Black-browed Reed Warbler in Hong Kong in autumn still growing the primaries, secondaries or tail. No data is available on the duration of this moult.

Feather abrasion, particularly in the primaries and tail, appears gradual, as most birds appear quite fresh or only slightly worn from November to January and range between slightly worn and heavily worn by March and April.

Of a sample of birds handled in Singapore between January and early April, none were in active wing or tail moult and all exhibited slight to moderate wear. From late March onwards there is a partial moult which involves replacement of the body feathers only. Later migrants reaching Hong Kong in May often have heavily abraded primaries. However, a minority of birds trapped in Hong Kong in April and May show fresh, unworn remiges and some or all of the rectrices are also fresh, suggesting these had recently been replaced.

HABITAT Closely associated with water and wetlands throughout the year. When breeding it is not confined to a particular wetland type and requires only dense cover, usually with shrubs and bushes from which it can establish a favoured song perch. Typical habitats include *Phragmites* reedbeds, river edges, lake borders, damp meadows, willow beds along rivers, sedge bogs, reed-filled ditches and moist forest. Almost any wetland suffices provided there is ample vegetation in which to nest.

On passage and in its winter quarters, it frequents similar habitat types as when breeding although it shows greater tolerance of sub-prime habitats. It usually prefers wetlands, especially *Phragmites* reedbeds, and bushes and scrub beside damp or wet ditches, but shows a wider tolerance than when breeding. Some birds will select tall grassland, dampened by early morning condensation, scrub bordering a damp ditch, often well away from standing water, or even small eutrophic pools with rank cover in disturbed industrial and urban environments.

BEHAVIOUR Not known to differ from other *Acrocephalus*. It is a shy and skulking species that usually remains within thick cover, typically including dense bushes and scrub, thick grasses or reedbeds. Birds sing from thick vegetation during the winter months and rarely reveal themselves. Males frequently sing on migration in spring and become more visible as they cling to the top of a *Phragmites* stem, or sing from the top of a bush. On the breeding grounds, newly returned migrants quickly establish a territory and males select a favoured song perch on a bush or low tree, from which the territorial song is delivered. Song is most vigorous from pre-dawn to late morning, then recommences in late afternoon, often continuing until well after dusk. Males sometimes sing in flight, flying low and swerving over the grasses, then diving into deep cover, sometimes pursuing the female.

BREEDING HABITS Males often sing during stopovers on spring migration and commence singing immediately on arrival in the breeding areas. In Honshu, Japan, the breeding season extends from May to July, while in the cooler climate of E Hokkaido and in Russia, it commences in early June and continues until August. The nest is built in reeds or adjacent scrubland, not necessarily over water, usually 0.5–1.5m above the ground. It is a deep, cup-shaped construction built from fine grass strips and other fibrous vegetable material. It is lined with fine, soft grasses and

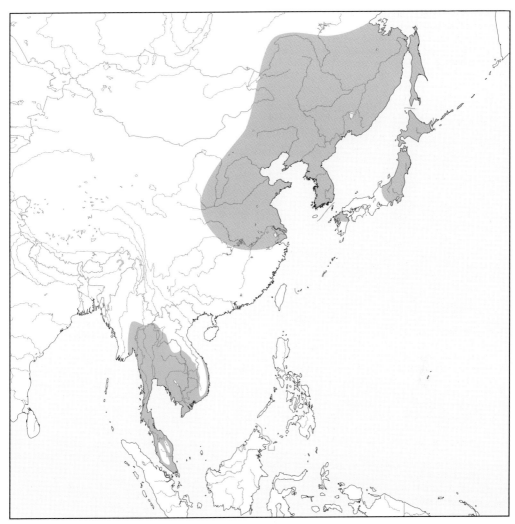

Black-browed Reed Warbler. Breeding range and winter distribution.

sometimes mammal hair. Three to six eggs are laid and incubation lasts 13–14 days. Both adults care for the young in the nest for approximately 14 days. After fledging, the young remain dependent on their parents for several days. Believed to be single brooded.

DISTRIBUTION

Breeding The breeding distribution encompasses much of the warm and temperate E Palearctic. The western limits lie in SE Transbaikalia and extreme E Mongolia in the reedbeds of the Khalka River (Vaurie 1964). It ranges through much of the lowlands of the Russian Far East, including the upper basins of the Amur and Ussuri Rivers east to the Pacific Ocean coastline, and the island of Sakhalin. It breeds commonly throughout the Korean peninsula and N Japan, where it is abundant on Hokkaido, particularly in coastal and low-lying wetlands, but occurs in smaller numbers up to and above the tree line. Locally common throughout N and C Honshu, particularly in the central highlands at 500–1,500m, and may be spreading and increasing along the valleys and coastal lowlands south to Chiba Prefecture

and the Tokyo area. Generally less numerous in S Honshu and an uncommon but regular breeder on Shikoku and Kyushu. It breeds widely in NE China, from Heilongjiang Province and the Nei Mongol Autonomous Region south to the Yangtze River. Throughout this region it is common in suitable wetlands although these have come under increasing pressure in recent years and may be affecting distribution and numbers. At the southern edge of its range in China, it becomes less numerous towards Henan and the Yangtze, while breeding is not known to occur south of the Yangtze.

Non-breeding Wintering birds are common and widespread in lowland wetlands throughout much of SE Asia. The main wintering range extends from N and C Thailand south to peninsula Malaysia and Singapore, where it can be found in reedbeds beside almost any wetland, no matter how small or unsavoury. It also winters on the plains of S Burma where Smythies (1968) found it to be not uncommon from November to mid April. To the west, small numbers regularly reach the Indian subcontinent to winter in Assam,

313

Manipur and lower Bengal (Ripley 1982), although these sight records are not supported by specimens (P. Rasmussen *in litt.*). Occasionally, birds will overwinter north of the normal range. Brazil (1991) noted birds on Iriomote-jima in the Nansei Shoto in S Japan in February and March and one or two occur in winter in most years in the Mai Po Marshes in Hong Kong (Carey *et al.* 2001).

MOVEMENTS Departure from the breeding areas begins during August, with a widespread exodus occurring from the end of the month, although many remain on Hokkaido into September, with stragglers still on Sakhalin and the Ussuri River region of the Russian Far East and in Honshu, Japan, until mid October (Brazil 1991). As a migrant, it becomes common and widespread throughout much of Japan, although rare in the Nansei Shoto, where it has been recorded from Tokashiki Island off Okinawa, Miyako-jima and Iriomote-jima. The latest record from Japan involving a presumed migrant comes from Izumi, Kagoshima Prefecture, on 2 November.

Locally it is common to abundant on passage at coastal sites in E and S China and likely to be numerous in the coastal provinces wherever suitable habitat exists. Passage at Hong Kong is protracted, lasting from late August to mid December, with a peak occurring in mid October, when several hundreds may be present, then declining until passage ceases in mid December. The earliest arrivals reach the Bangkok area of Thailand in early September and significant numbers are present here by the third week of the month (Round 2008).

It has occurred in Malaysia as early as 21 September (Medway & Wells 1976), but the main arrival here and in Singapore, takes place during late October and November. As many winter in this region, it is generally not possible to monitor new arrivals as numbers then remain high until April.

Return passage commences in late March although it is frequently encountered in Singapore until the end of April, but most birds have departed there by the end of the first week in May. A similar situation exists in Malaysia and Thailand where it is regularly recorded until the middle of May and some remain until the last week in May, with the latest being 30 May in Malaysia and 6 June in the Bangkok area (Round 2008). Northward passage is more rapid and concentrated in spring than in autumn, although peak numbers are generally similar or smaller. In Hong Kong, first arrivals occur in late March, with numbers peaking during the second half of April and into the first week of May, but becoming scarce after mid May. Many migrants pass through the Beidaihe region of NE China and the Korean peninsula throughout May. Returning birds reach southern Honshu from mid April onwards but first arrivals only reach Hokkaido in late May, suggesting these may follow a different route, to become widespread there in early June. In the Russian Far East, first arrivals reach the Lake Khanka region and Iman River in the third week in May, but those breeding in Sakhalin and the northern Amur region only arrive in early June (Dement'ev & Gladkov 1954).

It is a scarce migrant in Taiwan and the islands of the Nansei Shoto in S Japan, suggesting that the majority of birds travelling to and from Japan migrate via coastal China and possibly the Korea peninsula. Movement between China and Japan was confirmed by the recovery of a bird ringed in Hong Kong on 4 April 1993 and controlled in SW Honshu on 18 October 1996 (Melville & Leven 1999).

Vagrancy Vagrants have been to the east and west of the wintering range. It has been reported from Nepal on four occasions in the period January–March (Inskipp & Inskipp 1991; CI *in litt.*). It is also a vagrant to Sumatra, Indonesia: although lying close to Malaysia, there is just a single November sight record near Balige, Lake Toba in Utara (Marle & Voous 1988), although it seems likely that it is being overlooked here as it is common in Singapore in winter, within sight of Sumatra. There are just two records from the Philippines, both from Candaba, in April 2008 and March 2009. There have been no records from Borneo, Java or the Wallacean sub-region.

DESCRIPTION

Plumage – Adult fresh (September to November) Forehead and centre of crown variable from dull greyish brown with olivaceous tinge, to dull rufous-brown. Side of crown black, forming conspicuous band, broadest above and behind eye, narrower in front of eye, not usually extending to bill base. Below this, a conspicuous long and broad, creamy buff supercilium, flaring slightly behind eye and extending from bill base to rear of ear-coverts and terminating rather abruptly and squarely. A dark brown loral spot in front of eye, usually extending to bill base as a fine dark line. Behind eye, a diffuse dark brown eye-line, widening and merging with upper edge of ear-coverts and sides of nape. Ear-coverts pale greyish brown to warm tan, usually showing indistinct pale shaft streaks. Eye-ring narrow, upper part merging with supercilium, whitish lower part usually contrasting with darker ear-coverts. Nape, mantle and scapulars usually unmarked dull greyish brown with slight olivaceous tinge, often appearing slightly greyer than mantle and crown, but some dull rufous-brown to cinnamon-brown. Rump and uppertail-coverts usually dull rufous-brown, contrasting slightly with mantle, but matching mantle colour in brighter birds. Tail dark grey-brown to dull olive-brown, feathers broadly edged olive-brown and tipped whitish. Chin and throat creamy white. Rest of underparts variable. Breast usually dull creamy brown, slightly darker at side and merging with side of neck. Flanks creamy brown, slightly warmer than breast. In some birds, underparts much warmer and browner, almost peachy brown in extreme cases, with strongest wash on sides of breast and flanks. Belly paler than breast and flanks, whitish in typical birds, pale peachy buff in warmest-coloured birds. Undertail-coverts pale cream, unmarked. Lesser and median coverts dull greyish brown to dull rufous-brown with little contrast between feather centres and fringes. Greater coverts and tertials dark grey-brown to blackish with broad fringes, variable but matching mantle colour closely. Primary coverts, secondaries and primaries dark grey-brown, with edges again matching mantle colour. Primaries with narrow greyish white tips. Alula dull brown with narrow and slightly paler brown fringe. Underwing-coverts pale buff.

Adult worn (July–August) Warmer plumage tones tend to be lost. Head pattern usually becomes more pronounced, with supercilium whiter, black band on side of crown more extensive, often reaching bill base and loral line more conspicuous. Mantle and closed wing duller earth-brown, lacking warmer or olivaceous tones, often showing greater contrast with dull rufous-brown rump and uppertail-coverts. Underparts more uniform off-white, with buffy wash more confined to flanks. Tail feathers frequently without pale tips.

Juvenile Closely resembles adult but plumage loose-textured and slightly warmer than most adults, although matched by some fresh, dull rufous-brown adults, described above.

Dark band at sides of crown usually less well defined than in adult but quite variable in colour and extent. Usually browner, showing less contrast, only extending slightly in front of eye and diffusing into crown just behind eye. Sometimes darker and crisper, but again barely extending in front of eye. Supercilium less distinct, often narrower in front of eye and more diffuse behind, suffused warm buff towards rear. Upperparts as adult. Underparts pale, white to creamy white as pale adults. Undertail-coverts pale greyish white, unmarked.

Bare Parts Upper mandible dark grey with narrow pink cutting edge in adult. Lower mandible pink, unmarked. Juvenile as adult although some show a paler grey upper mandible. Mouth dull yellow. Tarsi and toes dull lead grey. Iris brown to reddish brown in adult, grey-brown in immature.

IN HAND CHARACTERS
Measurements

	Male	Female
Wing	53–60 (56.2; 50)	51–59 (54.2; 27)
Tail	42–52 (46.5; 13)	42–51 (46.0; 12)
Bill	13.5–15 (14.2; 13)	13.5–15 (14.2; 11)
Tarsus	20–22 (21.0; 12)	20–22 (20.7; 10)

Sexes combined:
Tail/wing ratio: 74–91% (84%; 26)
Bill width: 3.2–3.8 (3.5; 24)
Hind claw: 5.5–7.0 (6.3; 14)
Tail graduation: 8–12 (10.3; 22)

Structure

Wing formula (n = 12):

p1/pc	p2	p3e	p4e	p5e	p6	p7	p10
4–7.5	3–6	wp	wp	0–1.5	1–3	3–5	7–11

Wing rounded; p1 small. Wing point p3–4 [5]; p2 = p6/7–7/8; emargination on p3–5.

Figure 50. Wing of Black-browed Reed Warbler.

Tail strongly rounded; feathers broader, more rounded, than in Manchurian Reed Warbler or Streaked Reed Warbler.

Bill slim; slightly concave-sided with narrow tip. Tarsi slender; claws rather weak.

Recognition Plain-backed, but distinguished from Manchurian Reed and Paddyfield Warblers by bold black (rather than dark brown) lateral crown stripes. Tail length is commonly < 48mm, below the range of Manchurian Reed and Paddyfield. Bill length and width are usually also below the range of Manchurian Reed.

Ageing No plumage differences between adult and young birds after complete adult and post-juvenile moult in late summer, after which all birds have fresh primaries and broad fresh tail feathers. Ageing then depends on iris colour (warm brown in adults, dull greyish brown in young birds) and presence of tongue spots, which are usually retained in young birds until at least November and often until the following spring. Most cannot be safely aged after the turn of the year.

Weight Thailand, 6.5–11.7g (8.0; 338) (PDR unpublished data); Singapore, 6.4–8.6g (7.7; 18) (PRK unpublished data). Hong Kong, 6.9–15.0g (9.5; 1,681) (HKRG unpublished data). Typical lean weight 8–10g; commonly 11–13g at Hong Kong, Oct–Dec.

GEOGRAPHICAL VARIATION None recorded.

TAXONOMY AND SYSTEMATICS Manchurian Reed Warbler was formerly treated as a race of Black-browed Reed Warbler, but is now widely recognised as being a distinct species. No other issues arising.

▲ Adult, Hokkaido, June. Occupies a similar ecological niche to Sedge Warbler in Europe; this singing male is using an umbellifer as a song post in the same way a Sedge Warbler would (Gaku Tozuka).

▲ Adult, Hokkaido, July. Shows unmarked greyish brown upperparts, long, pale supercilium and characteristic blackish bands along sides of crown (Akiko Hidaka).

▲ Adult, Hokkaido, Japan, June. Typical bird with pale underparts, and whitish undertail-coverts not reaching to tip of shortest tail feather (Pete Morris).

▲ ▶ Adult, Hong Kong, October. An exceptionally warmly toned individual in fresh plumage. Few show such intense and richly coloured underparts, and most have whitish undertail-coverts. Note pale tips to the primaries and rectrices, which are lost on worn birds (Martin Hale).

▲ Adult, Taiwan, December. Juveniles and adults have a complete moult before leaving the breeding grounds, after which ageing is possible using iris colour; grey-brown in young birds, dark brown on adults (Liao Pen-shing).

▲ Adult, Taiwan, April. Adults in spring appear fresh after partial pre-breeding moult, with pale sandy buff underparts and supercilium, although this soon fades to dingy white (Liao Pen-shing).

MANCHURIAN REED WARBLER
Acrocephalus tangorum   **Plate 17**

Acrocephalus tangorum **La Touche, 1912.** *Bull. Brit. Orn. Club* 31: 10. Chinwangtao, northeastern Chihli, China.

A rare and little known *Acrocephalus* which breeds in *Phragmites* reedbeds in NE China and adjacent regions of SE Russia and winters in Thailand and probably elsewhere in Indochina. It has previously been treated as a race of both Paddyfield Warbler and Black-browed Reed Warbler. However, recent better understanding of its field characters, together with DNA sequence evidence, indicates that it is a distinct species, forming a superspecies with Paddyfield and Blunt-winged Warblers. Considered VULNERABLE by BirdLife International. Monotypic.

IDENTIFICATION Length 12cm. Wing 52–58mm. Tail/ wing 89–100%.

A small, unstreaked *Acrocephalus* with a bold supercilium that bulges in front of the eye, dark sides to the crown, and typically warmly toned plumage when fresh, becoming paler and colder when worn. Sexes alike.

Structure Resembles Paddyfield Warbler in overall proportions, showing similar short and rounded wings but a slightly longer tail with narrower and more pointed individual rectrices. The bill is also longer, deeper and broader across the base than in Paddyfield and Black-browed Reed Warblers, giving it a more robust structure. This larger-billed impression is accentuated further outside the breeding season by an entirely pale lower mandible. Wing averages longer than in Black-browed Reed Warbler but a short primary projection and longer, thinner tail creates the impression of a more rakish bird. The primary projection is generally 50% or less of the exposed tertial length and the closed wing usually shows six evenly spaced primary tips, the longest just reaching the base of the tail, the wing point being formed by p3–5. The secondaries are often visible beyond the tertials, a feature shared with Blunt-winged Warbler but not with Paddyfield Warbler (Fig. 54).

Plumage and bare parts On the wintering grounds, freshly moulted adults are bright cinnamon above and show warm, bright buff on the breast sides, flanks and undertail-coverts. The head pattern tends to be less contrasting than in Paddyfield Warbler since the darker lateral crown stripes are tipped with rusty brown. The supercilium is long and pale, appearing broadest in front of the eye where it bulges, but behind the eye it tapers towards the rear of the ear-coverts. In some individuals, however, it appears shorter and square-cut as in Black-browed Reed. Pale fringes to the fore-crown feathering give it a faintly mottled appearance which is unique to Manchurian Reed. The loral line is dark and conspicuous, extending from the base of the bill to the eye and there is an indistinct dark spot behind the eye but no obvious eye-ring. The closed wing appears rather uniform and the greater coverts lack the dark centres and contrasting fringes of Black-browed Reed. However, the tertials have broad, pale rufous-brown fringes and do show darker brown centres. Pale fringes to the primaries and secondaries are similar in colour to the coverts.

This bright and richly coloured appearance is retained for only a few weeks until feather tips and fringes abrade. As these are lost, the underlying duller rufous-brown plumage emerges. With continued abrasion and bleaching, the upperparts become paler and browner so that by late spring only the rump and uppertail-coverts retain a strong rufous

tone. The upperparts are then rather less rufous than in Paddyfield Warbler but warm and bright and lacking the olive tones typical of Black-browed Reed. When worn, the throat remains whitish, but the breast, flanks and undertail-coverts appear washed-out buff, similar to those of most Paddyfield and Black-browed Reed. Any warmer tones retained in the upperparts above are lost by late July and heavily abraded adults appear significantly paler and blotchy, although they are not known to attain the pallid, worn and bleached appearance that some adult Paddyfield Warblers attain at this time of the year. The supercilium can appear paler and the contrast with dark crown sides and dark lores becomes more conspicuous. Similarity to Black-browed Reed Warbler is perhaps greatest in mid summer.

First-winter Manchurian Reed Warbler resembles the freshly moulted adult, with bright cinnamon upperparts and little or no contrast between the mantle, rump and tail. Below, the throat is white, the breast and flanks warm brown, but paler, less bright than the upperparts. No other small *Acrocephalus* shows such bright upperpart plumage in August and September. By early November, these tones are much reduced through wear.

The bill of Manchurian Reed is dark grey with a pinkish orange lower mandible. Outside the breeding season it almost invariably lacks the dark shadow near the tip which is a feature in Paddyfield throughout the year. During the breeding season, however, the lower mandible often becomes darker with a dusky tip, this often being more extensive than Paddyfield Warbler would show. Leg colour ranges from orange-brown to reddish brown. The iris is pale warm brown in many spring adults.

SIMILAR SPECIES It often breeds in close proximity to the much commoner Black-browed Reed Warbler and may occur on passage and in winter in wetland habitat alongside Black-browed Reed and Blunt-winged Warblers. Its distinctive head pattern and long and thin rectrices should distinguish it fairly readily from these species. Separation from vagrant Paddyfield Warbler in E Asia is potentially more problematic and requires greater care.

Black-browed Reed Warbler greatly outnumbers Manchurian Reed so that any bird suspected of being the latter species will need to be closely examined. It overlaps with Manchurian Reed in the breeding and winter range and also on migration, and care is required at all times of the year. They share a similar combination of plain, unmarked upperparts and a long pale supercilium bordered by a darker band along the crown side. However, the bands on Black-browed Reed are broader, darker and more contrasting than those of Manchurian Reed. The supercilium is narrower in front of the eye and broader behind in Black-browed Reed; the opposite pattern to that shown by Manchurian where there is just a small dark spot in front of the eye, so the supercilium bulges onto the loral region. The shape and structure of the two species is quite different with Black-browed Reed showing a proportionately longer primary projection, usually more than 60%, compared with 50% or less of the exposed tertials in Black-browed Reed. It also has a shorter and darker tail than Manchurian Reed, with broader rectrices, and a finer and shorter bill.

Blunt-winged Warbler overlaps with Manchurian Reed on passage and in the wintering areas in SE Asia. Although Blunt-winged is often found in grassland in winter, both species frequent reedbeds and have been trapped in *Phragmites* at the same localities, e.g. Khao Sam Roi Yot in

Thailand. Blunt-winged Warbler is a plain, unstreaked and nondescript *Acrocephalus* which lacks the bold supercilium and dark sides to the crown of Manchurian Reed. So the long, broad and contrasting supercilium and the dark crown sides of Manchurian Reed should quickly eliminate Blunt-winged Warbler.

Paddyfield Warbler is a vagrant to E and SE Asia and Manchurian Reed has not been recorded from the Indian subcontinent, where Paddyfield winters. Both species have, however, occurred in Hong Kong and Paddyfield has also been recorded in Thailand, so the possibility of their occurrence in the same location is real. Separating Paddyfield requires great care since it closely resembles Manchurian Reed in all plumages and at all times of the year. Furthermore, the range and extent of variation is almost as great within both species, although Manchurian Reed appears not to approach the sandy grey and white appearance shown by some worn and bleached adult Paddyfield in late summer. Both species share a similar head pattern, combined with drab and unmarked upperparts. On Paddyfield Warbler, the supercilium does not bulge onto the lores in front of the eye as it does in Manchurian Reed; instead it tends to widen or flare behind the eye where, on Manchurian Reed, it narrows. An additional distinction is that Manchurian Reed tends not to show the characteristic pale half-collar of Paddyfield, that extends from the breast sides to the lower side of the nape.

Structural differences will always provide the best means of separating these species, Paddyfield, on average, being longer winged and shorter tailed than Manchurian Reed. It also has a narrower-based, finer and more delicate bill structure and always shows dark sides to the lower mandible near the tip throughout the year; this being unmarked in Manchurian Reed Warbler outside the breeding season. There is considerable overlap in wing length and this measurement alone cannot be relied upon to separate them. However, any bird with a wing length above 58mm should be outside the range of Manchurian Reed. Paddyfield also has a lower tail/wing ratio, ranging 88–95%, compared with 89–100% in Manchurian Reed.

VOICE The song resembles that of other small E Asian *Acrocephalus*, being a series of varied and predominantly high-pitched notes delivered with a slow and steady rhythm within a frequency range of 2–7kHz. Compared with Black-browed Reed, with which it often occurs during the breeding season, the song tends to be more musical and varied, with limited repetition. Typically just two or three short phrases are repeated, followed by a different sequence, again with limited repetition. Individual notes comprising the song are distinct and clearly different from the previous and subsequent notes. The song often continues without pause for several minutes and appears to contain little or no mimicry. In addition, the song includes distinctive short rattling '*thrrr-thrrr-thrrr*' sequence.

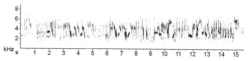

Part of song of Manchurian Reed Warbler, Zhalong, Qiqihar, Heilongjiang Province, China, June. (Per Alström)

Migrants appear to call infrequently and La Touche (1925–30) noted that it was always silent, even in spring. Distinguishing calls of wintering birds in Thailand from those of the more numerous Black-browed Reed Warblers has proved difficult, although P. D. Round (*in litt.*) noted the call as a soft '*tcheck*', softer and slightly more drawn-out than that of Black-browed Reed and also a frequently repeated, long drawn-out '*tchhht*'. A wintering bird in Hong Kong uttered a series of double '*grik-grik*' calls (Leader & Lewthwaite 1996).

MOULT Adults are faded and heavily abraded in late July. Most migrate to wintering areas in worn plumage, although some adults trapped in Hong Kong in late October have already replaced the body plumage and tertials but retain old primaries and secondaries. On arrival in Thailand, unmoulted birds undergo a full moult, and many are already in fresh body plumage by late October. Presumably birds that completed body moult before reaching Thailand also commence wing moult at this time. The earliest birds complete wing moult in mid or late November and most complete by the end of the year (Round & Rumsey 2003). A minority (*c.* 20%) suspend moult of the secondaries and renew these later in the winter, some weeks after the primaries and the rest of the plumage have been replaced.

Young birds are believed to undergo a post-juvenile body moult before autumn migration but this has to be confirmed. They then undertake a complete moult in Thailand, perhaps slightly later than in adults, but all appear to have completed body and primary moult by the end of the year (Round & Rumsey 2003).

Some birds may go on to replace a few feathers on the head and body in late winter but there appears to be no extensive pre-breeding moult (Round & Rumsey 2003). In late May, birds handled on passage at Beidaihe, Hebei Province in E China have moderately to heavily abraded flight and tail feathers and extensively worn and faded body plumage, supporting the view that it does not have an extensive pre-breeding moult.

HABITAT During both the breeding and non-breeding seasons, it appears to require extensive wetlands with large stands of *Phragmites* reed. At Khao Sam Roi Yot National Park in Thailand, it particularly favours stands of pure mature *Phragmites* in which older, dead reed stems remain (PDR *in litt*). It has also been observed in narrow reed-fringed drainage channels, towards the edge of the main

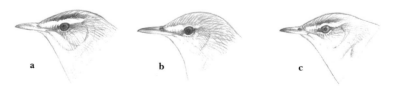

a   b   c

Figure 51. Comparison of head and bill of (a) Manchurian Reed Warbler (b) Blunt-winged Warbler and (c) Paddyfield Warbler.

marsh (PRK pers. obs.). Occasional records elsewhere in the Bangkok area include birds favouring *Typha* and other marginal habitats.

On migration it appears to use a wider range of habitats. When discovered in Hong Kong, the first few autumn records mostly came from areas of tall, wet grassland. Subsequent studies have, however, shown it to occur more frequently and in larger numbers in *Phragmites* reedbeds. At Beidaihe, where extensive reedbeds are lacking, spring migrants occupy flooded grassland, sedgy pools and *Phragmites*-filled ditches. It even occurs within open woodland where there are pools of standing water with adjacent cover. La Touche (1925–30) found it to be common in small millet fields in late August near Chinwangtao (Qinhuangdao, Hebei Province, China). The few reports from Cambodia suggest that wintering birds favour scrub and low sedges.

BEHAVIOUR Feeding birds may climb to the tops of reed stems with the tail cocked, behaviour which has not been observed in Black-browed Reed Warbler (Round 2008). Occasionally seen to chase flying insects. Otherwise not known to differ significantly from that of Paddyfield Warbler.

BREEDING HABITS Unknown.

DISTRIBUTION
Breeding The breeding range is apparently restricted to the extensive *Phragmites* reedbeds in NE China and adjacent marshes in the south of the Russian Far East, centred on Lake Khanka. This region is poorly known and it probably occurs more widely here than the few documented records suggest. Since 1976, Manchurian Reed Warbler has been found at several locations in SE Russia. It was first recorded in the Russian Far East near the Gnilye Lakes in 1976 (Gluschenko 1981) and subsequently found to be breeding around the entire southern and eastern shorelines of Lake Khanka in the Primorskiy Region, both in *Phragmites* reed and less commonly in wild rice. Given that it is widespread here, it seems likely that it was previously overlooked due to its resemblance to Black-browed Reed Warbler. To the north, a bird was caught near Khabarovsk on 23 August 2000 (Antonov 2003). In 2004, several singing birds were discovered in *Phragmites* reedbeds in the Muraviovka Nature Park in the Amur Region of the Russian Far East, along the northern shore of the Amur River to the west of Khabarovsk (PJL *in litt.*).

In China, there are unconfirmed breeding records from Dailing and Harbin, Heilongjiang Province, and Hulun Nor in the Nei Mongol Autonomous Region, but Alström *et al.* (1991) were unable to find it during searches of these localities. They did, however, find it breeding commonly in extensive *Phragmites* reedbeds in the Zhalong Nature Reserve near Qiqihar in Heilongjiang Province. A small population also breeds around the Chinese (northern) edge of Lake Khanka (Xingkai Hu). It has not been recorded as a breeding bird in Liaoning Province, but a worn adult was trapped in a reedbed at the Shuangtaizihekau National Nature Reserve near Panjin in July 1991 (Brazil 1992). As none were observed here during the breeding season, this bird may have bred elsewhere. Apparently suitable and extensive reedbeds occur widely throughout Liaoning, Jilin and Heilongjiang Provinces in NE China and it is expected that new breeding sites will be discovered.

Non-breeding The wintering range appears to be restricted to Thailand and perhaps also Cambodia, although occasional reports since 2000 suggest that small numbers

may also winter in Vietnam and Laos. In Thailand, a significant population returns each winter to a small region centred around the coastal marshes at Khao Sam Roi Yot National Park in Prachuap Khiri Khan Province (Round & Rumsey 2003; Round 2008). There are few records elsewhere, including single birds trapped at Bang Phra in October and Rangsit near Bangkok in March (PDR *in litt.*). In recent years, human encroachment at Khao Sam Roi Yot has reduced the available area of *Phragmites* and this may threaten the long-term viability of the reserve as a principal wintering site (BirdLife International 2000).

The first records from Cambodia came in March 2000, when a presumed wintering bird was trapped in Kompong Thom and at least 20 were seen at Krous Kraoum. Subsequently, at least three were seen at two locations in Preah Vihear (Robson 2000, 2001).

In S China, there is one documented record of a wintering bird, trapped in the Mai Po Marshes Nature Reserve, Hong Kong, on several dates in January 1995.

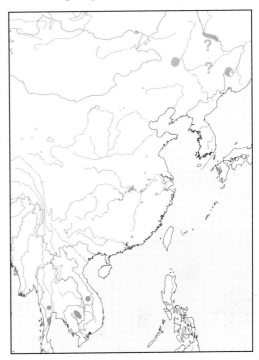

Manchurian Reed Warbler. Breeding range and winter distribution.

MOVEMENTS There are very few records of birds on migration. La Touche (1925–30) reported large numbers at Chinwangtao, Chihli (Qinhuangdao, Hebei Province) in NE China from mid August to mid September, often with Black-browed and Streaked Reed Warblers. Smaller numbers also occurred in spring between 20 May and 6 June. A century later, there is little more to add to these observations; small numbers are still recorded almost annually in NE China in spring and the location and timing of occurrence remain little changed. Coastal Hebei Province still attracts small numbers on spring migration between Qinhuangdao and Beidaihe, but there have been no sightings in recent autumns. Observations around Beidaihe (JH, *in litt.*) in 2004 (a particularly good year) showed passage occurred between 16 May and 17 June, with a peak of 25 birds on 24 May and 10 on 5 June. Migrants have been noted in the Beijing area in late May and again in mid September (Cai 1987).

On autumn passage it has occurred in Hong Kong fairly regularly since first being recorded here in 1995, suggesting that it may be becoming more numerous here. Up to 1997, seven birds had occurred, all but two in the period 17 to 27 September, the exceptions being the wintering bird referred to above (see **Distribution**) and another in November (Carey *et al.* 1999; Leader & Lewthwaite 1996). A subsequent study involving birds trapped for ringing in *Phragmites* reedbeds at the Mai Po Marshes has shown it to be a scarce but regular migrant from mid September to mid October with a total of 22 birds recorded to 2008 (PJL *in litt.*). In Vietnam, a bird at Xuan Thuy Nature Reserve, Nam Dinh Province, Vietnam, on 11 October 1997 (Tordoff & Eames 2001) is the only documented occurrence of what is presumably a migrant, between Hong Kong and known wintering areas to the south. The earliest arrival date in the wintering area at Khao Sam Roi Yot in Thailand, is 21 September. Wintering birds remain here well into April, with the latest record on 12 May (Round 2008).

DESCRIPTION

Plumage – Adult fresh (October to November) In late autumn and early winter, forehead feathers dark brown with narrow rufous-brown fringes, giving a distinct mottled effect. Crown bright fulvous-brown. Supercilium creamy white to pale rusty fawn and invariably conspicuous, broadest in front of and above eye, narrower behind it, extending to rear of ear-coverts and usually tapering to a point. Above this, a darker brown band along side of crown, partly obscured by brighter brown feather tips. Loral line dark, well marked and reaching base of bill, sometimes extending along moustachial line as a dark spur. Eye-line poorly marked behind eye, usually limited to an ill-defined spot or dusky shadow. Ear-coverts pale buff with diffuse, creamy white mottling, darkening towards upper edge to merge with eye-line. Pale eye-ring indistinct.

Nape, mantle and scapulars bright fulvous-brown, concolorous with crown and matching rump and uppertail-coverts when fresh. Tail warm brown, similar to mantle and uppertail-coverts, with brown feather shafts. Chin and throat creamy white to greyish white. Sides of breast and flanks bright sandy orange, slightly paler than upperparts, grading to warm buff on centre of breast. Belly creamy white to light buff. Undertail-coverts warm buff. Lesser, median and greater coverts fulvous-brown, without obvious dark centres, matching mantle colour. Tertials with darker brown centres and bright fulvous-brown fringes. Primary coverts, secondaries and primaries dark brown, with fulvous brown edges matching upperparts and tertial fringes. Alula dark brown with narrow, bright brown fringe. Underwing-coverts pale cinnamon-buff.

Adult worn (March to September) Distinctly paler and more washed out, but the head becomes more contrasting with wear. Supercilium paler, often almost white, and dark crown sides more conspicuous. Loral and eye-lines darker and more prominent and ear-coverts paler, slightly greyer, with whitish feather shafts. On forehead, inconspicuous narrow feather fringes usually remain well into summer. Crown, nape, mantle and scapulars fade to pale sandy brown. Rump and uppertail-coverts remain warm brown thus appearing brighter than mantle.

Underparts become paler as breast sides, flanks and undertail-coverts fade to pale buff.

The upperwing becomes plainer and less contrasting as edges to lesser, median, greater and primary coverts, tertials and alula lose brighter fringes and secondaries and primaries fade to uniform sandy brown, similar in colour to mantle.

Juvenile/first-winter Similar to fresh adult. Entire upperparts bright reddish ginger, forehead and crown with faint scaly effect due to indistinct brighter feather fringes. Supercilium pale buff, broadest in front of the eye, tapering towards rear of ear-coverts. Band along side of crown dark brown with brighter brown feather tips, so contrasts poorly with crown and more diffuse than in worn adult. Chin and throat white. Breast and flanks washed warm sandy buff. Belly and undertail-coverts slightly paler warm creamy buff. Fringes to upperwing-coverts, tertials and secondaries bright reddish ginger, closely matching mantle colour. Primaries usually with narrow pale brown tips. By November, brighter plumage tones are lost and appearance approaches that of worn adult.

Bare parts Upper mandible dark grey, sometimes with pale pink cutting edge. Lower mandible dull pink to dull orange in some breeding adults, with dusky sides near tip, but lacking dark sides in first-winter and adult birds outside breeding season. Mouth orange-flesh. Tarsi and toes plumbeous-brown to dull reddish brown or orange-brown. Iris mid brown to pale warm brown in adults, dull brown in immature birds.

IN HAND CHARACTERS
Measurements

	Male	Female
Wing	54–57 (55.2; 9)	52–54 (53.0; 3)
Tail	49–57 (52.8; 8)	49, 53 (2)
Bill	14.5–16 (15.3; 9)	14.5–16 (15.3; 3)
Tarsus	21–22.5 (21.7; 9)	21.5–22 (21.7; 3)

Sexes combined:
Tail/wing ratio: 89–100% (94%; 12)
Bill width: 3.8–4.3 (4.1; 12)
Hind claw: 6.1–7.2 (6.7; 12)
Tail graduation: 9–13 (10.7; 12)
Live wing length, Thailand: 52–58 (54.5; 105) (Round & Rumsey 2003).

Structure

Wing formula (n = 12):

p1/pc	p2	p3e	p4e	p5e	p6	p7	p10
1–4	4.5–7	0–0.5	wp	0–1	1.5–3	3–5	7–11

Wing rounded, p1 small. Wing point p(3) 4 [5]; p2 = p6/7–8 (8/9); emargination on p3–4, usually also p5.

Figure 52. Wing of Manchurian Reed Warbler.

Tail rather long, graduated; feathers narrow and rather pointed.

Bill strong, rather broad-based and straight-sided; tip of culmen distinctly decurved.

Tarsi and toes slightly stronger than in Paddyfield Warbler, claws larger.

Recognition Plain-backed, typically warmly and brightly coloured, with distinct dark lateral crown stripes as in Paddyfield Warbler; head less boldly striped than in Black-browed Reed Warbler. Best distinguished from Paddyfield by narrower central tail feathers (< 7mm wide) and by larger, straighter sided bill. Tail longer than in Black-browed Reed with feathers much narrower and bill much larger and broader; p1 smaller (> 4mm longer than pc in Black-browed).

Ageing In early autumn and on arrival in Thailand in October, the bright fresh plumage of first-winter birds allows ready separation from worn faded adults. Once moulted, young birds resemble adults and cannot be aged on plumage. Iris colour then helpful, warm brown in adults, dull brown in immature birds. Tongue spots are present on young birds up to the end of the year and possibly later.

Weight Thailand, Sep–Dec and Mar–Apr, 6.8–9.2g (8.0; 105) (Round & Rumsey 2003).

GEOGRAPHIC VARIATION None recorded.

TAXONOMY AND SYSTEMATICS Originally described by La Touche (1912) as a distinct species, and named

Acrocephalus tangorum in honour of his collectors, the brothers Tang. Manchurian Reed Warbler has since suffered a rather varied and ignominious taxonomic history. Vaurie (1959) considered it to be a race of Paddyfield Warbler, a species it resembles closely in appearance, and this was supported by Cheng (1987). Williamson (1968), however, decided to treat it as a race of Black-browed Reed Warbler. More recently, Alström *et al.* (1991) concluded *tangorum* to be a race of Paddyfield Warbler, based upon the response of birds to playback experiments on the breeding grounds in NE China. Sibley & Monroe (1990) elevated *tangorum* to specific status and a similar position was adopted by Kennerley & Leader (1992), who based their conclusions largely on its distinctive morphology and isolation from the breeding range of Paddyfield Warbler. Leisler *et al.* (1997) examined the DNA sequence of the mitochondrial cytochrome *b* gene from a range of *Acrocephalus* species, including Manchurian Reed, Paddyfield and Black-browed Reed Warblers. They demonstrated that *tangorum* was distinct from Paddyfield Warbler, although closely related to it. Rather surprisingly, Blunt-winged Warbler emerged as the closest relative of Manchurian Reed Warbler, while Black-browed Reed Warbler proved to be rather distantly related; their similar appearance apparently being largely coincidental. The original position adopted by La Touche has thus been vindicated and Manchurian Reed Warbler is widely recognised as a distinct species.

◄ Adult, Hong Kong, September. Shares prominent pale supercilium extending beyond the eye, dark brown side to crown, and short primary projection with Paddyfield Warbler. Differs by larger, more substantial bill with pale pink and mostly unmarked lower mandible. After breeding, adults have a partial moult, with this bird appearing to have replaced the body contour feathering; note rich brown fringe to fresh central tertial contrasting with old and faded tertials and flight feathers (Paul Leader).

▲ First-winter, Hong Kong, October. Young birds in autumn usually show considerably less wear than adults. Note the fresh, unworn flight feathers and narrow rectrices (Paul Leader).

▲ Adult, Hebei, China, May. Unlike Paddyfield Warbler, does not have an extensive pre-breeding body moult so birds returning to the breeding grounds in late May are worn and faded. Note the long tail with relatively narrow rectrices (Peter Kennerley).

BLUNT-WINGED WARBLER
Acrocephalus concinens   Plate 18

Calamoherpe concinens **Swinhoe, 1870**. *Proc. Zool. Soc. London.* p. 432. Peking.

A scarce *Acrocephalus* with a restricted and localised distribution, which breeds in three widely separated areas of Asia: E China, NE India to NW Burma, and the foothills of the NW Himalayas. Birds from China migrate to SE Asia but the other races appear to be either resident or short-distance altitudinal migrants. Formerly treated as a race of Paddyfield Warbler. Polytypic, with three discrete populations each recognised as a distinct race:

A. c. concinens (Swinhoe, 1870). NE and E China
A. c. haringtoni Witherby, 1920. Afghanistan to Kashmir
A. c. stevensi Stuart Baker, 1922. NE India and adjacent Bangladesh and Burma

IDENTIFICATION Length 12–13cm. Wing 52–59mm. Tail/wing 93–102%.

This nondescript and unstreaked *Acrocephalus* closely resembles several similarly sized *Acrocephalus* with which it occurs on migration and outside the breeding season in China and SE Asia. Of all the small, unstreaked *Acrocephalus* in Asia, Blunt-winged Warbler is the most unassuming, combining a poorly marked supercilium, lack of darker sides to the crown, warm brown plumage tones and an extremely short primary projection to give it a unique appearance. Sexes alike.

Structure Although similar in size to other small, unstreaked *Acrocephalus* in E Asia, Blunt-winged Warbler has proportionately the shortest and most rounded wings, and a shorter primary projection than any of the likely confusion species. Typically this is just 35–45% of the exposed tertial length, and five or six closely spaced primary tips are visible on the closed wing, which falls well short of the longest uppertail-coverts. It has a short first primary (p1), extending up to 7mm beyond the primary coverts in NW Himalayan birds but no more than 5.5mm in Chinese birds. The wing point is formed by p4–5, and occasionally p6 in the NW Himalayas.

The bunched secondaries project slightly beyond the tertials, a feature shared with Manchurian Reed Warbler and, to some extent, with Paddyfield Warbler, but is more conspicuous on Blunt-winged. The short wings help create a rather long-tailed impression but in reality the tail is no longer than in Paddyfield or Manchurian Reed Warblers. Blunt-winged shows a fairly long, deep-based bill which can appear quite stout in the field.

Plumage and bare parts Blunt-winged Warbler has a uniform appearance which other small, unstreaked *Acrocephalus* in E Asia lack. In particular, the head appears bland and nondescript when compared with the crisp and contrasting pattern in Manchurian Reed and Black-browed Reed Warblers. All birds show a diffuse and poorly defined pale creamy buff supercilium from the bill to the eye, where it merges with the upper edge of the eye-ring. This sometimes extends beyond the eye and may reach to the rear of the ear-coverts. Below the supercilium, a slightly darker brown loral spot is visible in front of the eye, on some birds forming a solid narrow line reaching to the bill. Behind the eye, however, there is little more than a poorly defined brown spot and the side of the head is otherwise plain and uniform. Only Blyth's Reed Warbler, a common winter visitor to the Indian subcontinent and a vagrant to E Asia,

and Eurasian Reed Warbler, also a vagrant to E Asia, share a similar unassuming head pattern.

In freshly moulted birds, the crown, nape, mantle, wing-coverts, tertial fringes and flight feather edges are uniform warm brown. The rump and uppertail-coverts are slightly warmer than the mantle, with their brighter appearance enhanced by the slightly darker tail, but the upperparts are surprisingly uniform and lack the contrasting appearance shown by Paddyfield Warbler. The dark brown-centred alula, if exposed, can contrast on an otherwise featureless closed wing. But this character is shared with both Paddyfield and Eurasian Reed Warbler and is of little use in their separation.

The underparts are nondescript, a whitish chin and throat merging with a light sandy brown wash across the breast. The breast sides and flanks are darker and richer brown than the breast and approach the upperparts in colour. When fresh, the flanks can sometimes be bright fulvous brown, even more colourful than the upperparts, and then contrast strikingly with the silvery white or creamy white belly.

When worn, the crown, nape and mantle become a paler and drabber brown, often with a slight greyish cast, giving an appearance suggesting the race *fuscus* of Eurasian Reed Warbler. At this stage, the contrast between the duller upperparts and warmer rump and uppertail-coverts becomes more pronounced. First-winter birds are not known to differ from adults.

In adults, the bill is dark grey with a pinkish lower mandible that may show greyish sides. The actual tip is usually paler. The legs and feet vary from dull straw to brownish flesh or greyish pink.

SIMILAR SPECIES Identification of Blunt-winged Warbler requires extreme care, particularly during migration when several similar species may occur together. Within its range in E Asia, the most frequently encountered unstreaked *Acrocephalus* is Black-browed Reed Warbler, but Manchurian Reed also occurs regularly, albeit in low numbers. To the west, Blyth's Reed and Paddyfield Warblers winter in large numbers within the Indian subcontinent where they overlap with Blunt-winged Warbler of the NW Himalayan race *haringtoni* and NE Indian race *stevensi*. Both Blyth's Reed and Paddyfield Warblers have occurred as vagrants in E Asia. Compounding the problem further is the recent discovery of wintering Large-billed Reed Warbler in Thailand where it has already occurred alongside Blunt-winged Warbler. Separation of these species requires prolonged observation with particular attention focused on the head pattern, and shape and structure of the closed wing. Ideally, any unfamiliar, small, unstreaked *Acrocephalus* in a vagrant context should be trapped to confirm identification.

Blyth's Reed Warbler winters throughout the Indian subcontinent where it overlaps in distribution with Blunt-winged Warbler of the races *haringtoni* and *stevensi*. Blyth's Reed is a nondescript *Acrocephalus* and separation from Blunt-winged will always require good and prolonged views. It shares a similar head pattern, including an indistinct supercilium that reaches to the rear of the eye, and sometimes beyond, and lacks contrastingly dark bands on the side of the crown. Adult Blyth's Reed differ in their duller, greyish olive upperparts, and this is particularly so when compared with *haringtoni* and *stevensi* which appear warmer, darker and richer than the nominate form. First-winter Blyth's Reed are browner than adults and more closely approach the colour of Blunt-winged. However,

Blyth's Reed always lacks the warmer and brighter tone to the rump and uppertail-coverts, which show little or no contrast with the mantle and tail.

There appears to be a fairly consistent difference in the head and bill structure. Blyth's Reed typically looks long-billed, with a long and sloping forehead and a low angular crown peaking behind the eye. In Blunt-winged, the bill looks shorter and often quite stout, and the crown appears rounded rather than angular. This may be a rather subjective distinction, but the combination of head and bill profile gives each species a distinctive character. Added to this is the proportionately shorter and less-rounded tail of Blyth's Reed.

Wing shape and structure will always provide the most reliable means of separating them, and although this is of most use in the hand, good views or photographs should enable some of the subtle differences discussed here to be appreciated when viewing a bird. Blyth's Reed is longer winged than Blunt-winged, and has a longer primary projection, typically 50–60% of exposed tertial length. It shows six to eight fairly evenly spaced primary tips and a minute first primary. This compares with a primary projection of 35–45% in Blunt-winged, with just five to six primary tips visible, and first primary extending beyond the primary coverts. Blyth's Reed usually lacks the emargination on p5 which Blunt-winged shows.

Large-billed Reed Warbler is so rare that any claim could not be upheld unless supported by measurements and photographs. Its overall appearance is extremely similar to Blunt-winged and Blyth's Reed Warblers, with which it shares a similar head pattern. As this species is so poorly known, the full range of plumage characters have not yet been established. It does, however, differ in its olive-brown upperparts which lack the rufescent tones of Blunt-winged Warbler.

Appreciating the subtle structural differences that separate Blunt-winged and Large-billed Reed Warblers is essential to their separation. As its name suggests, Large-billed Reed has a long bill, always longer than 18mm and beyond the length of the largest billed Blunt-winged Warbler. The wing shape and structure are similar to Blunt-winged when fresh, and minor differences will be lost as the primaries abrade. Both species share a short primary projection, c. 40% of tertial length, and both show a wing point at p3–5, each of which is emarginated. In Large-billed Reed, however, the first primary (p1) is shorter than in Blunt-winged, falling near the primary covert tips; p2 is longer and falls between p6/7 and p8, occasionally 8/9, while on Blunt-winged it falls between p8 and p9/10.

Paddyfield Warbler also winters in the Indian subcontinent where it overlaps during migration with Blunt-winged Warbler of the race *haringtoni* in N Pakistan and Kashmir, and possibly elsewhere in northwest India outside the breeding season. Paddyfield probably does not winter regularly within the range of *stevensi* in NE India, but seems likely to occur here, even if only occasionally.

Although all three taxa of Blunt-winged Warbler were formerly treated as races of Paddyfield, the two species are readily separable. The single most useful plumage feature is the conspicuous and contrastingly pale supercilium of Paddyfield which Blunt-winged lacks. On Paddyfield, this extends from the bill base to the rear of the ear-coverts, and often widens or flares behind the eye. Added to this is the faintly darker band which borders the side of the crown, and the dark brown lores and indistinct line behind the eye, while the lightly mottled ear-coverts give a paler appearance

to the side of the head than Blunt-winged shows. Otherwise, Paddyfield is quite variable in appearance, particularly in the colour of the upperparts, which vary with moult, wear and bleaching. Blunt-winged of the races *haringtoni* and *stevensi* are warm brown above and overlap with Paddyfield, so separation on plumage tones alone is considered unsound.

Although structurally similar to Blunt-winged, Paddyfield is slightly longer winged, with a primary projection approximately 50% of the tertial length and wing point formed by p3–4 (usually p4-5 in Blunt-winged). On average, it has a shorter p1 and longer p2, but other structural differences show considerable overlap; it shares with Blunt-winged six closely spaced visible primary tips and an emargination on p3 and p4, and often p5.

Manchurian Reed Warbler differs from Blunt-winged in many of the same aspects as Paddyfield Warbler does. The head of Manchurian Reed Warbler shows a prominent supercilium extending well behind the eye, bordered above by a diffuse dark brown band along the side of the crown, quite unlike the poorly marked head of Blunt-winged. The warm plumage tones of the two species are similar but the strongly tinged peachy buff underparts of fresh Manchurian Reed are brighter than ever shown by Blunt-winged.

Manchurian Reed resembles Blunt-winged in structure, but the primary projection tends to be slightly longer and closer to that of Paddyfield, the wing-tips extending closer to the longest uppertail-coverts. The bill of Manchurian Reed is broader towards the base.

Black-browed Reed Warbler is by far the most numerous and widespread of the smaller E Asian *Acrocephalus* and the most likely to be encountered alongside Blunt-winged at any time of the year. Their separation is quite straightforward using plumage characters alone but structural differences are also useful in the field. Although unstreaked above, Black-browed Reed is readily separated by the broad blackish bands along the side of the crown, and the long, broad, creamy white supercilium. Structural differences include a longer primary projection, typically 60–70% of the tertial length, and a proportionately shorter and a less rounded tail. Upperpart colours should be a useful supplementary feature on most birds, with the duller mid brown to slightly olive-brown upperparts of Black-browed never shown by Blunt-winged. However, some Black-browed appear warmer, richer brown when freshly moulted.

VOICE The song comprises a repetitive series of soft and melodic whistles interspersed with slurred churring sequences, and delivered at a slow tempo reminiscent of Eurasian Reed Warbler. It consists of varied phrases within a frequency range of 2–7kHz, each repeated three to six times to form a distinctive sequence lasting from four to eight seconds before a short pause. The entire song may last for several minutes, punctuated by many short pauses, each followed by a different song sequence. It is not known whether the songs of the three races differ significantly.

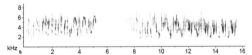

Song of Blunt-winged Warbler recorded within breeding range of *A. c. concinens*, Wu Yi Shan, Fujian Province, China, May. (Geoff Carey)

The song given by reedbed breeding birds in northern China is not recognisably different to that of birds breeding in the mountains of SE China.

Calls include a short, quiet '*tchek*' and a longer but softer and slightly slurred '*churr*'.

MOULT The nominate form has a complete moult on the breeding grounds prior to autumn migration. Newly arrived birds in the wintering areas in Thailand are in fresh plumage in October and November (Round 2008). It is not known whether there is a partial pre-breeding moult in the wintering range. In late spring, birds on migration and on the breeding grounds in E China show moderately abraded wing and tail feathers, and summer adults are fairly heavily worn. This suggests that there is no partial pre-breeding moult prior to northward migration. The timing and sequence of moult in other races is unknown.

HABITAT All three races breed in wetlands, especially those with *Phragmites* reedbeds or similar tall emergent reed. The nominate form was formerly a common breeder in the huge reedbeds along the lower Yangtze River in C China. Many of these reedbeds disappeared during the twentieth century but a reduced breeding population remains wherever suitable habitat exists. Elsewhere in China it also exploits reed-filled ditches and smaller patches of *Phragmites* fringing lakes, e.g. at the Summer Palace in Beijing. In Kashmir, the form *haringtoni* breeds around lakes and marshes in the Vale of Kashmir reaching elevations of approximately 1,700m in sedges and wet grasslands as well as *Phragmites* reedbeds. In Assam, the race *stevensi* breeds at lower elevations along the Brahmaputra River valley and associated wetlands, in rushes, tall and wet grasslands and reedbeds by rivers, large lakes and swamps.

In addition, some Blunt-winged Warblers also breed in dry scrub and bushes on hillsides away from wetlands, a trait noted in both the nominate race in China and the race *haringtoni* in Kashmir. These birds are not known to differ from their reedbed-breeding counterparts, and as yet no differences in plumage or vocalisations have been detected. In China, the nominate race also breeds in dry hillside scrub at upland locations in Guangdong, Fujian, Hebei and Sichuan Provinces, while in Kashmir, birds of the race *haringtoni* breed in rank scrub vegetation on dry hillsides up to 3,000m. This use of two distinct breeding habitats was first noted by La Touche (1925–30), who observed birds in the mountains in NW Fujian Province, and commented that birds were breeding commonly in hazel thickets in dry mountain valleys in Chihli (Hebei Province) as well as in the Peking (Beijing) reedbeds.

Migrants and wintering birds in Thailand are also found in both habitat types. Many occur in coastal freshwater marshes, for example at Khao Sam Roi Yot National Park, where it favours *Phragmites* reed, *Typha* and other marsh vegetation. Others winter in drier upland areas with rank *Imperata* grasslands, for example in Khao Yai National Park.

BEHAVIOUR Behaviour appears not to differ from that of similar small *Acrocephalus* warblers. It is generally very skulking and elusive, although males can be conspicuous when singing in calm conditions from an exposed *Phragmites* stem, tall herbaceous plant or bush top. In the wintering area, Round (2008) considered it to be more skulking than Manchurian Reed Warbler and less inclined to climb up reed stems.

BREEDING HABITS Most available data comes from studies of *haringtoni* in Kashmir by Bates & Lowther (1952). Breeding activity in the Vale of Kashmir and Wardwan Valley begins only when the herbaceous plants required for nesting are sufficiently tall to provide thick cover. Nest

building typically commences between mid June and early July. Some nests are built into tufts of sedge or tall grass over shallow water, while those on dry hillsides may be close to the ground in clumps of Dwarf Elder *Sambucus ebulus*. The nest is a small construction supported by three or four vertical stems, built of dry grass and lined with finer grasses, animal hair or vegetable cotton. Those nesting over water often incorporate moss into the construction. A clutch of three or four eggs is laid from late June onwards and the female is believed to carry out much of the incubation.

DISTRIBUTION

A. c. haringtoni **Breeding** This race is a summer visitor to the mountain valleys of Afghanistan and the NW Himalayas, where it occurs between 2,700m and 3,000m. From the Danaghori plain in N Afghanistan, the breeding range extends to the Hazara district in N Pakistan and into neighbouring Kashmir, India, where breeding has been recorded from the Vale of Kashmir down to 1,700m on the Kashmir Lakes, the Kagan valley, Gaghi Pass, Wardwan valley and upper Kishtwar. The winter quarters remain unknown but it is likely that some are resident at lower elevations, while those breeding in the mountains descend to the foothills of the Himalayas in Pakistan and NW India when the climate at higher altitudes becomes inhospitable. Its skulking behaviour and superficial resemblance to both Blyth's Reed and Paddyfield Warblers may be obscuring its presence during the winter months.

A. c. stevensi **Breeding** This form has the most restricted range, breeding only in extreme NE India, Burma and possibly Bangladesh, where it is believed to be largely resident or dispersive outside the breeding season. In India, it is thought to be resident in the floodplains bordering the Brahmaputra River in Assam. Breeding has not been proven in Burma but is suspected to have occurred near the Pegu canal (Smythies 1968).

Non-breeding Outside the breeding season, it has been recorded in the NE Indian states of Manipur, Meghalaya and West Bengal, as well as in the floodplains of the Brahmaputra River in Assam where it is resident. In neighbouring Nepal, it is an uncommon and extremely local winter visitor and passage migrant, recorded primarily from the Koshi River in the east of the country (Inskipp & Inskipp 1991; Baral 1996, 2000). Although these records are not supported by specimens, or positively attributed to *stevensi*, this is probably the most likely race to occur in E Nepal. In Burma Smythies (1968) also described it as being common during cold weather in the Sittang plain, the Karen Hills, northern Shan states, Karenni and North Tenasserim, suggesting that a substantial population breeds to the north in NW Burma or moves here from NE India during cold weather, although there is no record that such movements occur. This led Rasmussen & Anderton (2005) to propose an alternative suggestion, that these wintering birds could be of the nominate form.

A. c. concinens **Breeding** The breeding range of the nominate form extends over much of E and C China north to Beijing but probably not extending north of N Hebei Province. Cheng (1987) included the provinces of Hebei, Shaanxi, Hubei, Jiangxi and the Guangxi Zhuang Autonomous Region, to which can be added Sichuan and Guangdong Provinces, where singing males have been recorded in the breeding season. Within this large region, it is a scarce bird with a highly fragmented distribution.

The loss of reedbeds and the draining of wetlands which began in the twentieth century and is still ongoing must have contributed to the present patchy distribution and it is now absent from many apparently suitable wetlands.

Swinhoe originally discovered it breeding outside the city walls of Beijing, and La Touche (1925–30) quoted Père David who found it breeding widely in damp localities of the Great China Plain. Styan also found it plentiful along the lower Yangtze River at Kiukiang, Kiangsu (Jiujiang, Jiangsu Province), but La Touche failed to find it here and it would seem that by the late nineteenth century it was already becoming localised in E China, and perhaps it always was. La Touche described it as rare in NE Chihli (now Hebei Province) and managed to collect just one specimen, while to the south of the Yangtze River he encountered it just once, in the mountains of NW Fohkien (now Fujian Province).

The nominate race also breeds up to 2,100m in the mountains of E and SE China including Ba Bao Shan in Guangdong Province; Wu Yi Shan in Fujian Province; Old Peak in Hebei Province and Qingcheng Shan in Sichuan Province. This suggests it may be widespread in scrub and grasslands above 2,000m throughout much of E China. Similarly, in Kashmir, some birds of the race *haringtoni* breed in rank scrub vegetation on dry hillsides up to 3,000m.

Non-breeding Outside the breeding season, the winter range of the nominate form is centred on C and NW Thailand, where it is uncommon but widespread (Lekagul & Round 1991). Robson (2000) also includes N and C Laos in the wintering range, and also S and E Burma including Tenasserim. However, the race wintering here has not been examined, and the possibility that these birds could be *stevensi* has not been investigated.

MOVEMENTS Poorly known on migration. The limited information available relates mainly to migrants of the nominate race on passage through S China and the Indochinese countries to known wintering areas in Thailand. In Vietnam, Vo Quy & Nguyen Cu (1995) described it as a passage migrant of uncertain abundance, so five birds trapped in Cuc Phuong National Park, about 100km SSW of Hanoi in April 1995 suggest a fairly late departure from the wintering area (Mey 1997). There were just three records from Hong Kong prior to 2000 (Carey *et al.* 2001), but there have been seven subsequent records to 2006 (PJL *in litt.*), all trapped in *Phragmites* reedbeds at the Mai Po Marshes Nature Reserve. Six occurred between September and November, three were wintering birds in January and February: two of which two remained until April, plus a singing male on 20–21 April 1991. This spread of records provides few clues to its true status in SE China, other than it can occur on almost any date between September and April.

In NE China, it probably occurs annually in small numbers in the Beidaihe area in spring, but has not been reliably reported here in autumn. In most years, just one or two birds are recorded, with a maximum of seven in spring 1994 (JH pers. comm.). Beidaihe lies close to the northern limit of the breeding range, and records here span most of May, with the majority occurring near the end of the month.

The only documented movement of *haringtoni* comes from Whitehead, who reported large numbers on northward migration through Kohat, Pakistan (Roberts 1992).

DESCRIPTION *A. c. concinens*
Plumage – Adult fresh Forehead to nape, including sides of crown, uniform warm brown. Supercilium creamy white, fairly broad but short, from base of bill to rear edge of eye, sometimes continued as an indistinct, paler brown line beyond the eye. Lores with fairly conspicuous dark brown

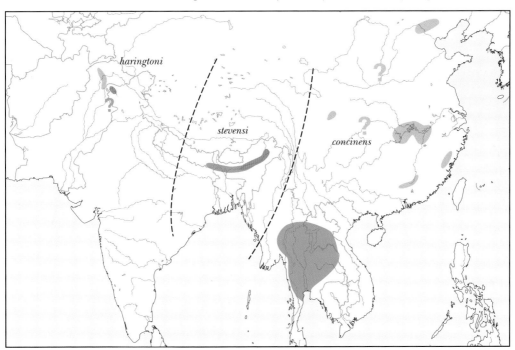

Blunt-winged Warbler. Breeding range and winter distribution. Outside of the breeding season only Chinese breeders undertake a long migration. Indian breeders are resident, dispersive or altitudinal migrants.

line from bill base to eye. Usually a small, indistinct dark brown spot immediately behind eye, but no eye-line. Ear-coverts warm brown, with indistinct paler shaft streaks but otherwise matching crown. Eye-ring narrow, usually white and appearing paler than supercilium; often quite conspicuous. Mantle and scapulars to uppertail-coverts uniform warm brown or fulvous-brown. Tail warm brown with darker feather shafts. Chin and throat white, often with creamy wash. Sides of breast and neck bright fulvous-brown, fading to warm brown wash across breast centre. Flanks bright fulvous-brown, slightly brighter than upperparts. Lower breast, belly and undertail-coverts creamy brown. Lesser and median coverts uniform fulvous-brown, greater coverts similar but with darker brown centres and diffuse, fulvous-brown fringes. Tertials mid brown with broad, diffuse fulvous-brown fringes. Primary coverts, secondaries and primaries grey-brown, edged fulvous-brown as upperparts, primaries with indistinct pale brown tips that contrast slightly with closed wing. Alula dark-centred with narrow brown fringe, often appearing as darkest feather on closed wing. Underwing-coverts pale warm buff.

Adult worn Warmer tones are lost and overall appearance becomes paler brown. Crown and upperparts mid brown to greyish brown, mantle and tail showing greater contrast with warmer-brown rump and uppertail-coverts. Supercilium slightly paler and more contrasting. Side of breast and flanks colder and paler, with variable sandy grey to dull peachy brown wash. Centre of breast washed pale grey-buff. Belly typically white with only faint creamy wash. Undertail-coverts pale warm buff. Tertials, primaries and secondaries earthy brown with sandy brown fringes. Alula faded, no longer contrasting with closed wing.

Juvenile/first-winter Not known to differ from fresh adult.

Bare parts Upper mandible dark grey with narrow pink cutting edge. Lower mandible pink, occasionally with indistinct greyish sides towards tip. Both upper and lower mandibles often with whitish tips. Mouth yellow. Tarsi and toes dull straw to brownish flesh or greyish pink; claws usually slightly darker. Iris hazel-brown in adults, grey-brown in first-winter.

IN HAND CHARACTERS
Measurements

A. c. haringtoni

	Male	Female
Wing	56–59 (57.8; 14)	54–59 (56.7; 15)
Tail	54–58 (56.8; 10)	52–58 (55.3; 10)
Bill	14.5–15.5 (15.0; 10)	14.5–15 (14.9; 8)
Tarsus	21.5–23 (22.2; 9)	21–22.5 (22.1; 10)

Sexes combined:
Tail/wing ratio: 93–102% (98%; 20)
Bill width: 3.8–4.2 (4.0; 8)
Hind claw: 6.0–7.0 (6.4; 10)
Tail graduation: 9–16 (12.2; 18)
A. c. concinens (sexes combined): *wing* 52–58 (55.1; 14); *tail* 49–55 (52.6;14); *bill* 15–16 (15.7; 12); *tarsus* 21–22 (21.8; 8).
A. c. stevensi (sexes combined): *wing* 53–57 (54.8; 21); *tail* 50–56 (53.7; 18); *bill* 15–16.5 (15.6; 17); *tarsus* 20.5–22 (21.6; 4).
Races *concinens* and *stevensi* have a shorter wing and tail than *haringtoni*, but slightly longer bill.

Structure

A. c. concinens

Wing formula (n = 7):

p1/pc	p2	p3e	p4e	p5e	p6	p7	p10
4–5.5	5.5–8	0.5–1.5	wp	0–1	1–2	3–5.5	8–9

Wing point at p4 (5); p2 = p8/9; emargination on p3–5.

Figure 53. Wing of Blunt-winged Warbler *A. c. concinens*.

Tail graduated; feathers broad with rounded tips.
Bill quite strong, straight sided; rather broader and deeper than in Paddyfield Warbler, less broad than in Manchurian Reed Warbler (Fig. 51).
Tarsi rather slender as in Paddyfield, but claws stronger.

A. c. haringtoni

Wing formula (n = 10):

p1/pc	p2	p3e	p4e	p5e	p6	p7	p10
4–7	6–9	0.5–2	wp	0–1	0–3	2.5–5	9–10.5

Wing similar to nominate *concinens* (Fig. 53) but p1 averages slightly longer. Wing point at p4 (5, 6); p2 = p 8–9/10; emargination on p3–5, sometimes also on p6.

Recognition One of three small, plain-backed, warmly coloured *Acrocephalus* of the E Palearctic and N Oriental regions but lacks the dark lateral crown stripe typical of Paddyfield and Manchurian Reed Warblers. Distinguished from Paddyfield and most Manchurian Reed by more strongly rounded wing, with p2 < p8; and from most Manchurian Reed by longer p1 (4mm or more > pc). A greater tail graduation (> 10mm) distinguishes most from Paddyfield. Broader, more rounded tail feathers provide further distinction from Manchurian Reed.

a   b   c

Figure 54. Closed wing structure of (a) Blunt-winged Warbler *A. c. concinens*, (b) Manchurian Reed Warbler and (c) Paddyfield Warbler.

Weight Thailand, Nov–Dec and Mar–Apr: 7.4–9.3g (8.3; 43) (PDR unpublished data). Hong Kong, 8.8–12.9g (10.2; 14) (HKRG unpublished data).

GEOGRAPHIC VARIATION Three races are recognised, all very similar in appearance and structure.

A. c. concinens (NE and central E China) Described above.

A. c. haringtoni (N Afghanistan to Kashmir) When fresh, warmer and brighter than the nominate race, with cinnamon-brown to russet-brown tones predominating. The entire upperparts including the crown, sides to the head, nape, mantle, wing-coverts, edges to the flight feathers and tail are russet-brown, while the rump and uppertail-coverts are slightly warmer and brighter cinnamon-brown. The supercilium is similar in shape and extent to that of nominate *concinens* but faintly cinnamon and less contrasting. The narrow eye-ring is faintly washed brown and less conspicuous.

The underparts are also warmly toned and, although paler than the upperparts, the flanks can appear particularly bright. The chin, throat and centre to the breast are lightly washed pale cream-buff to cinnamon-buff and contrast with the warm apricot wash on the sides of the breast, flanks and undertail-coverts. The lower breast and belly are warm buff, darkening slightly onto the undertail-coverts.

Worn birds are slightly paler, although cinnamon tones are retained on the rump and uppertail-coverts. However, *haringtoni* appears warmer and brighter than worn nominate *concinens*, with a stronger creamy brown wash below.

The bill shows dark sides that extend almost half the length of the lower mandible.

A. c. stevensi (NE India and adjacent Bangladesh and Burma) Closely resembles *haringtoni* closely, but has slightly darker upperparts and, in particular, shows rufous-brown rather than buff underparts, so there is little contrast between the throat and sides to the head. The bill is entirely pale and lacks dark sides to the tip.

TAXONOMY AND SYSTEMATICS Blunt-winged Warbler was originally described by Swinhoe (1870) but given the unfortunate English name Chinese Paddyfield Warbler. This subsequently resulted in it being treated as a race of Paddyfield Warbler despite clear morphological differences. The taxa *stevensi* and *haringtoni*, described in the early 1920s, were also treated as races of Paddyfield Warbler together with *concinens*. It was recognised that these three taxa formed a distinct grouping within Paddyfield Warbler, displaying clear morphological and biometric distinctions, but these were considered not sufficiently distinctive to merit specific treatment. Vaurie (1959) recommended a return to specific status for the *concinens* group but used the cumbersome English name of Blunt-winged Paddyfield Warbler, thus failing to sever the link with Paddyfield, and this split was not generally accepted. As further distinctions became better understood from the late 1980s, specific treatment gained popularity. It is now universally accepted that Blunt-winged Warbler is a full species and this is supported by molecular studies (Leisler *et al.* 1997). These have shown that it is most closely related to Manchurian Reed Warbler and is not the closest relative of Paddyfield Warbler, as had been expected.

As yet, no studies have been undertaken to establish the phylogeny of the three recognised races; *concinens*, *haringtoni* and *stevensi*.

To confuse the picture further, based upon slight plumage differences, Whistler (1930) described a fourth race *hokrae* from Hokra jheel in Kashmir and noted that it nested in reedbeds around the margins of lakes in the Vale of Kashmir, rather than in the dry scrub-covered hillsides frequented by *haringtoni*. Rasmussen & Anderton (2005), after examining specimens, considered *haringtoni* and *hokrae* to be separable using a number of criteria including differences in plumage colour, moult schedule, wing formula, morphometrics and breeding habitat. They did, however, acknowledge that some individuals are difficult to allocate to a specific race. We have examined specimens of *haringtoni* and *hokrae* held in the NHM, Tring, and find they are extremely similar. Although some *hokrae* match Whistler's (1930) description and are undeniably separable, appearing paler and slightly greyer than *haringtoni*, others show significant overlap and we could find no consistent morphological distinction between them. Given the close proximity of the breeding ranges, it is possible that birds described as *hokrae* represent a pale colour morph of *haringtoni*, which would explain the apparent inconsistency and overlap in characters.

A similar situation exists in E China with birds breeding in two distinct habitats; wetlands with *Phragmites* reedbeds in lowlands and dry hillsides in scrub habitats in the mountains of E and SE China. At present, therefore, we maintain *hokrae* as a synonym of *haringtoni* but recognise that this may change, and further studies may reveal two cryptic species.

◄ First-year *A. c. concinens*, Hong Kong, January. After complete moult in early autumn, adult and first-autumn birds appear identical, but can be separated by duller iris colour, this being a young bird. Has the shortest primary projection of the smaller *Acrocephalus*. Note the sandy brown upperparts, plain crown and lack of eye-stripe. Usually shows a poorly defined supercilium, although on this bird it is particularly well marked (Paul Leader).

▲ ▶ Adult *A. c. concinens*, Hong Kong, January. This freshly moulted bird shows relatively warm brown upperparts and typical, poorly defined supercilium barely visible beyond the eye. Note the relatively large bill and pinkish lower mandible which darkens subtly towards the tip. Grey-brown iris indicates first year bird (Paul Leader).

▲ Adult *A. c. concinens*, Hong Kong, April. When slightly worn in spring, upperparts are slightly paler and the supercilium only reaches to rear of eye. Also, the dark smudge on sides of the lower mandible is more conspicuous, and may become darker during the breeding season (Peter Kennerley).

PADDYFIELD WARBLER
Acrocephalus agricola   **Plate 18**

Sylvia (acrocephalus) agricola Jerdon, 1845. *Madras Jour. Lit. Sci.* 13(2): 131. Neighbourhood of Nellore, Madras.

A long distance migrant which breeds across the W and C Palearctic regions from the western coast of the Black Sea to C Asia and NW China and winters in the Indian subcontinent. It closely resembles Manchurian Reed Warbler, which was considered to be a race of Paddyfield Warbler until recently. Polytypic, with two races recognised:

A. a. agricola (Jerdon 1845). Caspian and Aral Seas east through Kazakhstan to W Mongolia and NW China, north to W Siberia and south to Tajikistan, E Iran, N Afghanistan and W Pakistan.

A. a. septima Gavrilenko 1954. Black Sea coast from Bulgaria and Romania, east through S Ukraine to the Lower Ural and Ilek Rivers.

IDENTIFICATION Length 12–13cm. Wing 54–62mm. Tail/wing 84–98%.

A small unstreaked *Acrocephalus* with a conspicuous pale supercilium bordered above by a diffuse dusky band along the side of the crown and typically warmly coloured upperparts, but showing extensive colour variation and marked seasonal variation in plumage tone. Many birds also show a distinctive pale half-collar extending onto the side of the neck. There is always a small dark smudge to the side of the lower mandible near the tip. Sexes alike.

Structure The structure resembles that of other small unstreaked *Acrocephalus* of the Western and Central Palearctic, although it is proportionately shorter-winged and longer tailed than any similar sympatric breeding species, including Eurasian Reed, Marsh and Blyth's Reed Warblers, giving it the highest tail/wing ratio of these species, ranging from 84% to 98%. Paddyfield Warbler frequently holds it wings loosely at the sides of the body, exposing the rump and uppertail-coverts. This also enhances the apparent tail length, which appears longer than in Eurasian Reed and Blyth's Reed Warbler. With the wings closed over the back, however, the primaries reach the base of the tail and much of this long-tailed appearance is lost.

Compared with these species, the crown can appear rather rounded and less angular, but this is a subtle and probably unreliable feature. The bill of Paddyfield Warbler is quite small and rather stubby, lacking the long and spiky appearance of Blyth's Reed and Eurasian Reed Warblers. The bill is closest in size and shape to that of Blunt-winged Warbler, but this usually lacks the dark shadow near the tip of the lower mandible, which is usually distinct in Paddyfield Warbler.

The wing is rather rounded, the typical primary projection being *c.* 50%, slightly shorter than in Blyth's Reed Warbler. It shows six fairly evenly spaced primary tips. This spacing is relatively easy to establish in first-winter and freshly moulted adults, but increasingly difficult as the primary tips become worn. The first primary is quite short, extending up to 6mm beyond the primary coverts. Emarginations are present on the outer webs of p3–4 and often p5; among *Acrocephalus* in Europe, only Blyth's Reed Warbler is similar. In eastern Asia, however, both Manchurian Reed and Blunt-winged Warbler have p3–5 emarginated, the latter usually with an additional emargination on p6.

Plumage and bare parts Amongst the small, unstreaked *Acrocephalus* breeding in Europe and C Asia, Paddyfield Warbler shows the most well marked head pattern, with a long and contrasting pale cream supercilium bordered above by a diffuse, dull brown band along the side of the crown. It has been likened to that of Sedge Warbler but, in reality, the supercilium is never so prominent or well defined, appearing long and pale, warmly tinged in freshly moulted birds but whiter in worn birds. It extends to the rear of the ear-coverts, sometimes flaring slightly behind the eye. A darker border is formed along its upper edge by darker sides to the crown. This can be quite conspicuous on worn birds, but is sometimes obscured by cinnamon-tipped feather fringes in freshly moulted birds. The supercilium is bordered below by a dark loral line and a less distinct brown line behind the eye and the lightly mottled ear-coverts give a paler appearance to the head side. Paddyfield also shows a surprisingly conspicuous pale half-collar that other small European and C Asian *Acrocephalus* lack. This extends from the side of the breast, below the ear-coverts and onto the side of the neck.

In fresh plumage, immediately after post-breeding moult in India, Paddyfield Warbler is the brightest of the smaller streaked *Acrocephalus*, approached only by Manchurian Reed. The upperparts are rich cinnamon-brown, while the breast, flanks and undertail-coverts are suffused rich orange-cinnamon. This appearance quickly changes becoming duller and browner as cinnamon-brown feather fringes are lost. This brighter plumage is briefly regained again in spring in N India following a partial pre-breeding moult, although they rarely appear as bright as fresh autumn birds. Some birds returning to Kazakhstan in May retain these warm tones, but most adults on the breeding grounds have lost the brighter feather tips, and are slightly worn, although many retain a cinnamon-brown wash on the rump and uppertail-coverts. The underparts, however, become much duller, with the breast and flanks appearing pale buffy brown, the chin and throat contrastingly white and the belly also whitish. As well as being brighter, the closed wing of Paddyfield Warbler shows darker centres to the tertials and greater coverts, which contrast with the cinnamon-brown fringes, and the alula appears as the darkest wing feather. By late summer, the worn upperparts become pale mousy brown or even pale sandy brown, and the underparts fade to dull white with little contrast between the throat and breast, with any buff or brown tones being confined to the flanks and undertail-coverts.

First-winter birds have warmly toned upperparts and a warm buff wash on breast, flanks and undertail-coverts. Initially they resemble spring adults, but lack the brighter cinnamon-brown tones of newly moulted adults in winter.

The bill is dark brown to blackish, with a pale pinkish yellow or straw-yellow base to the lower mandible and darker sides towards the tip. The legs and feet vary in colour, ranging from pale brown and pale grey-brown to pale yellowish brown.

The problem of pale birds Apparent plumage tones of *Acrocephalus* vary depending on light conditions. However some adult Paddyfield Warblers can appear exceptionally pale in July and August when the plumage becomes worn and bleached, looking quite different from typical spring birds. Occasionally, a first-winter bird can lack all traces of the usual warm plumage tones. We have no first-hand experience of such birds, and they must be rare, but it is important to be aware that they can occur. One such pale first-winter bird, trapped at Sheringham in Norfolk,

England in September 1993, was discussed by Bradshaw (1997) and the in-hand description is repeated below:

'Entire upperparts from forehead to upperside of tail almost uniform greyish brown with a slight olive cast to entirety. Uppertail-coverts slightly warmer coloured than rest of upperparts, pale brown with a buff tinge. No rufous on upperparts. Supercilium broad and white with a very slight buff suffusion, broadest in front of eye and fading behind eye to finish level with rear of ear-coverts. No dark upper edge to the supercilium. Iris dull greyish olive. Lores with grey-brown suffusion. Ear-coverts wholly greyish brown with restricted buff feathering below eye. Chin white. Throat white with restricted buff tipping. Breast white with more extensive buff tipping than throat, most buff on side of breast. Belly white. Flanks with extensive buff extending to sides of uppertail-coverts, where most buff. Undertail-coverts off-white, tips suffused buff. Wings uniform pale greyish brown with buff tinge. All wing feathers with pale buffish brown fringes, broadest on tertials, most narrow on all feathers of alula, hence alula looking darker. Primaries diffusely tipped off-white, less than 0.4mm at broadest tip (i.e. almost nothing there). Primaries all fresh. Tertials slightly worn (typical of first year *Acrocephalus*). Tail moderately worn with lots of castllations (typical for first year *Acrocephalus*). Legs pinkish grey; rear of legs paler. Soles pale yellow; claws mid grey'.

The appearance of this bird was particularly unusual for any small and unstreaked first-winter *Acrocephalus,* but it is interesting to note that subsequent field observations concluded that 'the supercilium was fairly obvious and there was a clear dark line above it'.

SIMILAR SPECIES Paddyfield Warbler is a particularly distinctive species that should not be mistaken for any other European or C Asian *Acrocephalus*. Although it shares a similar wing structure and overlaps in measurements with Blyth's Reed Warbler, which has a similar distribution throughout the year, albeit usually in different habitats, plumages differences are so great that their separation should not be difficult. Outside the breeding season, greater care is required to separate it in NW and NE India from the structurally similar Blunt-winged Warbler. Separation from Manchurian Reed Warbler and, especially, Booted Warbler requires care, and this potential pitfall is discussed in greater detail below.

Blyth's Reed Warbler has drab, cold olive-brown or greyish olive upperparts and lacks the warmer, bright plumage tones typical of Paddyfield Warbler. Some first-winter birds are warmer and browner above than adults, with olive tones largely suppressed and appear closer to Eurasian Reed Warbler in overall appearance. It also has a shorter, less prominent supercilium, most obvious in front of the eye but barely extending beyond it, and never shows dark crown sides. It also has a longer bill, a more attenuated head shape and the tail is relatively shorter than that of Paddyfield Warbler.

Blunt-winged Warbler is variable in appearance but appears warmly toned and similar to Paddyfield Warbler both above and below. However, the supercilium is less prominent, usually reaching the rear edge of the eye but not extending beyond it, and it lacks dark crown sides. Other differences include shorter, more rounded wings, a more rounded tail and a stouter bill.

Manchurian Reed Warbler breeds and winters to the east

of the range of Paddyfield, but vagrant Paddyfield Warbler has occurred within the range of Manchurian Reed. It is very similar in appearance to Paddyfield, in overall plumage coloration and head pattern and also wing structure, but the tail feathers are narrower. Its larger and broader bill appears heavier and more substantial than that of Paddyfield Warbler. Outside the breeding season it has an entirely pale lower mandible, but during the breeding season, the sides darken and take on the appearance of Paddyfield. These distinctions are subtle and best appreciated on a trapped bird. The separation of these species is discussed in greater detail within the Manchurian Reed Warbler account.

Eurasian Reed Warbler x Sedge Warbler have been known to hybridise occasionally. Such birds can show a conspicuous pale supercilium, dark crown sides and unstreaked upperparts. However, a hybrid would also be expected to share characters of each parent and so should be longer-winged than Paddyfield, with the wing point formed by p3, and only p3 would be emarginated.

Booted Warbler and Paddyfield Warblers share a similar head pattern and wing structure. First-winter and adult Booted Warblers in fresh plumage are paler and browner than Paddyfield and lack warm cinnamon tones, but confusion could occur between worn adults in mid to late summer, when the upperparts of both species fade to drab greyish brown. Measurements are of little use in their separation, with extensive overlap in wing length. Both species show emarginations on primaries p3–5, although Booted can also have an emarginated p6, and both have the second primary, p2, falling between p6 and p8.

Although they share a similar structure, their separation is usually straightforward. If confronted by the choice between Booted and Paddyfield Warbler, critical examination of the following features should result in the correct identification.

The supercilium is generally shorter in Booted, tapering as it fades above the ear-coverts.

The undertail-coverts are shorter in Booted, extending less than half the length of the visible tail. In Paddyfield they reach half way or more down the tail, although beware that some undertail-coverts may be missing or being replaced. Booted should never show the warm tone to the rump and uppertail-coverts which Paddyfield does.

A pale outer web to the outer tail feather is usually obvious in Booted, but is never found on Paddyfield. Occasionally Booted may lack this, particularly if an outer rectrix has been lost.

The tail of Booted is almost square, while in Paddyfield it is distinctly rounded, but beware the effects of abrasion. Booted typically shows a shorter, finer bill, but measurements show much overlap

Booted has a more delicate, rounded and domed head, giving it an appearance reminiscent of a *Phylloscopus* warbler.

Booted is more active than Paddyfield, regularly flicking its wings and tail and showing behaviour more typical of a *Phylloscopus* warbler.

VOICE The song is distinctive and sufficiently different from that of Marsh and Eurasian Reed Warblers to attract attention. It is slightly higher pitched than in these species, ranging between 2–8kHz, but shares the same extensive range of scratchy notes along with the '*chips*', '*chirrups*', '*churrs*' and whistles, common to many small *Acrocephalus*. It has a rapid delivery and a varied structure and tends to gradually rise and fall in pitch. Some passages are twittery and suggest Linnet, while others recall the scratchy song of Common Whitethroat. It perhaps most resembles the song of Marsh Warbler, although it lacks its liquid quality and range and variety of notes. Sample (2003) likened it to Moustached Warbler due to its slightly thinner quality and higher pitched delivery. It is quite different from the sedate, unhurried song of Eurasian Reed Warbler. Paddyfield Warbler is also a mimic and includes the songs and calls of many unrelated species within its repertoire. But mimicked phases are used less frequently than in Marsh Warbler and do not form the core of the song.

Song of Paddyfield Warbler recorded within breeding range of *A. a. agricola*, Buerjin, Xinjiang Uygur Autonomous Region, China, June. (Geoff Carey)

The most frequently heard call is a soft, quiet '*tuk*', '*chek*' or '*chak*', uttered regularly by foraging birds. It also gives a quiet churring '*cherr*' call

MOULT Adults usually replace some of the body and head feathers on the breeding grounds, but this moult varies in its extent, some individuals replacing the entire body plumage, others none at all. Moult recommences when birds arrive in Pakistan and N India from mid August onwards. All the old body contour feathering is replaced together with the remiges and rectrices. Active moult occurs in most birds in September and October and is completed by November. From February or early March there is a pre-breeding moult of body and head feathers, which may last into early April. This is variable in extent. Some birds replace most or all of the body feathering and appear as bright as fresh autumn birds, but a minority suppress this moult entirely. On reaching the breeding grounds, the latter appear worn and faded alongside freshly moulted birds.

Juveniles moult the head and body feathers and usually the lesser and median coverts, shortly after fledging. This post-juvenile moult is complete by early August, prior to migration. The main moult in first-year birds, involving the flight feathers, tail and entire contour feathering, occurs shortly after arrival on the wintering grounds. The variable late winter body moult presumably also affects first-year as well as older birds.

HABITAT Largely restricted in the breeding season to wetlands dominated by *Phragmites* reedbeds. In the arid steppe and semi-desert regions of C Asia and W China it utilises patches of *Phragmites* or *Typha* fringing small and often temporary lakes and slow-flowing rivers and irrigation ditches, and it is thriving and expanding its range into previously unsuitable areas where recently created irrigation schemes have provided reedbeds. To the west, where a wider range of wetland habitat is available, it is again widely scattered, with *Phragmites* reed usually an essential component of the environment, a habitat shared with Eurasian Reed and Great Reed Warblers. Great Reed prefers the tallest thick-stemmed reeds growing over water, but factors determining the distribution of Eurasian Reed and Paddyfield are not well understood. It has been suggested that Paddyfield prefers small reed patches close to the shore while Eurasian Reed tends to utilise denser stands further out over water. Paddyfield Warbler has benefited in

S Ukraine from the expansion of rice growing schemes.

Migrants prefer reedbeds where available, but will use other habitats associated with water, such as sedge beds, marshes, bushes and bramble patches. Wintering birds favour the tall damp grasslands of the Terai of N India and *Phragmites* reed, but also occur in other emergent vegetation over water, scrubby rank grassland with or without scattered bushes, and cultivated crops such as damp rice paddy and sugar cane.

BEHAVIOUR Rather shy and retiring when not breeding and only occasionally emerging from reeds or other thick vegetation. It tends to appear only briefly in exposed clearings, or when flying low and direct into the next patch of cover. Sometimes it feeds by flycatching within the reedbed and sallies out above the reeds briefly. At other times, birds feed on the ground among reed stems, flicking the tail nervously and calling persistently. Outside the breeding season it tends to be more difficult to observe than Blyth's Reed Warbler, keeping low within thick cover and feeding less frequently in the open shrub canopy. It often adopts a relaxed posture, with the wings held loosely drooped at the sides of the body, the flight feathers slightly spread and with the raised scapulars giving a ruffled, untidy appearance to the upperparts. This behaviour exposes the rump and uppertail-coverts, so the tail frequently appears longer than it really is and the habit of cocking it slightly and flicking it continuously enhances this impression. When flushed, tends to fly fast and low for a few yards before plunging into reeds with the tail spread.

On the breeding grounds, territorial males may sing throughout the day, with peak activity from dawn to mid morning and again in late evening, but they appear not to sing at night. Males will often perch in full view on a tall reed stem or seed head, seemingly preferring this to the more obscured perches typically used by Eurasian Reed Warbler. The forehead feathers may be raised when singing, giving a steeply rising and ragged appearance to the fore-crown.

BREEDING HABITS It is solitary and territorial and apparently monogamous, although nests may be as close as 5–10m apart where breeding density is high. In Crimea, in reedbeds of coastal spits in the Sea of Azov, breeding densities of 10–12 pairs/hectare have been recorded (Bronskov *et al.* 1989), while at Lake Durankulak, Bulgaria, one pair per 30–50m of shore was recorded (Nadler & Ihle 1988).

The nest is built by both sexes, or by the female with the male in accompaniment. It is placed in aquatic vegetation such as sparse reed and reedmace, or in sedges and low shrubs, close to or above water and between 0.1–2m up. It is a tightly made cylindrical cup of reeds and grasses, woven around several vertical stems and lined with grasses, reed flowers and sometimes plant down. A clutch of 3–6 eggs is incubated for about 12 days, apparently by the female only. The nestlings are fed by both parents, typically with items collected close to the nest. Normally single brooded. Laying peaks between mid May and early June, but extends into July. Hybridisation with Eurasian Reed Warbler has been reported from N Kazakhstan (Panov 1989).

DISTRIBUTION
Breeding
A. a. agricola Ranges through C Asia, generally to the south and east of Eurasian Reed Warbler but overlapping with it extensively in the northern part of its range.

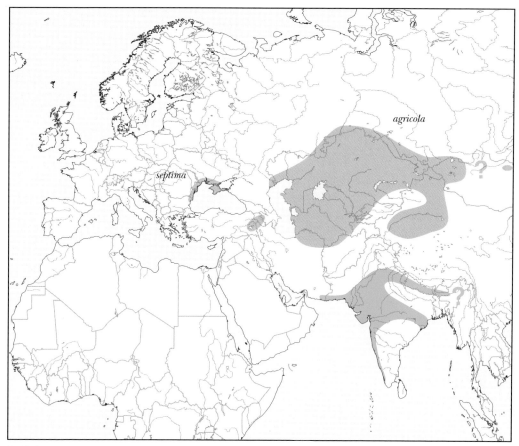

agricola

septima

Paddyfield Warbler. Breeding range and winter distribution.

The nominate form is widespread to the east of the Caspian Sea, where it breeds in reedbeds across SC Siberia north to *c.* 57°N along the middle Ural River in the region of Yekaterinburg. The northern limit then extends to the southeast including Novosibirsk and the Kulunda River, Barnaul, Biysk and the western foothills of the Altai Mountains. To the south, it breeds around the Aral Sea and east through much of Kazakhstan, where it is numerous on steppe lakes near Astana, the Ili River and Lake Balkhash region, Alakol Lake and the Zaysan Depression. It then extends into SE Kazakhstan, Tajikistan, E Iran and N Afghanistan. The eastern limit is reached in W Mongolia and W China, where it breeds in the Xinjiang Uygur Autonomous Region and it is apparently expanding its range due to irrigation projects. It now breeds at Bosten Hu and Korla in the northern Tarim Basin (Tarim Pendi), Kashi (near the Pakistan border) and the Zaidam depression (Qaidam Pendi).

A. a. septima This race breeds to the west of the nominate form, centred on the northern shores of the Caspian and Black Seas. Gavrilov & Gavrilov (2005) considered the eastern limit to extend along the northern shore of the Caspian Sea where it breeds along the lower Uil, Ural and Volga Rivers, on the Kamysh-Samarskiye Lakes and on the Kushan River at Dongulyukskoye reservoir.

The extent of its range along the western coast of the Caspian Sea is uncertain but it seems likely that breeding occurs wherever suitable habitat is found. Breeding certainly occurs in low-lying regions of Armenia, for example at the Armash Fish Ponds and in the Ararat area. In nearby E Turkey, a small population of breeding birds was discovered in the Lake Van marshes in the late 1980s, although it may have bred here for some time before this.

Along the Black Sea coast, it breeds widely in S Ukraine and through Crimea, which was colonised in the 1960s as rice cultivation expanded there. Its range has now expanded along the northern and western shores of the Black Sea where it is widespread in coastal Romania, following its discovery here in 1952. It has been a numerous breeding bird throughout the Danube delta since the 1970s. It was first recorded in NE Bulgaria in 1968 and now breeds regularly south to Lake Durankulak and Lake Sabla.

Non-breeding In winter, occurs widely throughout the Indian subcontinent, from Sind Province in S Pakistan, south through the lowlands of peninsula India, but is absent from Sri Lanka. The eastern limits are uncertain, but it winters throughout the Nepal lowlands, where it is numerous around the Koshi River. Records further to the east are open to question as here it encroaches into the range of Blunt-winged Warbler. There are just single records from the Kaziranga National Park in Assam and from Bhamo in N Burma. It is not known whether the race *septima* has a distinct wintering range, or whether it winters alongside the nominate form.

MOVEMENTS Adults leave breeding areas from mid July, with first-winter birds vacating the breeding areas a few weeks later. Passage commences in late July, with August being the peak period for migration of northern breeders through Kazakhstan and Uzbekistan. Most have departed by late September and the last stragglers remain in C Asia until early to mid October. Birds crossing from C Asia to the Indian subcontinent skirt the NW Himalayas, though still migrating over high passes and occasionally recorded up to 5,000m. The first arrivals reach NW India in early September, with birds moving quickly eastwards as far as Nepal. Some may pause here to complete moult before continuing to more S Indian wintering grounds, as in Blyth's Reed Warbler.

Departure from wintering areas begins in March, although many birds remain in India and Nepal into April. Passage through S Pakistan and E Iran peaks in April and continues into early May. Passage through S Kazakhstan is rapid, peaking in the third week of April and breeding birds occupy reedbeds from mid April onwards. First arrivals reach the breeding sites in W China from mid April, while those breeding in N Kazakhstan start to appear from the end of April, and S Siberian birds reach breeding sites from early May onwards.

The first returning birds reach the western limit of the breeding range relatively late, appearing in Crimea in late April and early May and Romania and Bulgaria during the first week of May, but becoming numerous here by the middle of the month. It is rare in Azerbaijan on the west coast of the Caspian Sea, even on autumn migration (KG).

Vagrancy There are very few reports of singing birds outside the known breeding range. Vagrants to Europe have occurred north to Finland, but Paddyfield Warbler is very rare in W Europe in spring. Post breeding season vagrancy into NW Europe has become increasingly frequent since the 1970s, with records of both adult and first-winter birds coming from many countries west to Ireland and north to Norway and the Faeroe Islands. One or two appear most years in the British Isles, usually first-winter birds between mid September and late October. A bird trapped on Fair Isle, Shetland, on 19 September 1996 had been ringed 11 days previously in Lithuania, almost 1,500km to the ESE and would seem to have been migrating in a mirror image of the direction required to take it to NW India. There have also been at least 14 records from Spain and three from Portugal since 1993, most of them birds captured by ringers on the Spanish east coast: they fall between 28 August and 24 April but eight were in November–February, as were three ringed in Corsica in winter 1993–94 (de Juana 2006; R. Gutiérrez pers. comm.).

East of the known range, vagrants have reached Hong Kong in SE China on at least nine occasions since 1992 on dates between October and March. There is also an old August specimen record from Xiushu in Jiangsu Province in E China. Birds have been trapped in N Thailand on three occasions between 4 February and 26 March and there are several unconfirmed reports from the Chiang Saen District of Chiang Rai Province (PDR *in litt.*). In Japan, a bird was photographed on Hegura-jima in the Sea of Japan on 5 May 1992.

DESCRIPTION *A. a. agricola*
Plumage – Adult fresh (October to November) Forehead to nape bright cinnamon-brown. Supercilium creamy, tinged warm buff, long and rather broad, extending from bill base and merging with crown and nape feathering above rear of ear-coverts, where broadening and often flaring behind eye. Sides of crown dark brown, forming ill-defined narrow dark band bordering upper edge of supercilium, often obscured by fine cinnamon-brown feather tips. A dark loral spot below supercilium, reaching base of bill and extending down as a spur in front of eye. Behind eye, a less distinct dull cinnamon-brown eye-line. Ear-coverts cinnamon-brown, with pale shaft streaks. Eye-ring narrow, buffish, poorly marked. Mantle and scapulars bright cinnamon-brown or orange-brown, becoming slightly paler and warmer, more orange-cinnamon, on rump and uppertail-coverts. Tail feathers dark grey-brown, fringed bright cinnamon-brown and with narrow pale buff tips. Chin and throat white, tinged orange-buff; rest of underparts washed orange-cinnamon, strongly so on side of breast, flanks and undertail-coverts. Lesser and median coverts cinnamon-brown, concolorous with scapulars. Greater coverts and tertials dark grey-brown with broad, bright cinnamon-brown fringes. Primary coverts and alula dark grey-brown, outer webs narrowly fringed cinnamon-brown. Primaries and secondaries dark grey-brown, edged bright cinnamon-brown, primary tips pale brownish white. Underwing-coverts white with slight rusty yellow wash.

When slightly worn from mid November onwards, crown is grey-brown and slightly darker than mantle. Mantle feathers lose bright cinnamon-brown fringes and tips so appear less bright but still remain warm brown, although rump and uppertail-coverts retain warmer cinnamon tones. Supercilium paler and more conspicuous, with narrow dark line bordering side of crown more distinct. Usually a warmer buff half-collar extends from side of upper breast, below ear-coverts and onto side of nape. Underparts paler, less bright, white chin and throat contrasting with buffy brown breast and flanks. Undertail-coverts paler buff and belly off-white. Pale tips to primaries often retained until spring. Many birds briefly acquire brighter body feathering in February and March in pre-breeding moult but tips again lost by April so birds on breeding areas from April onwards appear slightly worn.

Adult worn (June to August) Top of head and upperparts pale and uniform mousy brown, although rump usually warmer, more fulvous. Supercilium appears still paler, almost white and shows greater contrast with dark crown sides, loral spot and eye-line. Underparts white, with faint buff wash confined to side of breast and flanks. Remiges and rectrices dull grey-brown with faded mousy brown fringes and edgings. Primary tips abraded and pale tips lost.

First-winter Overall coloration similar to slightly worn adult. Top of head greyish brown, contrasting with warm buff half-collar extending below ear-coverts and onto sides of nape. Upperparts warm brown or cinnamon-brown, most brightly coloured on rump and uppertail-coverts. Supercilium pale buff, often with distinct dark upper border along side of crown. Head pattern otherwise as adult. Chin and throat white, tinged buff; breast and flanks washed buffy brown. Undertail-coverts pale buff. Belly whitish. Dark tertials, remiges and rectrices with warm brown or cinnamon-brown fringes and edges, broadest on tertials. Primaries with diffuse and narrow pale tips.

Juvenile Not known to differ from first-winter.

Bare Parts Upper mandible dark brown to blackish with pale pinkish cutting edge. Lower mandible pale flesh, pinkish- or straw-yellow, tip darker at sides. Mouth pale yellow; juveniles retain tongue spots until at least August. Tarsi and toes pale brown or pale grey-brown to yellowish brown or light flesh-brown; soles yellowish. Iris of adult variable, dark brown or olive-brown to light brown or pale straw, greyish brown in first-winter birds.

IN HAND CHARACTERS
Measurements

Races combined:

	Male	Female
Wing	54–62 (58.3; 48)	54–59 (56.8; 28)
Tail	49–58 (53.1; 45)	47–56 (51.6; 28)
Bill	13.5–16 (14.9; 57)	13–15 (14.5; 27)
Tarsus	20–23 (21.8; 35)	20–22.5 (21.5; 25)

Sexes combined:
Tail/wing ratio: 84–98% (91%; 73)
Bill width: 3.5–4.0 (3.8; 21)
Hind claw: 5.3–6.3 (5.8; 13)
Tail graduation: 6–9 (7.5; 25)
Juvenile wing as adult; tail on average *c.* 2mm shorter (Cramp 1992).

Structure

Wing formula (Cramp 1992):

p1/pc	p2	p3e	p4e	p5e	p6	p7	p10
0–6	3–6	wp	wp	0.5–1	1.5–3.5	3–6	7–10.5

Wing rounded; p1 small and narrow. Wing point p3–4; p2 = p6/8 (=6) [5/6]; emargination on p3–5; p2 notch below ss tips.

Figure 55. Wing of Paddyfield Warbler.

Tail medium, well rounded; feathers less broad, narrower tipped, than in Blunt-winged Warbler, not as narrow as in Manchurian Reed Warbler.

Bill shorter than in Eurasian Reed Warbler, straight and rather slim; straight sided or almost so (Fig. 51).

Tarsi more slender than in Eurasian Reed, claws smaller.

Recognition Plumage varies with fading and wear, but typically more warmly coloured than Blyth's Reed Warbler or the *fuscus* race of Eurasian Reed. Usually shows distinctive dark edge to crown sides and prominent supercilium. Legs tend to be paler and browner than in Blyth's Reed.

Shorter wing length separates it from Eurasian Reed, both in E Europe and C Asia. Shorter bill length (< 16mm) should separate it from most Blyth's Reed and all but the smallest Eurasian Reed. Second primary p2 is usually shorter than in Blyth's Reed (in which typically ≥ p6), but longer than in Blunt-winged Warbler (in which typically < p8) (Fig. 57). Most are distinguishable from both Blunt-winged and Manchurian Reed Warblers by a lesser tail graduation (any with t1–6 < 8mm being Paddyfield). For other structural differences from Manchurian Reed see under that species. Structurally similar to Booted Warbler, but tail more rounded (t1–6 usually > 5mm; < 5mm in Booted); also, p1 typically shorter (3–7mm > pc in Booted).

Ageing In early autumn, first year birds show fresh primaries and tail feathers while in unmoulted adults these are heavily abraded. Iris brown in adult but variable, paler grey-brown in immature.

Weight Range 7–14g. Typical lean weight 8–11g, but commonly reaches 12–14g prior to migration at Lake Alakol, Kazakhstan (AG, unpublished data).

GEOGRAPHIC VARIATION Two races are recognised. Differences in adult plumage colour have been described for birds breeding around the Black Sea, which Gavrilenko (1954) considered sufficiently distinct to treat as a separate race, which he named *A. a. septima*. These differences are slight and apparently depend on freshness of feathering (see **Identification** and **Description**) rather than geographical variation. Since Paddyfield Warbler is highly variable in appearance, there appear to be no consistent differences in either plumage coloration or measurements between *A. a. septima* in E Europe and W Asia and nominate *agricola* from C Asia.

A. a. agricola (Caspian and Aral Seas to W Mongolia and NW China, Tajikistan, E Iran and N Afghanistan) Described above.

A. a septima (Black Sea coast from Bulgaria and Romania to S Ukraine) Although averages slightly warmer than nominate *agricola*, we consider this race to be inseparable on plumage and structure from the nominate form (see **Taxonomy and Systematics** below). Vocalisations have not yet been studied in detail and playback may provide distinctions.

TAXONOMY AND SYSTEMATICS Historically, Manchurian Reed Warbler and Blunt-winged Warbler have been treated as races of Paddyfield Warbler. Leisler *et al.* (1997) examined the cytochrome *b* DNA sequences from a range of *Acrocephalus* species and demonstrated that these three taxa have diverged sufficiently to merit specific status. They also investigated the genetic divergence between Paddyfield Warblers from Crimea and those of E Kazakhstan, and discovered a 4.5% sequence divergence between them. Such a significant difference is usually associated with taxa that have diverged to such an extent that they are treated as distinct species. Sangster (1997) supported their findings and suggested that *A. a. septima* may be a cryptic species. Until further studies which investigate vocalisations and behaviour of European and Asian birds are published, we have retained *septima* as a race of Paddyfield Warbler but recognise that this position may change in the future.

We do not recognise the taxa *capistrata* (Severtsov 1872) or *brevipennis* (Severtsov 1872). These names appear to relate to the faded and worn plumage of the nominate form.

▲ Adult, Qinghai, China, May. An exceptionally pale and faded bird (Urban Olsson).

▲ Adult, Hong Kong, January. Following complete moult, adults and young birds are more richly toned than worn birds in autumn (Peter Kennerley).

▲ Adult, Turkey, May. Worn adult showing characteristic short primary projection, pale supercilium extending well beyond the eye, diffuse dark sides to crown most conspicuous above the lores, and dark tip to lower mandible (Johnny Salomonsson).

▲ Adult, Sweden, June. Characteristic pale half-collar extends below the ear-coverts and onto side of nape (Johannes Tallroth).

▲ First-winter, Ukraine, August. A particularly warmly toned individual (Stefan McElwee).

▲ ▶ First-winter, Shetland, Scotland, September. The long pale supercilium and diffuse pale half-collar contrasting with the darker brown mantle and greyish brown crown are clearly visible on this bird. First-winter birds in late summer and early autumn are readily separated from adults by their unworn plumage and grey-brown iris (Hugh Harrop).

BLYTH'S REED WARBLER
Acrocephalus dumetorum   Plate 19

Acrocephalus dumetorum **Blyth, 1849**. *J. Asiatic Soc. Bengal*, 18: 815. India.

A small unstreaked *Acrocephalus* which breeds in bush, scrub and woodland habitats from Finland east into C Siberia and C Asia and winters in the Indian subcontinent. Monotypic.

IDENTIFICATION Length 13cm. Wing 59–66mm. Tail/ wing 75–87%.

One of a group of small unstreaked *Acrocephalus* that breed across the temperate region of the Palearctic and are notoriously difficult to identify. In late spring and early summer the far-carrying, slow and repetitive song of Blyth's Reed Warbler provides the most reliable means of identification. Separation from silent Marsh and Eurasian Reed Warblers requires prolonged views in good light. Structural differences are important, particularly where two or more species occur together, so particular care is required when assessing structure and proportions. Essentially, Blyth's Reed has a combination of a relatively short primary projection and visible emargination on two primaries. Evaluation of plumage tone is more subjective as perceived colours vary with age, wear and light conditions. However, the uniform olive-brown tone to the upperparts of adult Blyth's Reed Warbler and the lack of a warmer rufescent rump, is often apparent. Calling birds give a single hard '*tuk*', quite different from the regularly heard calls of Marsh and Eurasian Reed Warblers. Sexes alike.

Structure Blyth's Reed shows the typical structure of a small *Acrocephalus* and is readily separated from the pale brown *Iduna* species, such as Sykes's Warbler, by its long and deep undertail-coverts which extend beyond the wingtip, as well as by its darker and browner appearance. In the field Blyth's Reed often gives the impression of being longer-billed and shorter-winged than either Marsh or Eurasian Reed Warblers and the tail seems proportionately longer than in either of these species. Although this long-tailed impression may be apparent in the field this is not supported by measurements, which show there is considerable overlap with Marsh and Eurasian Reed. In fact, the longer tailed appearance is an illusion created by the reduced primary projection compared with Eurasian Reed and Marsh Warblers. Additionally, Blyth's Reed is also said to adopt the so-called 'banana' posture, particularly when gleaning insects from the underside of leaves; at times it stretches the neck and raises the tail slightly, as well as spreading and drooping the wings across the flanks – probably just to maintain balance, but in doing so gives the body a slightly curved appearance. However, Eurasian Reed Warbler often feeds in a similar manner, particularly on migration when feeding in trees and scrub. When not feeding in trees, however, Blyth's Reed generally does not do this and then assumes postures shared with other small *Acrocephalus*. So the 'banana' posture is of little use in the specific identification of Blyth's Reed or the elimination of other species.

Wing structure is particularly important to identification and is essential to securing field identification of Blyth's Reed Warbler. The closed wing is distinctly more rounded than in Marsh and Eurasian Reed, with a shorter primary projection, typically 50–60% of the exposed tertial length. The wing point is formed by p3 and p4, and p5 is often so close in length that just six closely spaced primary tips are visible on the closed wing, fewer than in Marsh and Eurasian Reed. These can be difficult to see on slightly worn spring birds. Blyth's Reed also shows a distinct emargination on p3 and p4 which can be seen if viewing conditions are good.

The bill is often considered longer than in other small, unstreaked *Acrocephalus* species. While longer than in Paddyfield and most Marsh Warblers, it is similar in length to that of Eurasian Reed, but it is slightly deeper and broader-based, and so can appear more substantial. A rather long and sloping forehead and low angular crown, peaking just behind the eye, tend to exaggerate the apparent length of the bill. Other small *Acrocephalus* can at times adopt a similar tapered head and bill shape but this profile is particularly characteristic of Blyth's Reed.

Plumage and bare parts Blyth's Reed Warblers of all ages lack the warm tawny-brown tinge to the rump and uppertail-coverts characteristic of Eurasian Reed Warbler and appear browner (less greenish) than young Marsh Warbler, which may otherwise closely resemble Blyth's Reed.

Freshly moulted birds in winter are characterised by cold olive-brown upperparts and lack the brighter olive tones of fresh Marsh Warbler or the warm brown colour of nominate *scirpaceus* Eurasian Reed Warbler. The facial pattern is fairly crisp and sharp, with a small dark loral spot in front of the eye and a narrow eye-ring that is typically less pale and distinct than in Eurasian Reed. The shape and extent of the supercilium is important. In most, the lores are pale and unmarked and the creamy buff supercilium bulges in front of the eye to give Blyth's Reed a bland appearance to the head. The extent and prominence of the supercilium behind the eye is variable; on some birds there is little or no hint, while on others it can extend as a narrow, diffuse line over the ear-coverts, although it is invariably duller, poorly defined and less conspicuous than in front of the eye. On average, it extends behind the eye more often in Blyth's Reed than on Eurasian Reed and Marsh Warblers.

The olive-brown crown is concolorous with the upperparts, wings and sides to the head and there is no hint of darkening on the sides above the eye. The underparts are generally pale, with a brownish grey wash on the sides of the breast and flanks and a creamy white chin, throat and belly centre. There may be a faint tinge of yellow to the centre of the breast, but otherwise this is similar in colour to the throat and not as strong or extensive as typically seen in Marsh Warbler. The wing appears rather uniform with little contrast between the centres and fringes of the coverts and tertials.

On the breeding grounds, slightly worn adults resemble fresh birds but appear slightly duller, sometimes with a marginally greyer or greyish olive tone above. The underparts are distinctly whiter than in fresh adults or first autumn birds. They differ from spring Marsh Warblers, which have bright and fresh plumage, contrasting wing feather edgings and conspicuous pale primary tips.

Identification of first autumn Blyth's Reed Warblers is just as problematic as identifying adults and the same characters apply. They share the adults' features but, in general, they appear warmer and browner above than adults. Some may approach the upperpart colour of nominate Eurasian Reed Warbler but they always lack the rufescent tones and brighter rump and uppertail-coverts of Eurasian Reed. Also, there is often slight contrast between the slightly warmer-coloured edges and fringes to the coverts and remiges and the mantle and scapulars. The difference is slight but is usually noticeable as the wings often appear slightly warmer-toned than the upperparts and this contrast is more pronounced than in Eurasian Reed, particularly with the eastern form *fuscus*. Underpart colour and tones tend to appear slightly warmer and more sullied than on adults. There is a slight buff wash to the underparts, which is quite similar to some first autumn Eurasian Reed Warblers, so care is required as these birds, if silent, are readily overlooked as that species.

The bill is dark grey with a dull yellow or pale pinkish lower mandible that usually darkens slightly towards the tip. The legs are rather dark, varying from dull reddish brown to pinkish grey and are never pale brown, as commonly seen in Marsh Warbler

SIMILAR SPECIES Within the breeding range, confusion is most likely to occur with Marsh Warbler and the two races of Eurasian Reed Warbler, especially the eastern form *fuscus*. Separation from the rather different Paddyfield Warbler is more straightforward. The recent discovery of wintering Large-billed Reed Warbler in Thailand and India will present problems which have yet to be quantified, although behavioural differences may be useful. Care is also needed to distinguish Blyth's Reed Warbler from Sykes's Warbler, particularly worn birds on the wintering grounds, where they often occur together in similar habitats.

Eurasian Reed Warbler closely resembles Blyth's Reed Warbler and some silent birds, particularly fresh first-winter birds in autumn, may be inseparable. Singing adults, however, are readily identified. The simple, lazy and rhythmic song of Eurasian Reed generally contains little or no mimicry and is quite different from the rich and fluty song of Blyth's Reed, which is an outstanding mimic whose song includes a wide range of calls of unrelated species. Combined with its steady and unhurried rhythm and loud, energetic and far-carrying delivery, the song of Blyth's Reed is a particularly characteristic sound in the woodlands of NE Europe. Conversely, that of Eurasian Reed is often lost amongst the general *Acrocephalus* chatter heard within a reedbed community. Calls are extremely useful in their separation. The typical low nasal 'scherr' given by Eurasian Reed Warbler is very different from the characteristic hard 'tuk' or 'tak' regularly given by Blyth's Reed, which resembles that of Lesser Whitethroat or Blackcap. This is so different from the call of Eurasian Reed that it is worth investigating any small unstreaked *Acrocephalus* giving this call, as it is likely to prove to be Blyth's Reed.

In addition to calls, structural differences in the wing provide the best supporting characters to their separation and it is essential to correctly establish these if a silent bird is encountered, particularly in a potential vagrancy situation. Compared with Blyth's Reed, Eurasian Reed has a distinctly longer and quite pointed wing, with the primary projection reaching to 70–80% of the tertial length, compared with just 50–60% in Blyth's Reed, which gives the wing of Blyth's Reed a short and rather blunt appearance. Furthermore, in Eurasian Reed the wing point is formed by p3, which is also the only emarginated primary, while on Blyth's Reed, the wing point is formed by p3 and p4, both of which are also emarginated. As the spacing between the primaries on Blyth's Reed is closer than on Eurasian Reed, this gives a blunter appearance to the wing-tip of Blyth's Reed, in which the individual feather tips are difficult to see, especially on worn birds.

In appearance, adult Eurasian Reed Warbler closely resembles Blyth's Reed Warbler, but always shows a warm tawny-brown rump and uppertail-coverts, which Blyth's Reed lacks at all ages. Instead, Blyth's Reed shows drab greyish olive-brown upperparts with little or no contrast between the mantle and the rump and uppertail-coverts. Typically, immature Blyth's Reed Warbler appears slightly warmer and browner above than adults and may approach the colour of some Eurasian Reed Warblers, particularly *fuscus*. Despite this, they still lack the contrasting warmer rufescent tones and brighter rump and uppertail-coverts of Eurasian Reed Warbler and always appear quite uniform above. Furthermore, the tone to the underparts of Blyth's Reed is slightly colder and less sullied than that of Eurasian Reed and there is a tendency to show increased contrast with the upperparts.

Marsh Warbler is very different from Blyth's Reed in structure, which is as useful in their separation as plumage differences. Marsh tends to show a rather rounded crown and shorter bill, and thus has a less attenuated head than Blyth's Reed. The primary projection is much longer in Marsh, practically equal to the tertial length, and the wing point is formed by p3, which is the only emarginated primary. In Marsh, eight evenly spaced primary tips should be visible, remaining pale and conspicuous into June. Blyth's Reed does show six or seven slightly paler primary tips after moult in early winter, but they have abraded by April.

In spring Marsh Warbler is uniform olive-brown above. The olive tones are generally more pronounced than in Blyth's Reed and it appears slightly brighter. On the wings, the brighter fringes and darker centres to the tertials create a contrasting effect. The buff wash on the underparts is also usually tinged with yellow. The legs of Marsh are usually pale brown during the breeding season and generally paler than shown by Blyth's Reed throughout the year. Calls can be useful, but it should be remembered that Marsh has a 'teck' call, generally softer than the harsher, dryer 'tak' of Blyth's Reed. However, they can be confused.

Paddyfield Warbler is quite different in appearance from Blyth's Reed. It shows a broad and conspicuous supercilium extending to the rear of the ear-coverts, bordered above by a dark smudge or line on the side of the crown. The upperparts are warmer brown than Blyth's Reed and more contrasting, usually showing a greyish brown crown that is darker than the nape, a distinctive pale half-collar extending behind the ear-coverts and onto the sides of the nape, and warm brown fringes to the wing-coverts and tertials contrasting with the darker centres. The bill is shorter and blunter and the sides of the lower mandible are dark for the distal half, even on young birds in winter. Wing structure is similar to that of Blyth's Reed with much overlap and is considered unreliable in their separation, but the longer tail of Paddyfield is useful.

Large-billed Reed Warbler presents the greatest identification challenge within the small unstreaked *Acrocephalus*, in part because it is still uncertain just what it really looks like in the field and also because there are so few documented records, so the extent of variation and overlap with Blyth's Reed is unknown. These species are so similar that no reliable plumage differences have been established. In the hand, any Blyth's Reed with a bill length in excess of 18mm is worthy of further investigation. Their separation is discussed in detail within the Large-billed Reed Warbler account.

Sykes's Warbler is similar in size and structure to Blyth's Reed and it has been mooted as a likely confusion species. In our experience, this is unlikely if the bird is seen well. Confusion is perhaps most likely to occur when seen from below, particularly when feeding high in an Acacia in the Indian wintering grounds. Even then, the longer and deeper undertail-coverts and more rounded tail of Blyth's Reed should be apparent. Otherwise, the pale and washed-out appearance of Sykes's Warbler is closer to that of Eastern Olivaceous Warbler and is never approached by Blyth's Reed.

VOICE The song is remarkable for its rich and fluty quality and the extent of mimicry, and provides the most reliable identification feature in the field. It has a steady and unhurried rhythm and loud, energetic and far-carrying delivery, much more so than the racy song of Marsh Warbler. It is also quite different from the lazy, rhythmic song of Eurasian Reed Warbler or the more rushed songs of other Western Palearctic *Acrocephalus*. It typically includes the varied harsh rattling and churring notes common to all small *Acrocephalus* but these are interspersed with mimicked sequences. Each phrase is repeated within the sequence, usually three to eight times, before changing to a different phrase, giving a song structure and quality similar to that of Song Thrush. Mimicry is incorporated from a wide range of species encountered on the breeding grounds, including Black Kite, Common Sandpiper, Great Spotted Woodpecker, Barn Swallow, Blackbird, Song Thrush, Common Whitethroat, Blue Tit and Chaffinch. It also incorporates some calls from the wintering area, perhaps the most readily recognised being Red-wattled Lapwing. In addition, a powerful, melodious, slightly descending fluty phrase described as '*roo-de-roo-de-roo-de-roo-de-roo de*' or '*chu-e-loo...*' may be included and repeated several times in succession.

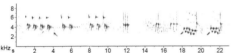

Part of song of Blyth's Reed Warbler, Highland Scotland, June. (Peter Kennerley)

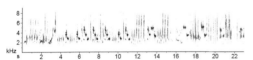

Part of song of Blyth's Reed Warbler, Finland, June. (Sample 2003)

The most frequently heard call is a short, hard '*tuk*', not dissimilar to that of Lesser Whitethroat or Dusky Warbler, but slightly softer. This call, given almost continuously at times, approximately one call every 1–2 seconds, is harder than the '*teck*' of Marsh Warbler and quite different from the normal harsh '*tcharr*' calls of Eurasian Reed Warbler. However, Blyth's Reed also has a harsh '*schaarr*' call, frequently heard in the winter and quite similar to that of Eurasian Reed Warbler.

MOULT Some adults begin body moult shortly after breeding in late July and early August. For most birds, this tends to be minimal, or completely lacking in more northern breeders. All adults appear to undergo full moult during a stopover in NW India. The earliest birds begin primary replacement in late August and almost all are actively moulting body, wing and tail feathers by early October. Moult is usually complete by early November, taking some 61–62 days in the individual bird. This is followed by a partial pre-breeding moult on the wintering

grounds between late February and early May, in which the head, body and smaller wing-coverts are replaced, but some birds may also renew one or more tertials.

Young birds have a post-juvenile moult of the head and body feathers, beginning shortly after fledging and finishing prior to migration. On arrival in India, the juvenile wing and tail feathers are replaced, the timing coinciding with the moult in adults, and the body feathers are again renewed. The late winter pre-breeding moult some five months later clearly affects first year as well as older birds.

HABITAT Breeds in dry or slightly damp, open and bushy habitats with dense luxuriant undergrowth of tall emergent growth such as nettles and a scattering of trees or large bushes that can be used as song-posts. Some also breed in tall forest provided there is a dense understorey of from which the nest can be hung. It typically prefers drier sites than those utilised by Marsh Warbler, including regenerating overgrown clearfell, bushy field edges and abandoned farmland. Many territories include open areas such as shorelines, road edges and forest clearings.

Wintering birds inhabit dry scrub, even in town gardens and parks and open forest throughout the lowlands in the Indian subcontinent and often alongside Sykes's Warbler. They forage in the canopy as well as in lower bushes and shrubs, usually well away from wetlands and luxuriant growth and appear to favour Acacia. Vagrants to Hong Kong were trapped in *Phragmites* reedbeds over water or adjacent scrub covered bunds. Ranges up to 2,100m in scrub-covered Himalayan foothills.

On migration, birds temporarily utilise a wide range of habitats from low scrub to woodland habitats, as do other small *Acrocephalus*.

BEHAVIOUR Not shy and rather easy to watch on the breeding grounds and, at times, in the wintering area, although migrants particularly in autumn tend to be more secretive. Typically it is solitary in winter, but several are sometimes found feeding close together, regularly calling to maintain contact. Outside the breeding season, migrants are quite vocal and call more frequently than most *Acrocephalus* warblers, often calling constantly in winter quarters and even on migration. It forages actively in the top and side foliage of bushes and trees and descends to low undergrowth or to open ground, where it may feed with hopping gait. Occasionally a bird will take insects in flight, sallying out from a bush top and returning to the same bush. It frequently raises, flicks and fans the tail in a nervous manner. In flitting flight over low cover, the short, rounded wings and fairly long and broad tail may suggest a Cetti's Warbler.

On the breeding grounds, males usually sing from a conspicuous perch on a bush or high branch of a tree 20m or more above ground, or even on open perches such as a telegraph wire. They frequently droop the wings along the flanks and dip the tail slightly in rhythm to the repetition of each song sequence. Song is given most vigorously by unmated males during the twilight hours and at night, as in Marsh Warbler, but also continues strongly after dawn. Singing becomes more sporadic as the morning progresses, but may continue whilst feeding. Singing birds will drop from a perch and give song bursts while foraging in undergrowth.

BREEDING HABITS Males arrive on the breeding grounds about eight days before females. They are solitary and territorial, but two or more males often nest in close proximity at sites with a high density of males. The song is often heard from migrants in May and commences immediately on arrival on the breeding territory. It is vigorous and continuous before pairing, but becomes less frequent in mated birds. Blyth's Reed Warbler is typically monogamous, but is occasionally polygynous, with males adopting successive females in different but adjacent territories.

The nest is built in 3-4 days, by both pair members or by the female alone. It is placed in dense vegetation such as nettles, reeds, shrubs or small trees, typically from 0.1–0.5m above the ground, but sometimes up to 1m. It is a neat and compact cup constructed from leaves, stems and plant down and lined with finer stems and hair. The usual clutch is 4–6 eggs which are laid between early June and mid July in Finland and W Siberia. The eggs are incubated for 12–14 days by both sexes but mainly by the female. The nestlings are fed by both parents and fledge after 11–13 days. The young remain dependent for a further 10–22 days, with the brood often divided between the two parents before dispersing. The male may disappear during the fledgling period, perhaps switching to another female, leaving the

original female to care for the brood. Believed to be single brooded.

Hybridisation with Marsh Warbler apparently occurs regularly in SE Finland and has been reported from the Netherlands. Also, a bird trapped in Kenya in December with plumage and structure of Blyth's Reed, but with a typically long primary projection, had the mtDNA of Marsh Warbler, and was presumably a hybrid.

DISTRIBUTION

Breeding Blyth's Reed Warbler breeds in the cooler temperate region of the W and C Palearctic. Its breeding range has expanded westwards throughout the twentieth century, reaching southern Finland sometime before 1950. It has subsequently spread into Estonia where the population has expanded rapidly and by 2002 was believed to range from 15,000 to 30,000 breeding pairs (Elts *et al.* 2003). It is also common and widespread in Latvia and has extended into S Sweden and possibly into E Poland, where small numbers breed. To the east, it is widespread from N Ukraine to the N Transcaspian region. Much of the breeding range lies within Russia, where it ranges

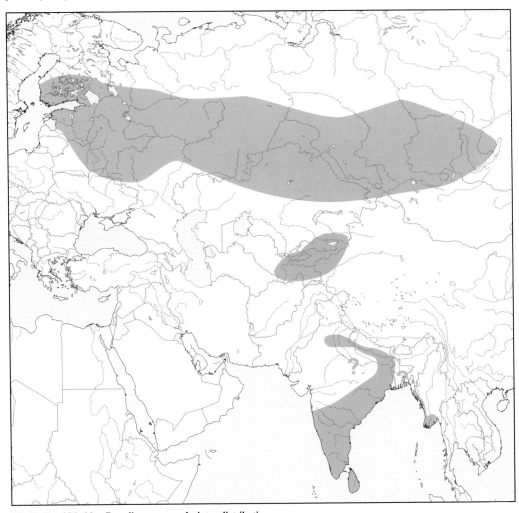

Blyth's Reed Warbler. Breeding range and winter distribution.

from Karelia east to the Urals and across S Siberia to the Lake Baikal region and western Yakutia, and also in the Russian Altai and into NW Mongolia and across the Kirghiz Steppes of Kazakhstan to the SW Altai and the Irtysh valley between Semipalatinsk and Usi-Kamenogorsk. To the south of its main range, a secondary population breeds in the foothills of the western and northern Tien Shan Mountains (Zailiyskiy Alatau) to the south of Almaty, west to E Uzbekistan and south into N Afghanistan and E Iran.

Non-breeding As a winter visitor it is widespread throughout the plains of the Indian subcontinent, regularly wintering up to 2,100m in the foothills of the Himalayas and south to Sri Lanka. It also winters throughout the lowlands of Nepal and Bhutan, Bangladesh and into W Burma, where it has been recorded from Arakan, the Sittang plain near Pegu and Karenni.

MOVEMENTS It is widespread and abundant on migration across much of C Asia. The breeding grounds are vacated from mid July onwards and almost all have left Finland by late August. Western breeders move east and south to join with others and numbers build as they converge through E Kazakhstan. Studies at Lake Sorbulak have shown that most birds passing through this region in early August are adults with juveniles peaking 2–3 weeks later. Birds breeding in E Iran and Afghanistan are still present in late August and passage occurs here throughout September. The first birds reach N Pakistan and NW India in late August and arrivals continue throughout September and many, perhaps the great majority, stop-over here to complete the full moult before moving south and east to final wintering destinations. Birds reach Nepal from mid October and Bangladesh and Burma soon afterwards. To the south, passage peaks at Point Callimere in Tamil Nadu in S India in November en-route to Sri Lankan wintering areas, where they arrive from late October onwards.

Spring migration begins in late March and the bulk of the population leaves the Indian subcontinent during April. Some birds remain in India to early May and there are exceptional records to early June. Arrival in Kazakhstan takes place from mid April onwards, with passage of northern breeders peaking here in mid May. At the northern breeding limit, birds reach the Yenisey River region of C Siberia between late May and mid June, while those breeding in Finland arrive from mid May onwards, but dates here depend on weather conditions. Cold, damp northerly winds deter many birds, while warm winds from the southeast bring larger breeding numbers.

Vagrancy With a better understanding of the field identification and vocalisations, Blyth's Reed Warbler is being regularly encountered as a rare migrant or vagrant outside the recognised breeding and wintering range. Occurrences are now annual in W Europe, west to the British Isles and north to Iceland. Most are first-winter birds that appear in September and October, but singing birds have been reported occasionally in spring from Germany, Holland, England and Scotland. It is being found to occur regularly in both autumn and spring in the United Arab Emirates. Birds occur regularly on both autumn and spring passage in the Xinjiang Uygur Autonomous Region of W China, but to the east it remains a rarity, e.g. it has been recorded once from Qinghai Province, on 6 September 2004. Vagrants occasionally reach Hong Kong in SE China, from where there are six records up to 2005, falling between 8 October and 30 March.

Published accounts of wintering birds in Africa (William-son 1963; Fry *et al.* 1974) are erroneous. These were based on misidentified African Reed Warblers from Nigeria (*A. b. cinnamomeus*), and short-winged Eurasian Reed Warblers from Tibesti (probably *A. s. scirpaceus*) and Eritrea (*A. s. avicenniae*).

DESCRIPTION

Plumage – Adult fresh (November to January) Forehead to nape uniform, light greyish, olive-brown. Supercilium pale grey-buff from base of bill to above middle of ear-coverts; broadest in front of eye, tapering and becoming ill-defined behind it, or absent. Dark loral spot immediately in front of eye. Pale eye-ring indistinct, broken in front of and behind eye, merging with supercilium above it. Ear-coverts greyish olive-brown, uniform with crown and nape. Upperparts greyish olive-brown, concolorous with crown, uppertail-coverts similar, occasionally slightly brighter and paler, never warmly coloured. Tail feathers dark greyish brown, with slightly browner outer edges and tips. Underparts generally pale; chin and throat creamy white with slight greyish white wash. Sides of upper breast with broad and diffuse brownish grey band, becoming pale creamy buff towards centre. Lower breast and upper belly greyish white or silvery white, duller than throat, sometimes tinged dull ochre. Flanks greyish brown as sides of upper breast, slightly paler than upperparts. Undertail-coverts white, sometimes tinged brownish, contrasting with lower belly. Lesser and median coverts concolorous with upperparts, lacking obvious fringing. Greater coverts and tertials greyish brown with barely discernible brownish fringe. Secondaries and primaries dark greyish brown, edges paler, concolorous with upperparts or sometimes slightly warmer and browner. Tips of primaries pale brown, usually contrasting only slightly with dark webs. Alula dark grey-brown with indistinct olive-brown outer web. Underwing-coverts pale greyish buff, similar to flanks but sometimes with slight yellowish wash.

Adult worn (June to September) In late summer resembles fresh adult but slightly paler and greyer, particularly on nape. Supercilium often appears paler and slightly more conspicuous than in fresh adult. Underparts greyish white, lacking brownish grey wash on breast.

Juvenile/first-winter Distinctly browner than fresh adult. Upperparts, including crown, ear-coverts, mantle and scapulars dull olive-brown, sometimes with faint warm wash. Rump and uppertail-coverts similar to mantle but sometimes browner and darker. Tail feathers browner than in adult. Supercilium creamy white, often fading out abruptly behind eye and merging with pale lores to give open-faced expression. Dark loral spot in front of eye. Underparts pale as fresh adult, but breast sides, flanks and lower belly tinged creamy brown, sometimes slightly olive-brown, but greyer tones of adult usually lacking. Upperwing-coverts, tertials and flight feather edges warm olive-brown and brighter than in adult, so contrasting with mantle and scapulars. Tertials with slightly dark centres and warmer brown fringes. Alula brown, contrasting little with coverts. Primaries with indistinct paler brownish tips when fresh.

Bare Parts Upper mandible mid to dark grey with pink cutting edge and sometimes a paler tip. Lower mandible dull yellow to pale pink, with an ill-defined dark subterminal smudge at sides near tip on adult, but rarely in first-winter. Mouth yellow. Tarsi and toes dark, varying from dull reddish brown to pinkish grey; claws grey-brown slightly darker; soles yellowish brown. Iris brown to warm brown in adult, dull greyish brown in first-winter birds.

IN HAND CHARACTERS
Measurements

	Male	Female
Wing	60–66 (62.8; 85)	59–65 (61.5; 46)
Tail	47–54 (50.3; 84)	46–52 (49.3; 44)
Bill	15.5–18.5 (17.2; 79)	15.5–18 (17.0; 43)
Tarsus	20.5–23.5 (22.3; 37)	20.5–22.5 (21.8; 19)

Sexes combined:
Tail/wing ratio: 75–87% (80%; 128)
Bill width: 3.8–4.6 (4.1; 34)
Hind claw: 5.2–6.5 (6.0; 36)
Tail graduation: 4–10 (6.0; 20)
Juvenile wing and tail length similar to those of adult (Cramp 1992).

Structure

Wing formula (Cramp 1992):

p1/pc	p2	p3e	p4e	p5	p6	p7	p10
(3)–3	3–6	wp	0–0.5	0.5–2.5	2–6	3–7	10–14

Wing rounded; p1 minute. Wing point p3 (4); p2 = p5/7 (7) [7/8]; emargination on p3–4 (occasionally p5 in adult). Notch on p2 at or below ss tips.

Figure 56. Wing of Blyth's Reed Warbler.

Tail rounded, structure as Eurasian Reed Warbler.

Bill as Eurasian Reed but slightly deeper and broader-based; sides usually slightly concave. Foot as in Marsh Warbler, toes and claws typically slightly shorter than in Eurasian Reed.

Recognition Shows uniform olive-brown upperparts, sometimes grey-tinged and without the general warm tone or the warmly coloured rump of Eurasian Reed Warbler. Typically duller above than Marsh Warbler, with whitish rather than yellow-buff washed underparts. Separated from Marsh and most Eurasian Reed by having p2 < p5 (often < p6) and p4 emarginated. Most birds (those with wing < 64mm) are below the wing length range of both Marsh and the 'large' *fuscus* Eurasian Reed of C Asia. Note that some Eurasian Reed have p2 < p5 and beware small Middle East *fuscus* which may also have an emarginated p4. Some African Reed Warblers have wing length and wing formula resembling those of Blyth's Reed, but these are unlikely to occur alongside it. Paddyfield Warbler with a similar rounded wing, has a shorter bill (< 16mm) and shorter wing (usually < 60mm); p1 tends to be longer than in Blyth's Reed and p2 shorter (often < p7), while p5 is always emarginated.

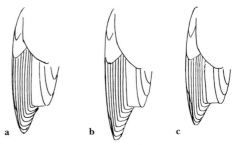

Figure 57. Closed wing structure of (a) Eurasian Reed Warbler (b) Marsh Warbler and (c) Blyth's Reed Warbler.

Eastern Olivaceous Warbler of race *elaeica* is similar to Blyth's Reed in bill length, wing length and wing formula. It tends to have a squarer tail however (t1–t6 < 5mm) with pale or whitish edged feather tips and p1 is usually longer (3–8mm > pc) and more rounded. Sykes's and Booted Warblers also differ from Blyth's Reed in having a longer p1 and (especially in Booted) a shorter bill. For distinction from Large-billed Reed Warbler see discussion under that species.

Ageing In early autumn, adults have worn flight feathers and tail and are easily separable from young birds in which these feathers are fairly fresh. Young birds are not distinguishable after the autumn moult in India.

Weight Range 8–20g. Typical lean weight 9–12g, but fattening birds commonly reach 13–16g prior to migration.

GEOGRAPHIC VARIATION Slight if any. Birds from Kazakhstan and Turkmenistan have previously been recognised as the race *A. d. turanicus*, based on a slightly longer wing. However, this is not consistent across the range and the validity of this form is no longer maintained.

TAXONOMY AND SYSTEMATICS No issues arising.

▲ Adult, Finland, June. Note faint olive wash to dull greyish brown upperparts, and dull rump and uppertail-coverts that lack the contrasting warmer tone of Eurasian Reed Warbler (Daniele Occhiato).

▲ Adult, Finland, June. Olive tones are more pronounced on this individual. Note short whitish supercilium above the lores, and worn primaries with short primary projection extending to *c.* 60% of tertial length (Daniele Occhiato).

▲ Adult, Poland, June. Some can show warmer, brown wings and tail contrasting with greyer upperparts. This interesting individual also shows a particularly long supercilium extending behind the eye, albeit faintly, and dark sides to the lower mandible (Mateusz Matysiak).

▲ Adult, Novosibirsk, Siberia, Russia, June. Worn adult still retains slight olive tone to upperparts. Note uniform appearance to mantle, rump and uppertail-coverts (Peter Kennerley).

▲ First-winter, Shetland, Scotland, October. A classic first-winter bird in autumn showing drab olive-brown upperparts, greyish brown iris and fresh primaries (Rebecca Nason).

▲ First-winter, Hong Kong, December. Warmly toned young birds more closely resemble Eurasian Reed Warbler but show shorter primary projection and emargination on p4 (Peter Kennerley).

LARGE-BILLED REED WARBLER
Acrocephalus orinus   **Plate 19**

Acrocephalus orinus **Oberholser, 1905**. *Proc. U.S. Nat. Mus.*, 28, p 899. Near Rampur, Sutlej Valley, Punjab Himalayas.

An overlooked and apparently rare species, with definite records confined to a recently discovered breeding population in NE Afghanistan and adjacent SE Tajikistan, three birds trapped in Thailand, and a small number of old museum specimens, most of them collected in non-breeding areas.

Treated as Data Deficient by BirdLife International. DNA analysis places this with the small, unstreaked *Acrocephalus* and indicates a close relationship with Blyth's Reed Warbler (Bensch & Pearson 2002; Round *et al.* 2007). Monotypic.

IDENTIFICATION Length 13–14cm. Wing 59–65mm. Tail/wing 86–98%.

A small *Acrocephalus* with plain olive-brown upperparts, a rounded wing and a relatively large bill. It is likely to occur in S Asia alongside three similar species: Blyth's Reed Warbler, Paddyfield Warbler and Blunt-winged Warbler. Its field characters are unknown, but it would be extremely difficult to distinguish from Blyth's Reed. Head profile and wing to tail proportion should provide useful guides. In the hand, measurements and wing formula should identify most birds, although some may not be separable from Blyth's Reed Warbler. Sexes alike.

Structure A small *Acrocephalus*, similar in size to Blyth's Reed and Blunt-winged Warblers. The bill is distinctly longer and proportionally stronger than in Blyth's Reed, tapering less towards the tip and much longer and more substantial than in Blunt-winged and Paddyfield Warblers. A long sloping forehead accentuates its long-billed appearance and the entire head can appear large and attenuated. The wings tend to be more rounded than in Blyth's Reed, the primaries projecting about 40% of exposed tertial length and falling well short of the longest uppertail-coverts. The first primary is very small, however, falling about level with the longest primary covert. The tail is longer and usually narrower than in Blyth's Reed. The legs are slightly stronger and the claws larger.

a   b

Figure 58. Comparison of head and bill shape of (a) Large-billed Reed Warbler and (b) Blyth's Reed Warbler.

Plumage and bare parts A nondescript *Acrocephalus* with olive-brown upperparts and crown, usually rather richer than in Blyth's Reed but lacking the strong rufescent tones of Blunt-winged. The head pattern is similar to that of Blyth's Reed, with a pale supercilium broadening onto rather pale lores, but fading out behind the eye. There is a dusky loral spot and a short darker eye-line above buffy ear-coverts. It lacks the dark crown edges commonly seen in Paddyfield Warbler. The underparts are whitish with a buffy wash on the breast, flanks and undertail-coverts. A rather uniform closed wing shows slightly warmer, lighter brown edges to the greater coverts, tertials and secondaries.

The appearance of young birds in autumn prior to the moult is unknown.

The bill is blackish above and entirely fleshy pink below. The legs are brownish grey.

SIMILAR SPECIES The type specimen of Large-billed Reed Warbler has been likened in the literature to Clamorous Reed Warbler and this has created a misleading impression of its size and affinities. Clamorous Reed is a much larger bird, especially the mainland Asian race *brunnescens*, and has robust dark legs and feet and a large narrower-tipped bill. With better recent understanding it can be stated that Large-billed Reed Warbler cannot be confused with Clamorous Reed. However, Blyth's Reed and Blunt-winged Warblers resemble Large-billed more closely.

Blyth's Reed Warbler is so similar that Large-billed has been overlooked as this species in museum collections, and presumably also in the field. As far as is known, there are no consistent plumage differences between these species and separation relies on measurements. The extent to which some of these overlap in the two species is still uncertain.

Blyth's Reed has a smaller bill, shorter tail and shorter claws and usually shows a less strongly rounded wing than Large-billed. Most Blyth's Reed have bill lengths below 18mm, the known minimum for Large-billed. The Blyth's Reed tail length range of 46–53mm and hind claw range of 5–6.5mm are usually well exceeded in Large-billed. Wing shape should also be a useful guide. Primary projection (10–14mm) tends to be greater in Blyth's Reed than in Large-billed (9–11mm), while p2 usually falls at p5–7 (above p6 in Large-billed) and p5 is rarely emarginated (see **In Hand Characters**).

Blunt-winged Warbler resembles Large-billed but has a much smaller bill, broader tail feathers and a shorter wing and its plumage is generally more richly rufescent. The two species have a similarly short primary projection, *c.* 40% of tertial length, but Blunt-winged has a larger first primary (p1), extending well beyond the primary coverts, and a more rounded wing with a shorter p2.

VOICE The song of a male recorded in Afghanistan in June contains a series of scratchy wheezes, rattles and whistles, given with a relaxed delivery at a steady pace. Unlike many of the smaller *Acrocephalus*, it includes much repetition, with individual notes repeated up to six times, followed by a different sequence of repeated notes. In this respect it resembles the song of Blyth's Reed Warbler but has a faster delivery within a frequency range of 2–7kHz, with an energy peak from 4–5kHz. In particular, it lacks some of the fluty notes and mimicry characteristic of that species. It is not known whether this song is typical, or whether there is substantial individual variation.

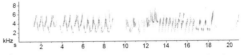

Part of song of Large-billed Reed Warbler, Afghanistan, June. (Rob Timmins)

MOULT Appears to have a complete moult lasting from September to November. The type specimen from N India, collected on 13 November, shows fresh body plumage, remiges and tail feathers. The secondaries are fully grown, but the outer primaries seem to be short of full length. Another October specimen from N India shows fresh body plumage, but has the outer four primaries and the secondaries growing and sheath present on the central tail feathers. The Thailand birds, trapped in late March, were slightly worn, with all flight feathers of uniform age. Specimens collected between May and August are all heavily worn.

HABITAT Specimens collected during the breeding season came from mountainous regions of C Asia, and it probably breeds on bushy slopes and in vegetated high-altitude valleys. In NE Afghanistan and adjacent Tajikistan birds were found breeding in scrubby riparian thickets at 2000–3200m (Timmins *et al.* 2009, Ayé *et al.* 2010). The preferred wintering habitat remains unknown. Birds trapped in Thailand came from grass filter beds (Round *et al.* 2007) and tall grass in an alluvial flood plain (Nimnuan & Round 2008), but it probably utilises lowland reedbeds, damp grasslands and other rank waterside vegetation.

BEHAVIOUR Unknown.

BREEDING HABITS Unknown.

DISTRIBUTION Breeding and wintering ranges remain to be fully established. The type specimen was collected in November 1865 in Himachal Pradesh, N India. Following capture and description of the first live bird at Laem Phak Bia, Phetchaburi, Thailand, on 27 March 2006 (Round *et al.* 2007), which was recaptured there on 21 March 2008, a further eleven specimens were found in museums in Britain and America. In addition to birds from N India (Uttar Pradesh in October and Punjab in May) and from

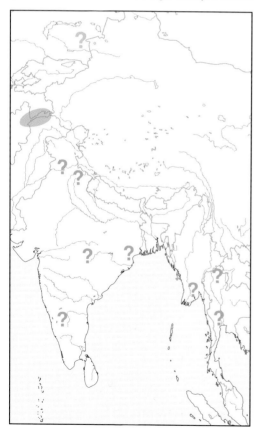

Large-billed Reed Warbler. Breeding range and winter distribution.

Burma (Lower Pegu in January and May), these included four July adults from NE Afghanistan and August juveniles from N Pakistan (Gilgit) and SE Kazakhstan (Zarkand) (Svensson *et al.* 2008). Five additional specimens from India with measurements of Large-billed Reed have been found by G. Jaffer (*in litt.*) in the Bombay Natural History Museum collection: one from Karnataka in February, three from Himachal Pradesh in mid to late May and one from Assam in early June. And birds claimed as this species were photographed in India, near Calcutta, W Bengal, in April 2007 (Sen *et al.* 2007) and in Kanha National Reserve, Madya Pradesh, in April 2008. Two further birds were trapped in Thailand during 2008, one at Nam Kham Nature Reserve near Chiang Saen on 27 March, the other at Bung Boraphet, Nakhon Sawan Province in C Thailand on 24 November (PDR *in litt.*). Then, in 2008–2009, breeding birds were discovered in NE Afghanistan, and 19 were trapped at four sites at the western end of the Wakhan Corridor (Timmins *et al.* 2009). Another eight were trapped at three nearby sites in SE Tajikistan (Ayé *et al.* 2010). Range probably encompasses the higher valleys and lower mountain slopes of the Hindu Kush, Pamir, Karakorum and W Tien Shan mountains in C Asia. But the winter records from Thailand and Burma would indicate other breeding areas much further east. The dates of birds in N India might suggest that breeding occurs south of the Himalayas, but these may have been migrants.

There is evidently a wide west/east wintering distribution across S Asia. It could winter alongside any of three races of Blunt-winged Warbler, as well as Blyth's Reed Warbler, and its similarity to these presumably explains how it went undetected for so long. It may well be rare, but large areas in Asia are poorly studied and a substantial population could exist.

MOVEMENTS No information.

DESCRIPTION
Plumage – Adult (March) Forehead to nape uniform olive-brown with a slight warm tinge. Supercilium creamy white, broadening above lores, becoming indistinct behind eye, linked to broken narrow creamy eye-ring. Lores pale creamy with dusky spot immediately in front of eye. Ear-coverts olive-buff, becoming darker greyish olive along upper edge and merging with pale buff cheeks. Mantle and scapulars olive-brown, concolorous with crown. Rump and uppertail-coverts slightly warmer tinged. Tail feathers dark greyish brown, narrowly edged warm brown, the tips with diffuse paler fringes. Chin and throat whitish. Remainder of underparts washed buff, most strongly across breast and on flanks and undertail-coverts. Lesser and median coverts concolorous with upperparts. Greater coverts and tertials greyish brown with diffusely demarcated light warm olive-brown fringes. Primary coverts, secondaries and primaries dark grey-brown, narrowly edged warm pale olive-brown. Alula dark grey-brown with narrow buffy fringe. (Round *et al.* 2007).
Bare parts Upper mandible blackish, strongly ridged on midline. Lower mandible entirely pinkish flesh. Tarsi and toes brownish grey; soles yellowish brown; claws darker grey. Iris dull brown.

IN HAND CHARACTERS
Measurements
Based on adult museum specimens and three live birds trapped in Thailand (includes data from L. Svensson *in litt.* and PDR *in litt.*).

Sexes combined:

Wing	60–65 (62.7; 10)
Tail	52–60 (56.0; 12)
Bill	18–20.5 (19.0; 13)
Tarsus	22.5–24 (23.5; 13)

Tail/wing ratio: 85–94% (89%; 10)
Bill width: 4.4–4.8 (4.7; 10)
Hind claw: 7.1–7.8 (7.4; 12)
Tail graduation: 7,8 (n=2)
Juvenile (n = 2): *wing* 61, 63; *tail* 53, 55.

Structure

Wing formula (Svensson *et al.* 2008):

p1/pc	p2	p3e	p4e	p5(e)	p6	p7	p10
(2.5)–1.5	4–7	0–1	wp	0–1.5	2–4	3.5–6	9–11

Wing rounded, p1 minute. Wing point p(3) 4 (5); p2 = p6/7–7/8 (8/9); p3–4 emarginated, also usually p5. Primaries typically broader than in Blyth's Reed Warbler.

Figure 59. Wing of Large-billed Reed Warbler.

Tail strongly rounded; feathers usually narrower than in Blyth's Reed.

Bill long, broad-based and quite deep; straight sided, narrowing less towards tip than in Blyth's Reed.

Toes and claws strong; hind claw longer than in Blyth's Reed.

Recognition Most birds are apparently separable from other *Acrocephalus* of similar size by longer bill (≥ 18.5mm), but some Blyth's Reed and the largest *fuscus* Eurasian Reed Warblers can approach this. Sides of bill straight and bill width usually > 4.5mm. Also distinguishable from Blyth's Reed by longer hindclaw (> 7mm) and usually by longer tail (>54mm) and higher tail/wing ratio (>85%, the maximum in Blyth's Reed). Typically, p2 is shorter than in Blyth's Reed (often ≤ p7) and p5 is commonly emarginated (rarely so in Blyth's Reed). Similar in coloration and head pattern to Blyth's Reed, but pinkish lower mandible usually unmarked and upper mandible typically blackish.

From Blunt-winged by much shorter p1 (usually 4–7mm beyond pc in Blunt-winged); p2 distinctly longer (usually > p8; = p8–9/10 in Blunt-winged).

Weight Thailand: 9.5g; 10.6g. (PDR unpublished data).

GEOGRAPHIC VARIATION None recorded.

TAXONOMY AND SYSTEMATICS Large-billed Reed Warbler was originally described as *Phyllopneuste macrorhyncha* (Hume (1869), but changed to *Acrocephalus macrorhynchus* (Hume 1871) when its generic affinity was established. It was renamed *Acrocephalus orinus* by Oberholzer (1905) who pointed out that *macrorhynchus* was preoccupied by *Calamoherpe macrorhyncha* (Müller 1853), from a specimen described from Egypt which is now treated as a synonym of *Acrocephalus stentoreus*.

Until 2006, the species was known from just the type specimen, whose validity was often questioned. Vaurie (1955) thought it represented a species closely related to Blunt-winged and Paddyfield Warblers. Williamson considered the unusual wing formula to be due to incomplete outer primary growth, but suggested the bird might represent an isolated form of Clamorous Reed Warbler *A. stentoreus*. Re-examination of the type specimen using mtDNA analysis (Bensch & Pearson 2002) confirmed it to be a distinct species allied to other small, unstreaked *Acrocephalus* warblers rather than to the *A. stentoreus* group. Results suggested its closest relative to be Blyth's Reed Warbler. Mitochrondrial DNA from birds trapped in Thailand in 2006 and 2008 closely matched that of the type specimen.

▲ ▶ Adult, Phetchaburi Province, Thailand, March. The first live bird, and only the second-ever record of this species. Shows features of both Blyth's Reed and Blunt-winged Warblers, but it was the particularly large bill which attracted attention and ultimately led to the identification being established (Philip Round/The Wetland Trust).

◄ Adult, Zebak District, Badakhshan Province, Afghanistan, June. Overall appearance closely resembles Blyth's Reed Warbler (Naqeeb Mostafawi and Stephane Ostrowski/WCS).

◄ Adult, Wakhan District, Badakhshan Province, Afghanistan, June. Note the exceptionally long bill of this individual (Hafizullah Noori, AliMadad Rajabi and Stephane Ostrowski/WCS).

◄ Adult, Narendrapur, Kolkata, India, April. Birds resembling Large-billed Reed Warbler have recently been discovered in small numbers on passage in late March and early April near Kolkata. Although they do appear to be this species, none have yet been trapped to establish the identification beyond all doubt (Sumit Sen).

MARSH WARBLER
Acrocephalus palustris   Plate 19

Sylvia palustris Bechstein, 1798. In: Latham's *Allgemeine Uebersicht der Vögel* 3: 545. Germany.

A long-distance migrant which breeds widely and commonly in rank herbaceous habitat across continental Europe to W Siberia, the Caucasus and NW Iran. It winters south of the equator in E and S Africa. Monotypic.

IDENTIFICATION Length 13cm. Wing 64–73mm. Tail/wing 71–79%.
A medium-sized *Acrocephalus* with plain olive-brown upperparts, pale underparts washed yellowish buff and a short supercilium that becomes indistinct behind the eye. In Europe and W Asia it forms a grouping with Eurasian Reed and Blyth's Reed Warblers, two species similar in size, structure and plumage. Unless singing, the identification of these three can prove challenging in the field. Even in the hand, the separation of Marsh from Eurasian Reed can be problematic, especially where first autumn birds are involved.
The mimetic song of Marsh Warbler is quite distinctive on the breeding grounds and in late winter in Africa, and some of its call notes differ from those given by Eurasian Reed and Blyth's Reed. Otherwise, field identification depends on the appreciation of subtle plumage tones and structural differences. Leg colour may be helpful in breeding birds, but is quite variable and of little value with first-autumn birds. In the hand, when Eurasian Reed is the only confusion species, adult Marsh Warbler and the majority of first autumn birds can be identified from wing formula. In W Europe, wing length can sometimes be helpful. Sexes alike.
Structure Structural features are of great importance when identifying the small, unstreaked *Acrocephalus* in Europe. Although differences are slight, and vary depending upon position and posture, when compared with Eurasian Reed and Blyth's Reed Warblers, Marsh Warbler appears rather compact with a full, deep-bodied look, accentuated by the long, full undertail-coverts. A further useful character is the less attenuated head profile. Appreciating this subtle feature can be difficult, but the bill is slightly shorter and broader, the forehead less flat and the crown can appear distinctly rounded, almost *Sylvia*-like at times. Excited birds raise the fore-crown feathers, producing a steep forehead and a crown that peaks slightly further forward than in Eurasian Reed or Blyth's Reed.
Marsh Warbler is particularly long-winged, with a primary projection 80–90% of exposed tertial length and reaching the end of the uppertail-coverts. Up to eight evenly-spaced primary tips are visible (Fig. 57). Emargination is only present on the third primary (p3), as in most Eurasian Reed Warblers, but this falls well short of the closed secondary tips (it typically extends close to the secondary tips in Eurasian Reed). The tarsi tend to be slightly thicker than in Eurasian Reed and the toes and claws smaller, but even in the hand these features can be difficult to evaluate.
Plumage and bare parts In fresh plumage, in spring and early summer, adult Marsh Warblers are rather light, uniform olive-brown above with a distinct greenish or ochreous tinge, slightly paler on the rump but without any warmth. The face pattern is moderately pronounced. A narrow creamy buff supercilium is well marked above the lores, joining a bright creamy eye-ring, but fades out shortly

behind the eye. This contrasts with a dark olive-brown triangle in front of the eye and rather dark buff-flecked olive-brown cheeks and ear-coverts. The pale underparts are washed yellowish buff, the whiter throat emphasised by a stronger olive-buff suffusion across the breast. The flanks are also suffused olive-buff while the undertail-coverts are paler creamy buff. On the upperwing, the blackish alula stands out and light olive-brown fringes to the greater coverts tend to contrast with darker feather centres. Well demarcated bright olive-brown fringes to dark-centred tertials can be a noticeable feature. The blackish flight feathers have narrow olive-brown edges, the primaries with prominent narrow greyish white tips which, due to the late winter moult, are still conspicuous in spring. The dark brown outer tail feathers show narrow and inconspicuous pale tips and inner edges.
Worn adults in late summer and early autumn are duller, somewhat greyer (less olive) above than spring birds and whiter below, but the tertial fringes and flight feather edges still remain olive-brown. There is usually an extensive autumn body moult in Ethiopia, so that by November most adults in Africa again show bright, green-tinged olive-brown upperparts and yellowish buff underparts, but these now contrast with the worn, greyer brown wings and tail.
Young Marsh Warblers in early autumn resemble spring adults, but the remiges and tail feathers are less blackish and the pale primary tips less prominent. On many birds the bright olive-brown upperparts and tertial fringes are less greenish, more ochreous or cinnamon-tinged than in adults, and the underparts show a more general buff suffusion. Some warmly-tinged birds resemble the colour of young Reed Warblers, especially on the rump and uppertail-coverts. Overall, young Marsh tend to look paler in Europe than young Reed, with a better-marked supercilium and face pattern, and with fringes to the tertials and greater coverts contrasting more sharply with dark centres.
Leg colour is variable and of limited value when identifying Marsh Warblers in the field. During the breeding season, the legs of European birds are often a distinctive pale brown or pinkish straw. There is much variation, however and adults in Africa commonly show mid brown or dark brown legs. In first autumn birds the legs may be pale or pinkish brown, but are more often mid brown, dark brown or greenish grey (similar to those of young Eurasian Reed). Occasional first year and even adult birds trapped in Kenya show very dark grey to blackish legs, but their breeding origin is unknown (DJP, unpublished). The bill, as in Eurasian Reed Warbler, is blackish above with a pale pinkish or yellowish lower mandible, commonly becoming dusky towards the tip, or with a subterminal dusky patch.

SIMILAR SPECIES Breeding Marsh Warbler overlaps widely in Europe with the nominate race of Eurasian Reed Warbler and also with Blyth's Reed Warbler from Finland and the E Baltic through W Russia. To the east, it breeds around the Caspian Sea and in NW Kazakhstan alongside Eurasian Reed of the race *fuscus*, which closely matches it in plumage tones and wing length. Some of the criteria useful in separation from Eurasian Reed in Europe are invalid when applied to *fuscus*. Migrant Marsh Warblers again occur with *fuscus* in the Middle East and in Africa. They also meet the mangrove-breeding race *avicenniae* of Eurasian Reed Warbler on the Red Sea coasts and various forms of the African Reed Warbler further south. Separation from the rather different Paddyfield Warbler is briefly discussed.
Eurasian Reed Warbler appears slimmer than Marsh, the

head less rounded, and it tends to have a slightly longer and narrower-based bill. Such perceived differences can be difficult to address objectively however. Differences in wing structure are slight and show extensive overlap, and most are of little use in the field. Many Eurasian Reed have a primary projection comparable with that of Marsh, but the spacing between the outer primary tips is usually less even and emargination on p3 tends to reach near the closed secondary tips.

Nominate Eurasian Reed are slightly darker than Marsh and differ in their warm-toned upperparts, warm buff flanks and lack of any yellow tinge below. The facial pattern tends to be slightly less crisp, more diffuse than in Marsh. In spring, most show slightly worn primaries which have lost pale tips. These are almost always conspicuous on the later moulting Marsh, which then has fresher wing feathers with more contrasting olive fringes and edges. On the breeding ground the mouth of singing Eurasian Reed is deep orange compared with the typically orange-yellow colour of Marsh.

In Asia, Eurasian Reed of the race *fuscus* are typically rather pallid olive-brown above with a greyish cast to the crown and nape. Some *fuscus* moult in late winter so their primaries appear fresh with pale tips in spring, further enhancing their similarity to Marsh Warbler. They usually, but not always, retain a warm tawny-brown tinge to the rump and uppertail-coverts, which contrasts somewhat with the mantle. They also differ from Marsh in having whitish rather than yellow-tinged underparts. But plumage distinctions between Marsh and *fuscus* Eurasian Reed can be minimal and are often lost in worn autumn birds.

The mangrove breeding race *avicenniae* of Eurasian Reed occurs along the Red Sea coast and matches Marsh quite closely in plumage colour, but is rather smaller. It has a narrower bill and much shorter and more rounded wings, with an emarginated p4.

African Reed Warbler is distinctly shorter winged and should not therefore be mistaken for Marsh. In S Africa, nominate *baeticatus* is much more warmly coloured than Marsh, while in E Africa the small race *cinnamomeus* has a particularly rounded wing and bright cinnamon-brown plumage.

Blyth's Reed Warbler is uniform olive-brown above like Marsh, but the spring adult is rather duller, colder and greyer. The underparts are paler with little or no yellowish wash. The wings are browner, more uniform and in spring lack the contrasting bright tertial fringes or the prominent pale primary tips of Marsh. The legs are greyish (never pale brown as in Marsh). Similar plumage distinctions apply between young Blyth's Reed and young Marsh in early autumn. The low forehead and slightly longer bill of Blyth's Reed usually give a more attenuated, flat headed appearance than in Marsh. The wing of Blyth's Reed is shorter and more rounded, with no more than six to seven primary tips visible and both p3 and p4 are emarginated.

Paddyfield Warbler is readily separated from Marsh Warbler by the contrasting appearance of the head, with a conspicuous pale supercilium that extends behind the eye, flaring slightly over the ear-coverts. This is bordered above by narrow, diffuse, dark sides to the crown which contrast with the warmer and browner centre. The entire upperparts and sides to the head are warm brown and contrast with a paler half-collar that extends from below the ear-coverts onto the sides of the nape. The bill is short and stubby and always shows dark sides to the tip of the lower mandible. The wing is short and rounded and the primary projection is extremely short, the shortest of all the European unstreaked

Acrocephalus. In structure, the wing overlaps with that of Blyth's Reed, showing six primary tips and emargination to the third (p3) and fourth primaries (p4), but never overlaps with Marsh.

VOICE The mimetic song of the adult male Marsh Warbler is outstanding; a varied, rapidly delivered warbling chatter, including clear liquid trills, sweet high-pitched notes, a characteristic repeated harsh '*zi-chay*' and other nasal wheezes. It encompasses the greatest frequency range of any European *Acrocephalus* song, from 1.5–9kHz. It is generally sweeter and higher-pitched than the song of Eurasian Reed Warbler and lacks any sustained underlying rhythm. It may be almost entirely imitative and combines a remarkable variety of mimicked bird notes and even mechanical sounds, into lively fluent sequences. Song may be almost continuous, lasting for hours with hardly a pause, but is usually broken up into sequences lasting from a few seconds up to a minute and separated by pauses of 2–12 seconds. At least 99 European and 113 African bird sounds were recognised in Marsh Warbler songs in a detailed study, with 63–84 different species in individual repertoires (Lemaire 1974; Dowsett-Lemaire 1979b). Each singer produces a consistent repertoire, learned during the first eight months of life.

Young birds have a simpler juvenile song in autumn and early winter, a subdued chatter without mimicry (Dowsett-Lemaire 1981b). Adult females on the breeding ground may sing a similar short grating non-imitative song.

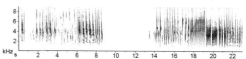

Part of song of Marsh Warbler, Poland, May. (Sample 2003)

The common call-note is a slightly nasal '*kerr*' or '*t-cherrr*', more grating than the similar call of Reed Warbler, but less buzzy than that of Sedge Warbler. Marsh Warbler often gives a short hard '*tek*' or '*chrek*', which may signal alarm; and a chattering '*chre-chre-chre…*'.

MOULT Some adults moult a few body feathers on the breeding grounds during July, beginning during the later stages of breeding. There follows a more extensive partial moult during autumn stopover in NE Africa, between September and November. The great majority of birds renew most or all of their body plumage and often some tertials, but wing-coverts, flight feathers and tail remain unmoulted (DJP unpublished). There is then a complete moult in winter quarters south of the equator, between January and early April. This involves renewal of tracts in typical passerine sequence and takes about 60 days to complete in individual birds (Dowsett-Lemaire & Dowsett 1987). Most birds are still growing outer primaries and inner secondaries in mid March.

After fledging, there is limited post-juvenile body moult. Scattered feathers growing during July and early August may represent addition to juvenile plumage rather than its replacement (Dowsett-Lemaire 1981a). Young birds usually have some autumn body moult in NE Africa, but this is less extensive than in adults and the tertials are never replaced. They have a complete moult in southern winter quarters, at the same time as adults.

HABITAT During the breeding season, it prefers rank herbage, especially fairly tall, tufty, erect plants such as nettles *Urtica*, meadowsweet *Filipendula* and willowherb

Epilobium (Hagemaijer & Blair 1997); also young osiers and alder, sometimes interspersed with reeds and bushes, or overshadowed by taller trees. It is often found in neglected marshy edges or depressions on moist or seasonally flooded soils, in moist scrub and hedgerows by standing crops and, in Russia, in abandoned orchards and open forests with rich undergrowth. Although a bird of thick cover, it prefers margins to deeper stands. Some birds do breed in waterside vegetation and mixed reedbeds with scattered bushes, but it is rarely attracted to extensive *Phragmites* reedbeds or swamps. It generally occupies damper and ranker sites than Blyth's Reed Warbler (Cramp 1992). In Europe, it is found mainly in lowland areas but breeds up to 1,500m in Switzerland. In the Caucasus it breeds among tall herbs above 1,500m, sometimes along river valleys to as high as 3,000m (K. Gauger pers. comm.).

In Africa, wintering birds utilise dense leafy thickets with rank grass and herbaceous growth, often along riverbanks and overgrown streambeds and also below open woodland and in open forest edge, mainly below 1,600m. During migration it occurs in a wider variety of habitats including scrubby *Lantana* thickets, acacia-grassland, thorn bush and coastal mangroves and ranges from sea level up to 2,400m. On southward passage through Kenya and Tanzania it follows the rains and exploits the rapid greening of semi-arid bushland.

BEHAVIOUR Usually stays concealed within vegetation, advertising its presence by calls or song, but is often less shy and skulking than Eurasian Reed Warbler. It spends much time in the herbaceous layer, but commonly forages up to 4m high in bushes and thickets and ventures into the tree canopy, feeding mainly by gleaning from foliage. It tends to adopt a horizontal posture when moving among twigs and within bushes, but is typically more upright when perched or on the move through vertical reed or herb stems and when singing. Excited birds raise their fore-crown feathers and frequently cock the head and flick their wings and tail. When disturbed from cover, flight is flitting and fluent before the bird drops swiftly back into a bush or herb patch.

On the breeding grounds, the male typically sings from a concealed perch 1–2m high, but sometimes from a taller bush or more exposed position, or from higher in a willow or other tree. On arrival in late May, song is often delivered continuously from before dawn and throughout the morning, then resumed from evening until after dark. Song output decreases markedly after pairing, with shorter quieter bursts interspersed with longer pauses. Song and territory defence continue through the incubation period, but cease after hatching, although occasionally the song is briefly resumed in July. Unpaired males in June can sing for hours throughout the morning and late evening.

In Africa, it tends to form loose wintering agglomerations within which individuals establish overlapping feeding territories, sometimes at quite high densities in prime habitat with up to 25 singing birds/ha recorded in Zambia (Kelsey 1989). On southward passage, this is in places the most numerous Palearctic migrant. It occurs in abundance on the Sudan coast and in SE Kenya and thousands can be attracted to lights or to small oases (Pearson & Backhurst 1976; DJP & G. Nikolaus). It shows strong fidelity to wintering sites, with almost half the birds in a Zambian study returning to the previous year's territory (Kelsey 1989). Song is infrequent and subdued in Africa during southward passage, but heard increasingly in the winter quarters between February and early April.

BREEDING HABITS The territory is established and defended by the male, who sings strongly on arrival. Pair formation may occur within a few days, although a high proportion of males (fewer females) remain unpaired. There is no mate fidelity between years and many surviving birds fail to return to the breeding grounds, the return rate being particularly low in females. Males are commonly polygynous and may leave one female with a nest and adopt a second one on a new territory, or will sometimes maintain more than one territory with more than one female at once. There is a high incidence of mate infidelity, males commonly mating with females in neighbouring territories (Cramp 1992).

The nest is built by the female in about five days, with the male in close attendance. The birds are then conspicuous, flitting low across the tops of vegetation, the female carrying nest material. The nest is sited 0.2–2.0m (usually *c.* 0.5m) from the ground among nettles, herbaceous tufts, bramble or osiers and attached to several (typically 3–4) vertical stems. It is a small tapering cup of leaves, dry grasses and other plant stems, lined with finer grasses, together with hair and plant down. It is shallower and less strongly built than most nests of Eurasian Reed Warbler, often with distinct handles woven from the rim around supporting stems. The clutch is usually 4–5 eggs (sometimes 3, rarely 6). Incubation lasts 12–14 days and is shared by the sexes. The young are usually fed in the nest by both parents and most broods fledge after 10–11 days, becoming independent after a further 15–19 days. The fledged brood typically divides, one group attaching to each parent (Cramp 1992). Normally single brooded.

Very occasionally, hybridisation has been recorded with both Eurasian Reed Warbler and Blyth's Reed Warbler, with Marsh Warbler usually the female of the pair.

DISTRIBUTION

Breeding Breeds widely across the cooler temperate latitudes of the West and Central Palearctic, from N and W Europe to C Siberia, The western limit reaches the Atlantic and North Sea coasts in N France, Belgium and the Netherlands, but it is largely absent from the British Isles. It is widespread across Europe from N and E France, north into S Norway, S Sweden and S Finland where it reaches 65°N. To the south it reaches N Italy and the N Balkans, then sporadically south to Greece and Bulgaria. It breeds widely through much of Belarus and N Ukraine but only sporadically south to Crimea. Within Russia, it is widespread and common west of the Urals and in the N Caspian Sea region, reaching the Volga delta and the Ural and Ilek Rivers in NW Kazakhstan. The eastern limit is uncertain but it is known to breed across the W Siberian Plain to the Ob River in the vicinity of Novosibirsk at *c.* 86°E (PRK). It is widespread and common in the Caucasus Mountains and also breeds at higher altitudes from NE Turkey and Armenia to NW Iran.

Within Europe, it is locally common to abundant, with over 1,000 pairs per 50-km square through much of the range (Hagemeijer & Blair 1997). Highest numbers are found in a band from Belgium and Holland through C and E Europe to the Baltic States, Russia, Belarus and Ukraine, where it is often the most numerous *Acrocephalus* warbler. South of the Alps and in SE Europe numbers are low and its distribution is patchy, but it can be abundant in the Caucasus. Its range has expanded markedly since 1900, especially at the northern limits in Scandinavia and perhaps also in Siberia. In England, a small population centred on

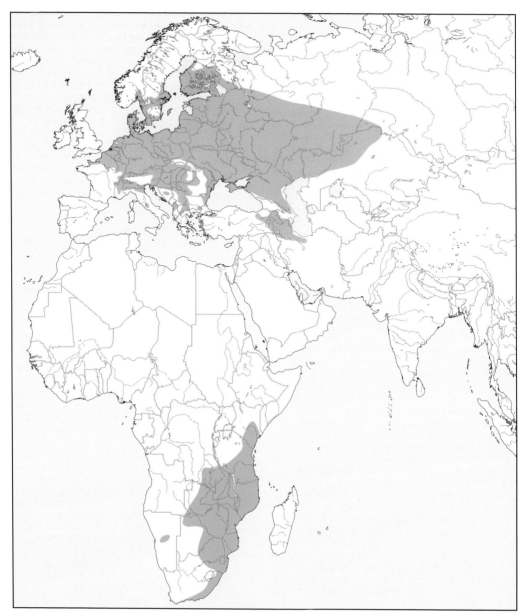

Marsh Warbler. Breeding range and winter distribution.

Worcestershire, dwindled from the 1950s and disappeared in the 1990s. It now breeds occasionally at south and east coast sites from Sussex and Kent to the Shetland Islands. The overall population for Europe has been estimated at 1.6–3 million breeding pairs (Hagemeijer & Blair 1997).

Non-breeding With winter quarters in SE and S Africa, this species performs the longest migration of any *Acrocephalus* warbler. Birds from all parts of the range converge on the Middle East in autumn, then migrate within narrow corridors through E Africa (Pearson 1990). Particularly heavy southward passage occurs on the Red Sea coast and through inland E Kenya. Birds winter from C and SE Kenya, where it is scarce and local, and NE and C Tanzania (where

poorly recorded) to extreme SE DR Congo (SE Katanga), Zambia (except the northwest), Malawi, Mozambique, Zimbabwe, N and E Botswana and N and E South Africa south to Eastern Cape. There are a few scattered records from C Namibia and vagrants have reached the Cape Peninsula in South Africa.

MOVEMENTS Autumn migration is a two-stage process. Adults leave the breeding grounds during late July and early August, with young birds following mainly during early to mid August, the last departing by early September. Birds from W and C Europe initially head southeast, passing through the Balkans to Turkey and the Levant, while Russian birds head south or southwest to the Caucasus. A few birds migrate through E Egypt but most apparently cross W and C Arabia. The main arrival in Africa takes place across the Red Sea coast of Sudan and probably N Eritrea, adults passing between mid August and early September, young birds from late August to late September, with stragglers into October. Birds then remain for two to three months in Ethiopia where most undergo a partial moult. The main Ethiopian stopover area must accommodate almost the entire world population during October, yet remains undiscovered. It is thought to lie west of the rift valley.

Onward migration follows a narrow route through inland Kenya, passing east of the central highlands and Mount Kilimanjaro, before turning south-southwest through Tanzania to Malawi, E Zambia and S Africa (Pearson 1990). This second stage begins in late October and early November and continues to mid January. Peak passage through Tsavo in SE Kenya is from mid November to mid December and many thousands of birds are caught and ringed annually there after being attracted to lights at Ngulia Safari Lodge. Birds arrive in Malawi and Zambia from late November, mainly during December.

Departure from winter quarters takes place between late March and mid April. Passage through E Africa is less protracted and less noticeable in spring than in autumn, with many birds apparently overflying. Migration is again channelled through SE Kenya, mainly during early and mid April, but with more birds appearing along the Tanzanian and Kenyan coasts than in autumn. It appears to be absent in spring from Sudan and scarce in W and C Ethiopia, indicating that the main route lies further east, through the Ogaden and N Somalia, where extensive pre-migratory fattening has been noted in trapped birds (JSA in litt., HB in litt.). Migration across Arabia and through Kuwait occurs mainly between late April and mid May and again tends to follow a more easterly route than in autumn. Many fat birds make a landfall near the coast of S Oman during early to mid May, when it is by far the most abundant passerine migrant (JSA & GN in litt.). Most birds presumably funnel through the Caucasus and NE Turkey, where it is often very common at this time. Birds reach the Black Sea coasts from late April, S Russia and E Europe from early May and C and W Europe from mid May onwards. European breeding grounds are occupied mainly during the latter half of May, with arrival at the western and northern range limits during late May and early June.

Over 180,000 birds caught in SE Kenya in November–December have provided 127 long-distance recoveries, including exchanges with breeding areas west to France and Belgium and north to the S Baltic and European Russia, and also with passage sites in Arabia. Kenya-ringed birds have also been found to the south between December and early April, in Malawi, C Mozambique, Zambia, Zimbabwe and SE DR Congo. Three Czech-ringed birds have been recovered in Malawi, one from Belgium in C Mozambique and one from Finland in South Africa.

DESCRIPTION

Plumage – Adult fresh (March–June) Forehead to nape olive-brown, tinged greenish. Supercilium olive-buff to creamy buff, well-marked in front of and above eye and linking with narrow buffy white eye-ring, but fading out just behind eye. Lores to below eye dark olive-brown with fine buff mottling. Cheeks and ear-coverts olive-brown, finely streaked buff. Mantle and scapulars to uppertail-coverts olive-brown, tinged greenish or ochreous, slightly paler on rump. Tail feathers dark grey-brown, narrowly edged olive-brown, the outermost with fine whitish fringe around distal inner edge and tip. Chin and throat whitish, tinged yellowish buff. Upper breast suffused yellowish olive-brown; lower breast and belly washed yellowish buff. Sides of breast light olive-buff; flanks and vent olive-buff. Undertail-coverts buffy white. Lesser and median coverts olive-brown, concolorous with scapulars. Greater coverts dark grey-brown with broad light olive-brown edges and tips. Primary coverts dark grey-brown, narrowly fringed light olive-brown. Alula blackish brown, finely edged light olive-brown. Remiges dark grey-brown or blackish brown; outer edges and tips of tertials with well demarcated, broad, bright olive-brown or greenish brown fringes. Primaries and secondaries with narrow light olive-brown or greenish brown edges, primaries with well-marked greyish white fringes around tips. Underwing-coverts buffy white.

Adult worn (August to December) In early autumn, top of head and upperparts much duller olive-brown, although still with greenish tinge. Supercilium paler buff. Underparts buffy white, less yellowish and paler on breast and flanks. Light olive-brown wing feather edgings retained but tertial fringes narrower, less contrasting. Alula less blackish. Pale primary tips worn away. By late autumn, following partial moult in NE Africa, top of head, mantle and scapulars to uppertail-coverts usually fresh olive-brown with strong greenish tinge. Ear-coverts, face and underparts as in spring, with marked yellowish wash. Wing feathers dull greyish brown with worn, light greyish olive edges, but some birds have one or more new bright-fringed tertials.

Juvenile/first-winter Top of head and upperparts olive-brown, generally slightly less greenish than in adults; some birds are lighter, more ochreous, others warmly tinged on mantle and scapulars and, especially, on rump and uppertail-coverts. Supercilium, face pattern and underparts as in fresh adult. Wing feather edges and broad fringes to tertials ochreous-brown to bright olive-brown, sometimes warmly tinged. Alula and flight feathers dark grey-brown, primary tips with finer, less conspicuous pale fringes than in spring adult. By late autumn, upperparts duller, underparts paler, wing feather edgings duller and greyer.

Bare Parts Upper mandible dark olive-brown with pale pinkish or yellowish flesh cutting edges. Lower mandible pale pinkish or yellowish flesh. Mouth orange to orange-yellow; newly fledged birds have two blackish tongue spots, but these are faint or absent by late August and rarely visible in late autumn. Tarsi and toes of adults mid brown to pale flesh-pink or pinkish straw, sometimes dark brown, rarely dark grey to blackish; soles dull yellow, claws greyish brown. Tarsi of first-autumn birds usually dark greenish brown to greenish grey, sometimes mid brown to pinkish brown, rarely blackish. Iris dark brown, olive-brown or light sepia-brown in adults; dark brown or dark grey-brown in first autumn birds.

IN HAND CHARACTERS
Measurements

	Male	Female
Wing	64–73 (69.2; 53)	64–70 (67.8; 33)
Tail	47–55 (51.4; 41)	48–55 (51.2; 19)
Bill	14.5–17 (15.9; 54)	14.5–17 (15.8; 34)
Tarsus	21.5–24 (22.7; 48)	21–23.5 (22.3; 31)

(Data from entire range; includes data from Cramp 1992)

Sexes combined:
Tail/wing ratio: 71–79% (75%; 43)
Bill width: 3.8–4.6 (4.2; 30)
Hind claw: 5.2–6.4 (5.8; 25)
Tail graduation: 2–8 (5.1; 35)
Juvenile wing averages *c.* 1mm shorter than that of adult, juvenile tail averages *c.* 1.5mm shorter.

Structure

Wing formula (Cramp 1992):

p1/pc	p2	p3e	p4	p5	p6	p7	p10
(4)–1	0–2	wp	1.5–3.5	3.5–6	6.5–9	8.5–12	14–19

Wing long with pointed tip; p1 minute, usually < pc. Wing point p(2)3; p2 = (p3) 3/4–4/5; p3 emarginated. Notch on p2 7.5–11mm from tip, falling at (p6) 6/7–8/9 [9] in both adults and juveniles.

Figure 60. Wing of Marsh Warbler.

Tail medium, slightly rounded.
Bill rather broad-based, sides straight or slightly concave; slightly broader and shorter than in Eurasian Reed Warbler, with length to rear of nostril 9–10.5mm (10–12.5mm in Eurasian Reed).

a   b

Figure 61. Comparision of bill profile of (a) Marsh Warbler and (b) Eurasian Reed Warbler.

Tarsi slightly thicker than in Eurasian Reed; toes and claws shorter.
Recognition Adults show uniform olive-brown upperparts, often with a clean greenish tinge, which distinguishes them from nominate Eurasian Reed (warmly toned above) and most *fuscus* (with tawny rump and uppertail-coverts) and also from the greyer Eastern Olivaceous Warbler of the race *elaeica*. Young Marsh are often warmly tinged on rump and uppertail-coverts, especially in August and September, but show brighter, more contrasting tertial fringes than young Eurasian Reed and more bronzy or golden (less rufescent) edges to secondaries and wing-coverts. Yellowish buff underparts are often distinctive in both adult and young birds (these are warm buff in nominate Eurasian Reed, whiter in *fuscus* and buff or whitish in Blyth's Reed).
Wing length is of limited value. Measurements over

67mm should exclude Blyth's Reed Warbler. Those above 70mm will exclude most nominate Eurasian Reed and Eastern Olivaceous but do not rule out *fuscus* Eurasian Reed. The more pointed wing of Marsh (with p2 > p5) and the lack of emargination on p4 separate it from Blyth's Reed and Eastern Olivaceous and from African Reed Warbler, but not from Eurasian Reed (Fig. 57).

Separation from Eurasian Reed may need to take into account wing structure, bill shape and foot structure. In adults the position of the notch on p2 on the closed wing is the best guide, falling at p6–9 in Marsh, usually below p9 in Eurasian Reed. It can occasionally fall as high as p7/8 in young Eurasian Reed and thus only conclusively separates a proportion of young Marsh. Secondary shortfall (distance from ss tips to wp): 17.5–21mm in Marsh, 15–19mm in Eurasian Reed, can provide another pointer in European birds (Grantham 2006). Marsh has a shorter, broader bill, with width/length (measured across and to rear of nostril) usually > 0.42 in live birds (< 0.42 in most Eurasian Reed). It also has a slightly smaller foot. Measurements of inner footspan (see Fig. 62) in C Europe and East Africa ranged from 16–18.5mm, compared to 18–21mm in Eurasian Reed (Leisler 1972; Pearson 1989). The claw on the inner toe of Marsh barely reaches the end of the middle toe, but usually extends 1–2mm beyond it in Eurasian Reed. Leg colour is of limited use but the pale ochreous to pinkish brown or light straw of most adult Marsh is characteristic. The greyish brown claws of Marsh are typically shorter and paler than those of Eurasian Reed, and the yellow soles are usually duller.

Figure 62. Left foot of Marsh Warbler to show 'inner footspan' and position of tip of inner toe claw.

Ageing In early autumn, young birds have bright fresh body plumage, contrasting bright fringes to the tertials and wing-coverts and fresh pale-tipped primaries. They are easily distinguished from adults with dull worn body plumage and wing feather edges and slightly to moderately abraded primary tips.

By November to December, ageing in Africa is more difficult. Young birds then have variably worn body plumage and wing-coverts. Some retain almost unworn primaries, but others have moderately abraded primaries and rather worn tails. In late autumn adults, abrasion of the primary tips and wing covert edges is typically more pronounced and tail feather wear more extreme than in young birds. They are best distinguished by a contrast between new greenish olive-brown mantle and scapular feathers and old greyer brown wing-coverts and flight feather edges. Some have diagnostic newly grown tertials. Some adults show a light olive-brown or hazel eye distinct from the dull dark brown eye of first-year birds. Birds with light straw-coloured or pinkish brown legs are more likely to be adults, while those with dark, greenish tinged legs are probably first years. Incomplete skull ossification separates first year birds until at least December.

Weight Range 8–23.5g; typically 10–12g in lean birds, commonly 13–17g in fattening migrants. In autumn, up to 20–23g in Ukraine and Turkey (GN & RV unpublished data). Often below 9g on S Sahara edge, but frequently above 13g during southward passage through Kenya (GN & DJP unpublished data). In spring, rarely above 14g in S Africa, but commonly 16–19g in Somalia and E Ethiopia (JSA, HB unpublished data).

GEOGRAPHIC VARIATION Slight, involving plumage colour only. Breeding birds in the southeast of the range in Iran have been separated as a distinct form, *laricus*, based on slightly paler plumage tones. A minority of spring birds examined in Kenya and S Africa do show colder and slightly greyer olive upperparts and whiter underparts and perhaps represent this population. It is unclear, however, whether this appearance fits all birds originating from the southeast of the range and we prefer not to recognise this race.

TAXONOMY AND SYSTEMATICS No issues arising.

▲ ▶ Adult, Czech Republic, May. Male singing from within a nettle bed, a typical habitat often used for breeding. Spring adults in fresh plumage show an olive wash to the upperparts, little or no warmth in the rump and uppertail-coverts, and conspicuous whitish tips to the primaries. Mouth often yellowish rather than bright orange of Eurasian Reed Warbler. Adults often show distinctive pale brown legs and feet, contrasting with short, darker claws. Note the long primary projection (Jiri Bohdal).

▲ Adult, Armenia, May. A slightly more warmly toned adult that retains olive tone to upperparts. Note the slightly shorter, stouter bill than Eurasian Reed Warbler would show (Peter Kennerley).

▲ Adult, Shetland, Scotland, June. The greyish appearance of this singing male is unusual, most are warmer and browner. Note long primary projection with eight primary tips visible, and fresh primary tips (Hugh Harrop).

◀ First-winter, Shetland, Scotland, September. Young birds in autumn are slightly warmer and browner than fresh adults in spring. Most differ from first-winter Eurasian Reed Warbler by olive-brown rump and uppertail-coverts, similar in colour to mantle, and slightly shorter, thicker bill (Robert Brookes).

EURASIAN REED WARBLER
Acrocephalus scirpaceus   **Plates 20 and 21**

Turdus scirpaceus Hermann, 1804. *Observ. Zool.* page 202. Alsace.

A long-distance migrant that breeds widely and commonly in reedbeds across the warm and temperate latitudes of Europe and C Asia and winters in Africa. Localised populations in NW and NE Africa and Arabia appear to be partially resident. The African Reed Warbler, which ranges widely within sub-Saharan Africa and has several races, is sometimes regarded as conspecific, but here we have treated it as a full species. The Red Sea mangrove breeding form *avicenniae* seems better included within Eurasian Reed rather than with African Reed. Eurasian Reed Warbler is thus polytypic, with three races recognised:

A. s. scirpaceus (Hermann 1804). NW Africa and Europe, north to the Baltic Sea, east to W Turkey and Ukraine and through Russia to the Don and Middle Volga Rivers.

A. s. fuscus (Hemprich & Ehrenberg 1833). C and E Turkey, Cyprus, the Levant to C Arabia, the S Caucasus to N and W Iran, the W and N Caspian Sea, W and S Kazakhstan, Uzbekistan and NW Xinjiang, China. Here we treat as *fuscus* all birds breeding within the traditionally recognised range of that race, although we believe that this arrangement is no longer satisfactory (see **Geographic Variation** below).

A. s. avicenniae (Ash, Pearson, Nikolaus & Colston 1989). Coasts of Sudan, Eritrea, SW Saudi Arabia, N Yemen and N Somalia, associated with mangroves.

IDENTIFICATION Length 12–14cm. Wing 60–74mm in Palearctic races, 56–62mm in *avicenniae*. Tail/wing 75–80% in Palearctic races, 78–85% in *avicenniae*.

One of four small, unstreaked *Acrocephalus* warblers which breed in the Western Palearctic, the others being the Marsh, Blyth's Reed and Paddyfield Warblers. This group poses identification challenges both in the field and in the hand and their separation is rarely straightforward. Vocalisations are particularly important. Species separation will otherwise depend on a combination of subtle plumage and structural characters and/or biometrics. Eurasian Reed Warbler is the most numerous and widespread member of this group in Europe and the species with which the others tend to be compared. It is also, however, the most variable. The nominate form overlaps extensively with Marsh Warbler in Europe, with Blyth's Reed Warbler east of the Baltic and with Paddyfield Warbler around the W and N Black Sea. The eastern race *fuscus* overlaps with both Paddyfield and Blyth's Reed Warblers through its C Asian breeding range. On migration throughout the Middle East and NE Africa and during the winter months in Africa, *fuscus* is likely to occur alongside Marsh Warbler. During migration, *fuscus* Eurasian Reed and Marsh Warblers occur alongside the mangrove-breeding race *avicenniae* in the Red Sea. Sexes alike.

Structure A small and relatively slim *Acrocephalus* with an attenuated head profile, the result of a low sloping forehead and relatively long slim bill. At times it raises the fore-crown feathers, changing the profile of the head and making it seem larger and more angular. Since other *Acrocephalus* also do this, it is of little importance in identification. The body is relatively slim and the medium-length tail is largely covered below by long, deep, undertail-coverts. The closed wing is

pointed with a long primary projection, some 70–80% of exposed tertial length. Up to eight primary tips are visible, as in Marsh Warbler, but the spacing tends to be less even, with the outer two tips falling closer together (Fig. 57). With good views, the emargination on just the third primary (p3) is usually visible. But caution is needed in the Middle East where small birds, treated within *fuscus*, have a slightly shorter wing and can show a distinct emargination on p4. Further south, around the Red Sea and Gulf of Aden, *avicenniae* has a still more rounded wing, with primary projection only about 50% and no more than six primary tips visible.

Plumage and bare parts This is a nondescript *Acrocephalus*, lacking distinctive plumage features, and its separation from similar species depends on subtle differences in colour tones. Difficulties are compounded by seasonal changes due to wear, bleaching and moult. The race *fuscus* is highly variable and overlaps in colour with various potential confusion species.

Nominate Eurasian Reed Warbler, when freshly moulted in Africa, is rich olive-brown on the crown and upperparts, with a warm tawny tinge, most pronounced on the rump and uppertail-coverts. The face pattern is fairly featureless with just a narrow buff supercilium contrasting with a dark loral triangle immediately in front of the eye. It joins with a distinct narrow whitish eye-ring, but barely extends behind the eye. The underparts are conspicuously paler than the upperparts. The whitish chin and throat contrast with a warm buff-tinged breast and warm brown-buff sides and flanks. The belly is whitish and contrasts with pale warm buff undertail-coverts. On the closed wing, the edges of the flight feathers and broad fringes to the tertials and greater coverts are warm brown, closely matching the mantle and scapular colour. The tips of the blackish brown primaries and dark brown tail feathers show only narrow and inconspicuous pale fringes.

Birds are already abraded on arrival in Europe and some of the features of fresh plumage will be lost. By May the warm brown upperparts are duller, with the olive tone subdued, sometimes with a slight greyish hue enhancing contrast with the warmer-coloured rump and uppertail-coverts. Being protected by the wings, these retain their brighter tone. The edges and fringes to the wing-coverts and tertials are also duller and few birds in Europe retain pale tips to the primaries. The underparts appear whiter than when fresh, the buff-brown flanks contrasting more with the breast and belly. By early autumn, despite some body moult, most adults appear still duller and paler with greyer wing feather edgings, but retain a tawny tinge above, particularly on the rump and uppertail-coverts.

Compared with fresh adults, juvenile and first-winter birds are slightly brighter with a richer rust tone to the upperparts. The supercilium and eye-ring are buffier and less contrasting, the underparts washed more extensively warm buff-brown and the wing-coverts and tertials brighter tawny brown. The primaries retain narrow pale buff tips until October, but the tail feathers usually lack pale fringes.

Central Asian *fuscus* typically differ from European birds in being paler olive-brown above and whiter below. When freshly moulted, the upperparts may match those of Marsh Warbler, but tend to be tinged more ochreous, less greenish, with a warm tawny tinge on the rump and uppertail-coverts. There is often a greyish cast to the crown and nape which then contrast slightly with the mantle. The underparts are off-white, with the buff wash on breast and flanks more restricted, less warm and less intense than in nominate birds. There are usually conspicuous whitish fringes to the tips of the outer tail feathers, those on the outermost pair extending broadly around the distal edge of the inner web. On the closed wing, the dark primary tips are prominently pale-fringed, but the centres of the tertials and greater coverts are less dark and contrasting than in Marsh Warbler. Many *fuscus* moult later in winter than the nominate race and such birds retain fresh plumage, including pale-tipped primaries, during spring passage and throughout May. Worn *fuscus* in early autumn tend to be paler and buffer-brown above than European birds, and decidedly whitish below.

Typical first-winter *fuscus* are duller olive-brown above than first-winter *scirpaceus*, with warmer brown feathering restricted to the rump and uppertail-coverts, and often show a greyish tinged crown and nape. They are whiter below with a more restricted buff wash.

Birds assigned to *fuscus* show considerable colour variation. Many of those migrating from E Africa and through the Middle East are more warmly tinged than the typical *fuscus* described above, yet show the whitish tipped tail feathers and longer wing length characteristic of C Asian birds. At the other extreme are birds that are greyish brown above and still whiter below, lacking any warm tones on the rump and uppertail-coverts.

The mangrove race *avicenniae* is similar in colour to typical *fuscus*.

The bill is dark greyish brown to blackish brown with a pale flesh brown to yellowish flesh lower mandible which darkens slightly at the sides towards the tip. The leg colour varies in all races from dark greyish or greenish brown in first autumn birds to mid brown or flesh-brown in older birds. The legs tend to be less pale than in Marsh Warbler, but there is extensive overlap.

SIMILAR SPECIES There seem to be no differences in behaviour, jizz or habitat preference that would consistently separate Eurasian Reed Warbler from Marsh, Blyth's Reed or Paddyfield Warblers. But subtle structural differences can be helpful in the field, particularly those of head and bill profile and primary projection. In the hand, wing formula and measurements will separate nearly all Eurasian Reed Warblers from the other three species, but a few first autumn birds may be indistinguishable from Marsh. In Europe, the wing length of Eurasian Reed overlaps with both Marsh and Blyth's Reed Warblers but, in C Asia, *fuscus* Eurasian Reed are decidedly longer winged than Blyth's Reed and much larger than Paddyfield, with a very different tail/wing ratio.

In good light, the warm brown tones of nominate Eurasian Reed Warbler should help separate it in Europe from Blyth's Reed Warbler and from adult (but not all first-winter) Marsh. On the other hand, the paler and greyer tones of *fuscus* should set it apart in C Asia from both Paddyfield and Blyth's Reed Warblers. But plumage colour may be of limited value, particularly as wear affects tones as the breeding season progresses.

Vocalisation provides the single most useful character when faced in Europe with an unidentified unstreaked *Acrocephalus* and separating singing Eurasian Reed from Marsh and Blyth's Reed is usually straightforward. Its slow and steady paced rhythmic song is quite distinct from the highly mimetic stream of chattering or chirruping notes produced by these species and should identify it readily on both breeding and wintering grounds. The call notes of Eurasian Reed Warbler on the other hand are less distinctive and overlap with some calls given by the other species.

Marsh Warbler has a rather more compact build than Eurasian Reed, a more domed crown, a slightly shorter, broader and deeper bill and longer wings. These differences are slight and often imperceptible in the field, but can give Marsh Warbler a less attenuated appearance and different 'feel' to Eurasian Reed. There is considerable overlap in wing structure and this is of limited use in the field, but the primary projection of Marsh is slightly longer, typically 80–90% of exposed tertial length, with spacing between the outer primaries more even.

In Europe, the paler olive-brown upperparts of adult Marsh, often with a distinct greenish tinge, should distinguish it from Eurasian Reed, and the underparts usually show a slight yellowish or creamy suffusion. Beware though that some first year birds in autumn are warmly tinged above, particularly on the rump and uppertail-coverts. The head pattern of Marsh closely resembles that of Eurasian Reed, although the supercilium above the lores tends to appear slightly sharper. Because it moults later in winter, Marsh retains contrasting olive fringes to the tertials and whitish tips to the primaries throughout spring when on most Eurasian Reed these have been worn away. In song, when breeding, the orange-yellowish mouth colour of Marsh differs from the deep orange of Eurasian Reed.

In the Middle East and in Africa, Marsh can be identical in upperpart colour and in head pattern to some *fuscus* Eurasian Reed. It is often rather greener, however, without the greyish head tinge and (except in some first autumn birds) lacks the contrasting tawny rump and uppertail-coverts. Most birds, adult and first-winter, show a yellowish suffusion below that *fuscus* lacks. Marsh is also close in coloration to the Red Sea mangrove race *avicenniae*, especially in autumn when young Marsh and newly moulted *avicenniae* are both in fresh plumage. In spring, however, all passage Marsh will appear fresh while *avicenniae* will be worn. The larger size and much longer wing of Marsh should readily separate it.

Blyth's Reed Warbler so closely resembles Eurasian Reed in appearance that some silent birds may be inseparable. Song provides the easiest means of distinction. That of Blyth's Reed is rich and fluty with a steady unhurried rhythm and loud, far-carrying delivery, quite different from the lazy, rhythmic song of Eurasian Reed. Calling birds give a hard '*tak*', similar to Lesser Whitethroat and outside the repertoire of Eurasian Reed.

Blyth's Reed has a low, flat, forehead and longish bill and shares the attenuated head shape of Eurasian Reed. But it has a shorter, more rounded wing with a primary projection, typically 50–60% of the exposed tertial length. The wing point is formed by p3 and p4 with p5 almost equal, so that only six or seven closely spaced primary tips may be visible on the closed wing, fewer than in Eurasian Reed. It also shows distinct emarginations on both p3 and p4. Because of this shorter wing it tends to appear longer-tailed than Eurasian Reed.

Adult Blyth's Reed is uniform cold olive-brown above and rather pale below, never matching the warm brown typical of nominate Eurasian Reed. It tends to show a better developed supercilium, broader above the lores and more often extending as a narrow line behind the eye. Worn adults appear dull above, sometimes with a greyish or greyish olive tone and distinctly whitish below.

First autumn Blyth's Reed could be more easily overlooked as Eurasian Reed. They are slightly browner above than adults and can appear buffier, more sullied below, but lack the strong rufescent tones and brighter rump and uppertail-coverts of Eurasian Reed. There is often a distinct contrast between the slightly warmer-toned edges to the wing-coverts and remiges and the mantle and scapulars, so that the wings can appear warmer than the upperparts and this effect is more pronounced than in Eurasian Reed.

Paddyfield Warbler is the most distinctive of this group and will rarely present problems, being the only one of the four to show a conspicuous supercilium that extends behind the eye. It is a smaller bird than Eurasian Reed with a shorter stubbier bill, a shorter, more rounded wing with an emarginated p4 and a proportionately longer tail. It has a more contrasting head pattern, with a conspicuous pale supercilium that extends well beyond the eye and emphasised by a narrow and diffuse dark band along the crown side. The warm brown upperparts tend to be brighter, particularly compared with those of *fuscus* in C Asia.

VOICE The highly distinctive song consists of a slow rhythmic series of softly grating and squeaky notes repeated two or three times: '*chup-chup-chir-chir-churric-churric-churric-whit-whit-whit churruc-churruc-* …', with frequent changes of pitch. It is often given in bursts of up to 20 seconds, starting slowly and ending rather abruptly, but may last several minutes without interruption. It is less interspersed with chattering and trills than in other *Acrocephalus* species. Delivery is lazy and lacks the variation and mimetic quality of Marsh Warbler song. It has a more uniform timing and slower tempo than in Marsh and is generally lower pitched and more grating. It is less exuberant, less chattering and buzzy than in Sedge Warbler. Brief imitations of other bird calls may be included, such as recognisable calls of Common Redshank, Common Tern and Bearded Tit. Some 'mixed singers' in continental Europe also imitate snatches of mimetic Marsh Warbler song.

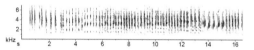

Part of song of Eurasian Reed Warbler, recorded within breeding range of *A. s. scirpaceus*, Suffolk, England, May. (Peter Kennerley)

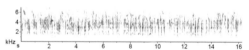

Part of song of Eurasian Reed Warbler, recorded within breeding range of *A. s. fuscus*, Buerjin, Xinjiang Uygur Autonomous Region, China, June. (Geoff Carey)

The commonest call is a low nasal '*scherr*', less grating than the similar call of Marsh Warbler. A conversational '*chrr-chrr*' is frequently heard and a louder, harsher '*skerr-*' is given in threat or alarm. A low and infrequently heard '*chk*' is less hard and emphatic than the various '*tuc*' or '*teck*' calls of Sedge, Marsh and Paddyfield Warblers and cannot be mistaken for the hard '*tak*' call given frequently by Blyth's Reed Warbler.

MOULT Timing varies according to race, location and latitude.

A. s. scirpaceus A few Iberian adults have a complete moult on the breeding grounds, and birds breeding in Morocco moult there rapidly from late August. Otherwise, most adults have a partial moult in late summer, involving a variable amount of the body and head plumage. After

migration they undergo complete moult in the northern tropics of Africa between October and December, some subsequently moving on to winter further south. Juveniles have an extensive moult into first-winter body and head plumage during July–September. After migration to Africa they moult completely, probably at the same time as adults.

A. s. fuscus The late summer partial moults of adults and juveniles are similar to those of nominate birds. A complete moult then takes place after migration. Its timing depends on the latitude in Africa where it occurs. Many birds moult in Ethiopia or Sudan between late September and December, after which a large proportion resume migration to winter quarters further south. Other birds wintering in equatorial or southern latitudes moult after arrival there, between December and March. An estimated 40% of birds wintering in Uganda moulted there after arrival, taking 65–75 days to complete and these included both young birds and adults (Pearson 1973). Most birds reaching S Africa also moult in the late winter (e.g. Tyler & Tyler 1997 for Botswana). Late moulting *fuscus* have primaries that are fresher and darker during spring passage than earlier moulting birds. In Uganda and Kenya these include long-winged warmly toned *fuscus* as well as typical olive-brown birds. Smaller *fuscus* which breed in the Middle East evidently moult rather earlier, presumably in autumn, as they show noticeably worn remiges in April on their territories in Arabia; the contrast with the fresher feathers of larger northbound passage birds is quite distinct (GN & JSA unpublished data).

A. s. avicenniae Adults moult completely during August and September.

HABITAT Usually breeds in mature *Phragmites* reeds above water or damp ground, including large freshwater reedbeds and stands fringing shallow lakes, slow rivers, brackish lagoons and estuaries. It also utilises small reed patches by ponds and strips of *Phragmites* along narrow ditches. In broad reedbeds, densities are highest around the edges of shallow lakes and meres and along watery channels. Mixed *Phragmites* and *Typha* is sometimes used and marsh edges tend to be favoured, where reeds are mingled with other plants and bushes. Drier marginal habitat sometimes occupied includes meadowsweet, willowherb and hawthorn. Breeding birds often leave reedbeds to feed in nearby mixed reed and *Carex* sedge, willow bushes, hedges and low trees. It occurs mainly in the lowlands, but ranges to above 1,000m in Switzerland, from 1,650m to 2,600m in the Caucasus in Georgia and from 1,200m to 2,500m in the Tien Shan (Dement'ev & Gladkov 1954).

Outside the breeding season it occupies a much wider habitat range and is no longer restricted to reeds. On passage, it occurs in damp herbaceous growth and scrub, hedges and thickets, fields of beans or roots, gardens, suburbs and parks. In Africa, on migration and in winter quarters, it frequents green thicket, tall grass and herbs, and reeds along river courses and lake shores. It is commonly found away from water in secondary bush, acacia, *Lantana* scrub, forest edge and garden hedges. Marshy habitats such as papyrus or *Typha* are used in some areas, but these tend to be avoided. It typically occurs below 1,400m, but winters up to 2,000m in Ethiopia and Kenya.

The race *avicenniae* appears to be confined to mangroves during the breeding season, but its preference at other times of the year is unknown.

BEHAVIOUR Often retiring and difficult to observe, but not particularly shy and will react inquisitively to disturbance with frequent angry calls. On the breeding grounds it is usually less demonstrative than Marsh Warbler. Males raise the fore-crown feathers when excited or angry and occasionally flick the wings and tail. It frequently sidles up and down reeds, both when foraging and singing and climbs easily with feet on separate stems, hopping from one to the next. On the ground, it hops and shuffles, often with both the head and tail raised, thus adopting the 'banana' posture – and birds on migration, feeding in the tree canopy, often also do this. Flight is fast and confident, the bird usually moving low and directly with the tail fanned and slightly drooping, before disappearing into cover. But in calm conditions, males may land on a reed top and begin to sing. When foraging, it moves purposefully among reeds, often in a near horizontal posture, but with tail typically held just below the wingtips. When feeding within bushes and thickets, it appears active and less heavy than when foraging in reedbeds. It pursues and takes insects from vegetation, sometimes leaping up or hovering and frequently chases and snaps at aerial prey and makes flycatching sallies.

Males sing strongly on arrival on breeding territories, typically from a reed head. Here they adopt an alert or upright attitude with the throat ruffled and conspicuous and the fore-crown feathers raised. They tend to have two or three main song posts within taller or thicker clumps of reed. Unpaired birds maintain intense and persistent song from before dawn and throughout most of the morning. Song is then resumed again in the evening and a few sing throughout most of the night. This 'advertising song' continues after pairing, but less intensely, with most activity confined to dawn and dusk. It is heard intermittently throughout summer, with a brief resurgence in July before second broods.

A shorter 'territorial song' may be given from low in the reeds, typically in response to intrusion by a rival male. Females may also give brief snatches of song when the nest is approached, or in support of the male during territorial disputes.

On the African wintering grounds, birds are usually secretive and remain within dense low cover except during short active periods at dawn and before dusk. Quiet song can be heard frequently from November onwards and often continues through the morning into the hot hours. This increases in volume and intensity towards the time of spring departure. Birds remain remarkably faithful to small, overlapping feeding territories and may occupy these year after year. They also defend temporary territories on passage.

BREEDING HABITS Males are usually monogamous and often pair with a mate from the previous season. They are loosely colonial and nests are often grouped together, sometimes only a few metres apart. Territories are small, typically only 300–400m² and tend to become smaller as more birds arrive through the season. Breeding densities may exceed 1,000 pairs/km² in well-grown *Phragmites* and tend to be higher in smaller reedbeds (Cramp 1992).

The first males reach the breeding marshes before females, and older adults of both sexes arrive before young birds. Most birds return to the same reedbed each year, but move territory slightly. A proportion of surviving young birds returns to the natal site. Males advertise their presence with persistent song and usually pair up within a few days of arrival. The female selects a site, then builds

and lines the nest in about a week. It is usually built in *Phragmites* reeds above water, but sometimes in osiers, or over dry ground in tall vegetation such as willowherb. It is typically placed 0.5–1.5m above the water, among old reed stems or a mixture of old and new. It is a deep cup woven around a few strong stems, composed of grasses, reed stems and leaves, sometimes with sedges, moss, plant down and spiders' web. It is lined with finer material such as dead reed heads, wool and feathers.

The clutch size is 3–5 eggs (occasionally 2–7). Incubation, mainly by the female, lasts 9–12 days. Both sexes care for the young, but the female broods while the male does most of the feeding. Almost all food is collected outside the territory, birds travelling up to 150m from the nest. The young fledge after 10–12 days (sometimes 9–13). They become independent after another 10–14 days, but then tend to remain in the natal reedbed for some weeks.

Egg laying takes place in W and C Europe mainly between late May and mid August; in NW Africa between late April and early June. Double broods are common, the second nest usually being built close to the first.

On the Sudan coast, *avicenniae* is thought to breed during April–June. The nest is a deep cup of seaweed, which may contain feathers, woven to the fork of a slender mangrove stem, 0.2m to 1.5m above the sea (GN *in litt.*).

DISTRIBUTION
A. s. scirpaceus **Breeding** Breeds commonly from the Atlantic coasts of Portugal, Spain and France and throughout W Europe north to S Scotland and S Scandinavia, extending to *c.* 65°N along the Baltic coasts of Sweden and Finland. It is widespread but more patchy and localised through S Europe and the Mediterranean region, including Corsica, Sardinia, Sicily, Crete and W Turkey. Its range also extends into N Africa where birds assigned to this race breed in Morocco south to the Middle Atlas, along the Atlantic coast to Oued Massa and in some Saharan oases; also in coastal N Algeria, in N Tunisia at Lake Ichkeul and probably in N Libya. It is common and widespread throughout C and E Europe, from the Baltic countries to the W and N shores of the Black Sea, east to the Sea of Azov and the Don River in Ukraine. In Russia, the northern limit lies at *c.* 60°N in regions near the Baltic and *c.* 56°N near Moscow. The eastern limit is unclear, but is not far to the east of Moscow, possibly reaching the middle Volga River.

The commonest reedbed bird throughout most of its range. Major population centres are associated with the huge reedbeds in the deltas of the Rhine, Rhone, Po and Danube Rivers, extensive shallow lakes including Neuseidlersee in Austria and Feharto in Hungary and the Dutch polders. The European population has been estimated at two to four million pairs (Hagemeijer & Blair 1997). Its range has expanded during the last few decades, especially in S Scandinavia, and numbers have increased significantly in NE Germany, N Poland and the Baltic States, as well as in Holland, due partly to reclamation of the polders. Numbers breeding in Ireland remain very small.

Small birds breeding in N and W Morocco are partially resident (J. Cortes *in litt;*, Jiguet *et al.* 2010). Birds in song in Libya during January and February, on the coast and at inland sites such as Houn and Jaghbub (M. Smart *in litt.*) involve local breeders, but appear to include African Reed Warblers at some localities (Hering *et al.* 2010).

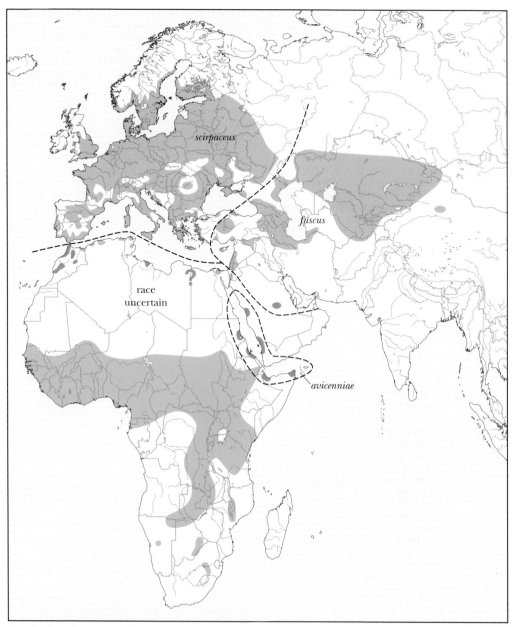

Eurasian Reed Warbler. Breeding range and winter distribution.

Non-breeding This race winters across the Sahel, Soudan and Guinea savanna zones of W and C Africa, from Senegal, Guinea and Liberia east through the Niger River delta, Ghana and Nigeria to S Chad and at least C and SW Sudan. It occurs south to Gabon and the northern edge of the Congo basin, but there is no convincing evidence that it reaches equatorial E or S Africa.

***A. s. fuscus* Breeding** Breeds almost entirely within Asia. In C Turkey, it breeds in the Goksu River delta and inland lakes to the north, then extends locally through E Turkey and the S Caucasus region to the W Caspian Sea coasts in Azerbaijan and Dagestan in Russia. Substantial

numbers breed along the Lower Volga River, the lower and middle Ural River to the region of Orenburg and Ural'sk in Russia, and the Ilek River in NW Kazakhstan, north to Sol'Iletsk.

Distribution within the steppe grasslands of C Asia is determined largely by availability of *Phragmites* reed stands. It breeds throughout Kazakhstan and is particularly numerous in wetlands across the north, including the region of Astana. In the more arid south, it is restricted to occasional lakes, but is common at Lake Balkhash and along the Ili River basin to Panfilov, Lake Alakol and the Zaisan depression. Further south and west, it breeds in the lower Tien Shan near Almaty, in the Tashkent region and along the Amu Darya in Uzbekistan and the Tedzhen and Morghab Rivers in Turkmenistan. It ranges east to the Xinjiang Uygur Autonomous Region in NW China, where it is known from Kashi on the western edge of the Taklamakan desert and Bosten Hu in the Tarim Basin.

Birds currently treated as *fuscus*, but distinctly smaller than those of C Asia, breed locally in the Middle East, in the Nile delta, Israel and Jordan and also at Riyadh, Saudi Arabia, where birds singing in January suggest that the population there is at least partly resident.

Non-breeding This race winters mainly in E Africa, from C and S Sudan and W and C Ethiopia to E DR Congo, Uganda, W and C Kenya and N and C Tanzania. Small numbers occur in SE DR Congo, Zambia, Malawi, N and E Botswana south to Francistown, and the Kavango and Bushmanland regions of N Namibia. It has also reached Windhoek in W Namibia and Gauteng Province, South Africa. Birds with short wing lengths, perhaps Middle East breeders, occur in autumn in coastal Sudan but do not reach Uganda or Kenya (G. Nikolaus & DJP).

A. s. avicenniae A resident or short distance migrant. Known from coastal mangroves in N Somalia (at Zeila, Garas Wadi and Alula), Eritrea (at Massawa, Zula and Scek Said Islands), Sudan (at Suakin), N Yemen (at Al'Urj) and W Saudi Arabia (at Yanbu-al-Sanaiyah and Shuqaia).

MOVEMENTS The nominate race shows a migratory divide within Europe. Western and northern populations move southwest in autumn through Iberia and Morocco. Ringing has shown that these birds eventually winter across W Africa east to Nigeria. Populations from the Czech Republic, Hungary and SE Europe migrate through the E Mediterranean and Egypt and presumably winter from Chad eastwards. In Britain and N Europe, adults begin to leave the breeding grounds in mid to late July and most have departed by mid to late August. The main passage of young birds lasts from early August to early September, but many remain within or close to their breeding range until late September, with stragglers remaining into early October. Passage peaks in Portugal in mid September and funnels through Morocco during September and October, with smaller numbers passing through Algeria. Passage through Cyprus and Egypt takes place mainly between late August and mid October, with late birds occurring into early November. Birds reach Senegal from mid September onwards and passage continues here to mid November. Arrival in Mali takes place during September and October. Movements into and through NE Nigeria and Chad occur between late September and early November, involving populations of unknown origin. Many birds apparently moult at stop-over sites in the northern tropics before moving further south in November and December.

Most birds depart from the W African wintering sites in late March or early April. There is a strong passage through Senegal from March to May and in N Nigeria and Chad from late February to mid May, peaking in late April. Spring passage is conspicuous throughout the whole of N Africa from late March to mid May, with many birds arriving in Saharan oases, indicating that migration takes place on a broader front than in autumn. Birds return to breeding grounds in SW Europe mainly in April, to Britain and NW Europe between late April and mid May and Scandinavia between mid May and early June.

Southward passage of *fuscus* from Kazakhstan com-

mences in late July and continues throughout August and September, with stragglers to mid October. Late birds linger in Uzbekistan to late October and the S Caucasus to early November. It is a common migrant through the S Caspian Sea area from August to October. Movement across Arabia spans late July to mid November, with the main passage in coastal Sudan between late August and mid October. To the south, arrival in Uganda and Kenya is much later. The earliest birds appear in late October and passage then continues into January. Local wintering birds arrive mainly in December and January. This delay indicates a lengthy stopover for many of these birds in Sudan or Ethiopia. Birds reach the southern extremity of the wintering range in Botswana between November and January and remain there to the end of March (Tyler & Tyler 1997). Wintering birds also remain in Zambia to late March or early April and in Uganda up to early or mid April. Northward passage occurs through C Kenya during April and early May and through C and E Ethiopia from mid April to late May. In Arabia and the Middle East, local breeding birds are already present in mid March, but a protracted passage lasts from March to early June. Larger *fuscus* pass through Turkey and Cyprus throughout April and the first arrivals appear in the lower Caucasus in late April. Central Asian breeders pass through Uzbekistan in April and May and most males are settled on breeding territories in N Kazakhstan by mid May. Passage in E Kazakhstan is rather later, beginning in late April, peaking in mid May and continuing to early June.

Warmly toned birds with long wing lengths winter alongside typical *fuscus* in E Africa. Such birds migrate in spring through Arabia and through Kuwait (D. J. Kelly *in litt.*) and occur in autumn on the Azerbaijan Caspian Sea coast (DJP pers. obs.). Considered here within *fuscus*, these birds presumably breed in the Caucasus region or around the Caspian Sea coasts further north.

E African ringed birds have been recovered as follows: Sudan (October) to Iran (May), Ethiopia (April) to Kuwait (September), Kenya (January) to Saudi Arabia (September) and Kenya (April) to Astrakhan, Russia (May).

A. s. avicenniae is a partial migrant, which fattens and departs from the Sudan coast during August, after breeding (GN *in litt.*). Its whereabouts outside the breeding season are unknown.

Vagrancy Outside the breeding range, vagrants have reached Iceland on 13 occasions to the end of 2002. Birds resembling *fuscus* have been reported from W Europe but no claims have proved to be acceptable. As a vagrant, *fuscus* occurred near Nanjing in Jiangsu Province, China, on 9 October 1921 (Kolthoff 1932).

DESCRIPTION *A. s. scirpaceus*

Plumage – Adult fresh (December to March) Forehead to nape warm olive-brown with a slight tawny tinge. Supercilium buff, narrow but well marked in front of eye, linking with narrow creamy white eye-ring; barely extending behind eye. Lores dark greyish olive, mottled buff, forming dark triangle in front of eye. Ear-coverts warm olive-brown, rather paler than crown, with fine buff streaks. Mantle and scapulars to uppertail-coverts warm olive-brown, mantle uniform with crown, rump paler with a stronger tawny or cinnamon tinge. Chin and throat white with slight buff tinge. Upper breast washed warm buff. Lower breast and belly white, with fainter buff wash. Sides of breast and flanks warm brownish-buff; undertail-coverts pale warm buff. Lesser and median coverts olive-brown, concolorous with scapulars. Greater coverts olive-brown with brighter tawny-brown fringes. Primary coverts and alula dark grey-brown, finely fringed light olive-brown. Tertials dark grey-brown, outer edges and tips with broad, light tawny-brown or cinnamon-brown fringes, not sharply defined. Primaries and secondaries dark grey-brown with narrow light olive-brown edges. Primary tips with distinct but narrow grey-buff fringes. Underwing-coverts pale warm buff. Tail feathers dark grey-brown, outer webs narrowly fringed olive-brown, outer feathers with narrow but usually poorly defined pale fringe around tip.

Worn adult (June to September) Upperparts duller brown, less olive, often with a greyer tone. Supercilium whiter. Underparts whiter, with buff at sides more restricted. Wing feathers already worn by June, with pale primary tips lost, becoming bleached and abraded by early autumn, with pale greyish edges.

Juvenile/first-winter Top of head and upperparts warm olive-brown or tawny-brown, becoming cinnamon-brown on rump and uppertail-coverts; slightly brighter above than adult. Supercilium and eye-ring warm buff, rather less well defined than in adult. Side of head and entire underparts washed warm buff, whitish areas restricted to throat and centre of belly. Fringes of flight feathers, tertials, wing-coverts and tail feathers brighter than in adult, more rust-brown or cinnamon-brown.

Bare Parts Upper mandible dark olive-brown, dark grey-brown or blackish brown, with pale flesh-brown or yellowish flesh cutting edges. Lower mandible pale flesh-brown or yellowish flesh, usually becoming dark greyish towards tip. Mouth orange or orange-red in adults, yellow or yellow-orange in first autumn birds; young birds have two black tongue spots, usually persisting until September or October. Tarsi and toes of adults dark greenish or greyish brown, becoming light brown or flesh-brown in older birds; in first autumn birds dark greenish grey to greyish brown, rarely light brown. Soles dull yellow to orange-yellow; claws dark grey-brown or brownish black above, contrasting with yellowish underside. Iris in adults dark brown or olive-brown, occasionally chestnut-brown; dark grey-brown in first autumn birds.

IN HAND CHARACTERS
Measurements

A. s. scirpaceus

	Male	Female
Wing	64–69 (66.7; 43)	63–69 (65.8; 28)
Tail	49–55 (51.4; 36)	48–54 (50.7; 21)
Bill	15.5–18 (17.2; 36)	15.5–17.5 (16.7; 26)
Tarsus	21.5–24.5 (22.9; 61)	21.5–24 (22.6; 37)

(W Europe, mainly Britain and Netherlands; includes data from Cramp 1992)

Sexes combined:
Tail/wing ratio: 75–80% (77%; 29)
Bill width: 3.7–4.2 (3.9; 28)
Hind claw: 5.6–7.2 (6.5; 28)
Tail graduation: 3–7 (5.5; 50)
Juvenile wing averages *c.* 1mm shorter than adult, tail *c.* 2mm shorter.

Iberian birds are smaller than those from elsewhere in W Europe, and Moroccan breeders are smaller still, while those from Scandinavia and E Europe are larger, see Table 6 (and **Appendix 2**).

A. s. fuscus Birds from C Asia and E African wintering areas: *wing*, ♂ 66–72 (67.9; 25), ♀ 65–72 (67.1; 16); (sexes combined) *tail* 49–56 (52.7; 32); *bill* 16.6–18.7 (17.6; 34); *tarsus* 21–24 (22.9; 32); bill width 3.8–4.3 (4.0; 19); hind claw 6.2–8.0 (6.9; 17).

These birds average larger than any European populations, but the wing length of typical *fuscus* and 'warmer *fuscus*' is similar (See Appendix 2). SW Asian breeding birds are shorter winged, however (see also Morgan 1998).

A. s. avicenniae (sexes combined, n = 19): *wing* 56–62 (58.8); *tail* 46–51 (48.0); *bill* 15.0–17.0 (15.8); *tarsus* 19.5–22.5 (20.7); hind claw 5.5–6.7 (6.2).

All measurements smaller than in *A. s. scirpaceus*.

Table 6. Wing length variation within Palearctic breeding populations of Eurasian Reed Warbler, based on live measurements of adults, sexes combined.

S Spain, breeding	60–68 (63.2; 141)	Grupo Ornitológico del Estreco, *in litt.*
Suffolk, England, July–August	62–70 (65.9; 693)	DJP unpublished data
Germany and Austria	63–71 (66.6; 104)	Leisler & Winkler 1977
C Sweden, June–July	62–72 (67.6; 1,011)	B. Neilsen & SB unpublished data
Azerbaijan, August	63–74 (68.5; 140)	DJP & GN unpublished data
E Kazakhstan, August	67–72 (69.2; 26)	DJP & GN unpublished data

Structure

A. s. scirpaceus

Wing formula (Cramp 1992):

p1/pc	p2	p3e	p4	p5	p6	p7	p10
(2)–3	1–3	wp	1–3	3.5–5	5–8	8–11	12–16

Wing rather long and pointed, p1 minute. Wing point p3; p2 = p3/4–4/5 (5); p3 emarginated. Notch on inner web of p2 10–13.5mm from tip in adults, 9–11.5mm in juveniles; falling at (p8/9) p9–ss tips in 61 adults; at (p7/8) p8–ss tips in 144 juveniles. (DJP)

Figure 63. Wing of Eurasian Reed Warbler *A. s. scirpaceus*.

Tail medium length, slightly rounded.
Bill straight, flattened at base; narrower than in Marsh Warbler, but broader and flatter than in Sedge Warbler; sides straight or slightly concave (Fig. 61).
Tarsi quite strong, but marginally more slender than in Marsh Warbler; toes and claws slightly longer than Marsh.

A. s. fuscus. Wing similar to nominate *scirpaceus* (Fig. 63), but p2 often slightly shorter (= p(3/4) 4–5 (5/6) in E Africa), and only p3 emarginated in C Asian birds, but also tip of p4 in some small Middle East birds.

A. s. avicenniae. Differs from other races in having wing rounded, with wing point at p3–4; p2 = (p5/6) 6–7 (7/8); p3–4 emarginated.

Figure 64. Wing of Eurasian Reed Warbler *A. s. avicenniae.*

Recognition European birds are rather uniform warm brown above and washed warm buff below. Asian birds, adult and first-winter, are paler, more olive-brown above and whiter below, but usually show warmly tinged uppertail-coverts and a greyer head, so their upperparts are usually less uniform than in either Marsh Warbler or Blyth's Reed Warbler.

In W Europe, smaller birds (with wing < 63mm) fall below the range of Marsh Warbler. Conversely, in Asia, most birds (with wing > 66mm) fall above the usual range of Blyth's Reed; and all have longer wings and longer bills than Paddyfield Warbler. Eurasian Reed is distinguishable from Blyth's by the longer p2 (usually > p5) and by lack of emargination on p4 (except in some small Middle East *fuscus*) (Fig. 57).

Adults and most first-winter birds are separable from Marsh by the position of the p2 notch falling below the tip of p9. Other useful structural features are the slightly longer, narrower bill of Eurasian Reed (a lower ratio of width to length) and its longer toes (see under Marsh Warbler for measurement details). In Eurasian Reed (but not in Marsh) the claw of the extended inner toe usually projects beyond the end of the middle toe.

The Red Sea breeding form *A. s. avicenniae* (Mangrove Reed Warbler) is closer in colour to both *A. s. fuscus* and Marsh Warbler, but easily separated from both by its shorter, more rounded wing (p2 usually < p6). It also lacks the rufescent upperparts of nominate Eurasian Reed and the nearest African Reed Warbler races *cinnamomeus* and *suahelicus*.

Ageing In early autumn, young birds have fresh body plumage and unworn primary tips. They are easily distinguished from adults with the whole plumage worn and primary tips abraded, or with partly new body plumage contrasting with worn greyish wing and tail feathers. By late autumn, unmoulted *fuscus* in Africa are difficult to age, but the primaries of young birds tend to be less badly abraded than those of adults. Birds with residual tongue spots are likely to be first-winter, while those with brighter brown or reddish brown eyes and/or pale brown legs are likely to be adults. Ageing after the complete moult may depend on bare part colours and must often be tentative. Skull ossification in young birds is incomplete until at least December.

Weight

A. s. scirpaceus and *A. s. fuscus*: range 7.5–23.5g. Typical lean weight 9.5–12g. Fattening migrants frequently reach 14–16g, less commonly 16–18g. Autumn weights in S

Turkey and spring weights in N Nigeria have exceeded 22g (RV & WP unpublished data, Fry *et al.* 1967). Some depleted autumn migrants in NE Sudan weighed below 8g (GN & DJP unpublished data). Small Moroccan birds weighed 7–11.5g (8.8; 78) (PP, unpublished data).

A. s. avicenniae: 7–10.5g (8.0; 20) (Ash *et al.* 1989).

GEOGRAPHIC VARIATION Variation is complex, involving size, coloration and, to a lesser extent, wing structure. Size tends to increase across the range from south and west to north and east, while colour saturation decreases from west to east. In Europe, coloration of nominate *scirpaceus* remains practically constant, but there are significant size differences. The birds from Iberia are small, while those from Sweden and Ukraine are distinctly larger. Partially resident birds breeding in Morocco are smaller still, and show a slightly more rounded wing (Jiguet *et al.* 2010). These may deserve recognition as a distinct race (see **Measurements**).

Compared with nominate *scirpaceus*, typical *fuscus* breeding from the Caspian Sea eastwards is paler, more olivaceous above, with any warmth restricted to the rump and uppertail-coverts, while the underparts are whiter with the buff wash reduced. But this is not the complete picture and variation in Asia is complex and not fully understood. Within the range of *fuscus* three colour variations, or morphs, can be recognised. In addition to typical *fuscus*, many E African wintering birds are as warmly coloured as nominate birds wintering in W Africa, yet exhibit the longer wing length and prominent pale tail feather tips associated with typically coloured *fuscus*. Such birds have also been noted on spring passage in Kuwait (D. J. Kelly *in litt.*) and in both spring and autumn on the Caspian Sea coast in Azerbaijan (DJP & GN). They would appear to originate from the western limit of the range of *fuscus* in E Turkey, the Caucasus or the W Caspian Sea area, rather than from Russia or Ukraine further to the west. Some wintering birds in Africa are distinctly greyer brown above than typical *fuscus* and still whiter below and lack any hint of the warmth on the rump. Their origin is unknown but presumed to be from the eastern part of the range. Intermediates between these three colour types have been noted.

Birds from the Caspian Sea region are similar in wing length to those of E Kazakhstan, but slightly larger than nominate *scirpaceus* on the Black Sea coast. They are also distinctly larger than *fuscus* populations breeding in S Israel and Arabia. Slight differences in wing structure are also apparent. Birds of the race *fuscus* from Kazakhstan tend to have the second primary (p2) marginally shorter than in European birds, usually < p4 and quite frequently = p5. The shorter winged SW Asian breeders reportedly have a still shorter second primary (p2) and p4 often emarginated. In Arabia, these birds appear duller olive-brown and more worn in spring than longer-winged *fuscus* passage birds, indicating that they have an earlier winter moult (GN *in litt.*).

Thus, racial boundaries may need redefining. Typical *fuscus* as recognised within its traditional range cannot always be differentiated by size or even by colour from nominate *scirpaceus*. Furthermore, the greyer brown Asian birds presently included within *fuscus* are as different in colour from typical *fuscus* as the latter are from nominate *scirpaceus*. These variations may involve distinct colour morphs or merely represent a west to east cline of decreasing colour saturation. Separation of the smaller SW Asian birds from C Asian *fuscus* appears to be warranted.

A. s. scirpaceus (NW Africa, Europe and W Turkey to the Middle Volga River) Described above.

A. s. fuscus (Asia from C and E Turkey, Middle East to C Asia) When fresh, typical C Asian *fuscus*, both adult and first-winter, lack the warm olive-brown crown and mantle of nominate *scirpaceus*. The upperparts are rather paler olive-brown, usually with a faint buffish or ochreous wash and with a greyish tinge to the nape. The rump and uppertail-coverts are paler ochreous or tawny-brown, contrasting distinctly with the mantle. The head pattern resembles that of nominate *scirpaceus* although colour tones are slightly different, with a pale buff supercilium and light olive-brown ear-coverts. The underparts are paler and lack the warmer tones of the nominate form. The chin and throat are off-white, the upper breast lightly washed pale buff. The side of the breast, flanks and undertail-coverts are pale buff, the lower breast and belly whitish. The fringes to the wing-coverts and tertials are light olive-brown or buffy brown, matching the mantle and scapulars and paler than the warm olive-brown to tawny-brown fringes of nominate *scirpaceus*. Unworn birds in spring often retain conspicuous pale greyish primary tips. Typical *fuscus* also shows greyish white tips to at least the outer three pairs of rectrices, that on the outermost (t6) extending around the distal border of the inner web. There appear to be no consistent differences in bare part colour between nominate *scirpaceus* and *fuscus*.

A. s. avicenniae (Coasts of Sudan, Eritrea, SW Saudi Arabia, N Yemen and N Somalia) Resembles *fuscus*. In fresh plumage (November), the upperparts are olive-brown, slightly paler on the top of the head and with a tawny tinge confined to the rump and uppertail-coverts. A narrow buff supercilium extends back to the eye. The underparts are off-white, with the breast washed creamy buff and the sides of the breast and flanks buff. The fringes of the greater coverts and tertials are olive-buff. In worn plumage (July–August), it is paler above, with a greyish cast and shows a whiter supercilium. The underparts are creamy white with a slight buff suffusion on the flanks. Smaller than the Palearctic races, with a more rounded wing.

TAXONOMY AND SYSTEMATICS Comparison of mtDNA sequences has indicated a divergence between birds from Europe and C Asia and it has been proposed that *scirpaceus* and *fuscus* be treated as separate species (Sangster *et al.* 1998). But plumage and morphological variation within Eurasian Reed Warbler is complex and partly clinal. Until variation within *fuscus* is better understood and fully supported by DNA evidence throughout its currently defined range, its treatment as a distinct species is premature and unwarranted. For the relationship with African Reed Warbler, see under that species. The recent discovery of short-winged reed warbler populations in Libya, some with mtDNA matching *A. baeticatus* but others matching *A. s. avicenniae* (Hering *et al.* 2010), would support the argument for treating Eurasian and African Reed Warblers as conspecific.

▲ Adult *A. s. scirpaceus*, Suffolk, England, May. Typical adult. Note contrast between warm brown mantle and slightly paler rump and uppertail-coverts (James Kennerley).

▲ Adult *A. s. scirpaceus*, Netherlands, June. This rather grey individual still retains the contrasting warmer rump and uppertail-coverts. Birds such as this can be mistaken for *fuscus* (Ran Schols).

▲ First-winter *A. s. scirpaceus*, France, September. Slightly warmer and brighter than adult, and shows less contrast between mantle and warmer rump and uppertail-coverts (Aurélien Audevard).

▲ First-winter *A. s. scirpaceus*, Italy, September. Slightly more warmly toned individual, aged as first-winter by fresh plumage and grey-brown iris (Daniele Occhiato).

▲ First-winter, Larache, Morocco, September. Racial affinity of N African breeders not fully established. When fresh, shows distinctive buff wash to supercilium, side of head and underparts (Pascal Provost).

▲ *A. s. fuscus*, March. Differs from nominate by colder, greyer upperparts and flanks, contrasting warmer rump and uppertail-coverts, colder tone to underparts and often a more conspicuous white eye-ring (Iva Hristova-Nikolova).

▲ Adult *A. s. fuscus*, Kuwait, March. Complete moult is later than in nominate race and, like Marsh Warbler, usually retains pale primary tips into early summer (Michael Pope).

▲ First-winter *A. s. fuscus*, first-winter, Israel, September. Although slightly warmer than adults, young *fuscus* are greyer than the nominate form and lack the brighter olive tone typical of Marsh Warbler (Lior Kislev).

▲ Adult *A. s. fuscus*, Goksu Delta, Turkey, May. A particularly warmly toned bird with fresh primaries. Such birds, with wing lengths typical *fuscus* and often a late-winter complete moult, occur regularly in E Africa. Although treated here within *fuscus*, they may represent a link between nominate *scirpaceus* and typical *fuscus* (Peter Kennerley).

▶ Adult *A. s. fuscus*, Israel, May. Birds breeding in the Middle East resemble typical *fuscus* in overall grey-brown coloration but are distinctly smaller. Probably moults earlier than central Asian breeders and appears heavily abraded in May (Amir Ben Dov).

AFRICAN REED WARBLER
Acrocephalus baeticatus   **Plate 21**

Sylvia baeticatus Vieillot, 1817. *Nouv. Dict. Hist. Nat.*, nouv. éd. 11: 195; based on 'L'Isabelle' of Levaillant, 1802, *Hist. Nat. Oiseaux Afrique* 3: 63, plate 121, figure 2. Knysna district, Cape Province.

A resident or short distance migrant which breeds in wetland and other moist habitats in sub-Saharan Africa. Polytypic. Five races are included here; some authorities recognise others.

A. s. baeticatus (Vieillot 1817). S, C and E South Africa to Zimbabwe and E Botswana.

A. s. cinnamomeus Reichenow 1908. S, E and W Africa from S Zambia, Malawi and inland Mozambique, north to S Sudan, S Somalia and Ethiopia and west to Nigeria and N Niger.

A. s. suahelicus Grote 1926. Coastal areas of Tanzania, Mozambique and E South Africa, associated with mangroves.

A. s. hallae White 1960. W South Africa to Namibia, NW Botswana, SW Zambia and (probably this race) S Angola.

A. s. guiersi Colston & Morel 1982. Senegal and (perhaps this race) Mali (Niger delta).

IDENTIFICATION Length 11.5–13cm. Wing 52–63mm. Tail/wing 77–88%

A rather small, slim warbler, appearing warm brown above and buffy below with a whitish throat and belly. The S African race *baeticatus* is strikingly similar in plumage to the nominate race of Eurasian Reed Warbler, but the widespread C and E African race *cinnamomeus* differs more substantially in size, structure and coloration. Sexes alike.

Structure Southern African birds are similar in size to Eurasian Reed Warbler, but C and E African birds average about 10% smaller. The attenuated head profile, with low sloping forehead and a longish and fairly narrow bill, are like those of Eurasian Reed. The main distinction is the much shorter, more rounded wing, with wing point usually at p3–5 and with both p3 and p4 (sometimes also p5) emarginated. Primary projection is only about 40% (compared with over 70% in Eurasian Reed) with up to six closely bunched primary tips visible. The legs are rather slender as in Eurasian Reed, but the claws are typically slightly larger and stronger. The small race *cinnamomeus* has the shortest, most rounded wing. It also has shorter undertail-coverts, covering just the basal half of the tail and this gives it a longer tailed appearance. The east coast race *suahelicus* has a larger bill than other African forms.

Plumage and bare parts The nominate race *baeticatus* appears very similar to the nominate form of Eurasian Reed Warbler. The two are almost identical in appearance, sharing warmly tinged brown upperparts and fringes and edges of the closed wing feathers, warm buffy brown flanks, underparts that are buff-washed and a whitish throat and belly centre. The face pattern, with a narrow but distinct buffy supercilium in front of the eye, is also like that of Eurasian Reed. Birds originating from SW Africa are paler and slightly greyer, while the east coast race *suahelicus* is more deeply rufescent. The widespread *cinnamomeus* is the brightest race, with rusty or cinnamon-brown upperparts and flanks and is washed rich buff on the breast.

The dark brown to blackish bill shows a pale flesh to yellowish lower mandible that darkens at the sides towards

the tip. The legs vary from greyish or greenish brown to pale brown.

SIMILAR SPECIES It occurs sympatrically with wintering Eurasian Reed Warblers throughout much of sub-Saharan Africa and overlaps with migrant Marsh Warblers in eastern and southern parts of the continent. In swamp edges and marshes it often occurs with both Lesser Swamp and Greater Swamp Warblers.

Eurasian Reed Warbler of the nominate race wintering in W Africa closely resembles the local races of African Reed and cannot be safely separated using plumage features alone. Its much longer primary projection (*c.* 70% of the tertial length) provides the only reliable means of distinguishing them, so separation relies upon obtaining a good view of the wing point. In E and S Africa the race *fuscus* is larger, paler and less brightly coloured than the African Reed races it is likely to meet.

Marsh Warbler should be readily separable from the more warmly coloured African Reed by its olive tone, larger size and much longer pointed wing. But difficulty can be experienced with birds moulting on the S African wintering grounds.

Lesser Swamp Warbler and **Greater Swamp Warbler** are unlikely to be confused with African Reed Warbler. They are respectively about 30% and 50% larger and much heavier bodied. Both have longer bills, longer, more graduated tails and stronger blackish legs.

VOICE African Reed Warbler and Eurasian Reed Warbler appear to be vocally identical. No differences in song were found between nominate *baeticatus* from S Africa and the race *guiersi* from Senegal, nor between these races and Eurasian Reed Warblers from Belgium (Dowsett-Lemaire & Dowsett 1987). All three forms responded equally well to playback of any combination of songs. Birds of the race *cinnamomeus* from Kenya and *suahelicus* from Pemba Island also give songs which are apparently identical to that of Eurasian Reed Warbler. For details of the song, see under Eurasian Reed Warbler. No differences in the call have been recognised.

Part of song of African Reed Warbler, recorded within breeding range of *A. b. cinnamomeus*, Athi River, Kenya, May. (David Pearson)

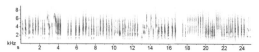

Part of song of African Reed Warbler, recorded within breeding range of *A. b. guiersi*, NW Senegal, February (Chappuis 2000)

Part of song of African Reed Warbler, recorded within breeding range of *A. b. baeticatus*, Ceres, Western Cape, South Africa, September. (Gibbon 2003)

MOULT The full moult takes place in adults shortly after breeding, during October and November in N Nigeria and April to June in Namibia and Botswana. However, many South African birds migrate north before moulting and wing moult has been recorded in birds wintering in Zambia during July–August. Juveniles appear to moult completely, soon after the adults. In S Malawi, non-breeding adults arriving in April and May retain old primaries or have suspended moult, with just the inner primaries replaced, and most complete moult by October. Unmoulted juveniles that arrived in Malawi in June and July mostly completed moult between October and December, and all appeared to complete moult before departure (Hanmer 1988).

HABITAT Breeds in a variety of wet or moist habitats but tends to avoid more extensive, deeply flooded reeds and swamp. In Senegal and Nigeria, it occupies reedbeds dominated by *Typha*, while in E and C Africa, *cinnamomeus* occurs in marshes with high grasses, swamp edges, patches of *Typha* and sedge and lush thickets. In S Africa, nominate *baeticatus* breeds in the edges of *Phragmites* reed-beds, in thin-stemmed *Cyperus* sedge mixed with *Typha*, scrub and *Typha* over mud, tufts of *Panicum* or thin reed and scrub along river banks, and small patches of reed at farm dams. It also utilises dense moist thickets and tall grass far from water. It occurs in drier places on migration and in winter, including sugarcane fields, gardens and wooded areas. Wintering birds in S Zambia occur in thickets of *Acacia*, *Lantana* and *Rhus* with patches of tall grass and reed, the same habitat as that occupied by migrant Eurasian Reed Warblers during the austral summer (Dowsett-Lemaire & Dowsett 1987). On the E African coast, *suahelicus* is typically found in mangroves, but also occurs in bushes and large trees on Pemba.

BEHAVIOUR Essentially like that of Eurasian Reed Warbler. Usually seen singly, in pairs, or in small family parties. It forages mainly at mid height or low down among reeds, or in thick grass and bushes and is typically difficult to see. It tends to feed nearer the reed bases than Lesser Swamp Warbler. It is reluctant to fly and usually does so low and over a short distance. Song is usually given from concealment. Males produce strong and prolonged song after arrival in South African breeding sites. They continue to sing after pairing, but with a decrease in both the frequency and length of the song bursts. Birds wintering in Zambia give subdued song, but this becomes quite loud by September, after completion of moult.

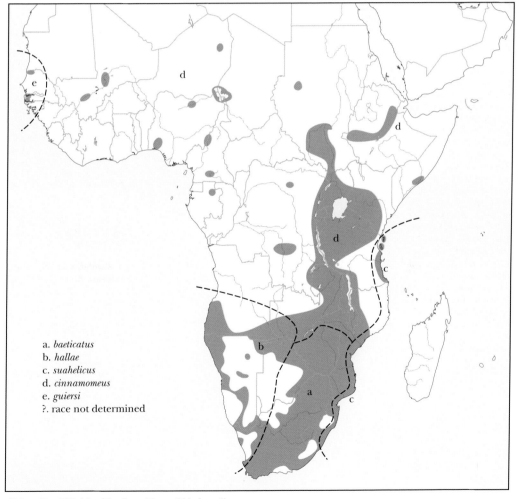

a. *baeticatus*
b. *hallae*
c. *suahelicus*
d. *cinnamomeus*
e. *guiersi*
?. race not determined

African Reed Warbler. Mostly resident within breeding range.

BREEDING HABITS Monogamous and territorial, but nests may be less than 50m apart in South Africa. In Namibia, territories averaging 350m² were strongly defended against intruders, but over 10% of pairs had one unrelated helper (Eising *et al.* 2001). It is generally less restricted to *Phragmites* reedbeds than Eurasian Reed Warbler and often flies to feed in dry herbaceous growth and low trees outside the territory.

The nest in South Africa is bound to upright stems of reeds, sedges or grasses, or to the leaves and flowers of large sedges or drooping willow branches, usually 0.6–1.5m up. It is a deep cup of grass and reeds lined with fine grasses. Clutch size in S Africa and in Senegal is 2–3 eggs, rarely four. Incubation lasts 12–14 days in S Africa. The young are fed and brooded by both parents and sometimes by helpers (Eising *et al.* 2001) and the fledging period is about 12–13 days. In S Africa, the breeding season extends from September to February or March, with egg laying mainly between October and December. Laying has been recorded in Zambia in February, in W Kenya in January, in Darfur in September–October and in Senegal in June–July.

DISTRIBUTION Rather common throughout southern Africa north to the Zambezi River, being absent only in the Kalahari. It is local and patchy elsewhere and in W Africa and the northern tropics is apparently confined to a few isolated populations.

A. b. guiersi Breeds in N Senegal at Lake Guiers and in S Senegal in Casamance. Those in Mali, where it is common in the Niger Valley and delta, may also belong to this race.

A. b. cinnamomeus A wide-ranging form, with local populations in W and C Africa in N Niger (Lake Arragai), Nigeria (Gashaka-Gumti National Park, Serti, Ibadan, Kano and Lake Chad). S Chad (Sarh and N'Djamena), S Cameroon (Akonolinga), N Gabon, Darfur in W Sudan and Uelle in N DR Congo. In E Africa, it is again somewhat sparse and local, but ranges through S Sudan, Uganda, W and S Kenya, N, inland E and S Tanzania, E and S DR Congo, E, C and S Zambia, Malawi and adjacent Mozambique, with outlying populations in W and C Ethiopia (Gambela and the Rift Valley) and S Somalia (Dannow).

A. b. suahelicus Ranges from coastal Tanzania (from Pemba and Zanzibar islands and Dar-es-Salaam) south to coastal Mozambique and KwaZulu-Natal, South Africa. Locally common and typically associated with mangroves.

A. b. baeticatus Breeds widely and commonly in South Africa, Zimbabwe, E Botswana and inland Mozambique; also in Lesotho and Swaziland.

A. b. hallae Replaces the nominate race in drier parts of W South Africa, Namibia and NW Botswana, extending also to S Angola and SW Zambia.

MOVEMENTS Southern populations of race *baeticatus* and at least some birds of the race *hallae*, are migrants that are present in South Africa from September to May, but disperse 1,000–2,000km to overwinter in C Africa when much of their breeding habitat dries out. Northern populations of the race *baeticatus* are predominantly resident. Non-breeding birds of nominate *baeticatus* are present in Zambia from May to November. The race *suahelicus* has occurred in Malawi where it is presumed to be a migrant from the Mozambique coast. Movements of *cinnamomeus* may be mostly local, but birds breeding in the S Saharan fringe areas are known mainly as summer visitors.

DESCRIPTION *A. b. baeticatus*

Plumage – Adult fresh (July to November) Forehead and crown olive brown, tinged tawny or cinnamon. Supercilium buff, narrow, well marked in front of the eye, linking with narrow creamy eye-ring. Lores dark greyish brown. Ear-coverts warm olive-brown, with buff streaks. Nape, upperside of neck, mantle and scapulars to uppertail-coverts uniform warm olive-brown. Tail feathers dark grey-brown, narrowly edged olive brown, outer feathers with pale fringe around tip. Chin and throat buffy white; upper breast washed cinnamon-buff; lower breast and belly white, with faint buff wash; side of breast and flanks warm brownish buff; undertail-coverts pale warm buff. Lesser and median coverts warm olive-brown, concolorous with scapulars; greater coverts olive-brown with bright cinnamon-brown fringes; alula and primary coverts dark grey-brown, finely fringed light olive-brown. Remiges dark grey-brown; tertials broadly fringed light tawny-brown or cinnamon-brown, primaries and secondaries narrowly edged light olive-brown, primary tips with distinct narrow pale fringes. Underwing-coverts warm buff.

Adult worn (December to March) During breeding, upperparts become duller and greyer, supercilium and underparts whiter, buff on sides more restricted. Wing feathers become abraded, with greyish brown edges.

Juvenile Similar to adult, but brighter, more cinnamon-tinged, above. Supercilium less well defined. Side of head and entire underparts washed cinnamon-buff, with whitish throat and belly more restricted. Fringes of wing and tail feathers brighter and warmer.

Bare parts Upper mandible dark olive-brown or dark grey-brown with pale flesh-brown or yellowish cutting edges. Lower mandible pale flesh-brown or yellowish, usually dark greyish towards tip. Mouth orange or orange-red. Tarsi and toes dark horn to flesh brown; soles yellow; claws dark grey-brown above, contrasting with orange-yellow underside. Iris dark brown or olive-brown, occasionally light warm brown.

IN HAND CHARACTERS

Measurements

A. b. baeticatus

	Male	Female
Wing	57–63 (60.2; 29)	56–61 (59.0; 19)
Tail	47–54 (50.2; 28)	47–53 (49.7; 19)
Bill	15.5–17.5 (16.5; 14)	15.5–17 (16.4; 7)
Tarsus	21.5–23.5 (22.5; 16)	21.5–23.5 (22.5; 6)

(Wing and tail includes data from Clancey 1975)

Sexes combined:
Tail/wing ratio: 77–88% (83%; 34)
Bill width: 3.5–4.1 (3.8; 19)
Hind claw: 6.8–8.2 (7.3; 20)
Tail graduation: 5–8 (6.6; 12)

A. b. hallae (sexes combined): *wing* 58–63 (60.2; 28); *tail* 48–55 (51.0; 27); *tarsus* 22–23 (22.3; 5) (wing and tail data mainly from Clancey 1975). Similar in size to *baeticatus*.

A. b. suahelicus (sexes combined): *wing* 56–63 (59.2; 15); *tail* 47–52 (48.9; 15); *bill* 16.8–18.3 (17.6; 13), *tarsus* 21–23 (21.9; 7); bill width 3.8–4.3 (4.1; 15). Size as *baeticatus*, but bill longer and broader.

A. b. cinnamomeus (sexes combined): *wing* 52–57 (54.3; 24); *tail* 41–48 (44.6; 24); *bill* 15.0–17.0 (15.8; 20); *tarsus* 20–22 (21.2; 16); bill width 3.4–3.8 (3.6; 18); hind claw 6.4–7.5 (6.9; 13). Much smaller than *baeticatus*.

A. b. guiersi (4 ♂♂, 1 ♀): *wing* 56–60 (58.0); *tail* 45–50 (47.2); *bill* 15.3–16.5 (16.0); *tarsus* 21–22 (21.4); hind claw 7.5–7.8 (7.7; 5). Slightly larger than *cinnamomeus*.

Structure

A. b. baeticatus

Wing formula (n = 12):

p1/pc	p2	p3e	p4e	p5(e)	p6	p7	p10
(1)–2	3–5.5	wp	wp	0–2	1.5–4	3.5–5.5	8–10

Wing rounded but p1 minute. Wing point p3–4 (5); p2 = p6/7–7/8; emargination on p3–4 and often p5. Depth of p2 notch 13–15mm; notch falls below ss tips.

Figure 65. Wing of African Reed Warbler *A. b. baeticatus.*

Structure otherwise as Eurasian Reed Warbler but claws distinctly larger.

A. b. cinnamomeus Wing similar to nominate *baeticatus* (Fig. 65), but typically shows a distinctly more rounded wing, with point at p3–5 and p2 = (p7) 7/8–8/9 (9/10).

Figure 66. Wing of African Reed Warbler *A. b. cinnamomeus.*

A. b. guiersi Wing less rounded than *cinnamomeus*. Wing point at p3–4; p2 = p6–7.

Recognition Generally more warmly coloured than migrant Eurasian Reed Warblers occurring alongside them, especially the small, bright race *cinnamomeus*, but effects of wear and bleaching render plumage differences unreliable. All races separable from Eurasian Reed by shorter p2, with tip at or below p6 (rarely below p5 in *A. s. scirpaceus* or *A. s. fuscus*). In African Reed p4 (and often p5) is emarginated but only a few smaller *fuscus* Eurasian Reed show this. This is potentially useful in a moulting bird with incompletely grown outer primaries, as too is the generally deeper p2 notch (usually > 13mm; 13mm or below in Eurasian Reed). Shorter wing length separates most African birds from wintering Eurasian Reed, but there is potential overlap at 59–62mm between the race *guiersi* of African Reed and

smaller Iberian and Moroccan breeding *A. s. scirpaceus*. Easily separated from Marsh Warbler, which has a much longer wing and a long p2 with shallower notch.

Ageing In S Africa, juvenile or first-winter birds are distinguishable from December to April (before moult) by their unworn primaries, when adults have worn primaries and tail feathers at this time. A similar age distinction applies from June to October in populations of the northern tropics.

Weight

A. b. baeticatus and *A. b. hallae*: S Africa, typically 9–12g, but extremes in a large Transvaal sample were 7g and 15.5g, some birds evidently fattening for migration (Urban *et al.* 1997); in N Namibia, 8.5–13g (9.8; 88) (Komen 1988).

A. b. cinnamomeus: Nigeria, 7.6–12.5g (8.9; 36) (Aidley & Wilkinson 1987); Kenya, 7.4–10.1g (8.6; 15) (Urban *et al.* 1997, ON unpublished data).

GEOGRAPHIC VARIATION Involves size and coloration and small differences in structure. Warmly coloured birds breeding in S Africa are replaced by paler birds in the dry southwest, and by similarly sized but more rufescent birds along the E African coast. Distinctly smaller birds occupy a wide range through C, E and W Africa, with isolated populations reaching the Sahara. These are typically brightly coloured, more cinnamon, but become duller and cooler toned in W Africa. Wings are slightly less rounded in the more migratory forms of S Africa. Libyan breeders, with wing length 58–65mm, are apparently larger than *cinnamomeus*.

A. b. baeticatus (South Africa, Zimbabwe and NE Botswana) Described above.

A. b. hallae (W South Africa to Namibia, NW Botswana, SW Zambia and S Angola) Resembles nominate *baeticatus*, but slightly paler, more olive-brown above and whiter below.

A. b. suahelicus (Coastal Tanzania, Mozambique and E South Africa) Slightly darker, more deeply rufescent above than *baeticatus* and tinged richer cinnamon-buff on the breast and flanks. Similar in size, but with a slightly larger bill.

A. b. cinnamomeus (S Zambia and Malawi, north to Ethiopia, Sudan and Nigeria) Tinged more strongly cinnamon brown than *baeticatus*, especially on the mantle and scapulars and becoming bright cinnamon-brown on the rump and on the fringes to the greater coverts and tertials. The breast and flanks are bright cinnamon-buff. Southern birds ('*fraterculus*' from Malawi and Mozambique) are a little darker, very close in colour to *suahelicus*, while Lake Chad birds ('*hopsoni*') are slightly browner. Smaller than the previous three races.

A. b. guiersi (Senegal and perhaps Mali) Differs from *cinnamomeus* in being colder brown above with a greyish tinge on the head and whiter below. Slightly larger than *cinnamomeus*.

TAXONOMY AND SYSTEMATICS African Reed Warblers have historically been regarded as specifically distinct from the migrant Palearctic Eurasian Reed Warbler and are usually all treated under *A. baeticatus*. However, Clancey (1975a) confined *A. baeticatus* to the birds of S Africa and coastal E Africa (races *baeticatus*, *hallae* and *suahelicus*). He grouped the smaller birds breeding further north as a separate species *A. cinnamomeus*. But this depended partly on the assumption that birds from the Middle Zambezi valley, thought to be *suahelicus*, were separated by small birds from the *suahelicus* of the east coast. Dowsett-Lemaire & Dowsett (1987) pointed out that these Zambian birds were probably all wintering nominate *baeticatus* from South Africa and considered the split of *cinnamomeus* from African Reed Warbler to be unjustified, a view later endorsed by Urban *et al.* (1997) and Hockey *et al.* (2005).

African Reed Warbler and Eurasian Reed Warbler have sometimes been treated as conspecific. Wing structure constitutes the only major morphological difference between them. Dowsett-Lemaire & Dowsett (1987) found the songs of *A. b. baeticatus*, *A. b. cinnamomeus* and nominate *A. scirpaceus* to be identical, and reported that all three reacted to each other's songs in tape playback experiments. *A. s. avicenniae*, described only in 1989, has a wing structure like that of the African races, but coloration similar to the race *fuscus* of Eurasian Reed Warbler, and appears to link African Reed and Eurasian Reed Warblers geographically. Comparison of the cytochrome *b* gene showed less

difference between *A. b. guiersi* and *A. s. scirpaceus* than between individuals of Eurasian Reed compared from western and eastern limits of the Palearctic breeding range (Leisler *et al.* 1997; Helbig & Siebold 1999), but DNA comparison is apparently still needed with the main forms of African Reed, notably nominate *baeticatus*.

Moroccan reed warblers are intermediate in size between SW European *A. s. scirpaceus* and W African *A. b. guiersi*, although they essentially resemble European birds in wing structure. However, short-winged resident populations found recently in various Libyan reedbeds match the mtDNA of *A. baeticatus* in some cases but of *A. s. avicenniae* in others, with little morphological difference between these (Hering *et al.* 2010). Although we opted here for the convenient course of retaining African Reed Warbler as a separate species, it seems that African and Eurasian birds may now have to be combined under *A. scirpaceus* as Common Reed Warbler.

▲ Adult *A. b. baeticatus*, KwaZulu-Natal, South Africa, June. The warm brown upperparts, warmly tinged flanks and white throat resemble those of nominate Eurasian Reed Warbler, but note the much shorter primary projection (Hugh Chittenden).

▲ Adult *A. b. guiersi*, Tiguet, Senegal, January. Closely resembles Eurasian Reed but note rounded wing structure with shorter p2 (Volker Salewski).

▲ Adult *A. b. baeticatus*, Gauteng, South Africa, February. The pale brown legs suggest that this is an older bird (Warwick Tarboton).

▲ Adult *A. b. baeticatus*, Gauteng, South Africa, September (Niall Perrins).

CAPE VERDE WARBLER
Acrocephalus brevipennis   **Plate 21**

Calamodyta brevipennis **Keulemans, 1866.** *Nederlandsch. Tijdschrift. Dierkunde* 3: 368. São Nicolau, Brava, São Tiago, Cape Verde Islands.

A resident, confined to three islands in the Cape Verde Archipelago. Its population is declining as a result of successive droughts and an increasing human population and it is considered ENDANGERED by BirdLife International. Monotypic.

IDENTIFICATION Length 14–15cm. Wing 62–69mm. Tail/wing 86–95%.

A mid sized, long-billed *Acrocephalus* with a nondescript, drab brown appearance. Geographically isolated and unlikely to come into contact with potentially confusing species except, perhaps, a vagrant Eurasian Reed Warbler or Western Olivaceous Warbler.

Structure Appears distinctly larger and more heavily built than Eurasian Reed Warbler. It also has longer and thicker tarsi and stronger toes, and a longer bill, although this is quite narrow, especially towards the tip. In wing formula and other structural characters it shows a closer resemblance to the Greater Swamp and Lesser Swamp Warblers of the African mainland and seems likely to have been derived from an African ancestral form. The wing is distinctly rounded with a long first primary (p1), a blunt wing-tip formed by p4–5 and a short primary projection. Emargination on primaries p3–6. The tail is relatively long with a graduated tip.

Plumage and bare parts The adult is rather dull olive-brown above but shows a greyish cast to the crown and neck and a warm tinge to the rump and uppertail-coverts. There is a narrow and indistinct greyish white supercilium that forms a diffuse line above dark lores and extends to the rear edge of the eye, but usually no further, and which merges with the inconspicuous whitish eye-ring. The wing feathers are fringed cold olive-brown or greyish brown and appear fairly uniform, but contrast with distinctly greyer upperparts. The chin and throat are off-white, contrasting with otherwise grey-brown underparts. The throat sometimes shows faint dark streaks.

Juveniles appear warmer brown and show gingery buff fringes to the tertials, wing-coverts and tail feathers and lack the greyish tones of the adult. The supercilium is washed buff and appears less distinct than in the adult. The whitish underparts show a buffy suffusion on the breast and flanks.

The bill is dark brown to blackish above, with a yellow-orange lower mandible and usually lacks a dusky tip. The legs are dark grey.

SIMILAR SPECIES No similar resident species occur in the Cape Verde islands but vagrant Eurasian Reed Warbler and Western Olivaceous Warbler could potentially cause confusion. Lesser Swamp and Greater Swamp Warblers are also compared briefly.

Eurasian Reed Warbler is a distinctly smaller bird that appears both warmer and browner but has a very different structure. It has rich, warm olive-brown upperparts, a more prominent supercilium in front of the eye and paler, buff-tinged underparts. The bill is smaller and more slender, the tail proportionately shorter and the wing much more pointed with a long primary projection and short first primary. In both this and Western Olivaceous Warbler the tarsi and toes are slender compared with those of Cape Verde Warbler.

Western Olivaceous Warbler is also distinctly smaller and slimmer than Cape Verde Warbler and appears paler sandy brown above, with conspicuously paler off-white underparts. The bill is long, but the flat fore-crown gives an attenuated head appearance that Cape Verde Warbler lacks. The tail appears fairly long and substantial, but has an almost square tip.

Lesser Swamp Warbler is similar in size and structure to Cape Verde Warbler, but less greyish, more warmly coloured, especially on the rump and uppertail-coverts. It has stronger legs and toes.

Greater Swamp Warbler is a larger, somewhat darker bird with drabber grey underparts. It has much stronger legs and larger toes and claws and a distinctly larger first primary.

VOICE The song is loud, resonant and low-pitched. It consists of short sequences lasting 1–3 seconds in which syllables tend to be repeated. These are interspersed with pauses of up to 6 seconds, although the bird will often call intermittently between them. Song closely resembles that of Lesser Swamp Warbler in structure, pitch and quality, being rather less harsh and throaty than in Greater Swamp Warbler. It includes some clear whistles and forceful churring. A sequence with an introductory '*put-dudloo*' followed by a bubbling, trilling '*doo-deedli-doo-deede-loo-deede-loo*', is strongly reminiscent of a bulbul *Pycnonotus*. Another sequence of deep rich notes, recalling Common Nightingale begins slowly and deliberately, then continues more rapidly with higher notes leading into a trill: '*chou-chou-chou keeup-keeup-keeup-kiririreoup*'.

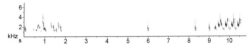

Song of Cape Verde Warbler, San Tiago, Cape Verde, September. (Chappuis 2000)

Calls include a throaty disyllabic '*pichow*' or '*kerrchow*'. Also a sparrow-like '*chuk*' or '*tuk*' and a repeated '*krrk*', similar to that of Great Reed Warbler but a little less harsh and guttural.

MOULT Adults apparently have a complete moult between January and April. Young birds have a partial post-juvenile moult soon after fledging. This is variable in extent but involves most of the head and body plumage and many wing-coverts, but usually few or none of the remiges or tail feathers.

BEHAVIOUR Skulking and difficult to see in dense cover, but can be tame and confiding in gardens and plantations. Sings throughout the year, but most intensely during the breeding season. Birds may then sing all day, typically from cover, perched upright on a reed or sugar-cane stem. It forms small groups when not breeding and commonly forages in trees, sometimes together with Blackcaps in fruiting figs. Birds often fly up to the canopy when flushed.

HABITAT The original habitat was probably scrub on mountain slopes and reedbeds in valleys, but it now occupies a broad range of habitat up to 500m. On Santiago, it shows a preference for well-vegetated valleys, especially undisturbed patches of Giant Reed *Arundo donax*, but has adapted to more open artificial situations and occurs in trees, bushes and gardens in villages. It has spread in sugar cane plantations, as these have expanded, and also breeds in banana plantations, manioc, oranges and coffee bushes, especially near running water. It also breeds in areas planted with introduced *Eucalyptus, Cupressus, Pinus* and Australian Silver-oak *Grevillea robusta* (Hering & Fuchs 2009).

On Fogo, it occupies a wider altitudinal range, mainly between 300m and 700m and occasionally to above 970m. It now occupies the extensive areas of cultivation in which introduced crops are dominant. It prefers coffee plantations interspersed with fruit trees. These are typically on terraced hillsides or in valleys and craters and are also used to grow maize, mango, banana, orange and papaya (Hering & Fuchs 2009). Below 400m, maize appears to be important within the birds' territories. In inaccessible gorges at higher altitude it was found in introduced *Lantana camara*. Mango trees were used as song-posts and were probably the most important nest site. Giant Reed, by contrast, was found in fewer than 20% of territories (Hering & Fuchs 2009).

On São Nicolau, it formerly bred in orange groves, coffee plantations and cultivated sugar cane. It is now restricted to areas with Giant Reed along dry riverbeds and often with large fruit trees (Hazevoet *et al.* 1999; Donald *et al.* 2004). The former population on Brava occurred around human settlements with established cultivation, in particular Vila Nova Sintra (Hering & Fuchs 2009).

BREEDING HABITS Breeds mainly from August to November, during and after the summer rains, but sometimes also in spring, during February and March. Nesting pairs are territorial although in prime habitat on Fogo the minimum distance between occupied nests was just 30m (Hering & Fuchs 2009).

On Santiago, the nest is usually built in Giant Reed, but often at up to 2m in sugarcane or up to 5m in bushes and trees. It is supported between stems of reed or sugarcane, or in the outer sprays of bush canopy with twigs passing through the rim. Of nine nests studied on Fogo by Hering & Fuchs (2009), seven were in mango trees and one each in guava and coffee bushes. They were situated at heights ranging from 2–15m and always woven into a fork of three vertically growing twigs in the outer branches. The nest was constructed by both sexes with coarse plant fibres up to 1cm thick, usually from the leaves and trunks of banana plants. They had substantial walls and a deep cup lined with fine plant fibres. Typically, 2–3 eggs are laid and both sexes take turns to incubate, sitting deep within the cup, often with only the head and part of the tail visible. After leaving the nest, the male almost always remains close by and gives an occasional short song burst. Incubation and fledging periods are unknown. Probably sometimes double brooded.

DISTRIBUTION Endemic to the Cape Verde Archipelago, where it is known from just four islands; Santiago, São Nicolau, Fogo and Brava, although believed to be extinct on the last of these.

It has long been known on Santiago, where the small population is declining due to habitat loss at the handful of sites in the interior. It also occurs at a few isolated sites in the south and west. The total population of the island is probably below 500 pairs. It was rediscovered on São Nicolau in 1998, having been last recorded there in 1924 (Hazevoet *et al.* 1999). Studies in 2001 and 2003 revealed no more than ten pairs, confined to just three sites (Hazevoet 2003;

Donald *et al.* 2004). On Brava, it has not been reported since 1969 and is presumed to be extinct due to increased desertification, habitat destruction and predator pressure (Hazevoet 1993, 1995).

In 2004, a large population was discovered for the first time on Fogo. Here, 129 territories were mapped by Hering and Fuchs (2009). They recorded the highest average density (19 territories/100 ha) in coffee plantations. Within its occupied range in the northern part of the island, they found an overall average density of 6.5 territories per 100 ha, which extrapolates to a total island population of about 500 pairs.

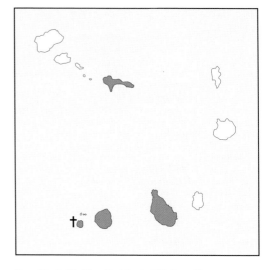

Cape Verde Warbler. Resident within breeding range.

MOVEMENTS Sedentary, with no inter-island movements reported.

DESCRIPTION

Plumage – Adult fresh (May to August) Forehead and crown grey-brown. Supercilium narrow and indistinct, above lores only, mottled grey and off-white, connecting with faint off-white eye-ring. Lores dark brownish grey. Cheeks and ear-coverts brownish grey with fine whitish streaks. Nape and upper side of neck brownish grey, merging with cold brownish grey mantle and scapulars and becoming slightly warmer, cinnamon-tinged, on rump and uppertail-coverts. Tail feathers dark grey-brown with narrow olive-brown edges. Chin and throat white, the latter often with faint dusky streaks. Centre of breast and belly greyish white. Lower side of neck, side of breast and upper flanks pale brownish grey. Lower flanks, vent and undertail-coverts pale grey-buff. Lesser and median coverts cold olive-brown. Greater coverts dark grey-brown with broad diffuse olive-brown fringes. Primary coverts, alula and remiges dark grey-brown with narrow olive-brown edges. Underwing-coverts greyish white.

Adult worn Upperparts duller, more greyish. Supercilium sometimes more distinct. Breast and belly whiter. Edges to tertials and flight feathers pale greyish.

First-winter Similar to juvenile, sometimes rather browner, but less grey than adult. Retains juvenile remiges and rectrices.

Juvenile Much less grey than adult. Upperparts and upperwing-coverts warm olive-brown, becoming cinnamon-brown on rump and uppertail-coverts. Sides of head greyish brown. Supercilium and eye-ring distinct, pale buff. Side of breast, upper breast and flanks pale buff, merging to white on chin and throat and mid belly. Fringes of flight feathers, tertials, greater coverts and tail feathers pale cinnamon-brown.

Bare parts Upper mandible dark brown or grey-black with pale yellowish horn cutting edges. Lower mandible pale yellowish horn, usually unmarked but sometimes with darker smudge towards tip. Tarsi and toes greenish grey to slate grey or lead grey; claws dark horn or black. Iris hazel in adult, olive-brown or ochre-brown in first-year bird.

IN HAND CHARACTERS
Measurements

	Male	Female
Wing	64–69 (66.6; 12)	62–67 (64.7; 6)
Tail	57–62 (60.3; 12)	58–62 (59.8; 6)
Bill	19.5–21 (20.3; 12)	19.5–21 (20.2; 6)
Tarsus	25.5–27.5 (26.5; 12)	25.5–27 (26.4; 6)

Sexes combined:
Tail/wing ratio: 86–95% (91%; 18)
Bill width: 4.4–4.8 (4.5; 11)
Hind claw: 7.0–8.3 (7.6; 11)
Tail graduation: 13–18

Structure

Wing formula (Cramp 1992):

p1/pc	p2	p3e	p4e	p5e	p6e	p7(e)	p10
10–16	8–10	1–3	wp	wp	0–1	1–2	6–8

Wing strongly rounded with fairly large p1 (40–50% p2). Wing point p4–5 (6); p2 = ss tips; emargination on p3–6, occasionally on tip of p7.

Figure 67. Wing of Cape Verde Warbler.

Tail medium, graduated, feathers rather broad and rounded.

Bill longish, rather narrow with concave sides and slender tip.

Tarsi strong; toes and claws smaller than in Lesser Swamp Warbler.

Structure similar to Lesser Swamp Warbler but bill relatively larger, legs and feet less robust.

Weight Range 15–17g (n = 3) (Cramp 1992).

GEOGRAPHIC VARIATION None recorded.

TAXONOMY AND SYSTEMATICS No issues arising.

▲ Adult male, Fogo, Cape Verde Islands, October. Shows a poorly marked supercilium, yellowish base to lower mandible and dark grey legs (Jens Hering).

▲ Adult, Fogo, Cape Verde Islands, December. Note the grey-brown upperparts, grey-washed underparts with whitish throat, short wings and well-graduated tail-tip (Jens Hering).

▲ Adult (upper) with juvenile (lower), Fogo, Cape Verde Islands, December (Jens Hering).

LESSER SWAMP WARBLER
Acrocephalus gracilirostris   **Plate 22**

Calamoherpe gracilirostris **Hartlaub, 1864**. In: Gurney, *Ibis*, page 348. Natal.

A resident, widespread in wetlands in E and S Africa and with isolated populations in W Africa. It forms a species group with Greater Swamp Warbler, Cape Verde Cane Warbler and Madagascar Swamp Warbler. Polytypic with eight races recognised:

A. g. gracilirostris (Hartlaub, 1864). South Africa (except extreme east and north) and S Namibia.

A. g. leptorhynchus (Reichenow, 1879). E Ethiopia, S Somalia, SE Kenya, E and S Tanzania, E Zambia, Zimbabwe, Mozambique and E South Africa.

A. g. parvus (Fischer & Reichenow, 1884). Kenya highlands, SW Ethiopia and N Tanzania.

A. g. jacksoni (Neumann, 1901). S Sudan, Uganda and adjacent DR Congo, W Kenya,

A. g. cunenensis (Hartert, 1903). SW Angola, N Namibia, N Botswana, SW and S Zambia and W Zimbabwe.

A. g. neglectus (Alexander, 1908). Lake Chad

A. g. tsanae (Bannerman, 1937). NW Ethiopia

A. g. winterbottomi (White, 1947). E Angola, NW and N Zambia, intergrading with *leptorhynchus* in SE DR Congo.

IDENTIFICATION Length 14–16cm. Wing 61–81mm, differing between races. Tail/wing 86–96%.

A mid sized and relatively long-billed *Acrocephalus*, slightly smaller than Greater Swamp Warbler, but substantially larger than African Reed Warbler. Shows considerable variation across its extensive range, affecting both plumage tone and size – there being no overlap in wing length between the smallest and largest races. All races show a distinct pale supercilium and rich brown upperparts. Sexes alike. **Structure** The bill is rather long and thin and combines with a low sloping forehead to give an attenuated head shape. It can be separated from any potentially confusing Palearctic migrant by its short and rounded wing structure, with a large first primary and wing point formed by p4–5 and sometimes p6. The tail is relatively long and slightly graduated and usually appears ragged and untidy. The legs are strong with large toes and claws. **Plumage and bare parts** There is considerable plumage variation across the extensive range, but all races are more warmly coloured than Greater Swamp Warbler and have paler underparts. In South Africa, adults of the nominate form are warm brown above, being brightest on the rump and uppertail-coverts, but rather darker and greyer on the top and sides of the head. A narrow whitish supercilium above the dark lores fades just behind the eye. The underparts are contrastingly paler with the chin and throat appearing whitish and the breast shows a light greyish brown wash, which becomes stronger, more buffy brown on the flanks and lower underparts. The wings are plain in appearance and show little contrast with the upperparts. The widespread eastern race *leptorhynchus* shows greater contrast between a paler and duller crown and mantle and bright warm brown rump and uppertail-coverts, and warmly tinged flanks. Inland E African birds (races *parvus*, *jacksoni* and *tsanae*) have darker upperparts and a pale throat that contrasts with darker, greyer underparts.

Juveniles resemble adults but are generally brighter and more rufescent.

The bill is dusky-brown with a pinkish grey lower mandible that darkens towards the tip. The legs and feet are dark grey in all races.

SIMILAR SPECIES Greater Swamp Warbler will be the main confusion species where its range overlaps with Lesser Swamp Warbler in N Nigeria and in inland E and southern C Africa. African Reed Warbler, although different structurally, is another potentially confusing resident. Various plain-backed migrant *Acrocephalus* occur in marshes with Lesser Swamp throughout its range.
Greater Swamp Warbler is larger and more robust than Lesser Swamp, although it is approached in size by Lesser Swamp from the Kenya highlands – and by those from South Africa where Greater Swamp is absent. It is darker olive-brown above, darker and greyer below and lacks the rufescent tones of Lesser Swamp. The bill is longer and stronger than in Lesser Swamp and the mouth lining is pale yellow.
African Reed Warbler is a much smaller bird than Lesser Swamp Warbler, with a smaller bill, shorter tail and more slender legs, which are brown rather than blackish. It is brighter above and paler below than most races of Lesser Swamp.
Basra Reed Warbler has a long slender bill and greyish legs like Lesser Swamp Warbler. It is colder olive-brown above, however, and has a long primary projection and a long whitish supercilium.

VOICE The chuckling song is loud, melodious and low-pitched, similar to that of Greater Swamp Warbler but less deep and throaty. In E Africa, it consists of varied simple sequences lasting 1–2.5 seconds, in which syllables are repeated several times: '*klieru-klieru-klieru... klikliu-klikli-klikliu-klee... kliew-klikliklikli...*'. Sequences are separated by short pauses, with a few ,*chorr*' or ,*chack*' notes interspersed between them. The frequency range is low, falling mainly between 1.5 and 3kHz.

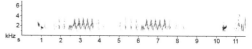

Song of Lesser Swamp Warbler recorded within breeding range of *A. g. parvus*, **Lake Naivasha, Kenya, July. (David Pearson)**

The song of nominate birds in S Africa sounds rather different, being a fluty bulbul *Pycnonotus*-like '*wewauwewau*', followed by a rattling trill of 8–11 notes lasting about one second.

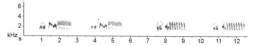

Song of Lesser Swamp Warbler recorded within breeding range of *A. g. gracilirostris*, **Western Cape, South Africa, September. (Gibbon 2003)**

Contact and alarm notes include a loud '*klierok*', a low '*chuck*' and a chattering' *chuk-uk-uk-k-k*'.

MOULT In Malawi, the race *leptorhynchus* has been found in full moult in all months of the year, but with a peak in numbers, of adults and immatures, starting in October and continuing until December (Hanmer 1988). Moult proceeds according to typical passerine tract sequences and takes some 60–90 days to complete. Young birds appear to have a post-juvenile body moult followed by a complete moult 2–3 months or more later. In S Zambia, most adults have a complete moult between November and April (Hockey *et al.* 2005). In Zimbabwe, they are found in primary moult from November to July (Manson 1985).

HABITAT Inhabits tall, dense growth over or close to water, around lakes and dams, in swamps and by rivers and estuaries. It is found in tall reeds, reedmace *Typha*, sedges, papyrus and in rank grass. The race *jacksoni* frequents leafy waterside shrubs and bushes on rocky islets in Lake Victoria. Where it occurs together with Greater Swamp Warbler, as at sites in W Kenya, S Sudan and Zambia, it keeps mainly to the swamp edges where it prefers vegetation other than papyrus, while Greater Swamp occupies the papyrus swamp interior. Ranges as high as 2,400m in Ethiopia and Kenya, but only to 1,500m in southern Africa.

BEHAVIOUR Often found in pairs or small groups. It usually forages in reeds and papyrus over water, from mid height down to the water level, moving easily among vertical stems with a rather upright carriage. It is highly vocal and

usually fairly conspicuous, often emerging onto the edges of reeds or picking food in the open from low or floating vegetation. It occasionally feeds in papyrus heads. Small frogs may be consumed in addition to the usual insect prey. Song may be given at any time of day, often by several birds in chorus. It is typically heard from within cover, usually 1–2m above water. Flight is low, rather weak and fluttery, usually no further than from one clump of vegetation to the next.

BREEDING HABITS It is monogamous and territorial, although several pairs often nest close together within a small patch of suitable habitat. Territories may be maintained year-round. The nest is a deep conical cup constructed from dry reed strips, coarse grass and occasionally water weed, and lined with fine strips, fine grass and sometimes a few feathers. It is usually built 0.2–1.8m above water or mud, around two or three upright stems, sometimes attached by 'handles', or in the fork of a shrub or small tree. The clutch is usually 2–3 eggs (occasionally four). Incubation is by both sexes for 13–14 days (Tarboton 2001), and the young are fed by both parents and fledge after 10–14 days. Breeds mainly during the rains, with laying recorded from March

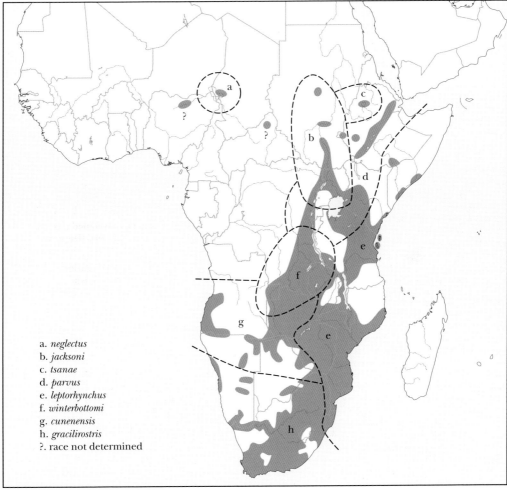

a. *neglectus*
b. *jacksoni*
c. *tsanae*
d. *parvus*
e. *leptorhynchus*
f. *winterbottomi*
g. *cunenensis*
h. *gracilirostris*
?. race not determined

Lesser Swamp Warbler. Mostly resident within breeding range.

to December in Kenya and Tanzania, January to August in Malawi and August to March in S Africa.

DISTRIBUTION Ranges widely through sub-Saharan Africa, from Nigeria to Ethiopia and south to the Cape. It is rather scarce in the northern tropics and known in W Africa only from isolated populations in N Nigeria, W Chad and N Central African Republic. To the east, it remains local and uncommon in Sudan, Ethiopia and S Somalia but becomes more widespread south of the equator and is often common in E and S Africa.

A. g. neglectus Known from W Chad (Sounta– Bahr Azoum confluence, Lake Chad). Birds in N Nigeria (Kano) and N Central African Republic (Manovo-Gounda-Saint Floris Nat. Park) may belong with this race.

A. g. jacksoni Breeds in Sudan in Kordofan and along the Upper Nile, to W and S Uganda and adjacent NE DR Congo: also Lake Victoria, W Kenya.

A. g. tsanae Restricted to the W highlands of Ethiopia, north to Lake Tana.

A. g. parvus Very common in the highlands of W and C Kenya. Similar but smaller birds assigned to this race occur in N Tanzania, from Monduli and Kilimanjaro to Mbulu, and to the NE shore of Lake Tanganyika (Burundi) and Lake Kivu (DR Congo); also commonly in Ethiopia in the rift valley and SW highlands.

A. g. leptorhynchus A wide-ranging eastern lowland race which occurs locally in SE Ethiopia, S Somalia, SE Kenya and E and S Tanzania; then more commonly and widely through Malawi, E and S Zambia, Zimbabwe and Mozambique to E Swaziland and E South Africa (E Limpopo Province, Mpumalanga and lowland KwuZulu-Natal).

A. g. winterbottomi Locally common in NW Zambia and adjacent E Angola and also in N Zambia in Northern and Luapala Provinces. This race (or *leptorhynchus* intergrades) is also found in neighbouring SE DR Congo and W Tanzania.

A. g. cunenensis Occurs locally in low rainfall country in W and SW Angola, N Namibia, N Botswana, SW Zambia, W Zimbabwe and N South Africa (NW Province, W Limpopo).

A. g. gracilirostris Common and widespread in most of South Africa, north to Gauteng and east to W Swaziland and interior KwaZulu-Natal. It also ranges sparsely into S Namibia.

MOVEMENTS Resident and mainly sedentary. In South Africa, also a partial migrant.

DESCRIPTION *A. g. gracilirostris*

Plumage – Adult fresh Forehead and crown rather dark brown. Supercilium well pronounced, greyish white, from base of bill to just behind eye. Lores, cheeks and ear-coverts dark greyish brown. No distinct eye-stripe. Nape, upper side of neck, mantle and scapulars to uppertail-coverts warm brown, becoming brighter, more rufescent-brown on rump and uppertail-coverts. Tail feathers dark brown with narrow, paler, warm brown edges. Chin and throat off-white. Centre of breast and belly greyish white. Lower side of neck, side of breast and upper flanks greyish brown. Lower flanks, vent and undertail-coverts warmer cinnamon-brown. Lesser, median and greater coverts uniform warm brown. Primary coverts, alula and remiges blackish brown with cinnamon-brown edges, these narrow on primaries, primary coverts and alula, broader on secondaries and tertials. Underwing-coverts pale buff.

Juvenile Similar to adult but more warmly toned. Mantle to uppertail-coverts more strongly rufescent. Breast side, flanks and undertail-coverts brighter cinnamon-brown and central underparts washed cinnamon-buff. Upperwing feathers with brighter, slightly broader, cinnamon-brown edges.

Bare parts Upper mandible dusky-brown. Lower mandible pinkish grey or pinkish buff with a dusky tip. Mouth orange. Tarsi and toes dark grey, tinged bluish or olive; soles dull yellow. Iris light brown.

IN HAND CHARACTERS

Measurements

A. g. gracilirostris

	Male	Female
Wing	73–79 (76.7; 9)	74–81 (75.7; 9)
Tail	65–73 (70.7; 9)	67–74 (69.2; 9)
Bill	19–21 (20.3; 9)	19–20.5 (20.0; 6)
Tarsus	27–30 (28.3; 9)	27–29 (28.2; 9)

Sexes combined:
Tail/wing ratio: 88–96% (92%; 19)
Bill width: 4.0–4.6 (4.3; 9)
Hind claw: 8.0–9.7 (9.0; 22)
Tail graduation: 13–19 (15.1; 9)

A. g. leptorhynchus

	Male	Female
Wing	63–68 (65.4; 28)	62–68 (64.3; 12)
Tail	56–60 (58.0; 9)	55–60 (59.0; 7)
Bill	18–20.5 (19.4; 9)	18–20 (18.9; 7)
Tarsus	25–27 (26.4; 7)	25–27 (25.9; 7)

Tail/wing ratio (sexes combined): 86–95% (90%; 16)

A. g. parvus Birds from Kenya highlands: *wing*, ♂ 70–78 (74.4; 18), ♀ 67–72 (69.2; 10). Sexes combined: *tail*, 60–74 (68.4; 7); *bill* 18.5–20 (19.5; 7). Birds from N Tanzania are smaller, sexes combined: *wing* 65–70 (67.3; 10); *tail* 58–64 (61.0; 7); *bill* 19–20 (19.4; 6).

A. g. jacksoni Birds from S Sudan, sexes combined: *wing* 61–66 (63.5; 9); *tail* 55–64 (57.9; 9); *bill* 17.5–19.5 (18.4; 9). Birds from Lake Victoria are larger, sexes combined: *wing* 65–70 (68.0; 5).

Other races (*wing*, sexes combined):
A. g. cunenensis 68–77 (72.1; 7); *A. g. winterbottomi* 67, 72, 74 (n = 3); *A. g. tsanae* 70–76 (72.4; 6); *A. g. neglectus* 62–68 (64.7; 6).

Structure

A. g. gracilirostris

Wing formula (n = 10):

p1/pc	p2	p3e	p4e	p5e	p6(e)	p7	p10
10–15	8–10	1.5–2.5	wp	wp	0–3	2.5–6	9–12

Wing strongly rounded with rather large p1 (*c.* 50% p2). Wing point p4–5 (6); p2 = p9–10; emargination on p3–5, usually also p6.

Figure 68. Wing of Lesser Swamp Warbler.

Tail medium, graduated; feathers rounded.

Bill long and strong, broad-based but concave-sided and narrow-tipped.

Tarsi and toes long and strong, claws large.

Other races mostly smaller, but structure similar.

Recognition All races are separable from Greater Swamp Warbler by warmly tinged upperparts and whiter (less greyish) underparts. In E Africa, wing length is below the range of Greater Swamp (< 72mm) where ranges overlap, but larger in the Ethiopian and Kenyan highlands where Greater Swamp is absent. Distinguished from other resident and migrant *Acrocephalus* in Africa by large first primary and strong dark legs and toes.

Weight

A. g. gracilirostris: 11.3–20.4g (16.7; 29) (Maclean 1993).

A. g. parvus: C. Kenya, 11.9–21.2g (16.5; 221) (Urban *et al*. 1997).

A. g. jacksoni: W Kenya, 12.5–16.2g (14.4; 9) (Britton 1978).

GEOGRAPHIC VARIATION There is considerable variation across the range, mainly involving plumage colour and size. Birds from the Nile valley and inland E Africa are darkest and greyest, while those from the eastern lowlands are warmly toned on the rump and uppertail-coverts, and those of S and SW Africa are palest below. Large birds occur in S Africa and in the Kenyan highlands. We recognise eight races here, but there is a case to be made for admitting two or three more.

A. g. gracilirostris (South Africa and S Namibia) The largest race. Described above

A. g. cunenensis (SW Angola to N Botswana and W Zimbabwe) Paler, less warmly tinged above than the nominate race. Distinctly whiter below with a paler buff wash on the flanks and undertail-coverts.

A. g. leptorhynchus (E Ethiopia and E Kenya to Malawi, Zimbabwe and E South Africa) Crown to mantle slightly paler and greyer, less warm than in the nominate race and contrasting more with the rufescent rump and uppertail-coverts. The underparts are whitish, faintly suffused with buff, and the lower flanks and undertail-coverts are tinged cinnamon. It is paler below than *cunenensis* and the supercilium is less prominent. Much smaller than the nominate race.

A. g. winterbottomi (E Angola to N Zambia) Upperparts darker and greyer than in the nominate race or *leptorhynchus* (matching those of *jacksoni*). Whitish below with greyer wash on flanks and undertail-coverts; chest and throat with indistinct streaks.

A. g. parvus (Kenya highlands, N Tanzania, SW Ethiopia) Rich brown above with greyer tone to the head and mantle, darker than in nominate race or *leptorhynchus*. Chin and throat creamy white, but underparts otherwise washed greyish, becoming browner on breast and upper flanks, and tawny-brown on lower flanks and undertail-coverts. The supercilium is subdued. Juveniles have a rich cinnamon tinge to the upperparts and underparts. Birds from the highlands of Kenya are large, but those from N Tanzania are smaller, not much larger than *leptorhynchus*.

A. g. jacksoni (S Sudan, Uganda, W Kenya) Rather dark and similar to *parvus*, but with brown upperparts more olive-tinged. The underparts are washed buffy grey, paler only on chin and throat. Birds from S Sudan are small and sometimes separated as a distinct form '*nuerensis*'. Birds from Uganda are similar in size to N Tanzanian *parvus*.

A. g. tsanae (W highlands of Ethiopia) Still darker above than *parvus* and greyer, especially on the head. Greyer below, with the grey-brown sides darker even than in *jacksoni*. Rather large.

A. g. neglectus (Lake Chad) Paler and more warmly toned than the preceding three races, more cinnamon-tinged on the rump and uppertail-coverts. The underparts are washed grey-buff rather than grey-brown. Compared with the nominate race, the upperparts are very similar, but the underparts are dingier, less whitish. Rather small.

TAXONOMY AND SYSTEMATICS This species and the Greater Swamp Warbler were earlier assigned to the genus *Calamocichla*, or to *Calamoecetor*, but since White (1963), Hall & Moreau (1970) and Benson *et al* (1970) they have been placed in *Acrocephalus*. Recent genetic studies show them to be quite closely related to the large plain-backed *Acrocephalus* species of Europe and Asia.

The form *zuluensis*, often recognised from NE South Africa and S Mozambique, is here treated as a synonym of *A. g. leptorhynchus*.

▲ ▶ Adult *A. g. leptorhynchus*, KwaZulu-Natal, South Africa, August. Shows the warm brown back and rump, greyish head, white throat, pale underparts, and short but distinct whitish supercilium. Note also the flesh-pink base to the lower mandible, and dark grey legs (Hugh Chittenden).

▲ ▶ Adult *A. g. parvus*, Nairobi, Kenya, May. This race is darker brown above than the nominate and shows a subdued supercilium. Grey-brown underparts contrast with a whitish throat (Peter Usher).

▲ Juvenile *A. g. parvus*, Nairobi, Kenya, September. Note the cinnamon-brown upperparts, bright wing feather-edges and warmly washed underparts (Peter Usher).

▲ Adult *A. g. gracilirostris*, Gauteng, South Africa, February. Shows warm brown upperparts and flanks and a prominent eye-ring. Note the long but rather slim bill (Warwick Tarboton).

GREATER SWAMP WARBLER
Acrocephalus rufescens   **Plate 23**

Bradypterus rufescens **Sharpe & Bouvier, 1876.** *Bull. Soc. Zool. France* 1: 307. Landana, Cabinda.

An Afrotropical resident, widely distributed south of the Sahara, mainly in extensive swamps. Together with Lesser Swamp Warbler, Madagascar Swamp Warbler and Cape Verde Warbler, it forms a distinct group of resident *Acrocephalus* species characterised by a strongly rounded wing with large first primary and a loud chuckling song. Polytypic, with four races recognised:

A. r. rufescens (Sharpe & Bouvier, 1876). Ghana to Nigeria (except Lake Chad), Cameroon, Bioko, NW DR Congo and NW Angola.

A. r. ansorgei (Hartert, 1906). S Sudan, Uganda and Kenya to E DR Congo, Zambia, W Zimbabwe, N Botswana and northern C Angola.

A. r. chadensis (Alexander, 1907). Restricted to Lake Chad.

A. r. senegalensis Colston & Morel, 1985. Senegal and Gambia.

IDENTIFICATION Length 16–18cm. Wing 67–85mm. Tail/wing 92–101%.

A large, long-billed *Acrocephalus* of wet swampland in sub-Saharan Africa, appearing dingy olive-brown above and greyish below, with a whiter throat and belly. Sexes alike.

Structure Has a distinctly more bulky structure than the sleeker Palearctic *Acrocephalus*, an effect enhanced by the short undertail-coverts and short wings. The head is attenuated, with a sloping forehead and long bill and the tail appears quite long and broad with a strongly graduated tip. The wing is strongly rounded, with a large first primary, wing point at p4–5 and an extremely short primary projection, about *c*. 20% of the tertial length. The legs are robust, the feet and claws large. The bill, although narrow, is relatively large and strong. It shares most of these features with Lesser Swamp Warbler, but is slightly larger and bulkier overall.

Plumage and bare parts Adults of the nominate race have dull olive-brown upperparts, with the top and side of the head slightly darker and greyer, and a more warmly tinged rump. The head is drab and unmarked except for a narrow and poorly defined pale greyish supercilium which extends to just behind the eye. The underparts are light greyish brown with a whitish throat and belly centre, the rear flanks and ventral region washed tawny-brown. The wings are plain and show little contrast with the upperparts. In the eastern and southern parts of the range, birds of the race *ansorgei* are darker and slightly larger than the nominate form, and usually show fine dark throat streaking.

Juveniles are quite different in colour from the adults, with tawny or yellowish brown upperparts and the underparts washed pale tawny.

The bill is dark with a pale yellowish or buff lower mandible which darkens at the sides. The legs are dark grey or blackish.

SIMILAR SPECIES Throughout much of its range it occurs alongside the similar Lesser Swamp Warbler, although the two tend to segregate in different habitats. It might possibly also be confused with migrant Great Reed and Basra Reed Warblers, although these are not swamp-dwelling birds in Africa.

Lesser Swamp Warbler varies in size from being slightly to

considerably smaller (depending on race) but is similar to Greater Swamp Warbler in overall structure. All races are warmer-toned, more richly coloured above than Greater Swamp and show a more distinct whitish supercilium. They tend to appear less greyish, paler and more warmly tinged below, with a whiter throat. The mouth lining is orange-red, unlike the dull yellow mouth of Greater Swamp.

Great Reed Warbler has a stouter bill, a broad, pale buff supercilium and pale underparts and usually shows pale brown legs. It has a completely different wing structure, with a minute first primary and a long primary projection.

Basra Reed Warbler has a long slender bill and greyish legs and in this respect resembles Greater Swamp Warbler. It is readily distinguished by its long primary projection (and minute p1) and by its long whitish supercilium and whitish underparts.

VOICE The song is loud, throaty and low-pitched, most syllables at 1–3kHz. It comprises a series of simple, varied sequences, typically lasting 1–3 seconds and separated by pauses of 5–10 seconds. Each sequence includes repetitions of low chuckling notes, variously transcribed as '*kwokwokwokwokwokwrrrryp*' or '*krup-krr-krr-krr... kikweu-kikweu-kikweu-kikweu... kieru-kwee-kwee-kwee...*' and is reminiscent of the song of a *Pycnonotus* bulbul. The song may be preceded by quiet '*chor*', '*chup*' or '*chuck*' elements and these may also be given between sequences.

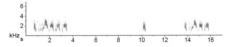

Song of Greater Swamp Warbler recorded within breeding range of *A. r. rufescens*, Buea, southwest Cameroon, November. (Chappuis 2000)

The song of the race *ansorgei* in Botswana differs in being more rolling and fluid, delivered at a slightly higher pitch. Sequences last approximately three seconds, followed by a pause of 3–4 seconds. Each consists of 10–12 low chipping notes on a rising scale, followed by a gurgling '*gweeweeeweeeweee...*'.

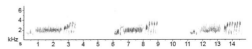

Song of Greater Swamp Warbler recorded within breeding range of *A. r. ansorgei*, Okavango, Botswana, April. (Gibbon 2003)

The usual contact and alarm note is a harsh '*kweeok*' or '*kierok*' and anxious birds may give a repeated '*klok, klok...*' call.

MOULT No information.

HABITAT A waterside species, typically found in tall emergent vegetation. In E and S Africa, it is closely associated with papyrus swamps and stands of papyrus along rivers and lakeshores, although in Zambia it occurs in *Phragmites*. In W Africa it utilises a wider range of habitats and occurs in reedbeds, wet elephant grass and sugar cane, as well as papyrus.

BEHAVIOUR A skulking species that tends to forage near water level, either singly or in pairs. Although it calls frequently it can be difficult to observe. When travelling through reedbeds, it moves easily among vertical stems, climbing up and down and hopping from one to the next. It feeds mainly on insects, generally collected at the base of papyrus clumps, although it will also take small frogs. Occasionally it flies out to feed in the open on lily pads.

BREEDING HABITS During the breeding season Greater Swamp Warbler is territorial and probably monogamous. Territories are small; a pair in Zimbabwe occupied *c.* 600m² (Hustler 1995). The nest is placed over deep water. Examples in Senegal were set low down between reed stems (De Naurois 1985), but In E and S Africa it is typically built 2–2.5m up within papyrus, slung between three or four vertical stems, or sometimes placed within an inflorescence, below the canopy. It is bulky with a deep cup, constructed from reed and grass or long strips of papyrus, and lined with finer strips and sometimes a few feathers. The clutch is 2–3 eggs. Incubation in Zimbabwe lasted at least 14 days (Hustler 1995), but the fledging period is unknown. Nestlings are fed by both parents. It breeds during the rainy season and so at different times throughout Africa,

from May to July in Senegal, April to October in Nigeria, March to April, July and October to November in Kenya and October to February in S Africa.

DISTRIBUTION Breeds in sub-Saharan Africa from Senegal east to S Sudan and south to Botswana. Within this extensive range, its distribution is highly fragmented but it tends to be locally common within its preferred habitat.

A. r. senegalensis Breeds in NW Senegal where it is locally common at Richard Toll and Mboro. Birds presumably of this race also breed near Tambacounda in SE Senegal, and in the Gambia at wetlands along the Gambia River between Tendaba and Jakhaly.

A. r. rufescens The main range extends from SE Ghana to S Nigeria, Cameroon and the island of Bioko. In addition, there are apparently isolated populations at Mole in N Ghana, Kano in N Nigeria, Ubangi River in NW DR Congo and in N Central African Republic. It is common in Cabinda (Angola) and near Boma on the Lower Congo River, and in NW Angola, where birds

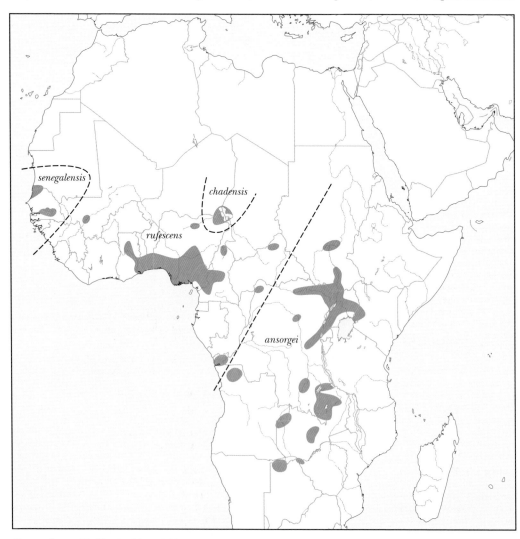

Greater Swamp Warbler. Resident within breeding range.

from Bengo and Luanda to N Cuanza Norte have been assigned to this race (Traylor 1963, Dean 2000).

A. r. chadensis Confined to Lake Chad, on the borders of W Chad and NE Nigeria.

A. r. ansorgei Ranges east and south of the nominate race. Breeds along the Upper Nile from S Sudan to NW, C and SW Uganda and N Rwanda and in adjacent E DR Congo. In NE DR Congo it is known from the Uele River and (perhaps this race) from the Congo River at Kisangani. In W Kenya it is locally common at Lake Victoria. Further south it breeds in NW Angola in Malange (the type locality) and S Cuanza Norte, reportedly just southeast of nominate *rufescens* (Traylor 1963; Dean 2000). It breeds in SE DR Congo at Lake Upemba and is locally quite common in Zambia (Luapala and W Northern Provinces, Lukanga and Busanga Swamps, Kafue and the Upper Zambezi), along the Middle Zambezi River (Zambia/W Zimbabwe border) and in the Okavango delta, N Botswana.

MOVEMENTS Apparently sedentary.

DESCRIPTION *A. r. rufescens*
Plumage – Adult Fresh Forehead and crown olive-brown with a greyish cast. Supercilium grey-buff, faint and narrow, above lores only. Lores greyish olive-brown. Cheeks and ear-coverts greyish olive-brown, streaked grey-buff. Nape, upper side of neck, mantle and scapulars olive-brown, tinged greyish, becoming lighter, slightly ochreous or cinnamon on rump and uppertail-coverts. Tail feathers dark grey-brown with narrow olive-brown edges. Chin and throat whitish, washed creamy-buff. Lower side of neck, breast and upper flanks darker greyish brown. Belly, lower flanks, vent and undertail-coverts more tawny-brown, becoming whiter on belly centre. Lesser, median and greater coverts greyish olive-brown, greater coverts with buffier edges. Primary coverts and alula dark grey-brown, edged warm buff. Tertials and flight feathers dark grey-brown, edged warm buff. Underwing-coverts creamy buff.
Juvenile Upperparts rich brown with cinnamon or yellowish tinge, brightest on rump and uppertail-coverts. Whole of underparts washed tawny-buff, with sides cinnamon-brown. Wing and tail feathers browner than in adult, remiges and wing-coverts with broader and brighter edges.
Bare parts Upper mandible dusky brown. Lower mandible pale yellowish grey or buff with dusky tip. Mouth dull yellow. Tarsi and toes dark bluish or greenish grey; soles yellowish. Iris light brown or reddish.

IN HAND CHARACTERS
Measurements

A. r. rufescens

	Male	Female
Wing	69–79 (74.4; 18)	67–75 (72.0; 13)
Tail	67–78 (72.3; 10)	64–69 (66.8; 10)
Bill	21–23 (22.0; 10)	20–22 (21.0; 8)
Tarsus	29–30.5 (30.1; 10)	28–30 (28.7; 8)

Sexes combined:
Tail/wing ratio: 92–99% (95%; 19)
Bill width: 4.8–5.2 (5.0; 10)
Hind claw: 8.8–10.8 (9.6; 13)
Tail graduation: 13–18 (14.4; 9)

A. r. ansorgei

East African birds:

	Male	Female
Wing	76–80 (78.3; 10)	72–78 (75.1; 10)
Tail	73–80 (77.1; 9)	71–75 (73.3; 10)
Bill	21–23 (22.1; 9)	20–22.5 (21.4; 9)
Tarsus	29–33 (31.2; 9)	28–31.5 (29.8; 10)

Sexes combined:
Tail/wing ratio: 95–101% (98%; 20)
Bill width: 4.8–5.4 (5.1; 9)
Hind claw: 10.6–12.5 (11.3; 13)
Tail graduation: 17–20 (18.4; 12)
   Averages larger than nominate race, with larger claws.
   Central African birds (SW Uganda and N Rwanda) are larger still: wing 80–85mm (White 1963).
   Southern African birds are also large with a longer but narrower bill: (n = 5, sexes combined) *wing* 76–82 (79.2); *tail* 74–78 (75.6); *bill* 23–23.5 (23.1); *tarsus* 30–33 (31.4); bill width 4.4–5.0 (4.7).
A. r. senegalensis (sexes combined, n = 3): *wing* 73, 76, 78; *tail* 66, 69, 70; *bill* 20, 21, 21.5; *tarsus* 29, 29, 30.
A. r. chadensis (sexes combined, n = 3): *wing* 72, 72, 74; *tail* 65, 65, 68; *bill* 19.5, 21, 21; *tarsus* 27, 29.

Structure

A. r. rufescens

Wing formula (n = 10):

p1/pc	p2	p3e	p4e	p5e	p6e	p7	p10
15–19	8–10	1.5–2.5	wp	wp	0–1.5	1–3	8–10

   Wing strongly rounded with large p1 (*c.* 60% p2). Wing point p4–5 (6); p2 = p10; emargination on p3–6.

Figure 69. Wing of Greater Swamp Warbler.

   Tail longish, graduated; feathers rather broad and rounded.
   Bill long, deep and broad-based, concave-sided.
   Tarsi thick and strong; toes long with large strong claws.
   A. r. ansorgei Similar to nominate *rufescens* but wing slightly more rounded, with p2 = tips of ss.
Recognition Large and long-billed, dark olive-brown above and greyish below with a whiter throat. Lacks warm tones and whiter underparts of Lesser Swamp Warbler. Wing length range overlaps with that of Lesser Swamp Warbler, but most birds (those with wing > 74mm in E Africa, >70mm

in W Africa) would be separable from Lesser Swamp races occurring with them. Easily distinguished from other *Acrocephalus* in Africa by large first primary and large dark tarsi and toes.

Weight

A. r. rufescens: (n = 9) mean 20.0g.

A. r. ansorgei: W Kenya, 18–29.3g (22.3; 81) (Britton 1978).

GEOGRAPHIC VARIATION Variation mainly affects plumage colour, but also size and structure. Nominate W African birds are paler and distinctly smaller than those of central, E and S Africa. Birds from the highlands of SW Uganda and N Rwanda ('*foxi*') are particularly large, while southern birds are also slightly larger than those of E Africa and appear to have narrower bills. These differences seem slight, however. We retain all eastern and southern populations within *ansorgei* and recognise four races.

A. r. rufescens (Ghana and Nigeria to NW Angola) Described above.

A. r. senegalensis (Senegal and Gambia) Differs from the nominate race in having a greyer crown and mantle and less warmly toned rump. The underparts, including the breast and upper flanks, are whiter (less grey) with a buffy brown wash confined to the lower flanks, belly and undertail-coverts

A. r. chadensis (Lake Chad) Similar to the nominate form but slightly paler. The upperparts are light olive-brown with an ochreous tinge, strongest on the rump. The underparts are whiter, with a reduced grey-brown suffusion on the breast and flanks.

A. r. ansorgei (S Sudan, Uganda and Kenya to Zambia, W Zimbabwe, N Botswana and C Angola) Darker and greyer than the nominate race above and below and distinctly larger. The upperparts are cold brown, becoming slightly paler and more distinctly tawny-brown on the rump and uppertail-coverts. The supercilium is dingy, very poorly marked and less conspicuous than in the nominate race. The entire underparts are suffused greyish brown, but with a tawny tinge to the lower flanks and undertail-coverts. The greyish brown chin and throat are slightly paler than the breast and there are a few dusky streaks on the throat. The edges to the flight feathers are buffy brown.

TAXONOMY AND SYSTEMATICS Birds from the Upper Nile, Kenya, E DR Congo and Zambia were originally assigned to race *nilotica*, while large birds of the SW Uganda and Rwanda highlands were described as the race *foxi*. But birds described as *ansorgei* from NW Angola were not very different and all E and S African populations are usually now treated as one race, within *ansorgei* as this name has precedence. It is curious that nominate *rufescens* is reported to breed in NW Angola, quite close to the *ansorgei* type locality.

This species and Lesser Swamp Warbler were long classified in the genus *Calamocichla*, or in *Calamoecetor*, but since White (1963), Hall & Moreau (1970) and Benson *et al.* (1970) they have been placed in *Acrocephalus*. Recent genetic studies show that they form a natural grouping together with the Cape Verde, Madagascar Swamp, Rodrigues and Seychelles Warblers, closely allied to the large, plain-backed *Acrocephalus* species of Europe and Asia (Leisler *et al.* 1997; Fregin *et al.* 2009).

▲ Adult *A. r. ansorgei*, Kalobo, W Zambia, May. Note the greyish head and grey underparts with contrasting paler throat (Peter Ryan).

▲ Adult *A. r. ansorgei*, Kalobo, W Zambia, May. A pair of adults (Peter Ryan).

▲ ▶ *A. r. ansorgei*, SW Uganda, August. A moulting bird, showing new greyish brown upperparts, grey underparts and long stout bill with yellow-based lower mandible (Augusto Faustino).

▲ Adult *A. r. ansorgei*, Kavango River, N Namibia, August. Freshly moulted. Reddish eye suggests an older bird. Note the plain greyish head with barely noticeable supercilium, and the dark grey leg (Hugh Chittenden).

▲ Adult *A. r. rufescens*, Edea, Cameroon, March. The underparts are paler than in *ansorgei*. Note the largely yellowish lower mandible (Nik Borrow).

MADAGASCAR SWAMP WARBLER
Acrocephalus newtoni   **Plate 23**

Calamoherpe newtoni **Hartlaub, 1863**. *Proc. Zool. Soc. London*, page 165. Near Soamandrikazay, Madagascar.

A marsh-dwelling resident *Acrocephalus* endemic to Madagascar, where it occurs in wetlands throughout the island. Monotypic.

IDENTIFICATION Length 18cm. Wing 64–73mm. Tail/wing 101–112%.

A large slender warbler. Drab olive-brown upperparts, olive-buff underparts and a conspicuously streaked throat separate it from all likely confusion species except perhaps Madagascar Brush Warbler. Its mellow song is distinctive however. Sexes alike.

Structure A large *Acrocephalus* with a longish bill, strong legs and a long, rather narrow, graduated tail. The wing is short and strongly rounded, with a large first primary and wing point formed by p4–5. In size and structure it is quite similar to the Lesser Swamp Warbler of mainland Africa

Plumage and bare parts The adult is pale olive-brown above, slightly darker and greyer on the crown, and shows a narrow and inconspicuous supercilium above dark greyish lores that does not extend far behind the eye. The sides of the head are faintly streaked dark greyish and olive-brown but show only slight contrast with the upperparts. The throat is buffy white with long, bold blackish streaks that extend onto the upper breast and upper flanks. Otherwise, the underparts are light olive-buff, with browner flanks and undertail-coverts. The dull brown tail appears darker than the rump. The wings are olive brown but the larger coverts and remiges show paler buffier edges and the closed flight feathers appear warmer and browner than the upperparts.

Juveniles are warmer brown above than adults and show a brighter tone to the rump. Below, they are warmer buff with shorter, browner and less conspicuous throat streaks and warm cinnamon-brown flanks and undertail-coverts.

The bill is dark grey with a pinkish base below. The legs are also dark grey.

SIMILAR SPECIES Two other warblers of similar size occur in marshy habitat in Madagascar; Madagascar Brush Warbler, which is likely to be mistaken for Madagascar Swamp Warbler although it is often found away from wetlands, and Grey Emutail, which bears only a cursory resemblance.

Madagascar Brush Warbler occurs alongside the swamp warbler in marshy habitats throughout Madagascar. It is similar in size and structure and also shows a conspicuously streaked throat, so care is required in their separation. It has similarly toned brownish upperparts but is darker and browner below and the throat streaking is usually softer and more diffuse. It has a proportionately longer tail but a smaller bill than the swamp warbler. Its vocalisations are quite different.

Grey Emutail has a smaller more rounded body than the swamp warbler and a much longer tail with a loose, degenerate structure, always appearing untidy. It also has a proportionately shorter bill, greyer and conspicuously streaked upperparts and paler underparts, which are conspicuously streaked, particularly on the throat and upper breast.

VOICE The song is simple, a short sequence of repeated

ringing notes. There is considerable individual variation, but the same sequence tends to be repeated several times, interspersed with short pauses during which an occasional, low chacking note may be heard. The most frequently heard song is a rather bulbul *Pycnonotus*-like '*chit-dweerd-wee*', which sometimes extends into a short trill with the final phrase repeated several times: '*chit-chtweerd-wee-wee-wee-wee*'. The song is repeated at intervals of 5–10 seconds.

Frequent variations include: '*teeee-tew-tew-tew-tew*', '*chipuchichichichichi*', '*pruchi-pruchi-pruchi-pruchi*', '*kerwi-kerwi-kerwi-kerwi-kerwi*' and a harsher '*chwer-chwer-chwer-chwer...*' and '*kercherweea-kerchwrweea-kercherweea...*'. The song is similar in structure to that of Lesser Swamp Warbler, but higher pitched and less throaty, with sequences typically shorter and syllables repeated more rapidly.

Song of Madagascar Swamp Warbler, Tararanle, Madagascar, August. (Jean C. Roche/British Library Sound Archive)

Calls are short and chacking, sometimes repeated in short series. It often gives a harsh '*k-cherr*' and a longer '*chercherchup*'.

MOULT No information.

HABITAT Usually found in reeds *Phragmites*, sedges *Cyperus*, *Typha* and other aquatic vegetation; sometimes also in tall grass, small trees, mangroves and coastal scrub. It frequents marshes and swamps, the edges of lakes, ponds, slow-moving rivers and old rice paddies. It occurs mainly below 1,800m, but ranges locally up to 2,050m in dry ericoid vegetation dominated by *Philippia*.

BEHAVIOUR Usually solitary and furtive and can be difficult to observe except when singing. Males may sing perched on a reed or stem but usually do so from within the cover of a dense shrub. Silent birds are likely to be seen briefly on a reed head or on other waterside before plunging back into cover. It is most at home in reedbeds where it climbs reed stems, moving from one vertical stalk to another. On the Andringitra Massif, it has frequently been reported clambering up and down thin *Philippia* trunks in the same way that it does reed stems. Flight between adjacent clumps of vegetation is slow and laboured, often with the tail spread.

BREEDING HABITS Apparently not studied; little information available. The nest is usually built in dense vegetation 0.5–1m above the water. It may be suspended from several vertical reed stalks, or built inside a dense bush. It is a cup made from dry grasses, woven together with bits of dry bark and down and lined with finer pieces of the same material and a few feathers (Langrand 1990). The clutch is usually three eggs. No information is available on incubation or fledging periods. Nesting is known to occur from May to January, with peak activity in November–December.

DISTRIBUTION Widely distributed in the east and west of Madagascar where it is common and widespread in all shrubby riverside, reedbed and marsh habitats, ranging from sea level to above 2,000m. It is absent from the extreme north of the island and less common in the drier south. An isolated population above the tree line on the Andringitra Massif cannot be differentiated using morphological or molecular characters (Goodman *et al.* 2000).

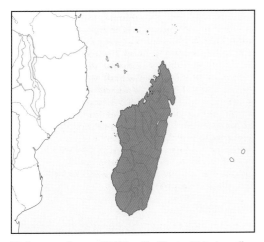

Madagascar Swamp Warbler. Resident within breeding range.

MOVEMENTS Believed to be sedentary.

DESCRIPTION

Plumage – Adult fresh Forehead and crown rather dark greyish olive-brown. Supercilium light brown, narrow and inconspicuous, extending back only to the eye. Lores and below eye dark greyish brown. Cheeks and ear-coverts light olive-brown with dark greyish brown streaks. Lower sides of neck light olive brown. Nape greyish olive-brown. Mantle and scapulars to uppertail-coverts olive brown, becoming slightly paler, more ochreous, on rump and uppertail-coverts. Tail feathers dark olive-brown. Chin and throat whitish, washed olive-buff, contrasting with olive-buff breast and belly. Throat and upper breast with bold blackish brown streaks. Flanks to undertail-coverts suffused greyish brown, lower flanks to undertail-coverts with a gingery tinge. Lesser and median coverts olive-brown. Greater and primary coverts olive-brown with diffuse lighter outer fringes. Remiges dark olive-brown, primaries and secondaries edged buffy brown. Alula olive-brown, edged pale olive-buff. Underwing-coverts olive-buff.

Juvenile Upperparts brown, tinged cinnamon, especially on rump and uppertail-coverts. Underparts washed gingery buff. Side of breast, flanks and undertail-coverts suffused cinnamon-brown. Throat streaks short and brownish.

Bare parts Upper mandible dark grey. Lower mandible mostly dark grey, with pinkish base. Tarsi and toes dark grey. Iris reddish brown in adult, darker brown in juvenile.

IN HAND CHARACTERS
Measurements

	Male	Female
Wing	67–73 (70.0; 8)	64–70 (66.4; 7)
Tail	70–78 (73.8; 8)	70–74 (72.0; 6)
Bill	18–20 (18.5; 8)	18–20 (18.6; 7)
Tarsus	25.5–28 (26.6; 8)	24–26 (25.0; 7)

Sexes combined:
Tail/wing ratio: 101–112% (107; 14)
Bill width: 4.0–4.6 (4.3; 10)
Hind claw: 6.8–8.0 (7.6; 12)
Tail graduation: 18–26 (21.3; 10)

Structure

Wing formula (n = 10):

p1/pc	p2	p3e	p4e	p5e	p6e	p7	p10
11–15	8–10	1–3	wp	wp	0–1.5	1.5–2.5	8–11

Wing similar to Greater Swamp Warbler (Fig. 69); strongly rounded with large p1 (*c.* 60% p2). Wing point p4–5 (6); p2 = p9/10–10/ss; emargination on p3–6.

Tail longish, more strongly graduated than in mainland African swamp warblers *A. rufescens* and *A. gracilirostris;* feathers rather narrow.

Bill longish, concave sided and fine tipped; rather smaller, more slender than in Lesser Swamp Warbler.

Tarsi long and strong, toes and claws long.

Weight 14.5–20.5g (16.8; 10) (Ravokatra *et al.* 2003).

GEOGRAPHIC VARIATION None recorded.

TAXONOMY AND SYSTEMATICS Morphological and vocal characters indicate that Madagascar Swamp Warbler belongs with *A. rufescens* and *A. gracilirostris* in the '*Calamocichla*' group of African swamp warblers. This is also confirmed by DNA analysis (Leisler *et al.* 1997; Fregin *et al.* 2009). The two former *Bebrornis* species of the W Indian Ocean, Seychelles Warbler and Rodrigues Warbler, also belong here.

▲ Adult, Antananarivo, Madagascar, September (Boedts Bruno).

▲ Adult, Madagascar, October. Greyish brown with a narrow supercilium, pale throat and bold breast streaks (Pete Morris).

▲ Adult, Ankarafantsika, Madagascar, October. Note the long narrow tail feathers and bright-based lower mandible (Jacques Erard).

SEYCHELLES WARBLER
Acrocephalus sechellensis **Plate 23**

Ellisia sechellensis **Oustalet, 1877.** *Bull. Soc. Philomath.* Paris, sér. 7(1): 103. Marianne Island, Seychelles.

A resident of scrub and woodland endemic to the Seychelles. Considered VULNERABLE by BirdLife International. Monotypic.

IDENTIFICATION Length 14cm. Wing 62–74mm. Tail/wing 81–88 %.
A medium-sized, rather plain greyish green or brownish green *Acrocephalus* with a long and fairly stout bill. The only warbler resident on the granitic Seychelles. Sexes alike.
Structure Although not a large *Acrocephalus*, it has a rather chunky appearance, enhanced by a proportionately large and rounded head and a strong, slightly decurved bill. The wings are short and strongly rounded with a large first primary and wing point formed by p5–6. It has a strongly graduated tail of ten feathers. The legs are long, relatively thick and strong.

a   b

Figure 70. Comparison of head and bill profiles of (a) Seychelles Warbler and (b) Rodrigues Warbler.

Plumage and bare parts The adult has uniform drab brown upperparts with a slight greenish or yellowish tinge. It shows a short and poorly marked supercilium above pale brown lores and a pale eye-ring of variable contrast, but the ear-coverts are concolorous with the crown and show no contrast. The yellowish buff or creamy buff underparts are contrastingly paler on the throat and undertail-coverts and often show a few faint breast streaks. The wing and tail feathers are darker brown than the upperparts and edged yellowish olive, with a contrasting pale panel on the closed secondaries. When fresh, the outer tail feathers show conspicuous pale tips, a feature atypical of *Acrocephalus*.
The juvenile resembles the adult but is darker, with some speckling on the breast.
The bill is dark brown with a pale yellowish pink lower mandible that darkens slightly at the sides towards the tip. The legs and feet are blue-grey. The eyes are reddish-brown in mature adults and lighter brown in younger adults, but greyish in juveniles.

SIMILAR SPECIES No similar species occur in the Seychelles. Within the Indian Ocean region, Rodrigues Warbler, endemic to Rodrigues in the Mascarene Islands, has similar yellow-tinged underparts and pale tail feather tips, but this is a smaller bird with a more slender bill (Fig. 70) and proportionately longer tail. The Lesser Swamp Warbler of Africa is rather similar in size and structure but has rufescent plumage tones, a narrower bill and 12 tail feathers.

VOICE The song is relatively short, simple and melodious. It is made up of repeated rich whistled notes and may be introduced by one or two short quieter notes, '*chu-ku-cheeoo-cheeoo-cheeoo-cheeoo*' or '*wichichu-wichichu-wichichu-wichichu-...*'.

It is low-pitched, most notes falling between 1.7 and 3kHz. Sequences lasting 1–3 seconds are separated by intervals of several seconds. Individuals produce substantial variety. Song structure is similar to those of the Greater Swamp and Lesser Swamp Warblers but less harsh and lacks their low chuckling quality. It is also less varied but with clearer repeated whistles. A low, fast, warbling sub-song is occasionally heard.

Song of Seychelles Warbler, Cousin Island, Seychelles, February. (Martijn Hammers)

The alarm call is a harsh nasal '*chk, chk*' and it gives a rapid, low, twittering contact call. Dependent juveniles give a persistent single wheezy begging call.

MOULT No information.

HABITAT Inhabits small, low islands with dense scrub vegetation and woodland dominated by *Pisonia grandis*, *Morinda citrifolia* and *Ochrosia oppositifolia*.

BEHAVIOUR Usually solitary but also found in pairs or small family parties. It can be tame and approachable, and juveniles can be very inquisitive, but is often unobtrusive as it moves steadily through vegetation, searching for insects and gleaning from leaves with deliberate movements. It may hang from twigs and peck at food from below. It typically makes only short flitting flights between bushes. Spontaneous song is infrequent and rarely sustained over long periods.

BREEDING HABITS Highly territorial and forms long-term breeding pairs, but has evolved a complex system of cooperative breeding; the only *Acrocephalus* species known to employ nest helpers (although Henderson Island Warbler often breeds in trios of unrelated birds, and a similar system of cooperation may occur). It produces a small clutch and relies on high adult survival. On Cousin, very small territories (average 0.15ha) are defended throughout the year until the occupant male dies. Each territory contains a pair of breeders together with any recently fledged dependent offspring and a variable number of independent young from previous breeding attempts, who may act as helpers. About one-third of territories on Cousin support subordinate individuals (Richardson *et al.* 2002). Such subordinates may act as helpers at the nest. The most successful groups have been shown to be those with a pair plus one helper (Komdeur 1994a). Helpers of both sexes engage in several aspects of parental care, including nest building (mainly females), incubation (females), nest defence (mainly males) and feeding young (both sexes) (Komdeur 1994a). In addition, joint-nesting by the primary female and the helper occurs frequently and there is a high incidence of extra-group paternity (Richardson *et al.* 2001).
The nest is cup-shaped, composed of grass stems, leaves and coconut fibres, with a finer lining of the same material. It is usually built in a fork of a tree or shrub, woven around three or four upright stems. The clutch is usually one egg, but occasionally two or three. These are incubated by the dominant breeding female and female helpers for approximately 18 days. Fledging occurs after *c.* 19 days, after which the young remain dependent for

up to three months. One brood per year is usual. Whereas single fledglings survive well, broods of three usually die before independence. Where the natal territory quality is high, young birds remain as helpers for longer and defer their own breeding. On Cousin, they often remained about two years and first bred at about four years. Remarkably, the sex ratio of the young can be biased depending on the environment. In territories with scarce food most eggs produce males, which move away. When food is plentiful, most eggs produce females, which tend to be recruited as helpers. Breeding activity peaks around June–July and, to a lesser extent, in January–February, but may continue throughout the year if insects are abundant (Diamond 1980; Komdeur 1992, 1996, 1996a, b; Komdeur *et al.* 1995; Skerrett *et al.* 2001).

DISTRIBUTION Endemic to the Seychelles, where it is now present on four small islands, Cousin, Aride, Cousine and Denis. In the 1960s it was confined to Cousin (area 0.3 km²) and on the brink of extinction with fewer than 30 individuals surviving in 1968. A spectacular recovery has since followed due to the regeneration of native woodland and the translocation of birds to the neighbouring islands of Aride (in 1988) and Cousine (in 1990) (Komdeur 1994a). Recent population estimates give about 320 birds on Cousin where the population seems to be stable, *c.* 230 on Cousine, *c.* 150 on Denis and *c.* 2,000 on Aride. Additional breeding populations may be established in the near future by translocation to predator-free islands. The natural range is unknown but it may have occurred previously on most of the granitic Seychelles islands, at least on Marianne, and possibly Cousine (M. Hammers *in litt.*).

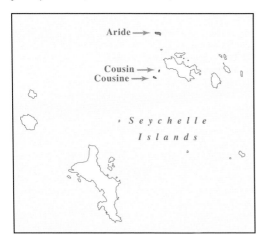

Seychelles Warbler. Resident within breeding range. Also introduced to Denis.

MOVEMENTS Sedentary. Inter-island migration is extremely rare. Only two cases of inter-island displacement were recorded in a 20-year study (Komdeur *et al.* 2004).

DESCRIPTION
Plumage – Adult fresh Forehead to nape olive-brown. Supercilium olive-buff, narrow and poorly marked, above lores only. Eye-ring creamy white and narrow. Lores dusky olive forming indistinct line from eye to bill, but lacks darker stripe behind eye. Ear-coverts olive-brown merging with the crown. Cheeks olive-brown, flecked yellowish buff, being palest below loral stripe. Mantle and scapulars to uppertail-

coverts uniform olive-brown, tinged yellowish. Tail feathers dark brown with narrow yellowish olive-brown outer edges, all except the central pair with a whitish fringe around the distal part and tip of the inner web. Chin and throat creamy buff. Breast and belly pale yellowish buff, upper breast often with a few dusky brown streaks. Sides of neck and breast light olive-brown. Flanks suffused olive-brown. Undertail-coverts pale creamy buff.

Upperwing-coverts dark brown, edged and tipped paler yellowish olive-brown. Alula similar but with pale yellowish edge. Remiges dark brown with olive-yellow edges, these becoming broader on secondaries and tertials to form contrasting pale panel. Underwing-coverts pale yellowish buff.
Juvenile As fresh adult but slightly darker, with faint speckling on breast.
Bare parts Upper mandible dark horn with yellowish cutting edges. Lower mandible yellowish flesh, usually with a variable dusky tip. Mouth yellow. Tarsi and toes bluish grey. Iris chestnut-brown in adult, blue-grey in young juvenile, becoming medium greyish brown in sub-adult (Skerrett *et al.* 2001).

IN HAND CHARACTERS
Measurements

	Male	Female
Wing	65–74 (68.0; 4)	62– 69 (65.7; 3)
Tail	56–60 (58.7; 3)	53–59 (56.0; 4)
Bill	18–19 (18.3; 4)	17.5–19 (18.3; 4)
Tarsus	25–27.5 (26.3; 4)	24–25.5 (24.9; 4)

Sexes combined:
Tail/wing ratio: 81–88% (86%; 6)
Bill width: 4.6–4.8 (4.7; 3)
Hind claw: 6.4–7.0 (6.7; 6)
Tail graduation: 12–15 (12.8; 4)

Structure

Wing formula (n = 5):

p1/pc	p2	p3e	p4e	p5e	p6e	p7	p10
13–17	6–9	1–3	0–1	wp	wp	0–2	7–9

Wing strongly rounded with large p1 (50–60% p2). Wing point p(4) 5–6; p2 = p9/10–10; emargination on p3–6.

Figure 71. Wing of Seychelles Warbler.

Tail medium, graduated, with ten quite broad, rounded rectrices.
Bill long, quite broad-based and straight-sided.
Tarsi long and strong; claws strong.

Weight 43 ♂♂, mean 16.9g, 25 ♀♀, mean 15.0g (Diamond 1980).

GEOGRAPHIC VARIATION None known.

TAXONOMY AND SYSTEMATICS This species and Rodrigues Warbler were formerly placed in the genus *Bebrornis*. Some authors then combined *Bebrornis* with *Nesillas*, a genus of brush warblers otherwise confined to Madagascar, the Comores and Aldabra. But the vocal and morphological characters of Seychelles and Rodrigues Warblers differ significantly from those of the *Nesillas* species and suggested a closer relationship with the Greater Swamp, Lesser Swamp and Madagascar Swamp Warblers (Diamond 1980). Further vocal and DNA studies have confirmed that the swamp warblers and the former *Bebrornis* species form a grouping within *Acrocephalus* (Dowsett-Lemaire 1994; Leisler *et al.* 1997; Fregin *et al.* 2009).

▲ Adult, Cousin Island, Seychelles, July. Shows the greenish olive upperparts, yellow-tinged underparts and strong grey legs (Martijn Hammers).

▲ Adult, Cousin Island, July. A browner-looking bird. Note the strong bill and the short wing projection (Martijn Hammers).

▲ Adult, Cousin Island, August. Note the conspicuous short supercilium and eye-ring (Martijn Hammers).

▲ Age uncertain. Cousin Island, August. A heavily worn and faded individual showing the strong bill and well-graduated tail. (Martijn Hammers).

RODRIGUES WARBLER
Acrocephalus rodericanus   Plate 23

Drymoeca rodericana **Newton, 1865**. *Proc. Zool. Soc. London*, page 47, Plate 1, figure 3. Rodrigues Island.

A resident of scrub and woodland on the small island of Rodrigues in the Indian Ocean and the only resident warbler on the Mascarene Islands. Considered ENDANGERED by BirdLife International. Monotypic.

IDENTIFICATION Length 13.5cm. Wing 59–65mm. Tail/wing 110–116%.

A small, light olive-brown warbler with yellow-tinged underparts and a long tail. Sexes similar, males slightly brighter than females.

Structure A medium sized *Acrocephalus* with a long, narrow bill and low head profile. The crown feathers tend to be raised when excited which gives it a large-headed look suggestive of a *Hippolais* warbler such as the Icterine or Melodious Warblers. This likeness is reinforced by its short undertail coverts and general plumage colour (Showler 1999). However, the wings are very short and rounded with a large first primary and wing point formed by p4–6. The graduated tail has ten feathers as in Seychelles Warbler, but is relatively long and narrow and frequently cocked above the back. The legs are robust, although less so than in Seychelles Warbler.

Plumage and bare parts Drab and nondescript, lacking any particularly distinctive features. When fresh, adults are uniform light olive brown above, with paler brown ear-coverts and cheeks. There is a short, rather indistinct, pale yellowish supercilium, noticeable only in front of the eye, which merges with a fairly obvious pale yellow eye-ring. The lores are pale yellow with a dusky spot in front of the eye that may extend from the bill. There is often a similar dusky line behind the eye. The entire underparts are distinctive pale lemon-yellow, slightly brighter in males than females. On the closed wing, the coverts are almost uniform with the scapulars. The remiges are darker brown, but with buffy yellow edges forming a broad pale panel in the wing. The tail is dark brown but the tips of the outer three pairs of feathers show conspicuous pale buff fringes. Worn birds are greyer above and drab greyish white below, with only a slight yellow tinge.

Young birds are variably yellow on throat and breast, with a whitish belly.

The bill is blackish with a pinkish lower mandible and the legs and feet are blue-grey. Usually, the reddish brown eyes are a noticeable feature.

SIMILAR SPECIES No similar species occur on Rodrigues or elsewhere in the Mascarene Archipelago. The related Seychelles Warbler is a more robust looking bird with darker upperparts and a shorter tail.

VOICE The song is short and simple, usually lasting 1–2 seconds. It consists of a few repetitions of a low melodious phrase, varying from one song to another, often preceded or followed by one or two short conversational notes; '*cherpeechupee-cherpeechupee...*', a more rapid '*chewichewichewi-chewi*', a harsher⁰ *chercherwer-chercherwer-chercherwer*', or a more strongly disyllabic '*ch-chu-werchi-werchi-werchi-ch-chu...*', reminiscent of a Great Tit. Like the song of Seychelles Warbler, it has a low frequency range and a structure recalling the songs of African swamp warblers. It is less loud and ringing than Seychelles Warbler song and lacks

the harsher chuckling and chacking sounds of the two swamp warblers.

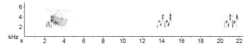

Song of Rodrigues Warbler, Rodrigues, July. (Kristy Swinnerton/British Library Sound Archive)

Calls are sharp and sparrow-like, described as '*chipipi*' and '*chitik*'.

MOULT No information.

HABITAT It formerly occurred in native forest, probably throughout the island. This has mostly been cleared and replaced by introduced trees, resulting in a dramatic population decline. The remaining birds are found mainly on moister northwest-facing slopes, which provide better protection from cyclones. Here it is confined to dense thickets in the remaining, largely exotic, vegetation. It is particularly attracted to patches of scrub and woodland dominated by Jamrosa (rose-apple) *Syzygium jambos*, with a mixture of Guava *Psidium cattleianum*, Mango *Mangifera indica*, *Litsea glutinosa*, *Tabebuia pallida* and other introduced trees. It is sometimes found in areas with little or no rose-apple, such as plantations of Mahogany *Swietenia mahogany* and Norfolk Island Pine *Araucaria cunninghamii*, but prefers a habitat with a dense structure of small branches (Showler *et al.* 2002).

BEHAVIOUR A quiet and unobtrusive species which usually occurs in pairs and keeps mainly to woodland sub-canopy 2–12m from the ground. It is often inquisitive and very active and agile (more so than Seychelles Warbler), moving continuously, gleaning from leaves and twigs and sometimes from the uppersides of large branches. It frequently cocks its tail at 45–60 degrees above its back and sometimes flicks it from side to side. Song is given infrequently and from anywhere within its territory, with no favourite song-posts.

BREEDING HABITS Apparently monogamous, with territories usually occupied by two birds. The nest is typically built about 2–3m up near the top of a guava bush, or 1.5–5m up beneath tall Jamrosa canopy. It is a rather deep cup, lined with a few feathers and supported in a fork of two or more slender branches. There are usually three eggs in the clutch, which are incubated by both sexes for 10–11 days. The fledging period has been estimated at *c.* 14 days and usually just one or two chicks are reared to fledging. The period of post-fledging care appears to be less extended than in Seychelles Warbler. The breeding season lasts from late September or early October to March and two broods may be raised during this period.

DISTRIBUTION Now restricted to the central uplands of Rodrigues where its distribution is fragmented, with birds confined mainly to seven small areas: Cascade Pigeon/La Source, Grande Montagne, Gros Mangue/Solitude, Mont Cimitiere, Mont Limon, Mont Malartic and Saint Gabriel.

It was once common and probably widespread throughout the island but its range contracted dramatically during the mid twentieth century due to loss and fragmentation of habitat and severe cyclones. By 1979, only 17 birds could be found. With habitat protection and reforestation since 1982, there has been a steady increase in range and in the number of thriving sub-populations. At least 150 birds were estimated in 1999, with up to 2.3 birds/ha in Jamrosa thickets (Showler *et al.* 2002). There has since been a large population increase coupled with woodland expansion.

Rodrigues Warbler. Resident within breeding range.

MOVEMENTS Believed to be sedentary.

DESCRIPTION
Plumage – Adult fresh Forehead to nape light olive-brown. Supercilium pale buffy yellow, rather narrow but extending to behind eye. Lores pale yellow with dusky spot in front of eye. Eye-ring narrow, pale yellow, broken posteriorly. Below eye to ear-coverts light olive-brown, flecked pale yellow. Mantle and scapulars to uppertail-coverts light olive-brown with slight yellow tinge. Tail feathers dark brown, narrowly edged light olive-brown, tips of t3–5 with buffy white fringes. Underparts, including lower cheeks and lower sides of neck lemon-yellow, sides of breast with olivaceous suffusion. Undertail-coverts slightly paler. Lesser, median and greater coverts light olive-brown with diffuse pale buffy edging. Primary coverts and alula dark brown, edged pale buffy yellow. Remiges dark brown, with pale buffy yellow edges, inclining to whitish on primaries, giving broad pale panel on closed wing. Underwing-coverts pale buffy yellow.
Adult worn Upperparts greyish brown, underparts drab greyish white with yellow cast.
Juvenile Similar to adult, but with varying amounts of yellow on throat and breast, contrasting with greyish white belly.

Bare Parts Upper mandible blackish with orange-pink cutting edges and tip. Lower mandible pink. Tarsi and toes mid blue-grey; soles whitish to yellowish grey. Iris reddish brown.

IN HAND CHARACTERS
Measurements

Sexes combined (n = 10):

Wing	59–65 (61.7)
Tail	65–74 (70.1)
Bill	16–18.5 (17.3)
Tarsus	22.5–24.5 (23.1)

No significant difference noted between sexes.
Tail/wing ratio: 110–116% (114%; 7)
Bill width: 3.8–4.4 (4.0; 5)
Hind claw: 5.8–6.3 (6.0; 7)
Tail graduation: 13–22 (17.6; 7)

Structure

Wing formula (n = 6):

p1/pc	p2	p3e	p4e	p5e	p6e	p7	p10
17–20	6–9	2–3	wp	wp	wp	0.5–2	7–8

Wing similar to Seychelles Warbler (Fig. 71); strongly rounded with very large p1 (*c.* 70% p2). Wing point p4–6; p2 = p9/10–10/ss; emargination on p3–6.
Tail longish, graduated, with ten narrow, bluntly pointed feathers.
Bill long, rather slender, narrow with concave sides.
Tarsi long, rather strong; toes slender.
Recognition Differs from Seychelles Warbler in its smaller size, narrower bill (Fig. 70) and much longer tail with narrower feathers.
Weight 11–13g (12.1; 7) (Showler 1999).

GEOGRAPHIC VARIATION None known.

TAXONOMY AND SYSTEMATICS Formerly placed together with the Seychelles Warbler in the genus *Bebrornis*, but following Diamond (1980) these species are now regarded as forming a natural grouping within *Acrocephalus* together with the *Calamocichla'* swamp warblers of Africa and Madagascar.

▲ Adult, Rodrigues, November. This bird shows the pale yellow underparts, narrow tail and slender grey legs (Jon Hornbuckle).

▲ Adult, Rodrigues, November. Note the slender bill and distinct narrow supercilium (Jon Hornbuckle).

▲ Adult, Rodrigues, May. A bird completing moult. Note the long graduated tail, bright pinkish lower mandible and dark red eye (David Showler).

▲ Adult, Rodrigues, November (Jon Hornbuckle).

BASRA REED WARBLER
Acrocephalus griseldis   Plate 24

Calamoherpe griseldis **Hartlaub, 1891**. *Abhandl. Naturwissen. Vereine Bremen*, 12 (1893): 7. Nguru, Kilosa district, Tanganyika Territory.

A restricted-range breeding species, largely confined to the Mesopotamian marshes of S Iraq. A long-distance migrant which winters in E Africa. Formerly regarded as a small race of Great Reed Warbler, but now widely recognised as a distinctive species which differs from Great Reed in structure, plumage and song. Considered to be ENDANGERED by BirdLife International. Monotypic.

IDENTIFICATION Length 15–16cm. Wing 77–89mm. Tail/wing 72–77%.

A medium-sized *Acrocephalus* with unstreaked olive-brown upperparts and a long slim bill. During migration and wintering seasons it can occur alongside the smaller Eurasian Reed and Marsh Warblers and the larger Great Reed and Clamorous Reed Warblers. If singing or seen reasonably well it should not be mistaken for any of these. It is also quite different from any of the swamp-dwelling resident *Acrocephalus* with which it could occur in Africa. Sexes alike.

Structure Its sleek appearance suggests one of the smaller *Acrocephalus* species rather than the larger, heavily built Great Reed and Clamorous Reed Warblers. It is some 20% longer than Eurasian Reed and Marsh Warblers, but appears generally slimmer and more attenuated, an effect enhanced by its proportionately longer bill. This is similar in length to the bill of Great Reed and Clamorous Reed but much more slender, less broad and less deep. The wings are long and pointed, reaching beyond the longest uppertail-coverts and showing a primary projection of some 80%. The wing point is formed by p3, the only emarginated primary and eight well-spaced primary tips may be visible on the closed wing of freshly moulted birds (Fig. 75). The tail is proportionately rather shorter than in Great Reed Warbler, appearing less ample in flight and the legs are less robust.

Plumage and bare parts In fresh plumage, the upperparts are a distinctive cold olive-brown and lack the warmer rump and uppertail-coverts usual in Eurasian Reed and Great Reed Warblers, or the greenish tinge typical of Marsh Warbler. The underparts are whitish with a buffy brown suffusion confined to the sides of the breast and flanks. A long whitish supercilium, extending well behind the eye, is more prominent than that of Eurasian Reed and Marsh Warblers, but narrower than in Great Reed Warbler. It is well defined above the lores and the triangle of dark feathers in front of the eye appears large and distinct. A pale eye-ring contrasts with the supercilium and ear-coverts. Freshly moulted birds show dark primaries with conspicuous pale tips and a noticeably dark brown tail that contrasts with the upperparts: both these features are noticeable in the field. Juveniles on the breeding grounds have a distinctly warm tinge to the body plumage and show pale buff edges to the brownish wing feathers and a hint of creamy buff to the underparts and supercilium. These tend to wear quickly, but the greater covert fringes can form a distinct pale wing-bar. First-winter birds are duller and greyer above than fresh adults.

The bill appears dark horn or dark grey above and pinkish below, often with dusky sides near the tip. The legs, unlike those of Eurasian Reed or Great Reed, are always dark grey, although in adults they show a distinct brownish

tinge. The eyes are usually dark brown or mid brown, but become bright reddish brown in many adults.

SIMILAR SPECIES This is one of five plain-backed *Acrocephalus* with generally similar plumage pattern that occur within its breeding or non-breeding range. Eurasian Reed and Marsh Warblers are considerably smaller with much smaller bills and a less pronounced supercilium and distinction from these should not be problematic. The larger Great Reed and Clamorous Reed Warblers are discussed below. The two African resident *Acrocephalus*, the Greater Swamp and Lesser Swamp Warblers, are also, surprisingly, potential confusion species.

Great Reed Warbler may occur alongside Basra Reed on migration and in E African wintering areas. It is the largest of the Palearctic *Acrocephalus*, approximately 15% larger (in length) and almost twice the weight of Basra Reed and the two can be separated by wing length alone. Great Reed has a much wider and stouter bill. It is long-winged, with a similar wing formula to Basra Reed, but the tail is proportionately larger and the legs are conspicuously thicker and paler. Great Reed shows a rather broader and typically buffier supercilium and a more restricted dark patch in front of the eye. The upperparts and particularly the rump and uppertail-coverts are warmer than in Basra Reed and the underparts usually show a more pronounced light brown wash. The throat of adults shows faint streaking which Basra Reed lacks.

Clamorous Reed Warbler has three races in the Middle East which could come into contact with Basra Reed. Birds of the race *brunnescens* are likely to occur with Basra Reed Warbler as it migrates through this region. The latter could also meet wintering *brunnescens* in Iraq, and resident Clamorous Reed of race *levantinus* at the breeding site in Israel. Clamorous Reed resembles Basra Reed in overall plumage pattern but has a short and relatively inconspicuous supercilium, warmer and browner upperparts and more strongly tinged underparts. Structural differences are pronounced. Clamorous Reed is only slightly larger than Basra Reed but is heavier and more bulky. It has a much thicker and stronger bill and thicker legs, more like those of Great Reed Warbler. It shows a shorter primary projection and a different wing formula, with p2 shorter than p5 and p3–4 emarginated. It also has a longer more graduated tail.

Lesser Swamp and **Greater Swamp Warblers** are resident in E African marshes and have sometimes been mistaken for Basra Reed Warbler. Although similar in size to Basra Reed and with long narrow bills, these have quite different short rounded wings. They are much darker on the underparts and show only an indistinct supercilium.

VOICE The song is a loose, rather hesitant, sequence of low throaty notes, delivered at about 1.5 notes per second within a frequency range of 1.5–3.5kHz: '*chrk-chri-chrk-chchuk-chrk-churrik …*'. This song is often sustained for several minutes without an obvious pause. On occasion the song speeds up so there is little or no pause between notes, but it soon slows down again. Although it has the distinctive structure and character of an *Acrocephalus*, it lacks the power and rhythm and the grating quality of Great Reed Warbler song.

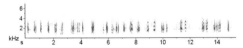

Part of song of Basra Reed Warbler, Mtito Andei, Kenya, February. (David Pearson)

The usual contact call is a harsh, complaining '*chaaarr*', similar to the call of Eurasian Reed Warbler, but stronger and more nasal.

MOULT All birds, adult and first year, undergo a complete moult in Africa. Adults replace some head and body feathers on the breeding grounds, but the extent of this post-breeding moult is unknown. Most renew their entire plumage between September and November, during the stopover in Ethiopia and then continue to winter quarters in fresh plumage. Others, however, suspend moult in Ethiopia and finish the replacement of their flight feathers in winter quarters after the second leg of migration. A few adults are still in fully old plumage during passage through Kenya and moult later in winter south of the equator. Young birds apparently replace much of their juvenile body feathering on the breeding grounds. In Africa, many then moult completely in Ethiopia, finishing by November or early December. But juvenile moult is more commonly suspended or delayed than in adults and some 30% of first year birds caught on passage in Kenya have fully old plumage (DJP). These moult further south, between January and March. Adult and first year birds that have a full moult during autumn show a partial replacement of body and head feathering in winter quarters during March.

HABITAT In Iraq it breeds in pure *Typha* vegetation near the shallow drying edges of saline inundated marshland, where recent reflooding has left the submerged remains of some terrestrial vegetation, but *Phragmites* reeds and sedges are absent (OF *in litt.*). Birds have been trapped in Israel at fishponds with surrounding thick cover of *Phragmites* and Blackberry *Rubus prucerus* bushes (Perlman & Geffen 2007). In Africa, it frequents dense moist thickets with tall rank grass and herbaceous undergrowth, especially along ditches and by drying pools; also herbaceous undergrowth in open woodland, coastal scrub, reeds, sedges, *Typha*, flooded grassland and sometimes papyrus by ponds and lakes. It favours flooded saltbush *Sueda monoeca* in coastal Kenya and occurs in Red Sea coastal mangroves on migration. Passage and wintering birds appear to seek the vicinity of water to a greater extent than either Eurasian Reed or Great Reed Warblers.

BEHAVIOUR Very active on their Iraq breeding territories. Readily approachable, but even the males remain largely out of sight within the *Typha* reedbeds (OF *in litt.*). In Africa, it forages within bushes or low down in reeds, picking items from leaves and stems and usually moving and perching with a slim, horizontal stance. Birds may emerge from cover to perch on a large stem close to the water surface, or feed while hopping on open mud. Flight is usually brief and low, the bird diving quickly back into cover; it is lighter and more agile than in Great Reed Warbler. Wintering birds are usually secretive and shy and are detected mainly by their call or song. Some occupy a territory for as long as three months, to which they return in later years. Of 112 birds netted at Nchalo, S Malawi, 17 returned in a subsequent winter, two of these up to eight years later (Hanmer 1989). A quiet song or sub-song is heard commonly, sometimes as early as November during an autumn stopover, but mainly in winter quarters during January to March, when birds can be vocal throughout the day.

BREEDING The nest is built 0.9–1.2m above water. It is a cone-shaped cup with an internal diameter of 7–9cm and attached to three vertical Typha stems (OF *in litt.*). Its mixed composition almost always includes snake skin. The

eggs, typically three but sometimes two, are usually laid during May. Young are fledged and independent in Iraq and in Israel early in July. Probably double-brooded. No other information.

DISTRIBUTION

Breeding As a breeding bird, almost entirely restricted to the Mesopotamian marshes of S and C Iraq, from Fao north to the Baghdad area and recently found further northwest along the Euphrates near Ar Ramadi (OF *in litt.*). Details of its distribution and population are poorly known but it is considered as endangered, an estimated 70–80% decline having occurred during recent decades due to drainage and destruction of marshes (BirdLife International). It probably also breeds in bordering areas of SW Iran (Ayé 2006) and in Kuwait, where birds are regularly heard in song each year

Basra Reed Warbler. Breeding range and winter distribution.

and have been observed collecting hairs for nesting material in late April. After occurring as a vagrant to Israel, breeding was proved in the Hula Valley in early July 2006, when two males, a female with a brood patch and a recently fledged juvenile were trapped (Perlman & Geffen 2007). Birds returned to breed here again in 2007 and 2008.

Non-breeding Winters from S Somalia and E Kenya south to Malawi and C Mozambique and has reached South Africa (Mpumalanga and KwaZulu-Natal) and Botswana (once, Gaborone). In Kenya, it winters in the hot low country east of the highlands, especially near the coast and there are few winter records from further inland. In Tanzania, it is also confined mainly to low-lying eastern areas, while in Malawi most records come from the Lower Shire Valley in the south. It is generally sparsely distributed within an African wintering range which far exceeds its breeding range. In Kenya, however, it is the main wintering *Acrocephalus* warbler on the floodplain of the lower Tana River, where densities of 10–20 birds/ha were found in delta salt bush (Pearson *et al.* 1978). It apparently occurs only as a passage migrant in Ethiopia and the few records from NE Sudan (August–October), S Sudan (once, October) and Uganda (three times, November) all relate to passage periods.

MOVEMENTS The Iraq breeding grounds are vacated mainly in late August (OF *in litt.*) but onward migration to the winter quarters near and south of the equator takes many weeks. On migration it passes through the Persian Gulf, Arabia and Ethiopia to reach E Africa. A few occur on the Sudan coast between late August and mid October. Birds spend two to three months in Ethiopia, where the first arrivals are in late August and most records come from the central Rift Valley in September and October. The first birds reach Kenya at the end of October, but the main passage through Tsavo is from mid November to early January and tens of birds are then trapped annually for ringing at Ngulia Safari Lodge. Birds reach coastal Kenyan wintering sites from late November onwards and arrive in Malawi from late November, but mainly in December. Spring migration is quite rapid. Birds leave wintering grounds in Kenya and Malawi in late March or early April and there are a few reports of migrants in Kenya in mid April. But the lack of spring passage records in NE Africa would indicate that large areas are overflown. There are only a few spring records from Arabia, but it is a common passage migrant in Kuwait from mid April to early May. Birds return to the Mesopotamian marshes from mid April onwards. A bird ringed in C Ethiopia (September) was recovered in C Mozambique (about early February). Another ringed in Kenya (December) was recovered in Saudi Arabia (August).

Vagrancy As a vagrant it has occurred in Cyprus in June 1981 and Syria in April 2006 (Yésou *et al.* 2007).

DESCRIPTION

Plumage – Adult fresh (November to March) Forehead to nape olive-brown with faint greyish tinge. Supercilium creamy white, prominent and fairly broad, from base of bill to above middle of ear-coverts; well-marked in front of eye, tapering and becoming more diffuse behind eye. Dark olive-brown triangular area on lores, linked below eye to ear-coverts. Ear-coverts cold olive-brown with slightly darker eye-line immediately behind eye and indistinct pale shaft streaks towards lower edge. A narrow, broken creamy white eye-ring, merging above eye with supercilium. Mantle and scapulars to uppertail-coverts olive-brown, rump and uppertail-coverts often marginally paler and warmer

than mantle. Tail dark brown, conspicuously darker than uppertail-coverts, feathers narrowly edged cold olive-brown and tips of t4–6 narrowly fringed brownish white. Chin and throat white with faint creamy buff tinge. Breast washed creamy buff, sides suffused cold olive-brown. Lower breast and belly whitish, tinged creamy buff. Flanks and undertail-coverts washed pale buff. Lesser, median and greater coverts cold olive-brown, fringes of median and edges and tips of greater coverts slightly paler, more ochreous, but poorly demarcated. Primary coverts dark brown, narrowly fringed buff-brown. Alula blackish brown, contrasting with surrounding feathers. Centres of tertials dull brown, merging with broad olive-brown outer borders and tips. Flight feathers dark greyish brown with narrow olive-brown outer edges, primary tips narrowly fringed brownish white. Underwing-coverts pale olive-buff.

Adult worn (May–August) Lacks brighter olive tones and becomes duller brown above. Supercilium whiter and head slightly greyer. Wing and tail feathers paler brown, the worn outer edges grey-buff. Primary tips usually already slightly worn by April.

First-winter Derived by some post-juvenile contour feather moult. Head and body plumage similar to that of adult but duller and greyer. Buff fringes on juvenile wing-coverts and tertials often present until at least October.

Juvenile Face pattern as adult, but supercilium and eye-ring tinged cinnamon-buff. Crown and upperpart feathers greyish olive-brown, tips tinged cinnamon-brown. Breast sides and flanks more strongly washed cinnamon-buff. Chin to breast with slight cream-buff wash. Upperwing-coverts with cinnamon-buff tips, those on median and greater coverts forming two distinct pale wing-bars. Tertials and alula with narrow pale buff fringes. Flight feathers narrowly edged and tipped pale buff. Tail feathers edged cinnamon-buff.

Bare Parts Upper mandible dark horn to blackish, narrowly edged pale flesh-pink. Lower mandible in adult pale flesh-pink with variable horn-brown to blackish tip; in first-autumn lower mandible usually with distal third to half dark. Two dark tongue spots usually persist faintly up to December. Tarsi and toes dark grey in adult with brownish tinge, dark grey or slate grey in first-autumn; soles greyish ochre or brownish; claws grey-brown. Iris olive-brown to rich chestnut-brown in adult, dull dark brown in first-autumn.

IN HAND CHARACTERS
Measurements

	Male	Female
Wing	81–85 (82.9; 7)	79–84 (81.6; 8)
Tail	61–65 (62.5; 6)	55–64 (60.8; 8)
Bill	20.5–23.5 (22.1; 6)	21.5–23 (22.2; 8)
Tarsus	25.5–26 (25.6; 6)	24–26 (24.9; 8)

(Cramp 1992)

Sexes combined:
Tail/wing ratio: 72–77% (75%; 9)
Bill width: 4.8–5.2 (5.0; 8)
Hind claw: 8.0–10.0 (8.9; 10)
Tail graduation: 4–8 (6.1; 8)

Live wing length, sexes combined: adult (Kenya, freshly moulted) 77–89 (83.0; 538); juvenile (Kenya, November, unmoulted) 73–85 (79.2; 89) (NRG).

Structure

Wing formula (n = 9):

p1/pc	p2	p3e	p4	p5	p6	p7	p10
(8)–(4)	0–2	wp	1.5–3	4–6	7.5–9	10–12	17–20

Wing pointed, first primary minute, much shorter than pc. Wing point p3 (sometimes also p2); p2 = p3–4; p3 emarginated; notch on p2 inner web = p7/8. Primary tips narrower than in Great Reed Warbler.

Figure 72. Wing of Basra Reed Warbler.

Tail rounded, proportionately shorter than in Great Reed Warbler.

Bill long and slim with concave sides and narrow tip (Fig. 73).

Tarsi, toes and claws strong.

Recognition The combination of rather cold olive-brown upperparts, very pale underparts, long whitish supercilium and grey legs is distinctive. Its narrower and much slimmer bill (depth 3.5–3.8mm) separates it from Great Reed Warbler (depth 5.1–5.6mm) and from Palearctic races

of Clamorous Reed Warbler. Wing length overlaps only marginally with the largest Eurasian Reed Warbler and Marsh Warbler and with the smallest Great Reed. Clamorous Reed (races *brunnescens* and *levantinus*) has a longer tail (68–82mm) with more graduated tip (t1–t6 = 8–21mm) and also a more rounded wing, with p2 = p5/7 and p3–5 emarginated.

Ageing In early autumn, young birds have unworn primaries and show pale buff tips to the greater and median coverts and buff-fringed tertials. Adults lack these pale fringes and have heavily worn body plumage and wing feathers. By November–December, ageing based on plumage is rarely possible, even in unmoulted birds. Most can still be assigned, however, on bare part colour. Adults show brown-tinged or brownish grey legs and usually a medium brown to bright chestnut-brown eye and they lack tongue spots. First year birds have dark grey or lead-grey legs with no brown tinge, a duller, typically darker brown eye and most show faint tongue spots. Incomplete skull ossification separates first year birds until at least December.

Weight Range 13–29g; typically 14–17g in lean, non-migrating birds. Fat southbound migrants in Kenya often reach 20–23g (NRG unpublished data); two spring birds about to leave the Tana River delta weighed 24g and 29g (Pearson *et al.* 1978).

GEOGRAPHIC VARIATION None recorded.

TAXONOMY AND SYSTEMATICS Although originally described as a distinct species, it was treated as a race of Great Reed Warbler for much of the twentieth century. Pearson & Backhurst (1988) emphasised the distinctiveness of its structure, plumage and voice and recommended its reinstatement as a full species. This has been supported by mtDNA comparisons, which have shown it to occupy a basal taxonomic position, outside the Great Reed Warbler and Clamorous Reed Warbler group of species (Leisler *et al.* 1997; Fregin *et al.* 2009).

▲ Adult, Kuwait, May. Separated from larger Great Reed Warbler by distinctive structure and smaller size; note relatively slight build, long and slim bill, and long primary projection, giving very different character to other large *Acrocephalus* (Pekka Fagel).

▲ Adult, Kuwait, May. With wear, brighter olive tones are lost. Note the slightly greyer head, dingy white supercilium, and duller grey-brown upperparts (AbdulRahman Al-Sirhan).

▲ Adult, Ngulia, Kenya, December. The majority have a complete moult in NE Africa between September and November before continuing migration. Once moulted, adults are usually separable from young birds by a brown tinge to the grey legs, and often by a warm brown iris (David Pearson).

▲ Juvenile, Kuwait, July. Shows warmer brown fringes to wing-coverts and whiter underparts than adult (Michael Pope).

GREAT REED WARBLER
Acrocephalus arundinaceus   **Plate 24**

Turdus arundinaceus **Linnaeus, 1758**. *Syst. Nat.* ed. 10: 170. Danzig.

A long-distance migrant, breeding widely and often abundantly in reedbeds throughout temperate continental Europe to C Asia and wintering entirely in sub-Saharan Africa. Until recently, Oriental Reed and Basra Reed Warblers were often regarded as races of Great Reed Warbler, but these are now widely treated as distinct species. Polytypic, with two poorly differentiated races:

A. a. arundinaceus (Linnaeus 1758). Continental Europe, NW Africa, Turkey and the Levant, east to the Urals, the Volga River and the W Caspian Sea.

A. a. zarudnyi Hartert 1907. NW Iran and east from the Caspian Sea through C Asia to NW Mongolia, Tajikistan and NW China. Intergrades with the nominate race from the Urals and SW Siberia to NW Kazakhstan.

IDENTIFICATION Length 18–20cm. Wing 89–104mm. Tail/wing 72–82%.

A large, powerful, plain-backed *Acrocephalus* with a long stout bill. Together with Oriental Reed, Basra Reed and Clamorous Reed Warblers, it forms a grouping of large, warm-brown or olive-brown *Acrocephalus* warblers which breed across the Palearctic. Their breeding ranges are broadly separated, but Great Reed Warbler overlaps marginally with Clamorous Reed in S Kazakhstan and may do so with Oriental Reed in Mongolia. Subtle differences in plumage tone, leg colour and face pattern may be useful in separating these species, but Great Reed and Clamorous Reed both show racial colour variation. Differences in wing, tail and bill structure are important in the field and in the hand measurements are diagnostic. The rhythmic grating song of Great Reed is particularly distinctive and quite different from the less intrusive songs of Clamorous Reed and Basra Reed. Sexes similar, but males are usually larger than females.

Structure The largest of the Palearctic *Acrocephalus*. The fairly long heavy bill, with a gently decurved culmen, appears almost thrush-like. The crown is somewhat rounded but becomes sharply peaked before or above the eye in a singing or excited bird and with throat feathers puffed out, the head then attains a characteristic shape which the smaller *Acrocephalus* never approach. The wings are long, reaching the end of the uppertail-coverts, and eight well-spaced primary tips are visible, forming a projection 80–90% of exposed tertial length (Fig. 75). The third primary forms the wing point and is the only primary with an emargination. The ample tail is fairly long and slightly rounded, covered below for more than half its length by long undertail-coverts.

Plumage and bare parts Adult European birds in fresh plumage show warm olive-brown upperparts, slightly darker on the crown and tail and paler and rather brighter on the rump and uppertail-coverts. A prominent pale buff supercilium broadens in front of the eye above a restricted dark loral triangle. It links with a narrow creamy eye-ring and extends well back above dark brown ear-coverts to give a strong facial expression. A whitish throat usually shows some faint narrow grey streaking. The rest of the underparts are washed tawny buff, strongly on the breast sides and flanks, but become whitish on the belly centre. On the wings, the greater coverts and inner remiges show rather bright olive brown or tawny brown edges, but the tertial fringes show limited contrast with darker brown centres. The dark brown alula is prominent and the dark primary tips show conspicuous whitish fringes. In flight, contrast is apparent between the darker brown tail and paler uppertail-coverts, and pale buff fringes and tips to the outer tail feathers may be noticeable. In Asian breeders (race *zarudnyi*) the olive-brown upperparts tend to be slightly paler, colder and lack the warm tones shown by nominate birds, and the underparts are paler and show a more restricted buff wash.

Many birds, especially in Western Europe, have lost the pale primary tips by April or May. Plumage continues to wear and fade through the summer months. The brown upperparts become duller and the underparts whiter, but with buff retained on the flanks and undertail-coverts. Juveniles are brighter, more warmly toned than adults, the underparts washed entirely with cinnamon-buff. First-winter birds are rather paler than fresh adults, distinctly buffy brown rather than olive-brown on the upperparts and wing feather edges and with a more gingery tone to the rump and uppertail-coverts. Below, they are tinged warm buff throughout, most strongly on breast and flanks, and throat streaks are usually absent. During autumn, before the main African moult, young birds can become faded sandy buff. The remiges and tail feathers become faded brown, although the primaries retain pale fringed tips up to October.

The bill is dark horn-brown above and on the tip, with a flesh-pink base to the lower mandible. The legs are pale brown, flesh-brown or greyish flesh in adults, but lead-grey or brownish grey in young birds. They are paler, at least in older birds, than the dull greyish legs of Clamorous and Oriental Reed Warblers.

SIMILAR SPECIES In Europe, there are no similar large warblers and the smaller unstreaked *Acrocephalus* such as Eurasian and Marsh Warblers are not considered potential confusion species. But during migration through the Middle East and C Asia, Great Reed Warbler is likely to occur alongside the slightly smaller Clamorous Reed and Basra Reed Warblers. It also meets the latter species in E Africa. Oriental Reed Warbler has occurred as a vagrant to Israel and Kuwait. It could meet Great Reed in C Asia, especially in Mongolia where their breeding ranges approach or meet.

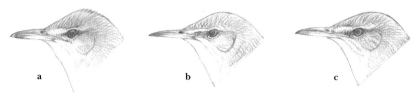

a   b   c

Figure 73. Comparison of head and bill shape of (a) Great Reed Warbler (b) Basra Reed Warbler and (c) Clamorous Reed Warbler *A. s. brunnescens.*

Clamorous Reed Warbler has three races breeding in warmer parts of the southern Palearctic and Great Reed Warbler could occur with any of these on migration. Clamorous Reed lacks the strong facial contrast and expression of Great Reed. The supercilium and eye-stripe are rather weakly defined in all races. The nominate Egyptian race is darker and more warmly coloured than Great Reed, particularly on the underparts, where white is largely restricted to the throat and belly centre. The race *brunnescens*, which migrates to India from C Asia and is also resident on the Arabia and Red Sea coasts, has a greyer tone to the olive upperparts and is whiter below than the nominate form and thus difficult to separate from many Great Reed on colour, especially in worn plumage. Clamorous Reed is slightly smaller than Great Reed and has a more attenuated head profile. The bill appears longer and more pointed, and that of nominate birds in Egypt and *levantinus* in Israel is decidedly narrower. The wing length and the primary projection are shorter, with only about six visible primary tips and with both p3 and p4 (sometimes also p5) emarginated. The tail is also longer and more graduated. These structural distinctions from Great Reed are more marked in resident birds than in migratory *brunnescens*.

Oriental Reed Warbler resembles Great Reed closely and measurements and structural differences provide the best means of separating them. Plumage differences are minor and the dull olive-brown or mouse-brown upperparts and pale underparts of Oriental Reed are extremely similar to those of the race *zarudnyi* of Great Reed. It tends to show sharper and more boldly marked streaks on the throat and upper breast and paler, more conspicuous tips to the tail feathers. It is slightly smaller than Great Reed and has a shorter primary projection (*c.* 75% of tertial length, intermediate between Great Reed and Clamorous Reed). It also has a slightly less pointed wing-tip, with p4 equal to p3 in some birds and sometimes emarginated – which it never is in Great Reed.

Basra Reed Warbler breeds to the south of Great Reed, but the two can occur together during migration through the Middle East and in E and S Africa. Although similar to Great Reed in wing and tail structure, it is about 15% smaller (in length) with almost no overlap in wing length. It is also slimmer, with a more attenuated head shape and a thinner bill. It shows colder olive-brown upperparts than Great Reed, darker wings and tail when freshly moulted, and whiter underparts which always lack throat streaking. The legs are always dark greyish.

VOICE The full song is loud and raucous, a steady rhythmic sequence of notes, each repeated about three times. Low grating elements alternate with high piping and creaky ones; '*karra-karra-karra gurk-gurk-gurk chirr-chirr, karra-karra, keet-keet-keet…*'. Sequences typically last about four seconds (*c.* 12 notes), but sometimes continue unbroken for ten seconds and are often separated by only a short pause. This song, used by males advertising for a mate, may be audible up to 1km away. Although characterised by its coarse and grating quality, it also contains some well-articulated high-pitched notes, reaching 7kHz and may include limited mimicry, such as imitations of gull and tern calls. Song is similar in general form and structure to that of Eurasian Reed Warbler but much louder, lower pitched and more stereotyped, and delivered slower and in shorter sequences. It is more rhythmic, more grating and less repetitive than the song of Clamorous Reed Warbler and each sequence

lasts considerably longer than the equivalent song sequence of Clamorous Reed.

The most elaborate songs are given by polygynous males in high quality territories. A short simpler song, lasting about one second with up to four syllables, is used in territorial encounters with rivals (Catchpole 1983). Following the complete moult, a fairly loud and sustained song is heard in wintering territories in Africa. Although less powerful and far-carrying than song on the breeding grounds, it is often given without a pause for half a minute or longer.

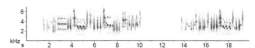

Part of song of Great Reed Warbler recorded within breeding range of *A. a. arundinaceus.* **France, May. (Sample 2003)**

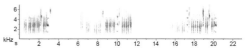

Part of song of Great Reed Warbler recorded within breeding range of *A. a. zarudnyi***, Buerjin, Xinjiang Uygur Autonomous Region, China, June. (Geoff Carey)**

The most frequently heard call is a hard *tack* or '*chack*'. A deep croaking '*kurrrr*' is also given and a shrike-like chatter when alarmed

MOULT In Europe, most adults have a partial moult in late summer when some or all of their body and head feathers are replaced. In S Europe the inner primaries may also be replaced and a few Iberian breeders have a complete moult before autumn migration. The great majority of adults have a complete moult in sub-Saharan Africa. In most, this occurs in the northern tropics between late September and December, before onward migration to equatorial and southern latitudes. But in birds wintering in S Africa, it is usually delayed until after arrival and takes place between January and March (Pearson 1975). First-year birds have an extensive post-juvenile moult of body and head feathers on the breeding grounds. They then undergo a complete moult in Africa along with adults, most in the northern tropics during an autumn stopover, but some in S Africa in late winter. Birds that complete the main moult in autumn (adult and first year) often have a partial pre-breeding moult of body and head plumage in February and March.

HABITAT In Europe, it breeds in reeds over fresh or brackish water, mainly by shallow lakes and sluggish rivers with fringing beds or islands of *Phragmites*. It prefers tall, strong, well-spaced reeds growing near open water edges and depends on old dead stems on arrival. It also uses other tall aquatic plants such as *Typha, Juncus* or *Scirpus* for singing. Birds may fly from the reeds to feed in marsh edge willows and adjacent shrubbery or low trees. In Russia and C Asia, it breeds by lakes and small steppe pools, in river backwaters and floodplains and near inland sea coasts. Most nest in reeds, but often in much smaller and thinner stands than those preferred in Europe. Some also nest in willows by streams, riverbank poplars and old orchards near water. In Europe, it breeds mainly in lowlands, although it occurs up to 650m in Switzerland. In Armenia and possibly elsewhere in Asia, it breeds much higher, in places up to 2,000m.

In Africa, wintering and passage birds occur in varied

moist habitat and not necessarily near water. They frequent beds of reed and *Typha* on marsh or lake edges, reeds and clumps of tall grass by rivers, rank growth and bushes along watercourses and green thickets including *Lantana* and acacia. Others use crops such as maize and sugar cane and shrubbery and garden hedges well away from water. They occur at low to medium altitude, ranging from sea level up to 1,800m in Kenya.

BEHAVIOUR A noisy and conspicuous species, less secretive and more easily observed in the open than most other *Acrocephalus*. Its movements are much heavier than in Eurasian Reed Warbler and it progresses through vegetation with short leaps and hops powerfully on the ground. Its postures are like those of an exaggerated Eurasian Reed Warbler, often near horizontal with tail held level with or just below the long wings, but more upright when climbing reeds and often very erect on a song-post. The crown feathers are raised frequently and the tail often fanned. Flight is usually direct and low above vegetation, often over distances of 100m or more before the bird plunges back into cover. It appears heavy with laboured-looking bursts of wing beats, the longish tail partly spread and held loosely below body level (Cramp 1992). It feeds low in reeds, or in bushes and trees, searching leaves and stems and often taking prey from the water surface or just beneath it. It sometimes leaps or fly-catches like a Eurasian Reed Warbler to take aerial prey, and feeds around the edge of open cover in an upright chat-like posture.

Males on the breeding grounds usually sing perched high on an old reed stem, but sometimes from a bush. They tend to move between several different song posts around the territory, They may also sing in the air, flying with even wing-beats, with head and tail raised and the tail slightly spread. Unpaired males sing a loud, long 'advertising' song, which may be sustained throughout most of the day and given in snatches through the night. This ceases once a female is attracted, but may begin again within a few days as the male attempts to find an additional mate. A shorter and quieter song is used by paired and unpaired males in territorial defence. Males sing little during incubation or feeding of the young. The song period in W and N Europe lasts from the end of April until late June.

In Africa, birds are often tame, inquisitive and approachable. They tend to occupy the same territory or thicket for many weeks and to be faithful to previously held wintering sites. Birds ringed in Malawi were recaptured up to eight years later (Hanmer 1989). Wintering birds sing strongly from within bushy cover between December and April.

BREEDING HABITS Solitary and territorial, but several territories are often grouped together near good feeding sites, with nests situated less than 100m apart. Territories are mostly between 0.15 and 0.6ha, but tend to be smaller where clustered (Cramp 1992). Males are often polygynous. In a Polish study 12–14% of males mated with more than one female, while in Austria up to 27% did so (Cramp 1992). In S Sweden, 40% of males mated with between two and four females (Hasselquist 1994). Polygyny was typical of older males, which arrived and began breeding earlier in better quality territories. Over half of adults returned to the same marsh in Sweden in successive years, but most of these settled in a different territory and very few mated with a former partner (Bensch & Hasselquist 1991).

The first males arrive in Sweden almost two weeks before females and select and advertise the best territories. A polygynous male will usually acquire two or three females

within the same territory. Each nest is built by the female in about a week, with the male guarding her. It is placed in stands of reed *Phragmites*, or sometimes *Typha*, up to 130cm (typically about 50cm) above water. It is supported on several thick stems, usually of old reed or a mixture of old and new. It is a deep, cylindrical, rather coarsely woven cup of reed and plant stems and leaves, plant down and spiders' web, lined with finer material, including hair and sometimes feathers. Compared to that of Eurasian Reed Warbler it is rather small for the size of the bird, with a cup diameter of just 5–6cm.

Eggs are laid in May; at the beginning of the month in S Europe but not until late May or early June in S Scandinavia and C Asia. The clutch size is usually 4–5 eggs, but occasionally 3–6, with clutch sizes declining through the season. Incubation is carried out entirely by the female and lasts about 14 days. The young are fed in the nest for 12–14 days by both parents. Food is mainly collected outside the territory, often from nearby bushes and trees. Once fledged, the young are tended in the nest area by both parents for a further 12–14 days. A polygynous male usually gives most nest assistance to the primary female (Cramp 1992). Each female is normally single brooded.

DISTRIBUTION
Breeding
A. a. arundinaceus Great Reed Warbler inhabits middle latitudes of the western and central Palearctic. In Europe, the nominate race breeds from Iberia, France and continental NW Europe to *c.* 60°N in S Sweden and 63°N in S Finland but is absent from the British Isles. It is widespread across much of C and E Europe and throughout the Mediterranean basin including the Balearic Islands, Corsica, Sardinia, Sicily and Crete. To the east it remains widespread and fairly common throughout Turkey, Ukraine, Russia north to *c.* 57°N in the S Ural Mountains and the lower Caucasus, where it breeds to 2,000m at Lake Sevan, Armenia. In NW Africa, small numbers breed in N Morocco, coastal N Algeria and Tunisia and in SW Asia there are isolated populations in N Israel, N Iraq and NW Iran. It is abundant around the Caspian Sea and along the lower Volga and Ural Rivers and in NW Iran, where many birds show characters of the race *zarudnyi*.

Distribution in the north and west of the range is local and patchy, but in S and E Europe and C Asia, it is often the most numerous *Acrocephalus*, outnumbering Eurasian Reed Warbler over wide areas. The highest populations occur around the larger lakes and in the Danube and Volga River deltas, and the total European population has been estimated at 2–3 million pairs (Hagemeijer & Blair 1997), *c.* 96% of which breed in E Europe. Expansion took place during the twentieth century along the northern range margins, into the Baltic States and Scandinavia. The Swedish population has increased ten-fold since 1970 and a few pairs now breed in coastal S Norway. Elsewhere, however, range contractions and declines of over 50% have been noted since 1970 in many parts of W, C and S Europe.

A. a. zarudnyi Replaces the nominate race in C Asia and SC Siberia, where it is widespread throughout much of Kazakhstan east to Zaisan and Alakol lakes and the southern foothills of the Altai. It ranges east in Siberia to the region of the Ob River near Novosibirsk and Kemerovo. Breeding occurs at Khar Us Nuur in NW Mongolia and may be more widespread within the

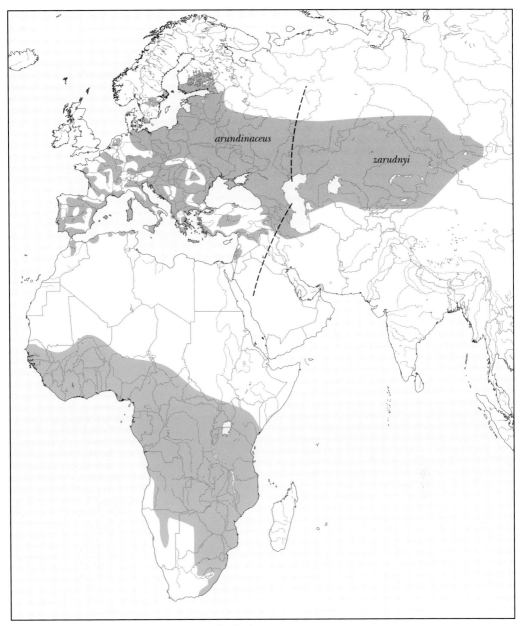

arundinaceus

zarudnyi

Great Reed Warbler. Breeding range and winter distribution.

country than is currently known. Breeding in NW China is restricted to wetlands and rivers in the desert regions of W and NW Xinjiang Uygur Autonomous Region north to the Ulungur River and several localities along the northern and western rim of the Tarim basin including Bosten (Boshteng) Hu and Karamay (Lewthwaite *et al.* 1998; Hornskov 2001; GJC & PJL pers. comm.). The southern breeding limit appears to lie along the Syr Darya in S Kazakhstan, the Naryn River in Kyrgyzstan and the Ili River through the Tien Shan in SE Kazakhstan and W Xinjiang. Appears to intergrade with the nominate race in SW Siberia and NW Kazakhstan.

Non-breeding Winters in Africa south of the Sahara, from Senegal, S Mali, Nigeria, Central African Republic, S and W Uganda and W and S Kenya south to Angola, NE Namibia, N and E Botswana and E South Africa (to KwaZulu-Natal and Eastern Cape). It also winters locally to 12°N in W and C Ethiopia. In W Africa, few birds remain in the Sahel and Soudan savannas. Most winter south of 9–10°N and from Ivory Coast to Cameroon and Gabon. The largest numbers winter south of the equator, particularly in S DR Congo, Zambia and Zimbabwe. Ringing has shown that birds from W and C Europe migrate to W Africa. Austrian-ringed birds were found south of 8°N from Ghana to Nigeria and one ringed in Sweden was recovered in SW Chad. Birds wintering in E and S Africa, which include many *zarudnyi*, are probably all from E Europe and Asia.

MOVEMENTS European birds initially head south in autumn, while those from Asia move southwest.

Northern and eastern parts of the range are vacated by early September. Passage through N and C Europe continues throughout August and September, with stragglers in the Mediterranean region to early November. There are few autumn records from N Africa, suggesting that birds fly non-stop from S Europe to the tropics. Some southward passage takes place through Egypt between late August and late September.

In Kazakhstan, the first birds leave breeding grounds in late July and most depart in August, the last at the end of September. Heavy migration continues through the S Caspian Sea region to October. Migration takes these birds southwest and across Arabia. The first birds reach the Sudan coast in late August, but arrivals continue to make landfall in NE Africa until mid October, with stragglers arriving to mid November. Arrival in the northern tropics is thus mainly during late September and October, but most birds destined for further south remain in NE Africa for about two months before continuing migration. In Zambia and Malawi, the first birds arrive in November, but most in December, and passage continues to January. The main route to S Africa appears to lie through Sudan and a sparse and patchy autumn occurrence in equatorial Africa suggests that large areas are overflown. A similar two-stage migration strategy, with onward movement from the northern tropics in November–December has been noted in W Africa (Hedenström *et al.* 1993).

Birds remain at wintering sites until late March or early April. In W Africa, most birds destined for Europe appear to depart from equatorial latitudes. Many make a landfall near the N African coast from late March and passage continues there until mid or late May. Birds return to breeding sites in S Europe and the Black Sea coasts from mid April and reach NW Europe and sites in the Caucasus from the end of April, but mainly in early and mid May. S Scandinavian breeders do not arrive until mid or late May.

The birds of E Europe and C Asia appear to follow a loop migration, most taking a more easterly route through Africa in spring than in autumn. There is a strong passage through Kenya throughout April and through Ethiopia from mid April to early May. Dement'ev & Gladkov (1954) consider that the first *zarudnyi* arrive earlier on the breeding grounds than nominate birds and mention arrivals on the lower Syr Darya from late March onwards. But the main passage through C Asia occurs later, through N Iran and W Kazakhstan from mid April, through Turkmenistan from mid April to late May, at the Ili River region in E Kazakhstan in the first week of May and in the western Altai foothills in the third week of May. Sites in C Kazakhstan are occupied from mid May onwards.

DESCRIPTION *A. a. arundinaceus*
Plumage – Adult fresh (December to April) Forehead to nape warm olive-brown with greyish tinge. Supercilium pale buff, prominent, extending from base of bill to above middle of ear-coverts, broadest above lores and linked to narrow creamy white eye-ring. A restricted dark greyish brown triangle in front of lower edge of eye and an indistinct eye-line behind eye. Ear-coverts dark olive-brown. Cheeks olive-brown, streaked buff. Mantle and scapulars to uppertail-coverts warm olive-brown, paler and

more cinnamon-brown on rump and uppertail-coverts. Tail feathers greyish olive-brown, narrowly edged warm buff, outer feathers with diffuse buffy white fringe around tip. Chin and throat whitish, with cinnamon-buff tinge and faint greyish shaft streaks on sides of throat and lower throat. Upper breast washed cinnamon-buff, sides of breast and flanks deeper cinnamon-buff. Lower breast and belly centre whitish with faint buff wash. Undertail-coverts pale cinnamon-buff. Lesser and median coverts warm olive-brown. Greater coverts greyish brown, edged light warm olive-brown or cinnamon-brown. Tertials with olive-brown outer borders and tips, not well demarcated from darker centres. Rest of upperwing feathers dark greyish brown, primary coverts and flight feathers narrowly edged warm olive-brown, primaries narrowly tipped greyish white. Underwing-coverts pale cinnamon-buff.
Adult worn (June to August) Olive-brown upperparts and upperwing-coverts rather duller and greyer, with cinnamon tinge more confined to rump. Supercilium and underparts whiter, breast, flanks and undertail-coverts with more restricted cinnamon-buff. Throat streaks sometimes more prominent. Flight feathers and tail feathers browner with pale edges more grey-buff and pale tips worn off.
First-winter Upperparts warm brown, slightly darker and more olive on crown and brighter cinnamon-brown on rump and uppertail-coverts. Supercilium and eye-ring warm buff, less prominent than in adult. Underparts washed cinnamon-buff, faintly on whitish chin, throat and belly centre, more strongly on sides and flanks. Grey throat streaks very faint or lacking. Wing feathers browner than in adult, remiges and greater coverts with paler, buffier edges. Tail paler brown, buff fringes on outer feather tips reduced or absent.
Juvenile Upperparts cinnamon-brown. Side of head and underparts cinnamon-buff. Wing and tail as first-winter.
Bare Parts Upper mandible dark horn-brown or blackish brown with flesh-pink to pinkish yellow cutting edges. Lower mandible flesh-pink to pinkish yellow with sides of distal third dark horn-brown. Mouth orange or orange-red in adult, orange-yellow in first-autumn; two dusky tongue spots, usually still present in November–December. Tarsi and toes variable but always pale in adult, varying from grey-brown or greyish flesh to pale brown or pinkish brown, darker grey or brownish grey in juvenile/first-autumn; soles greyish ochre; claws horn brown or dark grey-brown. Iris in adult mid brown, pale brown or yellow-brown; dark brown in juvenile/first-autumn.

IN HAND CHARACTERS
Measurements

A. a. arundinaceus

	Male	Female
Wing	94–101 (96.8; 48)	89–95 (92.3; 14)
Tail	71–80 (75.7; 41)	66–74 (70.4; 14)
Bill	22.4–25.3 (23.6; 45)	21.8–23.8 (22.7; 14)
Tarsus	28–31.1 (29.7; 39)	27.1–29.6 (28.6; 13)

(Cramp 1992)

Sexes combined:
Tail/wing ratio: 72–82% (77%; 63)
Bill width: 5.2–6.0 (5.7; 20)
Hind claw: 8.0–10.6 (9.4; 29)
Tail graduation: 6–12 (9.5; 20)

Juvenile wing length similar to that of adult, tail *c.* 1.5mm shorter (Cramp 1992).

In Europe, birds breeding in Sweden are long-winged, those in Spain relatively short-winged (see **Appendix 2**).

A. a. zarudnyi

	Male	Female
Wing	95–104 (98.4; 21)	92–97 (94.3; 10)
Tail	71–81 (75.3; 21)	68–76 (72.0; 10)
Bill	21–25 (23.5; 9)	22–24 (23.4; 10))
Tarsus	27.5–32 (30.0; 19)	27–30 (29.0; 10)

Structure

Wing formula (races combined, Cramp 1992):

p1/pc	p2	p3e	p4	p5	p6	p7	p10
(10)–(3)	0–2.5	wp	2–4.5	5.5–8	9–13	12–16	21–26

Wing long and pointed; p1 minute, always < pc. Wing point p(2)3; p2 = p3–4 [4/5]; p3 emarginated. Notch on inner web of p2 12–16mm from tip (10–14mm in juveniles); falls at p7–8 (9).

Figure 74. Wing of Great Reed Warbler.

Tail fairly long and rounded; feathers rounded in adult, narrower, more pointed in juvenile.

Bill long, stout and broad-based, tip of culmen decurved, sides slightly concave (Fig. 73).

Tarsi thick; toes and claws strong.

Recognition Characterised by large size, large thick bill, plain, often warmly coloured upperparts and prominent supercilium. Separated from Clamorous Reed Warbler by longer wing, with p2 usually > p4 (< p5 in *A. s. brunnescens*, < p6 in nominate *stentoreus*) and emargination confined to p3 (also p4 (5) in Clamorous Reed) (Fig. 75). Notch on p2 falls higher in Great Reed (below tips of ss in Clamorous Reed). Wing length is above that of nominate *stentoreus*, but overlaps with *brunnescens*. The tail is less graduated than that of most Clamorous Reed. Bill length in most females and some males is below range of Clamorous Reed (23.5–27mm); bill similar in shape to race *brunnescens*, but broader and thicker than in nominate *stentoreus*.

Larger than Oriental Reed Warbler, but wing length of female overlaps that of male Oriental Reed. Separated by longer second primary (p2 usually < p5 in Oriental Reed,

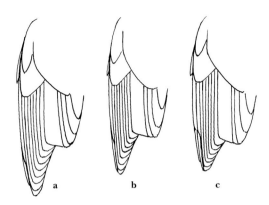

Figure 75. Closed wing structure of (a) Great Reed Warbler (b) Basra Reed Warbler and (c) Clamorous Reed Warbler *A. s. brunnescens* **compared.**

sometimes < p6), by lack of emargination on p4 and usually by higher position of p2 notch (below p8 in Oriental Reed). Much larger than Basra Reed Warbler with practically no overlap in wing, tail or tarsus measurements; bill broader and much thicker.

Ageing In early autumn, young birds are easily distinguished by relatively unworn body and tail feathers and unworn buff-edged wing feathers, the primaries pale-tipped. Adults have badly worn tail feathers, abraded, greyish edged wing feathers and head and body feathers old and worn, or partially replaced giving a variegated appearance. Unmoulted young birds bleach quickly during autumn, but tend to retain traces of pale primary tips to November. Ageing is more difficult in winter and spring after moult, but three characters are useful. First-year birds usually retain faint tongue spots until at least December; they have dark greyish or dark grey-brown legs whereas those of older birds are mid brown to pale or pinkish brown; and they usually have a dull, dark brown eye, while in most adults it is brighter olive-brown, yellowish brown or chestnut-brown. Skull ossification is incomplete in young birds to at least December.

Sexing Male measurements average significantly higher than those of females (see above). Many birds can be sexed on wing length.

Weight Range 19–56g. Lean birds usually weigh 24–32g, with males *c.* 10% heavier than females. Fattening migrants frequently exceed 40g, with autumn birds of 49g in Ukraine (GN unpublished data) and 56g in S Turkey (RV & WP unpublished data), and spring migrants of 46g in Ethiopia (JSA unpublished data) and 52g in Kenya (Pearson 1992). Depleted autumn migrants reaching coastal Sudan included birds of 19.5–22g (DJP & GN unpublished data).

GEOGRAPHIC VARIATION The slightly paler eastern race *zarudnyi* is poorly differentiated. Colour differences with the nominate form are slight in fresh plumage, but the greyer upperparts become enhanced on the breeding grounds by bleaching and wear. Birds resembling *zarudnyi* occur alongside darker birds resembling the nominate form over a large area from the Volga River east to southern C Siberia. Furthermore, a few birds resembling *zarudnyi* appear in W European populations. The two races might be regarded as colour morphs, the dark morph predominant in the west and the pale morph in the east.

A. a. arundinaceus (Europe east to the Volga River) Described above.

A. a. zarudnyi (C Asia) Fresh adults in winter quarters have olive-brown upperparts, rather paler on the rump and uppertail-coverts. They almost lack the warm tones of the nominate race and show a more pronounced greyish tinge on the head. The supercilium is buffy white. The underparts are off-white with a light buff wash on the upper breast and pale buff flanks and undertail-coverts. The throat has greyish streaks as in the nominate race. The wing feather edges are light olive-brown. In worn adults, racial differences are accentuated. Birds in Asian breeding areas appear distinctly pale and greyish

olive-brown above and whitish below compared to their European counterparts. First-autumn birds are more buffy, less olive, than adults with a tawny-brown rump and uppertail-coverts and appear very similar to young birds of the nominate race.

TAXONOMY AND SYSTEMATICS The validity of *zarudnyi* is discussed above. Note that Stepanyan (1978, 2003) treats *zarudnyi* as a synonym of *arundinaceus*.

In Kazakhstan, a hybrid with Clamorous Reed Warbler was caught at Chushkakol Lake and four similar hybrids were trapped at Stone Lake in May 2001 (Hansson *et al.* 2003).

▲ Adult *A. a. arundinaceus*, Poland, May. Singing male in characteristic pose with throat-feathering extended and fore-crown feathers raised (Mateusz Matysiak).

▲ Adult *A. a. arundinaceus*, Turkey, May. When relaxed, appearance is transformed into that of a neater, sleeker bird (Rafael Armada).

▲ Adult *A. a. zarudnyi*, Kuwait, May. Eastern birds are characterised by greyer upperparts, most apparent on worn birds during the breeding season (Gary Brown).

▲ Adult *A. a. arundinaceus*, Netherlands, May. This interesting individual shows a sandy wash to the flanks and undertail-coverts, and paler brown upperparts (Norman Deans van Swelm).

▲ First-winter *A. a. arundinaceus*, Italy, October. Young birds in autumn are fresher, more warmly toned than adults (Daniele Occhiato).

ORIENTAL REED WARBLER
Acrocephalus orientalis   Plate 25

Salicaria turdina orientalis **Temminck & Schlegel, 1847**. In: Siebold, *Fauna Japonica*, Aves, page 50, plate 20. Japan.

The eastern counterpart of Great Reed Warbler and regarded as conspecific with it until recently. It breeds in wetlands throughout much of the temperate E Palearctic and south into E China. Outside the breeding season it migrates to winter in SE Asia, where it is usually the most numerous wintering *Acrocephalus* and greatly outnumbers the more southerly breeding Clamorous Reed Warbler where the two come into contact. Monotypic.

IDENTIFICATION Length 18–19cm. Wing 76–95mm. Tail/wing 76–86%.

A large and bulky *Acrocephalus* with slow, ponderous behaviour and which closely resembles Great Reed and Clamorous Reed Warblers. Adults are dull olive-brown above with a slightly warmer and paler rump, and paler below with the chin and throat appearing almost white and with a necklace of faint streaks across the lower throat and onto the sides of the upper breast. The head shows a conspicuously pale supercilium bordered below by a contrastingly darker eye-stripe. Sexes similar, although males are usually distinctly larger than females.
Structure Slightly smaller than Great Reed Warbler but otherwise very similar in structure. The head appears rather stocky with a long, heavy and slightly decurved bill. This large-headed impression is accentuated by frequent raising of the fore-crown feathers when singing or alarmed, giving it a ragged, unkempt appearance. The wing is fairly long, with a conspicuous primary projection extending to *c.* 80% of the exposed tertial length and with seven or eight primary tips usually visible. However, the spacing between the longest primary (p3) and p4 is more difficult to discern than in Great Reed, and Oriental Reed often has an emargination on p4. The tail is long and slightly rounded and proportionately similar to that of Great Reed, but shorter and less strongly rounded than in Clamorous Reed. The undertail-coverts and uppertail-coverts are similar in length and extend beyond the longest primary, cloaking the proximal third of the tail.

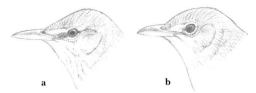

a   b

Figure 76. Comparison of head and bill shape of (a) Oriental Reed Warbler and (b) Thick-billed Warbler.

Plumage and bare parts Oriental Reed is very similar in appearance to Great Reed Warbler and also closely resembles some races of Clamorous Reed Warbler. In fact, the head pattern and overall coloration appear to be identical to those shown by Great Reed, particularly the eastern form *zarudnyi*. Consequently, large *Acrocephalus* in E Asia are generally assumed to be Oriental Reed unless proven otherwise and Great Reed has not yet been located among the huge wintering population of Oriental Reed Warblers, although its occurrence here seems likely.
Oriental Reed shows a fairly distinctive head pattern

with a conspicuous, pale, creamy buff supercilium and distinct greyish brown loral line. The upperparts including the wing-coverts are fairly uniform olive-brown although the crown may appear marginally greyer. The rump and uppertail-coverts are slightly warmer-toned and paler and contrast slightly with the mantle, particularly in flight. Only the darker alula, tertial centres and exposed primaries contrast with the paler, browner upperparts. The upper surface of the tail matches the mantle in colour but shows conspicuous pale brown to creamy white feather tips when fresh, but these are lost as the tail abrades. The underparts are dull creamy white, although the breast and belly show a faint buff wash and there is a stronger and more intense wash on the side of the breast, flanks and undertail-coverts, which varies from light buff to pale straw. Oriental Reed Warbler almost always shows fine dark brown streaking on side of the throat, becoming longer and slightly broader on the lower throat and breast, especially towards the sides. On some birds, this streaking can be quite conspicuous and extends across the entire breast, while on others the streaks are very fine, diffuse and barely perceptible. Streaking becomes more conspicuous as feather fringes are lost and is usually most obvious during the breeding season.

Juveniles resemble adults but the supercilium is less pronounced and the texture of the plumage is looser and less sleek. After the post-juvenile moult, which starts on the breeding grounds and is usually completed before late August and always by late September, there are no plumage or structural differences by which adults and immature birds can be separated.

The bill is dark bluish grey, although the lower mandible has a dull pink base that merges to dull greyish pink towards the tip. The legs, feet and claws are dull plumbeous-grey.

SIMILAR SPECIES Two similarly sized *Acrocephalus* occur in the temperate region of the Palearctic; the Great Reed and Clamorous Reed Warblers, as well as Thick-billed Warbler, while vagrant Oriental Reed has reached NW Australia on several occasions, and may occur here alongside the distinctly smaller Australian Reed Warbler.
Great Reed Warbler Great Reed Warbler of the eastern form *zarudnyi* and Oriental Reed Warblers may meet during the breeding season in N Mongolia, or occur together in an extralimital vagrant context, e.g. in Israel. Great Reed Warbler averages slightly larger than Oriental Reed, with a longer wing although there is overlap. It also has a slightly more pointed wing, with p2 equal to or longer than p4 (usually shorter than p4 in Oriental Reed) and unlike some Oriental Reed, it never has an emargination on p4.

Plumage differences between these species are slight, with the upperparts of both Oriental Reed and *zarudnyi* Great Reed appearing dull mouse-brown or olive-brown with a slight grey wash and generally duller than the warmer olive-brown upperparts of nominate Great Reed. The appearance of the underparts of Oriental Reed Warbler and *zarudnyi* is also similar, with both generally paler below than nominate Great Reed. Also, *zarudnyi* has a tendency towards faint streaking on the lower throat, although the throat and breast streaks in Oriental Reed tend to be better marked. On Oriental Reed, the pale tail feather tips are broader, paler and more conspicuous than *zarudnyi* would show.
Clamorous Reed Warbler is a highly variable species with several races, some of which occur within the non-breeding range of Oriental Reed Warbler. These vary considerably in size and appearance (see Clamorous Reed Warbler

account). Size alone will be sufficient to separate the smaller races from migrant or wintering Oriental Reed but the larger forms can cause a problem. In particular, the likelihood of confusion is greatest with the continental forms of Clamorous Reed; *A. s. brunnescens* (wintering in India) and *A. s. amyae* (resident in Burma and SW China), and the resident island forms *A. s. harterti* (Philippines) and *A. s. siebirsi* (Java). For convenience, these races can all be treated together since differences between them and Oriental Reed are consistent.

Plumage differences are important, the underparts of these four races of Clamorous Reed Warbler always being unstreaked, irrespective of the actual colour, whereas Oriental Reed Warbler invariably shows light streaking across the lower throat. The supercilium of Clamorous Reed is typically indistinct behind the eye but is obvious and contrasting in Oriental Reed. Other plumage differences are slight and less useful.

Structural features are also important in their separation. The bill of Clamorous Reed appears proportionately longer but rather finer than in Oriental Reed, giving the head a more elongated or 'snouted' appearance. Differences in wing structure are diagnostic. Clamorous Reed shows a relatively short primary projection, approximately half the exposed tertial length in resident races with just six primary tips visible, but slightly longer in the migratory C Asian form *brunnescens*. The wing of Clamorous Reed is distinctly more rounded than Oriental Reed, with p2 always being shorter than p5, and it shows emarginations on p3 and p4 and sometimes p5.

Australian Reed Warbler could occur alongside Oriental Reed in NW Australia, where Oriental Reed has occurred as a vagrant. Their separation is discussed in the Australian Reed Warbler account.

Thick-billed Warbler is the only similarly sized warbler that overlaps extensively with Oriental Reed in both its breeding and wintering areas. It is, however, quite different in appearance and the two species are readily separable throughout the year using a combination of plumage and structural characters. Its appearance is warmer toned and brighter than Oriental Reed, almost rufous-brown, particularly on the mantle, rump, uppertail-coverts and tail. It always lacks the conspicuous pale supercilium and the dark loral line and eye-stripe which Oriental Reed invariably shows, thus giving it an exceptionally 'plain-faced' appearance. The underparts are light buff, slightly warmer toned than in Oriental Reed and never show streaking on the throat or breast. Compared with Oriental Reed, it has a proportionately longer, more graduated tail, giving a very different structure and a tail/wing ratio of 97–105% compared with 76–86% in Oriental Reed. The wing is distinctly rounded with a much larger first primary (p1) that extends well beyond the primary coverts. The second primary (p2) is shorter than p7, with an emargination on p5 which Oriental Reed never shows.

VOICE The song consists of a series of loud, raucous calls strung together to form short, repetitive sequences within a frequency range of 1–5kHz. Its character is reminiscent of the songs of Great Reed and Clamorous Reed Warblers, but is slightly less harsh and lower pitched, slower in delivery and more structured. Each song sequence lasts approximately 6–8 seconds and comprises a loud '*ka-ka-ri-rik-rik-rik-rik-gurk-guwk-guwk-guwk-kawa-kawa-kawa-eek-eek-eek-eek…*', with a short pause before the next sequence commences. The song in Japan sounds slightly slower and

deeper than in the west of the breeding range in Mongolia, but it is not certain whether there is a consistent regional difference or whether this falls within individual variation found throughout the range.

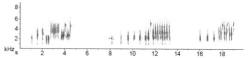

Part of song of Oriental Reed Warbler, Karuizawa, Honshu, Japan, May. (Ueda 1998)

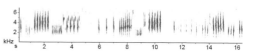

Part of song of Oriental Reed Warbler, Durur, eastern Mongolia, June. (Geoff Carey)

There are several calls, all loud, harsh and grating. These include a short '*kwak*' and a more rolling '*trrrr*', both similar to the calls given by Great Reed and Clamorous Reed Warblers.

MOULT Unusually among Palearctic *Acrocephalus*, adults and young birds have a complete moult on the breeding grounds that is completed prior to autumn migration (Ezaki 1984). In adults, this commences in mid July and is usually finished by early to mid September. Young birds begin their complete post-juvenile moult shortly after fledging in late July, but some late fledged second broods may not complete until mid or even late October. Juveniles take approximately 40 days to complete moult but the period for adults is unknown (Melville 1988). Most migrants on autumn passage through Hong Kong have fresh or slightly worn primaries (Melville 1988). Some young birds in Hong Kong in late August and early September are still growing their remiges and rectrices. As Oriental Reed Warbler does not breed in Hong Kong or neighbouring Guangdong Province, these birds are perhaps involved in local coastal dispersal movements from elsewhere in southern China, rather than migrants from the northern part of the range, which would be expected to arrive later.

During winter, both adult and first-winter birds have a partial moult involving the body feathering. The timing of this moult appears to differ between populations. For example, Medway & Wells (1972) recorded heavy body moult in Malaysia during March and April. In Hong Kong, however, April passage migrants have completed moult and show a combination of old and worn primaries, rectrices and usually the tertials, which contrast with the recently replaced fresh body plumage. Some passage birds in Hong Kong are known to breed in Japan (see **Movements** below).

HABITAT Always closely associated with wetlands throughout the year. During the breeding season, it requires *Phragmites* reedbeds in which it breeds. Foraging birds will readily move through scrub and bushes adjacent to reedbeds, but these are not essential and many breed in stands of pure *Phragmites*.

Migrants and wintering birds utilise a wider range of habitats associated with wetlands. These include thick scrub and bushes: usually near watercourses or damp ditches, mangroves, tall damp grasslands and dry, rank grassland on landfill sites, as well as *Phragmites* reedbeds and Papyrus where these are available. Passage birds occur at both coastal and inland sites. While many actively seek out *Phragmites*, others may appear in patches of tall grass moistened only by early morning condensation. In SE Asia, many birds establish winter territories well away from reedbeds and in these situations the primary requirement appears to be the availability of a damp area in which to forage. In Malaysia, the sexes have been found to differ in their habitat utilisation; males tend to occur in scrub, damp grassland and reed edges and females are more strictly confined to reedbeds (Nisbet & Medway 1976).

BEHAVIOUR Not known to differ in any significant way from that of Great Reed Warbler. Males sing during northward migration and continue when they reach the breeding grounds. Unmated males may begin to sing as early as 01:00 hrs and most males are in full song before dawn. Song then continues until late morning, when it gradually subsides, and is only heard occasionally during the heat of the day. Regular singing recommences in late afternoon and continues until 22:00 hrs, well after dusk.

In the wintering area, birds occur at high densities with overlapping territories and many individuals may utilise the same small patch of reeds or damp grassland. Harsh calls, presumably given by foraging birds, are regularly heard outside the breeding season but song is then infrequent.

BREEDING HABITS Males return to the breeding grounds up to ten days before females and immediately form territories. Pair formation commences with the arrival of the females, although nest construction may not start for a further ten days. Some males are polygynous; one study recorded one male paired with five females (Kikuchi *et al.* 1957). The nest is built around three or four reed stems or similar supporting vegetation, which hold in place a cradle of coarse grasses and small twigs that form a crude base to the nest, typically placed 0.5–1m above the water level. A deep cup-shaped nest, which incorporates the reed stems for support, is built on this base. It is made from dried coarse grasses and lined with finer grasses, although horsehair and sheep wool have been noted as lining materials. A clutch of three to five eggs is laid, commencing in mid May in S Japan, but not until early June in Hokkaido and the Russian Far East. One egg is laid each day and incubation starts when the clutch is complete. Incubation lasts for 11–12 days, the first eggs hatching in mid June in S Japan and from the last week in June further north, although the majority hatch during the first ten days in July. Fledging takes a further 12–14 days although by 11–12 days old the nestlings are too large for the nest and perch on its rim or on adjacent branches. Some pairs are double brooded in milder coastal regions where breeding begins earlier. The female then leaves the first brood to the care of the male and begins building a second nest within a few metres of the original. Incubation of this second clutch begins from mid July, while the male is still caring for the first brood. The second clutch hatches in late July and the second brood leave the nest in mid to late August.

DISTRIBUTION

Breeding Oriental Reed Warbler is an abundant breeding bird in wetlands with *Phragmites* reed throughout the temperate and warmer regions of the E Palearctic, and south through E China into the sub-tropical region south of the Yangtze River. It breeds in E Mongolia, extending northwest to the Tola River valley. It also ranges into adjacent regions of southeastern Russia to the east of the Baikal watershed and along the valleys of the Amur and Ussuri Rivers east to the Pacific coast. It is absent from Sakhalin and is uncommon in Hokkaido except in the southwest (Brazil 1991). Elsewhere in Japan, it is a common to abundant breeding bird on Honshu, Sado, Shikoku and N Kyushu, but is largely absent from S Kyushu and the Ryukyu Islands to the south. In continental Asia, it is widespread throughout the Korean Peninsula and N and E China. Cheng (1987) included the Xinjiang Uygur Autonomous Region in W China within its breeding range but this is not supported by recent observations, which have only recorded Great Reed Warbler in this region (Grimmet & Taylor 1992; JH pers. comm.; PJL pers. comm.). It certainly breeds regularly in Gansu Province and to the east throughout the northern part of Nei Mongol Autonomous Region, and abundantly in the provinces of Heilongjiang, Jilin and Liaoning. To the south, Cheng (1987) recorded it breeding widely throughout the lowland provinces of E China, including Hebei, Henan, Shandong, Shanxi, Shaanxi, Sichuan, Guizhou and Zhejiang. The southern limits of regular breeding lie in the Guangxi Zhuang Autonomous Region and Fujian Province. In Hong Kong, singing birds have been heard in June in the Mai Po Marshes Nature Reserve and Melville (1988) described a breeding attempt here in 1987. Where suitable habitat occurs, it can breed at very high densities. For example, Melville (1991) estimated 528,000 singing males in 24,000 ha of reedbed at the Shuangtaizihekou Nature Reserve in Liaoning Province.

Non-breeding It winters throughout SE Asia, with small numbers penetrating west to the eastern Indian subcontinent and into Indonesia. Its western limit within the subcontinent has yet to be established but it occurs regularly in the lowlands of NE India, including Assam, Manipur and Bengal, and on the Andaman Islands. In Burma, its status is uncertain due to past confusion with Clamorous Reed Warbler. However, Smythies (1968) considered it to be a winter visitor to Tenasserim in the south. It has occasionally overwintered in S and SE China, including Hong Kong, and in southernmost Japan.

The core wintering range extends through Laos and Cambodia, and into Vietnam except in the north. It is widespread and abundant at low elevations throughout Thailand and the Malay Peninsula south to Singapore. Large numbers also winter in Indonesia including the Riau islands, much of lowland Sumatra and W Java, where it is locally common east to the Jakarta region. It is common in the Philippines and widespread throughout the low-lying regions of Borneo, particularly in coastal regions. To the south and east, it becomes scarcer but still winters widely in wetlands of the Wallacean sub-region, where it has been recorded from the islands of Sulawesi, Sula, Buru, Ambon, Bacan, Halmahera, Ternate and Morotai and in the Lesser Sundas from Flores and Timor (White & Bruce 1986). It is likely that many birds are overlooked here and it occurs more widely than the few records suggest. The eastern limit of the regular wintering lies in Irian Jaya, Indonesia, where small numbers occur. It is apparently rare in Papua New Guinea, where recorded from the Kebar Valley, Vogelkop, Biak and the Aru Islands, Aroa lagoon, Central Province and Waigani Swamp, Central Province. Again, it is likely to have been overlooked here.

MOVEMENTS Departure from breeding grounds in Russia and Japan begins in August and continues throughout September, with stragglers remaining until mid October. Migrants pass through S Japan, including the Izu and Ryukyu Islands, and also commonly through Taiwan.

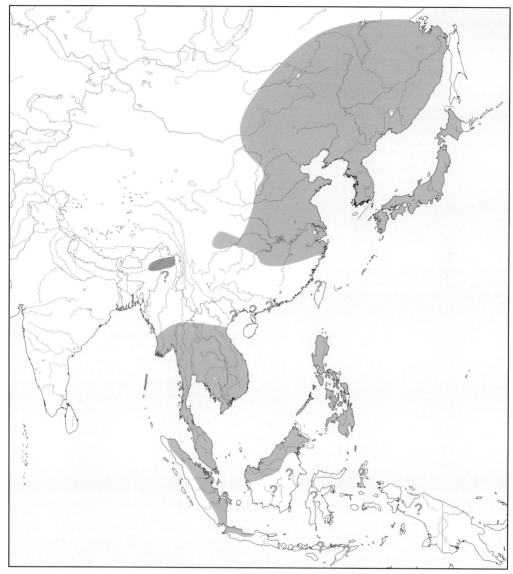

Oriental Reed Warbler. Breeding range and winter distribution.

Passage through China is rapid, with migrants reaching the south coast by the end of August. In Hong Kong, birds are occasionally recorded during July and August and these may be non-breeding, oversummering individuals. The first influx here usually occurs in the last week of August, with migration peaking from mid September to early October and continuing into November, with only occasional stragglers appearing in early December.

Southward passage is rapid through Thailand and the Malay Peninsula. In Malaysia, the first birds usually appear in mid September (earliest 28 August). At Selangor, the main influx occurred between late September and the third week in October (Medway & Wells 1976). It is common in Singapore by the end of September and numbers here continue to build rapidly through October and remain high in suitable habitat throughout the winter months.

Due to wintering abundance, it is uncertain when north-ward passage commences. It remains common in Singapore until late April. Males pass through Selangor, Malaysia, mainly from late April to mid May, with females moving up to two weeks later (Nisbet & Medway 1976). Northward passage through Hong Kong occurs earlier, however, usually in the last week in March and peaking in mid to late April, but numbers are lower than in autumn.

Birds return to their breeding grounds in southern Japan from mid April, but mainly in late April and early May. New arrivals continue throughout May, with the latest reaching Hokkaido in early June. Birds return to breeding areas in E China, near the Yangtze River, from late April onwards and NE China and SE Russia from early May, but it is not until the last week of May that they reach northernmost areas along the Amur River.

Several controls of ringed birds have established that migrants passing through Hong Kong breed in Japan. Given the early spring passage dates in Hong Kong, it seems likely that the bulk of migrants passing through here are Japanese breeders. Malaysia-wintering birds, with their later departure, perhaps breed towards the northern limit of the range in continental Asia or Hokkaido.

Vagrancy To the west of the known range, there are three winter records from Nepal; a sight record from Koshi on 20 February 1994 (Cottridge *et al.* 1994) and single birds trapped at Koshi Tappu Wildlife Reserve on 15 and 19 April 1997 (Giri & Choudhary 1997). There are also two records from Israel, which represent the only occurrences from the Western Palearctic: a bird remained at Eilat from 28 February to 13 April 1988 and a second was trapped there on 2 May 1990 (Shirihai 1996). Vagrants have also reached N Australia on at least five occasions between January and March. Records range from Western Australia to Queensland, and suggest it may be a rare wet season visitor (Higgins *et al.* 2006).

DESCRIPTION

Plumage – Adult fresh (August to November) Forehead, crown and nape dull greyish brown. Supercilium pale creamy buff, broad and conspicuous above lores, narrowing over the eye and fading above ear-coverts. Lores well-marked, with distinct greyish brown line extending to bill base. Eye-line limited to an ill-defined dark smudge immediately behind eye. Ear-coverts grey-brown, darker towards upper edge, paler creamy brown and usually mottled along lower edge. Pale eye-ring indistinct, merging with supercilium. Mantle and scapulars plain mousy brown or dull olive-brown, slightly browner than nape. Rump and uppertail-coverts slightly paler and warmer than mantle. Tail feathers blackish brown with cold greyish brown fringes and distinct pale brown to whitish tips. Chin and throat creamy white, the latter with short, narrow and indistinct dark greyish streaks at sides. Streaking slightly more apparent at sides of breast just above carpal bend. Breast and belly white with faint buff wash, this becoming brighter and more obvious on sides of breast and neck. Flanks and undertail-coverts pale straw, strongest on lower flanks and undertail-coverts. Lesser and median coverts dull mousy brown or olive-brown, unmarked and uniform. Greater coverts and tertials dark grey-brown with broad diffuse mousy brown or olive-brown fringes. Primary coverts, secondaries and primaries dark grey-brown with paler greyish brown edges, those on secondaries rather paler and brighter, forming slight pale wing panel. Alula dark grey-brown or blackish with a narrow, mousy brown fringe. Underwing-coverts light creamy buff to greyish brown, similar to flanks but sometimes with trace of pale yellow.

Adult worn (March to July) On breeding grounds, as fresh adult but with slightly paler, greyer and colder-toned appearance. Crown, upperparts and wing feather edges dull greyish brown, the brighter rump and uppertail-coverts tending to show more contrast. Supercilium whiter. Dark brown streaks on breast sides often more prominent and conspicuous. Breast and belly whiter, with reduced buff wash. Lower flanks and undertail-coverts remaining pale straw to dull buff.

Juvenile Resembles adult but plumage loose-textured and appearance rather blotchy. Overall slightly paler than adult, with supercilium narrower and less well marked. Median and greater coverts with paler, browner tips forming broad

but indistinct wing-bars. Tertials with conspicuously paler buff fringes than adult. Flight feathers and tail feathers paler and browner. Rectrices with diffuse pale brown tips, less contrasting than on adult, broadest on inner webs and extending *c.* 15mm from tip, on outer webs restricted to tip.

Bare parts Upper mandible dark bluish grey with narrow greyish pink cutting edge, some with a whitish tip. Lower mandible dull pink at base, shading to dull greyish pink towards tip. Mouth bright orange in adults, yellowish orange in immature birds; first-autumn birds show two dark tongue spots. Tarsi, toes and claws dull plumbeous-grey. Iris warm brown in older adults, dull greyish brown in first autumn birds.

IN HAND CHARACTERS
Measurements

	Male	Female
Wing	83–90 (85.8; 25)	76–86 (80.5; 26)
Tail	64–73 (69.6; 25)	60–72 (65.2; 26)
Bill	21.5–24.5 (22.7; 25)	21–23.5 (22.2; 25)
Tarsus	26.3–31 (28.7; 23)	26.5–29 (27.8; 25)

Sexes combined:
Tail/wing ratio: 76–86% (81%; 50)
Bill width: 4.9–5.6 (5.3; 20)
Hind claw: 8.2–10.0 (9.4; 19)
Tail graduation: 7–13 (9.6; 20)

Migrants on spring passage in Hong Kong are significantly longer-winged than those examined there in autumn. Mean wing lengths of birds wintering in Thailand and Singapore correspond with the shorter-winged population (Table 7). These data suggest that two populations occur on passage in Hong Kong.

Table 7. Comparison of live wing lengths of Oriental Reed Warbler captured at sites in E and SE Asia; sexes and age classes combined.

Location and season	Wing length	Source
Hong Kong, Mar–May	76–98 (87.0; 1,004)	HKRG
Hong Kong, Aug–Nov	73–97 (83.7; 3,561)	HKRG
Thailand, Sep–Apr	73–91 (83.0; 479)	PDR
Singapore, Oct–Apr	76–89 (82.3; 116)	PRK

Structure

Figure 77. Wing of Oriental Reed Warbler.

Wing formula (Cramp 1992):

p1/pc	p2	p3e	p4(e)	p5	p6	p7	p10
(7)–(1)	1–4	wp	0–2	2–6	5–9	7–11	15–19

Wing pointed with minute p1. Wing point p3 [4]; p2 = p(3/4) 4–5 [5/6]; emargination on p3, sometimes also p4; p2 notch falls at p9/ss (8/9).

Tail medium length, rounded.

Bill as in Great Reed Warbler; long, stout and broad-based, tip of culmen decurved, sides slightly concave.

Tarsi thick and strong; toes and claws large and strong.

Recognition A large warbler with plain olive-brown upperparts, a conspicuous supercilium and usually dark throat streaks. Separated from Great Reed Warbler by shorter wing (possible overlap above 88mm) and somewhat rounder wing-tip, with p2 nearly always < p4; also usually by emargination on p4. From Clamorous Reed Warbler by having p2 ≥ p5, with notch at or above ss tips (well below ss tips in Clamorous Reed); and from its resident island races by larger measurements and longer primary projection (p3–10 >15mm).

Most fresh-plumaged birds can be sexed on wing length. In Malaysia, those above 83mm were males, those below 82mm females (Nisbet & Medway 1972).

Ageing Once post-juvenile moult is complete in late summer, there are no plumage differences between immature birds and adults. Ageing then depends on iris colour (warm brown in adults, dull greyish brown in young birds), palate colour (bright orange in adults, paler yellowish orange in young birds,) and presence or absence of tongue spots (usually retained in young birds until at least November).

Weight Range 18–47g. In Malaysia, typically 20–23g during winter, increasing to 27–31g in late May (Nisbet & Medway 1972). In Hong Kong, August–November 18–44g (24.9; 3,591), March–May 19–47g (29.0; 1,046) (HKRG unpublished data).

GEOGRAPHIC VARIATION None recorded, but there is a significant difference in wing length between birds migrating through Hong Kong in autumn (mean 83.7mm) and spring (mean 87.0mm). Wing lengths of birds wintering in Thailand and Singapore correspond with the shorter-winged population.

TAXONOMY AND SYSTEMATICS Salomonsen (1929) treated several of the larger *Acrocephalus*, including Oriental Reed, Clamorous Reed and Basra Reed Warblers as races of Great Reed Warbler. Subsequently, these races were given differing taxonomic treatment by various authorities, although most adopted a conservative approach. These included Cramp (1992), who treated Clamorous Reed Warbler as specifically distinct while retaining the other taxa as races of Great Reed Warbler. Although Oriental Reed Warbler shares many morphological and structural similarities with Great Reed Warbler, mtDNA investigation of the larger *Acrocephalus* by Leisler *et al.* (1997) indicated it to be more closely related to Clamorous Reed than to Great Reed Warbler. Helbig & Seibold (1999) came to the same conclusion. Both studies supported the adoption of Oriental Reed Warbler as a distinct, monotypic species.

▲ Adult, Honshu, Japan, May. Closely resembles Great Reed Warbler, but note fine dark streaks on lower throat and upper breast, usually faint or absent on Great Reed (Akiko Hidaka).

▲ Adult, Honshu, Japan, May. This heavily abraded bird has lost the fine underpart streaking and would be difficult to separate from Great Reed Warbler in the field (Gaku Tozuka).

▲ First year, Hong Kong, October. After complete post-juvenile moult in the breeding area, adults and young birds are inseparable by plumage, although the grey-brown iris identifies this as a young bird (John and Jemi Holmes).

▲ First year, Singapore, February. By late winter, the upperparts become greyish brown and the underparts whiter, but the fine breast streaks remain conspicuous (Peter Kennerley).

▲ First year, Hong Kong October. Note primary projection at *c.* 75% of exposed tertial length, falling between that of Great Reed (80–90%) and Clamorous Reed (up to two-thirds in migratory *brunnescens*, shorter in other races) (John and Jemi Holmes).

▲ First year, Taiwan, November. Has slightly less pointed wing-tip than Great Reed, with p4 equal to p3 in some birds and often emarginated. Note slightly paler rump contrasting with warm brown upperparts, and indistinct throat-streaking (Liao Pen-shing).

CLAMOROUS REED WARBLER
Acrocephalus stentoreus   **Plates 26 and 27**

Curruca stentorea **Hemprich & Ehrenberg, 1833**. *Symb. Phys. Avium Decas I*, fol. bb. Damietta, lower Egypt.

A large, plain-backed *Acrocephalus* that breeds mainly in *Phragmites* reedbeds, *Typha* swamps and mangroves, from Egypt and the Middle East through C and S Asia to the islands of Indonesia and northern Australasia, east to the Solomon Islands. There is marked variation over this extensive range involving size, colour saturation, and relative length and shape of the bill. In addition, there are significant differences in song. It is mostly resident, although birds breeding in C Asia are migratory, wintering in the Indian subcontinent. Until recently, Australian birds were widely regarded as belonging within Clamorous Reed Warbler but they are now separated as a distinct species, Australian Reed Warbler. Birds breeding in eastern Indonesia and the islands of the Australasian region are quite distinct from those breeding to the west and may be better placed within Australian Reed Warbler or treated as a distinct species. Polytypic, with ten races recognised:

A. s. stentoreus (Hemprich & Ehrenberg, 1833). Nile Valley, Egypt, south to Lake Nasser.
A. s. brunnescens (Jerdon, 1839). Resident C and S Red Sea coasts, NW Somalia and Arabian Peninsula. Also breeds SC Asia south to Iraq and east to Iran, wintering Pakistan and N India.
A. s. meridionalis (Legge, 1875). Sri Lanka.
A. s. celebensis Heinroth, 1903. S Sulawesi.
A. s. amyae Stuart Baker, 1922. NE India to N Burma and (probably this race) SW China.
A. s. lentecaptus Hartert, 1924. Borneo, Lombok and Sumbawa.
A. s. sumbae Hartert, 1924. Buru, Sumba, Timor to New Guinea, Bismarck Islands and Solomon Islands.
A. s. harterti Salomonsen, 1928. Philippines.
A. s. siebersi Salomonsen, 1928. W Java.
A. s. levantinus Roselaar, 1994. N. Israel.

IDENTIFICATION Size differs greatly between races.
Central Asian *brunnescens*: Length 18–20cm. Wing 78–95mm. Tail/wing 80–91%.
Wallacean/Australasian *sumbae*: Length 14–15cm. Wing 65–71mm. Tail/wing 84–95%.

A mid sized to large, plain-backed and usually warmly coloured *Acrocephalus* with a proportionately long bill and tail. Palearctic forms share many plumage and structural similarities with Great Reed, Oriental Reed and, to a lesser extent, Basra Reed Warbler in the Middle East, while those resident in the eastern part of the range require separation from Australian Reed Warbler. The smallest form *sumbae* overlaps in size with Marsh Warbler. There is variation within each of these races and the effects of wear and bleaching compound identification problems. Sexes alike.
Structure All races have a relatively slender build, appearing slimmer than the other larger *Acrocephalus*. The long, narrow bill and sleek, flat crown give the head a characteristic long, attenuated and distinctly pointed appearance. Although heavier in continental Asian birds, the bill is less thick and 'thrush-like' than in Great Reed Warbler, with a more gradual decurvature along the length of the upper mandible. Birds resident In Egypt and Israel have a narrow-tipped, laterally compressed bill, although never

as slender as in Basra Reed. When singing, the fore-crown feathers are raised to give a distinct peak just behind the eye, but the head tends to lack the untidy, spiky appearance characteristic of singing Great Reed and Oriental Reed Warblers.

Clamorous Reed Warbler is proportionately shorter-winged than other large Palearctic *Acrocephalus*. In the resident races, the primary projection is approximately half of the exposed tertial length with only six primary tips visible (Fig. 75), but in the migrant form *brunnescens* it is slightly longer, extending up to two-thirds of the tertial length, with seven primary tips sometimes visible. The wing is distinctly rounded, with the second primary (p2) always shorter than the fifth (p5), and in most races shorter than the sixth (p6). The relatively long and strongly rounded tail enhances the slim appearance, although the extent of this differs between races.
Plumage and bare parts In the western races *stentoreus* and *levantinus* the supercilium is narrow and poorly defined, only slightly paler than the crown. The eye-stripe is also indistinct, appearing as a diffuse spot in front of the eye that sometimes extends across the lores. Behind the eye, the supercilium and eye-stripe are indistinct or absent and the side of the head appears uniform. The upperparts are rather bright olive-brown with a warm wash, especially on the rump and uppertail-coverts, and appear slightly darker and richer than in Great Reed Warbler. The unstreaked underparts are light fulvous-brown to cinnamon-brown or dark coffee-brown on the breast and flanks, always darker than in Great Reed. However, the throat and belly centre are contrastingly whitish. With wear, the upperparts become a duller, greyer brown and the underparts appear paler.

Migrant *brunnescens* from C and SW Asia is quite different in appearance to these races. It shows a better-defined head pattern, although this is still less bold and contrasting than that of Great Reed Warbler. The supercilium is paler and more contrasting than in *stentoreus*, extending further beyond the eye, while the eye-stripe is crisper in front of the eye and forms a dusky line behind it. The upperparts are uniform olive-brown with a slight greyish cast, similar to those of the race *zarudnyi* of Great Reed Warbler. Unlike *stentoreus*, the underparts are sullied white with a pale fulvous-brown wash on the side of the breast, which deepens on the lower flanks and ventral region. Fresh first-winter birds are brighter than adults, warm fulvous-brown above and buffy brown below, with the whitish chin, throat and belly centre lightly washed pale buff.

The bill is dark grey in all races, with a pale pink base to the lower mandible, which darkens towards the tip. The legs and feet are dark, ranging from plumbeous-grey or dark grey to greyish brown or pinkish grey.

The appearance of the other races and their separation from *brunnescens* is discussed within **Geographic Variation** below.

SIMILAR SPECIES Those races occurring from Egypt to W Java require separation from the other large, unstreaked *Acrocephalus* that can occur alongside them outside the breeding season. Oriental Reed Warbler is likely to overlap with races *amyae, siebersi, lentecaptus* and *harterti*, while Great Reed Warbler occurs alongside *stentoreus, levantinus* and *brunnescens*. The smaller Basra Reed Warbler is only likely to overlap with *brunnescens* although, given recent breeding records from Israel, sympatric breeding alongside *levantinus* is a possibility. The very different Thick-billed Warbler is unlikely to be mistaken for Clamorous Reed and their separation is discussed under the former species. Separation of the smaller races that resemble Australian Reed Warbler is summarised under that species.

Oriental Reed Warbler occurs alongside several races of Clamorous Reed including *amyae*, *siebersi*, *lentecaptus* and *harterti* during the winter months. Compared with these, it has a slightly shorter and thicker bill and more angular, less attenuated head profile. Differences in wing structure also provide a reliable means of separating them. In Oriental Reed, the primary projection is much longer, almost the length of the tertials, and the tail is slightly shorter and less graduated. In the hand, the longer wing of Oriental Reed is a reliable character, with the wing point formed by p3 (occasionally also p4), a shorter first primary (p1) and longer p2, and emargination well defined on p3 but rarely present on p4 and never on p5. Oriental Reed particularly resembles the two continental Asian forms of Clamorous Reed, *brunnescens* and *amyae*, which are paler and greyer than other races, although it shows whitish tips to the rectrices which Clamorous Reed lacks. There are no obvious differences in upperpart colour between Oriental Reed and these two races, but it usually shows distinct streaking on lower throat and upper breast, lacking in these races or at best faintly visible on some *amyae*. Some Indonesian races of Clamorous Reed also show indistinct streaking on the lower throat and upper breast, but its extent and prominence rarely approaches that of Oriental Reed. When fresh, the rufescent coloration of these resident forms should separate them from any large migrant *Acrocephalus* occurring alongside them. Worn birds can pose problems where they occur with wintering Oriental Reed Warbler.

Wintering Oriental Reed Warblers occur alongside *harterti* in the Philippines and *siebersi* in Java. Both these races are smaller and with proportionately smaller and finer bills, and when freshly moulted are slightly darker, more richly coloured than Oriental Reed, especially on the underparts. They do, however, show indistinct dark throat streaking. The effects of wear and bleaching result in these races becoming paler and tend to eliminate plumage distinctions, after which separation relies on size and structural differences.

Great Reed Warbler breeds to the north of Clamorous Reed in N Kazakhstan and S Siberia and winters in sub-Saharan Africa where the latter is absent. But on migration, the eastern race *zarudnyi* regularly moves through the C Asian breeding range of *brunnescens* Clamorous Reed. Further west, Great Reed also occurs on passage alongside Clamorous Reed of the races *stentoreus* in Egypt and *levantinus* in Israel, and on the coasts of the Red Sea and Arabian Peninsula where resident populations of *brunnescens* occur.

Great Reed is distinctly larger than all races of Clamorous Reed and its heavier structure and more clumsy behaviour are usually immediately apparent, while the longer, more pointed wing, longer primary projection and rather shorter, less graduated tail are additional reliable distinctions. Plumage differences between the two species are slight and are least marked in C and SW Asia where the greyer *zarudnyi* Great Reed meets the duller *brunnescens* Clamorous Reed. Great Reed has a long, broad and pale supercilium that extends well behind the eye and a narrow but contrastingly darker eye-stripe that is particularly conspicuous in front of the eye, giving it a bold and contrasting head pattern and fierce expression. Although the supercilium of *brunnescens*

can extend some way behind the eye, it invariably remains shorter and narrower and is usually obscured by a brown wash behind the eye and so appears less contrasting than that of Great Reed.

The olive-brown upperparts of freshly moulted *brunnescens* are slightly richer than those of *zarudnyi*, but both can show a greyish cast about the head. Below, fresh *brunnescens* tend to be warmer and brighter than *zarudnyi* but, when worn, both appear strikingly pale, with buff restricted to the flanks. Some *zarudnyi* can show discrete streaking on the throat which *brunnescens* lacks. Great Reed Warblers of the nominate form on migration through Egypt and Israel appear warmly toned but distinctly paler above than locally breeding Clamorous Reed. They are paler buff on flanks and underparts, with white less restricted to the throat and belly centre. In spring, they tend to have a brighter, fresher appearance to the plumage than Clamorous Reed and the primary tips are less heavily worn.

Basra Reed Warbler breeds in Iraq and winters in Africa, but migrants can occur alongside Clamorous Reed on the Red Sea, Arabian and Persian Gulf coasts, and also in Israel where it has recently been recorded breeding. Basra Reed is slightly smaller and decidedly slimmer than the two races of Clamorous Reed it is most likely to come into contact with; *A. s. brunnescens* in the Red Sea and Persian Gulf coasts and *A. s. levantinus* in Israel. In addition, it is appreciably longer winged and shorter tailed and has a more slender bill. Furthermore, it shows a long and conspicuously pale supercilium, while the upperparts are colder olive-brown and the underparts are paler.

Australian Reed Warbler is much smaller than the continental and Asian races of Clamorous Reed. However, the Wallacean taxa *celebensis* and *sumbae* are small races and overlap in size with Australian Reed Warbler. Their separation is discussed under that species.

Thick-billed Warbler is most unlikely to be mistaken for Clamorous Reed, but their separation is briefly discussed under the former species.

VOICE Song in the Middle East is loud and far carrying and includes the harsh chattering and grating notes typical of the large *Acrocephalus*. It differs from Great Reed and Oriental Reed Warbler songs in being less raucous, slightly more melodious, but also less varied. It is also distinctly slower in delivery and higher pitched, between 1–6kHz, than in Great Reed Warbler, and less sustained. Bursts consist of varied harsh and scratchy phrases, each repeated three or four times: *kerri-kerri-kerri, kureek-kureek-kureek-kureek, chi-kerruchi-kerruchi-kerruchi* …' to form a song sequence (Urban *et al.* 1997). In Israel, the song is often preceded by a series of '*tek-tek-tek*' calls, then delivered in a series of varied phrases '*karra-karra-karet-karet*', lasting two to eight seconds (Shirihai *et al.* 1995). Cramp (1992) mentioned a characteristic sequence '*ro-do-peek-kiss*' or '*rod-o-petch-iss*', with emphasis on the third or forth syllable. Some birds regularly include mimicry.

Songs of the western races, including *brunnescens*, resemble each other closely, with the slow-paced *kerri-kerri-kerri, kureek-kureek-kureek-kureek, chi-kerruchi-kerruchi-kerruchi* …' sequence common to all. It is not clear how much those of other Asian races differ. In Sri Lanka, *meridionalis* sound distinctly louder and more raucous than *brunnescens*. Although the style and pace of the delivery remains similar, it lacks the higher frequency notes above 5kHz and varied quality of *brunnescens*.

411

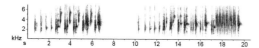

Song of Clamorous Reed Warbler recorded within breeding range of *A. s. leventinus*, Israel, April. (Sample 2003)

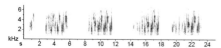

Song of Clamorous Reed Warbler recorded within breeding range of *A. s. brunnescens*, Shymkent, southern Kazakhstan, May. (Peter Kennerley)

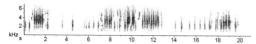

Song of Clamorous Reed Warbler recorded within breeding range of *A. s. meridionalis*, Bundala National Park, Sri Lanka, March. (Peter Kennerley)

At the southeastern limit of the range, the song of the small birds in the Bismarck Archipelago, Papua New Guinea and the Solomon Islands is quite different from that of Asian birds. It lacks the harsh and guttural notes and is slightly higher pitched and more varied, at times sounding quite fluty. It is always preceded by a series of calls '*cra cra cra*' or '*quark-quark*', which may be repeated several times before the next part of the song is added. This consists of short bursts lasting 1–2 seconds separated by slightly longer short pauses. Each sequence comprises a series of notes, variously transcribed as '*chek-chek-chek-tui-tui-tui-tui-tui*', or '*cra cra cra truut truut truut truut truut truut*' or minor variations on this. It also gives a slightly more guttural '*chu-chu-chu-chu*' rising in pitch, but higher pitched than heard from larger birds in Asia. After several repetitions of this sequence a rather nasal or fluty phrase may be included so the song extends to '*cra cra cra truut truut truut truut truut wheeecheet wheeecheet wheeecheet*'.

Despite the fact that this resident race is spread across many islands spanning several thousand kilometres the song is surprisingly consistent, certainly between the populations on the Bismarck Archipelago, Papua New Guinea and Bougainville in the Solomon Islands. Songs of birds on Buru, Sumba, Timor and Irian Jaya are unknown.

Song of Clamorous Reed Warbler recorded within breeding range of *A. s. sumbae*, New Ireland, Bismark Archipelago, Papua New Guinea, August. (Peter Kennerley)

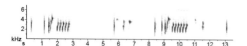

Song of Clamorous Reed Warbler recorded within breeding range of *A. s. sumbae*, Bougainville, Solomon Islands, Papua New Guinea, August. (McPherson Natural History Unit)

Several distinct calls include a distinctive hard '*tek*' that is given as a single call but also as a rapid series of '*tek-tek-*

tek-tek-tek...*' notes which run into each other. There is also a louder, harsher '*tak*' or '*chak*' similar to that of Great Reed Warbler, given singly or in pairs. Shirihai *et al.* (1995) described a softer '*karrk*' and Urban *et al.* (1997) mention a '*churr*' call, which may be the series of '*tek-tek-tek-tek-tek...*' forming a harsh dry churring rattle.

MOULT Adults undergo a full moult after breeding. In migrant *brunnescens* this is delayed until arrival in India and Pakistan, then completed between September and November. Resident *brunnescens* in Sudan begin moult in late July and August. Nominate *stentoreus* resident in Egypt moult between August and October or early November and similar timing is found in races *amyae* and *lentecaptus*. In other races, moult timing varies depending on local rainfall and breeding season. There does not appear to be a supplementary body moult. Races *brunnescens* and *stentoreus* show rather worn, faded body plumage and moderately abraded flight feathers by March and April. Young birds of resident populations appear to have a complete post-juvenile moult at the same time as adults moult. In migrant *brunnescens*, there is a post-juvenile body moult during July, followed by renewal of wing and tail (or probably all) feathers in autumn after arrival in the winter quarters.

HABITAT In Egypt and Israel, it inhabits waterways, lakes, swamps and riverside vegetation, preferring Papyrus *Cyperus papyrus* to *Phragmites* where available. Northern breeding *brunnescens* populations are more wide-ranging and opportunistic, breeding in S Kazakhstan in Papyrus and *Phragmites* beds around lakes, but also in small clumps of reed along mountain streams, and found singing from maize fields in Tajikistan. In Iran and Afghanistan, it frequents reedbeds, *Typha* swamps, emergent riverside vegetation and irrigation ditches from 700m to 1,200m. In Kashmir, it breeds commonly up to1,600m in reeds, marshes and adjacent willow scrub and breeds in similar wetland habitat in Kerala in S India. Reports of birds at 2,500m in the Pamirs and 3,000m in the Himalayas (Cramp 1992) presumably relate to migrants. Southern breeding *brunnescens* populations are confined mainly to the coasts of the Red Sea, Arabian Gulf and Persian Gulf and breed in mangroves. But with the spread of irrigation into these arid regions, there are recent reports of birds singing near artificial wetlands a short distance inland. Where the breeding range overlaps with Great Reed Warbler, as in Israel and S Kazakhstan, Clamorous Reed Warbler prefers to nest in Papyrus and Great Reed Warbler in *Phragmites* reed.

Wintering *brunnescens* occur in a wide range of habitats. In India, they occupy even small wetlands with restricted emergent vegetation and *Phragmites* is not essential. Many occur in Acacia woodland near wetlands and in cultivation. In Yemen, non-breeding birds appear in mangrove woodland, but it is not known whether these are migrant northern *brunnescens* or local migrants from nearby coasts.

Birds resident in S Asia occupy a range of wetland habitats including lakes, tanks, jheels and swamps with reeds, tall Papyrus stands and similar dense emergent vegetation. In Assam and Burma, *amyae* inhabits tall damp grassland, often away from open water, while in the Philippines, *harterti* breeds in wetlands, but also in bamboo thickets, well away from wetlands. In the Wallacean region birds occupy reeds, tall damp grassland and adjacent scrub, usually close to water, and singing birds have been noted from rice fields. Ranges from sea level to 800m on Sulawesi and up to 1,100m on Buru (Coates & Bishop 1997). Similar habitats are utilised in Papua New Guinea, the Bismarck Archipelago and the Solomon Islands, but usually at lower elevations.

BEHAVIOUR Occurs at high densities in favoured locations and then appears almost social, with singing males often less than 20m apart and largely unresponsive to songs of nearby males. Outside the breeding season, it tends to keep low within thick cover, giving only an occasional call that reveals its presence. Occasionally it feeds in the open, usually at the base of reeds or scrub just above water, or on emergent or floating vegetation. It is not particularly shy, but is often skulking, disappearing for several minutes before re-emerging. The movements of the larger races are fairly slow and deliberate, but less heavy or clumsy than those of Great Reed Warbler, while the smaller races tend to be less laborious in their movements and behave in a similar manner to the smaller *Acrocephalus*.

Males of the migrant populations of *brunnescens* return to breeding grounds before females and establish territories immediately. Song may be heard from deep cover, especially in windy conditions, but in calm weather it may be delivered from near the top of a reed stem or bush, but no territorial song-flight is known. The singing male ruffles its throat feathers and raises the feathers of forehead and crown, similar to Great Reed Warbler. Typical song begins before dawn and declines during the heat of the day, but can still be heard in the hottest periods. Song occurs with increasing frequency towards dusk and continues after sunset for several hours. Birds occasionally sing outside the breeding season and do so regularly on migration.

BREEDING HABITS Clamorous Reed Warbler is believed to be monogamous but sometimes polygynous with one male mated to two females. Territorial defence appears limited to the area immediately surrounding the nest. In the Nile delta, Egypt, singing males occur at a density of 10–20 per hectare (Meininger *et al.* 1986), while in Somalia 20 singing males were recorded along a 1km stretch of mangrove on Saad el Din island (Ash 1983). Similar densities occur in Papyrus beds in Kazakhstan, Sri Lanka and Java.

In Egypt, the nest is usually built close to the water, usually within 100–150mm of the surface. It is a deep cup of dry reed leaves, grasses and small stems, lined with finer material, sheep wool, which is attached to mangrove or reed stems (Urban *et al.* 1997). Three to six eggs are laid and incubation lasts 13–15 days. Both parents care for the young, which fledge after 11–13 days, but remain dependent for several more days.

Hybridisation with Great Reed Warbler has been recorded in S Kazakhstan (Hansson *et al.* 2003), where sympatric breeding occurs.

In Egypt, breeding begins in March and extends to late June (Urban *et al.* 1997), while in Israel it lasts from April to late July (Cramp 1992). In northerly migrant populations of *A. s. brunnescens* nest building commences in Tajikistan in mid May, with the earliest full clutch recorded here on 28 May and the latest on 22 July (Cramp 1992).

In resident populations of tropical and sub-tropical Asia, breeding takes place during the local wet season and may not follow an annual cycle. In Papua New Guinea and Bougainville, birds of the race *sumbae* appear to breed throughout the year (Hadden 1981). The nest is built over damp ground or open water, up to 2m above the ground and is often slung between reed or grass stems or similar

emergent vegetation. The clutch size in this region is usually 2–3 eggs but nothing more is known of its breeding habits.

DISTRIBUTION Clamorous Reed Warbler has an extensive although fragmented breeding distribution. It ranges from the Nile Valley and Red Sea coasts, across C and S Asia east to the Philippines, Lesser Sundas and Moluccas and through Papua New Guinea to the Solomon Islands. Northern populations are migratory, but birds breeding in the Middle East and in tropical S and SE Asia are believed to be resident. Its presence on some islands and absence from others appears random and may be indicative of a more extensive ancestral range in former times.

A. s. stentoreus The nominate race is abundant in the Nile delta and Suez Canal regions of N Egypt. It probably also breeds at El-Faiyum and Wadi el Rayan, and in the reedbeds at the Dakhla and Bahariya oases in the Western Desert (Urban *et al.* 1997). It has expanded its range south along the Nile Valley following the construction of the Aswan Dam and now reaches Lake Nasser and associated wetlands in N Sudan border areas.

A. s. levantinus The form *levantinus* is restricted to N Israel, breeding from the Hula Valley south along the Bet Shean and Jordan Valley to the northern Dead Sea; also along the Jezreel Valley towards the Mediterranean Sea and occasionally at other scattered sites south to Emeq HaSoreq (Shirihai 1996). Roselaar (1994) speculated that breeding may occur in Jordan but to date this remains unconfirmed.

A. s. brunnescens Larger birds united within *brunnescens* occur widely from the Red Sea to Kashmir and north to S Kazakhstan. This race has both migratory and resident populations and it is convenient to discuss these separately.

a) Migratory *brunnescens*

Breeding The northern migratory population breeds across southern C Asia from the Kopet Dagh in Turkmenistan and N Iran, to the southern shores of the Caspian Sea. It also breeds within the water catchments of the major rivers in this region, including the Morghab and Tedzhen Rivers in S Turkmenistan and N Afghanistan, the watersheds of the Amu Darya in Uzbekistan and the Syr Darya in S Kazakhstan and Uzbekistan to the Aral Sea. In S Kazakhstan it also nests close to Lake Sorbulak, near Almaty. To the south it ranges through Tajikistan to the Pamir Mountains and into Pakistan, where it breeds in Sind, Punjab, Baluchistan and North West Frontier Provinces, although its distribution here appears to be patchy and sporadic. In India, it breeds commonly up to 1,600m in the Vale of Kashmir and locally elsewhere at lower elevations in the Peninsula, including Sambhar Lake in Rajasthan, the Tapi (Tapti) River in Gujarat, several localities in the Bombay area, Vembanad Lake in Kerala and near Calcutta (Ripley 1982).

Non-breeding The wintering range extends from S Iraq and coastal S Iran to the Indian subcontinent, where it is common from Sind Province, Pakistan, east to Bengal and south to Tamil Nadu. It is a localised winter visitor and passage migrant to Nepal, where it is recorded mainly below 100m from wetlands in the south and east, most frequently from the Koshi River (CI pers. comm.). It has also been recorded from Sri Lanka, where it is undoubtedly overlooked amongst the

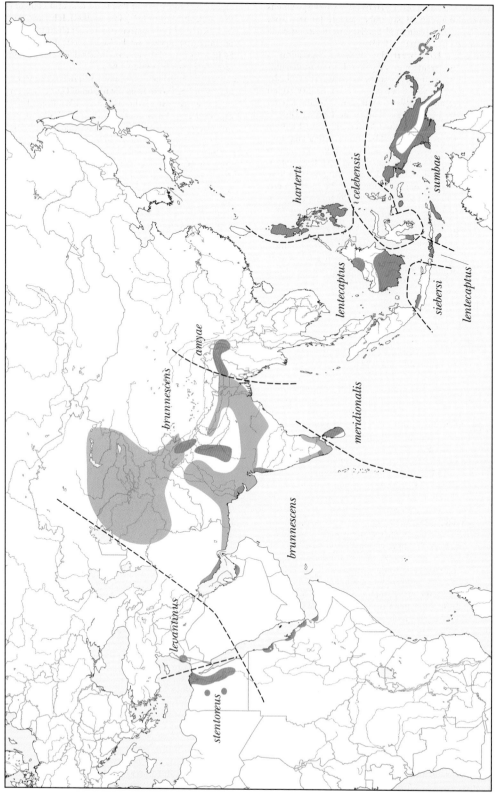

Clamorous Reed Warbler. Breeding range and winter distribution. Resident within breeding range in southern parts of range.

numerous resident form *meridionalis*. Three specimens collected between 29 November and 19 January from the Chiang Mai plain in N Thailand were attributed to *brunnescens* by Deignan (1963).

b) Resident *brunnescens* The southern population of *brunnescens* is resident or subject only to short-distance movements within coastal mangroves. It is locally common on the Red Sea coasts of Saudi Arabia, Sudan and Eritrea and in NW Somalia, but breeding has yet to be proved in Yemen. Within the Persian Gulf, it breeds in S Iran, the United Arab Emirates and Oman, where birds are augmented by non-breeding migrants, presumably from C Asia. It is absent from Bahrain and Qatar but appears to be spreading into the Eastern Province of Saudi Arabia. In Pakistan, singing birds have been recorded from mangroves up to 12 May (Roberts 1992) and together with a record on 25 July, suggest that breeding may occur, albeit occasionally, in mangroves along the Arabian Sea coast.

A. s. amyae Resident from E India into adjacent regions of Burma and SW China. Although this population is geographically isolated from breeding *brunnescens* and is resident or a short-distance migrant, wintering *brunnescens* may also occur within its range. In India, it appears to be confined to the floodplains and grasslands of the Brahmaputra River in Assam. Its status in Burma is unclear. There is a specimen from Taunggyi and all records from C Burma and the Shan States are probably this race (Smythies 1968), although see *brunnescens* (above) for Thai records. It certainly occurs at Moyingyi Reservoir in E Burma, a RAMSAR site to the northeast of Rangoon (PDR *in litt.*). In China, where the race involved is presumably *amyae*, Clamorous Reed Warbler is local and uncommon. Although there are very few confirmed records of breeding, it apparently breeds in C and NE Sichuan and S Guizhou Provinces (Cheng 1987) and singing birds have been heard in Yunnan Province at Er Hai in March and near Lijiang in April (JH *in litt.*).

A. s. meridionalis In Sri Lanka, this race is a widespread although localised resident throughout low-lying wetlands in both the wet and dry zones, north to the Jaffna Peninsular and south to at least Tissamaharma and Bundala National Park.

A. s. harterti In the Philippines, the race *harterti* occurs on the islands of Luzon, Mindoro, Leyte, Bohol and Mindanao, but is described as being uncommon by Dickinson *et al.* (1991). Confusion with wintering Oriental Reed Warbler has doubtless clouded its true status.

A. s. siebersi The range of *siebersi* on Java is poorly documented. It appears to be restricted to low-lying wetlands in the northwest, but there are very few recent reports of Clamorous Reed Warbler anywhere within Java. All recent reports come from wetlands near Jakarta, e.g. the Muara Angke reserve, on the western outskirts of Jakarta.

A. s. lentecaptus This race is resident on Lombok and Sumbawa, the westernmost of the Lesser Sundas. The resident birds on Kalimantan, Borneo, appear identical to *lentecaptus*, and Mees (1971) provisionally included them within *lentecaptus*. On Kalimantan, it is a rare resident and absent from many apparently suitable localities. It is known from Rantau in the south, and the swamps and lakes in the drainage basin of the Sungei Mahakam in the south and east, with singing birds found in the Amuntai and Alabio area in July 1995 (Holmes 1997). Singing birds have also been reported from the Sungei Negara basin

in January (van Balen & Prentice 1997) and Pontianak in March and April 1994 (Holmes 1994). It has not been recorded from the Malaysian states of Sabah and Sarawak, but birds in song were watched at Jerudong, Brunei, from 24 June to 7 July 1984 and are believed to belong to this race (Smythies & Davison 1999).

A. s. celebensis Restricted to Sulawesi, where it is apparently localised. It is known from the region of Ujung Pandang in the southwest of the island and Watling (1983) reported it to be common in the Palu Valley in the northwest of the island. Breeding occurs from sea level to 800m (Coates & Bishop 1997).

A. s. sumbae The easternmost race whose range includes the islands of Buru in the Moluccas and Sumba and Timor in the Lesser Sundas. It also extends east into the Australasian region, where it breeds across Irian Jaya (records from the Vogelkop Mountains, Wissel Lakes, Baliem Valley, Mamberamo and Noord Rivers); Papua New Guinea (records from Lake Daviumbu, the Bensbach River in Western Province, Chambri Lakes, Lake Kopiago and near Pureni in Southern Province, Kandep Lakes, Enga Province, Wahgi and Baiyer valleys and Ukarumpa, Eastern Highlands Province, Herzog Mountains, Popondetta area, Port Moresby district, eastern Central Province, and Orangerie Bay); the Bismarck Archipelago (where it breeds on New Britain, New Ireland, Umboi and Long); and throughout the Solomon Islands.

MOVEMENTS Departure of *brunnescens* from breeding grounds in Kazakhstan and Tajikistan begins in early to mid August and is largely complete by late September. Passage through N Pakistan occurs mainly during August and September and most birds have left Kashmir by early October. Arrivals reach the wintering areas in N India and Nepal from mid September onwards and continue into November, but birds wintering in S India may not arrive until December.

Birds begin to leave the wintering areas in India from March, although some remain up to May. Passage through Pakistan begins in late March with migrants becoming common in Sind Province from mid April to early May, with a few stragglers remaining to early June. Birds also reach Afghanistan and probably E Iran from mid April, but arrivals are reported in SW Turkmenistan from mid March and it is said to be common here by early April. Migrants reach the Tashkent region of Uzbekistan from mid April and presumably arrive on breeding sites in S Kazakhstan at this time. Almost all C Asian breeding grounds are occupied by early May.

Away from the recognised range, Abdulali (1965) confirmed the presence of migrants on the Andaman Islands, which he considered to be of the race *amyae*. Birds recorded in N and C Thailand, N Laos and C Annam, Vietnam, may be migrant *amyae* from cooler regions of S China, although Deignan considered the Thai specimens belonged with *brunnescens*. There is a single specimen of Clamorous Reed Warbler from the Malay Peninsula, taken in Penang in 1867. This is considered by Medway and Wells (1976) to be *brunnescens*, but they note that the provenance is uncertain. S Asian island populations are all considered sedentary.

DESCRIPTION *A. s. brunnescens*
Plumage – Adult fresh (November to February) Forehead to nape olive-brown with greyish tinge. Supercilium

broadest and most conspicuous between bill base and rear of eye, where whitish with slight brown wash. Behind eye mainly obscured by brown wash. Lores with well-defined dark brown line from bill base to eye. An indistinct dark brown eye-line extending from from rear of eye to rear of supercilium. Ear-coverts warm olive-brown, with whitish feather shafts giving a streaked appearance. Pale eye-ring narrow and inconspicuous. Mantle and scapulars olive-brown with warm tinge. Rump and uppertail-coverts slightly brighter than mantle. Tail dull olive-brown, with narrow warm buff fringes and tips. Chin, throat and malar region white with slight greyish wash, throat often with faint greyish shaft streaks. Centre of breast white, tinged greyish, warming to light fulvous-brown on side of breast and side of neck. Upper flanks washed light fulvous-brown, darkening to tawny-brown on lower flanks and vent. Belly greyish white, tinged warm buff. Undertail-coverts light buff, usually contrasting with darker lower flanks and vent. Lesser and median coverts uniform olive-brown, matching mantle colour. Greater coverts and tertials with wide warm olive-brown fringes, merging into darker greyish brown centres. Secondaries and primaries greyish brown with narrow warm brown edges, primaries with pale brown tips. Alula dark brown with narrow warm olive-brown fringe. Underwing-coverts creamy buff, slightly paler than flanks, sometimes with faint yellow tinge.

Adult worn (May to August) Supercilium whiter and often more obvious behind eye. Ear-coverts paler greyish brown. Crown, nape and mantle light brown to pale mousy brown. Rump and uppertail-coverts usually warmer olive-brown, but sometimes matching mantle. Tail drab mouse-brown with narrow, slightly browner edges. Underparts white with slight greyish wash, tinged light brown along flanks and creamy white on undertail-coverts. Wing-coverts and tertials similar in colour to mantle with little contrast between fringes and centres. Flight feathers rather darker than wing-coverts and upperparts, warm edges worn away. Alula remains darker and contrasting.

First-winter Similar to fresh adult in overall pattern, but warmer and brighter. Entire upperparts from forehead to uppertail-coverts warm rufous-brown to dull cinnamon. Supercilium washed pale cinnamon-buff. Underparts washed pale rufous-brown, palest on chin, throat and belly. Breast and upper flanks with warmer, more intense wash than in adult. Lower flanks and ventral region similar to mantle, but undertail-coverts slightly paler, light rufous-buff. Tail feathers warm brown with narrow warm rufous-brown fringes and tips. Lesser and median coverts warm rufous-brown to cinnamon, showing no contrast with mantle and scapulars. Greater coverts and tertials with fairly broad rufous-brown fringes and duller warm brown centres. Secondaries and primaries warm brown, edged rufous-cinnamon, giving uniform appearance to closed wing. Alula warm brown with rufous-brown to cinnamon fringe.

Juvenile As fresh first-winter plumage.

Bare parts Upper mandible dark grey with pale pink cutting edge. Lower mandible pale pink at base with darker, greyish sides towards tip. Mouth orange or orange-red. Tarsi and toes usually dark and greyish but variable, including sooty grey, plumbeous-grey, bright blue-grey, greenish horn, pinkish grey or light grey-brown; colour probably dependent on age; soles pale greenish to dull yellow. Iris warm brown in adults, slightly paler than in Great Reed Warbler; dark smoky-grey to dark brown in juveniles and first-winter birds (Cramp 1992).

IN HAND CHARACTERS
Measurements

A. s. brunnescens
a. Migrant *brunnescens* from C Asia, Afghanistan and Pakistan:

	Male	Female
Wing	81–95 (88.1; 59)	78–91 (83.8; 22)
Tail	69–84 (76.0; 57)	66–80 (70.9; 22)
Bill	23–26 (24.9; 48)	23–26 (24.1; 21)
Tarsus	26.5–30.5 (28.9; 41)	24–30 (27.7; 21)

Sexes combined:
Tail/wing ratio: 80–91% (86%; 79)
Bill width: 5.0–6.2 (5.3; 20)
Hind claw: 8.8–10.3 (9.6; 30)
Tail graduation: 10–17 (14.1; 30)
 Wing of juvenile averages *c*. 1.5mm shorter than adult, tail *c*. 5mm shorter (Cramp 1992).
 Breeding birds from Kazakhstan are particularly long-winged (see **Appendix 2**).
b. Resident mangrove-breeding *brunnescens* from Red Sea, N Somalia and S Arabia.

	Male	Female
Wing	80–88 (84.8; 8)	78–84 (80.5; 6)
Tail	72–79 (76.1; 7)	69–78 (74.6; 5)
Bill	24–26 (25.0; 7)	24–25 (24.7; 5)
Tarsus	26.5–29 (28.1; 7)	25.5–27.5 (25.6; 5)

(includes data from Cramp 1992)

 Tail/wing ratio: 87–98% (93%; 8)
 Wing thus shorter and tail/wing ratio higher than in C Asian migrant birds.

A. s. stentoreus

	Male	Female
Wing	80–84 (81.7; 18)	74–80 (76.6; 10)
Tail	69–81 (72.9; 18)	65–72 (68.2; 10)
Bill	24–27.5 (25.7; 17)	24–26 (25.1; 10)
Tarsus	27–30 (28.6; 17)	26–27.5 (27.0; 10)

Sexes combined:
Tail/wing ratio: 84–96% (89%; 28)
Bill width: 4.3–5.2 (4.8; 20)
Hind claw: 9.4–11.0 (9.9; 20)
Tail graduation: 11–18 (14.7; 25)
 Smaller than *brunnescens*, but bill and tarsus relatively long.
 Wing shorter and tail/wing ratio higher than in C Asian *brunnescens*, but similar to *brunnescens* from the Red Sea.

A. s. levantinus

	Male	Female
Wing	82–88 (84.6; 10)	75–82 (79.0; 3)
Tail	75–83 (79.8; 10)	72–74 (73.0; 2)
Bill	25.8–27.6 (26.5; 10)	23.8–24.5 (24.2; 3)
Tarsus	27.8–29.2 (28.4; 10)	26.4–28 (27.2; 3)

(Roselaar 1994)

Slightly larger and longer-tailed than nominate race.

Other races (sexes combined)

A. s. amyae: *wing* 81–90 (85.9; 10); *tail* 68–78 (73.7; 9); *bill* 23–26 (24.9; 10); *tarsus* 28.5–30 (29.3; 10); tail/wing ratio 82–89% (86%; 9). Large like *brunnescens*.

A. s. meridionalis: *wing* 77–84 (81.3; 16); *tail* 65–74 (68.1; 14); *bill* 23–26 (24.6; 15); *tarsus* 27–30.5 (28.3; 13); tail/wing ratio 79–89% (84%; 14). Wing and tail shorter than *brunnescens*.

A. s. lentecaptus: *wing* 73–84 (76.8; 4); *tail* 61–73 (67.0; 4); *bill* 22–24.5 (23.6; 4); *tarsus* 24–27 (26.3; 4). Smaller than *brunnescens*.

A. s. siebersi: *wing* 71–77 (74.4; 7); *tail* 62–67 (64.3; 7); *bill* 19.5–23 (21.4; 7); *tarsus* 26–29 (27.6; 7). Size similar to *lentecaptus*, but bill smaller.

A. s. harterti: *wing* 74–75 (74.7; 3); *tail* 68–71 (69.7; 3); *bill* 19–21 (20.2; 3); *tarsus* 26–27 (26.5; 3). Smaller than *brunnescens*, with relatively long tail but small bill.

A. s. sumbae: **a.** Sumba: *wing* 70–72 (71.5; 8) (Ernst Sutter unpublished data); **b.** populations from Buru to Solomon Islands combined: *wing* 65–71 (68.2; 13); *tail* 55–64 (60.5, 13); *bill* 19–21 (20.5, 13); *tarsus* 24.5–26 (25.0, 13); tail/wing ratio 84–95% (88%; 13); bill width 4.4–5.0; hind claw 8.5–9.5; tail graduation 9–11 (10.0; 8). The smallest race within *A. stentoreus*.

A. s. celebensis: (1 ♀, the type): *wing* 72; *tail* 63; *bill* 23; *tarsus* 21 (B. Leisler). Also (two juveniles): *wing* 70, 73; *tail* 59, 65; *bill* 21, 21.5; *tarsus* 24.5 (n = 1).

Structure

A. s. brunnescens

a. Migrants from C Asia, Afghanistan and Pakistan.

Wing formula (n = 10):

p1/pc	p2	p3e	p4e	p5(e)	p6	p7	p10
(6)–(1)	3–4.5	wp	wp	0.5–2	5–6	7–10	15–18

Wing rounded, but p1 minute (< pc). Wing point p3–4; p2 = p5/6; emargination on p3–4, occasionally also p5; p2 notch well below ss tips.

Figure 78. Wing of Clamorous Reed Warbler *A. s. brunnescens.*

Tail rather long, well rounded.

Bill strong and broad-based as in Great Reed Warbler, but with more concave sides and a longer narrower tip (Fig. 73).

Tarsi stout, toes and claws large and strong.

b. Resident mangrove birds from Red Sea, N Somalia, S Arabia.

Wing formula (n = 8):

p1/pc	p2	p3e	p4e	p5(e)	p6	p7	p10
(8)–0	4.5–6.5	0–2	wp	0–2.5	3–5	5.5–8	12–14

Wing more rounded than in C Asian birds (Fig. 78), with p2 usually shorter than p6. See also Roselaar (1994). Wing point p(3) 4 (5); p2 = p6/7 (7/8); emargination on p3–4, often faintly on p5.

A. s. stentoreus

Wing formula (Cramp 1992):

p1/pc	p2	p3e	p4e	p5(e)	p6	p7	p10
(6)–0	3–4.5	wp	0–0.5	1–2.5	4–5	6–8	14–17

Wing point p3–4; p2 = p5/6–6 (6/7); emargination on p3–4, occasionally also p5

Figure 79. Wing of Clamorous Reed Warbler *A. s. stentoreus.*

Tail on average more graduated than in *brunnescens*.

Bill less broad, more laterally compressed with much narrower tip (Fig. 80).

Toes and claws very strong.

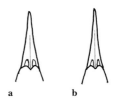

a   b

Figure 80. Comparision of bill profile of Clamorous Reed Warbler of the races (a) *A. s. brunnescens* **and (b)** *A. s. stentoreus.*

A. s. levantinus. As nominate *stentoreus* with long, laterally compressed bill, but tail/wing ratio apparently higher (*c.* 93%).

A. s. amyae, A. s. meridionalis. Wing formula as *stentoreus*, with p3–4 longest, p2 = p5/6–7, p3–5 emarginated, p10 shortfall 13–18mm. Bill and tail shape as *brunnescens*.

A. s. lentecaptus, A. s. siebersi. Wing formula as *stentoreus* but primary projection shorter. Bill of *lentecaptus* relatively large and broad based as in *brunnescens*, that of *siebersi* smaller.

A. s. harterti. Wing formula as *stentoreus*, with p3–4 longest and p2 = p6/7, but primary projection shorter, p10 shortfall 10–11.5mm. Emargination on p3–5.

417

Figure 81. Wing of Clamorous Reed Warbler *A. s. harterti.*

Bill smaller; broad based but with narrow tip. Tarsi and claws strong.

A. s. sumbae. Similar to nominate *stentoreus*. Wing point p3–4; p2 = p(5/6) 6/7–7/8; emargination on p3–5.

Figure 82. Wing of Clamorous Reed Warbler *A. s. sumbae.*

Wing formula (n = 6):

p1/pc	p2	p3e	p4e	p5e	p6	p7	p10
(3)–0	3.5–5	wp	wp	0.5–2	2–4	4–6	10.5–13

Tail markedly rounded.
Bill shape as *brunnescens*.
Tarsi and toes strong, claws relatively large.

A. s. celebensis. Wing formula apparently as *sumbae*.

Recognition Long-billed warbler with plain, rufescent upperparts, except in mainland Asian races. Size varies greatly, but all races are separable from Great Reed Warbler and Oriental Reed Warbler by more rounded wing (p2 < p5, usually < p6); also from Great Reed by emargination on p4, and from Oriental Reed by emargination (if present) on p5. Tail/wing ratio is commonly > 85% and tail graduation > 15mm, values beyond the upper limit for Great Reed and Oriental Reed. For separation of *sumbae* from Australian Reed Warbler see that species.

Ageing Criteria uncertain. Following post-juvenile moult, iris colour probably reliable, warm brown in adults, dark smoky-grey to dark brown in juveniles and first-winter birds (Cramp 1992).

Weight
A. s. brunnescens: C Asia and India, 21–34g (n = 23); S Kazakhstan, 21.6–35.0g (29.0; 235) (AG unpublished data); Sudan 21–29g (n = 14) (GN unpublished data).
A. s. levantinus: Israel, 21.5–28.5g (n = 13) (Cramp 1992).

GEOGRAPHIC VARIATION Across its vast range, there is substantial variation in size, structure and plumage, although all races are characterised by warm brown upperparts and an extensive warm wash below. Comparison here is mostly with *A. s. brunnescens* which is the most widespread race, occurring across C Asia, the Indian subcontinent and locally in the Middle East and NE Africa.

A. s. brunnescens (Coasts of Red Sea, Arabian Peninsula and C Asia) Described above.

A. s. stentoreus (Egypt) Darker and more richly coloured than *brunnescens*, warmer olive-brown above and darker tawny-buff below, with a contrasting whitish throat and belly centre. Rather large, but shorter-winged and shorter-tailed than *brunnescens*, with a relatively longer and finer, laterally compressed bill.

A. s. levantinus (N Israel) Structure similar to the nominate race, with a long, laterally compressed bill, but is slightly larger, with a longer wing and (especially) tail. Slightly darker and browner, less warmly coloured. Upperparts uniform dull brown, sometimes with olive wash. Throat and belly whitish, contrasting with cinnamon-brown breast and flanks. A dark morph, forming approximately 5% of the population, occurs in Israel (Laird 1992). This shows dark sepia-brown upperparts that contrast little with the almost equally dark but slightly warmer-toned underparts.

A. s. amyae (NE India, Burma, SW China) A large race, closely resembling *brunnescens*. In fresh plumage, the upperparts are slightly richer and browner, the underparts more strongly washed pale gingery buff, and the breast and flanks appear brighter fulvous-brown. The supercilium is narrower and less well marked behind eye, barely reaching to middle of ear-coverts even on better marked birds. It also shows slightly broader pale buffy tips to the outermost rectrices and vaguely defined streaking on the breast. When worn, these differences are largely lost.

A. s. meridionalis (Sri Lanka) Darker and more richly coloured than *brunnescens*. The upperparts are slightly darker than in *amyae*, with a slight rufescent tinge, and the underparts are a paler creamy white with fulvous-brown flanks and cinnamon-buff undertail-coverts. The throat is whitish with faint dusky striations that extend onto the upper breast. Slightly smaller than *brunnescens* and closer to nominate race in wing and tail length.

A. s. harterti (Philippines) Warmer, richer brown above than *brunnescens*. Underparts variable, some strongly washed fulvous-brown, others with white chin and throat contrasting with light fulvous-brown wash across the breast, which intensifies towards the sides and along the flanks. The belly is white, lightly tinged fulvous-brown and the undertail-coverts warm buff. One of the smaller races, the wing length of the largest birds being shorter than the smallest *brunnescens*. Distinctly short-billed.

A. s. siebersi (Java) Smaller and much darker than *brunnescens*. Upperparts dark warm brown. Underparts similar in colour and pattern to *brunnescens* and *amyae*, but frequently with faint striations at the sides of the upper breast, similar to or less obvious than those in *meridionalis*. The supercilium is variable, but generally less conspicuous than in *brunnescens* and often restricted to a warm buff line above the lores.

A. s. lentecaptus (Borneo, Lombok and Sumbawa) Closely resembles *siebersi* with similar dark, warm brown upperparts. When fresh, the underparts show a warmer orange-cinnamon wash than in *siebersi*, extending across the breast, flanks and belly. Supercilium usually more conspicuous, extending further above and behind the ear-coverts. When worn or faded some individuals are inseparable.

A. s. celebensis (Sulawesi) A small race that resembles *sumbae* in both plumage and structure. The entire upperparts are warm rufescent-brown, similar to or slightly paler than the warmest *sumbae*. The chin and throat are whitish, becoming pale cream on the breast and belly and darkening to warm creamy brown on the flanks and undertail-coverts. The supercilium is narrow and poorly defined, most obvious above the lores but barely visible behind the eye. It differs from *sumbae* in having a slightly longer bill with perhaps, a slightly straighter culmen.

A. s. sumbae (Buru, Sumba and Timor to the Solomon Islands) The smallest race, with wing length similar to that of Marsh Warbler but larger bodied. Variable in appearance, ranging from paler individuals resembling *celebensis* to darker birds similar to Australian Reed Warbler. Darker individuals show warm, rich brown upperparts, a light, creamy buff throat, dull cinnamon-buff breast, flanks and undertail-coverts and a slightly paler belly. The supercilium is dull buff and short, typically from bill base to the rear of the eye, but rarely beyond. It is unclear how much variation is due to wear and bleaching, or whether *sumbae* as recognised here actually comprises two or more taxa. Measurements given by Mayr (1948) demonstrate that populations on Sumba, Papua New Guinea (Anggi Lake in the Arfak Mountains, and Lake Daviumbu), New Britain and the Solomon Islands differ slightly, but there seems to be too much overlap to justify recognition of additional races.

TAXONOMY AND SYSTEMATICS Two distinct groups breed in the Palearctic. One comprises the nominate race, resident in Egypt, together with *levantinus*, a form recognised only recently from Israel (Roselaar 1994). These are large birds with long, laterally compressed and narrow-tipped bills. The second group includes still larger birds with heavier and broader bills, all treated under *brunnescens*. The latter breed widely in W and C Asia in two or more distinct populations. Some are resident in mangroves along the coasts of the Red Sea and Persian and Arabian Gulf. Others are migrants, breeding in C Asia and wintering in the Indian subcontinent. A third group breeds in isolated pockets in W India from Kashmir to Kerala and appears to be largely resident. The resident mangrove birds differ from the migratory C Asian birds in being shorter- and slightly rounder-winged and may merit recognition as a subspecies. Small-billed birds from SW Iran and smaller, paler birds from Kashmir also differ slightly from C Asian breeding *brunnescens* (Roselaar 1994). However, molecular studies have shown little genetic variation within Clamorous Reed Warbler in Asia. Mitochondrial DNA differences between *levantinus* from Israel, *brunnescens* from Arabia and *harterti* from the Philippines were found to be less than 1.1% (Helbig & Seibold 1999).

Australian Reed Warbler, with its races *A. a. australis* and

A. a. gouldi, was formerly included within Clamorous Reed Warbler. Even now, five insular races of Clamorous Reed are recognised from the islands of S and SE Asia and east to the Solomon Islands. Within the Wallacean sub-region both large and small forms occur and their distribution may reflect multiple colonisation events. We have limited the range of *lentecaptus* to the large birds on Lombok and Sumbawa, together with birds indistinguishable from these breeding in Borneo, and treated Javan breeders as *siebersi*, although Mees (1971) considered this synonymous with *lentecaptus*.

Further east, in the Moluccas and through New Guinea to the Solomon Islands, the taxonomic situation is still more confused. Some of these populations may be genetically closer to Australian Reed Warbler than to the isolated Wallacean island forms of Clamorous Reed. White & Bruce (1986) concluded that birds breeding on Sulawesi, Buru, Timor and Sumba belonged within a single form, *A. s. celebensis*. Others, however, restrict *celebensis* to S Sulawesi, a treatment that we have adopted here as this taxon is clearly distinct from those on Buru, Timor and Sumba.

The oldest name given to the small taxon widespread from the eastern Lesser Sundas, including Buru and Timor, east to the Solomon Islands is *Acrocephalus cervinus* (De Vis 1897). But as Mayr (1948) observed, the wing (80mm), tail (76mm) and culmen (14.5mm) measurements of the type specimen (which he did not examine) are 'impossibly large' for a New Guinea specimen, and this is supported by the measurements in **In Hand Characters** above. It seems likely that the bird De Vis described was an Oriental Reed Warbler. Use of *cervinus* has been abandoned and *sumbae* has been adopted into widespread usage. The race *sumbae* was originally described from Sumba, but it is uncertain whether *sumbae* can be applied to all island populations throughout such a vast region. Clements (2000) assigned the New Guinea, Bismarck Archipelago and Solomon Islands populations to *A. a. toxopei*, which he treated as a race of Australian Reed Warbler. We consider that this approach has merit and is certainly as valid as keeping these birds within Clamorous Reed. But Clements mistakenly retained the birds of Buru, from where *toxopei* was originally described, within *A. s. sumbae* as a race of Clamorous Reed Warbler.

As yet, no single authority appears to have a full grasp of this problem. Studies of phylogenetic relationships within the Clamorous Reed and Australian Reed Warbler complex in the Wallacean and Australasian region are clearly required. Until these are available, we will continue to regard *toxopei* and *meyeri* as synonyms of *A. s. sumbae* within Clamorous Reed Warbler. Maintaining this *status quo* is, we believe, preferable to adopting changes without supporting evidence. When the true relationships between these insular forms, the Asian taxa and Australian Reed Warbler are understood, it will almost certainly result in Clamorous Reed Warbler, as recognised here, being split into two or more species, with some races perhaps becoming subspecies of Australian Reed Warbler.

▲ Adult *A. s. stentoreus*, Egypt, April. Note lack of supercilium and rather uniform appearance, quite different to the Great Reed Warbler-like appearance of *brunnescens* (Vincent Legrand).

▲ Adult *A. s. stentoreus*, Egypt, April. Some may show a short, pale supercilium above the lores (Vincent Legrand).

▲ Adult *A. s. levantinus*, Israel, March. Closely resembles nominate but slightly darker, browner and less warmly coloured, giving a more uniform appearance (Daniele Occhiato).

▲ Adult *A. s. levantinus*, Israel, March. Uniquely, *levantinus* has a dark morph, forming approximately 5% of the population, with darker brown upperparts showing little contrast with the almost equally dark but slightly warmer-toned underparts (Daniele Occhiato).

▲ ▶ Adult *A. s. brunnescens*, Gujarat, India. April. Note short primary projection which readily separates Clamorous Reed Warbler from Basra Reed and Great Reed Warblers (Arpit Deomurari).

▲ ▶ Adult *A. s. amyae*, Burma, February. Closely resembles *brunnescens* but supercilium is narrower and less well-marked behind eye, barely reaching to middle of ear-coverts on well-marked birds. When fresh, upperparts are slightly richer and underparts more strongly washed pale gingery buff than on *brunnescens*. When worn, these differences are lost (Philip Round/The Wetland Trust).

▲ Adult *A. s. brunnescens*, Oman, November. Differs from western races by paler coloration and deeper bill with broader tip, giving them a rather Great Reed Warbler-like appearance (Hanne & Jens Eriksen).

▲ First-winter *A. s. harterti*, Luzon, Philippines, April. One of the smaller races, shorter-billed and shorter-winged than *brunnescens*. When fresh appears warmer, richer brown above than *brunnescens*, but on faded birds these differences become less apparent (Philip Round/The Wetland Trust).

AUSTRALIAN REED WARBLER
Acrocephalus australis   **Plate 27**

Calamoherpe australis **Gould, 1838**. In: Lewin, *Nat. Hist. Birds New South Wales*. Parramatta, New South Wales, Australia.

The only *Acrocephalus* occurring regularly in Australia, breeding mostly in SW and SE Australia and wintering throughout much of E and N Australia. Until recently, it was treated as a race of the similar Clamorous Reed Warbler. Appears closely related to the small eastern form *A. s. sumbae* of that species, which ranges from E Indonesia to the Solomon Islands. Polytypic, with two races recognised:
A. a. australis (Gould, 1838). SE Australia and Tasmania, wintering in N Australia.
A. a. gouldi Dubois, 1901. W Australia, wintering in NW Australia.

IDENTIFICATION Length 15–16cm. Wing 64–79mm. Tail/wing 78–91%.
A mid sized unstreaked and nondescript *Acrocephalus* of wetlands, swamps and lakes. Often skulking and difficult to see. Unlikely to occur alongside other *Acrocephalus*, but individual variation combined with the effects of wear and bleaching would complicate separation from similar species. Sexes alike.
Structure A mid sized, slim and sleek *Acrocephalus* with a relatively long, slender bill and flat crown, combining to give the head an attenuated structure. When singing or alarmed, the crown feathers are raised, giving the crown an untidy and ragged appearance The wings are fairly short and rounded, with the wing point formed by p3 and sometimes p4 and a short primary projection, *c.* 50% of the tertial length. The primary tips fall short of the longest uppertail-coverts. The tail is fairly long and broad and strongly rounded, which is often apparent together with the rounded wings when in low flight over reeds.
Plumage and bare parts Drab and nondescript. Fresh adults are uniform russet-brown above but slightly warmer on the rump and uppertail-coverts. The head shows a short creamy-buff supercilium, most conspicuous above the lores, but terminating at the rear edge of the eye, or just beyond. Below this, there is a slightly darker but rather diffuse eye-stripe, again most conspicuous in front of the eye but barely visible behind it. The underparts are paler than the upperparts, being washed warm creamy buff across the breast and along the flanks, which contrast with the large whitish throat patch and belly and dull rufous-brown undertail-coverts. As birds wear and bleach, they become distinctly paler and greyer; the upperparts olive-brown to greyish brown and the rump and uppertail-coverts slightly paler yellow-buff. With wear, the supercilium becomes paler and the eye-stripe darker, giving it a more contrasting head pattern.
The bill is dark grey with a pale flesh-pink base to the lower mandible, which darkens to pale grey at the sides towards the tip. The legs and feet are quite dark, greyish black in adults, but paler blue-grey in immature birds.

SIMILAR SPECIES Only two other *Acrocephalus* are known to occur within the Australasian region: Oriental Reed Warbler is a vagrant to NW Australia during the northern winter and Clamorous Reed Warbler (race *sumbae*) is resident in Papua New Guinea and other islands to the north of Australia, where Australian Reed is not known to occur.

Oriental Reed Warbler is only likely to occur in NW Australia during the austral summer when the majority of Australian Reed Warblers are breeding in the south. Song provides the most reliable method of separation. That of Oriental Reed consists of loud, raucous, croaking calls strung together in short, repetitive phrases. It is quite different to the melodic sequence of rich, sweet and fluty phrases given by Australian Reed.
Oriental Reed is significantly larger and more bulky than Australian Reed. It has a heavier and more powerful bill than nominate *australis*, but the bill of the western race *gouldi* is slightly deeper-based and closer to that of Oriental Reed, so care is required. It has a similar wing structure to Australian Reed, including wing point and primary projection, but has a longer p2, usually falling at p4–5. It only infrequently shows emargination on p4 and never on p5.

a   b

Figure 83. Comparison of head and bill shape of (a) Australian Reed Warbler and (b) Oriental Reed Warbler.

It resembles Australian Reed in plumage pattern and tone, but most can be separated by the fine dark greyish streaking on the lower throat which Australian Reed lacks, although this streaking is occasionally suppressed or entirely absent.
Clamorous Reed Warbler of the race *sumbae* (= *meyeri*) is believed to be resident within its Australasian range. But as Australian Reed could occur as a vagrant in Papua New Guinea where *sumbae* breeds, their separation is discussed.
The song of *sumbae* is quite different from that of Australian Reed. It is much shorter, less varied and distinctly harsher and lacks the rich, melodic quality of Australian Reed. On Papua New Guinea, it typically consists of 2–3 short '*quark-quark*' or '*cra cra cra*' calls followed by a short, rather guttural sequence '*deduwee-dwee-dwee-dwee-dwee*', '*chek-chek-chek-tui-tui-tui-tui-tui*', or similar.
There are no known plumage differences by which *sumbae* and Australian Reed can be separated, and wear and bleaching will affect the appearance of both species. Structural differences appear to provide a reliable guide in the hand. On average, *sumbae* is slightly smaller than Australian Reed, although there is considerable overlap in major measurements. But *sumbae* differs by having a slightly more rounded wing with the wing point at p3–4, emarginations on p3–5, p2 usually falling between p6/7 and p7/8, and it tends to show a shorter primary projection.

VOICE The song is a far-carrying, loud, varied and melodious warble, at times sounding rich, sweet and fluty, while other notes can be hard, metallic and even guttural. This variety makes it one of the most readily recognisable and pleasing bird sounds in Australia. It consists of a series of short, varied sequences in which the same combination of melodic phrases is repeated, in a similar manner to the delivery of a Song Thrush. This is followed by a pause of 3–5 seconds before singing recommences with a different combination of varied sequences.
Song sequences include '*whichee-whichee-whichee*', '*quarty-quarty-quarty-chutchee-chutchee- chutchee-dzree-fzree-dzree*' and

'*cheewip-cheewip-cheewip choo-choo-wheee-wheee-wheee*' plus several other equally varied combinations.

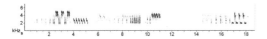

Song of Australian Reed Warbler recorded within breeding range of *A. a. australis*. Victoria, Australia, October. (McPherson Natural History Unit)

The most frequently heard call is a dry nasal buzzing '*chzzz*', or '*drzzz*'. Other calls include a sharp '*chat-chat*' and softer '*tchuck-tchuck*' and a harsh, scolding rattle.

MOULT Poorly understood, with almost no reports of adults in primary moult from breeding areas in Victoria, New South Wales, South Australia and SW Western Australia and very few reports of moulting birds from elsewhere. It appears that adults from the southern part of the range migrate to the north before replacing flight feathers, but it is not known when or where moult occurs. Adults have a complete post-breeding moult that appears to take place in N Australia during the austral autumn and winter months. This is apparently rapid. In the few moulting birds documented, all the inner primaries were replaced simultaneously and up to five primaries on each wing were found to be growing together. In NW Australia, birds in active moult have been recorded in February, April and September, while others in July showed no sign of moult. These dates suggest considerable variation in moult timing throughout the range.

It is not known whether there is a pre-breeding moult. Birds returning to the southern part of breeding range in spring have slightly worn primaries, which become further abraded during the breeding season and are extremely worn before departure. Further north, in N New South Wales, some birds replace their primaries at the breeding site after breeding.

Moult of immature birds is also poorly documented and it is unclear whether first-year birds have a complete post-juvenile moult. This seems unlikely as immature birds returning to breeding sites in spring have extremely worn primaries, more so than presumed adults, suggesting these are retained juvenile feathers, although the body contour plumage has been replaced.

HABITAT Occurs in a wide range of wetlands in fresh, brackish and saltwater environments, where it breeds in low-lying regions along the coast and inland. It occupies a wide range of natural wetlands including creeks, rivers, lakes, estuaries, ponds, swamps and lagoons. It is also found in many man-made and artificial wetlands including dams, irrigated farmland and sewage ponds, and in vegetation fringing lakes in parks, gardens and golf courses. It is common wherever there are reeds *Phragmites*, sedges *Typha*, rushes *Juncus* and other emergent vegetation, including *Baumea*, *Eleocharis* and *Cyperus* and grasses such as *Pennisetum*, *Brachiaria* and canegrass *Eragrostis*. It regularly forages in shrubland and riparian woodland fringing rivers and lakes, often quite high in the canopy. During years of drought, it may breed in scrubland away from water.

BEHAVIOUR Usually solitary or in pairs but will occasionally gather in large numbers in suitable habitat where food is abundant. Its skulking behaviour makes it difficult to determine the numbers present.

Forages for insects, spiders, small molluscs and seeds in dense aquatic vegetation and on open mud near the base of reeds and rushes. It typically clings sideways to reed stems and stretches to reach food items. It also feeds in shrubs and sometimes in trees, gleaning insects from leaves up to 30m above the ground. Occasionally it will sally after insects in flight, usually over open water.

Males commence singing on their return to the breeding grounds from July and August onwards, but not until September or early October in Tasmania. Song continues throughout the austral summer, regularly into January and occasionally February. It is generally elusive when singing and typically perches part way down a reed stem out of sight, but in calm conditions it sometimes sings from a reed head or bush. Singing males often raise the fore-crown feathering and puff out the throat feathers and their bodies appear to vibrate. Song is most frequently heard in the early morning but continues in more subdued form until late morning, even on the hottest days. It is often heard well into the night.

BREEDING HABITS Usually monogamous, occasionally polygamous. The nest is built in low aquatic vegetation, usually among reeds and rushes, at up to 1m above the ground or water, or up to 1.5m in willows, occasionally higher. It is usually placed close to, or over open water, but occasionally in shrubs and bushes up to 750m from water. It is built between reed or rush stems or occasionally supported in the fork of a tree or shrub. It is constructed from strips of rushes or reeds, plant fibres, grasses or other aquatic vegetation, the cup being lined with fine reeds, rushes, feathers, fine grasses and plant down. The usual clutch is 2–4 eggs. Incubation is mostly by the female for 12–13 days, occasionally 11–16 days. The young are fed in the nest by both parents for 11–13 days and continue to be dependent for up to 17 days after leaving the nest. Double brooded. Eggs have been recorded from early September to mid February.

DISTRIBUTION Ranges widely, breeding mostly south of 20°S in E and SE Australia and E Tasmania, and locally throughout W Western Australia where suitable wetlands occur.

A. a. australis Breeds throughout coastal E and SE Australia from C Queensland and the Brisbane region south to southernmost Victoria and west into South Australia, where it reaches the Eyre Peninsula and the Adelaide Plain in the region of Wirrabara and inland to Lake Eyre. It also breeds regularly in E Tasmania and formerly bred on the Furneaux Group in the Bass Strait. Inland, its range extends to the western and northern slopes of the Great Dividing Range, reaching Nanango in S Queensland and Mildura in NW Victoria. It has recently expanded its range to the north, breeding regularly in isolated locations, often dependent on artificial wetlands such as irrigation schemes and artesian boreholes. Significant extensions in the twentieth century include expansion into the Alice Springs region of Northern Territory and the Richmond area in NE Queensland. It may breed regularly in the southeast of the Gulf of Carpentaria.

Outside the breeding season it occurs throughout eastern Australia north to Kimberley Division in NE Western Australia, the Top End in Northern Territory, the Gulf of Carpentaria and the Cape York Peninsula.

A. a. gouldi Widespread in SW Western Australia, where it occurs at scattered well-watered sites. It is occasionally recorded along the south coast east to Eyre Bird Observatory and becomes more numerous and widespread to the west of a line running between Bremer Bay on the SW coast and the Pilbara region in NW Western Australia. Occasionally noted at the Great Sandy Desert where it has been recorded from Sandfire, Anna Plains, McLarty Hills and Dragon Tree Soak. To the north, recorded from scattered sites in Kimberley Division, with reports from near Broome to Lake Gladstone and from the region of Wyndham east to the Drysdale River, south to Lake Argyle, possibly reaching SW Arnhem Land in Northern Territory (although these may be *australis* or a third form *carterae*, see **Taxonomy and Systematics**).

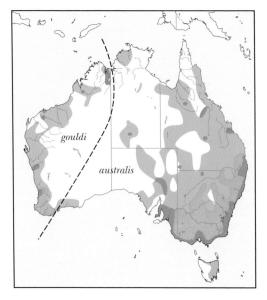

Australian Reed Warbler. Breeding range and non-breeding distribution.

MOVEMENTS Northern populations are largely sedentary but may undertake local dispersive movements in response to the availability of wetlands.

The vast majority of southern breeders, including those from Tasmania and southernmost South Australia and Victoria leave the breeding sites from February to April, although small numbers may remain in suitable wetlands in SE Australia throughout the year. Departures from breeding sites in S New South Wales occur mainly in March and April. Southern breeders disperse over a vast area of E Australia, with some reaching N Queensland, Northern Territory and possibly even N Western Australia. The earliest arrivals (perhaps birds which have failed to breed or remained to the north of the breeding range) occur in N Queensland in early December but most arrive in April. It remains common there until September. Some have reached the islands of the Torres Strait and it has been suspected, but not confirmed, to have occurred in S Papua New Guinea.

Returning birds appear to reach the breeding grounds almost simultaneously. Large numbers pass through coastal Queensland from late August to October and the first birds arrive on breeding sites in New South Wales in late August. It becomes widespread throughout SE Australia in September and the most southerly breeders return to sites in S Victoria and Tasmania mainly from early September to early October.

In Western Australia, departures begin in March, and

continue throughout April, although some remain near Perth, particularly along the Swan River, throughout the year. Further north, movements tend to be dispersive and associated with wetlands drying out, and many birds, such those along the Gascoyne River, tend to be sedentary. It is possible that western breeders may not reach N Western Australia and birds recorded here during the non-breeding season may be the nominate race from SE Australia.

Returning birds begin to reappear in August, with arrivals near Perth noted in September. At Manjimup birds arrive in two waves, the first in October and November and the second in December and January, with males slightly ahead of females. It is possible that the earlier birds are experienced adults and later arrivals mainly young birds.

Distribution in N Australia is patchy and poorly understood. It appears to be mostly a non-breeding visitor from SE Australia. The first arrivals reach the Darwin area in June and some remain until January, although it has bred here.

Most ringing recoveries have been within 10km of the ringing site. The only long-distance recovery concerns a bird ringed at Coleraine, Victoria, and recovered near Ingham, Queensland, a distance of 2,118km.

Vagrancy In New Zealand, a singing male was seen well and sound-recorded at St Annes Lagoon, Cheviot, South Island on 14–28 November 2004 (Allen 2004; N. Redman *in litt.*). Non-breeding migrants may reach S Papua New Guinea, but difficulties in separating this species from the small resident Clamorous Reed Warbler may mask its true status there.

DESCRIPTION *A. a. australis*
Plumage – Adult fresh (August to November) Forehead to nape russet-brown. Supercilium indistinct pale creamy-brown, appearing broadest and most conspicuous between bill base and rear of eye, becoming indistinct and fading to creamy white above ear-coverts. Lores with well-defined dark brown line from bill base to eye. An indistinct dark brown eye-line extends from the rear of the eye towards the rear of the supercilium, becoming indistinct towards rear. Ear-coverts dark brown with diffuse pale brown shafts, giving an indistinct streaked appearance. Eye-ring pale creamy brown, narrow and inconspicuous above and below eye. Sides of neck warm brown. Lower neck slightly greyer than crown. Mantle and scapulars warm russet-brown. Rump and uppertail-coverts warmer russet-brown to rufous-brown, brighter but slightly paler than mantle. Tail dark brown with narrow rufous brown to buff fringes and light brown to pale buff tips and inner webs, narrowest at tip of t1, becoming broader at tips of t4–6.

Chin, throat and malar region white to creamy white with slight greyish wash. Upper breast creamy white to light warm buff, very occasionally with indistinct and diffuse greyish streaking on breast. Sides of breast and flanks light brown to warm buff. Lower breast and belly creamy white to pale buff. Undertail-coverts dull rufous-brown, buff or pale brown.

Lesser, median and greater coverts dark brown with narrow, diffuse, russet-brown fringes closely matching mantle colour, those to tips of greater coverts forming indistinct russet-brown wing-bar. Tertials dark brown with narrow russet-brown tips and fringes to outer webs. Secondaries and primaries dark brown with narrow, pale brown to yellowish brown edges and creamy tips. Primaries usually with slightly paler edges, these not extending to tips. Primary coverts and alula dark brown to blackish brown with narrow russet-brown fringes to outer webs and tips.

Underwing-coverts buff to light yellow-brown.

Adult worn (February to April) Lacks warmer and browner tones and appears paler and greyer. Supercilium whiter, often more obvious behind eye, and eye-stripe darker and more contrasting. Ear-coverts paler greyish brown. Crown, nape and mantle olive-brown to greyish brown, with nape often slightly paler and greyer than mantle. Rump and uppertail-coverts pale brown to pale rufous-brown, usually warmer than mantle. Tail dark brown with narrower and paler buff edges and tips. Underparts paler than fresh adult, although chin, throat and malar region largely unchanged. Breast, sides of breast and flanks washed buff to grey-brown. Centre of breast to belly white with slight cream tinge. Undertail-coverts buff to pale cream, slightly richer than flanks. Wing-coverts and tertials paler brown with greyish brown fringes, similar to mantle, with reduced contrast between fringes and centres. Flight feathers lack warm brown edges, and are paler than wing-coverts.

Juvenile Closely resembles fresh adult. Differs only in slightly paler yellowish brown tone to rump and uppertail-coverts.

Bare parts Upper mandible dark grey to blackish with flesh-pink cutting edge. Lower mandible pale flesh-pink at base, becoming darker with greyish sides towards tip. Mouth orange-yellow to orange-red. Tarsi and toes usually dark grey-black in adults, but paler grey to dull blue-grey in juveniles. Iris dark warm brown in adults, light brown to grey-brown in immature birds.

IN HAND CHARACTERS
Measurements

A. a. australis

	Male	Female
Wing	68–76 (72.6; 22)	64–73 (68.5; 12)
Tail	59–69 (63.7; 21)	51–63 (58.5; 12)
Bill	17.6–21 (20.2; 21)	17.3–20.9 (19.8; 11)
Tarsus	22.8–26.8 (24.5; 20)	22.5–24.8 (23.7; 10)

(Higgins *et al.* 2006)

Sexes combined:
Tail/wing ratio: 78–87% (84%; 14)
Bill width: 4.0–4.8 (4.5; 14)
Hind claw: 7.7–8.7 (8.1; 13)
Tail graduation: 7–12 (9.2; 14)

Juvenile wing *c.* 1.5mm shorter than in adult, tail *c.* 2.5mm shorter.

A. a. gouldi

	Male	Female
Wing	71–79 (74.9; 16)	66–76 (71.2; 6)
Tail	64–71 (65.8; 16)	59–66 (62.7; 6)
Bill	21.5–22.8 (22.0; 10)	21.3–23.3 (22.0; 6)
Tarsus	21.2–26.7 (25.2; 10)	23.7–24.8 (24.4; 6)

(Higgins *et al.* 2006)

Sexes combined:
Tail/wing ratio: 82–91% (87%; 11)
Bill width: 4.5–5.1 (4.8; 10)
Hind claw: 8.2–9.2 (8.7; 10)
Tail graduation: 8–12 (10.3; 11)

Generally larger than nominate *australis*.

Structure

A. a. australis

Wing formula (Higgins *et al.* 2006).

p1/pc	p2	p3e	p4e	p5(e)	p6	p7	p10
(7)–(2)	1–4	wp	0–1	0.5–3	2–6	5–9	10–17

Wing rounded, but p1 minute (< pc). Wing point p3 (4); p2 = p5/6–6 (6/7); emargination on p3–4, occasionally also p5; p2 notch well below ss tips.

Figure 84. Wing of Australian Reed Warbler.

Tail rather long, well rounded.
Bill fairly strong; concave sided with narrow tip (Fig. 83).
Tarsi and toes strong; claws rather large.

Recognition Long-billed with plain, warm brown or rufescent upperparts. Very similar in size and structure to race *sumbae* of Clamorous Reed Warbler, but slightly longer-winged, with p2 usually = p6 (usually < p6 in *sumbae*) and little or no emargination on p5. Birds with wing length > 72mm are probably above range of Australasian *sumbae*.

Ageing Retained and worn primaries in spring suggest immature birds.

Weight *A. a. australis*: 13.8–22.8g (17.7; 142) (Higgins *et al.* 2006).

GEOGRAPHIC VARIATION Involves differences in size and colour tone Two discrete races are recognised.

A. a. australis (E Australia and Tasmania) Described above.

A. a. gouldi (W Australia) When fresh, darker than nominate race with warmer, more richly toned upperparts, and with extensive cinnamon-buff wash to underparts, appearing palest on the throat and most intense on the lower flanks. Worn birds closely resemble the nominate form. There are also slight differences in structure between the two races, with *gouldi* having a slightly longer wing and tail and a longer broader-based bill (Fig. 85).

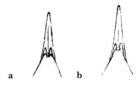

a   b

Figure 85. Comparison of bill profile of Australian Reed

Warbler of the races (a) *A. a. australis* **and (b)** *A. a. gouldi*.
On average, *gouldi* is slightly darker and more richly and warmly toned when fresh, but when worn it more closely resembles the nominate form, with some individuals being inseparable. When fresh, the upperparts including the mantle and scapulars and fringes to the wing-coverts, tertials and alula are richer and more rust-toned than in nominate *australis*. These contrast with the darker olive-brown tone to the crown and nape and the richer rufous-brown rump and uppertail-coverts. The underparts are more extensively washed and appear slightly darker and more warmly toned than nominate *australis*, ranging between rich yellowish brown to dull cinnamon-brown, particularly on the flanks and sides of the breast, but in some individuals this extends across most of the breast. On most birds, the centre of the belly and ventral region are pale rufous and conspicuously paler than the breast and belly. The undertail-coverts are warm buff.

TAXONOMY AND SYSTEMATICS Formerly treated as a race of Clamorous Reed Warbler but is now widely acknowledged to represent a distinct species.

Genetic studies by Leisler *et al.* (1997), which included analysis of 1,068 base pairs of the mitochondrial *b* gene established that Australian Reed is distinctive and merits recognition as a species distinct from Clamorous Reed Warbler (although the taxon *sumbae* was not included in this analysis – see below for discussion). They also established that its closest known relative is Pitcairn Island Warbler.

Two races are recognised, but it may be that the taxon *sumbae*, usually treated as a race of Clamorous Reed Warbler, is better placed within Australian Reed Warbler. Currently, *sumbae* is applied to a widespread taxon, ranging from the islands of the Lesser Sundas east to the Solomon Islands. Although there is surprisingly little variation across this vast region, it is unproven as yet whether genetic stability within *sumbae* is maintained across this region, especially where so many populations are isolated and restricted to

small islands. In fact, *toxopei* and *meyeri*, currently included as synonyms of *sumbae*, could be applied to birds originating from at least parts of this range. This approach would leave *sumbae* confined to Sumba and Timor in the Lesser Sundas, *toxopei* to Buru in the Moluccas and *meyeri* to become the name applied to the wide-ranging *Acrocephalus* extending throughout Irian Jaya and Papua New Guinea, the Bismarck Archipelago (New Britain, New Ireland, Umboi and Long), Bougainville, Buka, east to the eastern Solomon Islands.

Adopting this approach would still fail to address whether *sumbae*, *toxopei* or *meyeri* belong with Clamorous Reed as considered at present, with Australian Reed, or whether they represent one or more distinct species as seems likely. Without evidence to the contrary, we have elected to maintain the *status quo* and continue to include *sumbae* within Clamorous Reed Warbler. This treatment is subjective, however and is likely to be revised when sequencing of DNA from other populations has been undertaken and phylogenetic relationships are established.

The non-breeding ranges of *australis* and *gouldi* north of the breeding range remain poorly understood. Mayr (1948) suggested that birds from NE Queensland were intermediate in appearance between *australis* and *sumbae* from Papua New Guinea, while White & Bruce (1986) suggested that populations in NE Queensland may be clinal variants of *australis*, being slightly smaller than birds from southern Australia. Mayr (1948) recognised a third race of Australian Reed, *A. a. carterae*, in Kimberley Division of Western Australia. He described these as being longer billed than *gouldi*, but this was not confirmed by other researchers and this form is not recognised. However, Johnstone & Storr (2004) established that birds from Kimberley Division are resident and paler in appearance than *gouldi* and, based upon the small sample of specimens available to them, established that they are shorter-winged and shorter-tailed than *australis* and *gouldi*, but are longer-billed and have a longer tarsus. As yet, the taxonomic position of these birds has not been resolved.

▲ Adult *A. a. australis*, Canberra, Australia, September. Differs from Oriental Reed, the only other *Acrocephalus* recorded from Australia, by smaller size, slimmer build, shorter primary projection and finer, more delicate bill (Katerina Christenson).

▲ Adult *A. a. australis*, Canberra, Australia, September. Nominate race shows warm creamy buff wash to breast, flanks and belly, and duller rufous-brown undertail-coverts. Note lack of fine streaking on breast (Katerina Christenson).

▲ Adult *A. a. australis*, Canberra, Australia, September. When fresh, supercilium is poorly marked, but becomes more conspicuous with abrasion (Leo Berzins).

▲ Adult *A. a. australis*, Canberra, Australia, September. Note contrast between brown mantle and scapulars, and paler rufous-brown rump and uppertail-coverts (Julian Robinson).

▲ Adult *A. a. australis*, Canberra, Australia, September. A paler individual showing reduced wash on flanks and a fairly conspicuous supercilium (Julian Robinson).

▲ Adult *A. a. gouldi*, Western Australia, August. Western birds are characterised by warmer, darker, more richly toned upperparts, and extensive cinnamon-buff wash to underparts, palest on throat and most intense on lower flanks (Julian Robinson).

MILLERBIRD
Acrocephalus familiaris   Plate 28

Tatare familiaris Rothschild, 1892. *Ann. Mag. Nat. Hist.*, ser. 6(10): 109. Laysan, Leeward Hawaiian Chain.

Restricted to the island of Nihoa in the NW Hawaiian chain, where it is considered to be CRITICALLY ENDANGERED by BirdLife International. Formerly occurred on Laysan but became extinct here sometime between 1915 and 1923. The name 'Millerbird' is derived from the preference for feeding on moths, known locally as 'millers'. Two races recognised, one of which is extinct:
A. f. familiaris (Rothschild 1892). Laysan, Hawaii EXTINCT
A. f. kingi (Wetmore 1924). Nihoa, Hawaii.

IDENTIFICATION Length 14cm. Wing 60–65mm. Tail/wing 95–100%.
This drab, brown and nondescript *Acrocephalus* is the smallest of the resident *Acrocephalus* warblers occurring on Pacific islands and is the only warbler endemic to Hawaii. It is very different in both appearance and structure to many of the larger Pacific Island species, perhaps suggesting a different origin. Sexes alike.
Structure A small *Acrocephalus*, similar in size to Eurasian Reed Warbler *A. scirpaceus*, with a proportionately shorter and finer bill than most Pacific species. The head shows a somewhat domed crown, giving it a gentle appearance, and the body is slim, resembling some of the smaller mainland *Acrocephalus*. It differs from these, however, in the relatively short undertail-coverts, that extend to just beyond the closed wing-tip, and its relatively long tail. The wing structure suggests that of a migrant species, with a very short first primary (p1), a long second primary and a wing point formed by p4 and often p3.
Plumage and bare parts When fresh, the upperparts are drab, uniform brown or olive-brown with faint grey-brown feather fringes, although the rump and uppertail-coverts are plain and often slightly warmer-toned than the mantle and tail. A fine and poorly marked pale creamy brown supercilium barely reaches the base of the bill and fades away just behind the eye. The lores are dark but there is no eye-line extending behind the eye, so the uniformly dull brown of the ear-coverts merges with the nape, giving the sides of the head a rather featureless appearance. The chin and throat are pale creamy white with a light grey wash which merges into the lower ear-coverts. The remainder of the underparts are pale grey-brown with richer pale brown flanks and darker lower flanks and vent, which contrast with pale creamy brown undertail-coverts. The wings and tail appear plain and uniform dull brown in the field, but close examination of the closed wing reveals indistinctly warmer-toned fringes to the median coverts and greater coverts, which diffuse into the dark brown feather centres. The primary coverts, alula, tertials and flight feathers all have dark brown webs with narrow dull brown edges and tips.
When worn, birds appear greyer and slightly paler from crown to mantle, which may enhance contrast with warmer rump and uppertail-coverts. The supercilium tends to fade and almost disappear, even in front of the eye, leaving the darker loral line as the only feature on an otherwise uniform head side. The underparts fade to dull white, with the brown wash of fresh plumage restricted to the rear flanks.
A leucistic bird has been recorded once.
The bill is dark grey with a pale greyish pink base to the lower mandible. The legs and feet dark grey.

SIMILAR SPECIES The other passerine on Nihoa is the very different Nihoa Finch. The introduced Japanese Bush Warbler is found on the eastern high islands of Hawaii but not on Nihoa.

VOICE The song begins with a series of six or seven thin, harsh, metallic but relatively weak '*chit*' or '*chick*' calls given in rapid succession and gradually becoming louder. This is followed by a rapid series of scratchy, harsh and energetic notes in a short song sequence that lasts for *c.* 8–10 seconds. It is heard mainly during the breeding season (Pratt *et al.* 1987).
The delivery is rapid and varied and has a characteristic *Acrocephalus* structure, but is fairly quiet and does not carry far. In particular, the continuous calling of Sooty Terns breeding on the island tends to drown out the weaker song of the Millerbird.
Two calls are known, a weak '*chick*', delivered several times in quick succession and a quiet, short '*sweoo*', given occasionally.

MOULT No data on timing or strategy is available.

HABITAT Nihoa is a tiny, steep, rocky island with little vegetation that rises to a height of 275m. The centre of the island is covered in a layer of low scrub and bushes, in particular *Chenopodium oahuense*, *Solanum nelsoni*, *Eragrostis variabilis* and *Sida fallax*, much of which is considered to be suitable habitat for the Millerbird (BirdLife International 2000). However, the total vegetated area of Nihoa extends to just 40ha (68% of the island), of which just 0.32–0.41km² is considered suitable habitat (BirdLife International).

BEHAVIOUR Sedentary and highly territorial on Nihoa. Studies of colour-ringed birds revealed that most remained within 50m of the original ringing site for up to three years. Territory size varies between 0.2ha and 0.4ha. (Conant 1983). It mainly feeds by gleaning insects from low vegetation, but also picks from the leaf litter and the soil surface while walking or hopping and as well as hawking aerial insects. Its food consists entirely of insects and their larvae, particularly moths and caterpillars (Millers).

BREEDING HABITS Breeding takes place between January and September, with an apparent peak in activity in May and June. The lack of breeding observations during the remainder of the year is perhaps linked to lower rainfall and reduced food availability. It is a monogamous species and the nest is built by both sexes, taking up to two weeks to complete. It comprises a fairly deep cup of dry grass, rootlets and feathers and is situated close to the ground in dense scrub, usually *Chenopodium oahuense*, but also *Sida fallax* and *Solanum nelsoni*. The average height for 35 nests was 33cm, the height at which the vegetation is densest (Conant 1983). A clutch of 1–3 eggs (usually two) is produced. Incubation is by both sexes and lasts approximately 16 days, but the fledging period is unknown. Nestlings have been observed in February and March.

DISTRIBUTION Formerly occurred on Laysan, but is now confined to Nihoa, a tiny island of approximately 62ha in the NW Hawaiian Island chain, where its numbers are subject to significant fluctuations.
A. f. familiaris The nominate race formerly endemic to Laysan (25° 46'N, 171° 44'W) in the NW Hawaiian Islands but now extinct. This population was estimated at 1,500 birds in 1915, but numbers declined rapidly following the introduction of European Rabbits *Oryctolagus cuniculus*. It became extinct between 1916 and 1923.

A. f. kingi This race was discovered on Nihoa (23° 03'N, 166° 55'W) by the Tanager expedition in 1923, the year that extinction of the nominate form was confirmed. It faces many of the potential threats that overwhelmed the nominate population and its status is considered critical by BirdLife International (2000). Estimates on Nihoa since the late 1960s have ranged between 31 and 731 birds, the most recent count being 155 in July 1996 (BirdLife International, 2000). It has been calculated that the maximum population that the island could sustain would be approximately 600 individuals. The reasons for these evident fluctuations are unknown but may involve weather-related events such as tropical storms and drought.

Since both the size of the island and the remnant population are small, the risk of extinction remains high. Likely threats include severe tropical weather, changes in vegetation, accidental introduction of aggressive weeds or predators and also the spread of mosquito-borne disease – a significant factor in the extinction of many Pacific island bird populations. Part of the recovery plan for this species is to establish populations on other Hawaiian islands. Laysan, former home to the nominate race, would appear ideally suited. The vegetation on the island has now fully recovered from the devastation caused by rabbits that led to its extinction here.

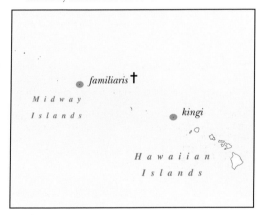

Millerbird. Resident within breeding range.

MOVEMENTS Believed to be sedentary. Despite there being several islands in the Hawaiian chain between Nihoa and Laysan, there are no records away from Nihoa (or Laysan).

DESCRIPTION *A. f. kingi*
Plumage – Adult fresh Forehead and crown dull brown, faintly tipped grey-brown. Supercilium narrow and poorly marked, barely reaching eye and extending only a short distance behind it, fading rapidly and merging with crown. Lores dark brown, contrasting sharply with supercilium. Eye-line barely visible, merging with ear-coverts. Ear-coverts uniform dull brown, darkest at upper edge, becoming paler towards throat. Eye-ring narrow, creamy brown, contrasting with supercilium and ear-coverts. Nape brown with faint grey wash, slightly greyer than crown. Mantle and scapulars dull brown with indistinct grey-brown fringes. Rump and uppertail-coverts plain warm brown. Tail dull brown, unmarked. Chin and throat white with faint grey-brown wash. Breast with grey-brown wash, this becoming distinctly colder brown on belly. Flanks pale brown, warmer

and browner than belly and becoming darker on lower flanks. Sides of breast ochre-buff. Undertail-coverts pale creamy brown. Lesser and median coverts dull brown with indistinct paler fringe. Greater coverts dark brown with broad, diffuse dull brown fringe. Tertials dark brown with narrow dull brown fringe. Primary coverts, secondaries and primaries dark brown with slightly paler dull brown edges and tips. Alula dark brown with narrow slightly paler dull brown fringe. Underwing-coverts ochre-buff.
Adult worn Duller and slightly greyer than fresh adult. Forehead and crown dull grey-brown. Supercilium barely distinct. Lores dark greyish brown. Slightly darker eye-line discernible immediately behind eye. Ear-coverts uniform dull grey-brown, paler towards lower edge. Mantle, scapulars, rump and uppertail-coverts uniform dull greyish brown. Tail feathers dull brown with narrow grey-brown fringes. Chin and throat whiter than on fresh bird. Breast white, washed pale grey, becoming whiter on upper belly but darkening to dull grey-buff on lower flanks. Lesser and median coverts dull brown, slightly greyer than in fresh bird. Greater coverts and tertials dark brown with broad, diffuse dull grey-brown fringe. Slightly paler edges and tips of primary coverts, secondaries and primaries usually lost so that wing appears uniform dark brown. Alula dark brown to black with indistinct, narrow dull-brown fringe.
Juvenile No details available.
Bare parts Upper mandible dark grey. Lower mandible dark grey with slightly paler greyish pink base. Tarsi, toes and claws dark grey. Iris dull brown.

IN HAND CHARACTERS
Measurements
A. f. familiaris (1 ♂, 1 ♀): wing, ♂ 64, ♀ 60; tail, ♂ 61, ♀ 61; bill, ♂ 19.1, ♀ 18.5; tarsus, ♂ 23.3, ♀ 20.4.
A. f. kingi (2 ♂♂, 1 ♀): wing, ♂ 63, 65, ♀ 62; tail, ♂ 62, 63, ♀ 60; bill, ♂ 18.6, 19.5, ♀ 18.9; tarsus, ♂ 24.5, 24.8, ♀ 23.7.
Races and sexes combined: tail graduation 8–12 (n = 3); hind claw 6.1–7.3 (n = 5).

Structure

Wing formula (races combined, n = 5):

p1/pc	p2	p3e	p4e	p5e	p6(e)	p7	p10
(2.5)–0	5–8	0–2.5	wp	0.5–0.1	2–3	3.5–5	9.5–10.5

Wing short and rounded, with minute p1. Wing point p(3) 4; p2 = p8–9; emargination on p3–5, sometimes p6.

Figure 86. Wing of Millerbird.

Tail longish, strongly rounded.
Bill shorter than in other Pacific *Acrocephalus* and rather slender; perhaps stouter in *kingi* (width 3.7, 3.9 in two nominate birds, 4.3–4.5 in three *kingi*).

Weight 15–21.5g (18.3; 56) (Morin *et al.* 1997).

GEOGRAPHIC VARIATION

A. f. kingi (Nihoa, Hawaii) Described above.

A. f. familiaris (formerly Laysan, Hawaii, now extinct) Closely resembled *kingi* in size and structure, but reported to differ from it slightly in appearance. Was said to be slightly greyer above, especially on the crown, nape and mantle, than *kingi*, with the pale brown wash on flanks and breast being slightly colder and greyer. It is not known whether these minor colour differences represent consistent differences between the races, individual variation or the effects of wear, or are due to colour changes occurring in long-dead specimens.

TAXONOMY AND SYSTEMATICS In a study to determine the relationship between the Millerbirds on Laysan and Nihoa, Fleischer *et al.* (2007) assessed the genetic variation in blood samples from 15 individuals in the modern Nihoa population using approximately 3,000 base pairs (bp) of mtDNA sequence and 14 microsatellite loci. These results were compared with up to 1,028 bp of mtDNA sequence from the fragmented DNA of museum specimens of three birds collected on Nihoa in 1923 and five birds collected on Laysan in 1902 and 1911. This study established that genetic variation was extremely low in the modern Nihoa population, but in the Laysan population, three mtDNA haplotypes were found amongst the five individuals examined, which indicated substantial genetic variation. The Nihoa and Laysan taxa differed by 1.7% uncorrected mtDNA sequence divergence, a magnitude that supports their recognition as distinct races.

▲ ▶ Adult, Nihoa, Hawaii, March. Quite unlike any of the other Pacific island *Acrocephalus*, but resembles smaller races of Clamorous Reed Warbler in its overall drab appearance (Ian Jones).

COOK ISLANDS WARBLER
Acrocephalus kerearako
Plate 28

Acrocephalus vaughani kerearako Holyoak, 1974. Bull. Brit. Orn. Club. 94: 149. Mangaia, Cook Islands.

Endemic to the Cook Islands in the Pacific Ocean, where it is resident on Mangaia and Mitiaro. Although only described as recently as 1974, its existence on Mangaia was known for many years prior to this (Christian 1920), but it was not until the collection of the type series from Mangaia and Mitiaro by Holyoak (1974a) that its presence became more widely appreciated. The scientific names are derived from the names used by the island inhabitants; that on Mangaia being known as 'Kerearako', while the Mitiaro bird is known to the islanders as 'Kaoko'. Considered NEAR THREATENED by BirdLife International. Polytypic, with two races recognised:

A. k. kerearako (Holyoak, 1974a). Mangaia, Cook Islands.
A. k. kaoko (Holyoak, 1974a). Mitiaro, Cook Islands.

IDENTIFICATION Length 16cm. Wing 76–80mm. Tail/wing 90–101%.

A plain and nondescript, medium sized Acrocephalus, appearing olive above and yellowish below, with a rather slender bill. It is strikingly different in appearance to Pitcairn Island Warbler with which it was formerly treated as conspecific. Sexes alike.

Structure This is a rather slim-bodied and long-tailed Acrocephalus with a distinctly rounded tail. The long-tailed appearance is enhanced by its short wings, with primaries that just reach the tail base and by the short undertail-coverts. It has a relatively long and straight bill that, although typical of several mid sized Pacific Acrocephalus, is proportionately finer than in the larger mainland Acrocephalus such as Clamorous Reed and Oriental Reed Warblers. The crown is usually rounded, but the feathering may be raised while singing, giving it an angular and ragged appearance. It shares a similar wing structure with other Pacific Acrocephalus, including a minute first primary, short primary projection and a wing point formed by p4 and often with p3 and p5.

Plumage and bare parts Cook Islands Warbler is a drab and nondescript Acrocephalus, lacking the bright and contrasting plumage of many of the Pacific species. It closely resembles some races of Clamorous Reed and Australian Reed Warblers, suggesting a possible origin for the ancestral Cook Islands colonists. It has plain warm brown to olive-brown upperparts, with the rump and uppertail-coverts slightly paler than the mantle and contrasting with the dull brown tail. The head shows a fine buff supercilium reaching from the bill base to the rear of the eye. The lores are dark but there is only a poorly defined eye-stripe behind the eye, so the unmarked yellowish buff ear-coverts merge with the sides of the crown and neck. The chin and throat are creamy white and contrast with the remainder of the underparts, which are lightly and variably washed yellowish buff. This wash is most intense on the lower flanks, but paler and yellower on the belly and undertail-coverts. On the closed wing, the warm brown fringes to the greater coverts, tertials and flight feathers contrast with darker feather centres and appear richer brown than the upperparts, particularly when fresh.

The bill is dark grey with a dull greyish pink base to the lower mandible, which darkens towards the tip. The legs and feet are light bluish grey.

SIMILAR SPECIES No similar species occur in the Cook Islands, where this is the only warbler.

VOICE Songs of the birds on Mangaia and Mitiaro share many similarities. Each has a simple structure with distinct single loud whistled phrases including loud 'shroo', 'chru' and 'wit' notes.

The song of kerearako on Mangaia has a more rapid delivery given in shorter bursts of 5–7 seconds, each followed by a pause of a similar length. It is more varied than that of kaoko with a slightly faster delivery and includes a greater variety of pleasant melodic fluty notes, within a frequency range of 1–5kHz. It is interspersed with harsher notes similar to those of the Mitiaro bird.

Song of Cook Islands Warbler recorded within breeding range of A. k. kerearako, Mangaia, Cook Islands Archipelago, October. (McPherson 1998)

Conversely, on Mitiaro, delivery is noticeably slower, simpler and more repetitive. It has clearly separated harsh whistles and lacks the faster and sweeter melodic whistles and phrases of kerearako. Delivery often continues for longer, with unbroken sequences of 20 seconds or more.

Song of Cook Islands Warbler recorded within breeding range of A. k. kaoko, Mitiaro, Cook Islands Archipelago, February (McPherson 1998)

The call is a harsh 'shroo' or 'chru', uttered intermittently at intervals of 1–5 seconds, but sometimes repeated continuously for several minutes. This call can often be heard within the song phrases.

MOULT No information on timing or duration.

HABITAT It occurs widely in a variety of habitats on both islands, where it is common and widespread. On Mangaia, it inhabits the wooded and bushy areas that comprise the makatea forest around the island periphery, but is adaptable and is also found in adjacent wooded, scrubby areas and introduced pine forest, and in the scrub zone on hills in the interior. On low-lying Mitiaro, it is common in any habitat that provides cover for feeding and nesting. Here it frequents trees and thick bushy scrub in the coastal coral zone and also reedbeds with Casuarina thickets in the interior wetlands. It is often found in gardens and villages on Mitiaro, but this has not been observed on Mangaia.

BEHAVIOUR Poorly known, but apparently little different from that of other Acrocephalus on low-lying Pacific islands. Males are highly territorial during the breeding season and frequently sing from a tree or bush, often partially concealed in the canopy as they move among leaves and twigs. The song is delivered mainly in the early morning or late evening, but occasionally for short periods during the middle of the day. Singing males often raise their crown feathers, puff out the throat and open and droop their wings slightly.

Diet is believed to consist entirely of small invertebrates, including small beetles, Diptera larvae, grasshoppers, moths and spiders. It actively forages from leaves and twigs within trees and bushes and among herbaceous plants. It has been observed feeding upside-down from a branch in the manner of a tit *Parus* sp., and catching insects among short plant tufts while hopping on the ground.

BREEDING HABITS Little studied and known mainly from collection specimens. Three occupied nests were located on Mitiaro in September 1973 together with several old and decomposed nests. Many of the birds collected at this time were in sexually active condition (Holyoak 1974a). Some nests were built in the canopy of trees and taller shrubs, well hidden by leaves, while others were placed in low scrub within 1m of the ground. The nest is a deep cup-shaped structure constructed from fine dry stems and fibres, including coconut palm fibres, and bound together around small branches and twigs. It is lined with similar, but finer, fibres and grasses. Each of the three occupied nests examined by Holyoak contained a single egg. According to local inhabitants, this is the normal clutch size, although two eggs are sometimes laid and, exceptionally, three. Incubation and fledging times are unknown.

DISTRIBUTION Confined to just two islands in the Cook Islands Archipelago, each occupied by an endemic race.

A. k. kerearako Widely distributed throughout Mangaia (21° 52'S, 157° 44'W), the most southerly of the Cook Islands, wherever suitable habitat occurs. This relatively large and well-wooded island covers an area of 51.8km² and rises in its centre to a height of 169m.

A. k. kaoko Restricted to Mitiaro (19° 50'S, 157° 42'W), also in the southern Cook Islands and approximately 220km northeast of Mangaia. This is a much smaller island than Mangaia, with a land area of 22.25km² and rising to just 10.9m. It is common in suitable habitat throughout the island.

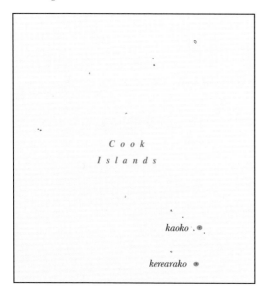

Cook Islands

kaoko

kerearako

Cook Islands Warbler. Resident within breeding range.

MOVEMENTS No inter-island movements have been recorded. It is probable that this must have occurred in the past for birds to become established on both Mangaia and Mitiaro. Whether populations ever existed on Mauke or Atui, which lie between these two islands, is unknown.

DESCRIPTION *A. k. kerearako*

Plumage – Adult fresh Forehead and crown plain warm brown to olive-brown. Narrow supercilium bright buff, most prominent between base of bill and eye, fading behind eye and merging with crown and eye-line. Lores dark brown forming dark line between eye and bill. Eye-line warm brown, sharply defined against supercilium but merging below with upper ear-coverts. Ear-coverts warm brown along upper edge, fading to warm buff at lower edge and colour merging with sides of throat and neck. Narrow eye-ring warm buff, contrasting with darker lores and eye-line. Nape, mantle and scapulars uniform warm brown. Rump and uppertail-coverts similar, but slightly paler. Tail warm brown, unmarked. Chin and throat buffy white, becoming warm buff to yellow at sides. Breast with variable warm buff to yellow wash, becoming stronger, often distinctly brownish on breast sides and along flanks. Belly pale yellow or sulphur-yellow, merging with flank coloration. Undertail-coverts pale yellow with faint sulphur or brownish tinge. Lesser and median coverts warm brown with poorly defined fringes. Greater coverts with dark brown centres and broad, diffuse bright tan fringes. Tertials dark brown with broad, crisp, warm brown fringes. Primary coverts, secondaries and primaries dark brown with narrow, warm brown fringes and tips. Alula blackish, fringed warm brown. Underwing-coverts olive-yellow.

Immature Undescribed.

Bare Parts Upper mandible uniform dark grey. Lower mandible dull greyish pink at base, becoming dark grey towards tip. Tarsi, toes and claws pale blue-grey. Iris dull brown.

IN HAND CHARACTERS

Measurements

A. k. kerearako (7 ♂♂): *wing* 76–79 (77); *tail* 77–80 (79); *bill* (exposed culmen) 15–17 (16); *tarsus* 28–29 (28) (Holyoak & Thibault 1984).

A. k. kaoko (6 ♂♂, 2 ♀♀): *wing*, ♂ 78–80 (79), ♀ 76, 79; *tail*, ♂ 76–79 (77), ♀ 69, 74; *bill*, ♂ 15–17 (16), ♀ 17; *tarsus*, ♂ 27–29 (28), ♀ 27, 28. (Holyoak & Thibault 1984).

Bill to skull: *kerearako* (2 ♂♂) 21.6, 23.1; *kaoko* (1 ♂) 22.4.

Races and sexes combined:
Tail/wing ratio: 90–101% (96%; 5)
Bill width: 4.8, 5.0 (n = 2)
Hind claw: 7.9–9.0 (8.5; 5)
Tail graduation: 10, 13 (n = 2)

Structure

A. k. kerearako

Wing formula (n = 4):

p1/pc	p2	p3(e)	p4e	p5(e)	p6	p7	p10
(3)–4	7–8	0–2	wp	0–0.5	2–3	4–5	8–11

Wing similar to Millerbird (Fig. 86), but emargination less obvious, usually most prominent on p4. Wing rounded, with p1 minute. Wing point p(3) 4 (5); p2 = p8/9–10; emargination on p4, sometimes also p3 and p5.

Tail longish, graduated, with rather narrow feathers.

Bill rather long but broad-based, similar to larger races of Clamorous Reed Warbler.

Tarsi long but relatively slender; claws fine.

Weight 17.3–28g (22.5; 40) (Dunning 2007)

GEOGRAPHIC VARIATION Two very similar races, each endemic to a single island.

A. k. kerearako (Mangaia) Described above.

A. k. kaoko (Mitiaro) When fresh, the upperparts including the edges to the flight feathers are slightly duller than in nominate race, while the rump and uppertail-coverts show only a faint tawny-brown wash that has little contrast with the mantle. The underparts, including the throat, breast and belly, tend to be paler yellow and show indistinct grey-brown streaking on the throat and breast, while the sides of the breast and lower flanks are tinged paler brown.

TAXONOMY AND SYSTEMATICS Holyoak (1974a) considered the Cook Islands taxa to represent races of Pitcairn Island Warbler and he initially described them as such. Despite this, he also acknowledged that they 'differ strikingly in showing no tendency to albinism, in having much heavier yellow lipoid pigmentation producing yellow underparts and olive upperparts and in measurements.' Subsequently, these factors, combined with the geographic isolation of Pitcairn Island from the Cook Islands, have led to the acceptance of Cook Islands Warbler as a distinct species with two races.

▲ Adult *A. k. kerearako*, Mangaia, Cook Islands, January. The intensity of yellow on the underparts varies individually on Mangaia; this is quite a bright individual (Jim Martin).

▲ Adult *A. k. kerearako*, Mangaia, Cook Islands, January (Jim Martin).

▲ Adult *A. k. kerearako*, Mangaia, Cook Islands, January (Jim Martin).

▲ Adult *A. k. kerearako*, Mangaia, Cook Islands, January. A considerably paler individual, some can match the appearance of the race *kaoko* on Mitiaro (Jim Martin).

PITCAIRN ISLAND WARBLER
Acrocephalus vaughani   Plate 28

Tatare vaughani **Sharpe, 1900**. *Bull. Brit. Orn. Club*, 11: 2. Pitcairn Island.

This distinctive *Acrocephalus* inhabits one of the most remote and isolated islands in the C Pacific, where it is the only resident passerine. It has previously been treated as a polytypic species with three races. Here, however, Henderson Island Warbler and Rimatara Warbler, former races of Pitcairn Island Warbler, are treated as distinct species. Considered to be ENDANGERED by BirdLife International. Monotypic.

IDENTIFICATION Length 17cm. Wing, male 80–85mm, female 74–79mm. Tail/wing 78–94%.

A large warbler with ash-grey upperparts, a pale rump and a variable extent of white in the wings and tail. The underparts are pale yellowish or creamy white. Sexes similar, but males are always larger than females.

Structure Similar in structure to Tuamotu, Tahiti and the Marquesan Warblers but is slightly smaller with a proportionately smaller bill and longer legs. Like these species, it has a long sloping forehead and rounded crown, except when the fore-crown feathering is raised, and the head becomes ragged and untidy. The body appears fairly large and rounded, but the wings are short, reaching only to the base of the tail and falling well short of the tips of the longest uppertail-coverts. Like many Pacific *Acrocephalus*, it has a fairly rounded wing with a short primary projection, but a wing formula suggestive of a migrant, with a short first primary (p1), a relatively long second primary (p2) and the wing point is formed by p4, often together with p3 and p5. There is a conspicuous emargination on p3 and p4.

Plumage and bare parts Adults are particularly distinctive *Acrocephalus* with ash-grey upperparts, each feather on the crown, mantle and scapulars being narrowly fringed whitish. When fresh, these fringes give a mottled or frosted appearance to the upperparts but as they abrade the upperparts become a more uniform and darker ash-grey. The rump and uppertail-coverts are slightly paler creamy white, so that as feather wear occurs these areas appear contrastingly paler than the mantle and tail. Most birds show a narrow and poorly marked supercilium extending from the bill base to the rear of the eye and most conspicuous above the dark and contrasting lores. Behind the eye, the supercilium and eye-stripe are indistinct, and the grey crown tends to merge with the pale ear-coverts which, in turn, merge with the whitish chin and throat. There is often a narrow but conspicuous white eye-ring. The underparts vary from creamy white to a more intense pale yellowish white, darkening to warm creamy buff or straw towards the flanks and undertail-coverts.

The plumage of Pitcairn Island Warbler is particularly prone to a variable but often high degree of leucism (or partial albinism) that affects the body and appears asymmetrically in the wings and tail, so that no two birds appear the same. This variation could be the result of a genetic bottleneck in this small isolated population, or it may partly reflect age or the effects of diet, but such explanations are speculative.

On some birds, the tail may be entirely black but most show a variable number of randomly and asymmetrically placed white feathers. Commonly, more than half the tail is white with white feather shafts, the vane colour varying from white to pale creamy yellow. Occasionally the entire tail can be white, but in less extreme individuals is limited to white tips or white fringes to otherwise black tail feathers. However, birds with white restricted just to the tail tip are unusual. The extent of leucism in the wing is equally variable. It is not unusual to see birds with a random mixture of black and white (or pale creamy yellow) remiges. Some birds may show narrow greyish fringes and white tips to dark secondaries and pale edges to dark primaries. Most, however, have dark grey lesser and median coverts with broad white fringes. The greater coverts are generally more variable. In some birds these are entirely white or pale creamy yellow, in others they show dark grey centres and broad whitish fringes, creating a chequered pattern across the closed wing. The primary coverts vary from being entirely black to entirely white, while the alula is usually black, sometimes with a crisp white fringe. The tertials are dark grey or black, with variable white fringing.

Juveniles are quite different in appearance from adults. They are generally browner above and show a fairly intense buffy wash below, especially on the flanks and undertail-coverts. The presence of white feathering in the juvenile plumage is unusual.

The bill is dark grey with a pale pink base to the lower mandible and the legs and feet are dark grey.

SIMILAR SPECIES No similar species occur on Pitcairn Island, where Pitcairn Island Warbler is the only resident passerine. It does, however, closely resemble Henderson Island and Rimatara Warblers.

VOICE Not known to produce an obvious or recognisable song. Nicoll (1904) noted only a quiet '*chack, chack*', while Chapin (writing in Mayr 1942a) heard no song during the breeding period. Williams (1960) noted only a monotonous and tuneless chirping during October and November, when birds were nesting. Consequently, Holyoak & Thibault (1984) concluded that Pitcairn Island Warbler did not sing in the manner of the larger *Acrocephalus* warblers on Tahiti and the Marquesas. However, Graves (1992) considered a series of thin, longer notes given by males to be the song. It seems certain that Pitcairn Island Warbler lacks the typical harsh and rapid *Acrocephalus* song.

The most frequently heard call is a harsh and screeching '*schaaar*', repeated at intervals of 1–4 seconds.

MOULT Little is known of the timing and frequency of moult. Some specimens from March 1922 were in moult while others had recently finished (Murphy & Mathews 1929).

HABITAT Widely distributed throughout the island wherever suitable habitat occurs. Pitcairn Island was originally covered with tall forest. Much has now been lost but the highest numbers of warblers are still to be found where it remains. Lower densities occur in scrub, which has replaced the forest, and also in gardens and cultivated areas close to human habitation, but it appears to be absent from cliffs and open ground (BirdLife International 2000).

BEHAVIOUR Poorly known. It is believed to feed entirely on insects that are gleaned from vegetation in a manner similar to the other Polynesian *Acrocephalus*.

BREEDING HABITS Poorly understood and no detailed studies have been made. Breeding probably occurs seasonally, as none of the birds collected by the Whitney Expedition in March 1922 were sexually active. However, Williams (1960) found occupied nests in October and

November 1956. The nest is an untidy structure, comprising a deep cup constructed from dry grasses and fibres of banana and other plants. Nest sites observed by Williams were quite varied, ranging from the base of a *Cordyline terminalis* leaf within 1m of the ground, to a fork in the canopy of a Mango *Mangifera indica*, approximately 10m above the ground. Most nests, however, were in bushes of *Eugenia jambos*, usually less than 5m high. The usual clutch is two eggs (Williams 1960) but incubation and fledging periods are unknown.

Unlike Henderson Island Warbler, Pitcairn Island Warbler is believed to nest only in pairs, and polyandrous or polygamous trios are unrecorded. Brooke & Hartley (1995) suggest that monogamous pairing occurred when the island was covered in primary forest and there was no shortage of suitable habitat. Subsequent fragmentation due to human activities reduced the extent of suitable habitat, but predation by cats has reduced the population, so habitat availability still exceeds demand. It remains to be seen whether breeding trios will form if the population increases to fill the available habitat.

DISTRIBUTION Endemic to Pitcairn Island (25° 03'S, 130° 08'W) in the C South Pacific Ocean, where Williams (1960) found it to be abundant in 1956. It is considered to be endangered due to the presence on the island of large numbers of introduced Pacific Rats *Rattus exulans* and feral cats. An attempt to eradicate cats began in 1997 and the warbler population responded with a marked increase to an estimated 2,000–3,000 individuals in 1998–99. By 2005, however, the populations of rats and cats had recovered and it seems inevitable that warbler numbers will decline again (BirdLife International).

MOVEMENTS Sedentary. There are no records away from Pitcairn Island.

DESCRIPTION
Plumage – Adult fresh Forehead and crown ash-grey, narrowly but conspicuously tipped white. Supercilium poorly marked, forming an indistinct creamy line from bill base to upper edge of eye but absent behind eye. Below this, a conspicuous black loral line. Eye-line poorly marked, barely visible between crown and ear-coverts. Ear-coverts pale ash-grey, faintly tipped cream, becoming paler and distinctly creamy towards lower edge. Eye-ring whitish, showing little contrast with supercilium and grey feathering below eye. Nape ash-grey, similar to crown but with narrower, less conspicuous dull cream fringes. Mantle and scapulars ash-grey, feathers fringed dull cream to white. Rump and uppertail-coverts pale grey-brown, warmer and paler than mantle and unmarked. Tail black, with a variable number of entirely white feathers in most individuals. Chin and throat white, faintly washed light grey. Breast white, washed creamy grey, with diffuse grey streaks on the sides of the upper breast and above carpal bend. Belly pale cream with faint yellow wash. Flanks creamy grey and unmarked, showing little tonal change from breast and belly. Undertail-coverts creamy white, slightly paler than flanks.

Wings with highly variable white feathering. Lesser and median coverts dark grey, median coverts broadly tipped white, lesser coverts only slightly so. Greater coverts broadly fringed and tipped white, especially on inner feathers, where brownish grey centres largely hidden. Tertials black, with variable white fringing; inconspicuous on some individuals, others with broad white fringes and tips to all

three tertials. Primary coverts white, unmarked. Secondaries and primaries either entirely white or black with a narrow white fringe, the number, pattern and position of white feathers varying randomly between individuals. Alula black, unmarked. Underwing-coverts creamy white, faintly mottled darker.

Juvenile Much darker and browner than adult, lacking white fringes and tips and white feathers. Forehead and crown dull olive-brown, indistinctly tipped buffy brown. Supercilium bright buff, short, extending from bill base to rear of eye. Lores blackish, indistinctly tipped buff. Eye-line barely discernible. Ear-coverts greyish brown, paler towards lower edge and merging with sides of throat. Eye-ring narrow, bright buff, contrasting with dark brown feathering below eye. Nape, mantle and scapulars dull olive-brown, indistinctly fringed pale grey. Rump and uppertail-coverts warm brown with slightly darker centres. Tail feathers dull brown with narrow, warm brown fringes. Chin and throat pale cream. Breast greyish, becoming browner and warmer at sides, similar to dull olive-brown nape. Belly white, washed pale yellowish brown, this wash becoming stronger and darker on flanks. Undertail-coverts warm buff. Lesser and median coverts mid brown with warmer brown fringes, slightly brighter than mantle. Greater coverts and tertials dark brown with diffuse warm brown fringes. Edges and tips to primary coverts, secondaries and primaries warm brown. Alula dark brown with narrow creamy fringe.

Bare parts Upper mandible dark grey with pale pink cutting edge. Lower mandible pale pink at base, darkening at sides towards tip. Tarsi, toes and claws dark grey. Iris dull brown.

IN HAND CHARACTERS
Measurements

	Male	Female
Wing	80–85 (82; 10)	74–79 (76; 8)
Tail	68–73 (70; 10)	64–67 (66; 8)
Bill*	17–18 (18; 10)	17–18 (17; 8)
Tarsus	29–31 (30; 10)	28–29 (29; 8)

(Holyoak & Thibault 1984) *exposed culmen

Bill to skull, (2 ♂♂): 19.5, 20.2; (1 ♀) 19.1.

Sexes combined:
Tail/wing ratio: 78–94% (85%; 8)
Bill width: 4.5–4.9 (4.7; 11)
Hind claw: 6.7–9.3 (8.4; 11)
Tail graduation: 12–18 (14.8; 9)

Structure

Wing formula (n = 8):

p1/pc	p2	p3e	p4e	p5	p6	p7	p10
(3)–0	4–7	0–0.5	wp	0.5–1.5	0.5–3.5	3–5	10–13

Wing similar to Millerbird (Fig. 86) but lacks emargination on p5–6. Wing rounded, p1 minute. Wing point p(3) 4; p2 = p7–8; emargination on p3–4.

Tail medium length, graduated, feathers rather narrow.

Bill longish and strong; almost straight-sided (Fig. 41).

Tarsi long and strong.

Generally much less robust, with a less exaggerated bill, than the *Acrocephalus* occupying the Marquesas, Society and Tuamotu Islands 1,000–2,000km to the northwest.
Weight ♂ 27g, ♀ 22g (Williams 1960).

GEOGRAPHIC VARIATION None recorded. However, in May 1968, an *Acrocephalus* was reported (heard only?) on the island of Raevavae (23° 49'S, 147° 41'W), which lies approximately half way between Rimatara and Pitcairn (Holyoak & Thibault 1984). It could not be located during a search in 1990 (Seitre & Seitre 1991) suggesting that if any *Acrocephalus* had occurred on the island, it may have already become extinct. If relocated, it is possible that this will represent a race of Pitcairn Island Warbler, Henderson Island Warbler or another distinct species.

TAXONOMY AND SYSTEMATICS Historically, Pitcairn Island Warbler has been treated as monotypic species as here, or as a polytypic species comprising three races; the nominate endemic to Pitcairn Island, *taiti* endemic to Henderson Island and *rimitarae* endemic to Rimatara. The structural and morphological differences between these three taxa are minimal. Greater differences can be found between the seven races of Tuamotu Warbler, which is recognised as a single species.

To date, no DNA studies have been published to suggest just how far these three taxa have diverged or whether they even share a common phylogeny. Given their geographical isolation there seems little prospect of interchange between islands. Consequently, we have treated each as a separate species.

▲ Adult, Pitcairn Island, April. The random positioning of white feathers in the primaries, secondaries, tertials and tail is characteristic of several closely related Pacific island *Acrocephalus*, including Henderson Island and Rimatara Warblers. All are extremely similar in appearance and can only be safely separated by distribution (Marcie Connelly-Lynn).

HENDERSON ISLAND WARBLER
Acrocephalus taiti   Plate 28

Acrocephalus taiti Ogilvie-Grant, 1913. *Bull. Brit. Orn. Club*, 31: 58. Henderson Island.

Endemic to remote Henderson Island in the C Pacific Ocean where it is the only resident passerine. Closely resembles Pitcairn Island Warbler and Rimatara Warbler and until recently regarded as a race of the former. Considered VULNERABLE by BirdLife International. Monotypic.

IDENTIFICATION Length 17cm. Wing 77–84mm. Tail/wing *c.* 85%.
A fairly large and extremely variable *Acrocephalus*. Adults appear largely white, particularly about the head, nape and underparts, while the upperparts are variably greyish white, palest on the rump and uppertail-coverts. The extent of white on the upperparts, including the wing-coverts and tertials, is dependent upon the width of the feather fringes, birds with the broadest fringes appearing particularly pale while those with narrower fringes have more conspicuous greyish feather bases, giving a variegated appearance. Almost all adults show a random and asymmetrical pattern of white and black remiges and rectrices. The reasons for this tendency towards leucism (or partial albinism) are not fully established. It may be a consequence of a genetic bottleneck in the small population established on the island combined with a lack of predators. Variation may be age-related. White feathering is largely absent in juveniles and apparently is most extensive in older adults.
Sexes similar, although males tend to have a greater number of white rectrices than females Males are slightly larger than females, although there is overlap.
Structure Not discernibly different from Pitcairn Island or Rimatara Warblers. Like these species, it has a long bill, sloping forehead, large rounded body and relatively short wings, and is conspicuously longer-legged than other Polynesian *Acrocephalus*.
Plumage and bare parts Adults are rather more variable than Pitcairn Island Warbler with most individuals exhibiting extensive white feathering or broad white feather fringes. Some birds appear almost entirely white. The upperparts are either entirely white, or pale ash-grey with broad whitish fringes. The underparts are white although some show a faint creamy wash which, when present, is never as well marked as in Pitcairn Island Warbler. Leucism is most pronounced on the head and mantle and many adults appear distinctly white-headed. The distribution of white remiges and rectrices is variable and often asymmetric. Individuals of both sexes invariably have one or more white rectrices but Brooke & Hartley (1995) demonstrated breeding males have more white rectrices (5.5 ± 3.7, n = 12) than females (1.8 ± 2.3, n =11). Males breeding in pairs tend to have more than those breeding in trios, suggesting that the number increases with age. Males are also more likely than females to have at least one white flight feather per wing.
Juveniles of Henderson Island and Pitcairn Island Warblers resemble each other closely. Both lack leucism, but the birds from Henderson Island are slightly paler.
The bill is dark grey with a pale pink lower mandible which darkens slightly at the sides towards the tip. The legs and feet are pale grey.

SIMILAR SPECIES No similar species occur on Henderson Island where Henderson Island Warbler is the only resident

passerine. It closely resembles Pitcairn Island and Rimatara Warblers but differs in being generally whiter about the head and underparts, while the white fringes to the upperparts are, on average, broader. It generally lacks the olivaceous upperpart tones and the creamy yellow wash to the flanks and undertail-coverts of Pitcairn Island Warbler. However, there is considerable individual variation, making it difficult to establish features that can reliably distinguish them.

VOICE No song has been described or recorded and, like Pitcairn Island Warbler, it is believed not to sing.
The call consists of a series of short, harsh screeches, with several sequences given in quick succession. Notes are similar in length but vary in pitch and tone throughout any given sequence.

MOULT No data available. It is likely that a complete moult occurs after the breeding season, between February and July.

HABITAT Henderson Island is a low-lying raised limestone plateau that extends to 3,700ha and forms the largest island in the Pitcairn group. It is uninhabited and largely covered with climax forest and has been designated as an UNESCO World Heritage Site. The warblers occur commonly throughout the forest, which consists of both native and introduced tree species.

BEHAVIOUR Not known to differ from Pitcairn Island Warbler. Feeds at all forest levels, from the canopy to the ground where it forages amongst fallen leaves. Takes small invertebrates including snails, ants, flies, moths, beetles, cockroaches and wasps, plus seeds and fruit pulp (BirdLife International 2000).

BREEDING HABITS Nesting occurs between late August and early January and birds are highly territorial during the breeding season (Brooke & Hartley 1995). The nest is placed 1.7–7.0m up (mean 3.6m) in the lower canopy of taller forest trees. Thin, spindly trees are preferred for nesting, including *Xylosma suaveolens*, *Thespesia populnea*, *Nesoluma st-johnianum* and *Ixora fragrans*, while *Eugenia reinwardtiana*, *Pisonia grandis*, *Psydrax odorata*, *Celtis pacifica* and *Glochidion pitcairnense* are sometimes used. An old nest, collected by Beck in 1922 (now at the AMNH), comprises a deep cup resembling that of other Pacific *Acrocephalus* and is constructed from dead leaves and plant fibres. The typical clutch is 2–3 eggs, although 4–5 may be present where two females lay in the same nest. With few predators, most chicks survive to fledging.
Using DNA fingerprinting, Brooke & Hartley (1995) established that Henderson Island Warbler commonly breeds in trios; either one male paired with two females (polygyny) or one female paired with two males (poly-andry), in both instances the three birds usually being unrelated. In a polygynous system, one or both females lay in the same nest, with the same male fathering all the chicks, and all three birds assist in raising the offspring. Where two males and one female share the nest, the dominant male and female share most of the incubation, with the subordinate male playing a minor part, but all members of the trio contribute to feeding of the young. Older birds are more likely to breed in pairs, while younger birds are more inclined to form trios.
The reasons for shared breeding are unclear, as it does not occur in Pitcairn Island Warbler. However, Seychelles Warbler, another species with a range restricted to small oceanic islands, usually breeds in trios, with one bird assisting the breeding pair. Brooke & Hartley suggested

that territorial vacancies in the stable, pristine habitat on Henderson Island are scarce and younger birds increase their chances of breeding by dispersing and forming a coalition with an inexperienced pair. This might increase the likelihood of securing a territory at a later date and enables the young bird to gain experience of breeding.

DISTRIBUTION Endemic to Henderson Island (24° 21'S, 128° 19'W) in the C South Pacific. It was considered to be common throughout the island during the Whitney Expedition of 1922 and was still apparently widespread 30 years later (Williams 1960). Its current status appears largely unchanged, but it is considered Vulnerable by BirdLife International due to the presence of the Pacific Rat *Rattus exulans* throughout the island. Rats are able to reach the upper branches of the forest trees and pose a potential threat to eggs and unfledged young. Despite this it remains abundant throughout the island although rats may be suppressing the population. Brooke & Hartley (1995) estimated a territory size of approximately 0.92ha. Extrapolation throughout suitable habitat equates to approximately 4,000 territories and an estimated population of 9,500 breeding adults. This compares with the estimate of a post-breeding population of 10,800 individuals (BirdLife International).

MOVEMENTS Sedentary. There are no records away from Henderson Island.

DESCRIPTION
Plumage – Adult fresh Forehead and crown dark ash-grey with white fringes, narrow in some birds, broad in others and creating a largely white crown. Supercilium pale greyish white, narrow and poorly marked, most conspicuous above lores and not extending beyond rear edge of eye. Below this a conspicuous black loral line between bill base and eye. Eyeline poorly defined, sides of crown merging with ear-coverts. Ear-coverts variable, usually matching nape and crown sides, but becoming paler, sometimes almost white, on lower edge towards throat. Eye-ring narrow, white and quite conspicuous, contrasting with greyer crown and ear-coverts. Nape ash-grey, with whitish fringes of variable width, appearing largely ash-grey or largely white. Mantle and scapular feathers ash-grey with whitish fringes, appearing ash-grey with only faint mottled effect when fringes are narrow, much paler and more strongly mottled when fringes are broad. Rump and uppertail-coverts pale greyish white, slightly mottled. Tail black with variable number of randomly placed, entirely white rectrices. Chin and throat white, merging with lower edge of ear-coverts. Breast and belly white with faint grey wash. Upper flanks white, darkening to pale sandy grey on lower flanks. Undertail-coverts white to creamy white.

Wing highly variable, with many asymmetric combinations of white primaries and secondaries. Lesser and median coverts dark grey with broad white fringes. Greater coverts entirely white in some birds, dark grey in others with broad white fringes which narrow towards outer edge of wing. Tertials charcoal-grey to black, with white fringes and tips of variable width. Primary coverts entirely black or entirely white. Secondaries and primaries typically black, but with a few entirely white. White secondaries often with greyish fringes, more conspicuous towards the tip; fringes entirely dark in some birds. Dark primaries and secondaries usually tipped white, sometimes with a crisp whitish fringe. Alula black, sometimes with a crisp whitish fringe. Underwing-coverts creamy white.
Juvenile Much darker and browner than adult, lacking white fringes, tips and feathers.
Bare parts Upper mandible dark grey with pale pink cutting

edge towards base. Lower mandible pale pink at base, darkening at sides towards tip. Tarsi, toes and claws pale grey. Iris dull brown.

IN HAND CHARACTERS
Measurements

	Male	Female
Wing	80–84 (82.1; 6)	77.5–82 (79.6; 4)
Tail	69–73 (71.0; 6)	67–73 (70.0; 4)
Bill*	16.5–17.8 (17.0; 6)	16.8–18 (17.5; 4)
Tarsus	28–30 (29.5; 6)	28–28.6 (28.3; 4)

(Murphy & Mathews 1929) *exposed culmen

Tail/wing ratio: *c.* 85%
Bill to skull: (2 ♂♂) 18.6, 19.4; (1 ♀) 16.9.
Bill width: 4.8–4.9 (n = 3)
Hind claw: 8–10 (n = 3)
Tail graduation: 14–17 (n = 3)

Structure

Wing formula (n = 3):

p1/pc	p2	p3e	p4e	p5	p6	p7	p10
(2)–5	7–10	0–1.5	wp	0–3	2.5–4.5	4–7	10–12

Wing similar to Millerbird (Fig. 86) but lacks emargination on p5–6. Wing rounded but p1 minute. Wing point (p3) 4 (5); p2 = p7/8–9/10; emargination on p3–4.

Tail, bill, tarsi and general size and structure similar to Pitcairn Island Warbler.
Weight ♂ 22.5–30.5g (25.8; 21), ♀ 21–25g (22.8; 19) (Graves 1992).

GEOGRAPHIC VARIATION Not recorded.

TAXONOMY AND SYSTEMATICS Henderson Island Warbler was originally described by Ogilvie-Grant (1913) as a distinct species *Acrocephalus taiti* but Murphy & Mathews (1929) concluded, after a detailed comparison of specimens from each island, that it represented a race of Pitcairn Island Warbler. This status remained unchanged until Graves (1992) suggested that it would be better treated as a distinct species. This treatment has since been adopted by most taxonomic authorities and is widely accepted.

▲ Adult, Henderson Island, September (Michael Brooke).

RIMATARA WARBLER
Acrocephalus rimitarae   **Plate 28**

Conopoderas vaughani rimitarae **Murphy & Mathews, 1929.**
Amer. Mus. Novit., 350: 20. Rimatara, Tubuai Islands.

Endemic to the remote island of Rimatara in the central
South Pacific. Previously considered to be a race of Pitcairn
Island Warbler but now usually treated as a distinct species.
Considered VULNERABLE by BirdLife International.
Monotypic.

IDENTIFICATION Size 17cm. Wing 80–88mm. Tail/wing
c. 83%.
  A large warbler, dull mottled brown above and whitish
below, with an indistinct pale yellow supercilium. Like
the closely related Pitcairn Island and Henderson Island
Warblers, it is predisposed to leucism, with white feathering
usually apparent on the head, back and wing-coverts,
while the wings and tail typically show an asymmetrical
combination of black and white feathers. Sexes alike.
Structure This large and relatively long-legged *Acrocephalus*
shares with Pitcairn Island Warbler a long sloping forehead, rounded crown and proportionally long bill.
There is considerable overlap in size and structure with
Pitcairn Island and Henderson Island Warblers, although
measurements suggest that it appears to be, on average,
longer tailed than the former. It is, however, smaller
and proportionately shorter billed than Tahiti and the
Marquesan Warblers. The wing structure is identical to that
of Pitcairn Island Warbler, with a short first primary (p1),
the wing point formed by p4, often together with p3 and p5,
and a conspicuous emargination on p3 and p4. The wings
are relatively short, reaching only to the shortest uppertail-
coverts. Although Rimatara Warbler averages slightly larger
than Pitcairn Island Warbler, there is considerable overlap
(see **In Hand Characters**), and there are no discernible
differences in structure or posture which separate them.
Plumage and bare parts Not known to be separable from
Pitcairn Island Warbler. It is a drab *Acrocephalus* with mottled
dull olive-brown to grey-brown crown, nape and mantle,
but slightly paler and more contrasting on the rump. The
head shows a poorly defined pale yellow supercilium that
contrasts with the dark eye-stripe and slightly paler brownish
white ear-coverts. Paler tips on the greater and median
coverts create two indistinct wing-bars on the closed wing
although these can be obscured or absent if the wing-coverts
are white. The underparts are lightly washed creamy white,
becoming pale yellow on the breast and belly, although the
sides of the upper breast are dull grey-brown.
  Like Pitcairn Island Warbler, it is predisposed to leucism
(or partial albinism), with white feathering appearing
randomly on the head, back and wing-coverts. The remiges
and rectrices usually show an asymmetrical combination of
black and white feathers. The extent and variation of the
white feathering is very similar to that found in Pitcairn
Island Warbler, which renders these species inseparable
on plumage features, so and specimens can only be reliably
identified from their origin.
  The bill is dark grey with a pinkish base and grey sides
to the lower mandible. The legs and feet are dark grey.

SIMILAR SPECIES No similar species occur on Rimatara.
Not safely distinguishable from Pitcairn Island or
Henderson Island Warblers, but these species are unlikely
to come into contact.

VOICE Unlike its counterparts on Pitcairn and Henderson
Islands, Rimatara Warbler has a recognisable song. This is
described as 'a succession of low and short whistling notes'.
It is said to be less powerful and elaborate than the songs
of Tahiti or Tuamotu Warblers and is typically of shorter
duration. Unlike the songs of these species, it is not given
throughout the year and is less frequent during the day but
it can be heard on bright, moonlit nights.
  Calls are similar to those of other Polynesian *Acrocephalus*.
These include alarm and contact calls and solicitation calls
given by the female and young (Thibault & Cibois 2006).
The most frequently heard call is a loud, grating and
unmelodic '*scarp*', given singly at intervals of several seconds,
or in quick succession to form an unmusical repeated
squealing, reminiscent of a child's toy. Other calls include
a '*chack*' or high-pitched '*chirp*' but these are only given
infrequently and are probably no more than variations of
the '*scarp*' call.

MOULT Adults trapped during October and November
had heavily worn plumage and had not started to moult
(Thibault & Cibois 2006). By contrast, most of the adult
specimens taken in March and held at AMNH were
moulting the flight feathers, the remainder of the plumage
being freshly moulted. This strongly suggests that adults
have a complete moult commencing at the end of the
breeding cycle. Young birds had fresh plumage in both
March and October–November and only one was in primary
moult in each period (Thibault & Cibois 2006).

HABITAT Occurs throughout Rimatara in trees, bushes,
brushy forest, plantations, reedbeds and other marsh
vegetation, from the coast to the highest part of the
island at 83m. It appears to favour wooded areas during
the breeding season, including undergrowth in coconut
plantations, mixed horticulture, coastal forest and natural
forest on limestone (Thibault & Cibois 2006), but avoids
the proximity of habitation.

BEHAVIOUR It is known to forage by gleaning insects from
vegetation like other Polynesian *Acrocephalus*. Its behaviour
and food preferences and requirements are likely to be
similar to those of Pitcairn Island and Henderson Island
Warblers. It has been recorded searching for insects in
vegetation on or close to the ground, but also actively in
trees. During the breeding season, the song can be heard
regularly in the early morning and evening and during
bright, moonlit nights (Thibault & Cibois 2006).

BREEDING HABITS The breeding season appears well
defined and seasonal, commencing in mid September and
continuing to at least late December (Thibault & Cibois
2006). Some birds among specimens collected in March and
April 1921 were still in sexually active condition (Murphy &
Mathews 1929) but others clearly were not. Some breeding
birds form trios that share in nest activities. This behaviour,
which occurs regularly in Henderson Island Warbler but
apparently not in Pitcairn Island Warbler, appears to be
widespread and perhaps the normal breeding strategy on
Rimatara (Thibault & Cibois 2006).
  The nest is placed in a fork or among vertical branches of
a tree, typically 4–7m from the ground. It is a large and untidy
cup built from plants and various fibres, including those of
coconut palm. Recorded nesting trees, many of which are not
native to the island, include *Hibiscus tiliaceus*, *Coffea arabica*,
Polyscias guilfoylei, *Thespesia populnea*, *Syzygium jambos*, *Falcataria
moluccana* and *Citrus aurantifolia*. The clutch is 1–2 eggs. The
incubation and fledging periods are unknown.

DISTRIBUTION Endemic to the island of Rimatara (22° 40'S, 152° 45'W) in the C South Pacific, which extends to just 8.6km² and rises to a height of 83m. Rimatara Warbler was considered to be fairly common when discovered here during the Whitney South Seas Expedition in 1929 and its status remains unchanged. The population may be as high as *c.* 2,600 individuals (BirdLife International) although other estimates place it much lower, in the region of 675 individuals (Thibault & Cibois 2006), but this seems too low. Breeding territories averaged 0.72ha and the population density was estimated at 2.4 adults/hectare (Thibault & Cibois) in 2004, when it was considered to be abundant over much of the island (BirdLife International).

The Pacific Rat *Rattus exulans* and the Brown Rat *Rattus norvegicus* are both present on the island, but appear not to be major threats. Predation by feral domestic cats was seen as a problem, but their impact seems to have stabilised. The potential risk of other alien predators being accidentally introduced remains the greatest threat to this population. The Common Myna, which has decimated other Pacific *Acrocephalus* populations, has reached nearby Rurutu and Tubuai and could have a significant impact on Rimatara Warbler if it were to become established on the island.

MOVEMENTS Sedentary. There are no records away from Rimatara.

DESCRIPTION

Plumage – Adult fresh Forehead and crown ash-grey to dull olive-brown, narrowly but conspicuously tipped white. Supercilium poorly marked, restricted to an indistinct pale yellowish line from bill base to upper edge of eye but absent behind eye. Below this, a conspicuous black loral line. Eye-line fairly well marked behind eye and separating crown from ear-coverts. Ear-coverts pale ash-grey, faintly tipped cream, becoming paler and distinctly creamy towards lower edge. Eye-ring whitish, showing little contrast with supercilium and grey feathering below eye. Nape dull olive-brown, slightly darker than crown and generally lacking paler fringes. Mantle and scapulars drab olive-brown with pale ash-grey fringes creating mottled effect. Rump and uppertail-coverts with small brown centres and broad pale ash-grey fringes, so appears paler than mantle. Tail dark brown to black, in most individuals with a variable number of entirely white feathers. Chin and throat white, faintly washed light grey. Breast and belly lightly washed pale yellow, with darker grey-brown wash on sides of upper breast in front of carpal bend. Flanks on some birds washed pale brown, on others creamy white to pale yellow, showing little tonal change from breast and belly. Undertail-coverts creamy white, similar to flanks.

Wings highly variable. On those individuals lacking white feathering lesser and median coverts dark greyish brown narrowly tipped pale brownish white. Greater coverts broadly fringed and tipped brownish white. Tertials dark brown with pale brown fringing. Primary coverts dark brown and unmarked. Secondaries and primaries dark brown with narrow pale brown fringes and tips. Alula dark brown with narrow, pale brown fringe. Underwing-coverts

creamy white. Most birds show a variable extent of leucism, with white feathers appearing randomly in wing-coverts and asymmetrically among secondaries, primaries and tertials. **Juvenile** Undescribed.

Bare parts Upper mandible dark grey with pale pink cutting edge. Lower mandible pale pink at base, darkening at sides towards tip. Tarsi, toes and claws dark grey. Iris dull brown.

IN HAND CHARACTERS

Measurements

	Male	Female
Wing	81–88 (84.3; 6)	79.5–84 (82; 6)
Tail	65–76 (71.6; 6)	67.5–74 (71.1; 6)
Bill*	17.8–20 (18.6; 6)	17–19 (18.2; 6)
Tarsus	29.2–32 (30.6; 6)	29 (n = 1)

(Murphy & Mathews 1929) *exposed culmen

Slightly larger than Pitcairn Island and Henderson Island Warblers.

Mean wing length in males 84.3mm (±0.95, n = 6) and exposed culmen length 18.6mm (±0.24, n = 6) compare with 82.2mm (±0.73, n = 10) and 17.7mm (±0.19, n = 10) respectively in Pitcairn Island Warbler and 82.1mm (±0.83, n = 10) and 17.2mm (±0.21, n = 10) in Henderson Island Warbler (Holyoak & Thibault 1977).

Structure Wing similar to Millerbird (Fig. 86) but lacks emargination on p5–6.

Weight 23–29g (26.5; 10) (Dunning 2007).

GEOGRAPHIC VARIATION Recognition of this form by Murphy & Mathews (1929) as distinct from Pitcairn Island Warbler was based upon the slightly larger size, particularly wing length, when compared with that species. Otherwise, the birds inhabiting Rimatara so closely resemble Pitcairn Island Warbler that it is impossible separate them using any combination of plumage characters. Murphy & Mathews suggested a tendency for Rimatara Warbler to exhibit a greater extent of partial albinism but this is not shown by all individuals, which otherwise appear identical to Pitcairn Island Warbler.

Just why Rimatara Warbler so closely resembles Pitcairn Island Warbler, when birds on Henderson Island, which lies much closer to Pitcairn, show a greater tendency towards albinism is uncertain. Murphy & Mathews speculated that birds from Pitcairn may have been transferred to Rimatara by the Polynesian inhabitants. While impossible to prove, this would go some way to explaining their extremely similar appearance and consistent differences from Henderson Island Warbler.

TAXONOMY AND SYSTEMATICS Formerly treated as a race of Pitcairn Island Warbler. Graves (1992) found this arrangement unsatisfactory and recommended that it should be recognised as a species distinct from Pitcairn Island and Henderson Island Warblers. This treatment has since been widely adopted.

KIRITIMATI WARBLER
Acrocephalus aequinoctialis   **Plate 28**

Sylvia aequinoctialis **Latham, 1790**. *Index Ornith.*, p. 533. Christmas Island, Line Islands.

Also known by its local name, Bokikokiko, this *Acrocephalus* is endemic to the Republic of Kiribati (Line Islands) in the C Pacific, where it formerly occurred on three islands, although it is now extinct on Tabueran. Despite this, it is considered by BirdLife International to be of LEAST CONCERN. Polytypic, with two races recognised:

A. a. aequinoctialis (Latham, 1790). Kiritimati (formerly Christmas Island), northern Line Islands.

A. a. pistor Tristram, 1883. Teraina (formerly Washington Island), northern Line Islands. Now extinct on Tabueran (formerly Fanning Island).

IDENTIFICATION Length 16cm. Wing 70–83mm. Tail/wing 80–85%.

A fairly bulky warbler with largely grey and white plumage and contrastingly pale rump. The only resident passerine in Kiribati. Sexes alike.

Structure Kiritimati Warbler is a relatively large *Acrocephalus*, similar in size to Australian Reed Warbler, but with slightly shorter wings, giving the appearance of a longer tail. Shows a relatively short bill, short undertail-coverts and a rounded wing. Despite being an island resident, it retains the short first primary (p1) typical of a migrant, but the primaries are fairly closely bunched and the wing point extends only to the tips of the shorter uppertail-coverts. There is a significant size difference between the two races, with *pistor* being distinctly larger than the nominate form.

Plumage and bare parts An attractive *Acrocephalus* with a contrasting grey and white appearance. The nominate form shows a clear grey crown, nape and mantle that contrast with pale ash-grey to greyish white uppertail-coverts and an unmarked dark grey tail except for narrow white tips and fringes. There is a conspicuous white supercilium which extends from the base of the bill to the rear of the ear-coverts, although it is often washed pale grey behind the eye. The wing-coverts are dark grey with conspicuous whitish tips that form prominent wing-bars, particularly on the greater coverts, while the narrower tips to the median coverts produce a thinner wing-bar. The dark grey-centred tertials show narrow whitish fringes and the whitish edges to the flight feathers create a pale panel in the closed wing. The entire underparts are white and often unmarked, but some birds show indistinct grey mottling above the carpal bend.

The bill is dark grey with a pale pink base to the lower mandible and the legs are also dark grey.

SIMILAR SPECIES There is no other *Acrocephalus* or, indeed, any other passerine species resident in the Line Islands, so Kiritimati Warbler cannot be mistaken within its range.

VOICE The song is simple and short. It combines the species' various calls and the local name, Bokikokiko, is a descriptive onomatopoeic rendition. Milder & Schreiber (1989) describe two song types, the 'short song' and 'long' song. The 'short song' includes three and occasionally up to five, short phrases, each being a simple combination of two to three of the call notes, the second usually rising slightly in inflection. It is typically used by mated birds, given from within cover and only occasionally from taller tree-tops. The

'long song' is a combination of the short song and individual call notes, performed over a longer period, with two to ten syllables forming each song sequence. It is used only by unmated males and is typically delivered conspicuously from a tree-top. This simple song is considered to have developed due to lack of interspecific interaction, a monogamous life style and large permanent territories that limit interaction between neighbours (Milder & Schreiber 1988)

Three calls are described, a disyllabic '*cha che*', a shorter, single harsh, grating '*chaaee*' and a high-pitched '*che*' (Milder & Schreiber 1989). These are similar and perceived differences most likely reflect single or repeated calls given quickly or being more drawn out, with slight differences involving only amplitude and frequency.

MOULT Poorly known and no published data available. Birds photographed in July show extensive body, wing and tail moult. One had replaced the inner primaries, tertials, inner primary coverts and greater coverts, but still retained heavily worn unmoulted outer primaries and tail feathers.

HABITAT On Kiritimati it frequents open and rather barren habitat dominated by Beach Heliotrope *Messerschmidia argentea* and Beach Scaevola *Scaevola frutescens*. Both are used extensively for foraging and breeding, although Beach Heliotrope, which grows to a height of 8m, is the preferred tree for nesting. Some territories include human habitation.

BEHAVIOUR Kiritimati Warbler is a typically skulking *Acrocephalus* but can be bold and inquisitive, showing little concern for the close presence of human observers when feeding young. Males will often sing for 2–3 hours, interspersed with short breaks. It is believed that only unmated males sing conspicuously from tree canopy, while mated males typically sing from deep within cover. Singing birds frequently raise the crown feathering and sometimes puff out the body feathers.

When feeding, it spends considerable periods in denser lower cover, where it perches on low, dead branches and drops to the ground to snatch prey items. It is believed to feed mostly on insects. One bird was observed to catch a dragonfly Odonata, crush it on a branch and feed it to one of its chicks, while another fed its incubating mate with a small skink Scincidae (Gallagher 1960). A photograph in Schreiber (1979) shows an adult feeding the tail of a small gecko *Hemidactylus* sp. or *Lepidodactylus lugubris* to young in the nest.

BREEDING HABITS Nest building has been recorded from February to April, with young birds fledging from mid March to late May (Gallacher 1960; Schreiber 1979; Milder & Schreiber 1989). With its breeding islands lying close to the equator, nesting possibly occurs at other times of year, but King (1955) found only old nests between October and December and none with eggs or young. It is believed to be monogamous and may pair for life, and there is no evidence of the polygyny found in some Pacific island *Acrocephalus* species. Pairs occupy rather large territories: three on Kiritimati ranged in size from 1.81–2.3ha and territories of other pairs were thought to be of similar size. Outside the breeding season the young remain within natal territories even while adults are rearing the next brood (Milder & Schreiber 1989).

Nests located by Schreiber (1979) were built just below the canopy in three or four branch forks of Beach Heliotrope, the tallest and most mature trees being preferred. Nest heights ranged from 1.8–8.1m above ground, although most were located between 6–7m. The nest is a cup built onto a base, constructed mainly of grasses, but usually including macerated coconut *Cocos nucifera* fronds, bark and fibre. Nests built close to human habitation may include man-made materials such as plastic. Several simpler 'cock nests' often appear to be built in the same tree before the final nest selection is made. A clutch of 2–4 eggs is incubated by the female only, but the nestlings are fed by both parents. No information is available on the timing of incubation or the fledging period.

DISTRIBUTION Endemic to the Republic of Kiribati (Line Islands) in the C Pacific, where it has been recorded on just three atolls, Kiritimati (Christmas Island), Tabueran (Fanning Island) and Teraina (Washington Island).

A. a. aequinoctialis Endemic to the island of Kiritimati (1° 52'N, 157° 20'W) where it remains fairly common and widespread and occupies much of the suitable habitat available. The total population was estimated at 300–400 birds (Clapp & King 1975). There appear to be no significant threats to its long-term existence, although urban expansion may impact upon some territories.

A. a. pistor Discovered in 1881 on the small atoll of Tabueran (3° 51'N, 159° 22'W), 244km northwest of Kiritimati. It was still known to be present here in 1924 but was considered extinct after unsuccessful attempts were made to find it in the mid 1960s (Bakus 1967; Clapp & King 1975).

Another geographically isolated population assigned to *pistor* was found in 1921, this time on Teraina (4° 43'N, 160° 24'W), a small atoll 120km northwest of Tabueran. Despite its small size, just 1,000ha, there is believed to be a substantial population here, in fact larger than that on Kiritimati. Clapp & King (1975) estimated several hundred birds present during 1964–67.

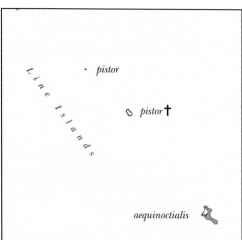

Kiritimati Warbler. Resident within breeding range.

MOVEMENTS Sedentary and no inter-island movements recorded.

DESCRIPTION *A. a. aequinoctialis*
Plumage – Adult fresh Forehead and crown pale grey with indistinct, narrow whitish fringes. Supercilium white, tinged grey and quite well demarcated in front of and over eye, becoming less obvious behind eye, where greyer and

narrowing towards rear of ear-coverts. Usually a faint black spot immediately in front of eye but loral line otherwise poorly defined. Eye-line restricted to inconspicuous dark spot immediately behind eye. Ear-coverts ash-grey at rear and upper edges with faint whitish fringes, merging with nape but contrasting with paler supercilium. Cheeks white with faint greyish wash. Narrow eye-ring white, contrasting only slightly with grey feathering below eye. Nape pale grey with indistinct whitish tips. Mantle and scapulars ash-grey, slightly darker than nape and narrowly fringed pale grey. Rump and uppertail-coverts distinctly paler than mantle, fading from ash-grey on upper rump to whitish grey on longest uppertail-coverts, often with slightly darker grey mottling. Tail feathers black with narrow white fringes and tips.

Chin and throat white, faintly washed grey, especially towards cheeks. Breast and belly white, breast usually with faint grey mottling, most noticeable above carpal bend. Flanks white and unmarked, sometimes with faint greyish wash on lower flanks. Undertail-coverts white to creamy white. Lesser and median coverts dark grey with narrow pale grey fringes. Greater coverts charcoal-grey with prominent whitish fringes, broadest on inner coverts and narrower towards outer edge of wing. Tertials charcoal-grey with narrow fringes, darker and less conspicuous than those on greater coverts. Primary coverts, secondaries and primaries black with narrow, whitish edges and tips. Alula black with narrow, crisp white fringe.

Juvenile Not described.

Bare Parts Upper mandible dark grey with pale pink cutting edge and whitish tip. Lower mandible dull pink at base, darkening at sides towards tip, but with tip itself whitish. Tarsi, toes and claws lead grey. Iris dull brown.

IN HAND CHARACTERS
Measurements

A. a. aequinoctialis

	Male	Female
Wing	70–76 (73.4; 11)	70–72 (71.3; 6)
Tail	57–64 (61.2; 11)	57–61 (58.4; 6)
Bill*	15.0–16.6 (15.8; 11)	15.0–15.8 (15.3; 6)
Tarsus	23–24.8 (24.0; 11)	23–24 (23.5; 6)

(Murphy & Mathews 1929) *exposed culmen

Sexes combined:
Tail/wing ratio: 80–85%
Bill to skull (n = 2): 20.5, 21.6
Bill width (n = 2): 4.0, 4.2
Hind claw (n = 3): 8.1–8.4
Tail graduation: 5–9

A. a. pistor

	Male	Female	Location
Wing	74–83 (8)	74–77 (5)	Teraina (Clapp & King 1975)
Wing	82, 79 (2)	77 (1)	Tabueran (Murphy & Mathews, 1929)
Tail	66, 69 (2)	61 (1)	
Bill*	17.8, 18.0 (2)	17.5 (1)	
Tarsus	28, 29 (2	29 (1)	

Also (mean values; Holyoak & Thibault 1984):

A. a. aequinoctialis Kiritimati: *wing*, ♂ 73.3 (16), ♀ 70.9 (11); *bill* (to nostril), ♂ 10.9 (16), ♀ 10.9 (11).

A. a. pistor Teraina: *wing*, ♂ 80.2 (8), ♀ 75.4 (5); *bill* (to nostril), ♂ 12.7 (6), ♀ 12.2 (4).

A. a. pistor Tabueran: *wing*, ♂ 79.5 (6), ♀ 70.9 (2).

Race *pistor* is substantially larger than nominate race, with a larger bill. Birds from Teraina and Tabueran do not differ significantly.

Structure

Wing formula (2 nominate *aequinoctialis*, 1 *pistor*):

p1/pc	p2	p3(e)	p4(e)	p5	p6	p7	p10
(2)–3	3–5	1	wp	0–2	1–5	3–7	10–12

Wing similar to the Marquesan Warblers (Fig. 87) but emargination on p3–4 less well defined. Wing rounded, but p1 minute. Wing point p4(5); p2 = p7–7/8; indistinct emargination on p3–4.

Tail medium length, rounded.

Bill medium length, proportions as in Australian Reed Warbler.

Weight 2 ♂♂, 25g (Dunning 2007).

GEOGRAPHIC VARIATION Two similar races differ slightly in size.

A. a. aequinoctialis (Kiritimati) Described above.

A. a. pistor (Teraina and formerly Tabueran where now extinct) Although this race is significantly larger than the nominate form, it is otherwise very similar. The main plumage difference lies in the colour of the underparts and supercilium, which are light grey rather than white. The upperparts of birds in fresh plumage from Tabueran were said to show broad white fringes, giving it the appearance of being dusted with flour, from which its derives its scientific name *pistor*, the Latin for a Roman baker. When worn, these fringes are believed wear to ash-grey, giving it an appearance similar to that of the nominate form. Birds from Teraina are not known to show these whitish fringes and more closely resemble the nominate form.

TAXONOMY AND SYSTEMATICS A study of relationships in the Polynesian *Acrocephalus* warblers by Cibois *et al.* (2007) established that Kiritimati Warbler is a sister taxon to the southern lineage of Marquesan Warbler. They also found that this clade also includes Australian Reed Warbler, suggesting that an ancestral *Acrocephalus* may have colonised this region from the Australasian region.

When the first male was collected on Teraina, Murphy & Mathews (1929) considered it intermediate in size between the nominate race and *pistor* on Tabueran. But with larger series available, Clapp & King (1975) concluded that birds on Teraina were identical in size and plumage. Clements (2000), Dickinson (2003) and Dyrcz (2006) included the Teraina population within *pistor*, and with the Tabueran now extinct there are no additional data to contradict this treatment.

▲ Adult *A. a. aequinoctialis*, Kiritimati, Republic of Kiribati, June. When fresh shows clean, cold-grey appearance and conspicuous white fringes and tips to primaries, secondaries, tertials and rectrices (Eric VanderWerf).

▲ Adult *A. a. aequinoctialis*, Kiritimati, Republic of Kiribati, June. Worn birds appear duller and drabber, and the striking white feather-fringes and tips are largely lost (Eric VanderWerf).

SOUTHERN MARQUESAN WARBLER
Acrocephalus mendanae   Plate 29

Acrocephalus mendanae Tristram, 1883. *Ibis*, p. 43, pl. 1. Hiva Oa, Marquesas Islands.

NORTHERN MARQUESAN WARBLER
Acrocephalus percernis   Plate 29

Conopoderas percernis Wetmore, 1919. *Bull. Mus. Comp. Zool.* 63: 213. Nuku Hiva, Marquesas Islands.

These two large *Acrocephalus* warblers are endemic to the Marquesas Archipelago in the C Pacific, where they occupy mutually exclusive island distributions. Until recently they were treated together as a single species, Marquesan Warbler *A. mendanae*, but recent mtDNA studies by Cibois *et al.* (2007) have established that Marquesan Warbler (*sensu lato*) is formed from two distinct lineages, and showed them to have very different origins. They recommended these be treated as two distinct polytypic species; Southern Marquesan Warbler *A. mendanae* and Northern Marquesan Warbler *A. percernis*, each with four races. Although minor differences in plumage and morphology exist between the various taxa, it has not yet been possible to establish whether there are any consistent characters that may enable the two species to be separated in the field or in the hand. Until this is established, identification will rely on distribution alone.

They are, therefore, most appropriately treated here within a single account. Where possible, we have attempted to give information relating to individual taxa. Differences in song (see **Voice**) or behaviour may provide clues to the separation of the two species, but these have not yet been studied in detail. See also **Taxonomy and Systematics**.

Southern Marquesan Warbler
A. m. mendanae Tristram 1983. Hiva Oa and Tahuata.
A. m. dido (Murphy & Mathews 1928). Ua Pou.
A. m. consobrina (Murphy & Mathews 1928). Mohotani.
A. m. fatuhivae (Murphy & Mathews 1928). Fatuhiva.

Northern Marquesan Warbler
A. p. percernis (Wetmore 1919). Nuku Hiva.
A. p. postremus (Murphy & Mathews 1928). Hatutaa.
A. p. aquilonis (Murphy & Mathews 1928). Eiao.
A. p. idae (Murphy & Mathews 1928). Ua Huka.

IDENTIFICATION
Southern Marquesan Warbler: Length 20–22cm. Wing 88–102mm. Tail/wing *c.* 84%.
Northern Marquesan Warbler: Length 20–22cm. Wing 85–103mm. Tail/wing *c.* 85%.

Two large, distinctive and almost identical *Acrocephalus*, combining a bulky structure and proportionately long bill, together with a combination of greenish upperparts, yellowish underparts and a yellow-tipped tail.
Structure Similar in size and structure to Tahiti Warbler. All taxa share a similar deep-breasted, thick-necked structure, with a relatively long tail, and short wings that do not reach the tips of the longest uppertail-coverts. The bill is long and strong, but appears slightly shorter and finer than that of Tahiti Warbler, with the upper mandible less distinctly decurved. The forehead is long and sloping and, together with the long bill, creates an attenuated appearance to the

head. This is transformed when the fore-crown feathering is raised, giving an angular appearance to the crown, and peaking just behind the eye. Nevertheless, the head remains less angular than in Tahiti Warbler. The wing is short and rounded with a short primary projection. The first primary (p1) usually falls short of the primary covert tips and the wing point is always formed by p4, with p3 and p5 sometimes being of equal length.

Plumage and bare parts The distinctive green and yellow plumage gives it a striking appearance, shared only with some Tahiti Warblers. The head is particularly distinctive, with the yellowish supercilium, ear-coverts and sides to the neck contrasting with the darker green crown, nape and eye-stripe. The upperparts including crown, nape, mantle and scapulars are dull olive-green diffusing into broad yellowish green fringes, while the distinctly yellow to yellowish buff rump and uppertail-coverts are particularly conspicuous during the song-flight. The tail is distinctive and quite unlike that of any other Pacific *Acrocephalus*, and most apparent when spread during the aerial display flight. The outermost feather (t6) is unmarked lemon yellow while the next (t5) has a yellow inner web. The remainder (t1–t4) are blackish but tipped bright yellow.

The underparts are yellow, the intensity varying between different races; some show a deep, rich burnt-yellow wash, while in others it is much paler yellow and tends toward yellowish white on the belly. For example, Southern Marquesan Warbler on Hiva Oa and Tahuata are paler than most forms, the lower breast and belly often appearing straw-yellow. Some of these paler individuals can approach a richly coloured Tahiti Warbler in appearance.

The closed wing appears bold and contrasting. There are two conspicuous wing-bars formed by the yellow tips of the greater and median coverts. The tertials show contrasting blackish centres and conspicuous pale yellow fringes which further enhance the contrast. There are also pale yellow edges to the secondaries which create a pale panel in the closed wing. Contrast in the wing is further enhanced by the blackish primaries which lack yellow edges, but which have obvious whitish tips.

The bill is dark bluish grey above and salmon-pink below. The legs are grey.

SIMILAR SPECIES No potential confusion species occur within the Marquesas Archipelago. They do, however, closely resemble Tahiti Warbler and their separation is discussed here.
Tahiti Warbler of the Society Islands will almost certainly never occur alongside either Marquesan Warbler so there should be no risk of confusion, despite their superficial similarity. All are large and long-billed *Acrocephalus*, appearing green above, yellow below and with two conspicuous yellow wing-bars on each wing. They are most readily separated by the patterns of the tail, rump and uppertail-coverts. In flight, the upperparts of the Marquesan Warblers appear contrasting green/black/yellow, with the tail being largely black with a yellow band across the tip, which is particularly conspicuous when the tail is spread during the parachuting song-flight. By contrast, the tail of Tahiti Warbler is entirely brown with, at best, indistinct buffy white tips to the rectrices. Furthermore, it does not appear to have a similar display flight.

The nominate race of Northern Marquesan Warbler has a deep yellow wash to the underparts and is quite unlike Tahiti Warbler, but Southern Marquesan Warbler can show a diluted yellow wash and resemble Tahiti Warbler more closely in overall plumage colour and tone. Perhaps because the underwing is visible during the parachute descent in the song-flight, the entire underwing, apart from the outer primaries, appears bright lemon-yellow, whereas in Tahiti Warbler it is buffy white with only the axillaries yellow.

VOICE The simple song consists of a random sequence of harsh '*churrs*' and '*tsharks*'. There appear to be small and subtle differences between the various taxa, although the extent of individual variation needs to be better understood before it can be established whether birds occupying each island race have a unique song. Southern Marquesan Warbler on Mohotani (*A. m. consobrina*) has a simple combination of harsh whistles, churrs, warbles and rasping scolds within a frequency range of 1–4kHz, similar to the song of Tahiti Warbler but less varied. Each sequence is brief, lasting up to seven seconds, separated by pauses of similar length. The song of birds on Uapo (*A. m. dido*) is similar to *A. m. consobrina* but with a slower tempo. Northern Marquesan Warbler on Ua Huka (*A. p. idae*) has a still slower song, comprising occasional harsh '*churrs*' that resemble the call, which then run into short fluid sequences lasting for one or two seconds. Finally, Northern Marquesan Warbler on Nuku Hiva (*A. p. percernis*) gives a loud series of rasping '*churrs*' interspersed with short fluty oriole-like phases, with much repetition. Song sequences on Nuku Hiva are longer than on other islands, lasting up to ten seconds with rather shorter breaks between sequences.

Southern Marquesan Warbler:

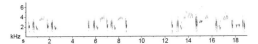

Song of Southern Marquesan Warbler recorded within breeding range of *A. m. consobrina*, Mohotani, Marquesas Archipelago, November. (McPherson 1998)

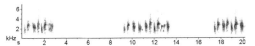

Song of Southern Marquesan Warbler recorded within breeding range of *A. m. dido*, Ua Pou, Marquesas Archipelago, October. (McPherson 1998)

Northern Marquesan Warbler:

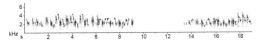

Song of Northern Marquesan Warbler recorded within breeding range of *A. p. percernis*, Nuku Hiva, Marquesas Archipelago, October. (McPherson 1998)

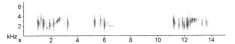

Song of Northern Marquesan Warbler recorded within breeding range of *A. p. idae*, Ua Huka, Marquesas Archipelago, November. (McPherson 1998)

The call is a single hard '*tsack*', as in Tahiti Warbler.

MOULT Recorded in January, April and August to November (Holyoak & Thibault 1984) and can perhaps occur at any time of year. Moult appears to be completed rapidly, with up to four primaries growing simultaneously on each wing. Some birds suspend primary moult when breeding.

HABITAT Highly adaptable, occurring in a wide variety of habitats, including scrub-covered hillsides, villages, gardens, coconut palm plantations, coastal scrub, secondary forest and montane forest up to at least 1,200m. On islands where they occur alongside one of the three endemic monarch *Pomerea* species, the monarchs frequent wetter areas with luxuriant vegetation, while Marquesan Warbler (*sensu lato*) prefer drier low-lying areas with xerophytic vegetation (Holyoak & Thibault 1984).

BEHAVIOUR Foraging behaviour and diet are not known to differ from those of Tahiti Warbler. They feed at all heights in trees and shrubs, primarily on insects, but will also take small lizards, small fruits and nectar. Song, courtship and display do, however, differ from Tahiti Warbler. Song can be heard throughout the day and often during the night (Holyoak & Thibault 1984), both from within deep cover or when the bird is in full view at the top of a tree or bush. Northern Marquesan Warbler on Nuku Hiva frequently perform a distinctive song-flight and territorial display, during which they fly to *c.* 20m above the tree canopy, often lower, and then parachute down in a long slow glide, still singing, with the tail spread and wings shivered, to land near the top of a prominent tree or bush, often still singing. It is not known whether Southern Marquesan Warbler has a similar display.

BREEDING HABITS There appears to be no clearly defined season. Birds in breeding condition have been recorded in January, May and August to December. Nestlings and recently fledged young have been collected from April to June and September to November (Holyoak & Thibault 1984). Nests are built in the upper part of a tree, usually 3–12m above the ground and supported in a fork. They have been recorded in many of the commoner trees of the archipelago including *Eugenia rariflora*, *Pandanus* sp., *Cordia lutea*, *Metrocideros collina* and *Ficus prolixa*. The nest is a large and untidy construction with a deep cup, constructed from leaves, coconut fibres, bark, moss and rootlets and lined with dry plants, small fibres and leaves. Materials such as cotton, wool, hair and feathers may be included if available. The clutch is 2–5 eggs, typically four (Bruner 1974). Both adults feed the young in the nest and for some time after fledging. No information is available on incubation and fledging periods.

DISTRIBUTION Endemic to the Marquesas Islands in the C Pacific, where the two species, comprising eight taxa, occur between nine islands throughout the archipelago. They are common on five of the six major islands but less numerous on Hiva Oa. Populations on the smaller islands of Eiao and Hatutaa are considered to be endangered. As recommended by Cibois *et al.* 2007, the distributions for Southern Marquesan and Northern Marquesan Warblers have been adopted here and the eight taxa are grouped within the respective lineages proposed. Status on the different islands was assessed during visits between 1971 and 1975 (Holyoak & Thibault 1984).

Southern Marquesan Warbler:

A. m. mendanae Restricted to two neighbouring islands, Hiva

Oa (9° 46'S, 138° 47'W) and Tahuata (9° 55'S, 139° 6'W). Still abundant on Tahuata but is less common on Hiva Oa, possibly due to the introduction of Common Myna.

A. m. dido Endemic to Ua Pou (Ua Pu), (9° 24'S, 140° 5'W). Widespread and abundant here during 1971–75.

A. m. consobrina Endemic to Mohotani (Motane Island), (10° 00'S, 138° 56'W). Described as being abundant when discovered by the Whitney Expedition in 1922, but by 1975 the population had fallen to 90–110 pairs, distributed throughout the island. Its current status is unknown but is probably endangered.

A. m. fatuhivae Endemic to Fatuhiva (Fatu Hiva), (10° 24'S, 149° 50'W) where it was common and widespread throughout the island in 1975.

Northern Marquesan Warbler:

A. p. percernis Endemic to Nuku Hiva (8° 57'S, 140° 15'W) where it is common throughout the island and occurs at a high density, particularly in the *Metrocideros collina* forest on the Toovii Plateau.

A. p. postremus Endemic to Hatutaa (Hatutu), (7° 56'S, 140° 38'W) where it is rare. It was discovered during the Whitney expedition in 1922 and considered rare even then. The population was estimated by Holyoak & Thibault (1984) to be in the region of 30–50 pairs, with birds restricted to a few thickets. Its current status is unknown.

A. p. aquilonis Endemic to Eiao (8° 2'S, 140° 41'W), where it is believed to be endangered or possibly extinct. It was apparently already scarce when it was discovered in 1922, but a remnant population was present in secondary scrub on the central plateau in the early 1970s. No recent information.

A. p. idae Endemic to Ua Huka (Huahuna), (8° 55'S, 139° 34'W), where it was described as abundant during 1971–75.

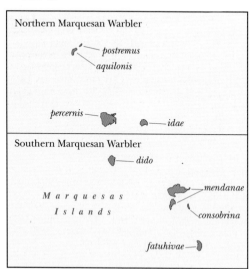

Northern Marquesan Warbler

postremus
aquilonis

percernis — *idae*

Southern Marquesan Warbler

dido

M a r q u e s a s
I s l a n d s

mendanae

consobrina

fatuhivae

Southern Marquesan Warbler and Northern Marquesan Warbler. Resident within breeding range.

MOVEMENTS All forms are believed to be sedentary. No movements have been recorded between any of the Marquesas islands.

DESCRIPTION Southern Marquesan Warbler *A. m. mendanae*

Plumage – Adult fresh Forehead and crown unmarked, dull olive-green. Supercilium bright yellow, broad and extending from base of bill to rear of ear-coverts. Dark olive-green loral spot, not extending to base of bill. Eyeline dull olive-green, extending to rear of ear-coverts, widening and merging into nape. Ear-coverts yellow and unmarked. No eye-ring. Nape and mantle dull olive-green, similar to crown, but lower mantle and scapulars indistinctly fringed olive-yellow. Rump and uppertail-coverts pale brown with broad yellow to yellowish buff fringes. Outer rectrices (t6) yellow; the rest blackish, although t5 with yellow inner web and all broadly tipped yellow or occasionally with dull creamy white tips. Chin and throat bright yellow, merging with ear-coverts. Breast and flanks to undertail-coverts straw-yellow, often whitish on belly. Lesser and median coverts dark grey with narrow yellow fringes. Greater coverts and tertials dark slate-grey with narrow, dull ochre fringes and tips. Primary coverts, secondaries and primaries dark slate-grey, narrowly edged and tipped dull ochre. Alula black with narrow ochre fringe. Underwing-coverts and axillaries pale to bright yellow.

Adult worn Resembles fresh adult. The upperparts appear drabber and browner as plumage wears and pale fringes to upperparts are lost.

Juvenile/immature Very similar to adult but slightly paler overall. Differs in having top of head and upperparts dull olive-green and yellow of supercilium, ear-coverts, chin and throat paler and colder. Tail feather markings and fringes to wing-coverts and tertials whitish. Edges and tips of flight feathers yellowish white.

Bare parts Upper mandible dark bluish grey above. Lower mandible salmon-pink. Legs grey.

IN HAND CHARACTERS
Measurements

Southern Marquesan Warbler:

A. m. mendanae

	Male	Female
Wing	97–102 (99.4; 20)	94–102 (97.0; 10)
Tail	79–85 (82.5; 20)	77–92 (79.6; 10)
Bill*	23–24.8 (23,8; 10)	23–24.6 (23.8; 10)
Tarsus	31.3–33 (32.1; 10)	30–33 (31.0; 10)

(Murphy & Mathews 1928) * exposed culmen

Sexes combined:
Tail/wing ratio: 79–86% (84%; 5)
Bill to skull: 28–33 (31.7; 7)
Bill width: 5.5–6.4 (5.8; 7)
Hind claw: 11.5–12.3 (11.8; 7)
Tail graduation: 14–17 (16.0; 3)

Other races (sexes combined, after Murphy & Mathews 1928)

A. m. dido: *wing* 88–96 (92.9; 15); *tail* 73–82 9 (77.6; 10); *bill** 20.5–22.5 (21.5; 10); *tarsus* 28–31 (29.7; 10).

A. m. consobrina: *wing* 92–99 (96.2; 15); *tail* 78–84 (80.6; 15); *bill** 20.5–22.5 (21.5; 10); *tarsus* 29.5–31.5 (30.9; 10).

A. m. fatuhivae: *wing* 93–101 (97.1; 15); *tail* 79–89 (82.8; 15); *bill** 23.5–26 (25.2; 10); *tarsus* 31–34 (32.6; 10).

Northern Marquesan Warbler:

A. p. percernis

	Male	Female
Wing	98–103 (100.6; 10)	95–102 (98; 5)
Tail	81–87 (85; 10)	79–86 (82.1; 5)
Bill*	22–24 (23; 5)	23–24.2 (23.5; 5)
Tarsus	31.5–32.6 (31.9; 5)	31–33 (31.8; 5)

(Murphy & Mathews 1928) * exposed culmen

Sexes combined:
Bill (to skull): 28–32 (30.5; 8)
Tail/wing ratio: 80–88% (84%; 8)
Bill width: 5.7–6.2 (5.9; 7)
Hind claw: 11.0–12.2 (11.7; 8)
Tail graduation: 13–18 (15.8; 5)

Other races (sexes combined, after Murphy & Mathews 1928)
A. p. postremus: *wing* 86–95 (90.0; 15); *tail* 71–81 (76.3; 15); *bill** 18.5–20 (20.1; 10); *tarsus* 28.5–30.5 (30.1; 10).
A. p. aquilonis: *wing* 88–98 (93.0; 15); *tail* 74–84 (79.8; 15); *bill** 19–20.5 (20.0; 10); *tarsus* 29–31.5 (30.4; 10).
A. p. idae: *wing* 85–93 (89.0; 15); *tail* 73–82 (76.4; 15); *bill** 18–19.5 (18.8; 10).

The largest taxa are thus *mendanae* and *fatuhivae* within Southern Marquesan Warbler, and *percernis* from Northern Marquesan Warbler. Southern Marquesan of the races *consobrina* and *dido*, and Northern Marquesan of the race *aquilonis*, are slightly smaller; and Northern Marquesan of the races *idae* and *postremus* considerably smaller. Wing and tail average *c.* 2% longer in males than females in all races.

Structure

Southern Marquesan Warbler

Wing formula (races *mendanae* and *fatuhivae* combined, n = 7):

p1/pc	p2	p3e	p4e	p5(e)	p6	p7	p10
(3)–3	6–10	0–1.5	wp	0–1	2–4	4–7	12–16

Wing rounded but p1 minute. Wing point p(3) 4 (5); p2 = p7/8–8/9; emargination on p3–4, often slight on p5.

Figure 87. Wing of Southern Marquesan Warbler *A. m. mendanae*.

Tail medium length, graduated, feathers rounded.
Bill very long, deep and broad-based, slightly concave-sided. Tip of upper mandible decurved (Fig. 41).
Tarsi robust, much stronger than in race *brunnescens* of Clamorous Reed Warbler. Claws very large and strong.
There are no evident structural differences between the two Marquesan Warbler species.
Smaller taxa resemble larger ones in proportions and structure.
Weight No data available.

GEOGRAPHIC VARIATION Eight taxa are recognised here within two species, all extremely similar, differing primarily in the tone of the yellow on the underparts. All are compared against the nominate form of Southern Marquesan Warbler.

Southern Marquesan Warbler:
A. m. mendanae (Hiva Oa and Tahuata) Described above.
A. m. dido (Ua Pou) Smaller than *mendanae* and *percernis*, but marginally larger than *idae*, with a distinctly larger bill. The brightest race, the yellow being particularly intense on the supercilium, ear-coverts and entire underparts, with the chin and throat appearing a rich, burnt yellow. Slightly greener above than *mendanae* with less contrasting fringes. The fringes to the wing-coverts and remiges are narrow, olive-yellow and less contrasting than in nominate *mendanae*, so the closed wing appears plainer.
A. m. consobrina (Mohotani) A poorly differentiated form that most closely resembles nominate *mendanae* of Hiva Oa and Tahuata, to which Mohotani is geographically close. On average, slightly smaller than *mendanae* with a distinctly shorter bill. The yellow wash on the upperparts and underparts is slightly more intense and yellowish fringes on mantle are marginally broader.
A. m. fatuhivae (Fatu Hiva) Similar in structure to *mendanae* and *percernis*, but with distinctly longer bill. The yellow tone to the supercilium, ear-coverts and underparts is closest to *percernis*, but it differs from both in having the rump and uppertail-coverts straw-yellow to bright warm buff, which merges with the flanks and undertail-coverts of similar colour. Crown, nape and mantle paler, brighter green when fresh, lacking the olive tones typical of *A. m. mendanae* and *A. p. percernis*. The fringes to the upperpart feathers are usually yellow, sometimes paler, giving a more frosted appearance than is typical in nominate *mendanae*. The fringes to the greater coverts and tertials are broader and more conspicuous. Edges and tips of the primaries and secondaries white.

Northern Marquesan Warbler:
A. p. percernis (Nuku Hiva) Size and structure as *A. m. mendanae*. Differs in having a rich citrine-yellow wash on the supercilium, ear-coverts and sides of neck, throat and breast, becoming less intense on flanks, belly and undertail-coverts, but always richer than the straw-yellow underparts of *A. m. mendanae*. Upperparts slightly greener, with brighter yellowish fringes.
A. p. postremus (Hatutaa) Similar to *aquilonis* on nearby Eiao, in size, structure and plumage, but the upperparts are slightly more olive or greyish green, less yellowish.
A. p. aquilonis (Eiao) Structure closely resembles *A. m. dido* but the bill is slightly smaller. Plumage is also similar to *dido* but is slightly darker above and the underparts are slightly paler, less intense yellow.
A. p. idae (Huahuna) The smallest race, with a short, slender

bill. The wing, bill and tarsus fall below the minima recorded for *A. m. mendanae* and *A. p. percernis*. Crown to mantle slightly paler than in *A. m mendanae*, and fringes to the greater coverts and tertials slightly broader and warmer yellow.

TAXONOMY AND SYSTEMATICS Although originally described as a distinct species by Tristram in 1883, Marquesan Warbler (*sensu lato*) has often been treated as a race of Tahiti Warbler (e.g. by Holyoak & Thibault 1984), together with Tuamotu Warbler. But recognition of its distinctive song and display flight and nesting behaviour, along with stable morphological differences led recent authors (e.g. Drycz 2006) to regard it as a distinct species. However, a recent investigation by Cibois *et al.* (2007), using mtDNA markers to develop a phylogeny of the *Acrocephalus* of eastern Polynesia, produced unexpected results. They found that Marquesan Warbler (*sensu lato*) is polyphyletic with two independent lineages, which are not each others' closest relatives and must, therefore, be treated as distinct species. The northern lineage, which they name *A. percernis* includes four races; *A. p. percernis, A. p. postremus, A. p. aquilonis* and *A. p. idae,* and is closely related to Tuamotu Warbler and Tahiti Warbler. The southern lineage, retained within *A. mendanae*, also has four races; *A. m. mendanae, A. m. dido, A. m. consobrina* and *A. m. fatuhivae*, and is a sister taxon to Kiritimati Warbler, a species endemic to two atolls in the Republic of Kiribati. Analyses of morphological characters established that all eight taxa exhibit a high degree of convergence in size, structure and plumage. The recommendations of Cibois *et al.* have been adopted here but, for clarity, we have treated the two species within a single account.

▲ ▶ Adult *A. p. idae,* Ua Huka, Marquesas Islands, French Polynesia, September (Pete Morris).

TAHITI WARBLER
Acrocephalus caffer   Plate 29

Sitta caffra **Sparrman, 1786**. *Mus. Carlsonianum,* fasc.1, No. 4, pl. 4. Tahiti, Society Islands.

Endemic to the Society Islands in the C Pacific, where it is now restricted to the mountains of interior Tahiti, although it was formerly more widespread. It is thought to be rare and probably still in decline and considered to be ENDANGERED by BirdLife International. Polytypic, with one extant and three extinct races recognised:

A. c. caffer (Sparrman 1786). Tahiti, Windward Group of Society Islands.

A. c. longirostris (Gmelin, 1789). Mo'orea, Windward Group of Society Islands. EXTINCT

A. c. musae (Forster, 1844). Raiatea, Leeward Group of Society Islands. EXTINCT

A. c. garretti Holyoak & Thibault, 1978. Huahine, Leeward Group of Society Islands. EXTINCT

IDENTIFICATION Length 20–22cm. Wing 92–100mm. Tail/wing 81–87%. (nominate race)

A large, heavy and long-billed warbler that occurs in two colour morphs. The typical morph is distinctly primrose-yellow in appearance while a dark morph appears blackish in the field. Sexes alike.

Structure One of the largest of all *Acrocephalus* with a characteristically deep-breasted and thick-necked appearance. The bill is strong and heavy and proportionately longer than most other *Acrocephalus*, with a distinctly decurved tip. When combined with the sloping forehead that peaks behind the eye, this gives the head a distinctive spiky and attenuated appearance. The wings are quite short and rounded, reaching only to the base of the tail, the wing point being formed by the fourth primary (p4), with p3 and p5 often of similar length. As in other Pacific *Acrocephalus*, the first primary (p1) is very short and, at best, extends just beyond the primary coverts. There is an emargination on the third primary and often indistinctly on p4. The legs and claws are large and strong.

Plumage and bare parts Adults of the typical morph show a pale creamy white to primrose-yellow wash to the supercilium, sides of the head and neck and also the entire underparts. The upperparts and wing-coverts are rather dark greyish brown to olive-brown with conspicuous and contrasting pale creamy white to primrose-yellow feather fringes. These fringes are narrow and less obvious on crown and nape, but increasingly broad from the mantle towards the uppertail-coverts, which can appear almost entirely pale when fresh. As these fringes abrade, the upperparts and especially the crown, become increasingly dark. The tail and flight feathers are edged creamy white to deep straw, but darker brown webs are often visible and contrast with the paler body plumage. The overall appearance is often of a large, pale warbler and frequently, from below, only the pale yellowish underparts will be visible.

Young birds resemble adults but are distinctly darker, with a sulphur-yellow wash to the supercilium, sides of the head and neck and underparts, particularly on the sides of the breast. The entire upperparts are dull olive-green and fringes are inconspicuous. In the closed wing, the greater coverts often show pale tips, forming an indistinct wing-bar. The fringes to the flight feathers are slightly paler than the mantle and form a contrasting panel in the wing. The tail is dark and although the fringes are dull olive, these show little contrast with the webs except towards the tips.

The bill is dark grey with an unmarked, entirely pinkish lower mandible. The legs and feet are plumbeous-grey.

Adults of the dark morph appear blackish with a slight brownish or sooty cast. The mantle, scapulars, wing-coverts, tertials, flight feathers and tail are smoky-black and entirely unmarked. The head and underparts appear similar in the field, but under ideal viewing conditions can show a slight brownish or olive wash. In this morph, the bill and legs are entirely black.

SIMILAR SPECIES No other warbler occurs on Tahiti, and confusion with other species is very unlikely. Only the entirely black male Tahiti Monarch remotely resembles the dark morph of Tahiti Warbler, but this is a much smaller bird with a very different structure and behaviour. For distinction from the Marquesan Warblers, see **Similar Species** under that species.

VOICE The song has fairly slow tempo and laboured delivery, comprising a varied series of harsh churrs and warbles, interspersed with loud whistles within a frequency range of 1–4kHz. In structure and composition, it recalls the song of Song Thrush, with varied repetitive sequences interspersed with short pauses; '*whiteewoo-whiteewoo-wheeo, kaark, gaaark, gaaark, gaaark, whiteewoo-whiteweewoo-weeo-weeo*'. A similar song was described by Holyoak & Thibault (1984) as '*shroo-shroo-shroo-whiteeoo-whiteeoo-wheeo, shroo-shroo-peewee-peewee-whet-shroo-shroo-peeoo shroo-shroo...*'. On Mo'orea, the song was said to have resembled that of the birds on Tahiti (Holyoak & Thibault 1984).

Song of Tahiti Warbler recorded within breeding range of *A. c. caffer*, Tahiti, September. (McPherson 1998)

The call is a frequently repeated harsh '*gaark*', '*shroo*' or '*rroo*', which can often be quietly heard just prior to the song sequence.

MOULT Moulting birds have been recorded in January, April and August to November. Very few birds are in moult and also sexually active, although some suspend moult while breeding (Holyoak & Thibault 1984). The flight feathers appear to be replaced rather quickly, with two to four primaries per wing growing simultaneously, but the moult duration is unknown.

HABITAT Occupies the lower slopes and steep-sided valleys on the eastern flank of Tahiti, ranging from sea level up to 1,700m, although Holyoak & Thibault (1984) encountered it most frequently between 50–700m. Due to habitat loss during the twentieth century, its range is believed to have contracted and it is now restricted to forest with bamboo groves, generally below 600m. It typically inhabits thick secondary forest with stands of Polynesian Bamboo *Schizostachyum glaucifolium* up to 25m in height and is often found close to small rivers and streams. Some birds formerly occurred in groves of *Hibiscus tiliaceus* and Coconut Palms *Coco nucifera* in the Tairei Valley.

Birds on Mo'orea formerly occurred in secondary forest between 300–600m.

BEHAVIOUR Tahiti Warbler is a rather shy and skulking *Acrocephalus* that often reveals its presence by frequent calling. Individual birds forage slowly through trees and bamboo; after landing on lower branches they search the trunk and leaves as they hop up towards the canopy; they then descend onto the next tree (Holyoak & Thibault 1984). They also pick up food items while hopping on the ground and occasionally catch prey in flight. The diet consists mainly of arthropods, but may include small molluscs, crayfish and small lizards and occasionally vegetable matter such as seeds, fruits and nectar. Bruner (1974) mentioned that lizards are dismembered while being held with one foot.

It appears to be highly territorial throughout the year. Singing males respond vigorously to songs of other males and pursue intruders aggressively within their territory. The song is given from a prominent perch, with the crown feathers raised and the wings held slightly open and away from the body, in the manner of a Great Reed Warbler. Males occasionally sing in flight, during territorial displays (Holyoak & Thibault 1984). The song can be heard at any time of day but is performed more or less continuously during the early morning and evening.

BREEDING HABITS Breeding is believed to occur during two periods, a peak season falling between August and December, followed by a secondary season from February to June (Holyoak & Thibault 1984). On Tahiti, most nests are built in *Hibiscus* stands or bamboo thickets, typically up to 15m above the ground. The nest is a large and untidy cup-shaped structure, much larger than a typical *Acrocephalus* nest and constructed from grasses, stems, roots and moss. No information is available on clutch size, incubation and fledging periods.

DISTRIBUTION Endemic to the Society Islands in the C Pacific, where it was formerly present on at least four islands but is now restricted to Tahiti. The population is small and perhaps, still declining.

A. c. caffer Once locally common over much of Tahiti (17° 39'S, 149° 26'W), But now confined to a few mountain valleys in the eastern interior, where it appears to be rare. During a survey between 1986 and 1991, it was found in just 12 of 39 suitable valleys investigated (BirdLife International 2000). It still inhabits many of the valleys in the east and centre of the island but is absent from the west side of the island and in the peninsula. There are estimated to be no more than 100–300 occupied territories (Cibois *et al.* 2008).

A. c. longirostris Endemic to Mo'orea (17° 32'S, 149° 50'W) where numbers were already greatly reduced by the early years of the twentieth century. Only two singing birds were discovered in the interior forests in 1972–73 and the last bird was seen on a bamboo grove in July 1981 (Holyoak & Thibault 1984). There have been no subsequent observations and it was apparently extinct by 1986.

A. c. garretti This race formerly occurred on Huahine (23° 22'S, 149° 28'W) but is now believed to be extinct. The first specimens were collected here by Garrett who lived on the island between 1870 and 1887. When the Whitney South Seas Expedition visited Huahine in December 1921 they failed to relocate it, suggesting that it was already very rare or extinct. There have been no subsequent observations.

A. c. musae Discovered on Raiatea (16° 50'S, 151° 25'W) during Captain Cook's second expedition (Forster 1844) and was collected here again by Garrett in the 1870s. The Whitney South Seas Expedition, which visited Raiatea in January 1922, failed to record it and

it apparently became extinct here between the 1870s and 1920s (Cibois *et al.* 2008). Very little is known of its former distribution on the island.

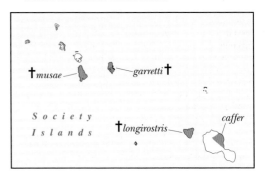

Tahiti Warbler. Resident within breeding range.

MOVEMENTS Resident, with no reported movements away from Tahiti, or even between neighbouring valleys on the island.

DESCRIPTION *A. c. caffer*
Plumage – Adult fresh, typical morph Forehead and crown dark brown, feathers fringed pale yellow, producing a scaly effect. Supercilium pale yellow, extending from base of bill to rear of ear-coverts. Dark spot on lores immediately in front of eye and narrow dark eye-line extending to rear of ear-coverts. Ear-coverts pale yellow, unmarked. No contrasting eye-ring. Nape similar to crown, but dark feather centres larger and pale yellow fringes broader. Mantle and scapular feather centres brownish yellow, slightly paler than on crown and nape and yellow fringes still broader, especially on lower mantle where slightly browner, contrasting less with centres. Rump and uppertail-coverts warm brown with broad diffuse yellowish brown fringes, although clear definition between centres and fringes largely lacking on uppertail-coverts. Tail feathers dull brown with paler fringes and whitish tips. Chin and throat pale yellow, merging with ear-coverts. Rest of underparts pale creamy buff to pale yellow, slightly more intense than on throat.

Lesser and median coverts dark brownish yellow, fringed pale yellow. Greater coverts dark brown, fringed cinnamon-yellow. Tertials similar, but with darker centres and broad cinnamon-brown fringes, warmer than those of mantle. Primary coverts blackish, fringed and tipped warm tan. Secondaries and primaries blackish brown, edged warm tan, tips fringed pale yellow. Alula black with broad cinnamon-brown fringe. Underwing-coverts pale yellow.

Adult worn Becomes slightly darker than fresh adult as pale fringes wear. Forehead and crown greyish black, crown feathers tipped pale yellowish white. Supercilium pale yellowish white. Black loral line between bill base and eye and black eye-line from rear of eye to nape more conspicuous. Ear-coverts white, tinged yellow, with darker feather bases giving faint mottling. Nape ash-grey with narrow pale yellowish-white fringes. Mantle and scapular feathers dark ash-grey with yellowish-white fringes of variable width, these becoming broader, paler and more diffuse towards rump. Rump and uppertail-coverts as mantle, but paler overall with feather fringes broader and grey centres smaller, so contrast is greater. Tail feathers grey-brown with pale yellowish-white fringes and white tips. Chin, throat and breast white with faint yellow wash. Flanks, belly and undertail-coverts with slightly stronger yellow wash. Lesser and median coverts similar to mantle. Greater and primary coverts and tertials dark grey with whitish fringes, broadest on tertials. Secondaries and primaries greyish with faint brownish yellow edges. Alula black with narrow yellowish white fringe.

Juvenile Forehead and crown dull olive-green with slightly paler olive-yellow feather tips. Supercilium paler than crown, ochre-yellow from base of bill to rear of eye, more olive-green and much less obvious above ear-coverts. Lores dull olive-green with ochre-yellow fringes, appearing faintly mottled. Narrow olive-green eye line extending to rear of ear-coverts and merging with nape. Ear-coverts olive-green with ochre-yellow tips giving indistinct mottling. Eye-ring ochre-yellow and inconspicuous. Nape, mantle and scapulars as crown but with indistinct olive-yellow mottling. Rump and uppertail-coverts olive-green and unmarked. Tail feathers dull brown with creamy white tips. Chin and throat ochre-yellow. Breast, flanks, belly and undertail-coverts deeper uniform olive-yellow. Lesser and median coverts similar to mantle. Greater coverts and tertials olive-green with ochre-yellow fringes. Edges and tips to primary coverts, secondaries and primaries ochre-yellow. Alula black with narrow ochre-yellow fringe.

Dark morph Entire head, upperparts, tail and underparts unmarked sooty-black. Lesser, median and greater coverts and tertials with sooty-black centres and slightly paler greyish fringes. Secondaries and primaries sooty-black, with blackish brown edges contrasting very slightly. Alula black.

Bare parts In typical morph, upper mandible dark grey, becoming salmon-pink towards cutting edge and greyish white at tip. Lower mandible salmon-pink and entirely unmarked. Tarsi, toes and claws lead grey; soles slightly paler. Iris dull brown in immature birds, slightly warmer in adults, but always dark.

In the dark morph, bill, tarsi, toes and claws always entirely black.

IN HAND CHARACTERS
Measurements

A. c. caffer

	Male	Female
Wing	94–100 (97; 10)	92–96 (93.5; 10)
Tail	73–81 (78; 10)	72–76 (74; 10)
Bill*	25–28 (27; 10)	26–27 (26.5; 10)
Tarsus	30–32 (31; 10)	30–31 (30; 10)

(Holyoak & Thibault 1984) * exposed culmen

Sexes combined:
Tail/wing ratio: 81–87% (83; 4)
Bill to skull: 31–39 (34.3; 6)
Bill width: 5.2–6.3 (5.8; 6)
Hind claw: 11–12 (11.3; 5)
Tail graduation: 10–18 (13.5; 4)
A. c. longirostris (2 ♂♂, 1 ♀): *wing* 103–106 (104); *tail* 85–90 (88); *bill* (culmen) 29–30 (29); *tarsus* 30–32 (31). (Holyoak & Thibault 1984)
A. c. garretti (2 unsexed, Holotype BMNH 98.9.1.2523 and Paratype AMNH 594897, Holyoak & Thibault 1984): *wing* 106; *tail* 88, 89; *bill* (culmen) 27, 28; *tarsus* 33, 33.5.

Structure

A. c. caffer

Wing formula (n = 5):

p1/pc	p2	p3e	p4(e)	p5	p6	p7	p10
2–4	3.5–6.5	0–1	wp	0–1	1–4	4–6	11–16

Wing similar to the Marquesan Warblers (Fig. 87); rounded with small p1. Wing point p(3) 4 (5); p2 = p7/8–8/9; emargination on p3, often faintly on p4.

Tail markedly rounded, feathers rather broad and rounded.

Bill very long, broad based but with narrow decurved tip.

Tarsi long and robust; toes and claws very strong.

Similar in structure to the Marquesan Warblers; bill equally long, but slightly less thick, with tip of culmen more strongly decurved.

Weight No data available.

GEOGRAPHIC VARIATION The four races closely resemble each other, and show only minor differences in plumage. But due to the paucity of specimens, the true extent of variation between and within each taxon is poorly understood. The dark morph appears to be confined to the nominate race on Tahiti. There are differences in size, the nominate form being slightly smaller than the birds from Raiatea, Huahine and Mo'orea. Again, the limited number of specimens from these islands may unduly influence these conclusions.

A. c. caffer (Tahiti) Described above.

A. c. longirostris (formerly Mo'orea, now extinct) Closely resembled the nominate race but believed to have lacked a dark morph. The tail differed, however, with all but the central pair of feathers being mainly pale cream to yellowish white. Distinctly larger than the nominate race.

A. c. garretti (formerly Huahine, now extinct) Very similar to the nominate form, but the pale cream fringes of the upperparts were slightly broader, especially on the rump and uppertail-coverts. Also, substantially larger, with wing and tail lengths overlapping with those of *longirostris* but with a slightly shorter bill. Differed from *longirostris* in having blackish brown rather than pale cream rectrices, although still with narrow, pale cream tips, these being somewhat broader on the outermost feathers.

A. c. musae (formerly Raiatea, now extinct) Known only from a single specimen housed in the Übersee-Museum, Bremen. In addition, a painting by George Forster illustrates the specimen described by his father (Forster 1844), and appears to show a bird with an exceptionally long bill. The bill length of the single specimen falls within the upper range of *longirostris*.

TAXONOMY AND SYSTEMATICS Marquesan Warbler (*sensu lato*) and Tuamotu Warbler have sometimes been regarded as races of Tahiti Warbler. But there are obvious morphological and behavioural differences between them and they are now widely regarded as three separate species.

Within the Society Islands it has been generally accepted that the four races of Tahiti Warbler are closely related and derived from a common ancestor. However, a study by Cibois *et al.* (2008) revealed that this may not be the case. Comparing the external morphology of the different populations and using DNA samples extracted from museum specimens, they proposed a molecular phylogeny based on partial cytochrome *b* gene sequences. This indicated that Tahiti Warbler is represented by three different lineages, found in Tahiti, Mo'orea and Raiatea–Huahine respectively. Birds from Tahiti and Mo'orea show marked genetic difference in addition to size and structural differences, despite the islands lying just 16km apart. Conversely, birds from Raiatea and Huahine separated by a 35km-wide channel, show only limited genetic and morphological differences, suggesting a more recent common ancestor. During periods of low sea level during the Pleistocene, these islands were not connected, leading the authors to conclude that colonisation events occurred within the Society Islands on several occasions.

They proposed that the Society Island *Acrocephalus* should be treated as three species:

Tahiti Warbler *Acrocephalus caffer* (Sparrman, 1786), monotypic and endemic to Tahiti.

Mo'orea Warbler *Acrocephalus longirostris* (Gmelin, 1789), monotypic and endemic to Mo'orea.

Leeward Islands Warbler *Acrocephalus musae* (Forster, 1844), polytypic with races *musae* on Raiatea and *garretti* on Huahine.

Because of the limited material available to Cibois *et al.* and taking into consideration that two of the proposed species are extinct, we feel it is premature to adopt this arrangement. It is likely that this will become widely accepted elsewhere in future. A further surprising discovery by Cibois *et al.* (2007) was the close relationship between the birds from Mo'orea with Tuamotu Warbler and Northern Marquesan Warbler. They suggest that colonisation of a large part of Polynesia originated from an ancestral *Acrocephalus* on Mo'orea which radiated widely throughout the region, although apparently not within the Society Islands.

▲ Adult, Tahiti, French Polynesia, September. Typical morph (Pete Morris).

▲ Adult, Tahiti, French Polynesia, September. Distinctive dark morph occurs alongside typical birds in tropical forest on the mountainous slopes of eastern Tahiti (Pete Morris).

TUAMOTU WARBLER
Acrocephalus atyphus **Plate 30**

Conopoderas atypha **Wetmore, 1919.** *Bull. Mus. Comp. Zool.,*
63: 206. Fakarava, Tuamotu Archipelago.

Endemic to the Tuamotu Archipelago in the C Pacific,
where it is resident on at least 40 atolls. Previously regarded
as conspecific with Tahiti Warbler and Marquesan Warbler
(*sensu lato*) but distinct morphological and behavioural
differences support their treatment as three separate
species. Differences between populations spread across
the Tuamotu Archipelago have led to the recognition of
six races.

A. a. atyphus (Wetmore, 1919). islands in N and W
Tuamotu.

A. a. palmarum (Murphy & Mathews, 1929). Anaa, WC
Tuamotu.

A. a. niauensis (Murphy & Mathews, 1929). Niau, NW
Tuamotu.

A. a. ravus (Wetmore, 1919). Seven atolls in SE Tuamotu.

A. a. eremus (Wetmore, 1919). Makatea, NW Tuamotu.

A. a. flavidus (Murphy & Mathews, 1929). Napukea, N
Tuamotu.

IDENTIFICATION Length *c.* 18cm. Wing 81–95mm. Tail/
wing 78–86%.

A large *Acrocephalus*, similar in size to Tahiti and the
Marquesan Warblers and Great Reed Warbler *A. arundinaceus*. Two colour morphs occur; a grey-and-white morph
and a brown morph. Sexes alike.

Structure Typical of the larger *Acrocephalus*. It has a long
and fairly slim bill, low forehead, relatively short wings that
do not reach the longest uppertail-coverts, a short primary
projection and relatively long and deep undertail-coverts.
It often adopts a horizontal stance, giving it a fairly sleek
structure for such a large warbler. When singing in the open,
it frequently raises the crown feathers and fluffs out the
body feathering, thus appearing more bulky, with the 'spiky'
appearance of the bill enhanced. The wing structure, with
the first primary (p1) only slightly longer than the primary
coverts and the wing point falling at p4, resembles that of a
migrant rather than a resident *Acrocephalus*.

Plumage and bare parts Rather featureless and nondescript
but quite variable in appearance and showing a tendency
towards two colour morphs, grey-and-white, and brown.
In the brown morph, the crown, ear-coverts and entire
upperparts are dull rufescent-brown. A pale creamy white
supercilium extends over the ear-coverts but is rather diffuse
behind the eye. It shows limited contrast with the poorly
defined eye-stripe which is restricted to a small dark spot
immediately in front of the eye and a diffuse line behind it.
The entire underparts are white with a warm peachy buff
wash restricted to the breast sides, flanks and undertail-
coverts. The tips to the greater and median coverts appear
slightly paler than the closed wing and form two indistinct
wing-bars. The edges to the tertials and secondaries are
often contrastingly paler and can produce a distinct pale
panel in the closed wing.

The grey-and-white morph shows a similar overall
pattern but the contrast between the paler and darker
areas is enhanced. On the head, the supercilium appears
more conspicuous and generally remains crisp behind the
eye and the eye-stripe is slightly darker and better defined.
The upperparts are rather cold greyish brown, with the
paler fringes to the greater and median coverts, tertials

and secondaries showing greater contrast with the closed
wing, so the wing-bars and the pale wing-panel appear more
conspicuous. The underparts are white, washed pale grey
across the upper breast and more strongly creamy grey on
flanks and undertail-coverts, but lack the warmer tones
shown by the brown morph.

Partial albinism or leucism occurs throughout the range
of the nominate form and appears to affect both colour
morphs equally. Many birds show random white feathering
in the body plumage, wings and tail. In some, the entire
head and upperparts and most of the tail feathers are largely
white. More commonly, the white is restricted to random
feathers and fringes on the mantle or to the tips of the tail
feathers. Occasionally an entire tail feather is white. Partial
albinism does not, however, affect all populations equally
and birds on some islands show little or no trace. Juveniles
have olive-brown tail feathers that are unmarked, or show
indistinct paler fringes.

The bill is dark grey with an unmarked salmon-pink
lower mandible. The legs and feet are brownish grey.

SIMILAR SPECIES No potential confusion species occur
within the Tuamotu Archipelago.

VOICE The song is a simple combination of whistles and
chattering notes, strung together to form a short song
sequence within a frequency range of 1–4kHz. There is
considerable variation throughout its extensive range
and individual island populations, even of the same race,
perform distinctly different songs. It is unknown whether
such variation results in reproductive isolation.

The song of *ravus*, recorded on Anu-Anurunga, is simple
and slow but pleasantly melodic and similar in structure
to that of Clamorous Reed Warbler, but lacks the harsher
quality of that species. It commences with a short '*che-
wuu-che*', quickly followed by a more continuous sequence
'*che-wuu-che*', *che-wuu-chaaa, che-wuu-che-we-we-we, che-wu-che-
wu*' lasting for 2–3 seconds. This is followed by a pause of
approximately eight seconds, before the next sequence,
during which an occasional call may be given.

The song of *eremus* recorded on Makatea is quite
different. It is much harsher and comprises a series of
raucous rasps and whistles with a short gap between each
note. The song sequence is longer than in *ravus*, lasting
c. 6–7 seconds, during which approximately 16 individual
notes are given, each clearly separated from the next '*charr-
wheeuu-charr-charr-wheeeeuu-wee-wee-chaaa-chaaa-chaaa-chaaa-
chaaa-weeuu-chaaa-wee-wee-weeuu*'.

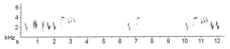

**Song of Tuamotu Warbler recorded within breeding range
of *A. a. ravus*, Anu-Anurunga, Tuamotu Archipelago,
January. (McPherson 1998)**

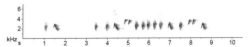

**Song of Tuamotu Warbler recorded within breeding range
of *A. a. eremus*, Makatea, Tuamotu Archipelago, January.
(McPherson 1998)**

The call is a low '*charr*', similar to that included within
the song sequence.

MOULT There are no published details of moult timing and sequence. Murphy & Mathews (1929) found adults from Taiaro in full moult in May, with body feathering in pin and the tail entirely lacking. Breeding birds may start to moult while still feeding young in the nest.

HABITAT The Tuamotu Archipelago comprises numerous low-lying atolls that reach only a few metres above sea level. Most are small and covered with dense low scrub and small trees, but some of the larger islands are well wooded. Tuamotu Warbler appears common on all atolls where it occurs and is as likely to be found in thick scrub adjacent to the sea as in more densely wooded areas. Many of the larger islands are inhabited but this seems to have little impact on its abundance and it is often common in and around gardens and coconut plantations.

BEHAVIOUR No behavioural studies have been reported. It is believed to be primarily insectivorous but will also take crustaceans and small lizards. It forages in coconut palms and scrub, but usually on or close to the ground and generally keeps low within thick cover. It occasionally hawks for insects. Strongly territorial during the breeding season.

BREEDING HABITS Poorly known. Murphy & Mathews (1929) documented nests with young during February to June, August and October to December and concluded that breeding occurs throughout the year. The nest is a deep cup of grass stems, twigs, long leaves and fine stems of vines and coconut fibres, lined with delicate fibres and small grasses. It is placed well above ground among trailing vines in a bush or tree. The clutch is 1–3 eggs. No information on incubation and fledging periods is available. Both parents feed the young in the nest.

DISTRIBUTION Confined to the small, vegetated atolls of the Tuamotu Archipelago. These extend over a huge area of the C Pacific, often separated by large distances. Many of the 76 atolls lack a resident warbler population but Pratt *et al.* (1987) stated that it occurs on 47 atolls. Birds were discovered on 37 of these by the Whitney expedition in 1921 and a further three were mentioned by Murphy & Mathews (1929).

A. t. atyphus was originally described from Fakarava and is the most widespread of the six recognised forms, occurring throughout the northern and western part of the archipelago. It is known from at least 30 atolls. Its current status on most of these is unknown but information from Takapoto suggests it is still common there. The atolls known to be occupied are: Ahe, Apataki, Aratika, Arutua, Faaite, Fakahina, Fakarava, Hereheretue, Hiti, Katiu, Kauehi, Kaukura, Makemo, Manihi, Matahiva, Nihiru, Rangiroa, Raraka, Taenga, Tahanea, Taiaro, Takapoto, Takaroa, Takume, Tauere, Tepoto, Tikahau, Tikei, Toau and Tuanaki. These lie between 14° 30'S and 19° 55'S and between 141° 30'W and 148° 10'W.

A. a. palmarum is restricted to Anaa (17° 30'S, 145° 30'W), an isolated atoll lying *c.* 65km to the south of Tahanea and Faaite. It is believed to be fairly common.

A. a. niauensis is still common on Niau (16° 10'S, 146° 20'W), a small, heavily wooded atoll approximately equidistant between Fakarava, Toau and Kaukura, all of which are occupied by the nominate form.

A. a. ravus occurs on seven atolls in the SE Tuamotus: Ahunui, Aki Aki, Hao, Paraoa, Pinaki, Tureia and Vanavana. These atolls lie between 18° 30' and 20° 45'S,

and between 138° 45'W and 140° 55'W. In addition, a bird believed to be of this form was sound-recorded on Anu-Anurunga (20° 40'S, 143° 20'W) in March 1990 (R. & J. Seitre *in litt.*).

A. a. eremus is restricted to Makatea (15° 50'S, 148° 12'W) where it is still numerous. Makatea lies close to Rangiroa, occupied by the nominate form.

A. a. flavidus was described from Napuka (14° 10'S, 141° 15'W), a well-wooded isolated atoll lying north of the archipelago and more than 180km from Takume and Fakahina.

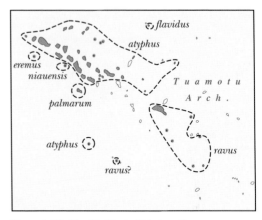

Tuamotu Warbler. Resident within breeding range.

MOVEMENTS No inter-island movements have been recorded but the fact that apparently identical populations occur on many widely separated atolls suggests that dispersal and colonisation events have occurred from time to time in the past.

DESCRIPTION *A. a. atyphus*
Plumage – Adult fresh, brown morph Forehead and crown grey-brown and unmarked. Supercilium conspicuous, whitish at base of bill, becoming cream above eye and pale brown over the ear-coverts. Lores pale with indistinct brown spot in front of eye. Eye-line dark brown, slightly darker than ear-coverts and merging into nape. Ear-coverts grey-brown, darkest at rear edge where meeting nape and eye-line, but warmer and paler near lower edge and below eye. Eye-ring narrow, creamy brown, blending with supercilium above eye but becoming paler and contrasting with ear-coverts below. Nape grey-brown, similar to crown. Mantle and scapulars warm brown with cinnamon feather tips, these being most conspicuous on lower back and scapulars where feathers are darker. Rump and uppertail-coverts warm brown, unmarked. Tail dull brown, plain and unmarked. Chin and throat pale cream, becoming pale peach towards sides and merging with ear-coverts. Breast pale peach, colour being most intense on flanks, especially lower flanks. Undertail-coverts strongly washed warm peach. Belly white with faint peach wash. Lesser, median and greater coverts warm brown with indistinct cinnamon fringes. Tertials dark brown with pale ash-brown fringes. Primary coverts dark brown with narrow ash-brown fringes. Secondaries dark brown with conspicuous pale ash-brown edges and tips forming pale panel in closed wing. Primaries dark brown, edged warm cinnamon brown, tipped whitish. Alula black with narrow ash-brown fringe. Underwing-coverts pale cream.

Adult worn Very similar to fresh adult but generally greyer.

Adult fresh, grey-and-white morph Forehead and crown ash-brown and unmarked. Supercilium white with faint brownish wash, most obvious at rear, extending from base of bill to nape. Indistinct loral line appears as dark spot in front of eye, sometimes extending as poorly defined dark line to bill base. Eye-line dark ash-brown, broadening behind eye and merging with nape. Ear-coverts white, washed pale creamy brown towards rear and merging with sides of neck and nape. Eye-ring whitish but inconspicuous. Nape ash-brown as crown. Mantle and scapulars ash-brown, often with ash-grey fringes. Rump and uppertail-coverts ash-brown. Tail dark grey-brown and unmarked. Chin and throat white, tinged grey and merging with ear-coverts. Breast greyish white, becoming warmer creamy brown on flanks and undertail-coverts. Lesser and median coverts as mantle but fringes slightly paler, pale tips to median coverts forming an indistinct wing-bar. Greater coverts ash-brown with broad, diffuse, paler grey-brown fringes forming a conspicuous wing-bar. Primary coverts ash-brown with narrow grey-brown fringes. Tertials dark brown with broad ash-grey fringes and tips. Edges and tips of secondaries pale ash-grey, producing pale panel in closed wing. Edges to primaries ash-brown, contrasting little with darker brown webs and pale ash-grey tips. Alula dark grey-brown with narrow pale ash-grey fringe.

Juvenile Not examined.

Bare parts Upper mandible dark grey with salmon-pink cutting edge. Lower mandible salmon-pink, generally unmarked. Tarsi brownish grey; toes and claws slightly greyer. Iris warm brown.

IN HAND CHARACTERS
Measurements

A. a. atyphus

	Male	Female
Wing	84–93 (88.3; 134)	81–90 (84.6; 79)
Tail	68–83 (74.6; 134)	66–77 (71.1; 79)
Bill*	19.6–22 (21; 134)	19–22 (20.6; 79)
Tarsus	29–33 (30; 134)	28–31.5 (29.7; 79)

(Murphy & Mathews 1929) * exposed culmen

Sexes combined (races **atyphus** and **ravus** combined):
Tail/wing ratio: 78–86%
Bill to skull: 26.9–27.8 (27.2; 7)
Bill width: 5.1–5.8 (5.4; 7)
Hind claw: 9.3–10.6 (9.9; 7)
Tail graduation: 12–15

Other races (from Murphy & Mathews 1929)
A. a. palmarum (5 ♂♂, 5 ♀♀): *wing*, ♂ 85–89 (86.8), ♀ 80–82 (80.8); *tail*, ♂ 68–73 (71.6), ♀ 60–68 (63.2); *bill* (culmen), ♂ 18.5–19.7 (19.2), ♀ 16.5–18.5 (17.5); *tarsus*, ♂ 28.3–29.3 (28.9), ♀ 27–29 (28.3).
A. a. niauensis (13 ♂♂, 3 ♀): *wing*, ♂ 82–87 (85.7), ♀ 79-80 (79.3); *tail*, ♂ 70–74 (71.4), ♀ 62–69 (65); *bill* (culmen), ♂ 18–19 (18.4), ♀ 18–19 (18.4); *tarsus*, ♂ 27–28.5 (28), ♀ 28.5–29 (28.7).
A. a. ravus (39 ♂♂, 23 ♀♀): *wing*, ♂ 84–93 (89.3), ♀ 82–88 (85.2); *tail*, ♂ 71–80 (76.2), ♀ 67–77 (71.3); *bill* (culmen), ♂ 20–22 (21.0), ♀ 19.2–21.6 (20.4); *tarsus*, ♂ 30–32 (30.9), ♀ 28.5–31 (29.5).

A. a. eremus (10 ♂♂, 8 ♀♀): *wing*, ♂ 88–95 (92.3), ♀ 85–92 (88.9); *tail*, ♂ 75–84 (80.6), ♀ 74–79 (76.6); *bill* (culmen), ♂ 22.5–25 (24), ♀ 23.5–24 (23.8); *tarsus*, ♂ 31–32 (31.5), ♀ 29.5–30 (29.8).
A. a. flavidus (n = 4, sexes combined): *wing*, 92–95 (93); *tail*, 73–78.5 (75.2); *bill* (culmen) 23.8–24 (24); *tarsus* 30–31.7 (31). Also (1 ♂), *bill* (to skull) 29.7, bill width 5.7, hind claw 11.3.

Thus, in comparison with nominate *atyphus*, races *palmarum* and *niauensis* are somewhat smaller, *ravus* is of similar size, *eremus* and *flavidus* are distinctly larger.

Structure

Wing formula (n = 5, races *atyphus* and *ravus*):

p1/pc	p2	p3e	p4e	p5e	p6	p7	p10
1.5–4	5.5–7	0–1.5	wp	0–1.5	1-3.5	4.5–5	10–13

Wing similar to the Marquesan Warblers (Fig. 87) but with a tendency to show emargination on p5. Wing rounded, but p1 small. Wing point p(3) p4 (5); p2 = p7–8; emargination on p3–5.

Tail medium length; graduated with rounded feathers.

Bill long and strong but concave-sided and narrow at tip, tip of culmen decurved.

Tarsi robust. Toes and claws very strong.

Structure thus similar to that of the Marquesan Warblers.

Weight No data available.

GEOGRAPHIC VARIATION There is considerable variation in plumage and size across the species' extensive range, with six races currently recognised. However, these are not evenly spread through the archipelago, with some races leapfrogging others. On current knowledge, the nominate form inhabits 30 atolls and the race *ravus* a further seven, while the remaining four races are each confined to a single atoll.
A. a. atyphus (At least 30 atolls in the northwest of the archipelago) Described above. Shows no significant size or structural differences between the many atolls in occupies. There is, however, considerable colour variation, apparently not related to age or sex, with brown and grey-and-white morphs occurring side by side on the same atolls. The ratio of these morphs varies, one or other tending to predominate on each island but matching specimens of either morph can usually to be found among birds from a neighbouring island. They show variable irregular white feathering on any part of the body and asymmetrical white, white-tipped or white-speckled tail feathers.

Murphy & Mathews (1929) investigated variability within the nominate form. Within each morph, this race shows no appreciable differences between islands apart from some variation in the extent of leucism or albinism. The population on Fakarava (where the species was originally described) occurs in both brown and grey-and-white morphs. The birds of Tikahao and Matahiva at the northwestern extremity of the archipelago resemble those of Fakarava. On Aritika, however, the brown morph predominates and albinism in the tail appears uncommon, while by contrast, the grey-and-white morph predominates on Fakahina. Birds on the five isolated northern atolls of Tikei, Takapoto, Takaroa, Manihi and Ahe are mostly the brown morph and appear otherwise indistinguishable from birds from the main archipelago. On Toau, birds show a greater tendency towards irregular white feathering, particularly on the mantle, wings and tail. Wetmore (1919) described birds from Rangiroa and Makemo as a distinct subspecies, but they appear inseparable from those on Fakarava (Murphy & Mathews 1929). On Takume, many birds closely resemble the nominate form although Murphy & Mathews considered some individuals perhaps better placed within *A. a. ravus*, which inhabits islands to the southeast. They did include the somewhat intermediate population of neighbouring Hao within *ravus*.

A. a. palmarum (Anaa) Closely resembles the nominate form and has both grey-and-white and brown morphs. However, the bill is significantly shorter, with the longest billed individuals matching the shortest bill length on nominate birds.

A. a. niauensis (Niau) Smaller and shorter-billed than both the nominate form and *palmarum* and in comparison with them appears rather plain and nondescript. Plumage differences are poorly marked but the upperparts are rather uniform, often with an olive-buff cast that is unusual in the nominate form. Furthermore, it lacks the paler tips to median and greater coverts and pale ash-grey fringes to primaries and secondaries shown in fresh birds of the nominate form. The supercilium is poorly defined and the head is plainer, less contrasting than typical in other races. The underparts are cream to pale buff and are rarely as pale as in nominate birds. In addition, this race appears to lack the tendency towards white feathering.

A. a. ravus (Seven atolls in the southeast of the archipelago) Structurally almost identical to the nominate form and shows wide individual variation. The upperparts are consistently browner than in the nominate form and the supercilium and underparts show a variable yellowish wash. Some birds are warm yellowish straw on the breast but others are paler with yellow tones more subdued. The undertail-coverts are typically darker, more buffy than in the nominate race.

A. a. eremus (Makatea) Resembles the nominate form closely in structure, but slightly larger and with a distinctly longer, deeper-based and slightly decurved bill. There is a strong cinnamon wash to the entire upperparts, and birds of this form appear more rufescent than even warmest birds of nominate form or *ravus*. The underparts are also warmer, being lightly washed pale cinnamon which tends to strengthen on the breast and belly. The flanks and undertail-coverts vary between pale and dark cinnamon although some appear similar in colour to the nominate race. The extent of random white feathering appears variable; some birds show occasional white body feathers and entirely brown rectrices, others have white tips to the brown outer rectrices, and a few show entirely white rectrices except for the central pair which remain brown.

A. a. flavidus (Napuka) A large and distinctive race with a longer bill and wing than the nominate form. The upperparts are dull brownish olive, similar to other races, but the scapulars, when fresh, have yellowish-olive fringes, giving the upperparts a slight greenish cast, so the pale olive-buff rump and uppertail-coverts contrast with the mantle. The entire underparts have a distinctive strong yellow wash.

TAXONOMY AND SYSTEMATICS No issues arising. Formerly treated as a race of Tahiti Warbler, but is quite different in both structure and appearance from that species.

Further research into the phylogeny of the various island populations may reveal that more than one species occurs in the archipelago.

▲ ▶ Adult *A. a. eremus*, Makatea, Tuamotu Archipelago, French Polynesia, September. Brown morph. Closely resembles nominate race but slightly larger and with longer, deeper-based and slightly decurved bill. Compared with nominate form, upperparts warmer with slight rufescent wash, and underparts warmer with pale cinnamon breast and flanks (Pete Morris).

NIGHTINGALE WARBLER
Acrocephalus luscinius   Plate 30

Thryothorus luscinius **Quoy & Gaimard, 1830.** In: Dumont, d'Urville, *Voyage Astrolabe, Zool.*, 1: 202. Guam.

A resident *Acrocephalus* endemic to the Mariana Islands in the W Pacific. Formerly occurred on several islands in the archipelago but now confined to Saipan, Alamagan and Agiguan. Sometimes treated as conspecific with Caroline Islands Warbler and Nauru Warbler, but is larger with a much longer bill and has a different song. Considered to be ENDANGERED by BirdLife International. Polytypic, with four races recognised, two of which are now extinct:

A. l. luscinius (Quoy & Gaimard, 1930). Saipan and Alamagan; formerly Guam.

A. l. nijoi (Yamashina, 1940). Agiguan.

A. l. yamashinae (Takatsukasa, 1931) Formerly on Pagan. EXTINCT

A. l. astrolabii Holyoak & Thibault, 1978. Origin uncertain. EXTINCT

IDENTIFICATION Length 18–19cm. Wing 85–91mm. Tail/wing *c.* 85%. (nominate form)

A large *Acrocephalus* with drab olive-brown upperparts, creamy underparts and an exceptionally long and slender bill. Only seven other passerine species occur on the three islands still occupied by Nightingale Warbler, none of which are warblers and likely to be confused with it. Sexes alike.

Structure Similar in size and structure to Tuamotu Warbler but has a much longer bill, similar in length to that of the considerably larger Tahiti Warbler and indeed proportionally longer than in any other *Acrocephalus*. The fore-crown feathers are raised during singing, giving the head a dishevelled and particularly spiky appearance. The wing is short and quite rounded, with a short primary projection and the wing point falling at p4, with p3 and p5 typically of similar length.

Plumage and bare parts The overall appearance is drab and nondescript, recalling some of the larger continental Asian *Acrocephalus,* such as Clamorous Reed and Oriental Reed Warblers, but its disproportionately long bill is particularly distinctive. When fresh, the entire upperparts including the wings are plain olive-brown, while the underparts shade from whitish on the chin though pale creamy brown on the breast to pale cream on the belly. The flanks are warmer-toned than the breast and the undertail-coverts are pale creamy brown. A conspicuous pale creamy brown supercilium extends from the base of the bill to the rear of the ear-coverts and a narrow olive-brown eye-line separates the supercilium and ear-coverts, but this is diffuse and indistinct on the lores. The ear-coverts and cheeks are warm creamy brown, giving a contrastingly paler appearance to the sides of the head.

When worn, the upperparts fade to a dull greyish brown, but the rump and uppertail-coverts tend to retain the richer tones and may contrast more with the mantle and tail. Both the supercilium and ear-coverts appear paler and more contrasting than on fresh birds. The underparts typically fade to dull white, with any remaining warm tones confined to the lower flanks.

The bill is dark grey with an entirely dull pink lower mandible. The legs and feet are bluish grey.

SIMILAR SPECIES No potential confusion species occur within the range of Nightingale Warbler.

VOICE The song of Nightingale Warbler on Saipan is a slow, loud, varied but simple melody spanning a frequency range of 1–5kHz. It is not dissimilar in structure and delivery to the song of a Common Blackbird, but harsher and less melodic and contains short and fluty warbling sections. Each song sequence comprises a series of varied notes, some short and harsh, others rather more slurred and melodic '*chark-chark-weeoo-wea-tweeo-wee-wee-wuuu-tsack-che-che*'. It can last for up to four seconds, followed by a pause of 6–10 seconds before another sequence begins. The song is frequently given at night (Pratt *et al.* 1987).

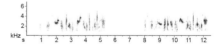

Song of Nightingale Warbler recorded within breeding range of *A. l. luscinius*, Saipan, Marianas Islands, February. (Steve Smith)

The call is a distinctive loud '*chuck*' or '*tchack*'.

MOULT No data available.

HABITAT On Saipan, it occupies a wide range of habitats but shows a distinct preference for introduced Tangan-tangan *Leucaena leucocephala* woodland, and mosaics of Tangan-tangan and Sword Grass or Elephant Grass. Otherwise it also shows a preference for wetlands, where it prefers thicker and more varied vegetation bordering wetland edges to monotypic stands of *Phragmites, Karka* or *Scirpus*. It also inhabits mangrove *Bruguiera gymnorrhiza* woodland, especially small stands with dense thickets of Sea Hibiscus *Hibiscus tiliaceus* and Rosewood *Thespesia populnea* (Mosher & Fancy 2002). Despite these preferences, it also occurs in grasslands, scrub, forest edge and clearings and scattered stands of tall Casuarina *Casuarina equisetifolia* and other native and introduced trees. Some territories, particularly those in Tangan-tangan may lack an understorey entirely, or include a layer of introduced Lantana *Lantana camara*. Territories in mangrove woodland also show a variable shrub understorey. On Saipan, it avoids nesting in native limestone forest (Mosher & Fancy 2002).

There are no wetlands on Agiguan and the highly endangered population here occurs (or occurred) in secondary growth forest and regenerating scrub with trees and thickets. The areas of secondary forest often lacked an understorey due to heavy grazing by goats, but it also occurred in scrub woodland from which goats have been excluded.

On Guam, it was formerly restricted to cane thickets and adjacent areas in and near fresh and brackish water marshes. The former small population on Pagan was restricted to vegetation around two small freshwater ponds (BirdLife International 2000).

BEHAVIOUR Highly territorial on Saipan during the peak breeding periods (Mosher & Fancy 2002), when males defend boundaries by vigorous singing from a perch close to the nest. Song is often heard during the night as well as in chorus at dawn, but declines in frequency and intensity outside the peak breeding periods. It is unclear whether birds then abandon territories. It is rather skulking when not breeding and forages mainly on or close to the ground, where it gleans insects from leaves and probes about amongst dead stubs. The diet consists primarily of insects and their larvae, but small lizards, snails and spiders have also been recorded as food items.

BREEDING HABITS Breeds throughout most of year, with peak periods from January to March in the dry season and from July to September in the wet season. It is believed to be monogamous.

The nest is built by the female and consists of a rather deep cup in one of two forms; either a compact and tightly woven structure, or a compact inner nest contained within a larger, bulky and untidy outer layer. It is constructed from vines, dry grass and strips of bark and sometimes incorporates spider's webs, twigs and leaves. Those nesting in Tangan-tangan woodland usually line the nest with Tangan-tangan petioles while those occupying mangrove woodland frequently use *Casuarina* branchlets as lining. Of nests studied by Mosher & Fancy (2002), most were in Tangan-tangan woodland but a few were found in mangrove woodland and just one in was in *Phragmites* reeds. Nests in trees ranged between 2.3–10m above the ground, while the single nest in *Phragmites* was 2.2m up. Nests constructed in Tangan-tangan or mangrove are typically attached to the main trunk and several lateral branches, with at least one branch providing support for the base. A clutch of 2–4 eggs is laid, but the incubation and fledging periods are unknown.

DISTRIBUTION Endemic to the Mariana Islands where it occurs, or formerly occurred, on the islands of Guam, Saipan, Alamagan, Agiguan and Pagan. Historically, it may also have occurred on Yap in the Caroline Islands, and it possibly also occurred prehistorically on Tinian (Steadman 1999). It is now extinct on some of these islands, but substantial populations survive on Saipan and Alamagan.

A. l. luscinius Substantial numbers remain on Saipan (15° 11'N, 145° 44'E) and Alamagam (17° 35'N, 145° 50'E), but these populations may be in decline. Recent estimates gave over 4,000 birds on Saipan and about 350 on Alamagan (BirdLife International) The population on Saipan is under threat from habitat loss and by introduced predators, including rats, cats and Monitor Lizards *Varanus indicus*. The nominate race formerly occurred on Guam (13° 27'N, 144° 45'E) but became extinct there in the late 1960s. The reasons for this are not well understood but may have included the effects of drainage, pesticides and loss of habitat due to fires. However, the introduction of the predatory Brown Tree Snake *Boiga irregularis* was almost certainly responsible for its ultimate demise.

A. l. nijoi Endemic to the small island of Agiguan (Aguijan) (14° 51'N, 145° 33'E), which lies to the south of Saipan. This race is extremely rare and only a tiny population remains, believed to number between two and ten individuals (BirdLife International, 2000). It is likely that destruction of habitat by introduced goats has pushed this form towards extinction.

A. l. yamashinae Restricted to the island of Pagan (18° 08'N, 145° 47'E). However, searches here since 1981 have failed to find any birds and it is now presumed extinct. It probably succumbed to the combined pressures of land drainage and predation.

A. l. astrolabii This is another race now considered to have become extinct, although it is uncertain where it formerly occurred. It was described by Holyoak & Thibault (1978) from two specimens collected during the Second Antarctic Expedition under the command of Captain J. Dumont D'Urville. This expedition visited numerous islands in Polynesia and Melanesia during 1838–39, along with several in Micronesia. The type specimen

chosen to represent *astrolabii* was originally labelled *A. syrinx*, with a collection location of Mangareva in the Gambier Islands of southern Polynesia. This location is, however, at odds with its appearance, as *astrolabii* closely resembles taxa inhabiting Micronesia and in particular *A. luscinius* and bears no resemblance to those occurring in Polynesia. The second specimen named Nouheva (or Nouhira) as the location, which casts doubt on the origin of both. The large size and plumage characters of *astrolabii* suggest it originated from Micronesia, where the expedition visited Losap, Truk, Guam, Yap and Peleliu (Holyoak & Thibault 1978). Guam and Truk are (or were) home to other distinctive *Acrocephalus* so these would be unlikely locations for *astrolabii*. Holyoak & Thibault (1978) speculated that the volcanic island of Yap (09° 32'N, 138° 07'E) might have been the origin of these specimens. Yap was not explored until many years after the Second Antarctic Expedition, by which time the warbler may have become extinct there. It is not possible to establish the origin of these specimens.

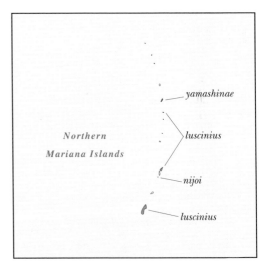

Nightingale Warbler. Resident within breeding range.

MOVEMENTS The population of each island is apparently resident and there are no records of inter-island movements. However, with the nominate form occurring on the islands of Saipan and (formerly) Guam some 200km apart, and also on Alamagan 350km north of Saipan, movements between these islands probably occurred in the past.

DESCRIPTION *A. l. luscinius*

Adult fresh Forehead and crown plain olive-brown. Supercilium broad, creamy brown from base of bill to eye, slightly duller over ear-coverts. Lores creamy brown as supercilium, with small dark loral spot in front of eye. Eye-line dull olive-brown, broadening and merging with nape. Ear-coverts creamy brown, contrasting sharply with eye-line and nape. Eye-ring pale cream and inconspicuous. Nape, mantle and scapulars uniform olive-brown. Rump and uppertail-coverts olive-brown, slightly paler and warmer than mantle. Tail dark brown and unmarked. Chin and throat white, becoming warm cream at sides and merging with ear-coverts. Breast pale creamy brown or yellowish brown, stronger in tone at sides and merging with warm creamy brown to peach flanks. Belly white to pale cream, usually with slight yellowish wash. Undertail-coverts creamy brown, slightly paler and less warm than flanks. Lesser and median coverts olive-brown without obvious fringe. Greater coverts dark brown with diffuse olive-brown fringes. Tertials dark brown with narrow but distinct olive-brown fringes. Primary coverts, secondaries and primaries dark brown with narrow olive-brown edges and tips. Alula blackish with olive-brown fringe. Underwing-coverts pale buff.

Adult worn Overall appearance greyer than fresh adult. Forehead and crown unmarked mid brown with faint greyish tinge. Lores and supercilium pale greyish white, the latter broad and conspicuous. Ear-coverts whitish, washed pale cream. Nape and mantle concolorous with crown, but rump and uppertail-coverts slightly warmer-toned and browner. Underparts white, washed greyish on breast and belly, faint buff on flanks and creamy white on undertail-coverts. Fringes to dark brown greater coverts and tertials, and edges to flight feathers, grey-brown and less well defined.

Juvenile Similar to adult, but lacks conspicuous supercilium and darker loral line. Entire upperparts brown. Breast, belly and undertail-coverts cream to light yellow; flanks buffy yellow. Edges and tips of flight feathers and tips of tail feathers with narrow buff fringes.

Bare parts Upper mandible dark grey with dull pink cutting edge towards tip. Lower mandible dull pink and unmarked. Tarsi, toes and claws lead grey. Iris dull brown.

IN HAND CHARACTERS
Measurements
A. l. luscinius (4 ♂♂): *wing* 85–91 (87.3; 4); *tail* 73–76 (74.3; 3); *bill* (to skull) 34.8–36 (35.3; 4); *tarsus* 30–34 (31.9; 4).

Also, mean values (19 ♂♂, 10 ♀♀): *wing*, ♂ 87, ♀ 82; *tail*, ♂ 83, ♀ 78; *bill* (from distal end of nostril), ♂ 23.0, ♀ 22.6; *tarsus* ♂ 34.8, ♀ 33.2. (Craig 1992).
Bill width: 5.9–6.0 (n = 3)
Hind claw: 10.8–12.2 (n = 3)
Tail graduation: 17 (n = 1)

A. l. nijoi No data available.

A. l. yamashinae (13 ♂♂, 6 ♀♀): *wing*, ♂ 75–80, ♀ 73–77; *tail*, ♂ 65–67, ♀ 60–65; *bill* (exposed culmen), ♂ 20–22, ♀ 20–22 (Takatsukasa & Yamashina 1931).

A. l. astrolabii (Only two specimens known, sex unknown): *wing* 99, 100; *tail* 83, 86.5; *bill* (exposed culmen) 29.5 (n = 1); *tarsus* 31.5, 33 (Holyoak & Thibault 1978).

Structure
A. l. luscinius
Wing formula (3 ♂♂):

p1/pc	p2	p3e	p4e	p5e	p6	p7	p10
(2)–5	5–9	0–1	wp	0–1.5	1.5–3	3–5	10–12.5

Wing structure similar to the Marquesan Warblers (Fig. 87) but usually shows emargination on p5. Wing rounded with minute p1. Wing point p(3) 4 (5); p2 = p8/9; emargination on p3–5.

Tail medium length, rounded.

Bill extremely long and strong, broad-based but laterally compressed and narrow towards tip; distal part of culmen decurved (Fig. 41).

Tarsi long and robust, toes and claws large.

Weight
A. l. luscinius: 27–38g (33.1; 10) (Dunning 2007). Also, ♂ average 35.9g (n = 19), ♀ average 32.0g (n = 9) (Craig 1992).
A. l. yamashinae: 24–28g (26.3; 9) (Dunning 2007).

GEOGRAPHIC VARIATION Although the geographical range is quite restricted, the islands on which it occurs are isolated, leading to significant variation between races.
A. l. luscinius (Saipan and Alamagam) Described above.
A. l. nijoi (Agiguan) Upperparts much less warm-toned than in the nominate race and the flanks and belly are also darker and brownish. Bill slightly shorter.
A. l. yamashinae (formerly Pagan, now extinct) A dark race and much smaller than the previous two races.
A. l. astrolabii (uncertain, possibly Yap, now extinct) Plumage closely resembled the nominate form with almost uniform upperparts, but lacked the pale feather fringes that are characteristic of many of the larger Polynesian *Acrocephalus*. Holyoak & Thibault (1978) described it as being much larger than the nominate form, but with a relatively short bill. The tarsi, toes and claws are extraordinarily stout, larger than any other warbler inhabiting Micronesia. Quite unique among any of the *Acrocephalus* warblers of Polynesia and continental Asia.

TAXONOMY AND SYSTEMATICS Caroline Islands Warbler and Nauru Warbler are sometimes considered to be races of Nightingale Warbler (e.g. Dickinson 2003). No other issues arising.

▲ ▶ Adult *A. l. luscinius*, Saipan, Northern Mariana Islands, January. Note the extraordinarily long bill (Jon Hornbuckle).

CAROLINE ISLANDS WARBLER
Acrocephalus syrinx   **Plate 30**

Sylvia syrinx **Kittlitz, 1835**. *Mém. Acad. Imp. Sci. St. Pétersbourg*, 2: 6, pl. 8. Lugunor and Uleei, Caroline Islands, Micronesia.

Resident throughout the Caroline Islands Archipelago in the C Pacific where it is the only warbler. Previously considered to be a race of Nightingale Warbler, but recent studies emphasising differences in song, behaviour and ecology, as well as plumage and structure, suggest it should regarded as a distinct species. Monotypic.

IDENTIFICATION Length 16cm. Wing 75–81mm. Tail/wing 81–91%.

A fairly large *Acrocephalus* with plain warm brown upperparts, a pale throat and cinnamon-buff underparts. Resembles Australian Reed Warbler but the bill is proportionally longer and heavier. Sexes alike.

Structure Slightly smaller than Nightingale Warbler, but with proportionately shorter wings and tail, which gives it a rather rounded and compact structure. The bill is proportionally much shorter than that of Nightingale Warbler and the head appears more rounded, less rakish or attenuated, even with the forehead feathers raised. It has a short, rounded wing, with the wing point formed by p3–5, but first primary (p1) is minute.

Plumage and bare parts This is a plain but warmly toned *Acrocephalus*, slightly darker and more richly coloured than Nightingale Warbler. The crown is dull greyish brown but brightens on the nape to become rich sepia-brown on the mantle and scapulars. The tail is similarly coloured but the individual rectrices are tipped pale sandy brown, giving a pale band across the tail tip. The rump and uppertail-coverts are often warmer rusty brown and the contrast with the duller mantle and tail can be quite marked, particularly in flight. The sides of the head appear pale, as in Nightingale Warbler, particularly so due to contrast with the rich sepia-brown upperparts. A prominent greyish white supercilium extends from the base of bill to the rear of the ear-coverts and is most conspicuous in front of and above the eye. There is a poorly defined eye-stripe that forms a narrow dark brown line behind the eye, but is often absent on the lores. Shows dark brown centres and warmer, richer sepia-brown fringes to the tertials and greater coverts, and warm brown edges and tips to the flight feathers. Apart from the pale greyish white chin and throat, the underparts are washed cinnamon-brown, warmer and more richly coloured on the lower flanks and ventral region.

The bill is dark grey with a pinkish grey lower mandible. The legs and feet are plumbeous-grey with a slight pinkish tinge.

SIMILAR SPECIES No similar species occur on the Caroline Islands, where this is the only warbler. It does, however, resemble Australian Reed Warbler and the easternmost race *sumbae* of Clamorous Reed Warbler in size, structure and some aspects of plumage, perhaps suggesting a common origin.

On Pohnpei, the vaguely similar Long-billed White-eye occurs. This is a large white-eye, similar in size to Caroline Islands Warbler and it lacks a conspicuous white eye-ring. It also lacks a supercilium, has a generally duller and drabber appearance and a slightly notched tail, unlike the rounded tail of Caroline Islands Warbler. In addition, the legs are

pale and the bill is long, thin and distinctly decurved. Its gregarious nature, moving rapidly through forest canopy in small flocks, is quite different from the sluggish and often solitary habits of Caroline Islands Warbler.

VOICE The song consists of a series of slow, loud and repetitive harsh rasping notes and fluty whistles that are clearly separated by a brief pause; '*chatt-chatt-wheett-wheett-wee-churr-wee-churr-wee-churr-weech-weech*'. The structure of the song is not dissimilar to that of the larger *Acrocephalus* species such as Clamorous Reed Warbler, although each sequence is slightly longer and more varied within a frequency range of 2–5kHz. Song bursts typically last two to three seconds, separated by long pauses, when the occasional call may be given. The song is less sustained than that of Nightingale Warbler.

Song of Caroline Islands Warbler, Truk, Caroline Islands, March. (Steve Smith)

The call can be either a single harsh rasping '*churr*' or a fluty whistling '*wee*', both of which are included in the song.

MOULT No available information.

HABITAT Occupies a wide range of habitats on the high islands, from mature, native montane rain forest to scrubby open lowland fields. It has adapted to environmental changes resulting from human activities, and regularly occurs near habitation, in gardens and in towns and villages. On Pohnpei, it is common in open country with a mixture of grasses or ferns with clumps of cane or bushes. It also frequents trees bordering grasslands, but avoids the extensive forests of the interior, except where there are dense *Pandanus* or *Hibiscus* thickets near streams. Smaller numbers occur in montane broadleaf forests, but it generally avoids palm forest. On Truk, it favours lowland scrub near overgrown fields, wetlands bordered by stands of *Phragmites* and patches of tall grass. It also occurs in secondary forest, preferring areas with small clearings and trails. On the coast, it avoids stands of pure mangrove, but occurs on the landward edges of mangrove woodland with adjacent rank grass or similar dense cover.

Smaller populations occur on many of the atolls and small offshore islets. It is believed to occupy most of the islets forming Ant Atoll, including Wolouna, a tiny isolated islet with less than a hectare of native strand vegetation. It also occurs on Nikalap Aru, where most of the native vegetation has been replaced with coconut palms but where it survives in the few remaining broadleaf trees and bushes.

BEHAVIOUR Typically occurs singly or in pairs and forages in dense bushy or grassy vegetation near the ground, as well as in the upper canopy, where it moves slowly and deliberately. Established adults appear to remain in the breeding territory throughout the year, but can often be difficult to locate when not nesting. Both birds of the pair are believed resident and there is no suggestion of territory occupation by other birds, or of fledged juveniles remaining within the parental territory. It feeds primarily on insects, picked or gleaned from foliage or snapped-up in flight. It often feeds opportunistically on exposed insects. On the main island of Weno in the Truk atoll, birds have often been observed feeding on recently mowed grass in an open field. Similar behaviour has been observed elsewhere in Truk, where birds have followed Bristle-thighed Curlews, which were uncovering clumps of mown grass with a flick of their bill; the warblers were presumably able to feed on disturbed insects.

BREEDING HABITS Apparent courtship display has been noted on Truk and Pohnpei which involved one bird, believed to be the female, remaining quietly on a perch while the male constantly sang a soft warbling sub-song and flew back and forth to her repeatedly (Holyoak & Thibault 1978). Nesting has been recorded in all months except January and March and apparently occurs throughout the year. The nest is typically built 2–14m above the ground and is well concealed, usually among dense foliage in a small tree or bush, but occasionally in cane swamps, taro plants, breadfruit trees, coconut trees, ivory nut palms or mango trees. It may be built in low scrub on some of the smaller islets where taller vegetation is absent. It is an untidy, bulky structure of coarse grasses, weed stems and leaves, lined with fine grasses. The clutch is normally two eggs. Incubation and fledging periods are unrecorded.

DISTRIBUTION Widespread throughout the Caroline Islands Archipelago in the Federated Sates of Micronesia, where it occurs on several of the high islands including Truk and Pohnpei. The eastern limit was formerly Kosrae but it is believed to have become extinct here (Pratt *et al.* 1987). It also occurs on many of the low-lying atolls throughout the archipelago west to Woleai (7° 20'N, 143° 50'E). The overall population is believed to be large and is not facing any immediate threats.

MOVEMENTS Sedentary. The population of each island is believed resident and there are no reported inter-island movements.

DESCRIPTION
Adult fresh Forehead and crown grey-brown. Supercilium broad and conspicuous, extending to rear of ear-coverts; generally greyish white in front of eye, becoming dull buff behind. Often a small dark brown loral spot in front of eye, becoming diffuse towards base of bill. Behind eye, a dull brown eye-line becomes diffuse and merges with coloration of head sides. Ear-coverts creamy, faintly flecked brown and paler than crown and nape, but becoming slightly darker towards rear edge. Eye-ring inconspicuous. Nape grey-brown. Mantle and scapulars warmer and richer brown than crown and nape. Rump and uppertail-coverts rufescent-brown, slightly brighter than mantle. Tail feathers dark brown with conspicuous warm brown fringes and pale sandy brown tips. Chin, throat and centre of breast white with faint greyish wash. Sides of breast and upper flanks light cinnamon-brown, becoming deeper cinnamon-brown on lower flanks and undertail-coverts. Pale cinnamon wash on belly merges into paler breast and darker flanks. Lesser and median coverts dark brown with broad, diffuse warm brown fringes. Greater coverts and tertials with darker brown centres and broader, warm brown fringes. Primary coverts dark brown with narrow, crisp, warm brown fringes and tips. Secondaries and primaries dark brown with narrow, warm brown fringes, primaries tipped whitish. Alula dark brown with ash-grey fringe. Underwing-coverts pale creamy white, distinctly paler than flanks.
Adult worn Not known to differ from fresh adult.
Juvenile Undescribed.
Bare Parts Upper mandible dark grey. Lower mandible uniform dull pinkish-grey. Tarsi and toes lead grey. Iris dull brown.

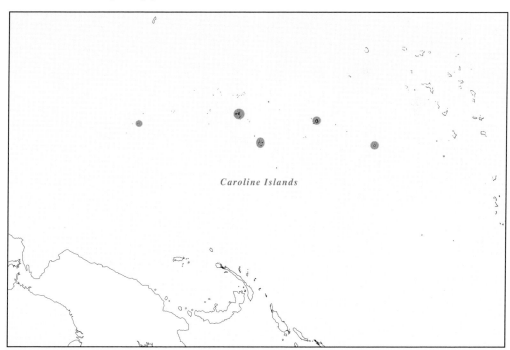

Caroline Islands

Caroline Islands Warbler. Widespread resident within breeding range.

IN HAND CHARACTERS
Measurements

Sexes combined:

Wing	75–81 (77.8; 12)
Tail	63–72 (67.2; 12)
Bill	24–27.5 (25.6; 11)
Tarsus	26–29 (27.2; 12)

Tail/wing ratio: 81–91% (86%; 9)
Bill width: 4.7–5.6 (5.1; 10)
Hind claw: 7.7–9.2 (8.5; 11)
Tail graduation: 10–13 (11.6; 9)

Also, mean values only: *wing*, ♂ 78.3 (n = 37), ♀ 75.8 (20); *tail*, ♂ 70.5 (37), ♀ 67.3 (20) (Holyoak & Thibault 1984).

Birds on Pohnpei show a slightly longer bill but shorter tarsus than those on Truk (Holyoak & Thibault 1984).

Structure

Wing formula (n = 8):

p1/pc	p2	p3(e)	p4	p5	p6	p7	p10
(4)–(2)	4–6	wp	0–1	0–1	3–3.5	4.5–6	10–12

Wing rounded; p1 minute. Wing point p3 (4–5); p2 = (p6/7) 7; emarginated poorly defined on p3–4, often absent.

Figure 88. Wing of Caroline Islands Warbler.

Tail longish, strongly rounded; feathers rounded but rather narrow.

Bill very long and straight, broad-based and concave-sided; much longer than in Australian Reed Warbler (Fig. 41).

Tarsi strong as in Australian Reed Warbler but claws rather weak.

Weight No data available.

GEOGRAPHIC VARIATION None recorded.

TAXONOMY AND SYSTEMATICS Formerly treated as a race of Nightingale Warbler.

▲ Adult, Chuuk, Federated States of Micronesia, January (Jon Hornbuckle).

▲ Adult, Weno, Federated States of Micronesia, April (Richard Porter).

NAURU WARBLER
Acrocephalus rehsei   **Plate 30**

Calamoherpe rehsei **Finsch, 1883**. *Ibis*, p. 143. Nawodo, Nauru, Micronesia.

An extremely poorly known *Acrocephalus* restricted to Nauru in the W Pacific, where it is the only passerine recorded from this isolated island. It most closely resembles two other *Acrocephalus* warblers occurring in Micronesia; Nightingale Warbler, with which is it sometimes considered conspecific, and Caroline Islands Warbler. However, its smaller size and shorter bill, together with its isolated location, justify treatment as a separate species. Considered to be VULNERABLE by BirdLife International. Monotypic.

IDENTIFICATION Length 15cm. Wing 67–72mm. Tail/wing *c.* 85%.

A medium sized, warmly coloured *Acrocephalus*, which is smaller than the superficially similar Caroline Islands Warbler, and much smaller than Nightingale Warbler. Sexes alike.

Structure Has a substantial bill, but is proportionately shorter than that of Caroline Islands Warbler, so that the head appears rather rounded and less rakish or spiky than it can appear in that species. Combined with its relatively small size and rather light overall build, it is reminiscent of the small race *sumbae* of Clamorous Reed Warbler. The closed wing is short and rounded, with the wing point formed by p3–5. The wing-tip falls well short of the tips of the shortest uppertail-coverts, which enhances the apparent tail length.

Plumage and bare parts Warmly and richly coloured like Caroline Islands Warbler but slightly darker. It shows only limited contrast on the side of the head as the pale rusty-brown ear-coverts are similar in colour to the crown and nape and also merge with the warmly toned chin and throat. A pale rusty brown supercilium extends from the bill to the ear-coverts but appears less contrasting than that of Caroline Islands Warbler. The entire upperparts and tail are dark rufescent-brown, the slightly warmer and brighter rump and uppertail-coverts contrasting with the mantle and tail. The closed wing appears uniform rufescent-brown, much as the mantle, although close views reveal slightly darker brown centres to the greater coverts and tertials. The underparts are distinctly warmer and darker than in Caroline Islands Warbler. The sides of the neck, breast and belly are warmer, paler rusty-brown, richer on the flanks and becoming darker towards the vent and undertail-coverts.

The bill is dark grey with a dull pink lower mandible which darkens slightly towards the tip. The legs and feet are dark grey.

SIMILAR SPECIES No similar species occur on Nauru.

VOICE Not studied. The song has been described as reminiscent of Song Thrush and Common Blackbird.

MOULT No information available on moult timing or strategy.

HABITAT Occurs widely in suitable scrub and bushes throughout the island, with highest densities occurring in remnant forest on the steep sides of the island escarpment. Also frequents gardens in coastal areas and residual scrub on the central plateau (BirdLife International, 2000).

BEHAVIOUR Little known and probably similar to Caroline Islands Warbler. Believed to forage for insects in the crowns of coastal coconut palms.

BREEDING Probably breeds throughout the year. The nest is built from *c.* 0.5–3m above the ground in a bush or in low undergrowth, or placed in forked branches of a *Hibiscus* or lime tree *Tilia*. Clutch size uncertain, probably three eggs. No information available on the incubation or fledging periods.

DISTRIBUTION Endemic to the isolated 21km² island of Nauru (0° 32'N, 144° 45'E) in the W South Pacific. The highest point on the island lies on the phosphate plateau, at just 61m. Much habitat was lost during the twentieth century when phosphate mining reduced up to 90% of the central plateau to a wasteland. Military operations in 1943–45 inflicted further damage to the remaining habitat. Phosphate mining has now largely ceased and the island is showing signs of recovery. In 1993, the warbler was found to be widely distributed and relatively common, with a population estimated at 5,000 individuals in 2006 (BirdLife International). However, the tiny range leaves the species susceptible to unpredictable chance events such as cyclones or introduction of predators.

MOVEMENTS Presumed to be sedentary. There are no reports of movements away from Nauru. Even the closest island, Banaba in the Republic of Kiribati, a similar phosphate-covered island with luxuriant vegetation 290km to the southeast, lacks a resident *Acrocephalus*.

DESCRIPTION
Plumage – Adult fresh Forehead and crown plain warm brown. Supercilium broad, creamy brown, extending from base of bill to rear of ear coverts, becoming slightly narrower and darker behind eye. Lores dark brown, forming obvious dark line between bill and eye. Behind eye, eye-line dark brown, widening and merging with nape coloration. Ear-coverts pale cinnamon-brown, becoming darker and merging imperceptibly with nape coloration. Eye-ring inconspicuous. Nape, mantle and scapulars plain rufescent-brown. Rump and uppertail-coverts slightly brighter, rusty-brown than mantle. Tail feathers dark brown with warm rufescent-brown fringes.

Chin and throat dull cream, slightly warmer and browner on lower throat. Breast dull brown with slight yellowish wash. Sides of breast and upper flanks rufescent-brown, becoming darker and richer on lower flanks and undertail-coverts. Lesser, median and greater coverts and tertials dark brown with broad, rather diffuse, warm rufescent-brown fringes. Primary coverts dark brown. Secondaries and primaries dark brown with narrow rufescent-brown fringes and tips. Alula dark brown with brown fringe. Underwing-coverts rufescent-brown.

Juvenile Undescribed.
Bare parts Upper mandible dark grey with dull pink cutting edge. Lower mandible dull pink, usually slightly darker towards tip. Tarsi, toes and claws plumbeous-grey. Iris dull brown.

IN HAND CHARACTERS
Measurements

Measurements of Finsch (1873) converted to metric by Holyoak & Thibault (1978):
wing, (2 ♂♂) 70, 72, (5 ♀♀) 67.5–70; *tail*, (2 ♂♂) 59.5, 63.5, (5 ♀♀) 57–59.5; *tarsus*, (2 ♂♂) 25.5, (1 ♀) 25.5
Also (1 ♀ specimen):

bill (skull) 22.2; tail graduation 10; bill width 4.9; hind claw 8.9.

Structure Wing similar to the Caroline Island Warbler (Fig. 88); rounded with p1 minute. Wing point p3–4; emargination on p3.

Tail markedly rounded. Bill longish, rather slender.

Weight No data available.

GEOGRAPHIC VARIATION None recorded.

TAXONOMY AND SYSTEMATICS Formerly treated as a race of Nightingale Warbler. Otherwise, no issues arising.

Genus *Hippolais* Conrad, 1827

[Gr. *hupolais* small unidentified ground-nesting bird mentioned by Aristotle, Theophrastus and Hesychius.]

A genus of just four species, all long-distance migrants that breed in the Western Palearctic and winter in Africa. All are medium sized warblers with long, strong, broad-based bills. Their wings range from long and pointed to shorter and more rounded, but with a small to minute first primary. The tails are squarer than in *Acrocephalus* and the undertail-coverts are shorter. The tarsi are quite strong, and show characteristic scutellation in front. The toes and claws tend to be smaller than in *Acrocephalus*. The rictal bristles are short. All have plain upperparts and a subdued head pattern with pale, unmarked lores and a moderately pronounced supercilium. Most show distinctive wing-panels when in fresh plumage.

Icterine Warbler and Melodious Warbler are greenish olive above and pale yellow below, and have unmarked tails. They form a species-pair in Europe, with parapatric distributions except where their ranges overlap in northeast France. Another species-pair is formed by Olive-tree Warbler and Upcher's Warbler which are largely parapatric except in SC Turkey, where their ranges overlap slightly but they are separated by habitat. Both species are greyish above and show narrow whitish tips and edges to the outer tail feathers.

All four species inhabit woodland and bushy growth, generally drier habitat than favoured by *Acrocephalus*. Icterine and Olive-tree Warblers are distinctly arboreal. Nests are neat and cup-shaped, usually built in a branch fork, sometimes up to a few metres high. All species have loud chattering warbling songs and hard tacking calls.

A further four species have traditionally been included in *Hippolais* but are treated here within the genus *Iduna*. Molecular analysis has shown a marked divergence between these and *Hippolais* (*sensu stricto*), such that the traditional larger *Hippolais* becomes non-monophyletic (Fregin *et al.* 2009).

ICTERINE WARBLER
Hippolais icterina   Plate 31

Sylvia icterina **Vieillot, 1817**. *Nouv. Dict. d'Hist. Nat., nouv. éd.* 11: 194. Nancy, France.

An arboreal species that breeds at middle and northern latitudes across N and E Europe to W Siberia, with an isolated population centred on the S Caspian Sea. A long-distance migrant that winters in Africa, mainly in the southern tropics. It forms a species-pair with the parapatric Melodious Warbler. Monotypic.

IDENTIFICATION Length 13.5cm. Wing 75–83mm. Tail/wing 62–71%.
   A medium-sized *Hippolais* with yellow or yellow-tinged underparts, long wings and dark grey legs. Migrants and wintering birds occur alongside the similar Melodious Warbler in W and S Europe and in parts of W Africa. Pale variants with little or no yellow can also be confused on migration with Eastern Olivaceous Warbler or, in S African winter quarters, with Olive-tree Warbler. Separation from these species relies upon careful assessment of plumage colour, head and bill shape, wing feather edgings and wing structure, while the song is highly distinctive. Measurements and wing formula are diagnostic in the hand. Sexes alike.
Structure Slightly larger than Melodious and Eastern Olivaceous Warblers, but smaller than Olive-tree Warbler. It appears slim, with a longish but broad-based bill, the apparent length accentuated by a flat fore-crown. The head tends to look more attenuated, less rounded, than in Melodious Warbler, although the crown feathers are raised when excited to produce a distinct peak above the eye. The bill is less long and less robust than in Olive-tree Warbler. The wings are long, with primary tips reaching beyond the uppertail-coverts and a primary projection similar in length to the exposed length of the tertials (Fig. 90). When fresh, the primaries show seven or eight exposed tips, those of the outer feathers falling progressively further apart.

Emarginations on the third and fourth primaries fall well beyond the tips of the closed secondaries. The tail is rather slim and square-cut, shorter than in Olive-tree Warbler, appearing square-cut or even slightly notched.
Plumage and bare parts Fresh adults are distinctive, with bright greenish olive on the crown and upperparts and lemon-yellow underparts with an olive tinge to the sides of the breast and flanks. They show a conspicuous pale wing-panel formed by the pale yellow to whitish edges of the secondaries, which contrast with the blackish webs to the larger wing feathers. The closed wing shows rather uniform olive wing-coverts, against which the blackish alula tends to stand out prominently. The head pattern is poorly marked and subdued. A yellow supercilium extends back to above the middle of the ear-coverts, but shows little contrast with the crown or ear-coverts. As the lores and eye-ring are a similar tone of yellow and merge with the supercilium in front of the eye, this gives Icterine Warbler an open-faced expression in which the dark eye is prominent. It lacks white markings on the tail feather tips.
   Later in the breeding season, adults become duller and greyer above with wear, the yellow underparts become paler and the pale wing-panel becomes narrower and less contrasting. Pale variants occur, accounting for *c.* 5% or less of adults in W Europe. These are greyish olive above, usually with a tinge of yellow on the supercilium and underparts and with whitish belly and undertail-coverts.
   Compared with fresh adults, juveniles are browner above, less strongly tinged with green, and the yellow underparts are paler, especially the throat and abdomen. The pale wing-panel is less prominent on juveniles than on fresh adults but tends to be more noticeable in autumn than that of worn adults. This juvenile plumage appears to be retained until the winter moult in Africa.
   The bill is dark brown to greyish horn and shows an unmarked dull yellow or pinkish lower mandible. The legs and feet are dark grey or blue-grey and appear quite distinctive at all ages.

SIMILAR SPECIES

Melodious Warbler most closely resembles Icterine but their separation is usually straightforward. However, care is required in spring when some adult Melodious can show a conspicuous pale panel in the closed wing. Olive-tree Warbler presents a greater challenge if a grey-and-white *Hippolais* is encountered and extreme care is required. Upcher's Warbler and all *Iduna* species lack the yellow underparts and strong olive tones to the upperparts, but usually show a paler fringe to the outer web of the outermost rectrix and at the tail feather tips.

Melodious Warbler resembles Icterine in plumage and size and shares a similar head pattern. Overall, adult Melodious tends to appear slightly duller than adult Icterine, with an indistinct brownish cast to the upperparts and a marginally richer yellow tone to the underparts. It usually lacks the contrasting pale wing-panel of Icterine but this may be present and it can be surprisingly conspicuous in a few. It has a much shorter primary projection and a more rounded wing-tip with shorter p2 and, usually, a longer p1. The tail tip tends to be more rounded. The legs are usually brownish grey but this is not diagnostic since leg colour in some resembles Icterine.

Confusion is most likely to occur in spring when some fresh adult Melodious can show surprisingly conspicuous whitish edges to the secondaries and tertials, creating a pale panel in the closed wing. Such birds closely resemble Icterine Warbler and separation then relies on establishing the diagnostically shorter primary projection of Melodious.

It has been suggested that birds with pale panels and short primary projections may be hybrids between Melodious and Icterine originating from the narrow contact zone in N France, Belgium and SE Holland. Faivre *et al.* (1999) demonstrated that hybrid pairings do occur in the contact zone in E Burgandy, France. Furthermore, comparison of wing length and wing characteristics between birds examined there in the periods 1965–76 and 1985–96 has shown a trend towards an overall reduction in wing length and wing characters of Icterine Warbler, approaching those of the Melodious Warbler, while no similar change was recorded for Melodious Warbler.

Olive-tree Warbler resembles a large grey-and-white Icterine Warbler. It has a long primary projection and shows a contrasting pale wing-panel in fresh plumage. Moreover, its attenuated structure and restless, dashing behaviour can give the impression of a slim and lightly-built *Hippolais*. However, the two species have quite different songs. Given good views, differences in size, structure and colour tone should allow most silent Olive-tree Warblers to be distinguished from pale variant Icterine.

Although their wing length ranges overlap, Olive-tree is a distinctly larger bird, typically some 20–25% heavier than an Icterine. It has a proportionately longer tail and a longer, deeper, spike-like bill with a distinctive orange-yellow base below. It shows darker cheeks and narrow white edges to the outer rectrices, and the tertial fringes and wing-panels are silvery grey, paler and more contrasting than on Icterine.

VOICE The song is loud, striking and highly varied, with a rapid delivery, and is often sustained for several minutes, interrupted by only brief pauses. It consists of a continuous flow of melodious calls, high sweet notes and strident sounds interspersed with chattering and musical warbling within a frequency range spanning 2–8kHz. It contains extensive mimicry and repetition. Notes, short

sequences and mimicked bird calls tend to be repeated several times before changing to a different sequence. There is a considerable range of pitch and volume and the song is more varied than the similar song of Marsh Warbler, with which this species overlaps throughout much of its range. As much of the repertoire appears to be learned, songs of adjacent singing males can show considerable difference, depending on the range of species imitated and the order in which phrases and sequences are included and repeated.

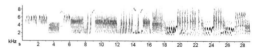

Part of song of Icterine Warbler, Suffolk, England, June. (Peter Kennerley)

Variation in song of same Icterine Warbler Suffolk, England, June. (Peter Kennerley)

A short, three-note '*tetetuî*' call, also described as an oriole-like '*deteroid*', is commonly given during the breeding season. This call is diagnostic and may also be included in the song. Otherwise, contact calls include a soft '*dett*' and a harder '*tek*', sometimes repeated two or three times. In addition, a *Phylloscopus*-like '*huit*' call is given, chiefly in late summer.

MOULT Adults replace a few head and body feathers prior to autumn migration and this partial moult may continue when adults reach the tropics. A complete moult takes place in winter quarters, mainly south of the African equator, between December and March, so that birds returning to the breeding areas are in fresh plumage. In Zambia this occurs from mid December and lasts approximately two months (Dowsett *et al.* 2008). The entire juvenile plumage is retained throughout the first autumn. Feathers grown in late July and August appear to be part of juvenile plumage development rather than plumage replacement. A full moult then takes place in winter quarters, as in adults.

HABITAT This arboreal species prefers the canopy of well-spaced trees. When breeding, it frequents sunny woodland edges and glades, broad-leaved copses, parks, orchards and gardens and tall hedges. It prefers trees with small light foliage, such as poplar, birch and alder, and favours a mixture of taller trees and tall bushy undergrowth. Birds may also be found in pure oak woodland, particularly in S Europe, and have been noted to prefer open stands of evergreen trees in Sweden. Breeds mainly in lowlands and river valleys, but extends up to 1,500m in foothills in some areas. On passage through Europe it occurs in all types of wooded, bushy and scrubby habitat, making the most of available thick cover. In dry areas of N Africa it occurs in palm groves, eucalyptus plantations, gardens, orchards and scattered desert scrub. In tropical Africa birds occupy open woodland or areas with plenty of trees and tall bushes, and range to well over 2,000m on passage. Wintering birds favour mature green *Acacia* and *Albizia* trees, often along water courses. In the southern tropics it also occurs in *Brachystegia* and broadleaved *Baikiaea* woodlands. In South Africa it is locally common in mature acacia and mixed woodlands.

BEHAVIOUR Mostly solitary, but forms small groups on migration. It forages restlessly in tree crowns, bush tops and high undergrowth, where it hops, clambers and jumps among foliage, but tends to stay concealed for much of the time. It takes insects while perched or fluttering on the edge of a bush and may emerge to make flycatching sallies. It has a more alert attitude and a more upright carriage than Eastern Olivaceous Warbler and the tail is flicked less persistently. Flight is fluent and dashing, showing its pointed wings and recalling that of Spotted Flycatcher. On arrival on the breeding grounds, song is intensive and persistent, maintained through the day and sometimes heard at night. Singing males adopt an upright stance and usually sing from within the cover of high foliage, although occasionally from an exposed perch. They reduce song frequency after pair formation and are then vocal mainly at dawn and dusk. The song period lasts until mid July. In winter quarters, birds tend to take up territories to which they may return year after year. Song is heard regularly then, mostly in February and March after completion of moult.

BREEDING HABITS Monogamous and territorial, occupying territories of 0.4–1.5ha (Cramp 1992). Most adults return to the same breeding site from year to year. The nest is usually placed in the fork of a tree or bush, between 1–4m up. It is a deep, well-built cup constructed from grasses, roots, leaves, moss, plant down and spiders'

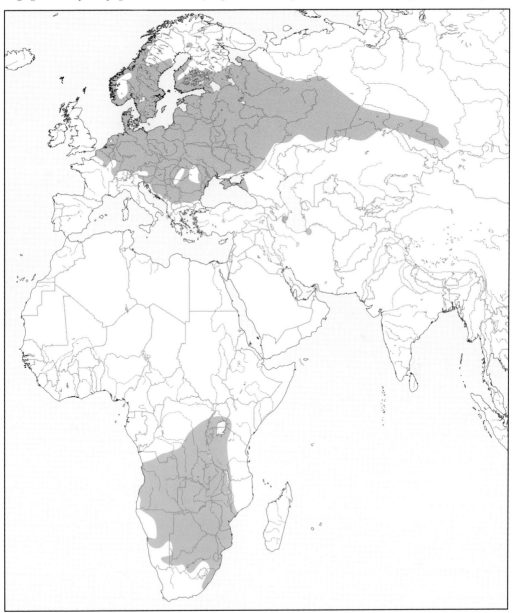

Icterine Warbler. Breeding range and winter distribution.

web and lined with hair, fine grasses and rootlets. It is often attached to surrounding twigs by fine grass loops and the outside may be adorned with pieces of bark, moss and wool (Cramp 1992). The clutch of 4–5 (sometimes 3 or 6) eggs is laid between late May and early July and incubated for 13–15 (sometimes 12–16) days. Incubation is mostly by the female although sometimes shared by the male. Nestlings are brooded by the female for the first week and are fed by both parents. The fledging period is 13–14 (12–16) days, after which the young quickly move into the tree canopy and become independent after about ten days. Single-brooded, late clutches are presumably replacements.

DISTRIBUTION

Breeding Breeds widely throughout the middle and northern latitudes of continental Europe, where range extends west to NE France and Belgium (where sympatric with Melodious Warbler) and the Netherlands. To the north it breeds throughout S Scandinavia including Denmark, much of Norway and Sweden to *c*. 67°N and Finland to *c*. 65°N. Here it is common to *c*. 62°N, but less so in the north of its range and in upland regions. It is a widespread and common bird throughout much of central Europe below 1,500m. In European Russia, it breeds north to Archangel on the White Sea coast and to about 60°N in the Ural Mountains. The southern range limit includes E France, N Switzerland, Austria, N Slovenia, N Serbia and N Bulgaria and more locally Croatia, Macedonia and S Bulgaria. It breeds in Ukraine south to the northern Black Sea coast and Crimea, then northeast through the Dnepropetrovsk region to the middle Volga and Ural Rivers in S Russia. East of the Urals, it ranges across the W Siberian Plain to the region of Omsk on the Irytsh River and to Novosibirsk and Tomsk on the Ob River. In extreme N Kazakhstan it is a rare breeding bird along the Ural River and in the Kokchetav region south of Omsk. A small and apparently disjunct population exists around the SW Caspian Sea, in Azerbaijan and N Iran.

In some places it is abundant and densities in prime broad-leaved habitats in France, Germany and Poland may reach one pair/hectare (Hagemeijer & Blair 1997). In the late twentieth century it declined considerably towards the western edge of its range in Belgium, France and Switzerland, especially where it breeds sympatrically with Melodious Warbler. It has increased in northern areas, in particular in Denmark, Sweden, Finland and Belarus. The European population has been estimated at 1.5 million pairs, with at least as many again breeding in Russia (Hagemeijer & Blair 1997).

Non-breeding Winters in Africa, mainly in the southern tropics. Between December and March, it is found from S and E DR Congo, S Uganda, SW Kenya and W Tanzania south to central Namibia, Botswana and N and E South Africa. The main wintering range appears to be centred from interior Angola, central Zambia and S Malawi south to Botswana and Zimbabwe, and the North West, Limpopo and Mpumalanga Provinces, South Africa. A few birds reach SE Namibia and Northern Cape, Free State, Kwazulu-Natal and Eastern Cape Provinces in South Africa. There are a few scattered reports spanning the period December to February from W Africa, including S Mali, Ivory Coast and S Nigeria. If valid these presumably refer to over-wintering birds.

MOVEMENTS Birds departing from NW Europe move east of south in autumn, those from Russia west of south. The main emigration from Europe apparently takes place across the central and E Mediterranean, with many birds pausing in Italy, the Balkans and Ukraine. Birds leaving W Siberia pass

through the N Caspian Sea area. Most European breeding areas are vacated between late July and early September, while Siberian breeders may remain until mid August. Passage through NW Europe peaks in early August, with stragglers occurring to mid September. In S Europe, passage continues throughout August and September and persists into early October. Birds move through the Crimea, Ukraine, between mid August and mid September. In N Africa, a few passage birds occur from Tunisia to Egypt from mid August onwards, but most probably overfly, continuing on directly to the northern tropics, where passage has been recorded through Chad and NE Nigeria between late August and mid October. Small numbers, perhaps Siberian breeders, occur along the Red Sea coasts of Sudan and Eritrea from late August to mid September. Further south, the main passage continues through DR Congo, Rwanda and Zambia, with rather few birds in Ethiopia or East Africa. The main arrival in S Africa takes place during late October and November.

Spring migration begins at the end of February, but most birds remain in their winter quarters to late March. Passage takes place through Zimbabwe and Zambia in late March and early April and through DR Congo to late April. A few birds occur in Kenya and Ethiopia during early and mid April. The main migration extends further west than in autumn to include Nigeria (peaking in late April) and Algeria. Scarce but regular in the Balearic Islands and uncommon in mainland Iberia, chiefly in the east. Many birds pause in spring in North Africa, where there is a strong passage from late April to mid May, with occasional records west to Morocco. There are very few reports from Arabia in spring, suggesting this region is largely avoided. Birds return to the breeding grounds quite late in spring, rarely before mid May in Poland, mid to late May in Sweden and late May to early June in N European Russia and Siberia. Movement through Europe lasts from late April to early June.

DESCRIPTION

Plumage – Adult fresh (March to May) Forehead to nape light olive-green to greenish olive-brown. Supercilium rather diffuse, pale lemon yellow in front of and above eye, becoming olive green above rear of ear-coverts. Eye-ring narrow but distinct, pale yellow. Lores pale yellow, mottled olive grey, merging with front part of supercilium and lacking darker loral line or spot. No eye-stripe. Ear-coverts and upper cheeks greenish olive with some yellow streaks, grading to lemon-yellow on lower cheeks. Mantle and scapulars to uppertail-coverts light olive-green to greenish olive-brown, slightly greener on rump. Tail greyish black, feathers narrowly edged pale yellow. Underparts lemon-yellow, slightly paler on belly and undertail-coverts and suffused with olive-brown on lower sides of neck, sides of breast and flanks. Lesser and median coverts olive-green. Greater coverts blackish, broadly edged pale grey-brown or pale greenish olive. Primary coverts blackish, finely fringed light olive-green. Alula conspicuously blackish with very narrow olive-green edge. Flight feathers and tertials blackish, primaries finely edged light greyish green, secondaries and tertials broadly edged pale yellow to whitish, to form a prominent pale panel on the closed wing. Tips of all flight feathers with fine greyish fringes. Underwing-coverts greyish white, tinged yellow. Leading edge at carpal joint brighter yellow.

Some individual variation independent of age occurs. Occasional birds have the top of the head, ear-coverts and upperparts olive-grey, with green tones subdued, supercilium and underparts off-white or with slight yellow tinge only.

Adult worn (July to October) Upperparts duller, more

greyish olive-brown (less greenish). Underparts paler yellow. Wing and tail feathers browner, fringes paler or completely worn off. Pale wing-panel persists until at least August, but gradually becomes narrower and less conspicuous and, eventually restricted to inner secondaries and outer tertial.

Juvenile Upperparts light olive-brown, with green tinge less pronounced than in adult. Underparts paler yellow, with yellow of throat, centre of breast, belly and undertail-coverts sometimes reduced to a faint yellowish tinge. Remiges and rectrices browner than in fresh adult and pale fringes to primary tips less prominent. Pale edges to secondaries and outer tertial less obviously white than adult, usually with slight yellow to pale buffish yellow fringe, so pale secondary panel still obvious and striking. Fringes to wing-coverts buffish brown, less green than in adult.

Bare Parts Upper mandible brownish or greyish horn with yellowish cutting edges. Lower mandible dull yellowish, becoming flesh or pinkish towards base. Mouth orange or orange-yellow; first autumn birds have two dark spots at base of tongue. Tarsi and toes dark olive-grey, slaty or blue-grey. Iris olive-brown or dark brown.

IN HAND CHARACTERS
Measurements

	Male	Female
Wing	76–83 (79.2; 80)	75–80 (77.8; 27)
Tail	49–55 (51.9; 50)	48–54 (51.3; 26)
Bill	15–17.5 (16.6; 79)	15.5–17.5 (16.5; 25)
Tarsus	19.5–22 (21.0; 49)	19.5–21.5 (20.5; 28)

(Includes data from Cramp 1992)

Sexes combined:
Tail/wing ratio: 62–71% (67%; 45)
Bill width: 4.4–5.2 (4.8; 20)
Hind claw: 4.8–6.2 (5.2; 21)
Tail graduation: (2)–3 (0.3; 20)
Juvenile wing *c.* 3mm shorter than in adult, tail 1–2mm shorter (Cramp 1992).

Structure

Wing formula (Cramp 1992):

p1/pc	p2	p3e	p4e	p5(e)	p6	p7	p10
(4)–2	1–4	wp	0–2.5	2.5–6	7–10	10–14	17–24

Wing long and pointed, with minute p1. Wing point p3 (4); p2 = p4–5 (5/6); emargination on p3–4, occasionally p5.

Figure 89. Wing of Icterine Warbler.

Tail rather short, tip square with t6 usually ≥ t1.

Bill flattened and broad at base, tip of culmen often slightly decurved; straight-sided (Fig. 92).

Tarsi quite strong, rather short; toes and claws small.

Recognition Usually distinguishable from all *Hippolais* and *Iduna* species except Melodious Warbler by yellow or yellow-tinged underparts, olive or greenish tinged upperparts and lack of pale markings on tail feather tips. Separated from Melodious by longer primary projection (wp to p10 17–24mm; 10–15mm in Melodious) (Fig. 90); by smaller, more pointed p1 (falling near primary covert tips); and longer p2 (falling at p4–5, rarely < p5; usually < p6 in Melodious). Almost all Icterine have wing length above 72mm (the maximum for Melodious). Marsh Warbler can appear faintly washed yellowish below, but has dark lores, no wing-panel, longer undertail-coverts, no emargination on p4 and a wing length below 75mm. Pale variant Icterine are easily separated from larger Olive-tree Warbler by shorter bill (< 18mm) and much shorter tail (< 58mm).

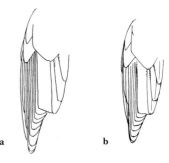

Figure 90. Closed wing structure of (a) Icterine Warbler and (b) Melodious Warbler.

Ageing In early autumn, young birds have fresh remiges and wing-coverts and show a pale mid wing-panel; the primaries are pale-tipped. Adults have worn remiges and wing-coverts and show little or no wing-panel. Young birds show two dark spots at base of tongue. These distinctions still apply in Africa during October–November.

Weight Range 8–24g; lean birds typically 11–14g. Frequently reaches pre-migratory weights of 16–18g, with very fat birds in Ukraine (autumn) and N Nigeria (spring) above 22g.

GEOGRAPHIC VARIATION None established, but see **Taxonomy and Systematics** below.

TAXONOMY AND SYSTEMATICS Two birds collected from Kuramabad in N Iran were described by Stresemann (1928) as a distinct race *H. i. alaris*. This form was said to differ from typical Icterine Warbler in having p2 shorter than p5, a shorter wing and slightly darker upperparts. However, a larger series from Iran included many birds resembling those of W Europe. Consequently the taxon *alaris* has been widely treated as a synonym of *icterina*. It is of interest, however, that of ten birds caught in SE Kenya in November and December, five had p2 equal to or shorter than p5. Icterine Warbler is treated here as a monotypic species.

▲ Adult, Czech Republic, June. Classic spring adult. Note distinctive pale wing-panel, long primary projection and pale tipped primaries (Jiri Bohdal).

▲ Adult, Poland, May. Shows brighter, yellower underparts compared with the drabber appearance of first-winter birds (Mateusz Matysiak).

▲ Juvenile, Cleveland, England, September. Typical first-winter bird with yellow tones most intense about head and throat, fading to drab greyish yellow on flanks. (Ian Boustead).

▲ Juvenile, Italy, September. Pale wing-panel remains conspicuous but duller, less striking than in adult (Daniele Occhiato).

▲ Juvenile, Kuwait, August. Note distinctive long primary projection and square-cut tail, both characteristic features (Pekka Fagel).

▲ Juvenile, Portugal, September. An exceptionally pale bird with green tones to upperparts replaced by pale sandy brown, and yellow underparts with creamy white. Remains recognisable as Icterine by the long primary projection. Pale birds account for ≤ 5% of birds in Western Europe (Ole Krogh).

MELODIOUS WARBLER
Hippolais polyglotta **Plate 31**

Sylvia polyglotta **Vieillot, 1817.** *Nouv. Dict. d'Hist. Nat., nouv. éd.* 11: 200. France.

Breeds in woodland and bushy growth in SW Europe and NW Africa and migrates to winter quarters in the tropics of W Africa. It forms a species pair with the parapatric Icterine Warbler *H. icterina*. Monotypic.

IDENTIFICATION Length 13cm. Wing 61–71mm. Tail/wing 71–78%.
A smallish *Hippolais* which, like Icterine Warbler, shows a combination of greenish upperparts, yellow or yellowish underparts and a rather plain facial pattern. During the breeding season it overlaps with Icterine in N France, S Belgium and, recently, SE Netherlands. It can occur with migrant Icterine outside the breeding season, particularly in Italy and the two species may meet in West Africa. Some Melodious Warblers are atypically pale and could be confused in Spain and NW Africa with Western Olivaceous Warbler. Separation of pale Melodious then relies on subtle differences in structure, plumage and bare part colour, although distinction of singing males should be straightforward. Sexes alike.
Structure A neat and compact warbler, slightly smaller than Icterine Warbler. The bill is quite long, but less broad-based than in Icterine and the head profile is distinctly more rounded. The wings are shorter and more rounded with wing point at p3–4. The closed primaries project half to two-thirds the exposed tertial length, so primary projection is much shorter than in Icterine (Fig. 90) and does not reach the end of the uppertail-coverts. Six or seven primary tips may be visible, but these are already worn and difficult to count by late spring.
Plumage and bare parts The striking yellow underparts and sides to the head distinguish Melodious Warbler from all *Hippolais* except Icterine. When fresh, adults show a yellow supercilium that extends to above the middle of the ear-coverts and largely yellow to yellowish grey lores with which the supercilium merges in front of the eye. A yellow eye-ring barely contrasts with the yellowish cheeks, so the face tends to appear bland and featureless and the contrastingly dark eye quite small and beady.
There is a slight buff suffusion to the rich yellow underparts, slightly darker on the sides of the breast and flanks. The upperparts and closed wings are olive-brown or greenish brown, rather warmer or browner in tone than in Icterine. A paler wing-panel, formed by yellowish buff edges to the secondaries and outer tertial, may be apparent in freshly moulted birds and can be retained until early April. These paler feather edges tend to appear as separated parallel lines so the wing-panel is rarely as contrasting as it appears in Icterine Warbler. Fresh adults in spring occasionally retain whitish fringes to the secondaries and tertials and show a more conspicuous pale wing-panel, and separation of such birds requires care. Like Icterine, Melodious lacks whitish fringes to the tail feather tips, but does show light brown outer edges to the outermost feathers. By late June and July worn birds lose their olive tones. The upperparts and wings then become more uniform brown or greyish brown and the underparts paler yellow. Pale variants occur with no trace of yellow and green in the plumage. Such birds, grey-brown above and creamy white to greyish white below, probably form fewer than 5% of the population in Iberia, on the basis

of ringing captures at Gibraltar (C. Perez pers. comm.).
Juveniles are rather browner above than fresh adults, with the supercilium and underparts paler, more buff-yellow. The edges to the tertials and secondaries are drab yellowish buff and may form a faint wing-panel, but this is never as conspicuous as in juvenile Icterine and has usually been lost to abrasion by August.
At all ages the dark bill has an unmarked pale yellowish flesh to pinkish orange lower mandible. The legs are typically brownish grey, but can sometimes approach blue-grey and resemble those of Icterine.

SIMILAR SPECIES Melodious and Icterine Warbler share many similarities, but their separation is usually straightforward. Pale variant Melodious closely resembles both Western Olivaceous and Eastern Olivaceous Warblers and their separation is potentially a much greater problem. **Icterine Warbler** is slightly larger and less richly coloured than Melodious, although there is considerable overlap due to the effects of wear and bleaching. Fresh Icterine always shows a conspicuous pale panel in the closed wing. However, some fresh Melodious can show a similar panel so this feature, although indicative, is not diagnostic of Icterine. Separation relies on wing structure with Icterine showing a conspicuously longer primary projection, almost equal to the tertial length and a pointed wing with eight primary tips visible. It always has dark grey or blue-grey legs, whereas on most Melodious these appear distinctly brown. However, some Melodious show grey legs and this character is not diagnostic.
Eastern Olivaceous Warbler occurs mainly as a vagrant within the breeding range of Melodious, although the race *elaeica* overlaps with it along the Adriatic coast of Slovenia and Croatia. On migration, Melodious also occurs within the breeding range of the race *reiseri* in desert regions of SE Morocco and Algeria. Eastern Olivaceous matches Melodious Warbler closely in size, structure and wing formula, and separation depends on differences in plumage and bare part colour. It lacks any hint of yellow and green in the plumage so most are readily separated by this feature alone, but it is very similar in appearance and coloration to pale variant Melodious. It also shows a slightly better marked supercilium than Melodious and often there is a dark spot in front of the eye, so it lacks the open-faced appearance of Melodious. The adult also has a white fringe to the edges and around the tip of the outermost tail feather and a whitish tip and inner web to t5. When fresh, Eastern Olivaceous has pale edges and tips to the secondaries which can form a distinct pale wing-panel, and a whitish line across the base of the visible primaries formed by the bunched pale secondary tips. It continuously dips it tail, giving a quiet '*tchack*' call at the same time, a behaviour unknown in Melodious.
Western Olivaceous Warbler overlaps with Melodious during the breeding season in Spain, Portugal and NW Africa and the two occur together in similar habitat in winter in parts of W Africa. There is overlap in size, structure and wing formula and the plumage of Western Olivaceous closely resembles that of pale variant Melodious. It shows many of the characters described for Eastern Olivaceous, but its resemblance to Melodious is even greater. It lacks the pale wing-panel of Eastern Olivaceous and the whitish edges and tips to the tail feathers are narrow and fairly inconspicuous. Separation from pale Melodious relies on its longer bill and flatter forehead, and a longer tail which gives it a more attenuated appearance. It does not constantly move its tail while foraging and in this respect resembles Melodious.
Eurasian Reed Warbler and **Marsh Warbler** are readily

separated from pale Melodious by structural differences, including longer undertail-coverts and a longer wing projection. Both species show dark lores and the underparts are washed pale warm brown to cream-buff.

VOICE The song consists of a varied and rapid chattering warble, with individual sequences falling within a frequency range of 2–8kHz. Individual song sequences last from 7–15 seconds and are separated by pauses of up to ten seconds, with occasional calls being given during these pauses. Each song sequence is typically introduced by a succession of repeated '*whi,whi,whi…*', '*pi, pi, pi…*' or '*chidi, chidi, chidi…*' notes, followed by a stuttering sparrow-like '*t-t-t-t…*', or even by a Song Thrush-like '*chuu, chuu…*'. In poor singers this introductory phase may dominate the song sequence, but in birds with a well-established vocabulary it is followed by a more varied and sustained musical warble. Compared with Icterine Warbler, the song lacks power and variety and sounds more rushed. It contains fewer pure-sounding notes and incorporates less mimicry. It is more musical, however, than the song of Western Olivaceous Warbler, but also more hurried and less rhythmic. It is slightly reminiscent of the song of a Sardinian Warbler or a very musical Common Whitethroat.

Part of song of Melodious Warbler, France, May. (Sample 2003)

The commonest calls are distinctive and sparrow-like, a monosyllabic '*terr*' or '*chuk*' and a disyllabic '*ter-terr*' or '*ter-cheek*', which may extend into an excited chatter. A brief '*hooeet*', recalling Willow Warbler, is mainly given in late summer.

MOULT After breeding, adults migrate to the wintering areas prior to moulting. The entire plumage is replaced shortly after arrival in W Africa, commencing in late September or early October and finishing in November or early December. Consequently, it moults earlier than Icterine so most birds are slightly worn when they return to the breeding grounds. The duration of the complete moult lasts about 50 days (Aidley & Wilkinson 1987). Some birds then replace at least part of their body contour plumage during February and early March, prior to return migration. There is apparently no post-juvenile moult in the breeding area. Young birds migrate in juvenile plumage, then undergo a complete moult in W Africa, probably at the same time as the adults.

HABITAT In Europe, it inhabits open woodland with bushy cover, woodland edge, thick scrub, riverine forest, trees and bushes around cultivation and along roadsides, and gardens and orchards in both rural and suburban environments. It prefers light foliaged trees with young growth, particularly tamarisk, elm and poplar, but regularly occurs in acacia, willow and stands of small or coppiced alder and oak (Cramp 1992). It tends to prefer less fragmented habitat than Icterine Warbler, with denser and lower growth, but readily uses tree crowns and the presence of some trees or taller bushes within the territory seems essential. Within its European breeding range, it occurs mainly in lowland areas, breeding no higher than 800–1,000m in Switzerland (Hagemeijer & Blair 1997). In NW Africa, it breeds in open woodland and bushy clearings, especially in forests of Cork Oak and Atlas Cedar, but also in Holm Oak coppice

on wooded and scrub covered hillsides up to 2,000m, and in willow, oleander and tamarisk along streams. In the W African wintering areas, it favours savanna woodland, forest edges and clearings, dense humid bush and secondary growth, gardens and even mangroves.

BEHAVIOUR Typically solitary and skulking. It feeds within scrub, bushes and low trees, keeping fairly low, usually no more than 3–4m above the ground. Some birds do feed in the tree canopy, gleaning and snapping at insect prey. Its foraging movements are rather heavy, with a horizontal carriage and frequent flicking of the tail. It appears less dashing than Icterine Warbler, with more fluttery, less fluent flight.

Breeding males may sing from within cover but often do so from an exposed perch. They also sing between perches in excited horizontal 'butterfly flight', with wings outspread and beating regularly. Song is continuous before pairing and may be heard throughout the day. It is infrequent during incubation and feeding of young, but can be renewed before replacement broods. Largely territorial in winter quarters and may sing persistently from December onwards, usually from thick-foliaged trees.

BREEDING HABITS Typically monogamous, perhaps sometimes polygynous. May form loose groups when nesting, with individual territory size ranging from 0.4ha to about 3ha. The nest is built by the female and placed in a bush or the fork of a shrub, usually 1–3m above the ground (Cramp 1992). It is a deep cup of leaves, plant stems and spiders' web, lined with rootlets, hair and plant down. The clutch of 4–5 eggs (sometimes just three) is incubated by the female for 12–13 days. The nestlings are brooded by the female for about five days and fed by both parents. They remain in the nest for about 12 days after hatching and are dependent on their parents for a further 9–10 days after fledging. Eggs are laid between mid May and early July. Usually single brooded,

DISTRIBUTION
Breeding Breeds throughout the Iberian peninsula and France, north to S Belgium, SE Netherlands, SW Germany and SW Switzerland; also on the Mediterranean island of Corsica, throughout Italy and into W Slovenia and NW Croatia. In NW Africa, it breeds in N Morocco (south to the Middle Atlas and High Atlas foothills), N Algeria (in the Tell and Atlas Saharienne) and NW Tunisia. The main stronghold is Iberia, with high numbers also in France and Italy. Densities may reach one pair/hectare in prime habitat. It is also widespread but less common in NW Africa. Since the mid twentieth century, the regular breeding range has expanded north to include Brittany in N France, Belgium, Germany and Switzerland. Breeding first occurred in the Netherlands in 1990 and by 2008 there were 14 singing males, all in Zuid Limburg in the extreme SE of the country. The European population is estimated to be between 1.3 and 2.7 million pairs (Hagemeijer & Blair 1997).
Non-breeding Winters in tropical W Africa, from Gambia, S Senegal, S Mali, S Burkina Faso and Nigeria (north to Kano) south to the Guinea coast, and extending east to C Cameroon and (rarely) W Central African Republic. Most birds winter in the guinea and derived savannah zones south of 8–9°N, between S Guinea and S Nigeria. Tens per hectare were found on Mount Nimba in SE Guinea (Brosset 1984). An olive and yellow bird trapped at Ngulia, Kenya, in November with the structure and biometrics of Melodious Warbler (Pearson *et al.* 1998) has since been shown to have mtDNA matching that of Eastern Olivaceous Warbler.

Melodious Warbler. Breeding range and winter distribution.

MOVEMENTS In Europe, departure from breeding sites begins in late July and passage continues to late September. Most birds move southwest and enter North Africa through S Iberia. Together with NW African populations, migrants continue south, most probably following a route close to the Atlantic coast. Passage through Morocco is mainly during August and early September, with stragglers to mid October. It is quite scarce throughout Morocco in autumn, however, suggesting that many birds overfly after staging in S Spain and Portugal. Migrants pass through Mauritania and Mali from August to October, and Senegal from late August to early November. It is common in N Nigeria from late September to late October, but most birds move on in November to the main guinea savannah wintering belt, where they start to arrive in mid October and become widespread in November.

Return passage has been noted in Senegal in late February and March, but most birds remain on the wintering grounds until early April and some stay into May. To the north of the wintering range, migrants occur in April in the northern tropics. Spring passage through Morocco and Algeria is more conspicuous than in autumn, beginning in early April and peaking from late April to mid May, with the last stragglers in early June. As birds return to NW African breeding sites during April and early May, some migrants in this region are probably mistaken for breeding birds. Passage occurs further to the east than in autumn, with occasional records coming from Tunisia and NW Libya. There is a strong passage through S Spain in early May. The first birds reach France at the end of April, but arrival near northern range limits is not until mid or late May.

Melodious Warbler is rare in Europe outside its breeding range, even in nearby countries such as Germany, Britain and Ireland. In the British Isles, it occurs mainly in the south and southwest but occasionally north to Shetland. The great majority of records relate to young birds between August and mid October, perhaps the result of random juvenile dispersal. Spring records are far fewer and occur between mid May and mid June. Elsewhere, it is a vagrant north and east of its breeding range, where it has occurred in Iceland, Norway, Sweden, Denmark, Poland, Czech Republic, Malta and Greece.

DESCRIPTION
Plumage – Adult fresh (November to February) Forehead to nape and upper sides of neck olive-brown, tinged greenish. Supercilium dull yellow or ochreous-yellow, extending from bill to above middle of ear-coverts. Narrow eye-ring yellow. Lores yellowish brown, merging with supercilium. Ear-coverts and upper cheeks olive-brown, tinged yellow, grading to light yellow on lower cheeks. Mantle and scapulars to uppertail-coverts greenish olive-brown, slightly lighter and greener on rump. Tail dark brown, t6 with paler grey-brown outer web and all feathers narrowly edged pale olive-yellow. Chin, throat and underparts light yellow with slight brownish cast, especially across breast. Lower sides of neck, sides of breast and flanks suffused olive-brown. Lesser and median coverts greenish olive-brown. Greater coverts blackish brown, broadly edged greenish olive-brown. Primary coverts and alula blackish, finely edged olive-brown. Flight feathers and tertials blackish brown, primaries finely edged light olive-brown, secondaries and tertials more broadly edged pale yellowish olive to buff-brown, occasionally whitish or yellowish white, to give a distinct pale wing-panel. Tips of primaries with fine greyish fringes. Underwing-coverts light yellow. By April and May, upperparts slightly greyer with fringes of greater coverts, tertials and secondaries narrower and greyer, so that wing-panel usually no longer distinct and pale edges and tips of primaries largely worn away.
Adult worn (June to August) Upperparts duller greyish brown. Underparts paler yellow or whitish. Wing and tail almost uniform grey brown with slight trace of greyish edging on inner secondaries only.
Juvenile Upperparts duller olive-brown than in fresh adult, with only a faint greenish tinge. Underparts paler, more buffy yellow, brown sides to breast and flanks less olive, more greyish. Wing and tail feathers dark brown (not blackish), pale tips to primaries narrow and inconspicuous. Buffy edges to secondaries and outermost tertial contrasting only slightly with darker edges to primaries. Tail dark brown, t6 with narrow greyish edge to outer web.
Bare Parts Upper mandible horn or dark brown with yellowish pink or pinkish orange cutting edges. Lower mandible yellowish pink or pinkish orange and unmarked. Mouth orange; first autumn birds have two tongue spots, usually lost by November. Tarsi and toes horn-brown to grey-brown or dark grey, often with a blue, olive or purplish tinge. Iris dark brown.

IN HAND CHARACTERS
Measurements

	Male	Female
Wing	63–71 (66.8; 83)	61–68 (63.9; 34)
Tail	47–54 (50.3; 83)	46–53 (48.5; 32)
Bill	14–17 (15.8; 77)	14.5–17 (15.7; 30)
Tarsus	19.5–21.5 (20.5; 71)	19–21 (20.2; 29)

(Includes data from Cramp 1992)

Sexes combined:
Tail/wing ratio: 71–78% (75%; 88)
Bill width: 3.9–4.7 (4.4; 20)
Hind claw: 4.5–5.6 (5.0; 20)
Tail graduation: 0–4 (1.8; 20)

Structure

Wing formula (Cramp 1992):

p1/pc	p2	p3e	p4e	p5e	p6	p7	p10
2–7	3–7	wp	0–1	0.5–1.5	2–4.5	5–8	11–15

Wing rounded, p1 small with rounded tip. Wing point p3 (and usually p4); p2 = p[5/6] 6, 6/7 [7/8]; emargination on p3–5, occasionally tip of p6.

Figure 91. Wing of Melodious Warbler.

Tail rather short, almost square, but t6 usually < t1 (cf. Icterine Warbler).

Bill flattened, tip of culmen often slightly decurved; sides straight or slightly concave (cf. Icterine Warbler Fig. 92).

Figure 92. Comparison of bill profile of (a) Melodious Warbler and (b) Icterine Warbler.

Tarsi quite strong, rather short; toes and claws small.

Recognition Most are distinguishable from all *Hippolais* and *Iduna* species except Icterine Warbler by yellow or yellow-tinged underparts. Adults also by absence of clean white fringes on tail feather tips. Wing structure and measurements can match those of *elaeica* race of Eastern Olivaceous Warbler. Separated from Icterine by shorter primary projection (wp to p10 < 15mm), longer, more rounded p1 (usually 3mm or more > pc) and shorter p2 (usually < p6) (Fig. 90). Wing length usually below 71mm (the minimum for Icterine). Spring adults and fresh juveniles lack the pronounced light wing-panel of Icterine but some may show indistinct panel. Eurasian Reed Warbler lacks any yellowish tinge below. It has dark lores, longer undertail-coverts and no emargination on p4–5.

Ageing In early autumn, young birds have fresh plumage, with unworn tail feathers and primary tips. Adults have heavily worn body plumage with grey bases to feathers showing through, worn wing and tail feathers and abraded primary tips. Young birds may remain distinguishable up to moult in late autumn, with residual light edging on wing feathers and primary tips only moderately worn.

Weight Range 8.0–22.8g; lean birds typically 10–13g. Birds often reach weights of 15–18g before migration, sometimes over 20g in spring in N Nigeria (Cramp 1992).

GEOGRAPHIC VARIATION None reported.

TAXONOMY AND SYSTEMATICS No issues arising.

▲ Adult, Italy, May. Note relatively short primary projection and uniform appearance to closed wing, together with slight brownish cast to upperparts and warmer yellow underparts (Daniele Occhiato).

▲ Adult, Netherlands, June. Has complete winter moult up to three months sooner than Icterine so adults in May appear more heavily worn than Icterine and usually lack pale primary tips (Ran Schols).

▲ Adult, Netherlands, June. A particularly drab individual with fairly prominent pale fringes to the tertials and secondaries. Overall coloration resembles a young bird but extent of wear is typical of an adult (Ran Schols).

▲ Adult, Italy, May. Slightly worn adult showing fairly prominent pale wing-panel, duller greyish green upperparts lacking brownish cast and drabber yellow underparts. Such birds can be mistaken for Icterine but the relatively short primary projection is diagnostic (Daniele Occhiato).

▲ ▶ Juvenile, Shetland, Scotland, August. Note greyish underparts and creamy yellow wash restricted to side of head and throat; young birds are duller and drabber than adults. The unworn appearance in autumn establishes this as a juvenile; adults would be more heavily abraded at this time of year. However, some young birds, even by late July, can show heavily abraded wings and tail, making ageing difficult. Note how light impacts upon perceived colour (Hugh Harrop).

OLIVE-TREE WARBLER
Hippolais olivetorum   Plate 31

Salicaria olivetorum **Strickland, 1837**. In: Gould, *Birds of Europe*, Vol 2, plate 107. Zante, Ionian Islands.

A long-distance migrant, breeding in the Adriatic, Mediterranean, Aegean and SW Black Sea regions of SE Europe and S Turkey and wintering mainly in S Africa. Monotypic.

IDENTIFICATION Length 15cm. Wing 81–92mm. Tail/wing 72–82%.

A large greyish warbler with a long, strong bill and long wings. Comparable in body weight to Garden Warbler and the impression that this is a bird of similar size to Barred Warbler or even Great Reed Warbler is misplaced. Throughout its range, it breeds alongside the similarly coloured but much smaller Eastern Olivaceous Warbler, and it could also be confused in Europe and in Africa with pale variant or strongly worn Icterine Warbler. On migration in the Middle East and in E Africa, it occurs with the somewhat similar Upcher's Warbler. Size, structure, bill colour and wing markings provide the most reliable clues to identification. Tail movements can also be useful in eliminating confusion species and the deep, raucous vocalisations are distinctive. Sexes alike.

Structure The largest of the *Hippolais* warblers. About 15% larger than Upcher's and Icterine Warblers, with a slim structure and an attenuated appearance to the head. The bill is strong and straight, with a fairly deep base, and appears both long and quite heavy. The forehead rises gradually from the bill base and a low rounded crown peaks behind the eye. The wings are proportionately long and extend to the middle of the uppertail-coverts. The closed primaries project some 80–100% of the length of the exposed tertials and seven or eight well-spaced primary tips are usually visible when fresh. Only Icterine Warbler among the *Hippolais* species shows such a conspicuously long wing point. The first primary is smaller than that of any other *Hippolais* or *Iduna* species. The legs and feet are robust.

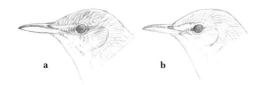

a   b

Figure 93. Comparison of head and bill shape of (a) Olive-tree Warbler and (b) Upcher's Warbler.

Plumage and bare parts In spring, when in fresh plumage, the upperparts of the adult are drab brownish grey. The wings are slightly darker and browner than the mantle and scapulars, but show a conspicuous pale panel formed by buffy white edges to the secondaries, outer tertial and tips of the greater coverts. The underparts are off-white with a creamy tinge, although there is a greyish wash to the breast and flanks. The facial pattern is poorly marked, but enhanced slightly by rather dark ear-coverts and cheeks that can give the head a distinctly hooded appearance. A greyish white supercilium extends back to the rear edge of the eye where it merges with a narrow white eye-ring. A variable dusky area is always present in front of the eye, sometimes restricted to a small spot, in other birds appearing more

extensive, but the pale grey of the lores tends to merge into the supercilium to create a rather bland and open-faced expression.

The greyish tail is similar to the mantle colour at the base and contrasts with the slightly paler sandy grey to grey-buff rump and uppertail-coverts, but darkens conspicuously along its length to become blackish grey towards the tip. It shows distinct whitish edges and the outer feathers are broadly fringed with white at the tip of the inner web. During the breeding season the wings and tail become browner with wear and contrast more with dull greyish upperparts. The pale wing-panel is reduced to a narrow band along the edges of the outer tertial and inner secondaries and is finally lost by late summer. However, the whitish edges and tips of the outer tail feathers tend to be retained. After an early autumn body moult, the contrast between fresh grey upperparts and faded brown wings and tail becomes even more pronounced.

Fresh juveniles are slightly paler and browner than fresh adults but otherwise resemble them closely. The pale wing-panel is extensive and conspicuous, but sandy buff rather than buffy white in colour, and the pale edges and tips to the outer tail feathers are less well defined. Later in autumn as plumages wears, first-winter birds appear very like worn adults.

At all ages, the bright, unmarked yellowish orange lower mandible is noticeable and the dark grey legs are a characteristic feature.

SIMILAR SPECIES Of the similar species likely to occur with Olive-tree Warbler, Upcher's Warbler most closely resembles it in terms of overall appearance and size. Barred Warbler also has greyish upperparts but is bulkier and very different in structure. If seen well, separation from the much smaller Eastern Olivaceous Warbler should present few problems. Pale variant Icterine Warbler presents a further pitfall, discussed below.

Upcher's Warbler is distinctly smaller than Olive-tree and is closer to Icterine Warbler in size. It has uniform light brownish grey upperparts and largely white underparts. When freshly moulted it shows a conspicuous pale wing-panel, but as the pale secondary edges are narrower this tends to be slightly less prominent than in Olive-tree Warbler. Fresh Upcher's also shows a prominent white outer edge and tip to the outermost tail feather. However, Upcher's is paler grey above than Olive-tree, with paler cheeks and a longer, whiter supercilium that extends to behind the eye. The lores are often more conspicuously marked and the head lacks the bland uniformity that Olive-tree tends to show. Structurally, Upcher's can be separated by its more slender bill, finer legs and shorter primary projection, about two-thirds the length of the exposed tertials. The tail is both broader and bulkier-looking than in Olive-tree. Both species show characteristic tail movements. In Upcher's these are deliberate and ritualised, the tail moving up and down and from side to side, quite slowly and often slightly spread. By contrast, Olive-tree dips its tail in a more random, shrike-like manner.

Eastern Olivaceous Warbler is a much smaller, more delicate warbler than Olive-tree, with a weaker bill, shorter wings and shorter primary projection, proportionately shorter tail and thinner legs. It is an active bird, continuously on the move, flitting among foliage and between bushes and regularly dipping its tail. Although Olive-tree does move and dip its tail, this is usually in a more random, less rhythmic manner. In coloration, the race *elaeica*, the form most likely to be encountered with Olive-tree, is significantly browner above, has a better-defined and slightly longer supercilium and paler, browner sides to the head. It can show a pale panel in the closed wing when fresh, but this is subdued compared to that of Olive-tree.

Icterine Warbler shares a conspicuous pale wing-panel and long primary projection with Olive-tree, but is distinctly smaller with a shorter and thinner bill and a much shorter tail that lacks white. The vast majority of Icterine Warblers appear distinctly yellow below and green above. However, pale variants, in which the yellow and green tones are replaced by white and grey-brown, can present a confusing scenario. Separation then relies on differences in structure, in particular tail length, bill length and depth and overall body size and bulk.

Barred Warbler occurs alongside Olive-tree both in Europe and East Africa. It is larger and more heavily built than Olive-tree and has a proportionately shorter primary projection, giving it a distinctly stocky appearance. Its shorter, blunter bill lacks the orange-yellow base of Olive-tree. Adults have a conspicuous pale iris and barred underparts and confusion at this age should never be an issue. Young birds are more uniform in appearance and lack the pale iris and barred underparts, but at all ages Barred Warbler shows pale tips to the greater and median coverts that form two distinct wing-bars, a feature not shown by Olive-tree Warbler.

VOICE The song is rather loud but low-pitched, combining a succession of discrete, throaty '*chroik*', '*chro*', '*chirk*' notes, delivered slowly and steadily, but in a random sequence and without repetition. It is delivered within a frequency range of 1–10kHz but typically sounds quite low pitched. The rhythm and harsh quality recall the song of Great Reed Warbler but it is less powerful and grating and does not appear to include mimicry. Individual song sequences usually last 3–15 seconds, separated by pauses of 4–8 seconds. The same or similar sequences are typically repeated several times and sometimes linked together by random calls.

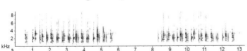

Part of song of Olive-tree Warbler, Turkey, May. (Peter Kennerley)

The common call-note is a deep and thick '*chack*' or '*chuk*', given singly or repeated at intervals of approximately 5–8 seconds. The alarm call is a prolonged rattling '*trrrrrr*' or combined to give '*chack-chack-trrrrrr*'. Calls are often given as a prelude to a song sequence. Trapped birds sometimes give a characteristic nasal '*chaarr*'.

MOULT Some adults appear to have a limited post-breeding moult of body feathers in July and August. After arrival in Africa in early autumn, but before reaching Kenya in November, there is an extensive partial moult during which most of the body and head plumage, most of the lesser and median coverts, the inner greater coverts and most of the tertials are replaced. The majority of birds passing through Kenya in November retain unmoulted flight feathers and tail feathers, but from late November onwards a few are already starting to moult the inner primaries. A complete winter moult takes place in S Africa. Most birds begin in December or January and finish in February or March. In addition to replacing the remiges and rectrices, there is a further renewal of the body plumage and, probably, some

of the tertials that were replaced in autumn.

Juveniles replace most of the body feathering and inner greater coverts in a post-juvenile moult that apparently occurs mainly in Europe prior to southward migration and certainly before reaching Kenya in November. As in adults, this is followed by a complete winter moult in S Africa.

HABITAT During the breeding season, it inhabits low-lying areas with well-spaced trees in warm and dry areas, such as olive groves, orchards, vineyards and open oak woodland. It tends to show an affinity for areas with a scattering of bushes, often on sloping ground.

In Africa, it occurs in bush country with scattered trees, dry open woodland and sometimes in gardens. It can frequently be found in degraded habitat and usually in areas below 1,200m. It is most commonly seen in low thorny trees and bushes and shows a preference for acacia woodland, in particular *Acacia tortilis* and *A. mellifera*.

BEHAVIOUR During the breeding season it forages mainly in the tree canopy where it can be difficult to see among foliage, although it also feeds in bushes and occasionally on the ground. When foraging, it can remain elusive and stationary for long periods, but when active its movements are rather heavy, ponderous and deliberate and short flights between trees are strong and buoyant. It usually maintains a horizontal carriage although this is accompanied by regular and frequently repeated movements of the tail, which can be waved in the manner of a shrike *Lanius*, or limited to shallow downward dips, similar to those of Eastern Olivaceous Warbler. During May and June, males sing persistently, usually from a concealed perch within a shrub or tree canopy. Song continues throughout incubation and may often be heard at night or during the hottest part of the day. On migration and in Africa, it is usually seen singly or in small groups and is unobtrusive but often quite approachable. In Kenya, it tends to be less skulking and more arboreal than Upcher's Warbler and is often seen feeding in open canopy and among the outer twigs of large acacia bushes (DJP pers. obs.). In Africa, a quiet song or sub-song may be heard from autumn passage migrants. Wintering birds show territorial behaviour and deliver a more sustained song, especially during February and March.

BREEDING HABITS Solitary and territorial, but several pairs may associate loosely together. The nest is built in the fork of a low tree, such as an olive or oak, or in a bush, typically between 0.5m and 3m from the ground. It is a rounded construction with a deep cup, made from grass, plant stems, bark strips and rootlets. It is lined with fine grasses and fibres, sometimes with horse hair and covered on the outside with spiders' web. A single clutch of 3–4 eggs is usually laid in late May or early June. The incubation period is no longer than 13 days but the duration of the fledging period is unknown. The young are fed by both parents.

DISTRIBUTION

Breeding Breeds from extreme SE Europe to S Turkey and Syria and there is also a small isolated population in N Israel. Along the Adriatic coastline it is confined to low-lying areas of Croatia, Serbia and Albania and rarely penetrates far inland. It breeds widely throughout Greece, including many of the islands in the Ionian and Aegean Seas south to Crete. To the north, range appears to be expanding in SE Bulgaria and it has spread along the Black Sea coast and recently bred in extreme SE Romania. In Turkey, it breeds around the Sea of Marmara and along the Mediterranean coast east to Hatay and into adjacent regions in NW Syria, in particular near Kassab. East of the Mediterranean, its range reaches inland along a belt through SE Anatolia to *c.* 40°E. Distribution is patchy throughout the range but it is locally common at low to medium altitudes in Greece and Albania, with significant numbers in Croatia and Bulgaria. The world population is small, with some 7,000 to 13,000 pairs estimated in the Balkan countries and a few thousand more in Turkey (Hagemeijer & Blair 1997). Numbers are apparently stable.

Non-breeding Migrates through NE and E Africa to winter south of the equator. A few overwinter in C and SE Kenya and in C and SW Tanzania, but most continue to S Zambia, Zimbabwe, C and S Mozambique, Botswana and NE South Africa. The main wintering concentration appears to be in the arid savanna of N Botswana and the eastern edge of the Kalahari in E Botswana and Limpopo Province, South Africa. A few birds reach C Namibia and N KwaZulu-Natal Province, South Africa.

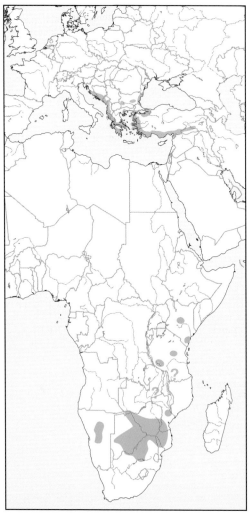

Olive-tree Warbler. Breeding range and winter distribution.

MOVEMENTS It leaves the breeding areas between the end of July and mid September. In Turkey, most have departed by the end of August and only stragglers remain into September (Kirwan *et al.* 2008). Movements during the next two months are poorly known but the initial direction of migration appears to be southeast, with birds skirting the E Mediterranean and passing through Syria and Israel. It is rare in Cyprus, but passage is noted during August and September in N and central Israel. North African records, between mid August and early September, are mainly from NE Egypt, with none confirmed west of the Nile. Birds pass through W and central Arabia during September and early October. There are a few autumn records from NE Sudan but practically none from the Horn of Africa and the species' whereabouts during October remains unknown. It reappears from early November in Kenya, where there is a small passage through central and southeast areas and scores are trapped and ringed annually at Ngulia (Tsavo) in November and early December. The first birds reach southern Africa in late November, but the main arrival is during December. Birds ringed in Kenya in November have been recovered in SE Botswana in January and in C Mozambique in mid March.

Return migration begins during the second half of March but a few remain in Botswana until early April. Small numbers have been recorded on passage in Zambia and Malawi to mid April and through E Kenya and Yemen during early to mid April. There are remarkably few spring records from NE Africa or the Middle East. The earliest returning birds are reported from Turkey in late March, but most arrive during the first three weeks in April, with passage continuing to mid May. It reaches breeding areas in the Balkans from the end of April, but the main arrival at the northwest limit of the range is in early May.

Vagrancy There are very few records of Olive-tree Warbler outside its known range. In Europe, there is just one record to the north and west of the breeding range, on the Shetland Islands, Scotland, on 16 August 2006 (Harrap *et al.* 2008).

DESCRIPTION

Plumage – Adult fresh (March to May) Forehead, crown and nape brownish grey with olive tinge. Supercilium rather diffuse, greyish white, extending only to rear of eye and merging with upper part of distinct, narrow, broken white eye-ring. Lores greyish white, variable mottled dusky grey area in front of eye. No stripe behind eye. Upper ear-coverts brownish grey, concolorous with crown and sides of neck. Lower ear-coverts and cheeks light brownish grey with faint dusky mottling. Mantle and scapulars brownish grey with olive tinge, becoming paler, more sandy grey or grey-buff on rump and uppertail-coverts. Tail dark grey-brown, feathers narrowly edged pale greyish, the outermost broadly edged greyish white. Tip and distal part of inner web of t4–6 (and sometimes t3) with white fringe, widest on tip of t6. Chin, throat, breast and belly white with a creamy tinge, sides of breast and flanks washed grey. Lesser and median coverts brownish grey. Greater coverts dark grey-brown, fringed pale grey-buff, tipped slightly paler buff-white. Tertials dark grey-brown, innermost fringed grey-buff, outermost more broadly fringed buffy white. Primary coverts, alula and primaries dark grey-brown or blackish brown, narrowly fringed pale grey-buff. Primaries narrowly tipped whitish. Outer web of secondaries broadly fringed buff-white: together with edges of outermost tertial and greater covert tips, form a conspicuous pale panel on closed wing. Underwing-coverts creamy white.

Adult worn (July to September) Upperparts duller, without olive tinge. Underparts off-white. Remiges and rectrices browner, with pale fringes worn, but pale edge to innermost secondaries and outer tertial usually retained until July or early August. Pale outer edge to outermost rectrix and whitish tip to inner web usually retained until November. In November after partial moult, fresh body and head feathers contrast with duller, worn brownish wings and tail. Fresh, dark-centred, broadly pale-fringed tertials and greater coverts contrast with retained and heavily worn and faded feathers.

First-winter Body and head plumage apparently as adult. Worn juvenile wing and tail feathers retained; already worn by November.

Juvenile Rather paler and browner above than fresh adult, underparts tinged grey-buff, less creamy. Pale edges to secondaries and tertials with buff tinge (less whitish). Pale edge to t6 narrower, more buff, than in adult, pale fringe at tip of inner web grey-buff and less distinct.

Bare Parts Upper mandible dark greyish horn with bright yellowish flesh cutting edge. Lower mandible rather bright yellowish flesh. Mouth orange-yellow. Tarsi and toes dark olive-grey or slate-grey; soles dull ochre; claws brownish grey. Iris dark brown.

IN HAND CHARACTERS
Measurements

	Male	Female
Wing	81–91 (87.1; 34)	82–92 (86.1; 19)
Tail	60–71 (65.7; 33)	62–68 (64.8; 19)
Bill	18.5–21 (19.9; 33)	19.5–21 (19.9; 18)
Tarsus	22.5–24.5 (23.6; 34)	22.5–25 (23.5; 19)

(Includes data from Cramp 1992)

Sexes combined:
Tail/wing ratio: 72–82% (75%; 23)
Bill width: 4.7–5.6 (5.1; 24)
Hind claw: 5.0–6.7 (5.7; 24)
Tail graduation: 2–7 (3.6; 22)

Juvenile wing averages *c.* 2mm shorter than adult (NRG unpublished data)

Structure

Wing formula (Cramp 1992):

p1/pc	p2	p3e	p4e	p5	p6	p7	p10
3–8	1.5–4	wp	0–3	3–7	7–11	10–14	18–23

Wing pointed, p1 minute and pointed. Wing point p3 (4); p2 = p4–4/5; emargination on p3–4 [5].

Figure 94. Wing of Olive-tree Warbler.

Tail slightly rounded, feathers narrower than in Upcher's Warbler.

Bill long and strong; broad-based and straight sided.

Tarsi strong; toes and claws relatively small.

Recognition Large and greyish, with rather dark cheeks and a poorly marked supercilium. Fresh-plumaged birds show prominent pale edges to secondaries and a white edge and white-fringed tip to outer tail feather.

Wing length (usually over 80mm) separates it from all except the largest Upcher's Warblers.

Distinguished from both Upcher's and Eastern Olivaceous Warblers by very short p1 (about half length of pc), longer p2 (> p5) and greater p10 shortfall (18–23mm). There is usually no emargination on p5.

Bill length (> 18.5mm) and width (usually > 5mm) should also be diagnostic.

Ageing In early autumn, young birds have fresh body plumage, unworn wing and tail feathers and a pale greyish white to buffy white wing-panel. Adults have worn body plumage, worn wing and tail feathers and no wing-panel. In late autumn, ageing is less easy. First year birds have slightly worn-looking upperparts, uniformly worn and faded tertials and wing-coverts and moderately worn primaries and tail feathers; but they usually retain distinct tongue spots until at least December. Adults then have fresh grey upperparts, fresh tertials and wing-coverts that contrast with a few very worn and faded old feathers, and very worn primaries and tail feathers; they also lack tongue spots. Skull ossification is usually incomplete in young birds up to November.

Weight Range 13–24g. Typical weight of lean birds 14–17g. Fat passage migrants in Kenya in November are commonly 20–23g (DJP).

GEOGRAPHIC VARIATION None reported.

TAXONOMY AND SYSTEMATICS No issues arising.

▲▶ Adult, Silifke, Turkey, May. Fresh adult in spring showing characteristic cold grey upperparts, whitish wing-panel, and long, pale-tipped primaries extending well beyond the tertials. Note conspicuous yellow-orange lower mandible. Structure appears robust and attenuated, exaggerated by long and slim bill, long primary projection and relatively long tail (Daniele Occhiato).

▲ Adult, Israel, May. A slightly drabber individual with a less well-pronounced supercilium, but whitish edges to replaced tertials and secondaries still form conspicuous wing-panel. At times can appear slim and sleek (Amir Ben Dov).

▲ Adult, Adrosan, Turkey, May. A rather drab individual showing little contrast between the grey flanks and upperparts (George Reszeter).

▲ First-winter, Ngulia, Kenya, December. This young bird has commenced moult of inner primaries while on migration. Note fresh greater and median coverts contrasting with worn primary coverts, alula and tertials (David Pearson).

▲ First-winter, Ngulia, Kenya, December. Body plumage replaced during autumn moult contrasts with browner remiges, rectrices and wing-coverts. Note abraded fringes to secondaries, so pale wing-panel lost (David Pearson).

480

UPCHER'S WARBLER
Hippolais languida   **Plate 32**

Curruca languida **Hemprich & Ehrenberg, 1833.** *Symb. Phys. Avium Decas I, fol. cc.* Syria.

A migrant that breeds in dry hills and semi-arid country in SW and C Asia and winters in similar dry scrub habitat within a restricted region of E Africa. Monotypic.

IDENTIFICATION Length *c.* 14cm. Wing 71–80mm. Tail/wing 76–83%.

A pale, grey-brown, medium sized *Hippolais* with a long-ish bill and a relatively long and bulky tail. Easily confused with two greyish species with which it can occur within its breeding range and in Africa, the larger Olive-tree Warbler and the smaller Eastern Olivaceous Warbler, particularly the eastern race of the latter, *elaeica*. It also overlaps in parts of C Asia with Sykes's Warbler and, to a lesser extent, with Booted Warbler, although these are considerably smaller and browner. Structure, face pattern and tail markings provide useful identification pointers, while its distinctive song, bold behaviour and unique tail movements are not shared with any similar species. Sexes alike.

Structure Comparable in size to Icterine Warbler, but with a slightly stockier appearance, accentuated by the much longer, broader tail. The bill is fairly broad-based, but slim, slightly longer than in Eastern Olivaceous, but similarly down-drooping at the tip. The low crown usually appears a little more rounded than Eastern Olivaceous would show, although when excited the fore-crown feathering is raised to give a steep forehead. On the closed wing, the primaries project *c.* 70% the length of the exposed tertials (slightly longer than in the *elaeica* race of Eastern Olivaceous), with six or seven pale primary tips visible when fresh. These fall well short of the tips of the uppertail-coverts. Emarginations are visible on p3–4 and sometimes near the tip of p5. The positioning of the tertials is often not symmetrical, the tip of the middle tertial falling closer to the longest, but this feature is also shared with some Eastern Olivaceous and Olive-tree Warblers.

Plumage and bare parts Upcher's Warbler can present a distinctly pale grey-and-white appearance not matched by other *Hippolais* or *Iduna* species, particularly when seen in strong sunlight. In fresh adult plumage, the upperparts are fairly uniform light grey-brown or light sandy-grey, offset by clean whitish underparts. There is a narrow but well marked whitish supercilium which extends from the bill base to just behind the eye and this contrasts in front of the eye with a diffuse dusky loral line, so that Upcher's lacks the open-faced appearance of some *Hippolais* warblers. There is a narrow white eye-ring which merges with the supercilium above the eye and with the cheeks below. The pale grey-brown of the ear-coverts merges with the still paler cheeks, which in turn merge with the whitish chin and throat, so that the sides of the head show little contrast. On the closed wing the dark grey remiges and primary and greater coverts contrast with the light grey mantle, scapulars and smaller wing-coverts, but pale edges to the secondaries and outer tertials form a conspicuous pale panel. The tail is much darker than the upperparts and this is particularly apparent in flight. Mid grey at the base, it becomes blackish towards the tip, so that white edges to the outermost feathers and broad white tips and inner web margins on the outer three pairs can appear particularly prominent. This character is not unique however and can also be shown by freshly moulted Olive-tree Warbler.

On the breeding grounds, most birds are heavily worn and faded, so that grey tones become duller and the wing-coverts, remiges and tail feathers become browner and less contrasting. The pale wing-panel disappears and the white edges and tips to the outer tail feathers are lost. First-winter birds in early autumn resemble fresh adults, but the wing and tail feathers are less dark. They show a distinct pale buff panel in the wing and pale fringes to the wing-coverts, but pale markings to the tail feather tips are poorly defined.

At all ages, the bill has a pale yellowish or pinkish lower mandible and the greyish legs are tinged brown or flesh.

SIMILAR SPECIES Upcher's Warbler overlaps with the *elaeica* race of Eastern Olivaceous Warbler throughout much of its breeding range and with Olive-tree Warbler in SC Turkey. It meets both these species in winter in E Africa. In C Asia it must be separated from the smaller Sykes's Warbler and can also come into contact with Booted Warbler, at least during migration.

Olive-tree Warbler is approximately 15% larger than Upcher's although this may not always be apparent. Compared with Upcher's it appears less bulky, more attenuated, with a larger bill, fairly long, almost flat forehead and longer primary projection. It is considerably darker above and shows darker cheeks, a shorter less clearly defined supercilium extending only to the eye and usually a diffusely darker spot in front of the eye rather than a dusky loral line. Olive-tree has a fairly bright orange-yellow lower mandible and relatively stout, dark grey legs.

Eastern Olivaceous Warbler (race *elaeica*) is significantly smaller than Upcher's (being slightly smaller than Eurasian Reed Warbler) and appears slimmer. It has a shorter, narrower tail and a slightly shorter, thinner bill. It shows a rather shorter primary projection typically half to no more than two-thirds of the tertial length, and usually fairly evenly spaced tertials. Both species have grey-brown upperparts, but these are usually distinctly browner in freshly moulted *elaeica*. The two show a similar head pattern and supercilium, but *elaeica* may show more contrast between the lower edge of the cheeks and the paler throat. Both show a pale wing-panel in fresh plumage in Africa, but in *elaeica* this is buffier in tone and more subdued. The tail in fresh *elaeica* is less dark than in Upcher's and white tips to the outer feathers tend to be narrower. The lower mandible is yellowish pink, rather than pinkish as in Upcher's, but leg colour is similar in the two species. Behavioural differences provide useful separation clues. Eastern Olivaceous is an active warbler, continuously on the move. It regularly dips its tail, giving a quiet '*tac*' call each time. Upcher's has slower, heavier and more deliberate movements and is more inclined to appear in open situations, feeding and singing on the sides or top of a bush or rock and hopping about in full view on the ground. It moves its tail vigorously, both up-and-down and from side-to-side, often randomly but sometimes in a circular pattern and often holding it slightly spread.

Sykes's Warbler and **Booted Warbler** are predominantly brown *Iduna* species and upperpart colour alone should preclude confusion with Upcher's. Both are much smaller than Upcher's, with a proportionately small fine bill and much shorter primary projection. Sykes's tends to have a relatively long tail, while that of Booted is shorter, but the tail is narrow in both species and lacks the bulk of Upcher's. Neither species displays the tail-waving behaviour shown by Upcher's.

VOICE The song is a lively, rapid and rather scratchy warbling, with a flowing delivery. It contains some melodious sequences and is constantly changing pitch between frequency ranges of 1–7kHz. Most sequences last 10–15 seconds, followed by a pause of 5–10 seconds, but song can be sustained for over half a minute. Each sequence usually consists of a repetition of short phrases, each of 2–3 seconds, or of two alternating phrases, but there is much individual variation. It is usually preceded and sometimes followed by the '*tuc*' call, or by ticking or thin '*ti*' notes. The flowing delivery suggests a *Sylvia* warbler, but is more musical and varied and less scratchy than, for example, Common Whitethroat. It is quite different from the undulating, chattering song of Eastern Olivaceous Warbler or the slower, harsher and more rhythmic delivery of Olive-tree Warbler.

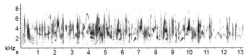

Part of song of Upcher's Warbler, Uzbekistan, May. (Peter Kennerley)

The common call is a rather quiet, dry '*tac*' or '*tuc*', heard frequently from birds in winter quarters or on passage. This call, likened to the sound of two stones being tapped together, is less hard and given less persistently than the foraging call of Eastern Olivaceous Warbler. When excited it may be repeated continuously 3–4 times per second. In alarm, a harsher shrike-like '*charrrrrr*' call is given.

MOULT After breeding, adults may replace some body plumage and tertials prior to migration, but this appears to vary individually. The complete moult takes place in Africa and is quite protracted, sometimes lasting 3–4 months. Many birds begin to replace the inner primaries in Somalia and Ethiopia during August and September and moult is well advanced in most birds reaching Kenya in November. Of birds (all ages) caught at Ngulia in SE Kenya in November and December, 5% had yet to start moult, 92% were in active primary moult (usually with 3–7 old primaries remaining on each wing) and just 3% had completed the moult (DJP, unpublished observations). Most birds complete moult in Kenya during January, but some, perhaps first-year birds, not until mid March. Young birds moult their juvenile body and head feathers shortly after fledging and then have a complete moult in Africa. This appears to coincide with the moult of adults and is well in progress in Kenya in November.

HABITAT Breeds in warm to hot arid regions, often at higher elevations than Eastern Olivaceous and Sykes's Warblers. Throughout its range it frequents semi-deserts, dry rocky hillsides often cut by deep winding valleys, ravines and gorges and enclaves of cultivation near villages. It requires patches of scattered scrub in which to forage and nest, such as tamarisk thickets and Wild Almond *Prunus jacquemontii*, but also occurs in saxaul scrub in sand dune areas, thorn bushes on stony hillsides and shrubby thickets in the valleys of large rivers (Cramp 1992). It breeds up to 1,600m in Lebanon on bushy hillsides, while in Uzbekistan, breeding occurs in the hills near Samarkand to *c*. 2,000m on dry hillsides with scattered scrub above wooded ravines and orchards. In Baluchistan, Pakistan, it breeds on dry hillsides with *Artemesia* scrub at altitudes between 1,800m and 2,400m (Roberts 1992).

On passage and in winter this is a species of dry bush country, with or without small trees. In east Africa, it occurs in scattered, often leafless, bushes and thickets and in low acacia and *Commiphora* woodlands, mainly in hot, arid or semi-arid areas below 1,200m. It prefers drier country than Eastern Olivaceous Warbler and is much less dependent on large acacia trees.

BEHAVIOUR Typically seen in ones and twos outside the breeding season but small parties may occur on passage. It is less arboreal than Eastern Olivaceous Warbler and prefers to forage within bushes, gleaning insects at all levels from leaves and twigs. Its movements are rather deliberate, recalling those of Olive-tree Warbler, usually less active than in Eastern Olivaceous. When excited, the head feathers are raised to give a peak at the centre of the crown. It is a bold and conspicuous species and appears to spend considerable periods foraging on stony ground around the base of small bushes, where it hops in a chat-like manner.

During the breeding season and also in winter it performs continuous deliberate movements of the tail, lowering it and slowly raising it again about once per second, at the same time often fanning it and moving it from side to side. The wings are flicked frequently and sometimes raised sideways or upward one at a time (Urban *et al.* 1997). Flight between bushes is low and direct and it may glide on spread wings at end of a longer flight with the tail slightly raised.

On return to the breeding grounds males sing almost continuously during daytime, sometimes hidden within foliage, but often perched prominently on the side or top of a bush or rock with a rather upright stance. Males sometimes perform a short song-flight, rising from the top of a bush with slow deliberate wing-beats, then gliding slowly down with wings raised. In windy conditions, a singing bird may hang in the wind with its wings outstretched above a cliff or rocky bluff and almost appear to float as it gains uplift from wind rising up a rock face. This behaviour may continue for several minutes, with the bird rising and falling in the updraft and singing regularly throughout. Song is heard mainly at the beginning of the breeding season and diminishes after pairing. In winter quarters, birds sing frequently and perform aggressive territorial chases during February and March, shortly before departure.

BREEDING HABITS Territorial, but like other *Hippolais* shows a tendency for several pairs to nest close together. The nest is built among branching twigs in scrubby bushes, or in low trees such as pistachio, oak and pear, typically between 0.5–2.5m from the ground. It is an untidy structure of small twigs and grasses, into which a neat rounded cup of grasses, stems, plant down and spiders' webs and egg cases is built and lined with finer grasses and animal hair. The usual clutch size is 3–5 eggs and these are incubated by the female for approximately 12 days, although the male will protect the eggs during the heat of the day. The young are fed by both parents and fledge after 11–12 days. Egg-laying takes place from mid May, but mostly in late May and early June, with little difference between dates in Turkey and Kazakhstan. Single brooded in Turkey and Kazakhstan, but clutches are replaced if lost early in the season.

DISTRIBUTION
Breeding The western breeding limit lies in S Turkey where it is a local and uncommon summer visitor but probably more widespread than is realised. Its range extends from the Taurus Mountains and the region of Gaziantep and across much of SE Turkey to the border with Iraq and Iran. To the

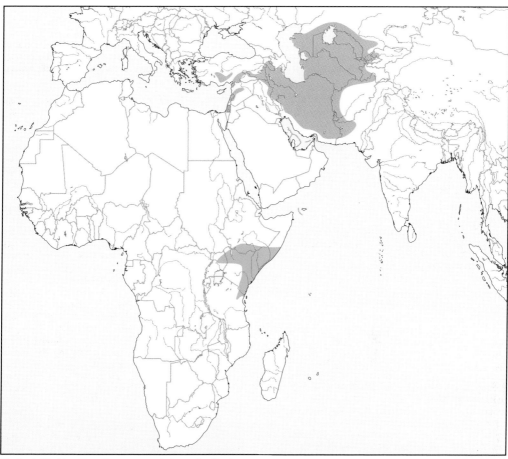

Upcher's Warbler. Breeding range and winter distribution.

south, it probably breeds in Syria and certainly does so in Lebanon, NE Israel and W Jordan. East of Turkey, it ranges from S Armenia and SW Azerbaijan, around the S Caspian Sea and throughout Iran to the W Baluchistan region of Pakistan. East of the Caspian Sea, it breeds widely throughout Turkmenistan and throughout Uzbekistan from the Aral Sea, through the Kyzyl Kum desert and into NE Afghanistan and the foothills of the Pamir Mountains in W Tajikistan. Its northern limit is in Kazakhstan, where it is widespread from the eastern shores of the Caspian Sea to the N Aral Sea, then southeast to the region of Shymkent and the foothills of the western Tien Shan Mountains. Within this range in C Asia it is generally common to locally abundant.

Non-breeding During the winter months it occupies a relatively small range in E Africa. It occurs sparingly in low country in S Ethiopia and N Kenya. It ranges more commonly through hot arid lowlands in S Somalia and E and SE Kenya, reaching extreme NE Tanzania where recorded from Moshi, Mkomazi and Amani. It has occurred locally in dry low bushland in SE Uganda.

MOVEMENTS Departure from the breeding areas begins in July and most have left Turkey by mid August, where it is rare by September. Departing birds from the main Central Asian population move southwest, with passage through Turkmenistan mainly in August and early September. There

is a large passage in E Iran in late September, then through E and S Arabia. Passage through the Gulf States lasts from early August to early October but is sparser here than in spring. Migrants move through N Yemen from July to early November and it appears this western route is favoured in autumn. Birds enter Africa through Eritrea and Somalia and are present in N Somalia from early August onwards. They are common along the coast of Eritrea from mid August to early October, and in C Ethiopia from the rift valley eastward to the end of October, but are rare in Sudan. Few birds reach Kenya or S Somalia until mid November. In SE Kenya, passage at Ngulia is mainly from late November to late December and most birds return to wintering sites in the Tsavo area during December and early January.

Return migration begins in March and most birds leave Kenyan wintering sites towards the end of this month. Passage through Ethiopia and Eritrea is much lighter than in autumn, mainly from mid March to early April. A few birds linger in Kenya to late April and in Somalia to early May. Migration across Arabia occurs mainly in the east and substantial numbers pass through Oman, UAE and Kuwait between mid March and early May, with a peak in early April. Reported from Iran from mid March, but passage occurs here mainly in April. In C Asia, most birds return to southern breeding areas in April and early May, but reach Kazakhstan between late April and mid May, with passage continuing to late May. Western breeders reach N Israel and Jordan from mid April and Turkey during late April and early May.

Outside the known breeding range, there is a single record of a singing bird from Istanbul on 24 May 1998, the only record for Europe (Kirwan *et al.* 2008).

DESCRIPTION

Plumage – Adult fresh (January to April) Forehead and crown to nape and upperside of neck light brownish grey. Supercilium greyish white, well marked and extending from base of bill to just behind eye. Lores pale greyish, with dusky area in front of eye contrasting with the supercilium. Ear-coverts grey-brown, sometimes with indistinct darker stripe behind eye, merging with paler grey-buff cheeks. Narrow eye-ring merges with white supercilium above eye. Mantle and scapulars to uppertail-coverts light greyish brown, usually with sandy or ochreous tinge to rump and uppertail-coverts. Tail dark grey-brown or blackish brown, especially towards tip, becoming paler grey-brown towards base, but darker than uppertail-coverts. Outermost feather (t6) with narrow whitish outer edge and broad whitish fringe around tip and onto inner web; t5 with similar but narrower fringe on tip and inner web, tips of t3–4 often also with trace of pale fringes. Chin, throat and underparts white, tinged greyish, becoming more strongly washed grey-buff on sides of breast, lower flanks and undertail-coverts. Lesser and median coverts light brownish grey. Greater coverts and tertials dark grey-brown with broad, light grey-brown fringes. Primary coverts and alula dark grey-brown with fine grey-buff fringes. Remiges dark grey-brown to blackish brown, edged pale sandy-grey to greyish white, tips with narrow grey-buff fringes. Broader edges of inner secondaries and outer two tertials form a distinct pale wing-panel.

Adult worn (July to November) Resembles fresh adult but upperparts paler and duller, supercilium and underparts whiter. Remiges and tail feathers browner and duller, with pale edges to secondaries mostly lost and pale wing-panel usually not apparent. Whitish tips to tail feathers usually lost.

Juvenile Similar to fresh adult, but upperparts more sandy-brown (less greyish); flanks with stronger buff tinge. Remiges less dark, with pale wing-panel more buffish (less grey) and with more distinct buff or sandy edges and tips to greater and median coverts. Tail feathers less blackish, less broadly rounded, with pale fringes at tips of outer feathers warm buff, narrower and less well-defined.

First-winter Fresh body plumage as adult, but juvenile remiges and rectrices retained. Most are worn and resemble adult by October–November.

Bare Parts Upper mandible blackish or dark greyish horn. Lower mandible entirely pale yellowish, pinkish yellow or flesh-pink. Mouth orange. Tarsi and toes grey or grey-brown, tinged pinkish; claws brownish grey. Iris dark brown, adults often with a distinct deep reddish tinge.

IN HAND CHARACTERS
Measurements

	Male	Female
Wing	72–80 (76.4; 16)	71–80 (75.4; 19)
Tail	55–63 (59.1; 16)	56–62 (58.8; 19)
Bill	17–20 (18.2; 15)	17–19 (18.1; 17)
Tarsus	20–23 (22.1; 14)	20.5–23 (22.1; 18)

Sexes combined:
Tail/wing ratio: 76–83% (78%; 35)
Bill width: 3.8–4.4 (4.2; 13)
Hind claw: 4.6–5.8 (5.2; 13)
Tail graduation: 2–9 (4.4; 17)

Juvenile wing and tail average *c.* 3mm shorter than in adult (Cramp 1992).

Structure

Wing formula (from Cramp 1992):

p1/pc	p2	p3e	p4e	p5(e)	p6	p7	p10
(4)–2	2–7	wp	0–0.5	0.5–2	2–5.5	6–9.5	14–18

Wing rounded, but p1 minute. Wing point p3 (4); p2 = p5–5/6 (6, 6/7); emargination on p3–4, often slightly on p5.

Figure 95. Wing of Upcher's Warbler.

Tail slightly rounded, feathers broad and rounded (Fig. 97).
Bill flattened, rather narrow-tipped with concave sides; tip of culmen slightly decurved.

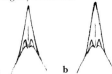

a   b

Figure 96. Comparison of bill profile of (a) Upcher's Warbler and (b) Olive-tree Warbler.

Tarsi slightly stronger than in Eastern Olivaceous Warbler; toes and claws small.

Recognition Slightly paler and greyer than the *elaeica* race of Eastern Olivaceous Warbler, with a longer bill but broader tail. Most are separable on wing length from both *elaeica* (with wing 72mm or below) and Olive-tree Warbler (with wing 79mm or above). First primary (p1) is about equal to or slightly shorter than pc, much shorter than in Eastern Olivaceous or Sykes's Warblers, but longer than in Olive-tree. Second primary (p2) is shorter than in Olive-tree (in which p2 > p5) and the p10 shortfall is less (14–18mm, compared with 18–23mm in Olive-tree).

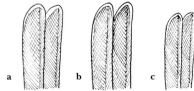

a   b   c

Figure 97. Comparison of the shape of the two outer tail feathers of (a) Upcher's Warbler (b) Olive-tree Warbler and (c) adult Eastern Olivaceous Warbler *I. p. elaeica*.

The tail feathers (and also the tertials) are much broader than in Eastern Olivaceous or Olive-tree (Fig. 97) and the more narrow-tipped, concave-sided bill is distinctive (Fig. 96).

Ageing In early autumn, young birds with fresh body plumage and unworn wing and tail feathers are readily distinguishable from adults in which these are badly abraded. By November, first year birds in Kenya are worn-looking like adults. Most have already started wing moult and are difficult or impossible to age. Some retain faint tongue spots. Adults may show a ruby-red tinge to the dark brown eye, but this is not easy to discern. Skull ossification is often incomplete in young birds up to November.

Weight Range 9.5–17g; typical weight of lean birds 10.5–13.5g. Spring migrants in Oman included many fat birds with weights 14–16.7g (GN unpublished data).

GEOGRAPHIC VARIATION Birds from C Asia were described by Severtsov as a distinct race, *H. l. magnirostris,* based on the paler and more sandy tone to the upperparts. The difference is slight and is not apparently consistent throughout the proposed range. Following Stepanyan (1978, 2003) we do not recognise *magnirostris.*

TAXONOMY AND SYSTEMATICS No issues arising.

▲ ▶ Adult, Gaziantep, Turkey, May. A rather browner individual with creamy white underparts, but still shows contrasting pale wing-panel. Note tip of central tertial lies closer to longest tertial than shortest, a characteristic feature of Upcher's although shared with some Olive-tree Warblers (Daniele Occhiato).

▲ Adult, Gaziantep, Turkey, May. In spring, males will sit conspicuously on top of a small tree or bush, or prominent rock, from where they make short, gliding song-flights to nearby bushes or rocks (Daniele Occhiato).

◀ ▲ Adult, Katha, Turkey, May. Appearance resembles Olive-tree Warbler including contrasting pale wing-panel. Separated by paler flanks, smaller bill (similar to that of Icterine Warbler), shorter primary projection and shorter tail, which darkens towards the tip (Daniele Occhiato).

485

Genus *Iduna* Keyserling & Blasius, 1840

[No explanation; perhaps from L. *idoneus* appropriate, suitable, or Gr. *idou* behold,
or a phonetic rendering of Gr. *aedonis* nightingale]

This genus consists of four Palearctic species included until recently in *Hippolais,* together with two Afrotropical species treated until now under *Chloropeta*. Recent DNA work has established that these belong in an acrocephalid lineage that also includes *Phragamaticola* and *Calamonastides*, and is distinct from the clade containing the four *Hippolais* species.

The Palearctic *Iduna* comprise two species-pairs, each formerly considered to be a single polytypic species. Western Olivaceous and Eastern Olivaceous Warblers are allopatric in Europe, the former migrating to winter in western Africa, the latter to eastern Africa. Eastern Olivaceous Warbler also has four African races, breeding in the Sahara and coastal Somalia. Sykes's Warbler was, until recently, treated as a race of Booted Warbler but it is now widely recognised that these are distinct species. Both breed in western Asia, with Booted to the north of Sykes's, although they apparently breed sympatrically in central Kazakhstan. Booted also extends west through temperate Russia to reach southeast Finland, and both species winter in the Indian subcontinent.

These Palearctic species are similar to *Hippolais* in plumage, structure and behaviour. They are small- to medium-sized warblers with longish, rather broad-based bills. Their wings are somewhat rounded but with a small first primary. Their tails are squarer than in *Acrocephalus* and the undertail-coverts shorter. The tarsi are scutellated as in *Hippolais*, but typically more slender, with rather small toes and claws. The rictal bristles are short and fine. The upperparts are plain, and the head pattern subdued, with the supercilium appearing poorly to moderately pronounced. All show pale to whitish outer webs to the outer tail feathers. All four inhabit dry woodland, bushy growth or scrub. Western Olivaceous and Eastern Olivaceous Warblers are often found in tree canopy. Nests are neat and cup-shaped, usually built in a forked branch. Their chattering or bubbling songs and tacking calls recall those of some of the smaller *Acrocephalus* warblers.

The two resident African species were formerly known as flycatcher-warblers. Molecular studies by Fregin *et al.* (2009) now confirm their place within the *Iduna* clade. Both are olive above and yellow below, with slender blackish legs, broad, flycatcher-like bills and long conspicuous rictal bristles, and short rounded wings with a large first primary. They frequent bushes and damp herbaceous growth and their feeding and nesting behaviour, and vocalisations, resemble those of Acrocephalid warblers.

EASTERN OLIVACEOUS WARBLER
Iduna pallida   Plates 32 and 33

Curruca pallida Hemprich & Ehrenberg, 1833. *Symb. Phys. Avium, fol. bb.* The Nile in Egypt and Nubia.

A long-distance migrant breeding widely in SE Europe, the Middle East and S Central Asia and wintering in NE and E Africa. Also resident or a local migrant in N and NE Africa, with breeding populations across the Sahara and in Somalia. We treat Western Olivaceous Warbler as a distinct species and thus recognise five races within *I. pallida*.
I. p. pallida (Hemprich & Ehrenberg 1833). Egypt to N Sudan (Nubia).
I. p. elaeica (Lindermayer 1843). SE Europe and Turkey, east to southern C Asia and south to Israel, Jordan, Iraq and W Iran.
I. p. reiseri (Hilgert 1908). Oases of the NW Sahara.
I. p. laeneni (Niethammer 1955). S Saharan borders from Lake Chad to W Sudan.

I. p. alulensis (Ash, Pearson & Bensch 2004). Red Sea and Gulf of Aden coasts.

IDENTIFICATION Length 11.5–13cm. Wing 58–71mm. Tail/wing 70–84%.

A small, pale greyish brown or buff-brown warbler usually showing a pale supercilium in front of the eye and sometimes a pale wing-panel. Vocalisations and tail movements are distinctive. Otherwise, field identification where it overlaps with similar species, relies largely on subtle details of structure and careful examination of facial pattern and wing and tail feather edgings. Sexes alike.
Structure Rather slim. The head profile, with a long, slim bill, flat forehead and low domed crown resembles that of Sykes's Warbler, but can also suggest Eurasian Reed or Blyth's Reed Warbler. At times it raises the crown feathering to form an untidy peak just behind the eye. The longish bill has straight or marginally concave sides and tends to have a downcurved tip to the upper mandible (Fig. 103). It is quite distinct from the larger, broader, slightly convex-sided bill of Western Olivaceous. In the migratory race *elaeica*, the

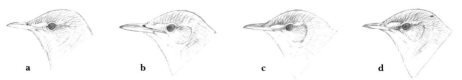

Figure 98. Comparison of head and bill shape of (a) Eastern Olivaceous Warbler (b) Western Olivaceous Warbler (c) Sykes's Warbler and (d) Booted Warbler.

primaries project about half to two-thirds the length of the exposed tertials, but far less in the resident African forms. Six or seven pale primary tips are typically visible when fresh, and emarginations on p3–5 fall about level with the tips of the secondaries. The tail appears neat and slim and is proportionately shorter and narrower than in Western Olivaceous and Upcher's Warblers.

Plumage and bare parts In fresh adult plumage in the African wintering range, the race *elaeica* is greyish brown above with an olive cast, and whitish or greyish white below with a tinge of creamy buff on the sides of the breast and flanks. It shows a narrow but well-marked creamy supercilium that usually extends to the back of the eye or slightly beyond. In front of the eye, there is a dusky spot or smudge on the otherwise pale and unmarked lores that merge with the supercilium to give an 'open-faced' expression. The ear-coverts and cheeks are darker than the crown, but paler than the throat, and the division between throat and cheek is usually quite well defined. On freshly moulted birds, there are narrow buff edges and tips to the flight feathers. Those on the secondaries and outermost tertial often form a faint but contrastingly paler panel in the closed wing and a pale line across the bunched secondaries, while paler tips to the greater coverts can suggest a narrow wing-bar. The outermost tail feathers have a narrow pale outer edge and the outer two pairs show well-demarcated whitish fringes near the tips that extend onto the distal inner web.

By May, birds on the breeding grounds are worn and bleached and appear drabber grey-brown above and whiter on the supercilium and underparts. Pale edgings to wing feathers have usually been lost and the pale wing-panel may not be apparent. The pale tail feather tips largely disappear during summer. First-winter birds in early autumn resemble fresh adults in overall colour and appearance. They show a faint buffy panel across the secondaries and there is often a more distinct pale bar across the greater coverts. Furthermore, they lack the whitish fringes near the tail feather tips.

Compared with *elaeica*, the Saharan races appear less grey, more buffish or sandy, but are otherwise similar in plumage pattern, with well-defined, pale wing feather edgings and tail tip markings. Although similar to *elaeica* in structure, they are slightly shorter-winged, particularly the race *laeneni* of the S Sahara. Nominate *pallida* of Egypt has buffy brown upperparts, similar in colour to Western Olivaceous Warbler, while the race *reiseri* of the NW Sahara is slightly paler and more sandy brown. Race *laeneni* resembles *reiseri* in colour but is still smaller. The small, short-winged race *alulensis* of Red Sea and N Somalia is closer in colour to *elaeica* than to the desert breeding forms.

In all races, the bill is dark greyish horn above with a paler cutting edge, and unmarked pinkish yellow below. The rather small and slender legs are typically grey-brown with a pinkish tinge.

SIMILAR SPECIES The Palearctic race *elaeica* overlaps in the Middle East and in SW and southern C Asia with the very similar Sykes's Warbler and great care is needed to separate these two, even in the hand. It also overlaps in SW Asia, Arabia and E Africa with the similar but distinctly larger Upcher's Warbler. On migration in southern C Asia, it occurs alongside Booted Warbler and Blyth's Reed Warbler and can occur with both Eurasian Reed and Marsh Warblers almost anywhere within its range. In Saharan Africa, the desert races must be distinguished from the larger, broader-billed Western Olivaceous Warbler.

Sykes's Warbler closely resembles the race *elaeica*, particularly during the breeding season when both are worn and faded. The two are similar in size, but Sykes's has a proportionately shorter wing and longer tail and a slightly smaller and thinner bill. It is distinctly browner above and shows a more uniform closed wing, but worn *elaeica* can appear similar once pale tertial and secondary fringes are lost. Sykes's usually shows paler, more pinkish legs than *elaeica*. Song and tail movement provide additional guides to separation. See further discussion under Sykes's Warbler.

Booted Warbler is a small *Iduna* whose distinction from *elaeica* is usually straightforward. It is a slighter bird, always active, randomly flicking its wings and tail like Sykes's Warbler. It has a long conspicuous supercilium that usually extends to the rear of the ear-coverts, dark lores and a short, fine *Phylloscopus*-like bill. See further discussion under Booted Warbler.

Upcher's Warbler has a longer, broader tail that is conspicuously waved about, quite unlike the steady rhythmic tail dipping of Eastern Olivaceous. It has a slightly longer but distinctly deeper bill, giving the head a heavier structure, and shows a conspicuously pinkish lower mandible. The upperparts are paler and distinctly greyer than in *elaeica*. When fresh it shows a more pronounced whitish panel on the closed wing, but this may become inconspicuous when birds return to breeding areas. The fresh tail is blackish, particularly towards the tip, fading to dark brown by May.

Western Olivaceous Warbler may meet the desert races, *reiseri* and *laeneni*, of Eastern Olivaceous in the W Sahara. It is slightly larger than these with a proportionately longer tail and thicker legs. It has a larger, deeper and much broader bill which often shows slightly convex sides. It is also rather darker and browner. Compared with race *elaeica* it is slightly warmer, less greyish and lacks any olive tones. It lacks the light edgings to the wing feathers and the more prominent whitish tail tip markings of fresh Eastern Olivaceous (all races). An important distinction is that when foraging it never dips the tail in the repetitive manner of Eastern Olivaceous.

Eurasian Reed Warbler and **Marsh Warbler** are usually darker, browner or more olive above than any race of Eastern Olivaceous, with strong buffy tones on the flanks and underparts. But note that race *fuscus* of Eurasian Reed often shows pale tipped tail feathers and the palest birds can approach the grey-brown upperparts and whitish underparts of *elaeica*. Compared with *elaeica*, both species have long undertail-coverts, a more rounded tail, a conspicuously longer primary projection and a different wing formula with only p3 emarginated.

Blyth's Reed Warbler has a wing formula and measurements similar to those of *elaeica* and can be confused with it, even in the hand. It is typically more olive-brown above, however and has long, deep undertail-coverts and a more rounded tail that lacks whitish markings.

VOICE The song is quite loud and vigorous, but repetitive, suggesting that of Eurasian Reed Warbler, although the delivery is slightly faster. It consists of a chattering sequence of notes with some softer notes interspersed. Song sequences are 2–5 seconds in length, each rising and falling again in volume and pitch between 2–7kHz and are repeated without pause in cyclic manner, occasionally for up to 30 seconds. Away from the breeding area, song is heard commonly on the African wintering grounds and occasionally from spring passage birds. This is a quieter version, with the same chattering sequence and underlying undulating rhythm, but more rambling and with a less clear cyclic pattern, but often sustained for long periods.

Part of song of Eastern Olivaceous Warbler, recorded within breeding range of *I. p. elaeica*, Goksu delta, Turkey, May. (Peter Kennerley)

The most commonly heard call is a persistent repeated hard '*tack…tack…tack*' or '*tchack…tchack*', often heard on the breeding grounds after pair formation and given constantly by feeding birds in winter. Other calls include a repeated '*trrt…trrt….trrt*' and a series of sharp ticking sounds, given by birds alarmed at the nest.

MOULT In *elaeica*, adults moult some body and head feathers in late July and August before autumn migration, but the complete moult takes place in Africa. Its timing is variable. Some commence primary moult in the northern tropics in October and November and a few are fully moulted when they reach Kenya by late November and December. However, the majority of East African wintering birds arrive in Kenya unmoulted, or with just the inner primaries replaced. Of birds on passage at Ngulia, SE Kenya, in November and December, 63% were unmoulted, 34% partly moulted (mostly suspended) and less than 1% fully moulted (DJP pers. obs.). Most are in active wing moult in E Africa in January and complete this in February. Occasionally, moult continues as late as mid March, perhaps in first-year birds. Juveniles have a partial moult involving head and body feathers shortly after fledging. This is followed by a complete moult from first-winter to adult plumage in Africa. Its timing is believed to coincide with that of adults.

In nominate *pallida*, most adults begin wing moult in Egypt in August and this is usually completed in Sudan during November and December. Juveniles have a partial post-juvenile body moult in the breeding area, followed by a complete moult in the non-breeding area after autumn migration. W Saharan birds also appear to have a partial post-juvenile moult on the breeding grounds, during July and August in *reiseri* and May and June in *laeneni*, but there is no information on the timing and duration of complete moult in these races.

HABITAT In the breeding season, *elaeica* in Europe inhabits warmer, drier country than other *Iduna* and *Hippolais* species. It occupies a variety of habitats, from bushy river valleys with scattered trees, scrub-covered hillsides and cultivation to steppe and semi-desert, ranging from sea level to 1,900m (Cramp 1992). It frequents gardens, orchards, olive groves, acacia thickets, tamarisk clumps and palms in oases. In the Middle East and C Asia it also breeds in semi-desert regions but usually near wetlands, rivers and irrigation channels, among thickets on riverside dunes and in low cover along ditches and edges of reedbeds. It may occur alongside Sykes's Warbler in C Asia, although that species shows a preference for even drier regions away from water. In Egypt, nominate *pallida* is typically a bird of cultivation with trees and it is found in suburban gardens and city centres. Saharan birds breed in oases, palm groves and acacia woodland. Birds in Somalia have been found in low coastal areas, in acacia and tamarisk trees along wadis, in irrigated gardens and in mangroves.

In E Africa, migrant *elaeica* occurs mainly in arid and semi-arid country below 1,600m, where it prefers dry open woodland, bushland and scrub thicket. In Kenya and Tanzania it inhabits acacia and *Commiphora* woodlands and grassy plains with scattered bushes and riverine trees. It is particularly attracted to tall *Balanites* bushes and the canopy of flat-topped acacias. It also occurs in mangroves on the NE African coasts, especially on migration.

BEHAVIOUR An active bird that forages restlessly with deliberate movements in the tops of bushes or in open tree canopy, regularly picking insects from vegetation. While foraging, it has the distinctive habit of frequently and persistently dipping its tail downwards, at the same time uttering its repeated hard '*tack*' call. This behaviour distinguishes it from various *Hippolais* confusion species. While singing, however, males may stop dipping the tail and then give only occasional random and occasional tail dips between song sequences. Sykes's and Booted Warblers twitch the tail in all directions with quick movements, often flicking the wings at the same time, but lack the deliberate motion of Eastern Olivaceous. Upcher's moves the tail constantly but slowly, raising and lowering it and waving it from side to side. Western Olivaceous does not flick the tail at all.

Not shy and may allow close approach, but usually remains partly hidden among foliage, giving only brief views and can be difficult to observe well. Males sing vigorously on their return to the breeding grounds, usually from a perch within cover near the top of a bush. They also sing in flight, while rising vertically and then during a diagonal descent, with raised wings, to a new perch. In Europe, song continues actively throughout the breeding season, to July or early August.

In Africa, migrants often form loose feeding groups or join mixed species parties in the tops of acacias. Song is regularly heard throughout the wintering period, often beginning before sunrise and maintained through the hot hours of the day. Wintering birds can be remarkably sedentary, using the same song post for several weeks at a time.

BREEDING HABITS Territorial, but with a strong tendency to form loose colonies. The nest is built in a tree, bush or creeper, usually about 1m from the ground, but sometimes up to 9m. It is a cup made from small twigs, grass and stems and lined with finer material such as hair and rootlets. In *elaeica*, laying begins in late May or June and the clutch is usually 3–4 eggs (sometimes 2 or 5). These are incubated for 11–13 days, mainly by the female. The nestlings are brooded at first by the female, then later fed by both parents. The fledging period is 11–15 days. It is often double-brooded.

Breeding is earlier in the African races. Nominate *pallida* in Egypt typically lays in April, *reiseri* in Algeria between mid April and late June, *laeneni* at Lake Chad between March and June (Urban *et al.* 1997). The clutch size in Egypt is 2–4 (usually 3), averaging fewer than in Europe.

DISTRIBUTION The Palearctic race *elaeica* is a long-distance migrant, wintering in E Africa. The remaining races breed in Africa where some are largely resident, others short-distance migrants.

I. p. elaeica **Breeding** Occupies an extensive range in SE Europe and SW Asia. It breeds commonly in the Balkans, along the Adriatic coast to Slovenia and north to S Hungary, where it is rare. It breeds along the western Black Sea coast from S Romania south through Bulgaria

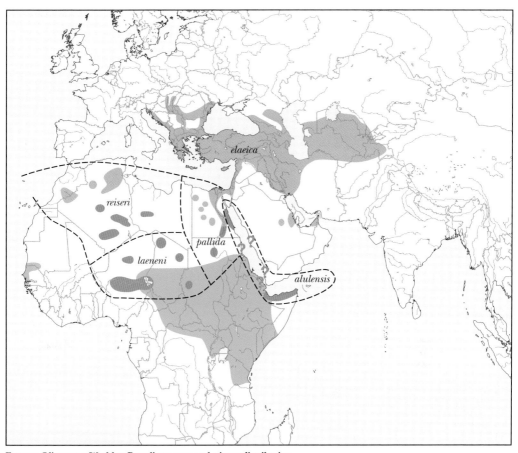

Eastern Olivaceous Warbler. Breeding range and winter distribution.

into Turkey. Its European stronghold lies in Greece, where it is common throughout and on many islands in the Aegean Sea south to Crete. It breeds widely on Cyprus and throughout Turkey, east to S Georgia, Armenia, Azerbaijan and the western Caspian Sea and south to C Israel, Syria and Jordan. It breeds in Iraq, Iran (in the west and north and possibly elsewhere) and N Afghanistan, and north throughout southern C Asia including much of Turkmenistan and Uzbekistan to the southern Aral Sea. It reaches its northern limit in S Kazakhstan, in the semi-desert area along the Syr Darya to the region of Shymkent, possibly extending north where irrigation has increased available habitat. Small numbers (probably referable to *elaeica*) breed locally in C and E Arabia. It often occurs at high densities, with six pairs in 0.1ha noted in Cyprus, one singing 'every 10 yards' in C Iraq and birds singing every 30–100m in deciduous woodland in N Turkey (Cramp 1992).

Non-breeding Migrates through Iran, Iraq, Arabia and Egypt to NE and E Africa. It winters commonly and often abundantly, from S Chad, C Sudan and Eritrea south to NE DR Congo, drier parts of Uganda, Kenya and SW Somalia; also in N Tanzania south and west to Dodoma. A few birds apparently also winter in coastal Arabia.

I. p. pallida Breeds in Egypt, in the Nile delta and valley, the Suez corridor and some of the Western Desert oases. It also extends south along the Nile into Sudan, south to Khartoum. It winters mainly in C and S Sudan, Eritrea and N Ethiopia and has occurred south to Kenya.

I. p. reiseri Has a restricted range in SE Morocco (Salewski *et al.* 2009) but breeds widely in Algeria in oases south of the Atlas, from Biskra to at least the region of In Salah at *c.* 27°N. It is also common at higher elevations on the Hoggar plains. It probably also breeds in Mauritania, S Tunisia and the Fezzan, Libya. It reaches N Senegal and is recorded outside the breeding season from S Mali.

I. p. laeneni Breeds in extreme N Nigeria, S Niger and the Lake Chad region, where it appears to be resident, as well as (presumably this race) in Darfur, W Sudan. Birds of the Aïr Massif in NW Niger are considered intermediate between this race and *reiseri*, as perhaps are those of Tibesti, Bol and Fada in N Chad.

I. p. alulensis Breeds in coastal regions of N Somalia between 43° and 51° E, and in mangroves along the Egyptian Red Sea coast from Hurghada south to Shalatein. Birds apparently of this race have also been reported from coastal Sudan, and from Red Sea mangroves in Djibouti, Yemen and Saudi Arabia north to Yanbu.

MOVEMENTS During migration, *elaeica* appears to avoid the Mediterranean region. Autumn movement begins in mid July and most birds vacate breeding areas during late July and August, although a few stragglers remain in SE Europe and S Turkey until late September. A heavy passage occurs at the Bosphorus between mid July and the third week of August and large numbers move through the Levant and E Egypt, mainly from August to October. Passage through Arabia lasts from July to November and it is common and widespread east to Oman in August and September. Migration across the Sudan coast and into Ethiopia begins early in August and most birds have moved through this region by mid September. The first birds appear in Kenya and Uganda about mid October, but most reach winter quarters in E Africa during November and December.

Departure from Kenya and Uganda occurs mainly between late March and mid April, with birds moving through NE Africa during this period. Late birds may remain in Ethiopia to mid May and Sudan to late May. Spring passage through Egypt occurs mainly from mid March to mid May. Birds return to breeding grounds in S Turkey from mid April, the S Balkans in late April and the N Balkans in early May. Spring passage through Arabia begins in mid March and peaks in April. Birds return to N Iran from mid April and reach S Kazakhstan in late April or early May.

Movements of the desert breeding races are not well understood. At the S Saharan oases, the race *laeneni* is believed to be resident. To the north, *reiseri* leaves sites on the N Sahara edge in September, after breeding and returns in March, but is believed to remain year-round in the more southerly Hoggar region. Nominate *pallida* leaves breeding areas in N Egypt during August and September and returns in late March and early April. It is common in Sudan from August to March.

Vagrancy It is rare to the west of the breeding range, with just 13 records from Britain to the end of 2008. Elsewhere in NW Europe it has reached Iceland (1), Norway (1), Sweden (3), Finland (3), Denmark (1), Germany (3), France (3) and Belgium (1).

DESCRIPTION *I. p. elaeica*

Plumage – Adult fresh (December to April) Forehead to nape grey-brown, tinged olive. Supercilium creamy buff, narrow but quite well marked in front of eye, extending from base of bill and tapering off sharply just beyond eye. Lores pale buff, merging with supercilium, offset by indistinct darker spot immediately in front of eye. Often some darker shading immediately behind eye, but no real eye-stripe. Ear-coverts uniform greyish brown merging with sides of the nape and crown, usually clearly demarcated from paler cheeks. Whitish eye-ring narrow and distinct, merging above eye with supercilium. Mantle and scapulars grey-brown with slight olive tinge. Rump and uppertail-coverts similar to mantle although slightly more olive-buff. Tail feathers dark grey-brown, outer web of t6 usually much paler than inner web. Both webs of t6 with distal white fringe, well demarcated and with dark feather centre usually protruding in a point along shaft, almost reaching the tip. White distal fringes on inner webs of other feathers narrow and variable; often present on t5 only, but sometimes on all feathers including t1. Chin and throat creamy white. Centre of breast, belly and vent white with slight greyish wash. Sides of breast and flanks lightly washed dull grey-buff, slightly warmer than the upperparts and underparts. Undertail-coverts creamy white, paler than flanks and warmer than rest of underparts.

Lesser and median coverts grey-brown with narrow, slightly paler fringes. Greater coverts and tertials dull greyish brown with broad, paler, sandy grey fringes. Primary coverts dark grey-brown, fringed pale grey-buff. Alula dark grey-brown with fine pale fringe, contrasting noticeably with surrounding feathers. Flight feathers dark grey-brown. Secondaries with sandy buff edges and tips, creating faint pale panel in closed wing and a pale line across bunched secondary tips. Primaries narrowly edged pale buff, tips with narrow grey-buff fringes.

Adult worn (June to September) Top of head and upperparts duller, more uniform, cold brownish grey. Supercilium creamy white. Lores pale, with darker spot in front of eye, or diffuse darker smudge reaching to base of bill. Eye ring less conspicuous. Tail grey-brown, slightly darker than upperparts. Whitish fringes usually still conspicuous near tip of t6, but often lost from other feathers by July. Chin, throat and rest of underparts greyish white, suffused brownish grey on sides of breast and flanks. Lesser, median and greater coverts grey-brown with slightly paler narrow fringes, but contrast between centres and fringes may be lost. Tertials grey-brown, usually with contrasting residual fringes. Primaries and secondaries uniform dull brown, with pale edges and tips lost, contrasting somewhat with grey-brown wing-coverts and upperparts.

First-winter Fresh first-winter plumage similar to fresh adult (greyer than in juvenile), but browner juvenile wing and tail feathers are retained, with distinct pale edges and tips to the greater coverts. Primary tips wear quickly and many birds are worn like adults by October and November.

Juvenile Upperparts more buffy brown, less greyish than in adult. Supercilium and underparts more strongly tinged pale buff. Pale fringes and tips to tertials and flight feathers broader than in adult and pale wing-panel apparent but contrasting less against browner feather webs. Pale buff tips to greater coverts form more distinct wing-bar. Lacks distinct pale outer edge to t6 and pale fringes at tail feather tips either absent, or brownish and obscure.

Bare Parts Upper mandible dark horn, paler towards cutting edges and tip. Lower mandible pale pinkish yellow, unmarked. Mouth yellow; first autumn birds have two tongue spots, usually very faint and sometimes absent by late autumn. Tarsi and toes dark grey-brown with a pinkish tinge; claws dull plumbeous brown, rather darker than toes. Iris dark brown.

IN HAND CHARACTERS

Measurements

I. p. elaeica

	Male	Female
Wing	64–71 (67.2; 84)	62–69 (65.5; 29)
Tail	46–54 (50.6; 82)	45–54 (49.5; 27)
Bill	14.5–17.5 (16.5; 73)	14.5–17 (16.0; 27)
Tarsus	20–22 (21.2; 63)	19–22 (20.6; 22)

(Includes data from Cramp 1992)

Sexes combined:
Tail/wing ratio: 70–82% (75%; 109)
Bill width: 3.8–4.4 (4.1; 20)
Hind claw: 4.6–5.5 (5.1; 20)
Tail graduation: 3–5 (3.5: 10)

Juvenile wing and tail average *c.* 1mm shorter than in adult (Cramp 1992).

Birds from C Asia ('*tamariceti*') are slightly longer-winged and longer-tailed, but shorter-billed, than those from Turkey and Europe (Cramp 1992; Svensson 2001).

Other races (sexes combined)

I. p. pallida: wing 61–67 (63.7; 38); *tail* 47–54 (50.2; 30); *bill* 14.5–17 (15.8; 48); *tarsus* 20–22 (21.1; 38); tail/wing ratio 75–83% (79%; 38).

I. p. reiseri: wing 62–68 (65.4; 18); *tail* 49–57 (52.7; 18); *bill* 14.8–16.2 (15.6; 20); *tarsus* 19.9–22.5 (21.2; 25) (from Cramp 1992); mean tail/wing ratio 81% (n = 18).

I. p. laeneni: wing 59–64 (61.6; 11); *tail* 46–54 (49.9; 11); *bill* 14.5–16.0 (15.3; 8); *tarsus* 19.0–21.5 (20.0; 11); tail/wing ratio 78–84% (81%; 11).

I. p. alulensis: (n = 4): *wing* 58–62 (60.3); *tail* 47–50 (49.0); *bill* 15–16 (15.4); *tarsus* 20–21 (20.4). Tail/wing ratio 78–84% (81%).

Structure

I. p. elaeica

Wing formula (Cramp 1992):

p1/pc	p2	p3e	p4e	p5e	p6	p7	p10
3–6	2.5–7	wp	0–1	0.5–2.5	2–6	6–9	12–15

Wing rounded, p1 small. Wing point p3 (4); p2 = p5/6–7; p3–5 emarginated (tip of p6 rarely).

Figure 99. Wing of Eastern Olivaceous Warbler *I. p. elaeica*.

Tail slightly rounded.

Bill rather flat; cutting edges straight or slightly concave, tip of culmen gently decurved (Fig. 103).

Tarsi rather slender, toes and claws small.

Races *pallida*, *reiseri*, *laeneni* and *alulensis*

Wing slightly shorter and more rounded than in *elaeica*. Wing point p3–p4 (p5) with p6 1–4mm shorter, p10 8–13mm shorter, p2 4–7mm shorter, p2 = p6/7–7/8 (sometimes = p8 in *laeneni*), p6 sometimes emarginated. Structure otherwise as *elaeica*.

Figure 100. Wing of Eastern Olivaceous Warbler *I. p. laeneni*.

Recognition Care is required to distinguish Eastern Olivaceous from several other migrant greyish brown, olive-brown or buffy brown warblers. Most *elaeica* and all African

races have a wing length below 70mm, the minimum in Upcher's Warbler, and all are much smaller than Olive-tree Warbler. The longer p1 (usually 3–8mm > pc) separates Eastern Olivaceous from Upcher's and Olive-tree Warblers and also from Eurasian Reed, African Reed, Marsh and Blyth's Reed Warblers. The narrower tail feathers provide an additional distinction from Upcher's (Fig. 97). The second primary (p2) in Eastern Olivaceous falls at p5–7 in race *elaeica* (usually at p6–7 in African races). This again separates it from Marsh and Eurasian Reed Warblers (with p2 > p5), although not usually from Upcher's (with p2 typically at p5–6), nor from Blyth's Reed and African Reed Warblers (or the Red Sea mangrove breeding form of Eurasian Reed Warbler *A. s. avicenniae*). Sykes's Warbler has a still shorter, more rounded wing, with p2 usually at p7–9. In *elaeica*, the larger p10 shortfall (usually 12–15mm) provides a good distinction from both Sykes's and Booted Warblers (with shortfall 8–12mm). Eastern Olivaceous (and especially *elaeica*) rarely shows the emargination on p6 present in most Sykes's and many Booted Warblers.

In all races, the bill is similar in shape to that of Sykes's, but longer and broader with less narrowed tip than in Booted. It is quite distinct from the very broad convex-sided bill of Western Olivaceous Warbler.

Plumage features to note include the prominence of the edgings of greater coverts, tertials and secondaries (broader in Eastern Olivaceous than in Sykes's, Booted or Western Olivaceous Warblers). Also, in adults, the pale pattern on the outer tail feather tips, the fringe on the distal inner web being more sharply demarcated, purer white and usually broader than in Sykes's or Booted.

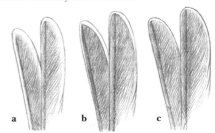

a   b   c

Figure 101. Comparison of extent of white in the two outer tail feathers of (a) Sykes's Warbler, (b) Eastern Olivaceous Warbler *I. p. elaeica* and (c) Western Olivaceous Warbler.

The greyer tones of *I. p. elaeica* should help separate it from the other small brown *Iduna* and the lack of yellow below normally distinguishes it from Melodious Warbler, which has very similar measurements and wing formula. The browner or buffier plumage of the desert races of Eastern Olivaceous is close to that of Western Olivaceous Warbler but paler.

Ageing In early autumn, first-winter *elaeica* are distinguishable by relatively unworn body plumage and flight feathers, adults then being badly worn and faded. By November, however, most young birds are already worn and ageing can be difficult. Some with relatively unabraded primary tips can be distinguished as first-winter, but ageing may otherwise depend on tongue spots. These are faintly present in most young birds in November, apparently absent in adults. Also, skull ossification is often incomplete up to November.

Weight

I. p. elaeica: Range 7–16g. Kenya, Nov–Dec, 7.0–11.2g (9.1; 461), typical lean weight 8.5–10.5g (NRG unpublished data). Autumn weights above 14g recorded Cyprus and S Turkey (Cramp 1992; RV unpublished data).

I. p. pallida: N Sudan, Aug–Sep, 7.5–12.5g (9.5; 101 (GN/JSA)

I. p. reiseri: Gambia, Jan–Feb, 7.9–9.8g (9.1; 14) (RR)

GEOGRAPHIC VARIATION Involves plumage colour, size and wing structure. The migratory Palearctic form *elaeica* is a grey-brown bird showing an olive tinge when fresh. It is relatively large and long-winged. Trends are evident within its range. Birds from C Asia, described as *'tamariceti'*, have slightly longer wings and tails, and shorter bills, than those of SE Europe, while Middle East birds are longer-tailed and shorter-billed but have short wings. These variations are apparently clinal.

African breeding populations are distinctly shorter-winged than *elaeica* but otherwise similar to it in structure and behaviour. The three Saharan races are much alike, buffier than *elaeica* without the greyish plumage tones. Southern *laeneni* is slightly smaller than *reiseri* but otherwise poorly differentiated. The Red Sea and N Somalian race *alulensis* is small and short-winged like the S Saharan birds, but resembles *elaeica* in colour, and mtDNA studies place it very close to the Palearctic race (SB *in litt.*). A few small grey-brown first-winter birds with prominent pale wing feather edgings and wing length below the range of *elaeica* were caught near the Sudan coast in August among other migrant Eastern Olivaceous Warblers (GN). It is likely that these were *alulensis*.

I. p. elaeica (SE Europe, SW Asia) Described above.

I. p. pallida (Egypt to N Sudan) Warmer, more buffy brown above than *elaeica*, without greyish tones, the rump and uppertail-coverts brighter, more tawny or ochreous. The underparts are more strongly washed with buff. The flight feather edges are buffy brown and paler than the mantle, contrasting as in *elaeica* with dark feather webs. Tail as in *elaeica*, with well demarcated whitish fringes at the tips of the outer feathers. Worn birds are less distinct from *elaeica*, but generally browner. Juveniles are paler, sandier brown than adults and show a paler buffy bar

across the greater covert tips, but pale primary tips are less conspicuous. First-winter birds before moult are similar in body plumage colour to fresh adults. Primary projection is shorter than in *elaeica*.

I. p. reiseri (NW Sahara) Like *pallida*, but slightly paler sandy buff-brown above, the rump more ochreous, less tawny. More creamy white below. Juvenile is very pale, with edges of wing-coverts and remiges more sandy than in *pallida*. Size and structure as *pallida*.

I. p. laeneni (S Sahara) Another pale desert race, like *reiseri* in coloration. Slightly but consistently smaller than *reiseri*, with a still shorter primary projection. Apparently intergrades with *reiseri*.

I. p. alulensis (Egypt to N Somalia) Greyish brown above like *elaeica* and off-white below, with a whitish supercilium; pale buff edges to wing feathers well-marked. Smaller than *elaeica*, with more rounded wing. Similar in size and structure to *laeneni*, but upperparts darker and greyer, underparts and supercilium less buff-tinged.

TAXONOMY AND SYSTEMATICS On present evidence, including DNA comparison, we have no reservation in retaining *elaeica* within the same species as the African forms. There are measurement differences within the range of *elaeica*, but these are apparently clinal and the recognition of *tamariceti* seems unjustified. We accept three Saharan races, but *laeneni* is poorly differentiated and its separation from *reiseri* may not be warranted if birds from NW Niger prove to be intermediate. Western Olivaceous Warbler has traditionally been regarded as a race of *I. pallida*, but here we follow Helbig & Seibold (1999) and Svensson (2001) and treat this as a distinct species (for further discussion see under that species).

DNA phylogenetic studies have shown that this and the other three *Iduna* species (all formerly in *Hippolais*) form a strongly related group to which the two former *Chloropeta* species also belong (Fregin *et al.* 2009). This group appears to be more closely allied to some of the *Acrocephalus* warblers than to the four species now retained in *Hippolais*.

▲ Adult *I. p. elaeica*, Israel, March. Note greyish brown upperparts, whitish underparts, pale wing-panel, relatively short primary projection – slightly more than 50% of tertial length – and evenly spaced tertials (Daniele Occhiato).

▲ Adult *I. p. elaeica*, Egypt, April. A drabber, greyer bird but still *elaeica*; the resident form, *pallida*, would appear more warmly toned (Vincent Legrand).

▲ First-winter *I. p. elaeica*, Lesvos, Greece, July. Young birds in early autumn are separated from adults by fresh, unworn plumage. Note crisp, pale edges and fringes to flight feathers, tertials and greater coverts, and broad whitish tips to secondaries, forming distinctive pale line perpendicular to wing-point (Steve Garvie).

▲ Adult *I. p. reiseri*, Ouarzazate, Morocco, April. Separation from the sympatric Western Olivaceous Warbler is difficult and differences in structure and plumage are subtle. Note indistinct dark spot in front of the eye, smaller, narrower, straight-sided bill, proportionately shorter and thinner tail and slightly thinner legs (Arnoud B. van den Berg/The Sound Approach).

◀ Adult *I. p. reiseri*, Gambia, February. Freshly moulted adult showing pale fringes and tips to flight feathers. Overall appearance subtly paler, sandy buff-brown than Western Olivaceous, which lacks pale fringes (Roger Riddington).

◀ First-winter *I. p. reiseri*, Gambia, February. Duller and drabber than adult and has lost pale edges to flight feathers so has more uniform appearance. Worn birds closely resemble Western Olivaceous and are probably not separable except by bill structure and wing length (Roger Riddington).

WESTERN OLIVACEOUS WARBLER
Iduna opaca   Plate 32

Hypolais opaca **Cabanis, 1851.** *Museum Heineanum* 1: 36.
Senegal.

A migrant breeding within a limited range in the Iberian
Peninsula and NW Africa and wintering in tropical W
Africa. Until recently, regarded as conspecific with Eastern
Olivaceous Warbler *I. pallida*. However, the two differ in
several aspects of structure and plumage, as well as vocally.
Moreover, they show a marked mtDNA sequence divergence
(Helbig & Seibold 1999). We follow these authors, together
with arguments offered by Svensson (2001), and treat
Western Olivaceous Warbler as a full species. Monotypic.

IDENTIFICATION Length 13.5cm. Wing 65–73mm. Tail/
wing 77–84%.

A rather uniform, slim and pale brown *Iduna* with a
relatively long tail and long, broad-based bill. In NW Africa
it occurs alongside the desert breeding race *reiseri* of the
similar but smaller-billed Eastern Olivaceous Warbler. It
occurs alongside Melodious Warbler in both its summer
and winter range and could be mistaken for the uncommon
variant in which yellow and green tones are subdued or
absent. Bill shape, body and wing colour, tail proportions
and patterning and vocalisations are important characters
for separating from these species. Sexes alike.

Structure Western Olivaceous has the characteristic *Iduna/
Hippolais* appearance, but its proportionally large bill is
distinctive. It is long, strong and very broad-based, usually
with distinctly convex sides (Fig. 103). The long bill and long
flat fore-crown give the head a more attenuated appearance
than in any of the potential confusion species. The legs are
stronger than in Eastern Olivaceous and in comparison with
race *elaeica* the tail appears longer and fuller, an effect due
in part to a slightly shorter wing-tip. The closed primaries
project about half the length of the exposed tertials. The
wing point is formed by p4 (often with p3) and p3–5 are
emarginated.

Plumage and bare parts The upperparts of spring adults
are light brown, the rump slightly warmer, more ochreous,
than the mantle. It is less greyish than the Palearctic race
elaeica of Eastern Olivaceous Warbler, with no hint of an olive
tinge. It is closer in colour to the Saharan breeding race
reiseri, but slightly less pale and sandy. There is a buff wash
to the breast sides and flanks but otherwise the underparts
are off-white. The head appears plainer than in *elaeica* and
a short, light sandy buff supercilium shows little contrast
with the crown. The supercilium extends from the bill base
to the front edge of the eye where it merges with a whitish
eye-ring. The ear-coverts and cheeks appear uniform light
brown, with no distinct eye-stripe. This coloration merges
with that of the crown and nape and diffuses into the sides
of the throat. The head thus has a bland and uniform
appearance, at best showing a faint dusky line in front of
the eye, giving it a similar 'open-faced' expression to that
of Melodious Warbler.

The wings appear plain and uniform when fresh
with only the alula showing slightly darker. They lack
contrastingly paler edges to the secondaries and do not
show the pale panel characteristic of Eastern Olivaceous and
some other *Hippolais* species. The tail is similar in colour to
the upperparts, but the outer feathers have brownish white
fringes at the tip, usually narrow and ill defined. As adults
become worn during summer they become drab brown but

otherwise change little in appearance. First-winter birds
resemble fresh adults but lack distinct pale tips to the tail
feathers.

The bill is dark grey-brown with a dull yellowish brown
or flesh lower mandible. The legs and feet are grey-brown
or greyish flesh.

SIMILAR SPECIES Most closely resembles the Saharan
race *reiseri* and Palearctic race *elaeica* of Eastern Olivaceous
Warbler, but confusion also possible with pale Melodious
and even Eurasian Reed Warbler.
Eastern Olivaceous Warbler (race *reiseri*) can occur
alongside Western Olivaceous in the W Sahara, particularly
in SE Morocco and Algeria where it breeds south of the
Atlas Mountains, and also in W Africa outside the breeding
season. It is distinctly smaller than Western Olivaceous and
has a smaller and narrower bill, a proportionately shorter
and thinner tail and finer legs, but shares a short primary
projection of about half the length of the tertials. The head
lacks the snouted, attenuated appearance characteristic of
Western Olivaceous. When fresh, the upperparts of *reiseri*
are paler and sandier than in Western Olivaceous and it
shows paler edging to the wing feathers and a distinct pale
wing-panel.

Eastern Olivaceous (all races) shows a more contrasting
head pattern, due to the slightly longer and more striking
supercilium and darker lores. Adults have a whitish edge to
the outer tail feather which becomes broad and conspicuous
at the tip and along the inner web, and is usually much more
conspicuous than on Western Olivaceous.

As adults wear and fade and pale wing and tail feather
edges are lost, plumage differences between Eastern and
Western Olivaceous become blurred. Differences in
structure may still be reliable, but some worn adults may
be impossible to identify in the field in late summer.
Melodious Warbler is often found in similar habitats to
Western Olivaceous and occasional variant birds appear
pale and colourless below. Under good conditions, these
should show darker, more olive upperparts. Melodious
has a more rounded crown and smaller bill than Western
Olivaceous and tends to show pale unmarked lores. It is
also slightly shorter-tailed and appears marginally heavier
and more robust, but this is rather subjective and difficult
to apply to a bird in the tree canopy. Neither species shows
tail movements relative to the body and even in the hand,
there is complete overlap in wing formula. A pale Melodious
with any hint of yellow below should be identifiable, but in
rare individuals with yellow and green tones completely
suppressed, separation may not be possible, particularly in
worn adults. In the hand, there is complete overlap in wing
formula. The rapid and varied song of Melodious is quite
distinctive and singing males are readily separable.
Eurasian Reed Warbler has darker, more warmly tinged
upperparts than Western Olivaceous, warm creamy underparts and slightly bolder face pattern. The long undertail-
coverts extend to over half the length of the tail. It also
has a narrower bill and a longer primary projection and
different wing structure.

VOICE The song is quite loud with a varied and vigorous
delivery within a frequency range 2–8kHz. At times, it can
sound rather repetitive and the chattering warble may
suggest the song of an *Acrocephalus* warbler. Song sequences
usually last between 2–10 seconds and are separated by short
pauses and are often introduced by calling. Some birds may
sing for longer periods. The song is similarly paced to that of

the *elaeica* race of Eastern Olivaceous Warbler, but includes more sweet wheezy or nasal sounds and the underlying Eurasian Reed Warbler-like rhythm is less pronounced. Overall, the general pattern is more uniform and lacks the cyclical 'rise and fall' in pitch which is characteristic of *elaeica* Eastern Olivaceous.

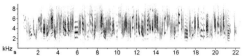

Part of song of Western Olivaceous Warbler, Spain, April. (Sample 2003)

The usual call is a hard *Sylvia*-like '*tack*' or '*tec-tec*', often separated from other calls by a pause of 2–3 seconds. Other calls include a nasal '*jerr*', a churring anxiety call '*trrrt-trrtrt*'; a ticking, alarming '*tchick-tick-tick-tick*' is given at the nest.

MOULT Adults moult some body and head feathers during August prior to migration. The complete moult takes place shortly after arrival in W Africa. It commences in October and is usually completed in December or January. Juveniles replace the head and body feathers during a post-juvenile moult, shortly after fledging and before southward migration. Like adults, they have a complete winter moult which is believed to coincide with the timing of adults. Some, possibly first year birds, are still replacing their primaries in February.

HABITAT Breeds in warm, dry country, where it prefers olive groves, orchards and gardens, willows and poplars along riverbanks and bushes such as tamarisk and *Nerium oleander* near water. It occurs mainly in lowlands but ranges up to 1,200–1,400m in the Moroccan High Atlas. In N Morocco it can be found in dense vegetation (*Olea, Quercus*) far from water. In S Morocco breeding is restricted to oases and palm groves (Thevenot *et al.* 2003). In the West African tropics it winters mainly in the arid north, where it frequents tall trees, gardens and coastal scrub, and concentrates in dense patches of riverine *Acacia nilotica*. It avoids the *Acacia tortilis* steppe.

BEHAVIOUR Active and confiding. Forages mainly in the tree and shrub canopy, hopping rather powerfully with a distinctly level carriage and frequently giving a hard '*tec*' call note. Migrants, in particular, will occasionally drop to the ground to take insect prey, but soon return back into the canopy. In contrast to Eastern Olivaceous Warbler, it invariably holds its tail still while feeding and calling and does not flick, wave or dip it in the manner of most other *Hippolais/Iduna*. When agitated, the crown feathers are raised, forming an untidy peak just behind the eye. In spring, males sing during migration and from arrival on breeding grounds in April and May until early July. Song is often heard throughout the day, sometimes delivered from an exposed branch, but usually from within the cover of foliage. On migration it often travels in small groups of up to 4–5 birds. In the winter quarters it is solitary, often remaining within the same territory for two months or more, and it tends to return to the same site each year. Song is frequently heard in W Africa from November onwards and becomes prolonged during March, prior to departure.

BREEDING HABITS Territorial, but several pairs may associate to form a loose breeding group. The nest is usually built in a shrub or small tree such as a tamarisk,

well above the ground; in Morocco, typically 0.7–2.5m but exceptionally to 4–6m (Thevenot *et al.* 2003). It is a well-built cup woven to plant stems and branches, constructed from grass stems, fine twigs, sedges and hair and lined with fine fibres, hair or feathers. The usual clutch is 3–4 (sometimes 2 or 5) eggs. In NW Africa, laying spans a prolonged period from mid April to early July and it is often double brooded. In Spain, laying begins later and lasts from about mid May to mid June.

DISTRIBUTION

Breeding In Europe, confined to the Iberian Peninsula where only a few thousand pairs breed. These are almost entirely restricted to Spain where it is locally common in the south, but the range extends into extreme SE Portugal. It becomes scarce and irregular to the north and east, ranging to Valencia and the Ebro Valley. Outside Europe it breeds in the Maghreb region of NW Africa, where it is widespread and common in N Morocco south to the Anti-Atlas. It is scarcer and more localised in N Algeria, breeding in the Atlas Saharien and near the northeast coast, and in Tunisia where it breeds south to Gafsa and Gabes. It extends east to NW Tripolitania in Libya.

Non-breeding Winters in West Africa, mainly in the Sahel and Sudan savanna zones, from S Mauritania and Senegal to S Niger and W Chad and south to N Guinea, N Ghana, central Nigeria and N Cameroon. A few occasionally reach Ivory Coast, S Ghana and S Nigeria. It frequently over-summers in the W African Sahel region but breeding has not been proved to occur.

Western Olivaceous Warbler. Breeding range and winter distribution.

MOVEMENTS Spanish breeding grounds are vacated between late July and September, those in NW Africa between mid August and mid October. Autumn passage at Gibraltar lasts from mid July to mid September. It peaks in Morocco between mid August and mid September, with stragglers remaining on the Atlantic coast until late October or early November. Birds reach the Sahel from the end of August, but the main arrival is during September and October. The earliest birds reach Gambia from mid October, but Ghana only from November onwards.

Spring migration begins late. Most birds leave winter quarters during April, although many remain in the Malian Sahel and N Nigeria until May and some until June. It returns to NW African breeding grounds from late March, but mainly between mid April and early May. Spring passage through Morocco and S Spain peaks in early May and continues to early June and it is common on spring passage in the W Saharan oases. Migrants occur further east in spring than autumn, frequently reaching E Libya (Cyrenaica) and occasionally W Egypt. It is extremely rare to the north of its breeding range, with only four records from France and an old specimen from Greece (13 July 1861). Past records from Britain and elsewhere in NW Europe are no longer considered acceptable.

DESCRIPTION

Plumage – Adult fresh (January to April) Forehead to nape light brown with greyish tinge. Supercilium pale buff, rather narrow and poorly defined, extending back only to the eye to meet a distinct buffish white eye-ring. Lores pale buff, mottled greyish brown, with a faint darker line in front of eye. Ear-coverts light brown, concolorous with crown, grading to whitish on lower cheeks. Side of neck, mantle and scapulars to uppertail-coverts light brown with grey tinge, inclining to ochreous brown or buffish brown on rump. Tail feathers greyish brown, narrowly edged light buff-brown; t6 with narrow brownish white outer edge and whitish fringe at tip, broadest on inner web and usually merging into dark feather centre; tip of t5 usually with narrower whitish fringe on inner web, rarely on outer. Chin and throat off-white. Remainder of underparts with faint buffish brown wash, sides of breast and flanks more strongly suffused greyish brown. Undertail-coverts white. Lesser and median coverts light brown. Greater coverts and tertials greyish brown with paler, buffier fringes. Primary coverts and alula greyish brown with narrow buff-brown fringes. Primaries and secondaries dark greyish brown, narrowly edged light buff-brown, primary tips with narrow and inconspicuous brownish white fringes. Underwing-coverts creamy white.

Adult worn (May to October) Slightly paler, duller brown above and whiter below. Pale markings at tip of t6 retained until at least July.

First-winter Fresh body plumage as in adult, but juvenile wing and tail feathers retained. Worn and probably indistinguishable from adult by October.

Juvenile Paler above than adult, especially on top and sides of head. Underparts whiter. Pale eye-ring less buffish. Upperwing rather plain with buff feather edgings poorly defined. Remiges, greater coverts and alula paler than in fresh adult, without noticeable pale tips to primaries. Tail feathers paler and browner than in fresh adult, t6 without distinct pale fringe at tip.

Bare Parts Upper mandible dark grey-brown or greyish horn. Lower mandible dull yellowish brown or flesh. Mouth yellow; nestling shows three tongue spots (Crespo 1988). Tarsi grey-brown or greyish flesh. Iris dark brown.

IN HAND CHARACTERS
Measurements

	Male	Female
Wing	68–73 (70.2; 18)	65–72 (68.2; 10)
Tail	54–60 (56.5; 18)	53–59 (54.8; 10)
Bill	17–19 (18.0; 17)	17–18 (17.8; 11)
Tarsus	22–24 (23.0; 17)	22–24 (22.8; 11)

(Includes data from Cramp 1992)

Sexes combined:
Tail/wing ratio: 77–84% (81%; 26)
Bill width: 4.7–5.6 (5.2; 20)
Hind claw: 5.2–6.3 (5.8; 20)
Tail graduation: 3–6 (4.5; 10)

Structure

Wing formula (Cramp 1992):

p1/pc	p2	p3e	p4e	p5e	p6	p7	p10
4–9	5–8	0–1	wp	0.5–1.5	3–5	5–8	12–15

Wing rounded with small p1. Wing point p(3) 4; p2 = p6/7–8; emargination on p3–5, rarely on p6.

Figure 102. Wing of Western Olivaceous Warbler.

Tail rounded, rather long; feathers slightly broader and tips more rounded than in Eastern Olivaceous Warbler.

Bill longish, rather flat and broad, usually with convex sides; tip of culmen gently decurved; lower mandible appears rounded rather than keeled (Fig. 103).

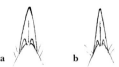

a   b

Figure 103. Comparison of bill profile of (a) Western Olivaceous Warbler and (b) Eastern Olivaceous Warbler *I. p. elaeica*.

Tarsi stronger than in Eastern Olivaceous; toes and claws small.

Recognition Separation from Eastern Olivaceous Warbler depends largely on bill size and shape and tail length. All birds have bill longer and broader than in *I. p. reiseri* and most (those with length > 17.5mm or width > 4.8mm) are above the range of *I. p. elaeica*. Most have a convex-sided bill with rounded and swollen appearance unlike the straight or slightly concave sides and more keeled mandible in Eastern Olivaceous (Fig. 103). Most have tail longer than 58mm, thus outside the range of both *elaeica* and *reiseri*. Compared to *elaeica* (but not *reiseri*) the wing tends to be more rounded, with p2 often < p7. The narrower, less prominent, wing feather edges and less well defined pale tail feather tips may help to separate from Eastern Olivaceous.

Melodious Warbler is similar in wing length and wing formula to Western Olivaceous (and sometimes lacks yellow on the underparts), but has a shorter narrower bill and shorter tail, with little overlap in these measurements. Eurasian Reed Warbler has a longer p2 than Western Olivaceous (> p5) and a much smaller p1.

Ageing In early autumn, young birds have relatively unworn body plumage and primary tips, while in adults these are very worn and faded.

Weight Range 8.3–16.8g. Typical winter weight 9–12g; some birds fatten substantially before the spring Sahara crossing (SJRR unpublished data).

GEOGRAPHIC VARIATION None reported.

TAXONOMY AND SYSTEMATICS Formerly included as a race of Olivaceous Warbler (*sensu lato*). Due to well marked morphological differences, together with differences in song and tail movements, Svensson (2001) proposed that *opaca* should be treated as a distinct monotypic species. All other taxa within the olivaceous warbler complex are

retained within *I. pallida*. This treatment is supported by a 9.6% sequence divergence between Eastern Olivaceous and Western Olivaceous Warblers in the mitochondrial cytochrome *b* gene (Helbig & Seibold 1999).

▲ Adult, Erg Chebbi, Morocco, May. Slightly larger and more robust than Eastern Olivaceous Warbler, with a broader, more substantial tail and distinctly thicker legs. Note overall pallid appearance, and slightly swollen bill structure with unmarked, pale pinkish orange lower mandible. Never dips tail in repetitive manner of Eastern Olivaceous Warbler (Augusto Faustino).

▲ ▶ Adult, Gorges du Dadès, Morocco, July. Compared with Eastern Olivaceous, note pale lores and lack of supercilium giving uniform appearance to head. Worn adults in late summer may be impossible to separate from equally worn *reiseri* Eastern Olivaceous which lack pale wing-panel and show similarly plain head (Ferran Lopez).

▲ Adult, Taroudannt, Morocco, April. Compared with the partially sympatric *reiseri* Eastern Olivaceous, note the slightly larger, broader and bulbous bill structure, with an unmarked yellowish pink lower mandible, plain lores and more substantial tail (Arnoud B. van den Berg/The Sound Approach).

▲ Adult, Gambia, February. Separation of silent birds from *reiseri* Eastern Olivaceous in the winter range is difficult except in the hand, where longer wing and larger bill structure are diagnostic (Roger Riddington).

SYKES'S WARBLER
Iduna rama   Plate 33

Sylvia rama Sykes, 1832. *Proc. Zool. Soc. London*, page 89.
Dukhun, India.

A migrant that breeds in the steppes and semi-deserts of SW
and C Asia and winters mainly in the Indian subcontinent.
Regarded until recently as a race of Booted Warbler but
now widely recognised as a distinct species, with different
structure, behaviour and song. This treatment is supported
by mtDNA studies (Helbig & Siebold 1999) and by sympatric
breeding of Sykes's and Booted Warblers in S Kazakhstan
(Svensson 2001). Monotypic.

IDENTIFICATION Length 12cm. Wing 58–65mm. Tail/
wing 76–90%.

A small, drab greyish brown and rather plain warbler
with a longish tail and relatively short rounded wing. It can
be extremely difficult to separate from Booted and Eastern
Olivaceous Warblers, both of which can occur alongside it
in southern C Asia. Differences between these species in
overall plumage colour and in wing and tail markings are
subtle. The field identification of Sykes's Warbler requires
careful assessment of wing, tail and bill structure and close
attention to voice and behaviour. Sexes alike.
Structure Slim like Eastern Olivaceous Warbler. The rather
flat crown and longish bill tend to give an impression of an
Acrocephalus, rather than of a *Phylloscopus*, as often occurs in
the case of Booted Warbler. In size, it falls between the slightly
larger Eastern Olivaceous (race *elaeica*) and marginally
smaller Booted, but there is overlap in measurements with
both species. The bill is similar in shape to that of *elaeica* but
slightly shorter and thinner, and it lacks the down-drooping
tip often apparent in Eastern Olivaceous. It is larger and less
fine-tipped than in Booted, and straight sided when viewed
from above whereas that of Booted is distinctly 'pinched in'
(Fig. 106). The tail appears longer than in either *elaeica* or
Booted. This character is accentuated by a short primary
projection, about a third or less of the length of the tertials,
with no more than five pale primary tips visible in fresh-
plumaged birds. Emarginations on the third (p3) to fifth
primaries (p5) and usually also the sixth (p6), fall well within
the tips of the secondaries. These and other structural and
wing formula differences are best assessed in the hand.
Plumage and bare parts The plainest and drabbest of the
small grey-brown *Iduna* and *Hippolais* species. In fresh adult
plumage (in India) the upperparts are light greyish brown
('milky-tea'). It lacks the warm tones of freshly moulted
Booted or the olive-grey of *elaeica* Eastern Olivaceous.
The wing is slightly browner and plainer than in *elaeica*,
with less pronounced pale feather edgings. In particular,
there is little or no contrast between the tertial centres
and fringes, so the closed wing appears uniform and lacks
a pale secondary panel. Sykes's has a poorly marked head
pattern, with a short off-white supercilium and rather pale
ear-coverts. The supercilium is most prominent in front of
the eye and contrasts with a dark loral spot. It extends to
the back of the eye but often no further. Most adults show a
slightly darker line above the supercilium, but over the lores
only. The underparts are pale, appearing off-white to silvery
white with, at best, only a faint buff tinge to the breast. The
outer tail feathers are edged whitish and bordered whitish
around the tip and on the distal part of the inner web, but
without the sharp demarcation from dark centres as seen
in Eastern Olivaceous Warbler.

Adults returning to the breeding grounds are slightly
worn, paler and greyer brown above and whiter below
than when fresh. The wings appear uniformly brown, the
primaries without distinct pale tips. At this season they
differ from Booted in lacking olive tones above or any buff
tinge below but, as the plumage of Booted also fades, these
differences become minimal.

After fledging, juveniles show pale cinnamon-tinged
upperparts and buffy white underparts. Rather uniform
brown wings lack the contrasting fringes to the coverts
typical of young *elaeica*. After a body moult, first-year birds
in August and September are similar in colour to freshly
moulted winter adults, although more sandy brown with
paler brown wing and tail feathers. They usually lack the
faint dark line above the lores seen in some adult Sykes's
and regularly in Booted.

The upper mandible of Sykes's is brownish at all ages.
The lower mandible appears pale pinkish, often with a dark
smudge behind the tip, but not the extensive dark tip usual
in Booted. Light brownish or pinkish legs are similar to
those of Booted, but paler, less grey than in *elaeica* Eastern
Olivaceous.

SIMILAR SPECIES Sykes's Warbler meets Booted Warbler
on passage and in winter and locally during the breeding
season in S Kazakhstan, NW China and possibly elsewhere.
It also overlaps widely with race *elaeica* of Eastern Olivaceous
Warbler in Turkmenistan, Uzbekistan and Iran. Any vagrant
Sykes's in NE Africa could occur with local desert breeding
races of Eastern Olivaceous. Sykes's also shows a similarity
to Blyth's Reed Warbler, with which it can occur in the
non-breeding season.
Booted Warbler and its separation from Sykes's Warbler
presents a daunting identification challenge. These species
are extremely similar and there is no single character
which can separate them reliably. Booted has the 'feel' of a
smaller, *Phylloscopus*-like warbler, with its shorter, narrower,
more 'pinched-in' bill, shorter tail, 'larger-looking' eye
and more compact structure. Occasionally, the bill may
be larger and approach the structure of Sykes's. It shows
a more conspicuous supercilium that extends behind the
eye, sometimes reaching the rear of the ear-coverts. When
fresh, the olive-brown upperparts are generally warmly or
even cinnamon-toned and the pale creamy underparts are
slightly richer than Sykes's would show. Worn birds are paler
and sometimes inseparable from Sykes's on colour. See also
discussion under Booted Warbler.
Eastern Olivaceous Warbler (race *elaeica*) can usually be
separated from Sykes's using a combination of plumage,
size and behavioural differences. The upperparts are slightly
greyer. The supercilium is poorly defined behind the eye
as in Sykes's and there is no hint of a darker eye-stripe, but
darker sides to the fore-crown are absent, giving *elaeica* a
more bland and featureless expression. On fresh *elaeica*,
including first-winter birds, pale edges to the secondaries
are more prominent than the primary edges and tend to
form a contrasting panel on the closed wing. This pale panel
is absent in Sykes's, which shows uniform brown fringes to
the secondaries.

Eastern Olivaceous of the race *elaeica* is a slightly larger
bird than Sykes's and can appear heavier-bodied and larger-
headed. It has a longer wing, the primaries projecting half to,
occasionally, two-thirds of the length of the exposed tertials.
Emarginations on the third to fifth primaries (p3–5) fall close
to the secondary tips, not within them as in Sykes's. The bill
is quite long and rather heavier looking, the upper mandible

showing distinct decurvature towards the tip. The lower mandible is entirely pale and unmarked. In comparison, the bill of Sykes's, although also quite long, is thinner based and the upper mandible is relatively straight towards the tip. The *elaeica* race of Eastern Olivaceous shows rather dark greyish legs while those of Sykes's Warbler are browner and paler.

Tail and wing movements should also provide a reliable guide for separating *elaeica* from Sykes's (and Booted) Warblers. Regular, continuous tail dipping is characteristic and never seems to be shown by Sykes's. In contrast, Sykes's continuously flicks its tail and wings in all directions in a nervous manner reminiscent of a *Phylloscopus* warbler. The song of Eastern Olivaceous, if heard, should readily distinguish it from Sykes's.

The African races of Eastern Olivaceous are smaller and shorter-winged than *elaeica*, thus very close in structure to Sykes's. Typically, they are distinctly paler, more buffish or sandy in overall tone. However, the small greyish brown race *alulensis* in N Somalia more nearly resembles Sykes's in coloration and is also shorter-winged, making their separation extremely problematic. Even in the hand it is very difficult to distinguish a worn *alulensis* from Sykes's.

Blyth's Reed Warbler is slightly larger and more bulky than Sykes's Warbler. Although both species are somewhat drab and featureless, Blyth's Reed differs in both structure and plumage tones. Its longer and deeper undertail-coverts extend roughly half the length of the tail. It always lacks pale edges and tips to the outer rectrices and the plain brown upperparts, conspicuously washed with olive, are quite unlike those of the paler Sykes's Warbler.

VOICE The song is a rapid chattering warble, usually given in short bursts of 3–6 seconds, interspersed with pauses of similar duration. A singing male will typically give five or six song bursts per minute. Amongst the similarly plumaged *Iduna* species, its song is particularly stereotyped and characteristic. Compared with the song of Booted Warbler, it is louder, faster and more chattering and spans a slightly wider frequency range of 1–8kHz. Individual syllables sound more distinct and the song includes more harsh grating notes and shriller sounds. By contrast, the song of Booted is more bubbling and undulating, delivered in longer bursts of 8–18 seconds. Compared with that of Eastern Olivaceous Warbler the song of Sykes's is faster, more stuttering and jerky and the cyclic structure (going repetitively up and down the scale) is less noticeable.

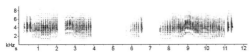

Part of song of Sykes's Warbler, Shymkent, southern Kazakhstan, May. (Peter Kennerley)

Svensson (2001) described a very different dawn song consisting of piping or chirping notes given in a slow staccato rhythm, '*zeeh…sirri…zree…tsretsre…zeeh…zrih…*' etc., delivered at about two notes per second.

The usual call is a short, hard '*tec*', '*zek*' or '*tk*', given twice or more in rapid succession, interspersed with pauses of several seconds. It is very similar to the contact call of Booted Warbler but lacks the grating, r-sounding quality of that species, which is replaced by a distinct strong s-sound, giving Sykes's call a liquid quality. In addition, Svensson (2003) mentions a fuller, less penetrating sound, described as '*tslek*' and reminiscent of the call of Bluethroat. He considers this call strongly indicative of Sykes's.

MOULT Adults begin to moult in the breeding area early in August. This involves replacement of some of the head and body feathers and perhaps occasionally some of the primaries. A full moult is usually completed in NW India, after migration. This is evidently rapid, taking place mainly between late August and early October. The earliest birds begin in late July and finish in mid September. Young birds may moult some of their juvenile body plumage in late summer. They evidently undergo a complete moult of wing, tail and body feathers in India together with the adults or shortly afterwards. A variable body moult may affect some birds during January to March.

HABITAT When breeding, it inhabits dry, semi-desert country in C Asia. It avoids barren open areas but is common and widespread in stone or sand deserts with scattered bushes. It requires tall shrubs and herbage in which to nest and prefers taller bushes (1.5–3m), especially tamarisk and saxaul, but also *Eurotia*, *Calligonum* and willow. The presence of taller trees, e.g. along irrigation channels, does not appear to discourage it. Expanding irrigation has resulted in growth of luxuriant scrub along water channels and Sykes's has spread into riverside plantations, orchards, gardens, woodland and plantations. In the northeast of its range, it breeds in mountain river valleys with thorny shrubs up to *c*. 1,600m, while in Iran and Pakistan it is said to breed abundantly in rose hedges. In the Taukum Desert, SE Kazakhstan, and much of its range in Uzbekistan and Turkmenistan, it often breeds alongside Asian Desert Warbler.

Wintering birds in India occur in dry scrubby woodland, particularly acacia, a habitat shared with Blyth's Reed Warbler. It also frequents tamarisks and bushes along rivers and canals, bushy thickets and low scrub. In the Persian Gulf, the resident population apparently breeds and winters in coastal mangroves and is unknown from inland locations.

BEHAVIOUR During the breeding season and in winter it feeds mainly in scrub and bushes or within low tree canopy. It is thus less skulking and more easily observed than Booted Warbler. On migration, however, it occurs in dense cover and can be as difficult to view as other skulking *Iduna* and *Hippolais*. It is typically more active and restless than Eastern Olivaceous Warbler. It frequently twitches its tail, but with fine movements and in all directions. The wings are often flicked at the same time, or when hopping to a new perch.

Males sing strongly on arrival on the breeding grounds, often from dawn to dusk and sometimes at night. The song is often given from a high perch on a bush or the inner branch of a tree. Birds may however sing continuously from deep within a tamarisk and only occasionally appear in the open, particularly during the heat of the day. Occasionally, a male will sing while flying from bush to bush, or when rising 1–2m in a short song-flight. Song becomes intermittent after pairing, but continues to be heard in Kazakhstan until mid July. A quiet sub-song is given in winter quarters in India and Sri Lanka and this develops into an almost incessant song shortly before spring departure.

BREEDING HABITS Apparently monogamous. It is solitary and territorial but territories may be contiguous in the southern parts of the range where breeding density is high. The nest is built by the female, accompanied by the singing male. It is typically located in dense scrub or thicket and close to the ground, although occasionally up to 1.8m.

Nests have also been recorded in tall herbs, in a low tree or in a bush close to the edge of a reedbed. The nest is a thick cup of fine twigs and grass stalks, with added plant down, cotton fibres and camel hair and is lined with finer material such as feathers, hair, down and cobwebs. A clutch of 3–5 eggs is typical, laid from mid May to early June. Incubation is mainly by the female, lasting for 12–14 days. Both male and female brood the nestlings for the first 2–3 days and supply them with food collected near the nest. The fledging period is usually 11–13 days. Usually single brooded, but replacement clutches are often laid.

DISTRIBUTION
Breeding The breeding range lies south of that of Booted Warbler, although there is limited overlap in NW China and S Kazakhstan. Sykes's breeds widely throughout the drier regions of Central Asia, from the lower Volga and Ural Rivers and the N Caspian Sea coast, through much of Kazakhstan south of 47°N, including the Karatau foothills, Betpak-Dala region, the Taukum Desert south of Lake Balkhash and the Tarbagatay range. It extends through the semi-deserts of Dzungaria, NW China, centred on the Gurbantungut Desert (Junggar Pendi) but ranging north to Ulungur Lake and the Irtysh River near Habahe. To the south, range includes the semi-desert regions of Uzbekistan, Turkmenistan and E and central Iran and extends to W and S Afghanistan and W Baluchistan, Pakistan. A discrete population is resident in mangroves fringing both shores of the Persian Gulf, including Khor Khalba and Ras el Khaimah in UAE (Pearson *et al.* 2004) and Batinah in N Oman.

Throughout much of its range, it is common to locally abundant and a density of 130–140 pairs/km² was recorded in S Kazakhstan (Cramp 1992). High numbers have been noted breeding in Kazakhstan in the Karakum desert and in the valleys of the Amu Darya and Syr Darya rivers, and also in S Turkmenistan.

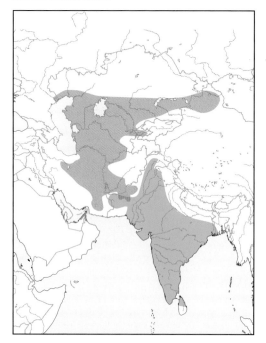

Sykes's Warbler. Breeding range and winter distribution.

Non-breeding Winters mainly in Pakistan, and in India from the Delhi region east to Bengal and south throughout much of the peninsula to N Sri Lanka. A small contingent also winters in eastern Arabia, south to Oman and S Yemen. There is one specimen record from Africa (Eritrea, November 1951).

MOVEMENTS Autumn migration begins early, commencing in Kazakhstan in late July, with the latest stragglers in early September. Passage is well in progress through Turkmenistan by early August and occurs widely through Pakistan, south to the Mekran coast and through E and S Iran during August and early September. Breeding grounds in NW Pakistan are vacated toward the end of August. Autumn migrants occur at over 2,500m in the mountains of Kyrgistan and Tajikistan. The first birds reach N India at the end of July, but the majority arrive between mid August and early September. The timing of progress through India in uncertain as most birds moult upon arrival. Some are reported in S India by the end of September but arrival in Sri Lanka is not until November.

Birds depart from Sri Lanka in late March and passage through India take place throughout April. Northward migration is rapid, with birds reaching S Turkmenistan from mid April and they are numerous at Chardzhou from late April to mid May. Breeding areas in Uzbekistan and S Kazakhstan are occupied early in May, but those in E Kazakhstan and W China not until mid May.

Vagrancy Sykes's Warbler is a vagrant to Europe. Most have occurred in Britain, with ten since 1959, peaking in late August. Others have reached Iceland (1), Norway (2), Ireland (1), Netherlands (1) and Germany (1). It has also reached Hong Kong (September 1994 and 1998).

DESCRIPTION
Plumage – Adult fresh (October to January) Forehead to nape uniform greyish brown, faintly tinged olive. Supercilium creamy white to pale buff, prominent in front of eye where narrow but crisp; absent or weakly defined behind eye, diffusing into crown sides and not extending beyond middle of ear-coverts. Dusky brown loral spot in front of eye, sometimes extending to form loral line, but lores usually pale buff merging with supercilium. Eye-line absent or restricted to dusky brown spot immediately behind eye. Upper cheeks pale brown. Ear-coverts greyish brown, tinged olive, faintly streaked paler. Mantle and scapulars to uppertail-coverts uniform light greyish brown with only faint hint of olive; becoming slightly paler, more ochreous, on rump and uppertail-coverts. Tail feathers mid brown, slightly darker than mantle, with narrow buff edges and narrow whitish fringe at tips; the outermost (t6) with a broader whitish fringe, extending around tip and along distal border, but merging with brown centre, not sharply demarcated; t5 similar on inner web and around tip but lacks whitish outer edge. Tail feather shafts concolorous with webs. Underparts greyish white, but creamy white on throat and undertail-coverts and with pale buff wash across breast and sides of neck. Sides of breast and flanks dull buffy brown to greyish brown.

Lesser and median coverts drab brown, broadly fringed light greyish brown as upperparts. Greater coverts similar but contrast between centres and fringes better defined. Tertials mid brown with slightly paler greyish brown fringes. Alula dark brown with barely perceptible pale fringe, usually the darkest part of wing. Primaries and secondaries edged greyish brown. Primaries tipped pale greyish brown, contrasting with darker greyish webs. Underwing-coverts creamy buff. Closed wing appears uniform and matches upperpart colour.

Adult worn (April to August) Differs from fresh adult in having upperparts greyer and duller, the warmer rump and uppertail-coverts contrasting slightly; underparts whiter; flanks slightly greyer, contrasting with whitish breast. Fringes to wing feathers faded and match upperpart colour; pale primary tips lost. Whitish fringes and tips to tail feathers reduced or lost.

First-winter Crown and upperparts pale brown or sandy brown, usually lacking greyish or olivaceous tones of fresh adult. Supercilium creamy white, slightly paler than in adult, most conspicuous in front of eye where it merges with lores; absent or indistinct over ear-coverts. Loral spot and eye-line as fresh adult. Ear-coverts sandy brown, faintly streaked whitish and slightly paler than adult. Tail sandy brown as upperparts; outer web of t6 rather paler, but distal part of t6 and t5 without distinct pale inner web border. Underparts as fresh adult, but slightly warmer and browner on breast and flanks. Closed wing as fresh adult but fringes and edges pale sandy brown, slightly more conspicuous and contrasting. Fringes to lesser and median coverts slightly paler than the mantle. Pale sandy brown fringes to greater coverts and tertials broad, merging with greyish brown centres. Flight feathers edged pale sandy brown, exposed primaries pale greyish brown with narrow pale tips. Alula dark brown with little or no fringe.

Juvenile As first-winter, but upperpart feathering initially pale buffy brown with a marked cinnamon or gingery tinge; underparts pale cinnamon-buff. Whether change to paler first-winter plumage involves moult or is due to feather fading is uncertain.

Bare Parts Upper mandible dark pinkish brown with narrow pink cutting edge and often a minute pale tip. Lower mandible pale pinkish, sometimes with small dark smudge on sides towards tip. Tarsi brownish grey or pinkish grey. Iris dark brown.

IN HAND CHARACTERS
Measurements

	Male	Female
Wing	58–65 (61.4; 67)	58–64 (60.9; 33)
Tail	48–56 (51.9; 66)	46–55 (51.7; 33)
Bill	14–16.5 (15.4; 62)	14–17 (15.2; 30)
Tarsus	19.5–21.5 (20.4; 32)	19.5–21 (20.5; 21)

Sexes combined:
Tail/wing ratio: 76–90% (85%; 96)
Bill width: 3.6–4.3 (4.0; 20)
Hind claw: 4.4–52 (4.8; 19)
Tail graduation: 2–7 (4.6; 20)

Structure

Wing formula (n = 20):

p1/pc	p2	p3e	p4e	p5e	p6(e)	p7	p10
3.5–10	4–6	0–1	wp	0–1	1–3	3–6.5	8–11

Wing rounded, p1 small. Wing point p(3) 4 (5); p2 = p(6/7) 7–8/9 (9); emargination on p3–5, usually slightly on p6.

Figure 104. Wing of Sykes's Warbler.

Tail longish, slightly rounded.

Bill rather flat; cutting edges straight or slightly concave (Fig. 106).

Tarsi slender, toes and claws small.

Recognition Slightly browner, less olive-grey than Eastern Olivaceous Warbler (race *elaeica*) with a plainer wing; pale edgings to the remiges and greater coverts narrow and indistinct; pale fringes to the outer tail feather tips of adults buffier (less white) and less sharply demarcated. Best separated on wing formula and measurements. The shortfall from the wing-tip of p10 (< 11mm) and p6 (< 3mm) is less than in *elaeica*; p2 is usually shorter than p7 (longer in *elaeica*); the distance p2 > p1 is nearly always 26mm or less (27mm or more in *elaeica*; Svensson 2002); and p6 typically shows a distinct emargination (lacking in *elaeica*). Sykes's has a higher tail/wing ratio than Eastern Olivaceous (usually over 80%; under 80% in *elaeica*) and many birds have a wing length below 62mm (the minimum for *elaeica*).

Sykes's cannot be separated from Booted on wing measurements alone, but usually has the tail longer than 50mm (the maximum in Booted) and a higher tail/wing ratio (this usually < 81% in Booted). It also has a distinctly longer, less fine-tipped bill (Fig. 106). It lacks the olive or warm tones of Booted, has whiter underparts and browner (less dark) centres to the remiges and tail feathers.

Ageing Young birds are readily distinguishable in late summer and early autumn by their unworn plumage, especially the fresh appearance to the primaries and relatively unworn tail-feathers. Adults have badly abraded wing and tail feathers by June-August and very worn greyish body plumage. The pale, gingery tinged plumage of juvenile Sykes's seems to be characteristic, but is lost during post-juvenile moult. Ageing first year birds on plumage is not possible after the complete moult in autumn.

Weight Range 7–11g (Cramp 1992); Kazakhstan, 8.3–10.3g (9.1; 22) (AG unpublished data).

GEOGRAPHIC VARIATION None reported.

TAXONOMY AND SYSTEMATICS Previously regarded as a race of Booted Warbler but this treatment is untenable. Molecular study has shown that mtDNA divergence between Sykes's and Booted Warblers is similar to that between Icterine and Melodious Warblers (Helbig & Seibold 1999). Moreover, Svensson (2001) reported breeding Sykes's and Booted in adjacent territories in Kazakhstan, confirming that the two co-exist and behave here as distinct species.

DNA comparisons have shown that Sykes's and Booted Warblers are closely related to Eastern Olivaceous and Western Olivaceous Warblers. These species, now placed in *Iduna*, are more closely allied to some of the *Acrocephalus* warblers than to the four species retained in *Hippolais* (Fregin *et al.* 2009).

▲ Adult, S Kazakhstan, May. Central Asian breeders are usually slightly warmer and browner than those breeding in coastal mangroves in the Middle East (Colin Bradshaw).

▲ ▶ Adult, Oman, April. Differs from Booted by shorter, less conspicuous supercilium and slightly longer bill. Often lacks dark loral line that Booted shows; typically only has a dark spot in front of the eye, giving Sykes's a plainer head pattern. Adults often show cleaner white, less dingy underparts than Booted (Markus Römhild).

▲ ▶ First-winter, Shetland, Scotland, September. Although closely resembling Booted appears paler and slightly greyer, and has longer bill that typically lacks dark shadow near tip of lower mandible. Supercilium narrower and slightly less pronounced than Booted. Note slightly longer tail than Booted, giving the body a more attenuated structure. Tertials are plainer than in Booted and show subdued contrast between the centres and fringes (Hugh Harrop).

BOOTED WARBLER
Iduna caligata   **Plate 33**

Sylvia caligata **Lichtenstein, 1823**. In: Eversmann, *Reise von Orenburg nach Buchara*, page 128. Ilek River, near Orenburg.

A long-distance migrant, breeding in open scrub and forest edge from E Finland to C Siberia and C Asia and wintering in India. Traditionally regarded as conspecific with Sykes's Warbler, but following Stepanyan (1978, 1983, 2003) we treat them as separate species. This treatment is supported by mtDNA studies (Helbig & Siebold 1999) and observations of sympatry of Booted and Sykes's Warblers in S Kazakhstan (Svensson 2001). Monotypic.

IDENTIFICATION Length 11.5cm. Wing 56–65mm. Tail/wing 72–84%.
A small brown warbler, sometimes appearing no larger than a Common Chiffchaff, with a rather short rounded wing and a small narrow-tipped bill. Extremely difficult to separate from Sykes's Warbler, with which it overlaps widely on passage and in winter. It also occurs alongside Eastern Olivaceous Warbler on migration in southern C Asia. It has been confused at times with Paddyfield Warbler and also with some of the plain-plumaged *Phylloscopus* species. In the field, careful attention to colour tones and wing and head pattern are important. Identification will also depend on appreciation of general structure, head and bill shape, behaviour and voice. Sexes alike.
Structure Slightly smaller than Sykes's Warbler and decidedly smaller than Eastern Olivaceous (race *elaeica*). It is more compact looking than either of these and the rounded crown and small, fine bill create the impression of a *Phylloscopus* warbler rather than an *Acrocephalus* or *Hippolais*. The wings are rather short, the primaries reaching only to the base of the tail and projecting a third to a half the length of the exposed tertials (slightly shorter than in the *elaeica* race of Eastern Olivaceous Warbler). Six pale primary tips may be visible on the closed wing and emarginations on p3–5 (sometimes also p6) fall well inside the tips of the secondaries. The tail is shorter than in Sykes's Warbler. Tail and bill measurements together with wing formula details are essential to establish identification in the hand.
Plumage and bare parts In freshly moulted birds (in India) the upperparts are rather warm olive-brown, sometimes with a rufous tinge never seen in Sykes's Warbler. The breast and sides are washed buff or cinnamon-buff and the throat and central underparts are whitish. The head has a more varied and 'interesting' appearance than in Sykes's or Eastern Olivaceous Warblers. There is a prominent light buff supercilium from the base of the bill and extending well behind the eye. It is most conspicuous in front of the eye, but tends to flare, fade and become diffuse behind it. This is offset below by a dark brown loral line and often by a short, dark eye-stripe. A conspicuous pale buff eye-ring merges with the supercilium above, but encircles and accentuates the size and prominence of the eye. A narrow line of dark feather tips is usually evident above the supercilium, occasionally extending back over the eye. The wing lacks a pale secondary panel, but the tertials, greater coverts and tail feathers are rather darker-centred than in Sykes's, the paler edges better defined and more contrasting. The outermost tail feather has a narrow whitish outer edge which broadens and extends around the tip and onto the distal portion of the inner web. The second outermost (t5) also

has a pale tip that extends onto the inner web but this is narrower and less conspicuous.
By spring, adults are moderately worn and warmer tones are lost. The upperparts are drab mid brown, usually with an olive or ochreous tinge, the underparts off-white with buff confined to the sides of the breast and flanks. The supercilium remains prominent but the dark shadow above the loral region is usually not apparent. Worn birds later in summer tend to appear uniform and greyish, but less so than in either Sykes's or Eastern Olivaceous Warblers, and the contrast between the darker centres and paler fringes to the tertials may be lost.
Young birds in autumn are light olive-brown above with an ochreous tinge, and lack the warm tones of fresh adults. The underparts are off-white and the supercilium, cheeks, breast and flanks have a buff wash not present in Sykes's. Light buff edges to the remiges and wing-coverts are more prominent than in adults (and more contrasting than in young Sykes's), but there is no suggestion of a paler or contrasting secondary panel or greater covert bar. The outer tail feathers lack distal whitish fringes.
At all ages, the upper mandible is blackish, while the pale lower mandible often has an extensive dark smudge at the tip, not seen in either Sykes's or Eastern Olivaceous Warblers. The legs are pinkish or light brown with a grey or blue-grey tinge.

SIMILAR SPECIES Sykes's Warbler and Eastern Olivaceous Warbler (race *elaeica*) are the two species most likely to be confused with Booted Warbler within its breeding range. Sykes's is extremely similar and separation is discussed in detail below. Eastern Olivaceous is more easily distinguished. Paddyfield Warbler has also been mistaken for Booted at times.
Sykes's Warbler closely resembles Booted but tends to be slightly plainer and more nondescript. It is a longer-tailed and marginally shorter-winged bird with a slightly shorter primary projection. It is also slightly longer-billed, although there is considerable overlap. Bill colour and shape are also indicative. In Sykes's, the upper mandible is dark brownish pink with a pale tip, the lower mandible conspicuously pale with only a small dusky smudge near the tip. In Booted, the bill is blacker above with a dark tip and the lower mandible tends to show more conspicuous darkening towards the tip. In the hand, the bill of Sykes's shows straight sides, while in Booted these are decidedly concave.
The head pattern of Sykes's Warbler is plainer than that of Booted. The length and prominence of the supercilium is variable in both species but it tends to be paler and more contrasting in Booted, especially behind the eye. Although Sykes's can show slightly darker sides to the crown above the loral region, this tendency is less marked than in Booted. The lores of Sykes's are poorly marked, the spot in front of the eye browner, less contrasting than in Booted. In fresh adult Sykes's the upperparts are plain greyish brown, with at best a faint olivaceous wash and invariably lacking the warmer rufescent tones of fresh Booted. The tertials and greater coverts are paler, plainer and less contrasting and the tail feathers lack the darker contrasting shafts shown by Booted: although it should be noted that worn and faded adult Booted can closely resemble Sykes's. Both species show a whitish edge to the outer tail feather and their pale tail tip markings are very similar. The underparts of Sykes's are generally whiter, less buffy, than in Booted. It is stressed that these plumage differences are subtle, readily affected by light conditions and become less apparent in worn birds.

There are no obvious behavioural differences between Booted and Sykes's Warblers. Both show random, nervous twitching tail movements. The quiet ticking calls of the two species are identical but the songs differ. Sykes's lacks the quieter hesitant opening of Booted, sounds slightly harder and scratchier and is inclined to be more repetitive and delivered in shorter sequences of only 5–8 seconds. Song is louder than in Booted, readily audible up to 250m.

Eastern Olivaceous Warbler (race *elaeica*) is a larger bird than Booted with a slightly longer primary projection, appearing heavier bodied and larger headed. The bill is slightly longer and deeper, the upper mandible showing slight decurvature towards the tip. The lower mandible lacks the darker tip that Booted invariably shows. The greyish legs appear less pale than the brownish legs of Booted. Race *elaeica* shows greyer upperparts than Booted and a more bland, less contrasting head pattern. It lacks a distinct eye-stripe or darker sides to the fore-crown and the eye-ring is obscure. Although conspicuous in front of the eye, the supercilium is poorly defined behind it. The closed wing is rather more patterned than in Booted, with more prominent pale edges and tips to the secondaries. Regular, continuous tail dipping is characteristic of Eastern Olivaceous Warbler

Paddyfield Warbler shares several features with Booted, including a fairly prominent supercilium, dark sides to the crown and dusky sides to the lower mandible and is similar in size, primary projection and wing formula. But it has longer undertail-coverts, a rather longer bill and a more rounded tail without white at the feather tips. Worn adults could be confusing however in late summer. See also under Paddyfield Warbler.

Plain *Phylloscopus* species have finer, more delicate bills and legs than Booted and most show olive-green and yellow plumage tones.

VOICE The song is a lively chattering warble, delivered rapidly and with a characteristic rising and falling in pitch within a frequency range spanning 1–6kHz. It begins slowly and quietly with 8–12 repeated introductory notes which increase in volume, before quickly building into the chattering, undulating warble which continues for 8–18 seconds. There follows a short pause before this song sequence is repeated. Within each sequence, individual syllables are less distinct than in Sykes's Warbler. Song includes harsher grating notes, shriller sounds and whistles, but it lacks the volume of Sykes's and is easily overlooked amongst background birdsong.

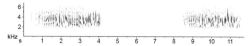

Part of song of Booted Warbler, Kemerovo region, Siberia, Russia, June. (Veprintsev 2007)

The usual call is a short and quiet but grating '*chk*' or '*chrrt*' and this is presumably the call described as '*chek*', '*tett*' or '*zek*' by Svensson (2001). It is usually given singly but may be repeated, at intervals of approximately one second. This is not a hard call; it is quite different from that of Lesser Whitethroat, more reminiscent of Common Stonechat. It is similar to the call of Sykes's Warbler, but drier, rather more grating and slightly lower-pitched, and is quieter, less sharp than the '*tac*' call of Eastern Olivaceous Warbler.

MOULT Adults moult some head and body feathers in the

breeding area from mid July. This is followed by a full moult immediately after arrival in NW India. This is evidently rapid and begins in some birds in early August. It takes place in most between late August and early October. Birds wintering in central and S India are already fully moulted when they arrive from late September onwards. Young birds moult body and head feathers shortly after fledging (Cramp 1992). They then have a complete moult in NW India, starting rather later than the adults. Most are still unmoulted in India during late August and early September. A variable moult of head and body feathers takes place in many birds between January and early April, prior to departure from the wintering grounds.

HABITAT Occupies a wide range of low scrub habitats across the cool, temperate lowlands of NE Europe and Asia, reaching 400m on bush-covered slopes in the Altai foothills. It frequents bushy glades and regrown patches of scrub in taiga and deciduous forest, meadows with *Salix* scrub, riverbanks, young birch woodland with mixed grassland and weedy borders of cultivated fields. It often breeds alongside Common Whitethroat and Grasshopper Warbler in low thickets, tall thistles, cornfields, high grass and weeds, bushy gardens and sometimes in reedy ditches. It does not particularly seek out wetlands in the northern part of the range, although breeding sites are regularly soaked with early morning dew. In the south of its range, in the semi-desert zone in central and S Kazakhstan, it tends to prefer the vicinity of water. Where it occurs alongside Sykes's Warbler, Svensson (2001) reported that it preferred low pea scrub, while Sykes's selected areas with taller tamarisk and saxaul bushes. Breeding in this region was unknown in the first half of the twentieth century (Dement'ev & Gladkov 1954) and its expansion here may be as a result of irrigation schemes.

A recent range expansion into N Europe may be a consequence of the demise of agriculture over large areas of the former Soviet Union. Huge regions have reverted to dense scrub-woodland ideally suited to the needs of Booted Warbler.

On migration and during winter, it frequents a wide range of dense vegetation including low bushy thickets, scrub tangles, scattered plots of cultivation with bushy fringes, reed edges, tree-scrub, gardens, groves, reedbeds etc. It seems to avoid the acacia woodland favoured by Sykes's Warbler.

BEHAVIOUR Usually rather shy and secretive. It spends much time in low vegetation, among grass, crops, edges of cultivation, clumps of vegetation or in low bushes. Typically it hops on the ground with the body held nearly horizontal and climbs up and down grass stems, picking food from leaves. Also feeds in the edges and canopy of small trees, although this may reflect lack of low cover. It appears to have an exclusively insect diet. Its movements are quick and active and reminiscent of a *Phylloscopus*. It continuously flicks its wings and tail in a nervous manner, the tail movements being shallow and random in direction. Males sing strongly, usually from within cover, in late winter and during spring migration, and continuously throughout the day and night once they reach the breeding grounds.

BREEDING HABITS Solitary and territorial. Birds pair quickly after arrival. The nest is usually built on the ground among shoots of shrubbery or grass stems, often in a slight hollow. It may rest on the branch of a bush or among large stalks, usually less than 30cm above the ground. It is a strong cup of twigs, roots, stems and leaves, with a lining that may include feathers, hair and plant down. A clutch of 4–6 eggs is usually laid in late May or early June in the south of the range, in late June in the north. Incubation is mainly by the female and the young are fed by both parents with food collected near the nest. The fledging period is 13–14 days and the young are fed for a further 12–14 days after leaving the nest until they become independent. Normally single brooded.

DISTRIBUTION

Breeding Breeds in NE Europe from SE Finland and the Lake Ladoga region of Karelia to *c.* 62°N and east through Russia to the western and eastern foothills of the Urals to *c.* 58°N. To the south, it ranges through the Moscow area, the upper Don River, the Volga River south to Volgograd and the Ural River south to Orenburg and Ural'sk, but appears not to reach the Caspian Sea, where it is replaced by Sykes's Warbler. It breeds across the W Siberian Plain north to *c.* 61°N, reaching the upper Yenisey River and the region of Chuna (Chunskiy) at *c.* 98°E. It is widespread throughout N Kazakhstan south to the Syr Darya delta, the Sarysu River, Lake Balkash and the northern part of the Alakol depression, extending east to northernmost Xinjiang in NW China and the Altai Mountains of S Russia and NW Mongolia.

It is common to abundant over much of this range, but distribution becomes local and patchy in the south where Svensson (2001) described its breeding alongside Sykes's Warbler. Densities of up to 5–6 pairs/hectare have been recorded in forest steppe in S Russia and central Siberia and it can also be abundant in scrub and herbaceous thickets. It is much scarcer in northern taiga forest regions.

Breeding expanded west in Russia during the second half of the twentieth century. It was first recorded in Finland in 1981 and has since become an annual summer visitor to the east in small numbers. Eleven singing males were recorded in late June 2000 when breeding was confirmed in Värtsilä (Davies 2001).

Non-breeding Booted Warbler winters in the Indian subcontinent, mainly from Madya Pradesh and the Ganges southward to Tamil Nadu and east to Bengal and Bangladesh.

MOVEMENTS Autumn departure from Russian breeding grounds begins shortly after the young have fledged, so that southern birds leave before northern breeders, the earliest passing through S Russia and Kazakhstan from the end of July. Around Orenburg birds begin to disperse in July and all have moved by the end of the month and it is presumably these southern breeders that pass through Turkmenistan, where passage peaks in the first half of August. Most northern areas are vacated by mid or late August. In central Kazakhstan (e.g. at the Kurgaldzhin Reserve) passage is heavy in late July and early August, but ceases by mid August. Migration through Tajikistan, Kyrgystan, Afghanistan and Pakistan occurs from late July to mid September. Adults reach Pakistan and N India from late July, mainly in August; juveniles from mid August. Arrival in C and S India is during September.

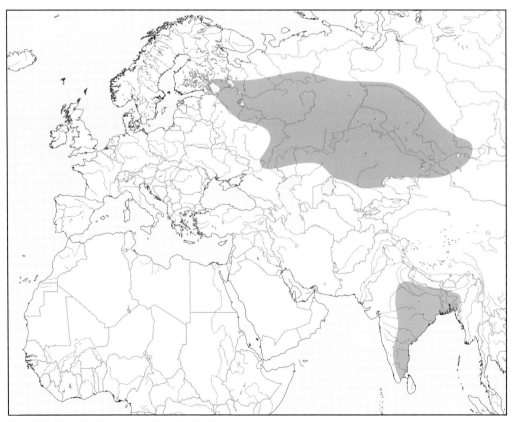

Booted Warbler. Breeding range and winter distribution.

Departure from the wintering grounds takes place mainly in April and some birds remain in India until the end of the month and probably into early May. Migrants are occasionally recorded in Nepal and Sikkim between late March and mid April. Passage through Afghanistan and Turkmenistan is rapid, occurring in late April and early May. The first birds reach Orenburg in the third week in April and the main passage occurs here during mid May. Breeding sites in N Kazakhstan and S Russia are occupied from mid May onwards. Birds return to some European Russian breeding sites from early May, but arrive in the Moscow area during the third week. They arrive at the extreme range limits, in Finland, on the Yenisey River and in the Altai Mountains, between the end of May and mid June.

Vagrancy Booted Warbler reaches W Europe regularly and the numbers arriving have shown a sharp increase since the late 1970s, coinciding with the westward expansion of the breeding range. It occurs annually in Britain, with 115 records to the end of 2008, all but three since 1975. Most occur between late August and late September, coinciding with the departure of northern breeders, but there are a few late October and early November records, plus five reports of singing males in June. Elsewhere in Europe, vagrants have reached Estonia, Sweden, Norway, Denmark, Germany, Netherlands, Belgium, Ireland, France, Switzerland, Spain, Italy and Greece. Booted Warbler is a vagrant to Turkey, although Kirwan *et al.* (2008) consider it may be a near-regular passage migrant in small numbers through the eastern two-thirds of the country. Vagrants have also reached Israel, Lebanon, the Nile delta, Egypt and Sri Lanka.

DESCRIPTION

Plumage – Adult fresh (October to January) Forehead to nape warm olive-brown, with a variable cinnamon tinge. Supercilium white, tinged buff or cinnamon-buff, rather narrow but well defined, extending from base of bill to about middle of ear-coverts. Lores pale buff as supercilium, marked with a small dark spot immediately in front of eye. Behind eye, a narrow, dark brown eye-stripe extends to rear of ear-coverts where it merges with sides of nape. Side of fore-crown above lores slightly darker than crown, forming a narrow line above supercilium in front of eye. Ear-coverts and upper cheeks warm olive-brown, grading to pale buff on lower cheeks. Eye-ring pale buff, narrow and indistinct. Upperparts olive-brown, with a variable, often strong cinnamon or rufous tinge, slightly paler cinnamon-brown on rump and uppertail-coverts. Tail dark grey-brown with slightly darker feather shafts. T6 with pale buff or greyish edge extending length of outer web, sometimes narrow and inconspicuous; t6 and t5 with pale tips and pale buff edges to distal inner webs. Underparts washed warm buff, paler creamy white on chin, throat and belly. Sides of breast and flanks more strongly suffused warm buff to rufous-buff. Undertail-coverts creamy white. Lesser and median coverts warm olive-brown. Greater coverts and tertials dark greyish brown with contrasting broad warm brown fringes. Primary coverts and alula dark greyish, fringed buffy brown. Flight feathers dark greyish brown, secondaries edged warm brown, primaries finely edged warm buff and with narrow pale greyish fringes and tips. Underwing-coverts warm buff.

Adult worn (May to August) Paler, with warm plumage tones almost entirely absent. Upperparts duller brown or olive-brown, but becoming paler sandy brown, often with slight greyish tinge by July. Paler rump and uppertail-coverts less cinnamon, more buffy or ochreous. Supercilium less contrasting, but dark sides to fore-crown more distinct, forming diffuse dark brown line or shadow above supercilium between the bill base and eye. Tail faded sandy brown but retains darker brown feather shafts; pale feather edges and tips usually narrow or absent by May. Underparts buffy white, becoming greyish white by July, but faint ochre-buff tinge usually retained on sides of upper breast and flanks. Undertail-coverts white. Closed wing paler, matching upperpart colour. Fringes to greater coverts and tertials pale sandy buff. Pale primary tips usually already lost by April. Tertials may appear uniformly pale in heavily worn birds.

First-winter Paler than fresh adult, without warm cinnamon tones. Supercilium pale buff, quite prominent in front of eye, less conspicuous over ear-coverts, contrasting in front of eye with dark loral spot. Diffuse dark brown sides to fore-crown usually conspicuous. Eye-ring often more contrasting than in adult. Ear-coverts pale sandy brown. Upperparts light buffy brown or olive-brown, slightly paler, more ochreous on rump and uppertail-coverts. Tail feathers dull sandy brown with darker brown shaft and narrow buffy edges; t6 with buffy outer web, but t5 and t6 lacking pale buff fringes on distal inner webs.

Chin, throat and undertail-coverts creamy white, becoming richer creamy buff on breast and darker greyish buff on flanks. Belly white, tinged greyish. Upperwing-coverts dark brown; lesser and median coverts with broad buffy brown tips, greater coverts fringed buff and primary coverts narrowly so. Tertials warm brown to dull greyish brown with broad, pale sandy brown fringes. Flight feathers dark brown, with sandy buff edges better-defined than in adult; primaries with narrow light sandy brown tips. No contrasting pale panel on secondaries, but closed remiges and greater coverts form rather paler area than adjacent upperparts. Alula dark brown with narrow, greyish brown fringe prominent along outer web.

Juvenile Resembles first-winter but upperparts and buffy breast warmly tinged.

Bare parts Upper mandible dark grey to blackish with narrow, pale pink cutting edge and dark tip. Lower mandible pink at base but with dark grey sides towards tip. Tarsi dull reddish brown in adults, reddish brown to pinkish grey in young birds with rear usually slightly darker than sides; soles flesh brown; claws horn brown. Iris dark brown.

IN HAND CHARACTERS
Measurements

	Male	Female
Wing	58–64 (60.6; 52)	56–65 (59.8; 38)
Tail	44–49 (46.4; 51)	42–49 (46.2; 38)
Bill	12.5–15 (13.7; 49)	12.5–15 (13.4; 35)
Tarsus	18.5–21 (19.9; 41)	19–21 (19.8; 32)

Sexes combined:
Tail/wing ratio: 72–84% (77%; 89)
Bill width: 3.3–3.8 (3.6; 17)
Hind claw: 4.0–5.5 (4.8; 21)
Tail graduation: 1–5 (3.2; 20)

Structure

Wing formula (Cramp 1992):

p1/pc	p2	p3e	p4e	p5e	p6(e)	p7	p10
3–8	4–8	0–1	wp	0–1	1–3.5	4–6	9–11

Wing rounded, p1 small. Wing point p(3) 4 (5); p2 = p(6) 6/7–7/8 [8]; emarginations on p3–5, sometimes slightly on p6.

Figure 105. Wing of Booted Warbler.

Tail rather short, almost square to slightly rounded.
Bill rather small, concave sided with narrow tip (Fig. 106).

Figure 106. Comparison of bill profile of (a) Booted Warbler and (b) Sykes's Warbler.

Tarsi slender, toes and claws small.

Recognition Differs from Sykes's Warbler in having slightly darker, warmer or more olive (less greyish brown) upperparts, buffier (less whitish) underparts, more prominent supercilium and dark tip to lower mandible. Structurally, length and shape of the bill, and tail length, are important in separation from Sykes's. Most Booted have bill (to skull) < 14mm (the minimum for Sykes's), with concave sides (not straight sided as in Sykes's, see Fig. 106). Most Booted (but very few Sykes's) have tail < 50mm and tail/wing ratio < 80%. Booted also tends to have a slightly longer second primary (commonly > p7, exceptionally = p8; in Sykes's, rarely > p7, commonly = p8 or 8/9), but there is much overlap and many cannot be separated.

Distinctly browner, less greyish, than the race *elaeica* of Eastern Olivaceous Warbler, with plainer wing, the pale edges of the remiges and greater coverts narrow and indistinct. In adult Booted, pale fringes to tips of outer tail feathers buffier (less white) and less sharply demarcated. The smaller p10 shortfall (usually < 12mm) should distinguish Booted from *elaeica* in the hand, as also should bill measurement (rarely < 14.5mm in *elaeica*). Most birds have wing length below 62mm (the minimum in *elaeica*).

Separated from Paddyfield Warbler by shorter, squarer tail (tail/wing ratio > 85% in Paddyfield, t1–6 6–9mm); longer p1 (0–4mm > pc in Paddyfield); and (where present) emargination on p6. Also by narrower supercilium and lack of distinct eye-stripe. Young Paddyfield in autumn usually show slightly darker, browner plumage.

Ageing In early autumn, young birds are readily distinguishable by their unworn plumage, with dark, pale-tipped primaries. Adults have abraded wing and tail feathers during June-August and worn faded body plumage. Ageing on plumage is not possible after complete autumn moult.

Weight Range 7.7–10.8g (Cramp 1992); Kazakhstan, 7.5–10.7g (8.9; 69) (AG unpublished data).

GEOGRAPHIC VARIATION None reported, but see discussion of *annectens* in **Taxonomy and Systematics** below.

TAXONOMY AND SYSTEMATICS Helbig & Seibold (1999) found a sequence difference of almost 7% between the cytochrome *b* genes of *caligata* and *rama*. Although based on just one specimen of each taxon (*caligata* from W Mongolia and *rama* from W Turkmenistan), this indicated substantial divergence. This mtDNA difference was less than that for other similar *Iduna* pair comparisons (e.g. 10% between *I. pallida elaeica* and *I. rama*, 9% between *elaeica* and *caligata*) but was greater than that found commonly elsewhere between recognised biological species. Svensson (2001) quoted an additional finding that the cytochrome *b* gene of *caligata* from Kazakhstan did not differ from that of birds trapped in Finland. He also reported breeding *caligata* and *rama* in Kazakhstan in adjacent territories, *caligata* showing a preference for low pea scrub, *rama* for taller tamarisk and saxaul bushes. These findings confirm that the two co-exist and behave as distinct species in that region.

In addition to *caligata* and *rama*, a third taxon, *annectens*, was proposed by Sushkin (1925) for birds from SC Siberia and neighbouring W Mongolia, E Kazakhstan and NW China, centred on the Junggar Pendi Desert. They are described as having the smaller size and structure of Booted, but being closer to Sykes's Warbler in overall colour, slightly more greyish olive above and whiter below with greyer tinged flanks than typical Booted. In addition, the outermost rectrix was said to have a more distinct white inner border and tip. It was proposed that *annectens* might have arisen as a result of secondary hybridisation between Booted and Sykes's Warblers. However, hybridisation has not been reported between these species where their breeding ranges are now known to come into contact (Svennson 2001).

Stepanyan (1978, 1983, 2003) acknowledged the validity of *annectens* as a pale race of Booted Warbler. But Svensson (2001) examined 23 of the 40 specimens used by Sushkin to describe *annectens*. He found that *caligata* and *annectens* were not sufficiently differentiated on colour to merit subspecific separation and commented that many of the cyanotypes of *annectens* did not differ at all from *caligata*. Dickinson (2003) recognised *annectens* but treated it as a race of Sykes's Warbler. Here we follow Svensson's arrangement and treat Booted and Sykes's Warblers as distinct, monotypic species, and with *annectens* being regarded as a synonym of *caligata*.

▲ Adult, Kazakhstan, June. Worn adults on the breeding grounds lack pale fringes of fresh birds but still retain conspicuous supercilium. Note short primary projection (Jyrki Normaja).

▲ Adult, Kazakhstan, May. The smallest *Iduna*. Note the particularly short, fine bill. This individual shows paler, less contrasting lores and lacks darker sides to crown (Hanne and Jens Eriksen).

▲ Adult, Novosibirsk, Siberia, June. Worn adult, with poorly marked supercilium terminating at rear of the eye. Also lacks dark shadow on side of crown, giving rather Sykes's Warbler-like appearance to head. However, bill structure and pattern, dark loral line and darker tertial centres are typical of Booted (Peter Kennerley).

▲ First-winter, Shetland, Scotland, September. Can appear *Phylloscopus*-like in structure and behaviour. Closed wing lacks pale wing-panel and secondary tips shown by Eastern Olivaceous. This individual shows a relatively long primary projection, perhaps exaggerated by the slightly displaced wing, but longer than in Sykes's (Hugh Harrop).

▲ ▶ First-winter, Shetland, Scotland, September. Young birds show characteristic appearance to head, with pale supercilium extending behind eye, dark shadow on side of crown above lores and rather delicate bill with dark sides on lower mandible near tip. Note contrast between dark tertial centres and paler fringes; contrast is less pronounced or largely absent on first-winter Sykes's Warbler. When worn and faded, these pale fringes and tips are lost and identification then becomes more difficult. This combination of characters should separate Booted from similar first-winter *Iduna* species in early autumn (Hugh Harrop).

DARK-CAPPED YELLOW WARBLER
Iduna natalensis   **Plate 34**

Chloropeta natalensis **Smith, 1847.** *Illus. Zool. South Africa, Aves,* plate 112, figure 2 (and text). Near Port Natal (Durban), Natal.

A widespread Afrotropical resident and local migrant of forest edges and bush-lined streams that ranges from C and E Africa to E South Africa. It overlaps geographically and ecologically with Mountain Yellow Warbler. Polytypic, with four races recognised:

I. n. natalensis Smith, 1847. S Tanzania and E Zambia to E Zimbabwe and E South Africa.

I. n. massaica Fischer & Reichenow, 1884. SE Sudan and Ethiopia to E DR Congo, Uganda, Kenya and Tanzania, intergrading in S Tanzania with *natalensis*.

I. n. major Hartert, 1904. Gabon and Angola to S DR Congo, N and W Zambia and N and C Zimbabwe.

I. n. batesi Sharpe, 1905. SE Nigeria and Cameroon to N DR Congo.

IDENTIFICATION Length 13–14cm. Wing 56–70mm. Tail/wing 86–95%.

A medium sized warbler, olive above and rich yellow below, some races showing a contrasting darker cap. In East Africa, it occurs mainly at lower altitudes than Mountain Yellow Warbler but overlaps with it at about 2,000m and both species may occur in the same habitat. The song is distinctive, a series of short phrases, typically ending with a ringing flourish. Sexes alike.

Structure Suggests a typical *Hippolais/Iduna* warbler in size and shape but has a conspicuously broad-based, often slightly convex-sided bill and a rather rounded crown. The wing differs from the migratory *Iduna* species, being short and rounded, with a large first primary (p1) and a very short primary projection, the wing point formed by p4–5 and sometimes p6. The slightly rounded tail has only ten feathers. Perched birds often adopt an upright flycatcher-like posture when the forehead, formed by raised crown feathers, can appear particularly angular.

Plumage and bare parts The adult is primarily yellow below. It shows olive-brown upperparts with a conspicuous yellow tinge and (except in the race *major*) a contrastingly darker top to the head, usually dark brown but blackish in race *massaica*. A narrow yellow supercilium reaches to above the rear of the eye and there is an indistinct narrow yellow eye-ring. These stand out against dark olive lores, cheeks and ear-coverts which, in turn, contrast sharply with a bright yellow chin and throat. The entire underparts are yellow, duller and suffused with olive on the flanks. The edges and fringes to the closed wing appear yellower than the upperparts. Yellowish green fringes to the greater coverts and tertials contrast with blackish centres and broad yellowish green edges to the secondaries and form a bright panel that contrasts with the blackish primaries. The brown tail shows bright yellowish feather edges.

In juveniles, the underparts and supercilium are rich tawny buff rather than yellow, the upperparts are light cinnamon brown and the crown is browner than in the adult. The pale edges to the wing and tail feathers are tawny-buff.

The bill is black above and fleshy white to bright horn below. The legs are dark grey or blackish.

SIMILAR SPECIES Occurs sympatrically in parts of its range with the rather similar Mountain Yellow Warbler and their separation is discussed below. Melodious and Icterine Warblers reach the Afrotropics during the northern winter and could present potential sources of confusion.

Mountain Yellow Warbler is slightly duller and greener above than Dark-capped and always lacks a contrastingly darker crown. It also has browner wing and tail feathers with the yellow edgings less bright and contrasting. Its habits are less flycatcher-like when feeding.

Melodious Warbler and **Icterine Warbler** are both paler yellow below than Dark-capped Yellow Warbler, and have paler, uniform olive-green rather than yellow tinged olive-brown upperparts. They also have paler lores and a much less broad bill. Being migrants, both show a noticeably longer primary projection.

VOICE The song is loud, brief and far-carrying, with a distinctive quality. In S Africa, it consists of a series of short sequences, each lasting *c.* 2 seconds and separated by brief pauses of *c.* 1 second. Each sequence may be introduced by three or four short chipping calls, followed by two or three varied, rather fluty bulbul *Pycnonotus*-like notes, leading into a trilling or rattling flourish: '*chut-chut-chut-wezur-wezur-wewewewewewe*'.

Part of song of Dark-capped Yellow Warbler recorded within breeding range of *I. n. natalensis*, Natal, South Africa, November. (Gibbon 2003)

Songs in Kenya are slightly different and have a throaty quality reminiscent of Lesser Swamp Warbler. Here the song again consists of brief sequences of *c.* 2 seconds in which short introductory notes typically lead into a ringing trill or flourish: '*chip-chip-titit-reep-reep-reep-reep*', '*trip-trip-trelelelelelel*', or '*twiya twiya, wichu-wichu-wichu*'. However, intervening pauses are longer, often over ten seconds. A loud, descending, wheezing call sometimes follows the song.

Part of song of Dark-capped Yellow Warbler recorded within breeding range of *I. n. massaica*, Taita Hills, Kenya, November. (Chappuis 2000)

The most frequently heard calls include a harsh '*check*' and a nasal '*chaaar*' given in alarm.

MOULT In Zimbabwe, adults are in primary moult in February and March (Hockey *et al.* 2005).

HABITAT A bird of moist places, utilising a wide variety of rank vegetation. It is found in tall grass, bracken-briar, nettle-beds, tangled growth along streams, bushy places near lakes and rivers, overgrown waste ground and gardens, and dense herbage on the edge of forest. It has a wide altitudinal range, occurring from sea level to lower montane elevations. In East Africa it is typically a bird of mid elevations, occurring between 500m and 2,300m. It ranges up to 2,150m in Cameroon and as high as 2,600m in Ethiopia. Wintering birds frequent coastal scrub in South Africa.

BEHAVIOUR Usually found alone or in pairs. Shy and seen mainly when it emerges to sing from an exposed perch, but it drops down quickly when disturbed and creeps away. It feeds as a typical warbler, creeping among low shrubs and herbage and sidling up and down stems. It snaps disturbed prey, often with short flutters. It also gleans insects from leaves in trees like a *Phylloscopus* warbler and makes short fly-catching sallies. It will defend its territory with much song and crest raising, adjacent males singing against each other.

BREEDING HABITS It is monogamous, solitary and territorial. The nest is built in a low bush, or among bracken, reeds or herbaceous plants, often by a stream or swamp, typically placed in an upright fork or slung between upright stems about 1m from the ground. It is a deep, often bulky cup of grass or reed blades, rootlets and other fibres, lined with fine grasses, stems, plant fibres and hair. The clutch is usually two eggs (sometimes one or three) and these are incubated for 12 days. The fledging period is 14–16 days. Breeding usually occurs during rainy seasons. North of the equator, eggs are laid mainly between April and July, in southern Africa between October and February.

DISTRIBUTION Has a wide but rather patchy distribution in C Africa both north and south of the Congo forest belt and through E Africa from Ethiopia south to Zimbabwe and E South Africa. It is locally common at mid to lower montane levels in eastern and southern parts of its range.

I. n. batesi Ranges from the E Nigerian highlands, through the southern lowlands and highlands of Cameroon (north to Bamenda and Mount Oku) to SW Central African Republic, and around the edge of the forest zone in northern DR Congo to Ituri.

I. n. major Occurs mainly south of the Congo forest, breeding from S Gabon, S PR Congo and Cabinda (Angola) south to the central plateau and E highlands of Angola and across S DR Congo (Kasai and Katanga) to N, C and S Zambia and N and C Zimbabwe.

I. n. massaica Occurs in the S Sudan highlands, E DR Congo (south to Itombwe), Rwanda, NE Burundi, W and S Uganda, W Tanzania (south to Kasulu) and the highlands of W and SE Ethiopia, W, C and SE Kenya and NE and E Tanzania. Intergrades with nominate *natalensis* in S Tanzania.

I. n. natalensis Ranges from S Tanzania to NE and E Zambia, Malawi and the highlands of NW Mozambique. South of the Zambezi it breeds in the Zimbabwe highlands and adjacent W Mozambique, and in South Africa through E Limpopo Province, Mpumalanga and lowland KwaZulu-Natal to coastal Eastern Cape; also in Swaziland.

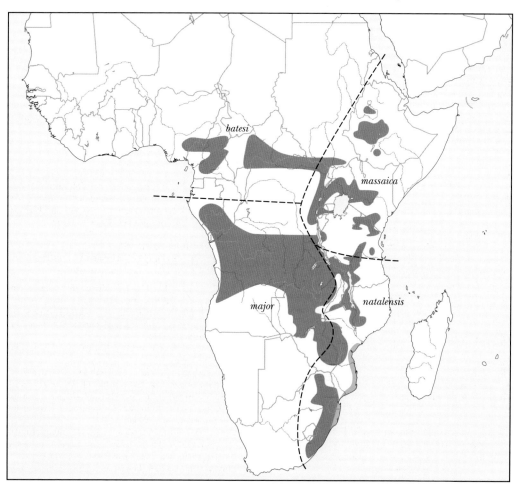

Dark-capped Yellow Warbler. Breeding range and non-breeding distribution.

MOVEMENTS In southern Africa, birds undertake short movements and appear at lower levels during the cool non-breeding season. In South Africa, there is a regular movement from the higher parts of KwaZulu-Natal (> 1,500m) to mid levels during May and some reach the coast. Birds of the race *major* breeding on the Zimbabwe Plateau apparently winter on the Mozambique coastal plain (Hockey *et al.* 2005).

DESCRIPTION *I. n. massaica*

Plumage – Adult Forehead and crown blackish brown. Supercilium yellow, well-defined but narrow, extending from bill base to front of ear-coverts. Eye-ring yellow, narrow but distinct. Lores dark olive-brown, forming triangle in front of eye, linked below eye with yellowish-flecked olive-brown cheeks and ear-coverts. Nape, mantle and scapulars to uppertail-coverts yellowish olive-brown, palest on rump and contrasting with dark cap. Tail blackish brown, feathers with narrow olive-yellow fringes. Chin, throat and lower sides of neck bright yellow. Remainder of underparts yellow, suffused dark olive on sides of breast and flanks. Lesser coverts yellowish olive-brown. Median and greater coverts and tertials blackish brown, broadly fringed yellowish olive-green. Primary coverts and alula blackish, edged olive-yellow. Feathers along carpal edge bright yellow. Primaries and secondaries blackish brown with sharply defined yellowish olive-green edges, fine yellowish tips and broad yellow inner borders. Underwing-coverts bright yellow.

Juvenile Patterned as adult, but top and sides of head browner. Supercilium and eye-ring yellow-ochre. Mantle and scapulars to uppertail-coverts light cinnamon-brown. Underparts rich yellow ochre to rich tawny buff, paler on the belly. Fringes of tail feathers, upperwing-coverts and tertials, and edges of flight feathers cinnamon-buff.

Bare parts Upper mandible black. Lower mandible pinkish or fleshy white to bright horn. Mouth bright orange. Tarsi dark grey-brown, dark grey or blackish. Iris mid to dark brown.

IN HAND CHARACTERS

Measurements

I. n. massaica

	Male	Female
Wing	58–67 (62.4; 19)	59–63 (61.5; 14)
Tail	52–58 (55.6; 10)	51–60 (56.1; 9)
Bill	14.5–16 (15.5; 10)	14.5–16 (15.4; 8)
Tarsus	20.5–22 (21.1; 10)	20.5–21.5 (21.0; 9)

Sexes combined:
Tail/wing ratio: 86–95% (91%; 21)
Bill width: 5.7–6.5 (6.1; 20)
Hind claw: 5.8–7.5 (6.7; 11)
Tail graduation: 5–8
Other races (sexes combined)
I. n. natalensis: *wing* 56–65 (61.4; 27); *tail*, 53–62 (56.6; 21); *bill* 14–16.5 (15.5; 12); *tarsus* 19–22 (21.2; 12).
I. n. major: *wing* 61–70 (65.3; 11); *tail* 52–59 (56.1; 11); *bill* 15–16.5 (16.0; 11); *tarsus* 21–23 (22.0; 11). Tail/wing ratio apparently lower than in other races (84–89%, n = 11).
I. n. batesi: *wing* 57–61 (59.1; 20); *tail* 51–58 (53.5; 19); *bill* 15–16.5 (15.5; 12); *tarsus* 19.5–21 (20.5; 12).

Structure *I. n. massaica*

Wing formula (n = 9):

p1/pc	p2	p3e	p4e	p5e	p6e	p7(e)	p10
14–17	7–10	0.5–3	wp	wp	0–1	1.5–3.5	7–10

Wing strongly rounded with large p1 (*c.* 70% p2). Wing point p4–5 (6); p2 ≤ p10, p3 = p6–7; emargination on p3–6, sometimes slightly on p7.

Figure 107. Wing of Dark-capped Yellow Warbler *I. n. massaica*.

Tail medium, rounded, with ten rounded feathers.
Bill medium length, very broad and flattened with convex sides.

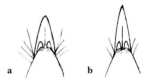

Figure 108. Comparison of bill profile of (a) Dark-capped Yellow Warbler and (b) Papyrus Yellow Warbler

Taris and toes rather slender.
Other races similar in structure.
Recognition A distinctive warbler with yellow underparts and a broad bill. Distinguished from Mountain Yellow Warbler by olive-brown rather than greenish upperparts, contrasting dark crown (except race *major*) and blackish wing feathers with contrasting yellowish edging.
Weight
I. n. massaica: 10–11.5g (10.7; 5).
I. n. natalensis: 9–13.6g (11.7; 77) (Hockey *et al.* 2005).
I. n. major: 12–13g (12.3) (Urban *et al.* 1997).

GEOGRAPHIC VARIATION W African birds are smaller and duller; those of S central Africa larger and brighter. Birds of S Africa and particularly those of E Africa, are characterised by a contrasting dark crown. There are four well differentiated races.
I. n. massaica (Ethiopia to E DR Congo and N Tanzania)
  Described above.
I. n. natalensis (S Tanzania and E Zambia to E South Africa)
  Resembles *massaica*, but the top of the head is dark olive-brown rather than blackish and shows less contrast with the yellowish olive-brown upperparts. The yellow underparts are slightly less bright.
I. n. major (Gabon and Angola to N and W Zambia, N and C Zimbabwe) Differs from *massaica* and *natalensis* in having the top of the head yellowish olive-brown, uniform with the mantle. It is also slightly paler above than *massaica* and the wing and tail feathers are browner (less blackish) and show yellower edges. The underparts are bright

yellow as in *massaica*, but the sides of the breast appear less olive. Larger than other races.

I. n. batesi (Nigeria to N DR Congo) Differs from *massaica* in having a dark brown crown and darker, less yellowish, olive-brown upperparts and thus shows only slight contrast between crown and mantle. The yellow underparts are paler and less bright. Slightly smaller than *massaica*.

TAXONOMY AND SYSTEMATICS This species and the Mountain Yellow Warbler, with their broad bills and bright coloration, were formerly treated as monarch-flycatchers, but their general habits, feeding movements and calls indicated a relationship with the *Acrocephalus/Hippolais* warblers. This has now been supported by DNA studies (Helbig & Siebold 1999, Fregin *et al.* 2009), which place these two species in a clade together with four former *Hippolais* species. These six species now make up the genus *Iduna*, within which the two yellow warblers appear to be most closely related to Eastern Olivaceous and Western Olivaceous Warblers.

▲ Adult *I. n. massaica*, Nairobi, Kenya. September. A freshly moulted bird showing the blackish crown, contrasting greenish olive upperparts and bright yellow underparts. Yellowish wing and tail feather-edges are conspicuous, and yellow tips form prominent bars across the median and greater coverts (Peter Usher).

▲ Adult *I. n. massaica*, Nairobi, Kenya, August. Shows the dark top and side to head, narrow yellow supraloral stripe and eye-ring, and broad bill (Peter Usher).

▲ Adult *I. n. batesi*, Banekane, Cameroon, March. Paler than *massaica*, the olive crown matching the mantle (Nik Borrow).

▲ Adult *I. n. massaica*, Nairobi, Kenya, November. The crown feathers are raised in alarm (Nik Borrow).

▲ Adult *I. n. natalensis*, KwaZulu-Natal, South Africa, December. Yellow underparts and a yellowish wing panel contrast with olive-brown upperparts. Note the short primary projection and slender dark grey legs (Hugh Chittenden).

▲ Adult *I. n. natalensis*, KwaZulu-Natal, South Africa, December. The crown feathers are raised in typical alert posture. Note the broad bill. The crown is only slightly darker than the mantle in this race (Warwick Tarboton).

▲ Adult *I. n. natalensis*, KwaZulu-Natal, South Africa, December. This incubating bird shows the subdued head pattern and short, weakly defined supercilium (Warwick Tarboton).

MOUNTAIN YELLOW WARBLER
Iduna similis   Plate 34

Chloropeta similis Richmond, 1897. *Auk* 14: 163. Mount Kilimanjaro, Tanganyika. 10,000 feet.

A resident, confined to bushy habitat in the highlands of E Africa. Monotypic.

IDENTIFICATION Length 13cm. Wing 55–64mm. Tail/wing 86–95%.

A medium-sized warbler of montane forest edge, appearing olive-green above and yellow below. Its geographical range overlaps that of Dark-capped Yellow Warbler, but the two are usually separated altitudinally, with Mountain Yellow occurring at higher elevations. Its varied musical song is quite different from that of Dark-capped Yellow Warbler. Sexes alike.

Structure Similar in structure to Dark-capped Yellow but the bill is slightly less broad and carriage and behaviour are less flycatcher-like. It has short and very rounded wings, with a large first primary (p1) and the wing point usually formed by p5–6. The tail is rather longer and more graduated than that of Dark-capped Yellow Warbler and has 12 rather than ten rectrices that are narrower and more pointed.

Plumage and bare parts The adult is dark olive green above, the top of the head being uniform with the mantle. A narrow yellow supercilium extends only to the rear of the eye and a fine yellow eye-ring is inconspicuous. The lores and sides of the head are dark olive-green, matching the upperparts. The entire underparts are bright yellow, tinged with olive on the sides of the breast. The wing lacks the blackish appearance shown by Dark-capped Yellow Warbler and the coverts appear more uniform, with olive-green fringes obscuring dark centres. Olive-green edges to the remiges create a brighter wing-panel, but this is not prominent.

Juveniles resemble adults but show a cinnamon-brown tinge above. They have paler yellow underparts and paler and yellower wing feather edges.

The bill is blackish or dark horn with a bright yellowish or orange brown lower mandible, most conspicuous towards the base. The legs are dark grey.

SIMILAR SPECIES See discussion under Dark-capped Yellow Warbler.

Dark-capped Yellow Warbler has browner upperparts and a contrasting dark cap (except race *major* which occurs outside the range of Mountain Yellow Warbler). The wing is more strongly patterned, with blacker feather centres and a more conspicuous yellowish wing-panel. It also displays flycatcher-like feeding behaviour more often than Mountain Yellow, and has a very different voice.

VOICE The song consists of a series of varied and melodic sequences, each lasting about 4–5 seconds and followed by a pause of 3–4 seconds before a slightly different sequence is given. This may continue for minutes at a time. Each sequence is a pleasant medley of slurred whistles and canary-like warbling and trills, with a large frequency range. Most notes are clear and musical, though some of the lowest have a nasal *Acrocephalus*-like quality.

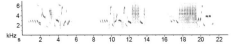

Song of Mountain Yellow Warbler, Aberdares, Kenya, September. (Chappuis 2000)

The alarm call is described as '*cha-cha-cha*' (Urban *et al.* 1997).

MOULT No information available.

HABITAT A bird of rank growth or bushes that occurs in a variety of highland habitats. Found in primary forest, especially along edges or in swampy clearings, but also in secondary growth, woodland undergrowth, heath scrub, bracken-briar and overgrown cultivation. It often frequents vegetation along streams and swampy valleys. It ranges from 1,800m to above 3,000m and occurs locally up to 3,400m in Kenya and to 3,700m in E DR Congo. There is limited overlap with Dark-capped Yellow Warbler between 1,800m and 2,200m, for example on the Nyika Plateau in Malawi where they occupy the same bracken-briar habitat (Dowsett-Lemaire 1989).

BEHAVIOUR Typically found in pairs and only occasionally associates with other species. It feeds in a typical warbler manner, usually keeping fairly low in thickets and young growth but sometimes foraging up to 10m above the ground in creepers or in the crowns of low montane forest trees. It adopts a rather horizontal carriage and moves with short hops, gleaning prey items from leaves and branches and making occasional sallies to catch flying insects. Birds tend to sing from within thick cover and are usually less conspicuous than Dark-capped Yellow Warbler.

BREEDING HABITS Territorial, sometimes holding a territory for 2–3 years (Dowsett 1985). The nest is built about 1m above the ground in a fork in a low shrub or bush, often near a stream. It is a thick-walled cup constructed from grass blades, leaves and seed heads, together with ferns and moss, bound with cobwebs and lined with feathers, hair and plant fibres. It tends to be bulkier than that of Dark-capped Yellow Warbler (Urban *et al.* 1997). Two eggs are usually laid (sometimes only one). Incubation and fledging periods are unknown. Breeding tends to take place during the rainy seasons. Egg laying has been noted in Sudan in April and October, DR Congo in April to June and October, W Kenya in July, August and November, Tanzania in September and December, and Zambia and Malawi from December to February.

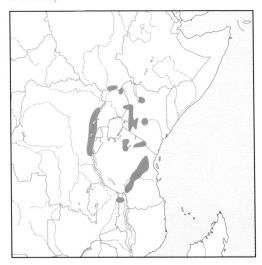

Mountain Yellow Warbler. Resident within breeding range.

DISTRIBUTION Has a restricted and fragmented distribution in the highlands of E Africa, but is often locally common. It occurs in the Imatong and Dongatona Mountains of S Sudan and on nearby Mount Morongole in NE Uganda. It occupies the mountains either side of the Albertine Rift, from the Rwenzoris south to Itombwe and Mount Kabobo (in E DR Congo, W and SW Uganda, W Rwanda and W Burundi). It occurs on Mount Elgon and in the highlands of W and C Kenya, including Mount Nyiru and Mount Kenya. It is present in N Tanzania on Mount Kilimanjaro and Mount Meru and in the Crater Highlands, in E Tanzania from the Nguru, Ukaguru and Uluguru Mountains to the Udzungwas and Mount Njombe, and on the Nyika Plateau in N Malawi and adjacent Zambia.

MOVEMENTS Believed to be sedentary.

DESCRIPTION

Plumage – Adult Forehead to nape and upperside of neck dark olive-green. Supercilium yellow, narrow and tapering off above rear of eye. Yellow eye-ring narrow and inconspicuous. Triangular loral spot dark olive-green, joining with similarly coloured upper cheeks and ear-coverts. Mantle and scapulars dark olive-green, merging with nape and crown but becoming rather paler and yellower on rump and uppertail-coverts. Tail dark olive-brown, feathers fringed yellowish olive-green. Lower cheeks, chin, throat, lower sides of neck and rest of underparts bright yellow, sides of breast suffused with dusky olive. Upperwing-coverts olive-green, with dark centres to feathers obscured. Tertials dark olive-brown with olive-green fringes. Primaries and secondaries dark brown, narrowly edged olive-green; borders of inner webs yellow-ochre. Underwing-coverts bright yellow.

Juvenile Similar to adult, but upperparts slightly browner with distinct cinnamon tinge, especially on rump and uppertail-coverts. Underparts warm buff, throat and breast pale yellow-buff. Edges of flight feathers and fringes of tertials paler, warm buff to yellowish olive (less green).

Bare parts Upper mandible dark horn or blackish. Lower mandible yellowish or salmon pink, especially at base, becoming darker towards tip. Mouth light reddish orange. Tarsi dark grey, greenish grey or blackish. Iris hazel, brown or dark brown.

IN HAND CHARACTERS
Measurements

	Male	Female
Wing	57–64 (59.4; 19)	55–62 (57.9; 14)
Tail	54–63 (56.8; 10)	53–60 (56.2; 9)
Bill	15–16.5 (15.7; 10)	14.5–16 (5.3; 10)
Tarsus	21.5–23 (22.6; 10)	21.5–23 (22.4; 10)

Sexes combined:
Tail/wing ratio: 86–95% (90%; 21)
Bill width: 4.8–5.8 (5.4; 18)

Hind claw: 5.0–6.1 (5.7; 10)
Tail graduation: 8–12

Structure

Wing formula (n = 10):

p1/pc	p2	p3e	p4e	p5e	p6e	p7(e)	p10
13–16	9–12	2.5–4	0–1	wp	wp	0–2.5	5–7

Wing similar to Dark-capped Yellow Warbler (Fig. 107); strongly rounded with large p1 (*c.* 65% p2). Wing point p(4) 5–6[7]; p2 < ss tips, p3 = p7–9; emargination on p3–6, usually slight on p7.

Tail more strongly graduated than in Dark-capped Yellow Warbler, with 12 rather narrow feathers (Fig. 112).

Bill broad and flattened; sides straight or slightly convex, as Dark-capped Yellow Warbler (Fig. 108).

Tarsi rather slender, but longer than in Dark-capped Yellow Warbler; claws weaker than in Dark-capped Yellow Warbler.

Recognition Distinguished from Dark-capped Yellow Warbler by greenish upperparts with the crown uniform with the mantle, brownish wing feathers with less sharply demarcated yellow edges, narrower tail feathers (Fig. 112) and greater t1–6 difference (usually > 8mm).
Weight 9–15g (11.1; 23) (Urban *et al.* 1997).

GEOGRAPHIC VARIATION None described.

TAXONOMY AND SYSTEMATICS See under Dark-capped Yellow Warbler.

▲ Adult, Ngorongoro, Tanzania, February (Martin Goodey).

Genus *Phragamaticola* Blyth, 1849

[L. *phragmites* kind of reed growing in hedgerows; *-cola* dweller (*colere* to dwell)]

A monotypic genus with just a single migratory species, Thick-billed Warbler, which inhabits dense undergrowth in central and southeast Siberia to northeast China, and migrates to winter in India and southeast Asia. Although this large, unstreaked warbler is often included within *Acrocephalus*, it differs significantly from the large plain-backed *Acrocephalus* species. These differences include its much shorter and thick-based bill, domed crown, a fairly long first primary combined with a more rounded wing structure, a strongly graduated tail and an unmarked head pattern. Note that *Phragmaticola* is an incorrect subsequent spelling for this genus, and *Phragamaticola* remains the correct spelling (Dickinson & Gregory 2006).

THICK-BILLED WARBLER
Phragamaticola aedon   Plate 25

Muscicapa Aëdon **Pallas, 1776**. *Reise Verschiedene Provinzen Russischen Reichs* 3: 695. Dauria.

An unusual and distinctive large warbler with unique structural characters and a preference for shrubbery and dense undergrowth, rather than wetlands. It breeds across the Eastern Palearctic and migrates to winter from India to SE Asia. Two races are recognised:

P. a. aedon (Pallas, 1776). SC Siberia and adjacent NW Mongolia.

P. a. stegmanni Watson, 1985. NE Mongolia and Amurland region of E Siberia to Sea of Japan and NE China.

IDENTIFICATION Length 18–19cm. Wing 73–86mm. Tail/wing 97–105%.

A large and warmly coloured warbler with a short, thick bill, relatively short and rounded wings and an exceptionally long tail. Its distribution overlaps in E and SE Asia with Oriental Reed Warbler throughout the year, with Clamorous Reed Warbler in India and Burma during the winter months and with Great Reed Warbler in W Siberia during the breeding season. Sexes alike.

Structure Thick-billed Warbler has a unique structure including a short, deep-based bill, an exceptionally long tail and a domed crown, giving it an overall structure reminiscent of one of the smaller shrikes *Lanius*. The bill is much shorter than the dagger shaped bills of Oriental Reed and Great Reed Warblers (Fig. 76), so although it appears thick, it is actually no deeper at the base than that of Oriental Reed. Like the bill of a shrike, it retains fairly uniform thickness until the distal third, when both mandibles curve towards the tip. The crown feathering is normally held flat against the head, giving it the characteristic rounded appearance, but when agitated, the crown feathers are raised. This gives an appearance distinct from that of the large *Acrocephalus*, which raise only the fore-crown feathers.

Although Thick-billed Warbler resembles a large *Acrocephalus*, it has a short and relatively rounded wing with the wing point formed by p4, often together with p3 and p5. The primary projection is short, usually half to two-thirds of the exposed tertial length, and the wing-tip falls about one-third of the way along the uppertail- and undertail-coverts. The relatively long and broad first primary (p1) extends well beyond the primary coverts, a feature not found among the large Palearctic *Acrocephalus*. This is often visible on a slightly spread wing, as is the emargination on p3–5, which is also diagnostic. The tail is particularly long, narrow and strongly graduated, giving it a tail/wing ratio about 100%, higher than that of any of the larger Palaearctic *Acrocephalus*.

Plumage The plainest of the larger warblers of mainland Asia. It has no distinctive plumage features and even lacks a contrasting supercilium or distinct eye-stripe, which all the large *Acrocephalus* show. Only the slightly paler lores and large dark eye provide contrast on the otherwise uniform sides to the head. The head, upperparts and closed wings are uniform warm fulvous-brown to cinnamon-brown with a slight olivaceous tinge, showing slight contrast with the typically slightly warmer and brighter rump. The tail is rufous-brown and often the brightest part of the bird. The creamy white chin and throat merge with the uniformly pale sandy brown underparts, which darken to warm cinnamon-buff towards the lower flanks and undertail-coverts.

Worn birds on the breeding grounds show slightly duller upperparts and there is often a greyish cast to the nape, giving the crown a slightly warmer-toned and capped appearance. The warmer brown rump, uppertail-coverts and, in particular, the tail then tend to show greater contrast with the mantle. The underparts are also then paler and the belly can appear conspicuously silvery white although the flanks usually retain a dull buffy straw wash.

Throughout its range, in both autumn and spring, some are paler, less richly coloured than typical birds, with duller olive-brown upperparts, wings and tail, and whitish underparts with warmer tones restricted to the upper breast and flanks, but the chin, lower breast and belly are white. Birds with this appearance include known young birds, but it is uncertain whether adults can also resemble this. From October onwards, following the complete moult by both adults and juveniles, there are no established plumage features by which they can be separated, although iris colour remains reliable; dark brown in adults and greyish brown in young birds.

The pale greyish brown bill shows an unmarked lower mandible, pale pink in adults, but slightly more yellowish in young birds. The legs and feet are greyish.

SIMILAR SPECIES Within its range, Thick-billed Warbler overlaps with Great Reed, Oriental Reed and Clamorous Reed Warblers. Although similar in size and coloration, the resemblance of these species to Thick-billed Warbler is superficial and there is little risk of confusion.

Oriental Reed Warbler and **Great Reed Warbler** closely resemble each other and share similar distinctions from Thick-billed Warbler, so it is convenient to treat them together here. They show a prominent supercilium, distinct eye-stripe and angular crown, giving them a characteristic fierce expression, enhanced by their long dagger-like bills (Fig. 76). This is quite unlike the round headed, open-faced appearance of Thick-billed, further softened by its large dark eye. The dull olive-brown or mousy brown upperparts of Oriental Reed and Great Reed are generally paler, less warm and rich, than those of Thick-billed. Their paler, dull creamy white underparts are also less rich, particularly on the flanks, ventral region and undertail-coverts.

The tails of Oriental Reed and Great Reed Warblers are proportionately shorter, broader and less graduated than that of Thick-billed Warbler (Fig. 110). Structural differences in the closed wing are also diagnostic. In Oriental Reed and Great Reed Warbler, the primary projection appears long and pointed and can approach the tertial length, while in Thick-billed Warbler, it typically ranges between half and two thirds of the tertial length. With good views, the rounded wing structure of Thick-billed is diagnostic. In Oriental Reed and Great Reed Warblers, the first primary (p1) invariably falls short of the primary coverts, whereas in Thick-billed it is relatively long and broad, extending 5–10mm beyond them. The wing point is formed by p3–4 in Oriental Reed and Great Reed, and never by p5, and they lack the emargination on p5 shown by Thick-billed.

Clamorous Reed Warbler has several races which breed in Asia but only two are likely to come into contact with Thick-billed and only during the winter months; the migratory form *brunnescens* in India and the resident form *amyae* in NE India, SW China and N Burma. Both races are very similar in appearance to Oriental Reed and Great Reed Warblers, and have a similar head pattern and upperpart colour. They are thus quite different from the warmer, browner and more richly coloured appearance of Thick-billed Warbler. Structural differences are also diagnostic. Clamorous Reed has a distinctively long, slim and blackish bill which is proportionately longer than that of Oriental Reed, giving it a more attenuated head profile to that of Thick-billed Warbler. Differences in the wing structure are less pronounced and there is some overlap with Thick-billed, but the minute p1 of Clamorous Reed provides an immediate distinction.

VOICE The song is quite different from that of the large *Acrocephalus*. It is introduced by characteristic '*tschok, tschok*' phrases, repeated several times. There then follows a distinctive soft and relatively musical warble or babble, lacking in harsher notes and interspersed with imitations of the calls and songs of other species occurring nearby. Each phrase is repeated several times before there is an abrupt change to a different phrase. In this respect, it is similar to the song of Blyth's Reed Warbler, but is more lively and rapid. In Amurland, Neufeldt (1967) mentioned that the song includes considerable mimicry including song or calls of Brown Shrike, Gray's Grasshopper Warbler, Black-browed Reed Warbler, Siberian Rubythroat and Black-tailed Hawfinch. Shirihai *et al.* (1995) liken the song to that of a loud Marsh Warbler, but deeper and lacking the coarser tones.

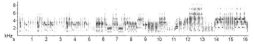

Part of song of Thick-billed Warbler recorded within breeding range of *P. a. aedon*, Chita region, Siberia, Russia, July. (Veprintsev 2007)

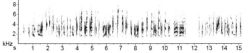

Part of song of Thick-billed Warbler recorded within breeding range of *P. a. stegmanni*, northeast China, May. (Sample 2003)

The call is a loud harsh '*tack*' or '*tschok*', continuously repeated, either singly or in pairs, at intervals of a second or less. A less frequently heard '*tchurr*' is occasionally given.

MOULT Most adults and juveniles appear to have a complete moult prior to departure from the breeding area. Dement'ev & Gladkov (1954) stated that adults have a post-breeding moult beginning between mid June and late July and completed by the end of August.

Although Williamson (1968) considered that adults and possibly young birds begin a complete moult immediately after arrival in the wintering areas, data from birds trapped in Thailand do not support this. Of 40 individuals handled between late October and early January, only seven were found to be replacing either primaries, secondaries or the tail (PDR *in litt.*), suggesting most had moulted before arrival. Of these seven, all had completed secondary moult, three were still in primary moult, three were replacing the tertials and two replacing the rectrices. Round (2008) also commented that the plumage remains unworn throughout the winter and even spring birds show only slight wear.

Young birds have a complete post-juvenile moult prior to autumn migration, although some may suspend during migration. For example, a young bird in Hong Kong in late October was in suspended moult, with the primaries and tertials replaced but had retained the five outer secondaries. There are no data to indicate a partial moult prior to spring migration, but it would seem likely that this takes place, perhaps during March and April.

HABITAT Thick-billed Warbler shows no particular affinity towards wetlands and reedbeds during the breeding season, on migration or on the wintering grounds. It will breed in almost any habitat containing thick shrubbery and a luxuriant undergrowth. In Amurland, Neufeldt (1967) recorded it breeding in impenetrable thickets of hazel, both on hill slopes and into the lowlands. It is also regularly found in birch forests with a thick scrub layer, and also on dry hillsides where fires and felling have enabled a heavy growth of hazel, rose, oak and lespedeza to form dense thickets. It does not, however, shun wetlands completely and can be found in damp meadows provided there is a dense growth of thick grasses and scattered shrubs.

It also favours dense scrub and undergrowth during migration and during the winter months. For example, in Hong Kong it is rare in the *Phragmites* reedbeds and is more frequently located in dry scrub and dense undergrowth on hillsides well away from water. In Thailand, wintering birds retain their attachment to thick undergrowth, bushes and scrub in dry open or cleared areas and invariably avoid primary and secondary forest.

BEHAVIOUR Typically shy and skulking, often remaining deep within cover and betraying its presence only by the occasional call. Movement and progression through dense undergrowth tends to be slow and ponderous and flights between adjacent scrub patches are short and slow. When excited, it gives a series of alarm calls that merge into a harsh, loud chattering. When alarmed, it frequently raises the rear crown feathers and cocks the tail or waves it in a rather stiff shrike-like manner, as if using it to balance. Song can be heard occasionally throughout the winter months and on spring migration, but only becomes regular on the breeding grounds, when it is a strictly diurnal songster (Neufeldt 1967).

BREEDING HABITS On return to the breeding grounds, singing males immediately occupy territories and pair formation commences with the arrival of the females. Nest construction by the female follows and completed nests have been found in Amurland as early as 8 June (Neufeldt 1967). The nest is built in the upper branches of a small bush or scrub 0.6–1.0m above the ground. Unlike that of Oriental Reed Warbler, the nest is never built in *Phragmites* or over water. It is an untidy and flimsy structure of coarse grasses, lined with finer grass and rootlets, quite unlike the neat nest of an *Acrocephalus*. The first eggs are laid from mid June and nests with fresh eggs have been found up to early July. The full clutch usually comprises five eggs, but sometimes four or six. Incubation by the female typically lasts for 13–14 days and the young remain in the nest for about 14 days but may depart earlier if disturbed.

DISTRIBUTION

Breeding Breeds widely throughout the temperate regions of the Eastern Palearctic, where it is fairly common and appears to have expanded its range westward during the twentieth century.

P. a. aedon The nominate form ranges west to the basin of the Ob River in the region of Novosibirsk at *c.* 83°E. In the western part of the range, it occupies a narrow band extending north to *c.* 56°N, close to Mariinsk in Krasnoyarsk and the northern end of Lake Baikal

(Neufeldt 1967), but to the south it remains unrecorded from Kazakhstan. Its eastern limits are poorly defined but believed to include the SE Transbaikalia region of Russia and the Khanghai and Kentai Mountains in N Mongolia.

P. a. stegmanni The breeding range lies east of the nominate form, centred on the western and central parts of the Amur River basin and Ussuriland and north of Khabarovsk to Lake Petropavlovskoje in the Russian Far East. It breeds widely in suitable habitat in adjacent NE China, throughout Heilongjiang, Jilin and Liaoning Provinces, and south to the hills of Hebei Province north of Beijing. It also breeds in NE Mongolia and neighbouring areas in the Nei Mongol Autonomous Region of N China, possibly intergrading here with the nominate form (Cheng 1987).

Non-breeding The two races are not safely separable outside the breeding season and it is unclear where they winter or to what extent they overlap. However, wintering birds in India exhibit a wing length compared with that of the nominate race in C Siberia. To the east, through Burma, SW China and Thailand, mean wing length gradually decreases but remains longer than in birds breeding in NE China and SE Siberia, suggesting both races winter here.

Most birds wintering in the Indian subcontinent are

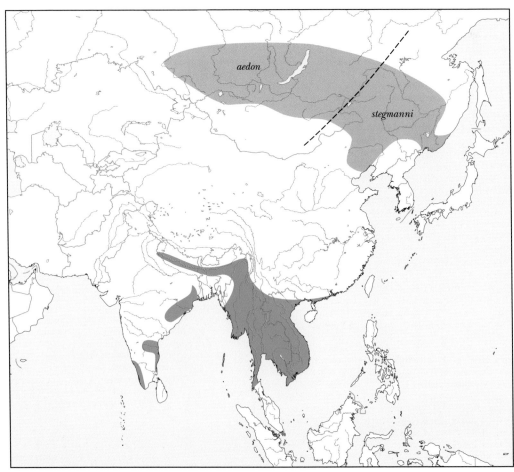

Thick-billed Warbler. Breeding range and winter distribution.

probably of the nominate race. It occurs widely throughout N and E India, west to Nepal but becomes rare further west, although it has occurred near Bharatpur in Rajasthan and Kutch in Gujarat. It regularly reaches the Western Ghats in Tamil Nadu and Kerala, but records are scattered and irregular elsewhere in the peninsula. In Nepal it is rare in the west with just one documented record from the low-lying Royal Sukla Phanta Wildlife Reserve (Choudhary 1997). To the east, it is uncommon but regular in the south of the country where it has been recorded up to 1,500m from Pokhara, the Kathmandu Valley, Hetaura and Chatra and frequently from the low-lying Koshi Tappu in E Nepal (Inskipp & Inskipp 1991; CI *in litt.*). It becomes progressively more numerous in NE India, including Orissa and Bengal and through low-lying parts of the Brahmaputra valley in Assam and into Bangladesh. It has also been recorded on the Andaman Islands.

It winters abundantly at lower elevations in Burma, where both races probably occur. In S China, small numbers regularly remain in S Yunnan Province, but elsewhere it is a rare winter visitor to coastal regions of Guangxi and Guangdong Provinces east to Hong Kong. In SE Asia, it is a widespread winter visitor to lower elevations in Thailand, Cambodia, Laos and Vietnam. Below 1,500m in the northern and central provinces of Thailand, it is extremely common but occurs less frequently in the peninsula, with Phuket marking the southern limit.

MOVEMENTS Departure from Siberian breeding grounds begins in August and most birds have left by early September. Passage migrants regularly cross Mongolia and the Gobi desert from mid to late August with stragglers into mid October. It tends to leave breeding grounds in NE China slightly later, typically between late August and the end of September. Both races migrate across eastern China (Cheng 1987), where it is common in autumn throughout the coastal provinces from Hebei south to Guangdong, but it occurs less than annually in Hong Kong. Migrants pass through the Chinese hinterland, but it is scarcer inland than along the coast. The first birds appear on the wintering grounds in India from early September, Thailand from 12 September (Round 2008) and in Nepal from mid October.

Return passage through India begins early in April and most birds have left Nepal by the middle of the month. Eastern breeders generally begin to move north later with many remaining in Thailand until mid May, with the latest recorded here on 20 May (Round 2008). Migrants stop-over for several weeks in Burma, some lingering to early June. Migration through Beidaihe in coastal Hebei Province, China, peaks between mid May and early June. Occasional birds appear on the breeding grounds from early May and there is an exceptional record from NE Mongolia on 5 April. Most birds return to their breeding grounds along the Amur and Ussuri Rivers in the Russian Far East in late May and early June and most territories are occupied by mid June.

Vagrancy There are few Asian records outside the known range. It is a vagrant to Malaysia, where there is just a single record involving a bird collected at Rantan Panjang in Selangor on 22 April 1973. It is rare but presumably overlooked on migration in South Korea. It is also a vagrant to Japan with just two records from Honshu, from Nagano-ko in May 1927 and Shizuoka-ko between February and April 1997 (Eguchi *et al.* 2000). Westward vagrancy is also unusual. There have been seven documented occurrences

in W Europe, six in the autumn spanning the period 14 September to 11 October and one in spring. Three of the autumn records are from the Shetland Islands in Scotland, with single birds on Fair Isle on 6 October 1955 (Williamson *et al.* 1956), Whalsay on 23 September 1971 (Simpson 1973) and Out Skerries on 14 September 2001 (Harvey 2001). Other autumn occurrences involved one at Lågskär, Norrskär, Finland on 11 October 1994 (Eischer 1995) and two from the island of Utsira, Norway, on 6 October 2004 and 3 October 2005. The single spring bird occurred on Fair Isle on 16–17 May 2003 (Shaw 2003). An additional record for the W Palearctic comes from Santa Katherina in Sinai, Egypt, on 20 November 1991 (Greive 1992).

DESCRIPTION *P. a. aedon*

Plumage – Adult fresh (October to January) Forehead and crown uniform fulvous olive-brown. Lores creamy buff, plain and unmarked, slightly paler than crown and ear-coverts. Ear-coverts warm cinnamon-buff along upper edge but paler and slightly greyer on lower edge. Lacks dark eye-line and pale supercilium, so sides of head uniform. Eye-ring narrow, often whitish and contrasting with sides of the head, sometimes browner with little contrast. Nape, mantle and scapulars uniform fulvous olive-brown, usually with faint cinnamon wash, concolorous with crown. Rump and uppertail-coverts similar to mantle, with little or no contrast. Tail feathers dull brown with broad warm brown fringes matching uppertail-coverts. Chin and throat white with faint creamy wash. Breast slightly warmer, washed sandy brown, this strengthening and darkening towards sides. Upper flanks pale sandy brown to warm cinnamon-buff, colour intensifying on lower flanks and undertail-coverts. Belly creamy white. Lesser, median and greater coverts warm brown with faint olive tinge, lacking darker centres. Tertials dull brown with broad, warm brown fringes. Primary coverts, secondaries and primaries dull brown with narrow, warm brown edges. Alula dull brown with a narrow, crisp, warm brown fringe. Underwing-coverts vary from rich warm buff to pale sandy brown.

Adult worn (May to July) Head pattern unchanged, but eye-ring often paler, more prominent. Upperparts and edges to remiges warm brown, but rather duller, tinged more olive. Nape often with greyish wash. Cinnamon tinge retained only on rump and uppertail-coverts, which contrast more with mantle. Chin to breast paler, less creamy and belly whiter. Flanks with dull buffy straw wash.

Juvenile Similar to fresh adult, but crown, mantle, scapulars and closed wing uniform pale brown, with slight olive tinge but lacking cinnamon wash. Nape often faintly greyish. Rump and uppertail-coverts warm cinnamon-brown, contrasting with duller mantle. Tail warm brown, slightly brighter than mantle but duller, less warm than uppertail-coverts. Underparts white with creamy wash on throat and breast. Breast sides and flanks pale sandy brown.

Bare parts Upper mandible dull greyish brown with fairly broad, pale pink cutting edge. Lower mandible entirely pale pink and unmarked. In first autumn, upper mandible paler brown with pale yellowish pink cutting edge and tip. Lower mandible yellowish and unmarked. Bill darkens throughout first winter and the yellow lower mandible becomes pinker. Mouth orange-flesh. Tarsi and toes greenish grey to plumbeous-grey in adult; in first autumn birds greyish blue, slightly pinker on rear; toes pinkish grey. Iris hazel-brown in adult, greyish brown to dull brown in immature.

IN HAND CHARACTERS
Measurements

P. a. aedon

	Male	Female
Wing	78–86 (80.7; 54)	76–85 (79.6; 27)
Tail	76–90 (81.9; 54)	77–86 (80.1; 25)
Bill	17.5–20.5 (19.0; 54)	17.5–20 (19.0; 25)
Tarsus	27–29.5 (27.8; 32)	27–30 (27.8; 18)

Sexes combined:
Tail/wing ratio: 97–105% (102%; 20)
Bill width: 5.4–6.3 (5.8; 20)
Hind claw: 7.0–8.5 (7.9; 20)
Tail graduation: 18–30
P. a. stegmanni (sexes combined): *wing* 73–79 (77.5; 15); *tail* 70–81 (76.5; 15); *bill* 17.5–19.5 (18.4; 14). Slightly smaller than nominate.

Structure

P. a. aedon

Wing formula (Cramp 1992):

p1/pc	p2	p3e	p4e	p5e	p6	p7	p10
5–10	7–12	0–1	wp	0–1	2–4	5–8	12–16

Wing strongly rounded; p1 fairly small but rounded, 30–40% p2. Wing point p(3) 4 (5); p2 = p7–8/9 (9/10); emargination on p3–5. Notch on inner web of p2 falls below ss tips.

Figure 109. Wing of Thick-billed Warbler.

Tail long, strongly graduated; feathers narrow and rather pointed in comparison with larger *Acrocephalus* (Fig. 110).

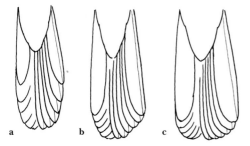

a   b   c

Figure 110. Comparison of tail structure of (a) Thick-billed Warbler (b) Clamorous Reed Warbler *A. s. brunnescens* and (c) Great Reed Warbler.

Bill relatively short, but stout and broad-based; distal part of culmen strongly decurved. See Fig. 76 for comparison with Oriental Reed Warbler.

Tarsi long and strong, but toes and claws relatively small.

Recognition Distinguished from Great Reed, Oriental Reed and Clamorous Reed Warblers by absence of light supercilium and dark loral stripe. Separated structurally from Great Reed and Oriental Reed by shorter bill (< 21.5mm), rounded wing (with longer p1, shorter p2, wing point at p3–5 and emarginated p5) and more graduated tail (t1–t6 > 17mm). Clamorous Reed exceptionally has t1–t6 up to 26mm and is closer to Thick-billed in wing structure, but has a minute p1 and a much longer bill (> 23mm in continental Asian races).

Ageing In early autumn, young birds with unworn primaries are readily distinguished from adults in which primaries and tail feathers are abraded. Criteria for ageing birds after the autumn moult are not known.

Weight
P. a. aedon: India, winter 22–28g (25.9; 9) (Ali & Ripley 1973).
P. a. stegmenni: E China 15–31g (22.4; 29) (Shaw 1936).
Races combined: Thailand, Oct–May, 20–29g (23.6; 63) (PDR unpublished data).

GEOGRAPHIC VARIATION Two races are recognised which closely resemble each other.
P. a. aedon (SC Siberia and adjacent NW Mongolia) Described above.
P. a. stegmanni (NE Mongolia to SE Siberia and NE China) When fresh, the upperparts including the tail, are marginally darker and more rufescent than those of the nominate race. This distinction is only apparent when comparing series and is not readily detectable in a single individual. Both races fade to duller brown with wear, effectively becoming inseparable. Justification for retaining *stegmanni* is poor, and relies on its slightly smaller size and shorter wing. There is, however, considerable overlap and many cannot be positively assigned to a specific race.

TAXONOMY AND SYSTEMATICS Thick-billed Warbler is often included within *Acrocephalus* although its many distinctive structural characters, together with its habitat preferences and distinctive song have been used to justify its inclusion within the monotypic genus *Phragamaticola*. In their summary of relationships within the *Acrocephalus* and *Hippolais* warblers of the Western Palearctic, Parkin *et al.* (2004) concluded that Thick-billed Warbler has more in common with the large *Acrocephalus* species such as Great Reed and Clamorous Reed Warblers than with any other group within the *Acrocephalus*/*Hippolais* complex, and recommended that it should be retained within *Acrocephalus*. However, the findings of a more recent molecular phylogenetic study (Fregin *et al.* (2009) indicated that Thick-billed Warbler should be returned to *Phragamaticola*, and we have followed this recommendation.

▲ ▶ Adult, Shetland, Scotland, May. Superficially resembles the larger *Acrocephalus* species but note characteristic shrike-like structure with proportionately long tail and short primary projection. Lacks supercilium and eye-stripe, and combination of uniform side to head, unmarked lores and relatively short, thick bill create an open-faced expression. Often raises crown feathers when nervous or agitated (Hugh Harrop).

▲ Adult, Hong Kong, October. Recently moulted bird in fresh plumage showing warm brown upperparts and reddish brown tail (Peter Kennerley).

▲ First year, Hong Kong, October. A rather drab individual with faint olive wash to upperparts and warmer tones suppressed. After complete post-juvenile moult in early autumn, young birds and adults are inseparable using plumage features alone; the grey-brown iris and retained juvenile secondaries establish this as a first-year bird (James Kennerley).

Genus *Calamonastides* Grant & Mackworth-Praed, 1940

[Gr. *kalamos* reed; *astes* singer (*ado* to sing); *-ides* resembling. Modified from Genus *Calamonastes* Sharpe, 1883]

A monotypic genus containing one resident species in Africa, Papyrus Yellow Warbler, which frequents swamps. It is characterised by its olive and yellow plumage, broad bill, strong blackish legs, long tail and short rounded wings. In many respects it resembles the Dark-capped Yellow and Mountain Yellow Warblers now placed in *Iduna*, and was often included with them in the genus *Chloropeta*. It differs from them in having much larger feet and claws and a very different voice. Molecular studies place it firmly within the Acrocephalidae, but as sister to the *Iduna* clade (Fregin *et al.* 2009).

PAPYRUS YELLOW WARBLER
Calamonastides gracilirostris   Plate 34

Chloropeta gracilirostris Ogilvie-Grant, 1906. *Bull. Brit Orn. Club* 19: 33. SE slopes of Ruwenzori mountains, Uganda, 3,400 feet.

A localised resident, endemic to swamps in C and E Africa. Considered VULNERABLE by Birdlife International due to its small and fragmented population and loss of habitat due to drainage and exploitation. Polytypic, with two races recognised:

C. g. gracilirostris (Ogilvie-Grant, 1906). E DR Congo, Rwanda, Burundi, SW Uganda, W Kenya.
C. g. bensoni (Amadon, 1954). Lake Mweru, Zambia.

IDENTIFICATION Length *c.* 13.5cm. Wing 55–68mm. Tail/wing *c.* 99%.

A medium-sized warbler of swamp and papyrus, with warm brown or olive green upperparts and dull yellow underparts, lacking a distinct supercilium. Its habitat preference separates it from the two *Iduna* yellow warblers which are largely unknown from papyrus swamps. Sexes alike.

Structure Its general appearance suggests a short-winged and rather compact *Acrocephalus* warbler. The longer tail and longer legs and toes set it apart from the *Iduna* yellow warblers and although smaller, it appears closer in structure to the African Greater Swamp and Lesser Swamp Warblers. It shows a low domed crown and a longish, thin bill. The latter is quite broad-based but much less so than in Dark-capped Yellow Warbler (Fig. 108). The wing is short and rounded, with a large rounded first primary (p1), the wing point formed by p4–6 and a very short primary projection. The tail is strongly graduated, with 12 fairly broad and rounded feathers. The tarsi are quite strong, but less robust than in the swamp warblers. The long but rather fine claws are adapted for grasping papyrus.

Plumage and bare parts Adults of the nominate race are rather dark olive-brown above, tinged greenish on the head and mantle, but with a warm cinnamon or rufous wash on the rump and uppertail-coverts, and also on the closed wing and tail. There is no supercilium or supraloral stripe and although the lores and a short stripe behind the eye can appear slightly darker, the sides of the head, including the upper cheeks, essentially match the crown. The underparts are conspicuously yellow, brightest on the chin and throat, but duller and paler on the breast, which is tinged and diffusely streaked with olive. The flanks and undertail-coverts are washed warm ochre.

The bill is dark grey above and pinkish brown below. The legs and feet are dark grey. It also shows a conspicuous orange-red eye.

Juveniles lack the green and yellow plumage tones of the adult. The head is uniform dull greyish brown and contrasts with rich buffy brown upperparts. The underparts are warm peach, most intense across breast, becoming rich bright buff on the flanks and undertail-coverts. Orange-brown tips to the greater and median coverts form two conspicuous wing-bars.

Zambian birds of race *bensoni* are more uniform olive-brown above and lack the warm tinge on the wings, uppertail-coverts and lower underparts. They have a pale yellow eye.

SIMILAR SPECIES Its yellow underparts and simple song distinguish it from other marsh-dwelling warblers.

Dark-capped Yellow Warbler can occur on the edges of papyrus swamps and is a potential source of confusion. It has greener upperparts, with a distinctly darker cap, shows a narrow yellow supercilium and has blacker wing and tail feathers with prominent yellowish edges. It has a much broader bill than Papyrus Yellow Warbler, a shorter and less graduated tail and more slender tarsi. Its loud ringing song is distinctive.

Lesser Swamp Warbler and **Greater Swamp Warbler** are larger (especially Greater Swamp) and lack yellow on the underparts. Both have short but distinct supercilia. They have much louder, lower pitched songs and calls.

African Reed Warbler *A. b. cinnamomeus* is rather smaller and slimmer looking, with cinnamon-buff (not yellow) underparts. It has a shorter tail and paler, more slender legs and toes with shorter claws.

VOICE The song is weak and sibilant. It consists of repeated short (0.5–0.8 seconds) and rather plaintive whistled sequences of just one or two notes, separated by pauses of a few seconds.

In Kenya, these are simple and consist of either a single slightly metallic '*cotcheeow*' or a double '*choweet-choweet*'. Rather different sequences in SW Uganda include 4-5 sibilant notes '*gwo-gwo-gwo-gwo*'; four rattling notes with the first two lower and quieter, '*brob-brob-chrip-chrip*'; and a quick note followed by a rapid higher pitched trill, '*cotreeeeeel*'. In Zambia, four main sequences consist of a three part '*thweet-slow-wheee*', a three-part musical warble '*phwit-slrrlrlr-ow*' and a high pitched trilling '*putdreeeeeel*', similar to the trilling call of Uganda birds (Maclean *et al.* 2003).

The song has also been transcribed as '*t-tslowee.....to-tslowee.....tee-tschleewo....tslo-tschleewo.... tschleew...*' (Urban *et al.* 1997).

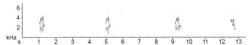

Song of Papyrus Yellow Warbler recorded within breeding range of *C. g. gracilirostris*, Nyika Plateau, eastern Zambia. (Chappuis 2000)

The call is unknown.

MOULT No information.

HABITAT Primarily a bird of papyrus swamp, but also found in reed swamp and mixed vegetation. It is apparently restricted to papyrus at Lakes Edward and George in Uganda and at lower, drier sites in Rwanda, while in Kenya it prefers tall, undisturbed papyrus, particularly over water and is absent from smaller more isolated fragments (Maclean *et al.* 2003). However, it utilises reeds in favoured wetter swamps in N Rwanda at 1,850–2,050m. In SW Uganda it occurs in mixed patches of papyrus and other vegetation, in *Cladium* swamps at 1,300m and in reedy marshes fringing lake edges up to above 2,000m. In Zambia, at Lake Mweru, it is found in papyrus over deep water with an outer fringe of reeds.

BEHAVIOUR Usually occurs singly or in pairs. It forages in papyrus at all levels, typically over water, hopping from stem to stem like a swamp warbler, searching for small insects. It often utters its song while moving about in low vegetation.

BREEDING HABITS Unknown.

DISTRIBUTION Confined to swamps in C and E Africa. Three disjunct populations are known: one in the Albertine rift valley, based mainly in Rwanda, N Burundi and SW Uganda; one in W Kenya; and a third confined to N Zambia and adjacent DR Congo. It can be quite common locally but its swamp habitat is threatened in parts of Rwanda and W Kenya by drainage and by the cutting and burning of papyrus. Its habitat in SW Uganda is also under serious threat.

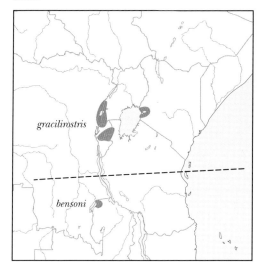

Papyrus Yellow Warbler. Resident within breeding range.

C. g. gracilirostris Present at a number of localities in eastern C Africa on either side of the Albertine Rift. It is recorded from DR Congo on the western shore of Lake Edward and from south of the Virunga volcanoes. It is known from several sites in Rwanda, around Lake Lubondo and Lake Bulera and the nearby Rugeyi and Mulindi Swamps in the north, and in Akanyaru swamp and the Kigogo and Kibaya valleys further south. In N Burundi it occurs near Karuzi in the Ndurumu valley and along the Ruvubu River on the Tanzanian border. In SW Uganda, it is present in the rift around Lake Edward and

Lake George, at the higher Lakes Bunyoni and Mutanda, and in many other small disturbed lake-edge marshes (Maclean *et al.* 2003). In Kenya, the same race reappears around Lake Victoria, where it is locally common at Lake Kanyaboli and the Yala swamp, at swamps near Kisumu and at Kendu Bay. Despite a few unconfirmed reports from S Uganda, the Albertine Rift and W Kenyan populations appear to be separated.

C. g. bensoni Known only from the mouth of the Luapala River where it enters Lake Mweru on the border of N Zambia and from Nkole in adjacent SE DR Congo.

MOVEMENTS Sedentary.

DESCRIPTION *C. g. gracilirostris*
Plumage – Adult Forehead, crown and nape olive-brown, tinged greenish. No supercilium or supraloral stripe, or noticeable eye-ring. Lores, upper cheeks and ear-coverts greenish olive-brown, darkest on lores and on a short stripe through the upper ear-coverts. Mantle and scapulars to uppertail-coverts rich olive-brown with cinnamon-brown tinge, uppertail-coverts more strongly washed cinnamon-brown. Tail feathers dark brown with narrow cinnamon-buff fringes. Lower cheek, chin, throat and lower sides of neck bright yellow. Breast and belly yellow. Sides of breast and upper breast suffused or diffusely streaked with broad band of dark olive green. Flanks, vent and undertail-coverts yellowish, washed cinnamon. Upperwing-coverts olive-brown, edges of greater coverts cinnamon-brown. Tertials and flight feathers dark brown with narrow cinnamon-brown edges, appearing palest on primaries. Inner borders of flight feathers whitish. Underwing-coverts pale yellow.
Juvenile Yellow and green tones largely absent. Forehead, crown, lores and side of head uniform dull grey-brown. No supercilium. Eye-line behind eye indistinct and only slightly darker than side of head. Nape slightly warmer than crown, merging with unmarked, rich buffy brown mantle and scapulars. Chin and throat pale buffy white to creamy yellow. Breast and flanks pinkish buff, colouring most intense across breast, becoming rich bright buff on flanks and undertail-coverts. Belly whitish, tinged pale buff. Greater and median coverts blackish with warm brown edges and broad rich orange-brown tips which create two conspicuous wing-bars. Primaries and secondaries edged warm brown.
Bare Parts Upper mandible mid grey. Lower mandible pinkish brown or orange-brown, becoming dusky towards tip. Juvenile as adult but lower mandible bright orange-yellow and unmarked at sides.
Mouth bright orange in adult, yellowish in juvenile with blackish tongue spots. Tarsi and toes dark grey or blackish. Iris reddish brown or orange-red in adult, pale brown in juvenile.

IN HAND CHARACTERS
Measurements

C. g. gracilirostris

Sexes combined:

Wing	57–64 (61.8; 5)
Tail	56–66 (61.2; 4)
Bill	15.5–16 (15.9; 4)
Tarsus	21–24.5 (23.3; 5)

(Includes data from Urban *et al.* 1997)

Tail/wing ratio: mean 99% (n = 5)

Bill width: *c.* 5.0 (n = 1)

Hind claw: 10, 10.7 (n = 2)

Tail graduation: 10–18

Live wing length, adult, W Kenya, sexes combined: 59–68 (62.4; 65) (ON unpublished data).

C. g. bensoni (n = 2): *wing* 55, 58; *tail* 55, 58; *bill* 14.5, 15.5; *tarsus* 20, 21 (n = 1); bill width 4.6; hind claw 9.5.

Structure

Wing formula (nominate race, Kenya, n = 2):

p1/pc	p2	p3e	p4e	p5e	p6e	p7(e)	p10
14	10–11	2.5–3.5	wp	wp	wp	1.5–2	6–7

Wing strongly rounded with large rounded p1 (*c.* 70% p2). Wing point p4–6; p2 < ss tips, p3 = p7–9; emargination on p3–6, often slightly on p7.

Figure 111. Wing of Papyrus Yellow Warbler.

Tail graduated, with 12 broad rounded feathers (Fig. 112).

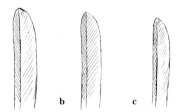

Figure 112. Comparison of a central tail feather of (a) Papyrus Yellow Warbler (b) Dark-capped Yellow Warbler and (c) Mountain Yellow Warbler.

Bill longish, slim, broad-based and straight sided.

Tarsi slender; toes long and slender; claws long and fine-tipped.

Weight Kenya, 9.6–12.5g (10.6; 62) (ON unpublished data)

GEOGRAPHIC VARIATION The two northern populations show subtle plumage differences and differ vocally (Maclean *et al.* 2003). The southern population forms a smaller, well-differentiated race.

C. g. gracilirostris (eastern C Africa, Kenya) Birds from Kenya are described above. SW Ugandan birds are similar, but appear slightly more uniform dull brown, less olive on mantle, rump, tail and wing-coverts and slightly more rufescent on the flanks and undertail-coverts. They also show a more contrasting, paler yellow throat (Maclean *et al.* 2003).

C. g. bensoni (Zambia) Differs from the nominate race in being darker, more uniform olive-brown above, with a less pronounced greenish tinge on the head and mantle. It lacks the warm tone to the rump and uppertail-coverts and the tertials and flight feathers are edged dull olive-brown. The underparts are duller, green and cinnamon tones being replaced with dusky olive and brown. The flanks and vent are dark olive-brown and the undertail-coverts pale yellow. The eye is pale yellow. Slightly smaller than the nominate race.

TAXONOMY AND SYSTEMATICS Papyrus Yellow Warbler was described under *Chloropeta* based upon its yellow plumage and rather broad bill, and it has since been retained within that genus by most authors. However, Grant & Mackworth-Praed (1940) considered that with its longer bill and very large feet it was more closely related to the '*Calamocichla*' swamp warblers and they made it the type of a monotypic genus *Calamonastides*. Recent DNA studies have confirmed a near relationship with *Acrocephalus* and shown that the two former *Chloropeta* species, Dark-capped Yellow Warbler and Mountain Yellow Warbler, group within the *Iduna* clade of former *Hippolais* warblers (Fregin *et al.* 2009). Papyrus Yellow Warbler lies outside this clade, however, and we therefore return it to *Calamonastides*.

Irwin & Turner (2001) suggested that the two recognised races might represent good species, based upon an apparent difference in bill shape, which has subsequently been found to be due to methods of specimen preparation. Subsequently, Maclean *et al.* (2003) considered that differences between the Albertine Rift and W Kenyan populations might warrant a further subspecies split, but mtDNA differences them do not support this (I. Maclean *in litt.*).

▲ Juvenile *C. g. gracilirostris*, SW Uganda, August. Warm buffy brown with dull grey-brown head, creamy throat, and bright cinnamon-buff wing-bars (Augusto Faustino).

◀ Adult *C. g. gracilirostris*, SW Uganda, February. Note the plain olive-green head, yellow throat, warmly tinged upperparts, wings and flanks, and red eye (Gareth Knass).

▲ Adult *C. g. gracilirostris*, Lake Bunyonyi, Uganda, July. Note the longish tail and strong grey legs (Pete Morris).

▲ Adult *C. g. bensoni*, Luapala, Zambia, January. This race lacks warm brown tones and has a pale yellow eye (Pete Leonard)

Genus *Nesillas* Oberholser, 1899

[Gr. *nesos* island (= Madagascar); *illas* thrush]

A group of five resident species endemic to the Malagasy Region. One species, Aldabra Brush Warbler, is recently believed to have become extinct. They are medium-sized warblers with rather long, strong bills, short rounded wings and long graduated tails. The upperparts vary from olive-brown or greenish brown to grey-brown. The underparts are washed olive-brown to greyish with soft dusky streaks on the throat and upper breast. Their heads are rather plain but have distinct, narrow pale supercilia.

They inhabit bushes and undergrowth and sometimes the lower tree canopy outside forest as well as the lower to middle storey within forest. Their deep cup-shaped nests are usually built among thick vegetation close to the ground, but occasionally (in Moheli Brush Warbler) up to 9m above the ground among tree foliage. All give simple harsh chacking notes and low structureless rattles. Two species, Moheli Brush Warbler and Grande Comore Brush Warbler also have more complex vocalisations. Madagascar Brush Warbler and Lantz's Brush Warbler are parapatric on Madagascar but have only recently been separated as distinct species. Another distinctive taxon, *obscura*, occurring in W Madagascar, may also warrant species status. In the Comoros, the taxon *longicaudata* is sometimes treated as a full species, but following Benson (1960) and Louette *et al.* (1988), we retain it here as a race of Madagascar Brush Warbler. In the Comoro islands, Moheli Brush Warbler and Madagascar Brush Warbler occur sympatrically on Moheli but otherwise no island hosts more than one species.

MADAGASCAR BRUSH WARBLER
Nesillas typica   Plate 35

Ellisia typica Hartlaub, 1860. *J. Ornithol.* 8: 92. Madagascar.

A common resident of forest understorey and dense undergrowth, endemic to Madagascar and the Comoro Islands. Polytypic, with five races recognised:

N. t. typica (Hartlaub, 1860). Humid E, S and C Madagascar.

N. t. ellisii (Schlegel & Pollen, 1868). Humid N and NE Madagascar.

N. t. longicaudata (Newton, 1877). Anjouan, Comoro Islands.

N. t. obscura Delacour, 1931. Savanna of NW and W Madagascar.

N. t. moheliensis Benson, 1960. Moheli, Comoro Islands.

IDENTIFICATION Length 17–18cm. Wing 57–72mm. Tail/wing 106–135%.

A rather large, slim olive-brown warbler with short wings and a long graduated tail. Sexes alike.

Structure A fairly large *Nesillas* with a low forehead and crown and a relatively long but quite robust bill. Together with the very long, narrow and strongly graduated tail, which can have either ten or 12 feathers, these give the bird a sleek and attenuated appearance. The closed wing is short and rounded, with a long first primary and very short primary projection. Races on the Comoros are equally long-tailed, but bulkier, with slightly larger bills and tarsi.

Plumage and bare parts The nominate race on Madagascar has olive-brown upperparts that appear darkest on the crown and usually show a greenish tinge on the mantle. A narrow but fairly conspicuous pale buff supercilium extends beyond the eye above a distinct, narrow dark eye-stripe. Otherwise, the sides of the head are dark olive-brown, but with yellowish mottling on the ear-coverts. The underparts are contrastingly paler. They are washed yellowish buff, whiter on the throat and belly and becoming light olive-brown on the flanks and undertail-coverts. A band of soft greyish streaks extends across the throat and upper breast. The wing feathers are darker than the mantle, the greater coverts and tertials having well-defined greenish olive

fringes and the flight feathers showing narrower greenish olive edges. The dark brown tail also shows greenish olive feather edges when fresh.

The bill is blackish with a dull pink base to the lower mandible. The legs are greyish.

The distinctive race *obscura* from W Madagascar is darker and duller above and much darker and greyer below without the yellow tinge. The two races on the Comoros resemble nominate *typica* of Madagascar but *moheliensis* is warmer brown while *longicaudata* is slightly paler and greener.

SIMILAR SPECIES This is the only *Nesillas* present throughout much of Madagascar, but it can occur locally with the parapatric Lantz's Brush Warbler in the extreme south. Other Madagascan warblers which might cause confusion are Madagascar Swamp Warbler, found in and around marshes throughout the island, and Thamnornis Warbler in parts of the southwest. On the Comoro Islands, the only sympatric confusion species is Moheli Brush Warbler on Moheli.

Lantz's Brush Warbler is much paler and has distinctive calls. It is restricted to SW Madagascar from where Madagascar Brush Warbler is largely absent.

Madagascar Swamp Warbler is paler below and tends to show more conspicuous and better defined throat streaking. It also has a conspicuous red-brown eye and a larger bill. Its song is mellow and more complex than that of Madagascar Brush Warbler.

Moheli Brush Warbler is smaller and shorter-tailed than race *moheliensis* of Madagascar Brush Warbler and tends to be more arboreal in behaviour. It is paler and greener, with no obvious supercilium and has a reddish orbital ring, albeit inconspicuous in the field. Some vocalisations are very distinct, with scratchy warbling song phrases, although both species give simple rattles.

Thamnornis Warbler has a grey head, bright greenish edges to the wing and tail feathers, white-tipped outer tail feathers, a stronger bill with a pale orange lower mandible and a distinctive voice.

VOICE Appears to lack a structured song. What passes for 'song' in this species appears to be a series of calls strung together to form a sequence.

'Song' of Madagascar Brush Warbler, recorded within breeding range of *N. t. longicaudata*, Anjouan, Comoro Islands. (Herremanns 2001)

The usual call of nominate birds on Madagascar is a series of shrill clipped notes, '*krak-trak-trak-trak-trak-trak...*' and also a variety of loud rattling calls, variously described as '*trrrrrrrk*', '*tkatrk*', '*trk*' etc.

On Anjouan, *longicaudata* gives a series of similar but rather higher-pitched rattling calls that run into each other to form a rapid chattering '*pirrik-pirrik-pik-pik-pik...*'. Several simple chacking notes are also given.

On Moheli, the fast 'machine-gun' rattle and short staccato notes of *moheliensis* are very similar to those of *longicaudata*.

MOULT No information available.

HABITAT In Madagascar, it inhabits forest ground cover. Nominate *typica* and race *ellisii* prefer the typically denser undergrowth of montane forest. It is also found in secondary brush, including scattered patches on grasslands (Rand 1936) and even in town gardens. Disturbed and regenerating areas, such as scrub along river margins, may be preferred to adjacent areas of closed forest (Goodman *et al.* 1997). In the northwest, it is recorded from marshy areas and riverbanks, where it has been observed foraging among aquatic ferns. The race *obscura* occurs in deciduous and semi-deciduous forest on limestone, but in the north it is also found on wooded plains and in gallery forest.

On Anjouan, *longicaudata* occurs in almost all habitats with dense undergrowth, including native forest, exotic plantations, coastal thickets in or near towns and villages, and lakeside sedges and grasses.

On Moheli, where habitat choice is reduced, *moheliensis* is restricted to the undergrowth of evergreen forest (Louette *et al.* 1988). Apparently suitable undergrowth in lowlands outside forest is unoccupied by *Nesillas*.

BEHAVIOUR Usually found singly or in pairs and often first detected by its rattling or chattering calls. Not particularly shy and can be quite inquisitive, approaching intruders while giving scolding calls.

It skulks in low vegetation, sometimes descending to the ground, and can thus be difficult to observe. When undisturbed, it is lively and active, moving quickly and with agility through dense vegetation in pursuit of small insects, but its flight is weak and usually only over short distances between low patches of vegetation. On Anjouin, it hops between vertical stems in the forest herb layer, but also ascends to 3m and occasionally as high as 10m, where it picks food items from moss on tree branches (Safford & Evans 1992). Birds on Madagascar have been observed to perch on bush tops in open view, raising the tail at 45° to the body and flitting it from side to side in the manner of a *Prinia* (Benson 1960). The crown feathers are often raised to form a rounded crest.

BREEDING HABITS The few nests of nominate *typica* described in Madagascar were about 0.5m above ground, in a variety of situations: in tall grass on a grass- and brush-covered hillside, in dense herbaceous growth in a copse of small bushes, in secondary vegetation next to a forest stream, hidden among the dry leaves of a fallen tree in open secondary growth areas and in a bush in dense secondary

forest (Rand 1936; Benson *et al.* 1977). They consisted of a deep cup, loosely constructed of broad dead grass blades, with an inner layer and lining of finer grass. Other materials recorded include small twigs bound outside with threads from caterpillar cocoons (Milne-Edwards & Crandidier 1881) and a lining of fine flower stalks.

Four nests of the race *longicaudata* on Anjouan were situated approximately 1m above ground level among climbers on larger trees, or in grass tussocks, and all were well hidden. Nests here were loosely constructed, deep cups of coarse grass, lined with very fine grass (Benson 1960).

The usual clutch on Madagascar is two eggs, rarely three. On Anjouin, the clutch is also usually two eggs. The nest and eggs of *N. t. moheliensis* and *N. t. obscura* are unknown.

No information is available on incubation or the development and care of the young.

The nominate race breeds on Madagascar from July to December, with most observations between September and November. The few data for *obscura* indicate breeding occurs between November and March. The race *N. t. moheliensis* breeds from at least September to December or January, while *longicaudata* on Anjouan breeds in September and October and probably also later (Benson 1960).

DISTRIBUTION Restricted to Madagascar and the Comoro Islands. It occurs widely throughout most of Madagascar, being most numerous in the north and east. It ranges from sea level to the highest mountains, reaching 2,750m on Tsaratanana and 2,450m on Andringitra and tends to be more numerous at higher altitudes. Distribution becomes patchier in W Madagascar, where it is typically confined to forest on calcareous substrate.

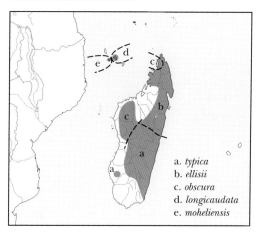

a. *typica*
b. *ellisii*
c. *obscura*
d. *longicaudata*
e. *moheliensis*

Madagascar Brush Warbler. Resident within breeding range.

N. t. typica Widespread and common in humid parts of S and C Madagascar, south to the Fort Dauphin area and including much of the central plateau. It ranges into the eastern edge of the western savanna, where birds from the Tsiandro area may intergrade with the race *obscura* (Rand 1936). It possibly occurs more widely in the west, separated from *obscura* by habitat. In the southeast, it occurs from Marovony Forest south through the humid forests of the Anosyenne and Vohimena mountains to Manantantely Forest, and in littoral forest south to Manafiafy. It is parapatric with Lantz's Brush Warbler in the south and southwest of the island, where sight records suggest that it occurs west to Beroroha on Mangoky River, and in the Isalo area. An apparently disjunct population occurs in the humid forest at Analavelona, in the southwest mountains (Raherilalao & Goodman 2005).

N. t. ellisii Widespread and very common in humid parts of N and NE Madagascar, including Mount d'Ambre and the Sambirano River valley in the northwest, and ranging south in the eastern forests and brushlands to about 18°S.

N. t. obscura Present in two separate regions of Madagascar: in limestone massifs in the north, where best known from around Ankarana, and in the west, where recorded from Bemaraha and Namoroka. Its range appears to be bisected along the Sambirano River valley by that of *ellisii*. Its distribution is probably restricted to forest on limestone karst and much more local than mapped.

N. t. moheliensis Restricted to Moheli in the Comoros, where it is known only from the forested ridge above 400m and could be threatened by forest loss. It is markedly scarcer than the sympatric Moheli Brush Warbler.

N. t. longicaudata Common throughout Anjouan in the Comoros, occurring from sea level to mountain tops (Louette 1988).

DESCRIPTION N. t. typica

Plumage – Adult Forehead to nape dark olive-brown. Supercilium narrow, pale buff, extending from base of bill to above middle of ear-coverts. Lores to below eye dark olive-brown. Short, poorly marked, dark olive-brown stripe behind eye. Ear-coverts and sides of neck greenish olive-brown. Lower ear-coverts olive-brown, mottled yellowish buff. Mantle and scapulars olive-brown, tinged greenish, brighter than crown. Rump and uppertail-coverts slightly browner than mantle. Tail feathers dark brown, edged greenish olive-brown. Chin to breast and belly pale yellowish buff, whiter on chin and throat. Breast tinged olive-brown with soft olive-grey streaks extending from chin to upper breast. Flanks light olive-brown, becoming warmer olive-brown posteriorly and on vent and undertail-coverts. Lesser and median coverts greenish olive-brown. Greater coverts and tertials dark brown, broadly fringed and tipped greenish olive-brown. Primaries, secondaries and primary coverts dark brown, edged greenish olive-brown. Alula dark brown, fringed greenish olive-brown. Underwing-coverts yellowish buff.

Juvenile Similar to adult, but top of head, upperparts and flanks warmer brown, less olive. Tail feathers warm brown. Underparts washed warm buff, strongly so across breast, where darker streaks are indistinct or absent. Fringes to wing-coverts and tertials, and edges to flight feathers, warm brown or cinnamon-brown.

Bare parts Upper mandible dark grey or blackish. Lower mandible yellowish grey or light pinkish yellow. Mouth orange-yellow. Tarsi brownish grey to dull bluish grey; claws brown. Iris dark brown or red-brown.

IN HAND CHARACTERS

Measurements

N. t. typica

	Male	Female
Wing	62–70 (66.1; 17)	58–67 (61.8; 10)
Tail	72–93 (84.9; 17)	67–83 (76.3; 9)
Bill	14.5–17 (15.7; 16)	15–16.5 (15.5; 9)
Tarsus	23–26.5 (25.3; 12)	23–26 (24.4; 10)

Sexes combined:
Tail/wing: 106–135% (127%; 26)
Bill width: 4.0–4.6 (4.3; 9)
Hind claw: 6.2–7.2 (6.6; 10)
Tail graduation: 35–55

N. t. ellisii

	Male	Female
Wing	58–67 (62.3; 29)	57–63 (59.0; 14)
Tail	68–85 (77.6; 29)	67–76 (71.9; 14)
Bill	15–17 (16.1; 28)	14.5–17 (16.1; 14)
Tarsus	23.5–27 (25.4; 22)	22.5–26 (24.5; 14)

N. t. obscura

	Male	Female
Wing	65–72 (70.0; 7)	59–68 (63.7; 3)
Tail	76–83 (81.3; 7)	67–78 (75.7; 3)
Bill	16–18.5 (17.5; 7)	16.5–18 (17.3; 3)
Tarsus	24.5–27 (25.6; 7)	24–24.5 (24.2; 3)

N. t. moheliensis (sexes combined): *wing* 62–68.5 (64.8; 8); *tail* 70–82 (77.3; 8); *bill* 16.5–18 (17.3; 8); *tarsus* 24.5–28.5 (25.9; 7) (Louette *et al.* 1988).

N. t. longicaudata (sexes combined): *wing* 59.5–65 (62.3; 9); *tail* 73.5–82.5 (78.0; 9); *bill* 16–18 (16.9; 10); *tarsus* 23.5–26 (25.2; 10) (Louette *et al.* 1988).

Structure

N. t. typica

Wing formula (n = 9):

p1/pc	p2	p3e	p4e	p5e	p6e	p7(e)	p10
13–17	10–12	3–4	wp	wp	wp	0.5–2.5	5–8

Wing strongly rounded with large p1 (*c.* 60% p2). Wing point p4–6; p2 < ss tips, p3 = p8/9; emargination on p3–6, often slightly on p7.

Figure 113. Wing of Madagascar Brush Warbler N. t. typica.

Tail very long, usually 12 feathers but sometimes ten; extremely graduated (outer feather *c.* 40% t1); feathers narrow but with rounded tips (Fig. 114).

Bill medium length; rather strong and straight, somewhat concave-sided.

Tarsi quite long and strong, claws relatively small.

Other races are similar. *N. t. obscura* has 12 tail feathers, *moheliensis* 12 or ten, and *longicaudata* just ten. In all of these, outer tail feathers only 35–45% of t1 (Louette *et al.* 1988).

Recognition A plain-backed warbler with dark olive-brown upperparts and a very long tail, most races tinged yellowish below. Bill length is less than that of Madagascar Swamp Warbler, as usually is wing length.

Weight

N. t. typica: 14–22g (18.1; 100).

N. t. moheliensis: 19–24g (21.4; 9).

N. t. longicaudata: unsexed 19, 19.5g (n = 2).

Louette *et al.* (1988).

GEOGRAPHIC VARIATION Two similar races occupy humid N, E and C areas of Madagascar. *N. t. ellisii* in the north has slightly more saturated plumage tones than nominate *typica* and shows some biometric differences. Drier calcareous areas of W Madagascar are occupied by a distinctive darker race *obscura*. The two races on the Comoro Islands resemble nominate *typica* and *ellisii* more closely than does *obscura*.

N. t. typica (N, E and C Madagascar) Described above.

N. t. ellisii (N and NE Madagascar) Similar to the nominate race but shows slightly warmer olive brown upperparts. The underparts are more strongly washed with ochreous buff, the breast sides and flanks darker and browner than in nominate *typica*. Wing and tail average shorter, but bill slightly longer than in *typica*.

N. t. obscura (W Madagascar) Distinctly darker, less greenish than the nominate race. The crown and head sides are greyer, the upperparts more greyish olive. The underparts are much darker, with practically no yellow tinge. Underwing-coverts greyish brown. Longer-winged and larger-billed than nominate *typica*.

N. t. moheliensis (Moheli) Upperparts warmer brown, less olive, than in the nominate race, with the rump and uppertail-coverts tinged cinnamon. The underparts are more strongly washed with yellow, the throat less pale and the flanks tinged warmer brown. Streaking extends from the chin to the upper breast and is stronger and more prominent. Bulkier than nominate *typica*, with a longer bill and tarsus.

N. t. longicaudata (Anjouan) Similar to the nominate form, but slightly paler, greenish olive-brown above with the crown slightly greyer than the mantle. Streaks on the breast and throat are narrower and mostly confined to the upper breast. Slightly smaller than *moheliensis*.

TAXONOMY AND SYSTEMATICS See under Lantz's Brush Warbler for discussion of the separation of that taxon from Madagascar Brush Warbler. Following Louette *et al.* (1988) we treat the Anjouan form *longicaudata* as a well-differentiated race of *N. typica*. Its calls are restricted to harsh '*tak*' and rattle sounds similar to those of nominate *typica* and *moheliensis* and it has a similarly long tail, albeit of ten feathers. In Madagascar, the race *obscura* is poorly known but it appears to have specialised habitat requirements. It may well prove to be a distinct species when further biological and molecular evidence is available.

▲ Adult *N. t. longicaudata*, Anjouin, Comoro Islands, October. Paler, more greenish olive-brown than nominate *typica*. This bird shows pale brown legs (Pete Morris).

▲ Adult *N. t. longicaudata*, Anjouin, Comoro Islands, October. Note the poorly defined supercilium and absence of breast streaks (Pete Morris).

▲ Adult *N. t. typica*, Antananarivo, Madagascar, September. Note the dark tawny brown plumage, long narrow graduated tail, subdued supercilium, blackish bill and diffuse breast streaks (Boedts Bruno).

529

LANTZ'S BRUSH WARBLER
Nesillas lantzii   Plate 35

Ellisia Lantzii **Crandidier, 1867.** *Rev. Mag. Zool. Paris*, sér. 2, 19: 86. West coast of Madagascar.

A resident of dry spiny forest and coastal scrub in SW Madagascar. Formerly treated as a race of Madagascar Brush Warbler. Monotypic.

IDENTIFICATION Length 17cm. Wing 57–66mm. Tail/wing 112–135%.

A distinctive pale greyish *Nesillas* with a proportionately long tail. Sexes alike.

Structure Similar in size, general structure and wing formula to Madagascar Brush Warbler but the tail always has 12 feathers and tends to be less extremely graduated: the outer feathers are about 50% of the length of the central pair.

Plumage and bare parts A pale nondescript *Nesillas* that shows a distinct buffy white supercilium from the bill to behind the eye, bordered below by a darker eye-stripe. There is also an inconspicuous narrow white eye-ring. This well-marked head pattern is enhanced by the overall pallid appearance of the bird. The upperparts are light greyish brown, including the top and sides of the head and the wing-coverts, although the rump and uppertail-coverts are slightly more ochreous and the tail is distinctly darker grey-brown. The flight feathers are marginally darker than the mantle, but with pale grey-buff edges when fresh. The underparts are buffy white, with a warmer greyish brown wash to the flanks. A band of faint dusky streaks extends across the upper breast.

The bill is blackish with a pale yellowish base to the lower mandible and the legs are dark bluish grey.

SIMILAR SPECIES Within Madagascar, the closely related Madagascar Brush Warbler presents the most likely source of confusion. However, Thamnornis Warbler is similar in size and overall coloration and the two species occur sympatrically within S Madagascar.

Madagascar Brush Warbler avoids the sub-desert scrub and coastal regions in S Madagascar and the two species generally have parapatric distributions, although they do occur together in localised pockets where preferred habitats coincide. Madagascar Brush is much darker and browner in overall appearance, especially on the underparts and shows a less well-marked supercilium. The call is much lower-pitched and more rasping. Furthermore, the tail often has just ten tail feathers, whereas Lantz's Brush Warbler always has 12.

Thamnornis Warbler overlaps widely with Lantz's Brush Warbler in spiny sub-desert habitat. But its proportionately larger head, shorter tail and shorter, thicker bill give it a very different structure and character. It has a greyer head and distinctive yellowish green edges to the wing and tail feathers and also shows white tips to the outer tail feathers. The songs of the two are quite different, that of Thamnornis Warbler being a loud '*tewtewtewtewtew*'.

VOICE Appears to lack a structured song. Its rattling contact call comprises a short series of '*thratt-thratt-thratt-thratt-…*' calls, usually three to five given in a short sequence. It is similar in structure to that of Madagascar Brush Warbler but higher pitched and thinner, less grating.

MOULT No information available.

HABITAT Common in intact to heavily disturbed sub-desert

spiny forest and littoral forest and also found in low scrub and gardens (Goodman *et al.* 1997). Inland, it reaches the fringes of lowland evergreen humid forest and degraded *Didierea* forest, but does not breed in these habitats, being replaced there by Madagascar Scrub Warbler.

BEHAVIOUR Forages close to the ground for insects, alone or in pairs, and skulks in thick low cover and understorey. Usually detected by its rattling call.

BREEDING HABITS Very poorly known. Breeding has been recorded from August to February, but mainly between October and December. It nests close to the ground in a grass clump or bush and lays a clutch of two eggs.

DISTRIBUTION Common in low arid regions of SW Madagascar. Its range extends along the coast from Mangokey River south to Cap St. Marie and east to Fort Dauphin. Inland, it reaches the limit of the sub-desert forest, being confined to elevations below 200m. It is mainly parapatric with Madagascar Brush Warbler but the two occur together in places, for example near Fort Dauphin and in Andohahela.

Lantz's Brush Warbler. Resident within breeding range.

DESCRIPTION

Plumage – Adult Forehead to nape light greyish brown. Supercilium buffy white, extending back to middle of ear-coverts. Narrow buffy white eye-ring. Lores dark grey. A dark greyish brown line behind eye, contrasting slightly with paler greyish brown ear-coverts and sides of neck. Mantle and scapulars light greyish brown, grading to ochreous-brown on uppertail-coverts. Tail grey-brown, feathers edged grey-buff, tips of outer feathers fringed buffy white when fresh. Underparts buffy white, flanks with a grey-buff wash becoming deeper and warmer posteriorly, upper breast with short, faint dusky streaks; undertail-coverts pale grey-buff. Lesser and median coverts light greyish brown. Greater coverts and tertials dark grey-brown with narrow grey-buff fringes. Flight feathers and primary coverts dark grey-brown, narrowly edged grey-buff. Alula dark grey-brown with grey-buff outer webs. Underwing-coverts buffy white.

Juvenile Resembles adult closely, but slightly duller, more uniform grey.

Bare parts Upper mandible dark grey or blackish with yellow cutting edge. Lower mandible yellowish grey or light pinkish yellow with a darker sub-terminal spot. Mouth yellow. Tarsi and toes dull bluish grey. Iris mid brown.

IN HAND CHARACTERS
Measurements

	Male	Female
Wing	62–66 (63.8; 6)	57–63 (60.4; 7)
Tail	77–83 (80.2; 6)	68–76 (73.5; 7)
Bill	15.5–16.5 (16.1; 5)	14.5–17 (15.9; 7)
Tarsus	23.5–25 (24.3; 6)	22.5–25 (23.2; 7)

Sexes combined:
Tail/wing: 112–135% (124%; 11)
Bill width: 3.7–4.3 (4.1; 10)
Hind claw: 6.0–7.0 (6.5; 10)
Tail graduation: 36–42

Structure

Wing formula (n = 5):

p1/pc	p2	p3e	p4e	p5e	p6e	p7	p10
14–16	8–10	2–2.5	wp	wp	0–1	2–3.5	6–8

Wing similar to Madagascar Brush Warbler (Fig. 113); strongly rounded with large p1 (*c.* 60% p2). Wing point p4–5 (6); p2 = ss tips; emargination on p3–6.

Tail very long, 12 feathers, narrow and loose textured; strongly graduated with t6 *c.* 50% t1.

Bill and leg structure as nominate race of Madagascar Brush Warbler.

Recognition A plain-backed grey-brown warbler with whitish underparts and faintly streaked breast. Separated from Thamnornis Warbler by longer tail (usually > 70mm) without white feather tips and by lack of greenish wing and tail feather edges.

Weight Unsexed, 15–20g (17.5; 11) (Ravokatra *et al.* 2003).

GEOGRAPHIC VARIATION None recorded.

TAXONOMY AND SYSTEMATICS Lantz's Brush Warbler was formerly regarded as a race of Madagascar Brush Warbler but the two are now known to occur sympatrically in parts of SE Madagascar with no reported instances of hybridisation. Work by Schulenberg *et al.* (1993) showed that the two are genetically isolated and should be considered separate species.

▲ Adult, S Madagascar, October. A bird with faint breast streaks. Note the mainly yellow lower mandible and grey legs (Pete Morris).

▲ Age uncertain, La Table, S Madagascar, October. This bird, perhaps a juvenile, lacks breast streaks (Jacques Erard).

▲ Adult, S Madagascar, October. A slim, pale, greyish warbler with white underparts and long, narrow, graduated tail. This individual shows prominent narrow breast streaks (Pete Morris).

GRANDE COMORE BRUSH WARBLER
Nesillas brevicaudata   Plate 35

Ellisia brevicaudata Milne-Edwards & Oustalet, 1888. *Nouv. Archives Mus. Nat. Hist. Paris*, sér. 2, 10: 249. Grand Comoro Island.

A common endemic resident in the higher hills of Grande Comore in the Comoro Islands. It has previously been considered a race of Madagascar Brush Warbler but is now usually treated as a full species. Monotypic

IDENTIFICATION Length 15–16cm. Wing 61–69mm. Tail/wing 97–103%.

A warmly tinged *Nesillas* with well-marked throat streaking and a proportionately shorter tail than other members of the genus. The only resident warbler on Grande Comore. Sexes alike.

Structure The low head profile, strong bill and short rounded wing resemble those of other *Nesillas* but it appears more compact. The narrow tail, with 12 feathers, is strongly rounded but much shorter than that of Madagascar Brush Warbler and less extremely graduated.

Plumage and bare parts The upperparts are warm olive-brown, slightly more rufous on the rump and uppertail-coverts. The head shows a narrow but contrasting pale supercilium, extending well behind the eye and a distinct narrow dark eye-stripe. Conspicuous dark streaking extends from the chin to the upper breast and onto the neck sides. The throat is pale, but the underparts are otherwise darker and browner than in races *typica* and *longicaudata* of Madagascar Brush Warbler. The lower flanks and undertail-coverts are warmly tinged brown. Dark brown centres to the greater coverts and tertials contrast with warm olive-brown fringes. The dark flight feathers and tail feathers are also edged olive-brown.
The bill is blackish with a flesh-pink base to the lower mandible. The legs are greyish.

SIMILAR SPECIES Three *Nesillas* species occur in the Comoros but only Grand Comore Brush Warbler is present on Grande Comore. Madagascar Brush Warbler occurs on Moheli (race *moheliensis*) and Anjouan (race *longicaudata*), with Moheli Brush Warbler also on Moheli. As both are resident, they are unlikely to come into contact with Grande Comore Brush Warbler.
Madagascar Brush Warbler is larger and darker with a longer tail and it is much less arboreal than Grande Comore Brush Warbler.
Moheli Brush Warbler is closer in size, structure and habits but is paler and greener.

VOICE Like Madagascar Brush and Lantz's Brush Warblers, it appears to lack a structured song. It often gives a shrill chatter, '*ch-r-r-r ch-r-r-r- ch-r-r-r*', which may represent a 'song'. This is much less staccato than the race *typica* of Madagascar Brush Warbler.

The contact call is a short, low pitched, nasal, sparrow-like '*peut*'. When agitated, it gives a loud '*chik-puyk*', both notes of which appear to have harmonics; also a rapid scolding, uniform in rhythm, possibly in alarm from a family flock (Louette *et al.* 1988).

MOULT No data available.

HABITAT Occurs widely in tall forest as well as in *Philippia* stands and in thickets (Benson 1960; Louette 2004). It also frequents exotic thickets dominated by Strawberry Guava *Psidium cattleianum* (R. J. Safford *in litt.*).

BEHAVIOUR Usually seen singly, or 2–3 birds together, often with mixed species parties. It perches from low levels to the canopy of taller trees, sometimes up to 12m from the ground, but it prefers the shrub layer or the low trees and lower canopy above this to the herb layer. Thus generally more arboreal than other *Nesillas* apart from Moheli Brush Warbler (Louette *et al.* 1988). In forest, it hops along mossy branches and trunks, often with the tail cocked, picking at tiny food items, jumping between foliage masses and leaf-gleaning (Benson 1960; Safford & Evans 1992). It feeds nearer the ground in the heath zone, where the vegetation is lower (Safford & Evans 1992).

BREEDING HABITS Poorly known, with little information on laying dates. An apparently dependent juvenile was noted in April (Safford & Evans 1992). Data is available from just one nest containing two well-grown young (photo in Louette *et al.* 1988). This was situated just above the ground, apparently in mixed undergrowth at the base of a Strawberry Guava sapling. It was a deep cup built of grasses and fine woody material, with moss and filmy ferns added to the exterior.

DISTRIBUTION An endemic resident on Grande Comore. Common and widespread above 500m in all vegetational zones including *Philippia* heath, virtually to the top of Mount Karthala at nearly 2,300m, and on the second peak, La Grille. Numbers increase with altitude from 500m towards 2,000m (Louette *et al.* 1988; Louette 2004).

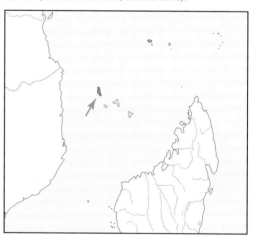

Grande Comore Brush Warbler. Resident within breeding range.

DESCRIPTION
Plumage – Adult Forehead to nape rather dark olive-brown. Supercilium buffish, narrow but distinct, extending just behind the eye. Lores dark brown. A faint darker brown stripe extends behind eye along upper border of ear-coverts. Rest of ear-coverts and sides of neck olive-brown, paler and rather greyer than crown, with a buffy crescent below eye. Malar area streaked buff. Mantle and scapulars olive-brown, rather lighter and warmer than crown, becoming cinnamon-brown on rump and uppertail-coverts. Tail dark brown, feathers edged light olive-brown. Chin and throat pale buff; breast buff with olive-brown wash; belly pale buff. Chin to upper breast with soft greyish brown streaks. Flanks olive-brown, becoming warm brown on rear flanks, vent and undertail-coverts. Lesser and median coverts warm olive-

brown. Greater coverts and tertials dark brown, fringed and tipped warm olive-brown. Primary coverts and alula dark brown, narrowly fringed light olive-brown. Flight feathers dark brown, edged light olive-brown. Underwing-coverts light olive-brown.

Juvenile No information available.

Bare parts Upper mandible blackish. Lower mandible flesh with sepia tip. Mouth bright reddish orange. Tarsi and toes light greyish brown. Iris dark brown.

IN HAND CHARACTERS
Measurements

	Male	Female	Sexes combined*
Wing	64–68 (66.0; 3)	62–66 (64.0; 3)	61–69 (63.6; 29)
Tail	66–67 (66.3; 3)	61–64 (62.3; 3)	58–68 (63.4; 27)
Bill	17–18 (17.2; 3)	16–17 (16.5; 3)	16–18.5 (17.6; 22)
Tarsus	26.5, 27 (2)	25–26 (25.7; 3)	25–28 (26.1; 29)

(*Louette *et al.* 1988)

Sexes combined:
Tail/wing: 97–103% (99%; 7)
Bill width: 4.3–4.7 (4.5; 7)
Hind claw: 7.0–7.5 (7.2; 7)
Tail graduation: 28–34 (31.3; 6)

Structure

Wing formula (n = 5):

p1/pc	p2	p3e	p4e	p5e	p6e	p7(e)	p10
10–15	11–13	3–4	0–0.5	wp	0–1	2.5–4	9–10

Wing similar to Madagascar Brush Warbler (Fig. 113); strongly rounded with large p1 (*c.* 60% p2). Wing point p4–6; p2 < ss tips; emargination on p3–6, sometimes slightly on p7.

Tail of 12 narrow feathers; medium length, strongly graduated (t6 *c.* 50% t1), t6 very small and narrow, cf. Madagascar Brush Warbler *N. t. longicaudata* (Fig. 114).

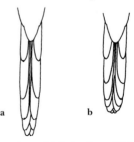

Fig. 114. Comparison of tail structure of (a) Madagascar Brush Warbler *N. t. longicaudata* and (b) Grand Comore Brush Warbler.

Bill medium length; rather stout, almost straight-sided. Tarsi strong, claws relatively small.

Recognition A plain-backed warbler with warm brown upperparts and distinct throat streaks. Tail/wing ratio (< 105%) is below that of *N. typica* races.

Weight 14.0–19.0g (16.1; 17) (Louette *et al.* 1988).

GEOGRAPHIC VARIATION None.

TAXONOMY AND SYSTEMATICS In view of its distinctive voice and different tail structure, Louette *et al.* (1988) suggested that Grande Comore Brush Warbler had different origins to those of the longer-tailed brush warblers of Anjouan (*N. t. longicaudata*) and Moheli (*N. t. moheliensis*). They treat it as a full species, a course that we have followed here.

▲ Adult, Grande Gomore, Comoro Islands, October. Note the rather plain head side, tawny brown upperparts, short primary projection and strongly graduated tail of moderate length (Pete Morris).

▲ Adult, Grande Gomore, October. Shows the brown-washed underparts with diffuse dusky breast-streaking (Pete Morris).

MOHELI BRUSH WARBLER
Nesillas mariae   **Plate 35**

Nesillas mariae Benson, 1960. *Ibis* 103: 81. Bandamale, Moheli, Comoro Islands, altitude 500 metres.

An endemic resident of forest and thick scrub on Moheli, Comoro Islands. Monotypic.

IDENTIFICATION Length 15–16cm. Wing 58–64mm. Tail/wing *c.* 110%.

A pale greenish grey warbler with a proportionately long tail. Sympatric on Moheli with the endemic race *moheliensis* of Madagascar Brush Warbler *N. typica*. Sexes alike.
Structure The smallest of the *Nesillas* warblers. Appears slim, but the narrow tail of 12 feathers is shorter and less strongly graduated than in Madagascar Brush Warbler. The bill is slightly smaller and the legs, although strong, are shorter than in other members of the genus.
Plumage and bare parts The upperparts are uniform drab light olive-green, the rump and uppertail-coverts slightly brighter than the mantle. The crown and ear-coverts are concolorous with the mantle, but paler yellowish buff cheeks contrast with the greener neck sides. A narrow buffish supercilium is poorly defined, appearing most prominent above the lores and extending only as a faint diffuse line over the ear-coverts. A narrow reddish orbital ring distinguishes this from other members of the genus, but this is inconspicuous in the field. The yellowish buff underparts are paler on the throat and belly centre, but tinged warm brown on the flanks and undertail-coverts. A band of faint soft greyish streaks extends across the throat and upper breast. The closed wing is similar in colour to the mantle, with light olive-green fringes and edges to the coverts and remiges. The tail is also tinged and edged greenish.

The bill is blackish with a flesh-toned base to the lower mandible that darkens at the sides towards the tip. The legs and feet are greyish brown.

SIMILAR SPECIES On Moheli, the only similar species is the endemic race of Madagascar Brush Warbler. Among allopatric *Nesillas* warblers, Grande Comore Brush Warbler most closely resembles Moheli Brush Warbler in habits, voice and morphology.
Madagascar Brush Warbler (race *moheliensis*) is distinctly larger, much longer-tailed and both darker and browner than Moheli Brush Warbler. Its vocalisations lack the complexity shown by Moheli Brush Warbler. These species also tend to be separated on Moheli by habitat selection, Moheli Brush Warbler being more arboreal.

VOICE Vocalisations are well structured and often varied and complex, unlike those of other *Nesillas* species. The song consists of a series of loud, high-pitched scratchy notes, slightly separated and rather similar to staccato sounds made by a child's squeaky toy. It has also been likened to the song of a Barn Swallow or a *Nectarinia* sunbird.

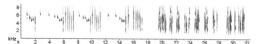

Part of song of Moheli Brush Warbler, Moheli, Comoro Islands, November. (Herremans 2001)

It also utters a series of loud '*teeeep-teeeep-teeeep…*' phrases, believed to form part of the song. Pairs foraging together give a clear '*chinkechoyit-chetwie*'.

The call when alarmed is a rapid rattle like that of Grande Comore Brush Warbler. It is also similar to the repertoire of structureless sounds of Madagascar Brush Warbler, although higher pitched and more uniform in rhythm (Louette *et al.* 1988). Also given is a series of rapidly repeated '*chit-chit-chit-chit…*' calls, with 20 or more uttered in rapid succession.

MOULT No data available.

HABITAT Prefers upland forested areas in the centre of the island, particularly where there is almost complete cover of herb and shrub layers and low trees are frequent. In the lower parts of the island it occurs outside forest in woody vegetation with small trees and in streamside scrub (Cheke & Diamond 1986). It shows a consistent difference in habitat use compared with the sympatric Madagascar Brush Warbler, which is less associated with low trees and usually remains below 3m in the shrub or herb layers. Habitat selection is closest to that of Grande Comore Brush Warbler (Cheke & Diamond 1986; Louette *et al.* 1988; Safford & Evans 1992).

BEHAVIOUR Forages in shrubs and bush tops and the lower parts of trees, typically about 7–8m above ground, although often above or well below this (Bijnens *et al.* 1987). Feeds by gleaning invertebrates from leaves.

BREEDING HABITS A nest under construction by both pair members on 20 February was described by Cheke & Diamond (1986) as being 9m above the ground in a tall Mango *Mangifera indica* tree, in the foliage at the end of a long horizontal branch. It consisted of a small cup of moss and grass with untidy bits of grass hanging below and with dead leaves and tiny twigs added when nearly complete. The eggs and young remain undescribed and no other details of breeding are known.

DISTRIBUTION Endemic to Moheli in the Comoro Islands where it is widespread on the forested ridge, but occurs in secondary habitats down to 150m. Common in forest, with highest densities occurring at higher altitudes and less numerous in lowland secondary vegetation (Louette *et al.* 1988). Typically more numerous than the sympatric Madagascar Brush Warbler.

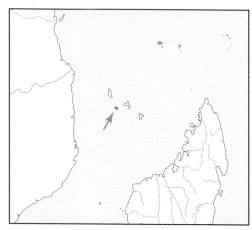

Moheli Brush Warbler. Resident within breeding range.

DESCRIPTION
Plumage – Adult Top of head dull olive-green. Supercilium buffish, poorly defined, evident mainly above lores. Ear-

coverts and sides of neck light olive-green, concolorous with crown. Mantle and scapulars dull olive-green, becoming brighter on rump and uppertail-coverts. Tail dark greyish brown, feathers tinged and edged greenish. Entire underparts including lower cheeks ochreous buff, palest on chin, throat and centre of belly. Throat and upper breast with soft greyish streaks. Flanks browner; lower flanks, vent and undertail-coverts tinged cinnamon. Lesser and median coverts olive-green. Greater coverts dark grey-brown, broadly but diffusely edged and tipped olive-green. Remiges, primary coverts and alula dark grey-brown, edged light olive-green, rather broadly but diffusely on tertials and alula. Underwing-coverts ochreous buff.

Juvenile Apparently undescribed.

Bare parts Upper mandible blackish. Lower mandible fleshy with dusky sides towards tip. Tarsi and toes dark greyish brown. Iris dark brown. Orbital ring narrow, reddish.

IN HAND CHARACTERS
Measurements

Sexes combined:

Wing	58–64 (61.0; 9)
Tail	63.5–71 (66.2; 10)
Bill	16–18 (16.7; 9)
Tarsus	21–23.5 (22.2; 10)

(Louette *et al.* 1988)

Bill width: (n = 1) 4.2
Hind claw: (n = 1) 5.8
Tail graduation: 33

Structure Wing similar to Madagascar Brush Warbler (Fig. 113); strongly rounded with large p1. Wing point p4–6; p2 < ss tips; emargination on p3–7.

Tail of 12 feathers strongly graduated (t6 *c.* 50% t1); shorter than in *N. typica*, only slightly longer than wing length.

Bill rather smaller and slimmer than in other Comoros *Nesillas* taxa, and tarsi shorter and more slender.

Recognition Distinguished from sympatric race of Madagascar Brush Warbler by paler greenish upperparts and by shorter tail (usually < 70mm) and shorter tarsi (usually < 24mm); also by narrow red orbital ring.

Weight 14–17g (15.6; 8) (Louette *et al.* 1988).

GEOGRAPHIC VARIATION None recorded.

TAXONOMY AND SYSTEMATICS No issues arising.

▲ Adult, Moheli, Comoro Islands, October. Note the pale plumage, green-tinged back and wings, red eye-ring and rather slender bill (Claire Spottiswoode).

ALDABRA BRUSH WARBLER
Nesillas aldabranus   Plate 35

Nesillas aldabranus Benson & Penny, 1968. *Bull. Brit. Orn. Club* 88: 102. Western extremity of Middle Island, north coast of Aldabra Atoll.

An endemic resident on Aldabra, known up to the 1980s from one small area of dense coastal scrub on Ile Malabar (Middle Island). Considered EXTINCT by Birdlife International, but included here in case an undiscovered population remains. Monotypic.

IDENTIFICATION Length 18–20cm. Wing 63–70mm. Tail/wing *c.* 130%.
    Formerly the only warbler resident on Aldabra. Sexes alike.
Structure A large *Nesillas* with an attenuated head shape, short rounded wings and a proportionately long graduated tail comprising 12 feathers. The bill is long and strong. Sexes alike.
Plumage and bare parts Plain, rather pale, and nondescript. The upperparts are earth-brown but slightly warmer and more rufescent on the rump and uppertail-coverts, sometimes with a greyish tinge on the crown. The side of the head is greyish brown, with pale greyish lores and a well-marked greyish white supercilium that extends behind the eye above a darker eye-stripe. The underparts are whitish on the chin, throat and belly centre, with a light buff wash on the breast and pale tawny-brown flanks and undertail-coverts. The upper breast shows variable, often indistinct dusky streaking, most obvious at the sides. The wings are darker brown than the mantle, with light tawny feather edges.
    The bill is dark horn with a paler or flesh-toned lower mandible. The legs are grey.

SIMILAR SPECIES No similar species occur on Aldabra.

VOICE Usually silent. The most commonly given call was a '*tak*', sometimes repeated rapidly (Prŷs-Jones 1979), to form a rattle, similar to the presumed alarm calls of Grande Comore Brush and Moheli Brush Warblers. A short '*chinkachoy*' or '*chak-chir*' resembles the clear foraging call given by Moheli Brush Warbler (Louette *et al.* 1988).

MOULT No data available.

HABITAT It formerly occurred in tall, dense, closed-canopy scrub up to 5m high, with a good leaf litter and/or soil layer. It particularly favoured areas with large stands of *Pandanus tectorius* or an abundance of *Dracaena reflexa*, both of which were much used for foraging.

BEHAVIOUR Skulking and would typically only fly short distances. Birds foraged silently for small invertebrates, mainly within 1.5m of the ground. They fed by picking from the ground or leaves, or probing in leaf litter, sometimes making a jump or short flight to snatch prey (Skerrett *et al.* 2000).

BREEDING HABITS Territories extended to c. 0.75ha and were occupied throughout the year. Breeding probably coincided with the wet months from October to January (Prŷs-Jones 1979). A nest with a clutch of three eggs found in December 1967 was 0.6m above the ground in the leaf bases of young *Pandanus* scrub. Two empty nests discovered in 1968 were, respectively, 3.2m up in a thicket between stems of *Mystroxylon* and 1.5m above ground in forking stems of *Pemphis* (Benson & Penny 1968).

DISTRIBUTION Following its discovery in 1967, it remained up to the early 1980s in a 50m-wide strip of scrub that extended for *c.* 2km along the north coast of Ile Malabar, Aldabra. It was, apparently, always rare here and a study in 1974–75 located just five birds. Extrapolation of this figure indicated a population of about 25 birds in a 9km-strip of suitable habitat. Unfortunately, this was reduced in size by goats and giant tortoises *Geochelone gigantea* so that by 1977 only two males were known to have survived. The last sighting was made in 1983. Intensive searches in 1986 confirmed that the species was extinct, probably because of predation by rats. Goats and giant tortoises are now absent from the remaining potentially suitable dense scrub of W Malabar.

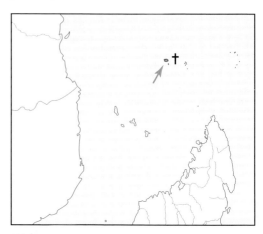

Aldabra Brush Warbler. Resident within breeding range.

DESCRIPTION
Plumage – Adult fresh Forehead to nape warm brown, sometimes with greyish cast. Supercilium well-marked, greyish white, from bill to behind eye. Lores mottled dark grey-brown. A short dark brown stripe extends behind the eye. Ear-coverts greyish brown. Mantle and scapulars warm brown, becoming brighter, more cinnamon-brown on rump and uppertail-coverts. Tail dark brown. Chin to breast and belly greyish white, breast with brownish wash. Lower throat and upper breast with variable faint dusky streaking. Flanks, vent and undertail-coverts pale tawny-brown. Upperwing-coverts and tertials dark brown with diffuse tawny-brown edges. Primaries and secondaries dark brown, edged lighter tawny-brown. Underwing-coverts off-white.
Juvenile Undescribed.
Bare parts Upper mandible dark brown or sepia with pale cutting edge. Lower mandible light horn or fleshy, unmarked. Mouth orange. Tarsi grey. Iris reddish brown or mid brown.

IN HAND CHARACTERS
Measurements

	Male	Female
Wing	67–70 (68.6; 4)	63, 65 (2)
Tail	85, 91 (2)	86 (1)
Bill	18–20 (19.0; 3)	18 (2)
Tarsus	24–26.5 (25.3; 3)	23.5, 24 (2)

(Includes data from Prŷs-Jones 1979)

Structure Similar to *N. typica*.

Weight 18.0–19.7g (19.2; 4) (Prŷs-Jones 1979).

GEOGRAPHIC VARIATION None.

TAXONOMY AND SYSTEMATICS Due to similarities in vocalisations and tail structure, Louette *et al.* (1988) suggested that Aldabra Brush Warbler was most closely related to Grand Comoro Brush Warbler and Moheli Brush Warbler.

▲ Adult, Aldabra. Note the generally pale brown upperparts, strong grey legs, and strong bill with bright pale brown lower mandible (Robert Prŷs-Jones).

▲ Adult, Aldabra. This singing bird shows tawny-edged wing-feathers, greyish white cheeks and breast, a prominent pale supercilium and a well-marked eye-stripe (Robert Prŷs-Jones).

Genus *Oligura* Hodgson, 1844

[Gr. *oligos* short, small; *oura* tail]

A monotypic genus comprising just a single species, Chestnut-headed Tesia, which is an altitudinal migrant breeding in montane forest undergrowth in the Himalayas and mountains of western China and northern Indochina. It differs from the *Tesia* species in having bright yellow underparts and a chestnut head, a slightly longer tail comprising ten rectrices, and much smaller bill, as well as a characteristic, short, rising and falling song.

CHESTNUT-HEADED TESIA
Oligura castaneocoronata   Plate 36

Oligura castaneocoronata **Burton, 1836.** *Sylvia? castaneocoronata* Burton, 1836. *Proc. Zool. Soc. London* (1835), p. 152. No locality (= Himalayas).

A tiny warbler that frequents dense undergrowth and dark ravines and gullies in montane forest of the Himalayas, Burma and W China, and winters in the adjacent foothills and lowlands. Polytypic, with three races recognised:

O. c. castaneocoronata Burton, 1836. Himalayas.
O. c. abadiei (Delacour & Jabouille, 1930). Chapa (Tonkin), altitude 1,600 metres, N Vietnam.
O. c. ripleyi Deignan, 1951. Likiang Mountains, Yunnan Province, China.

IDENTIFICATION Length *c.* 8cm. Wing 45–67mm. Tail/wing 41–54%.

A stunningly bright sprite of the forest floor with a red head, dull green upperparts, yellow underparts, an extremely short tail and a simple but powerful song
Structure A tiny warbler with an extremely short tail that barely extends beyond the wings. This is usually held in line with the body axis and not held cocked in the manner of a Northern Wren, sometimes making it appear tail-less, particularly in the gloomy undergrowth of the forest floor. The bill is short and fine, but the legs are proportionately quite long and it often straightens them when stretching up to increase its height, especially when curious. The wing is short and rounded, with a long first primary (p1) and the wing point formed by p5–6.
Plumage and bare parts Has a highly distinctive plumage not shared with any other species. The entire crown, nape and side of the head are uniform rich cinnamon-red, offset only by a small whitish spot immediately behind the eye. Otherwise the entire upperparts, including the tail, are drab olive-green, although the webs to the wing-coverts, tertials and flight feathers are darker but still edged olive-green. The closed wings usually appear slightly darker than the upperparts since the duller webs are often exposed as the bird nervously flicks its wings.

The chin and throat are bright yellow and sharply defined from the cinnamon-red lower ear-coverts and cheeks. The remainder of the underparts are duller, the breast being yellow with dull olive-green feather fringes, forming a wash across the breast and belly. This darkens to olive-green towards the flanks and side of the neck, where it appears slightly greener and brighter than the upperparts. The tibia is feathered olive-green to the tibio-tarsal joint.

Juveniles appear quite different from adults. The entire upperparts are uniform dark brown with a trace of olive, while the entire underparts are uniform warm, rich orange-brown.

The bill has an entirely dark greyish brown upper mandible and a pale yellow lower mandible. The legs and feet are pale fleshy yellow.

SIMILAR SPECIES No similar species occur in the montane forests of the Himalayas and E Asia. The closely related *Tesia* species are largely green above and grey below.

VOICE The simple song is one of the most characteristic sounds of the Himalayan montane forests. It comprises a four-syllable sequence, '*si si-see-dee*', or '*sip, sip-it-up*', which rises and falls in pitch but descends from *c.* 7kHz to 3kHz throughout delivery. Emphasis is placed on the first three syllables, the fourth always being given at the lowest frequency. This simple song, lasting for *c.* 1 second, is repeated continuously at intervals of 4–6 seconds. There is limited variation, mostly in frequency range, but also in the intervals between sequences, some birds interspersing these pauses with one or more calls.

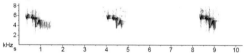

Song of Chestnut-headed Tesia recorded within the breeding range of *O. c. castaneocoronata*, Sengor, Bhutan, May. (Peter Kennerley)

The call is a harsh and high pitched '*si-si-si-si-si-si...*', repeated at intervals of approximately one second. It is often given prior to the start of the song.

MOULT No details available. Adults probably have complete moult after the breeding season in August–September, prior to post-breeding dispersal. The distinctive juvenile plumage appears to be retained for only a short period and is probably replaced in a complete moult at the same time as that of the adult.

HABITAT During the breeding season it frequents dense undergrowth in montane forest, from 1,800m to 3,300m, but is most numerous above 2,400m. Birds have been recorded to 3,900m in Nepal. It occupies the lowest storey of the forest, often on or very close to the ground in a dense undergrowth of ferns Dryopteridaceae, nettles Urticaceae, light scrub, bushes and dwarf bamboo Bambusoideae. It is most frequently found in dark, dank overgrown gullies and along the courses of streams and small rivulets, but also in dense undergrowth on slopes of undulating forest floors.

Outside the breeding season it frequents similar habitats at lower elevations, but also occurs in more open situations such as a shady section of a nullah, or in more open secondary forest. Migrants can occur in almost dense undergrowth, including bamboo scrub in city parks.

BEHAVIOUR Typically solitary and elusive but not a shy bird. It is often bold and will closely approach a stationary observer, nervously flicking its wings above its back. Its bright plumage and bold behaviour ensure that it is often readily located and easily observed. It always keeps close to the forest floor, rarely more than 1m above the ground and almost never flying other than between the low branches, fallen logs and moss-covered rocks, on which it usually hops rapidly from perch to perch. It rarely remains stationary for more than a few seconds. It appears to be entirely insectivorous.

Ali & Ripley (1973) published details of what appears to be a complex courtship ritual witnessed by D. Proud (*J. Bombay Nat. Hist. Soc.* 55: 349). 'Two birds were in the same bush, one keeping mostly to the upper branches where it ran or rather strutted backwards and forwards with wings drooping, bill turned straight upwards, yellow throat puffed out, tiny tail held bolt upright, uttering a continual, rapid '*tsk tsk tsk...*'. The second bird behaved in exactly the same way in the lower part of the bush. Every now and again the two birds would approach each other, the excitement rising to fever pitch, but when about two inches apart they would turn away and resume their initial positions. This was repeated again and again for an hour. It was never discovered if they were a pair in courtship display or two males challenging each other.'

BREEDING HABITS The nest comprises a superbly camouflaged ball of moss lined with feathers. It is usually built close to the ground in a bush or on a low branch amongst other similarly sized growths of moss. It is occasionally built amongst the moss on a tree-trunk or found hanging from a branch, but is always difficult to find. A clutch of three, or occasionally four eggs is laid in June or July (Stuart Baker 1922).

DISTRIBUTION Three races occur extensively throughout the montane forests of the Himalayas and into the mountains of N Burma, SW China, N Thailand and N Indochina.

Breeding

O. c. castaneocoronata In the Himalayas, breeding occurs in India from the Kulu and Parbati valleys at Bhawan in Himachal Pradesh, east through Uttaranchal to Arunachal Pradesh. Elsewhere in NE India it breeds in Mizoram (Lushai Hills), Nagaland and Meghalaya and possibly Manipur. Ali & Ripley (1973) claimed breeding in the Chittagong Hill Tracts of Bangladesh although this is contradicted by Rasmussen & Anderton (2005), who state there are no supporting specimens from the country. It also breeds in Nepal, Sikkim and Bhutan and into neighbouring regions of Tibet (Xizang Autonomous Region) (Cheng 1987). Cheng considers this race to occupy much of the species' range in China, including NE Yunnan and C Sichuan Provinces, while restricting *O. c. ripleyi* to the type locality at the Lijiang region in Yunnan Province.

In Burma, it breeds from the border with India south through the Chin Hills, including Mount Victoria and to the Southern Shan States and Karenni. It range also extends into N Laos and NW Thailand, where it is apparently restricted to Doi Pha Hom Pok, where it is common, and Doi Inthanon, Doi Ang Khang and Doi Chiang Dao, where it is less numerous, breeding from 1,400m to the summit of Doi Inthanon at 2,590m. It is uncertain, however, which race breeds in this region, particularly in N Laos, which lies adjacent to the range of *ripleyi* in S Yunnan.

O. c. abadiei Restricted to W and E Tonkin in N Vietnam, where it occurs from 1,600m to 2,800m. It is apparently resident in the Sa Pa - Hoang Lien National Park, which includes Fan Si Pan from where this race was described.

It also breeds in Tam Dao National Park and is probably widespread in forests of the higher hills throughout the north.

O. c. ripleyi According to Cheng (1987), this race is restricted to southern Yunnan Province in China, where it is known from the type locality at Lijiang and also from the Nujiang and Longchuan (Nanhua) River valleys. Cheng attributes birds breeding in northern Yunnan and Sichuan Provinces to the nominate form. It has not been possible to confirm or contradict these distributions.

Non-breeding Most descend from the breeding grounds to winter in the foothills and lowlands, although some can be found throughout the year towards the lower limits of the breeding range. In Bhutan, Spierenburg (2005) found it occurred most frequently from 800m to 2,600m. Ali & Ripley (1973) noted that it winters from *c.* 1,800m down to the foothills and onto adjacent plains of the Brahmaputra Valley in Assam, while Barua & Sharma (2005) considered it to be a common winter visitor to Nameri National Park in the foothills of the Himalayas in Assam.

In Vietnam, the type specimen of *O. c. abadiei* was collected at 1,600m in December 1929.

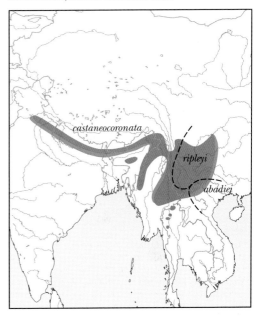

Chestnut-headed Tesia. Breeding range and winter distribution. Birds breeding at lower elevations are resident throughout the year.

MOVEMENTS Birds breeding at higher elevations are altitudinal migrants that descend to the foothills outside the breeding season. Birds in Vietnam are believed to be resident.

Spierenburg (2005) described it as an altitudinal migrant in Bhutan, wintering down to 800m and sometimes as low as 200m. Birds depart from the breeding areas between October and mid December and return in April. There are few observations of migrants in China; one in a park in Chengdu, Sichuan Province, China, on 27 October (PRK pers. obs.), provides some indication of the likely departure period from the breeding area and suggests that some birds may winter away from the foothills.

DESCRIPTION *O. c. castaneocoronata*

Plumage – Adult fresh Forehead, crown, nape, lores, ear-coverts and eye-ring rich cinnamon-red. No supercilium or eye-stripe. There is usually a conspicuous white to yellowish white spot immediately behind eye, and a similar but much smaller spot in front of eye, but this is occasionally absent. Mantle, scapulars, rump, uppertail-coverts and upper surface of tail dark olive-green. Chin and throat bright dandelion-yellow at tips with white bases to feathers, sharply demarcated from cinnamon-red lores and ear-coverts. Upper breast yellow with olive-green wash, becoming duller yellow with an olive-green wash towards the lower breast. Side of neck darkens to dark-olive green towards nape. Sides of breast bright yellow with olive-green wash. Flanks olive-green with slight yellow wash. Belly dull ochre yellow. Undertail-coverts olive-green with slight yellow wash. Lesser, median and greater coverts and tertials dark olive brown with indistinct dark olive-green fringes. Primary coverts and alula dark olive-green. Primaries and secondaries dark brown with dark olive-green outer web. The tibia is feathered olive-green to the tibio-tarsal joint. Underwing-coverts dull greyish yellow.

Adult worn Not known to differ from fresh adult.

Juvenile Quite different from adult. Forehead, crown, nape, lores and ear-coverts and eye-ring very dark brown, tinged olive. No supercilium or eye-stripe. Eye-ring slightly paler than ear-coverts but inconspicuous. Mantle, scapulars, rump, uppertail-coverts and upper surface of tail dark brown tinged olive, this slightly more conspicuous than on head. Chin, throat and side of neck rich burnt cinnamon. Breast and flanks similar burnt sienna but slightly darker. Belly and undertail-coverts rich burnt cinnamon. Lesser, median and greater coverts, tertials, primary coverts, underwing-coverts, alula, primaries and secondaries dark olive-brown with dark olive-green fringes.

Bare parts Upper mandible dark grey to black. Lower mandible unmarked pale straw, or darkening at sides towards tip on some birds. Juvenile lacks dark tip to lower mandible. Tarsi, toes and claws pale fleshy yellow. Iris dark brown.

IN HAND CHARACTERS
Measurements
O. c. castaneocoronata

	Male	Female
Wing	47–53 (50.5; 20)	46–50 (47.9; 13)
Tail	20–27 (23.9; 18)	20–24 (22.4; 11)
Bill	11.5–13.5 (12.3; 20)	11.5–13 (12.4; 11)
Tarsus	21–23.5 (22.2; 17)	20.5–23.5 (22.0; 11)

Sexes combined:
Tail/wing ratio: 41–54% (47%; 29)
Bill width: 3.2–3.5 (3.3; 16)
Hind claw: 5.1–6.5 (5.9; 19)
Tail graduation: 2–5
Also, from Deignan (1951):
O. c. castaneocoronata: *wing* 45–50 (47.25; 16); *tail* 21–26 (23.5; 12).
O. c. ripleyi: *wing* 52–57 (55.4; 7); *tail* 28–32 (30.3; 7).
O. c. abadiei: *wing* 50–53 (51.5; 4); *tail* 27–29 (28.0; 4).

Structure *O. c. castaneocoronata*

Wing formula (n = 10):

p1/pc	p2	p3e	p4e	p5e	p6e	p7	p10
12–15	9–13	3–5	0–1.5	wp	wp	0.5–1.5	4–5

Wing similar to Grey-bellied Tesia (Fig. 115); short and strongly rounded with large p1. Wing point at p5–6; p2 < ss tips; emargination on p3–6.

Tail very short, slightly rounded; longer than in *Tesia* species, feathers less narrow.

Bill rather flat, straight-sided with fine pointed tip; much smaller than in Grey-bellied Tesia.

Tarsi and toes long and slender, claws smaller and finer than in Grey-bellied Tesia.

Recognition A tiny warbler with an extremely short tail hidden below closed wings. Told from all *Tesia* species by the distinctive combination of a bright chestnut head, dull green upperparts and conspicuously yellow underparts.

Weight 8–10g (Ali & Ripley 1973).

GEOGRAPHIC VARIATION Slight, limited to minor differences in colour and size.

O. c. castaneocoronata (Himalayas) Described above.

O. c. abadiei (N Vietnam) Differs from nominate race in its overall duller appearance, particularly about the head. Crown slightly duller cinnamon-red with a slight brownish cast and nape dark olive-green rather than cinnamon-red. Chin and throat yellow but slightly paler and less richly coloured, similar to breast. The division between the lower edges of the cinnamon-red lores and ear-coverts and yellow chin and throat is less distinct than in nominate race.

O. c. ripleyi (SW China) Plumage as nominate race although forehead to nape slightly paler and brighter. Differs mainly in longer wing and tail measurements (see **In Hand Characters**).

TAXONOMY AND SYSTEMATICS Often included in the genus *Tesia*, but the highly distinctive plumage and longer tail justify separation from these species and placement in *Oligura*.

▲ Adult, Sichuan Province, China, April. Distinctive structure and colourful appearance make this species unmistakable (Yang Xianwei).

Genus *Tesia* Hodgson, 1837

[Nepalese name *Tisi* for the Grey-bellied Tesia *Tesia cyaniventer*]

Four tiny, apparently tail-less, ground-dwelling warblers that are resident or undertake short, altitudinal migrations. The tail appears to comprise eight rectrices, although the short length makes this difficult to establish with certainty. They frequent undergrowth in montane forest in SE Asia. All are dome-headed and plump-bodied, with fairly small but broad-based bills, rather long legs and an upright stance. Their coloration varies from olive-green to plain brown above, and slate-grey to greyish white below. One species, Javan Tesia, exhibits a long, prominent whitish supercilium. The songs are short, simple and quite loud. The nest is usually ball-shaped with a side entrance and placed close to the ground amongst moss. Russet-capped Tesia was formerly included in the genus *Urosphena* but its vocalisations and tail/wing ratio place it firmly within *Tesia*.

GREY-BELLIED TESIA
Tesia cyaniventer   Plate 36

Tesia cyaniventer **Hodgson, 1837**. *J. Asiatic Soc. Bengal* 6: 101. Nepal.

A tiny warbler of dense undergrowth and the forest floor in mountain ranges from the lower Himalayas to N Vietnam, where some are resident and others descend to winter in adjacent foothills and lowlands. Monotypic.

IDENTIFICATION Length 8–8.5cm. Wing 45–53mm. Tail/wing 31–37%.

A minute, 'tail-less' and drably coloured warbler with dull green upperparts, grey underparts, a distinctive bright green supercilium and a dark grey eye-stripe. Closely resembles Slaty-belled Tesia. Sexes alike.

Structure A diminutive warbler with an extremely short tail that does not extend to the tips of the primaries and is always hidden by the wings. Otherwise, the overall structure, including the short and rounded wing shape, is very similar to that of Slaty-bellied and Chestnut-headed Tesias, with a long first primary (p1) and the wing point formed by p5–6.

Plumage and bare parts Has a contrasting head pattern not shown by other Himalayan tesia species. In particular it shows a long and broad bright lime-green supercilium, broadest in front of the eye and extending onto the forehead above the bill. It narrows slightly behind the eye but remains conspicuous to the side of the nape. Below this, a dark grey eye-stripe extends from the bill to the rear of the ear-coverts and contrasts with the paler grey ear-coverts and cheeks. Otherwise, the upperparts, from the crown and nape to the uppertail-coverts and tail and also the wing-coverts and the edges to the flight feathers, are dull, uniform moss-green. The underparts are grey and also unmarked but vary in colour from greyish white on the chin to mid grey on the breast and dark grey on the flanks.

The bill is dark brown to blackish with an orange-yellow lower mandible that darkens slightly towards the tip. The legs and feet are dark brown.

SIMILAR SPECIES Within its range, only likely to be mistaken for Slaty-belled Tesia.

Slaty-bellied Tesia closely resembles Grey-bellied and care is required in their separation in the dense undergrowth on the forest floor or in gloomy ravines and gullies. Slaty-bellied always lacks the distinctive green supercilium and dark grey eye-stripe of Grey-bellied, instead showing a rich golden-yellow crown and nape with a slight iridescence, quite unlike the darker crown and nape of Grey-bellied.

The underparts are slate-grey, slightly darker than on Grey-bellied, but this is of little use in separating them since both keep close to the forest floor where low light levels make this difficult to discern.

The colour of the lower mandible also differs, being bright orange-red to vivid orange in Slaty-bellied Tesia but much duller orange-yellow in Grey-bellied, although slightly darker at the sides towards the tip in both species.

VOICE The song is surprisingly loud with a rich, almost explosive quality and is one of the most frequently heard and characteristic sounds in the Himalayan forests. It is usually uttered as the bird moves within *c.* 0.5m of the ground. It is the lowest-pitched and has the richest delivery of the songs of the three Himalayan tesia species. An introduction of two or three separate and slightly slurred '*tsiti*' notes, given in quick succession on more or less the same pitch, is followed by a distinctive rippling trill, descending in frequency from 5–2kHz and composed of several jumbled and rapidly down-slurred notes given in a quick terminal flourish. Each complete song sequence lasts for about two seconds and is repeated after a pause of 6–8 seconds.

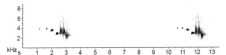

Song of Grey-bellied Tesia, Yonkhola, Bhutan, May. (Peter Kennerley)

The call is sharp '*tsik*', or a double '*tsik-tsik*' followed by a short pause, but repeated continuously for several minutes. It lacks the spluttering delivery of the call of Slaty-bellied Tesia and is harsher.

MOULT No details available. Probably similar to that of Slaty-bellied Tesia.

HABITAT Occurs in dense undergrowth in cool, shady broadleaf forest, often near small streams and rivulets in wet ravines with a tangled undergrowth of ferns Dryopteridaceae, nettles Urticaceae and dwarf bamboo Bambusoideae. In winter it frequents similar habitats at lower elevations in Sal *Shorea robusta*, evergreen and secondary forest, provided there is ample shade, and dank ravines along stream courses. Although it occurs in exactly the same habitats as Slaty-bellied Tesia, with which it overlaps throughout much of its breeding range, Spierenburg (2005) considered there to be a gradual transition between the two species, with Grey-bellied being more numerous above 1,700m. Where it is common during the breeding season, every nullah, stream and rivulet holds a singing bird, while others occur in bamboo undergrowth along ridge tops or beside roads.

BEHAVIOUR Typically solitary and elusive but, like other tesias, not shy and will approach a stationary observer closely, hopping back and forth and darting rapidly between branches, nervously flicking its wings above its back and calling when alarmed, but rarely remaining still. Invariably found on or close to the forest floor amongst dense undergrowth, usually keeping to the darkest niches along deep ravines with small streams. Birds often disappear into crevices between rocks or into hollow tree trunks and reappear elsewhere. Very occasionally a bird will ascend up to 6m in a tree. It rarely flies, instead preferring to hop between branches or onto moss-covered rocks, often pausing to sing, but it can be difficult to follow in gloomy undergrowth. Singing birds can continue for an hour or more, repeating the same sequence or a slight variation of it. Singing commences in March and reaches a peak in the second half of April, but can continue until at least August. Believed to be entirely insectivorous.

BREEDING HABITS The breeding season extends from April to June, continuing into July at higher elevations. The nest is a neat, well-camouflaged ball with a side opening, constructed from moss and lined with moss roots and is extremely hard to find. It is usually situated in a tangle of creepers or amongst the tiny lower branches of a thick, low bush. Some nests are built in dense moss against a tree or stump, on a steep bank or against a rock or heap of boulders. The usual clutch size is 3–4 eggs, occasionally five. The incubation and fledging periods are unknown.

DISTRIBUTION Breeds in the Himalayas and mountains of SW China, Burma and Indochina where it is resident between 1,500m and 2,500m, although some descend to lower elevations in the cooler months.

Breeding The western limit lies in W Nepal, although it occurs in neighbouring regions of Uttaranchal, NW India, to the west and may breed there. From Nepal, it breeds east through Sikkim and Bhutan to Arunachal Pradesh and also in the S Assam hills, including Meghalaya to the Lushai Hills, Nagaland, Manipur and the Chittagong Hill Tracts in Bangladesh. Within China, it breeds in the Xizang Autonomous Region (Tibet) in regions adjacent to the Indian border, then south and east through S Yunnan Province, with an isolated population on the Yao Shan range in Guangxi Province (Cheng 1987). Elsewhere in SE Asia, it breeds widely throughout the major hill ranges of Burma, including the Chin Hills, where it occurs between 1,800m and 2,100m on Mount Victoria and south through the southern Arakan Mountains down to *c.* 750m. It is widespread in N Burma where it has been recorded at *c.* 2,000m in April and in the South Shan States. It is extremely rare in N Thailand where it has only been recorded from Doi Phu Kha, Doi Inthanon and Doi Chiang Dao, although these are probably altitudinal migrants from neighbouring regions of Burma or Laos. To the east the breeding range extends through adjacent regions of NW Laos and into W Tonkin in N Vietnam, where it breeds in the Sa Pa - Hoang Lien National Park, which includes Fan Si Pan where it is believed to be resident, having been recorded here at 1,700m in November and December. In S Vietnam, an isolated population exists on the Da Lat Plateau and Lang Bian Mountains in Lam Dong Province between 1,500m and 2,100m in S Annam. Another isolated population was

discovered in March 2000 when birds were collected in the Cardamom Mountains in SW Cambodia, at 1,250m on Mount Tumpor and at 1,400m on Mount Khmaoch (Eames *et al.* 2002). These two isolated mountain populations lie at the southern limit of its range in SE Asia.

Non-breeding Reported to be resident in some parts of its range but birds breeding at higher elevations descend to the lowlands in winter. Ali & Ripley (1973) noted that it winters in the foothills of the Himalayas and sparingly enters the plains of the Brahmaputra. Spierenburg (2005) considered it to be an altitudinal migrant in Bhutan, breeding between 1,400m and 2,600m and descending to winter between 200m and 1,800m. In Burma, it occurs in Upper Chindwin and North-east Burma in the winter but it has not been observed in the foothills in S Burma (Smythies 1968).

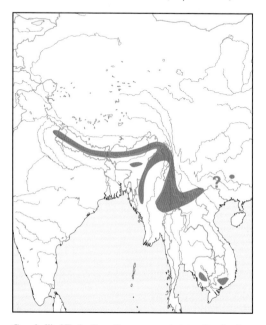

Grey-bellied Tesia. Breeding range and winter distribution. Birds breeding at lower elevations are resident throughout the year.

MOVEMENTS There are no documented reports of movements from breeding to wintering areas. In Bhutan, Spierenburg (2005) considered it a frequently recorded altitudinal migrant throughout the temperate zone and in the central and eastern valleys. The timing of the descent to wintering areas is uncertain. Birds are still present on the breeding grounds until September, but are in the lowest part of the winter range from November to January. They return to breeding territories by late March and are readily located when singing.

DESCRIPTION

Plumage – Adult fresh Forehead, crown and nape dark moss-green, each feather with a very narrow dark fringe giving slightly scaly appearance. Contrasting supercilium brighter lime-green, broadest in front of eye, and meeting across the bill base and reaching the rear of ear coverts. Dark, contrasting eye-stripe formed by dark grey lores and broad blackish eye-line behind eye extends to the rear of the ear-coverts and contrasts with the brighter supercilium and paler ear-coverts. Ear-coverts dark ash-grey with white shafts.

Indistinct whitish eye-ring visible on lower edge of eye only. Eye-ring on upper edge of eye bright lime-green, merging with supercilium. Mantle, scapulars, rump and uppertail-coverts dark moss-green as head, but without darker fringes, so lacks scaly appearance. Tail dark moss-green.

Chin and throat pale grey. Breast, side of neck and side of breast mid grey, belly pale grey, flanks dark grey. Undertail-coverts mid grey. Lesser, median and greater coverts dark moss green. Tertials dark brown with narrow, poorly contrasting moss green fringe. Primary coverts dark moss green, slightly darker than edges to primaries and secondaries. Primaries, secondaries and alula dark brown edged dark moss green. Underwing-coverts green, slightly paler than mantle.

Adult worn As fresh adult.

Juvenile Not known to differ from fresh adult.

Bare parts Upper mandible dark brown to blackish with whitish tip. Lower mandible orange-yellow, slightly darker at sides towards tip. Tarsi and toes dark brown; claws slightly paler.

IN HAND CHARACTERS
Measurements

	Male	Female
Wing	48–53 (50.6; 32)	45–51 (48.1; 19)
Tail	16–19 (17.5; 13)	15–17 (15.9; 7)
Bill	13.5–15.5 (14.7; 32)	13.5–15 (14.2; 19)
Tarsus	23–25 (23.7; 27)	21.5–24 (22.9; 18)

Sexes combined:
Tail/wing ratio: 31–37% (34%; 20)
Bill width: 3.7–4.4 (4.2; 20)
Hind claw: 6.0–7.7 (6.7; 21)

Tail graduation: *c.* 2

Structure

Wing formula (n = 10):

p1/pc	p2	p3e	p4e	p5e	p6e	p7	p10
10–16	9–11	2.5–4	0–0.5	wp	wp	0.5–2	5–7

Wing short and strongly rounded with large p1 (*c.* 50% p2). Wing point p5–6; p2 < ss tips; emargination on p3–6.

Figure 115. Wing of Grey-bellied Tesia.

Tail extremely short, almost square; feathers very narrow.

Bill broad-based, rather flat, straight-sided with fine pointed tip.

Tarsi and toes long and slender.

Recognition A tiny 'tail-less' warbler with green upperparts and grey underparts. Readily separated from the similar Slaty-bellied Tesia by its bright green supercilium and contrasting broad blackish eye-stripe.

Weight 8.4–12g (9.7; 5) (Ali & Ripley 1973)

GEOGRAPHIC VARIATION None recorded.

TAXONOMY AND SYSTEMATICS No issues arising.

▲ Adult, Corbett NP, Uttarakhand, India, February. Note the dark eye-stripe and contrasting brighter green supercilium (Ramki Sreenivasan).

SLATY-BELLIED TESIA
Tesia olivea   **Plate 36**

Saxicola? olivea McClelland, 1840. *Proc. Zool. Soc. London*
(1839), p. 161. Assam.

A diminutive warbler occupying the lowest altitudinal zone
among the Himalayan *Tesia* species. It occurs in thick
undergrowth and low vegetation along small streams
and shady gullies from the Himalayas to Burma and N
Indochina. Some are resident while others winter in
adjacent foothills and lowlands. Polytypic, with two races
recognised:

T. o. olivea (McClelland, 1840). Himalayas to N Burma.

T. o. chiangmaiensis Renner *et al.* 2008. NW Thailand, N
   Laos and N Vietnam.

IDENTIFICATION Length 7.5–8cm. Wing 42–52mm. Tail/
wing 30–40%.

A minute 'tail-less' warbler with a spritely, energetic
character, always active but keeping close to the forest floor
where its dull green upperparts and grey underparts provide
ideal camouflage. Its drab appearance is offset only by the
bright, slightly iridescent golden-yellow wash on the crown
and nape. Sexes alike.

Structure A diminutive warbler with an extremely short
tail that does not extend to the tips of the primaries and is
always hidden by the wings. Overall structure very similar
to that of Slaty-bellied Tesia.

Plumage and bare parts Adults show a conspicuous bright
golden-yellow cap that has a slight iridescence when caught
in sunlight, but this is rarely noticeable in the shady forest
that it frequents. This cap extends from the bill base to
the lower nape and down to the upper edge of the eye
and upper ear-coverts. A narrow, poorly defined dark grey
eye-stripe extends from the bill base to the rear of the
ear-coverts, but is much less conspicuous than that of Grey-
bellied Tesia. The upperparts from mantle to tail, including
the uppertail-coverts, wing-coverts and closed wing, are
uniform dull moss-green. The entire underparts, including
the ear-coverts and cheeks, are uniform dark slate-grey with
a slight bluish cast.

Young birds resemble adults but the moss-green crown
and nape lacks the golden-yellow feather tips.

The bill is dark brown to blackish with a bright orange-
red lower mandible that darkens slightly towards the tip.
The legs and feet are dark brown.

SIMILAR SPECIES Only likely to be mistaken for Grey-
bellied Tesia. Differences are discussed under that
species.

VOICE The song is slightly higher pitched than in Grey-
bellied Tesia, more scratchy and less tuneful and powerful.
Each song sequence is introduced by 6–9 slightly discordant
and hesitant whistled '*tsip*' notes that vary and undulate in
pitch from 4–7kHz over a period of *c.* 2 seconds. These lead
into a short, rapid terminal flourish of several loud, jumbled
and rapidly down-slurred notes '*tsito-tjutjutju-tjowi*', starting
at *c.* 7kHz and descending to *c.* 3kHz within two seconds.
The complete sequence '*tsip tsip tsip tsip tsip tsip tsip tsito-
tjutjutju-tjowi*' lasts approximately four seconds, with a short
pause of *c.* 2 seconds before being repeated.

The song of *chiangmaiensis* is similar to that of the
nominate race, with only minor differences in the number
of introductory notes and the frequency range within the
terminal flourish.

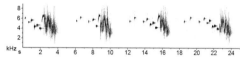

Song of Slaty-bellied Tesia recorded within breeding range
of *T. o. olivea*, Yonkhola, Bhutan, May. (Peter Kennerley)

The most frequently heard call is a spluttering '*trrrrt,
trrrrt, trrrrt*' with a soft, liquid quality. It is usually given three
or four times in quick succession followed by only a brief
pause, but it may continue for several minutes when the
bird is agitated.

MOULT No details available.

HABITAT In the Himalayas and mountains of SW China
and N Burma it breeds in moist, temperate oak *Quercus* and
rhododendron forests with a dense understorey, where it
frequents small streams and dark ravines with moss-covered
stones and boulders, fallen tree trunks and tangles of fallen
branches. Here it appears to occupy exactly the same niche
as Grey-bellied Tesia. However, these species are separated
by altitude, with Slaty-bellied occurring most frequently
from 1,400m to 2,000m and occasionally to 2,400m. It
overlaps with Grey-bellied Tesia above 1,700m and appears
to occur in exactly the same habitats, the two sometimes
being found almost side by side. Outside the breeding
season, Himalayan birds of the two species occupy similar
habitats at elevations from 800m to 1,800m and occasionally
down to 200m.

In N Thailand and N Indochina, it occupies a similar
niche in moist evergreen forest on the mid to upper slopes
of the higher mountains, in N Thailand occurring from
c. 1,200m to the summit of Doi Inthanon at 2,590m. In C
Laos, it is reportedly common in dry evergreen forest above
1,000m and also in *Fokienia* dominated forest from 1,400 to
1,800m. Although it occurs above 1,800m its abundance is
uncertain (Evans & Timmins 1998).

BEHAVIOUR Not known to differ from Grey-bellied
Tesia.

BREEDING HABITS Not known to differ from Grey-
bellied Tesia.

DISTRIBUTION Breeds in the Himalayas and mountains
of SW China, Burma and N Indochina where it is resident
between 1,200m and 2,500m, although some descend to
lower elevations in the cooler months.

T. o. olivea Breeds in the foothills of the Himalayas between
1,400m and 2,000m from E Nepal east through
Sikkim and Bhutan to NE India, where found from SE
Arunachal Pradesh and the S Assam hills to Nagaland
and E Meghalaya. It also breeds in the Chittagong Hill
Tracts in NE Bangladesh, although Rasmussen and
Anderton (2005) note that there are no specimens from
the country. It breeds in adjacent mountainous regions
of Yunnan Province in SW China and north to *c.* 29°N
in the Ebian region of S Sichuan Province and east in
Guizhou Province to *c.* 108°E at Leishan (Cheng 1987).
Its distribution in neighbouring Burma is uncertain
due to past confusion with Grey-bellied Tesia, but it
appears that both species occur together throughout the
mountains in the north and east, but that Slaty-bellied is
absent from the Chin Hills and the lowlands (e.g. Pegu
Yomas National Park), and from Tenasserim in the south
(Smythies 1986). Outside the breeding season, northern
breeders descend to avoid cold weather and are usually

found below 1,000m, occasionally down to 200m.

It breeds at high densities in suitable habitats. In Bhutan, Spierenburg (2005) noted 10–30 singing males annually along *c.* 10km of road in the Mo Chhu valley between Rimchu and Tashithang.

T. o. chiangmaiensis Breeds widely in the higher mountains of NW Thailand from *c.* 1,200m to the summit of Doi Inthanon at 2,590m. Occurs at similar altitudes in neighbouring N Laos, south to the Nakay-Nam Thuen National Biodiversity Conservation Area in the provinces of Khammouane and Bolikhamsai in C Laos, where discovered only in 1994 (Evans & Timmins 1998). In N Vietnam, breeds in W and E Tonkin including the Sa Pa–Hoang Lien National Park and N Annam. Birds of this race are believed to be resident on breeding territories throughout the year.

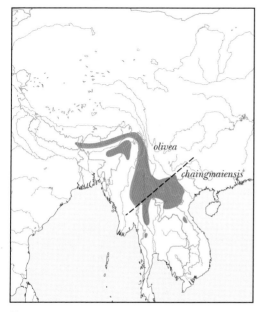

Slaty-bellied Tesia. Breeding range and winter distribution. Birds breeding at lower elevations are resident throughout the year.

MOVEMENTS Poorly documented. In Bhutan, Spierenburg (2005) noted singing birds still present at breeding sites to late September, but at lower elevations by November. The first singing birds return to breeding sites in the second half of March.

DESCRIPTION *T. o. olivea*
Plumage – Adult fresh Forehead, crown and nape bright-moss green, with brighter iridescent golden-yellow feather tips. No supercilium. No eye-ring. A narrow and diffuse blackish grey loral line runs from the bill base to the upper edge of the eye and a similar eye-line extends to the side of nape. Ear-coverts uniform dark slate-grey with a slight bluish cast.

Mantle, scapulars, rump, uppertail-coverts and tail uniform, drab moss-green. Underparts including chin, throat, breast, sides of neck and breast, flanks, belly and undertail-coverts dark slate-grey with a slight bluish cast, merging with ear-coverts, lower breast similar but usually with paler grey fringes.

Lesser, median and greater coverts uniform, drab

moss green. Tertials and primary coverts dull brown with drab, moss-green fringes. Primaries, secondaries and alula dull brown with drab moss-green fringes to outer webs. Underwing-coverts dark grey.
Adult worn Not known to differ from fresh adult.
Juvenile Resembles adult but lacks iridescent golden-yellow tips to crown and nape feathering.
Bare parts Upper mandible dark brown. Lower mandible bright orange-red, usually with darker sides towards tip. Tarsi, toes and claws horn-brown to dark brown. Iris dark brown.

IN HAND CHARACTERS
Measurements

T. o. olivea

	Male	Female
Wing	46–52 (48.0; 13)	42–49 (46.2; 17)
Tail	16–19 (17.2; 9)	13–19 (15.5; 13)
Bill	13–14.5 (13.9; 11)	12–15 (13.9; 16)
Tarsus	21.5–24 (22.4; 12)	19.5–23 (21.8; 16)

Sexes combined:
Tail/wing ratio: 30–40% (34%; 22)
Bill width: 3.7–4.5 (4.1; 12)
Hind claw: 6.0–6.8 (6.4; 14)
Tail graduation: *c.* 2

Also, from Renner *et al.* (2008), wing in natural position:
T. o. olivea: *wing* 39–50 (45.2; 21); *tarsus* 20.7–24.2 (23.4; 26).
T. o. chiangmaiensis: *wing* 39–47 (43.3; 28); *tarsus* 20.6–23.2 (22.2; 26).

Structure

Wing formula (n = 10):

p1/pc	p2	p3e	p4e	p5e	p6e	p7	p10
11–15	9–12	2.5–4.5	0–1.5	wp	wp	0–2	3.5–5.5

Wing similar to Grey-bellied Tesia (Fig. 115); short and strongly rounded with large p1. Wing point at p5–6; p2 < ss tips; emargination on p3–6.

Tail extremely short, almost square, with eight rectrices.

Bill broad-based, rather flat, straight-sided; tip rather blunter than in Grey-bellied Tesia.

Tarsi and toes long and very slender.
Identification A 'tail-less' warbler with dull green upperparts and dark grey underparts. Separated from similar Grey-bellied Tesia by unmarked sides of head, lacking green supercilium and broad, dark grey eye-stripe.
Weight Range 8–9g (8.7; 3) (Ali & Ripley 1973); 6.0–8.5g (7.7; 5) (Renner *et al.* 2008).

GEOGRAPHIC VARIATION Slight, limited to differences in size and colour.
T. o. olivea Described above.
T. o. chiangmaiensis Differs from nominate race in having slightly shorter wings and tarsus. Adults also lack the iridescent golden-yellow crown and nape, and the upperparts are slightly greyer, less noticeably olive-green. Renner *et al.* (2008) noted two specimens from India lacking an iridescent crown and nape but these were considered to be immature nominate *olivea*.

TAXONOMY AND SYSTEMATICS Slaty-bellied and Grey-bellied Tesias were not recognised as different species until the late 1930s. Their different appearance was earlier ascribed to age or sex differences, to different colour morphs or to races within one species. Many early accounts of distribution or behaviour are therefore difficult to assign to one species or the other, especially as few of these give information on breeding season elevation.

Ludlow & Kinnear (1937) studied specimens collected in Bhutan during the breeding season, for which the sex and altitude of collection was carefully recorded, and were the first to suggest that two species were involved. Of 26 specimens, 20 were described as being pale (= Grey-bellied Tesia). All of these were obtained in temperate forest between 6,000 and 8,000 feet (c. 1,800–2,400m) where no birds of the dark form (= Slaty-bellied Tesia) were collected. Six dark birds were all obtained in tropical forest at or below 3,000 feet (c. 900m). This indicated the existence of a high-altitude pale form and a low-altitude dark form separated during the breeding season within

the same forests and therefore behaving as two good species.

▲ Adult *T. o. olivea*, Sikkim, India, June. Shows uniform side to head and golden-yellow cap with slight iridescence (Rajneesh Suvarna).

JAVAN TESIA
Tesia superciliaris   **Plate 36**

Microura superciliaris **Bonaparte, 1850**. *Consp. Gen. Avium* 1: 258. Java.

A tiny warbler of dense undergrowth and the forest floor endemic to the mountains of W Java in Indonesia, where it is resident. Monotypic.

IDENTIFICATION Length 8.5–9cm. Wing 47–51mm. Tail/wing < 30%.
    A minute, 'tail-less' and drably coloured warbler with dull olive-green upperparts, grey underparts and supercilium and a broad, dark charcoal-grey eye-stripe. Sexes alike.
Structure Characterised by its extremely small size and a short tail that does not extend to the tips of the primaries and is always hidden by the wings. Otherwise, the overall structure, including the short and rounded wing shape, is very similar to that of Slaty-bellied and Grey-bellied Tesias, with a long first primary (p1) and the wing point formed by p5–6. It has thicker legs and exceptionally large feet when compared with other tesias, which may be an adaptation to clinging onto moss-covered tree trunks when feeding.
Plumage and bare parts A drably plumaged warbler, dull olive-green above, including the wing-coverts and edges to the flight feathers, and grey below, with a grey head. A dark charcoal-grey crown tapers to a point above the bill base and separates the broad ash-grey supercilia that extend onto the sides of the forehead but do not quite meet. Each supercilium is particularly conspicuous and broad, reaching back to the side of the nape. It is bordered below by a broad, charcoal-grey eye-stripe that widens behind the eye and flares down onto the upper ear-coverts. The ash-grey ear-coverts and cheeks merge with the similarly coloured sides to the neck and upper breast. The underparts are greyish white on the chin, darkening towards ash-grey on the breast, while the dull olive-green lower flanks and undertail-coverts closely match the upperparts.
    The bill is dark grey to blackish with a yellow lower mandible that often shows slight darkening at the sides towards the tip. The legs and feet vary from warm brown to reddish brown.

SIMILAR SPECIES No similar species occur on Java.

VOICE The song is a pleasantly melodic and sweetly variable trill, initially fluctuating in frequency while dropping from *c.* 5kHz to *c.* 3kHz, then rising quickly into a melodic terminal flourish at *c.* 7kHz. It lacks the sequence of individually separated introductory notes typically given by Himalayan tesias, although there is often a single quiet '*hueet*' or '*weeecht*' at the start of the song. This immediately leads into the melodic, descending warbling '*tseeuuweechhee*' sequence, to be followed by a rapidly rising '*cheeuueeeet*' sequence. The complete '*weeecht-tseeuuweechhee-cheeuueeeeet*' lasts for approximately 2.5 seconds and is followed by a pause of *c.* 15–20 seconds before being repeated.

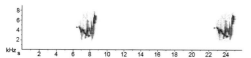

Song of Javan Tesia, Gunung Gede, Java, Indonesia, October. (Peter Kennerley)

    Two distinctly different calls are known; a spluttering

'*trrrrt, trrrrt, trrrrt*' with a soft, rattling quality, usually given three or four times in quick succession but almost continuously when the bird is alarmed. It also has a harsher '*queut*' with a slight chipping quality, given as a single note and repeated about once per second.

MOULT No details available.

HABITAT Occurs in moist evergreen forest with dense undergrowth and tangles of fallen branches, and a ground storey of ferns, vines, moss-covered rocks and fallen tree-trunks. At lower elevations, tree ferns are common and branches are draped with a luxuriant growth of epiphytes that grow abundantly in the moist conditions. Above 1,000m it is found in montane forest, with *Anemone, Aster, Berberis, Galium, Gaultheria, Lonicera, Primula, Ranunculus, Rhododendron, Veronica* and *Viola* commonly represented. The most abundant montane tree species in the lower montane zone are *Lithocarpus, Quercus, Castanopsis* and laurels (Fagaceae and Lauraceae).
    Aerobryum mosses are a dominant feature above 1,500m and coat all exposed surfaces on tree trunks, branches, vines and also the rocks and boulders on the forest floor and along gullies and streams, where Pitcher plants and Begonias are also common.

BEHAVIOUR Displays the characteristic skulking behaviour typical of all tesia species, keeping close to the ground in shady cover amongst moss-covered rocks and in the lower branches of bushes, vines and creepers, but often not actually on the ground. It rarely flies and when it does so, this is usually over very short distances. It often clings to the side of a moss-covered tree trunk, where its thicker tarsus and larger feet compared with other tesia species may be an adaptation to this behaviour. When nervous or disturbed, it displays a distinctive habit of hopping or 'bouncing' rapidly back and forth along a low branch continuously flicking its wings while doing so. It sometimes ascends into vines and creepers 6–8m above the forest floor, something which other tesias rarely do.

BREEDING HABITS Unknown.

DISTRIBUTION Restricted to the mountains of W Java, where it is resident in the montane rain forest from

Javan Tesia. Resident within breeding range.

Gunung Halimun National Park and Gunung Salak east to Gunung Papandayan and Gunung Ciremay. It is generally common and readily located, for example in the Gunung Gede–Pangrango National Park.

MOVEMENTS Believed to be resident. No movements recorded.

DESCRIPTION
Plumage – Adult fresh Forehead, crown and nape dark charcoal-black. Supercilium ash-grey, broad, reaching from base of upper mandible to side of nape. Lores and eye-line dark charcoal-black, forming a broad eye-stripe reaching the side of the nape. Ear-coverts ash-grey with whitish shaft streaks. No eye-ring. Mantle, scapulars, rump, uppertail-coverts and tail dark olive-green with a slight brownish cast. Chin pale grey. Throat slightly darker ash-grey. Sides of neck and breast ash-grey with a slight brownish wash and whitish shafts. Upper flanks dull olive-brown with a slight greenish tinge, becoming dark olive-green with slight brownish cast on the lower flanks, as upperparts. Belly pale grey. Undertail-coverts dark olive-green with a slight brownish cast. Lesser, median and greater coverts dark olive-green with a slight brownish cast. Tertials and primary coverts dark brown with dark olive-green fringes. Primaries, secondaries and alula dark brown, edged dark olive-green. Underwing-coverts mid grey.
Adult worn As fresh adult.
Juvenile Not known to differ from fresh adult.
Bare Parts Upper mandible dark grey to blackish, usually with a small pale yellow to whitish tip. Lower mandible yellow with a greyish smudge on sides towards tip. Tarsi, toes and claws pale warm brown to reddish brown. Iris dark brown.

IN HAND CHARACTERS
Measurements

Sexes combined:

Wing	47–51 (48.6; 5)
Tail	< 15
Bill	14–15 (14.5; 5)
Tarsus	22.5–25.5 (24.3; 5)

Tail/wing ratio: < 30%
Bill width: 4.3–4.6 (4.5; 5)
Hind claw: 6.2–6.7 (6.4; 5)

Structure

Wing formula (n = 4):

p1/pc	p2	p3e	p4e	p5e	p6e	p7	p10
12–14	8–10.5	3–4	0–1	wp	wp	0–1	4–5

Wing similar to Grey-bellied Tesia (Fig. 115); short and strongly rounded with large p1 (*c.* 60% p2). Wing point at p5–6; p2 < ss tips; slight emargination on p3–6.
Tail extremely short; feathers very narrow.
Bill broad-based, rather flat, straight-sided; broader and stronger than in Grey-bellied Tesia.
Tarsi and toes long, longer and stronger than in Grey-bellied Tesia.
Weight No data available.

GEOGRAPHIC VARIATION None recorded.

TAXONOMY AND SYSTEMATICS No issues arising.

▲ Adult, Gunung Gede, Java, July (James Eaton/Birdtour Asia).

▲ Adult, Gunung Gede, Java, July (James Eaton/Birdtour Asia).

RUSSET-CAPPED TESIA
Tesia everetti   **Plate 36**

Orthnocichla everetti **Hartert, 1879**. *Novit. Zool.* 4: 170. Flores.

A tiny warbler endemic to Flores and Sumbawa in the Lesser Sundas, Indonesia, where it is a common resident. Polytypic, with two races recognised:

T. e. everetti (Hartert, 1879). Flores and (possibly this race) Adonara.

T. e. sumbawana (Rensch, 1928). Batoe Doelang (= Batudulang), Sumbawa, altitude 800–1,000 meters.

IDENTIFICATION Length 8.5–9cm. Wing 50–54mm. Tail/wing 32–37%.

A minute, 'tail-less' and drably coloured warbler, but with a rich russet-brown cap and slightly paler reddish brown sides to the head. It shows a narrow and poorly defined supercilium and a marginally darker brown eye-stripe. Otherwise the dull brown upperparts and greyish underparts are particularly featureless. Sexes alike.

Structure Characterised by extremely small size and a short tail that does not reach the tips of the primaries and remains hidden by the wings. Overall structure, including the short, rounded wing shape, with long first primary (p1), is very similar to that of other tesias. It shows a slightly longer p7, which also forms the wing point together with p5–6. It also has a proportionately slightly longer and finer bill, giving the head a more attenuated character. Like Javan Tesia, it has relatively thick legs and large feet.

Plumage and bare parts Although drably plumaged, it shows a distinctive rich, warm russet-brown crown and upper nape and slightly paler reddish brown sides to the head. The head itself is poorly marked, many birds showing no trace of a contrasting supercilium, eye-stripe or eye-ring. Others do show slight contrast, with a narrow, poorly defined supercilium behind the eye and a marginally darker shadow below this along the upper edge of the ear-coverts.

The upperparts including the wings are drab, unmarked olive-brown, although the edges to the primaries and secondaries are slightly paler olive-green and contrast with the darker body. The chin and upper throat are pale greyish white, the rest of the underparts drab grey, appearing ash-grey on the breast and slightly paler in the belly. They darken to slate-grey with a brownish cast on the flanks, although still paler than the upperparts.

The bill is blackish with a pale yellowish orange lower mandible, the legs and feet pale reddish brown to light straw.

SIMILAR SPECIES No similar species occur on Flores or Sumbawa.

VOICE The call is a single, harsh '*tscheeet*', given rapidly and continuously but erratically, sometimes two or three calls per second, then none for a second or two. Typically, however, several calls are delivered in quick succession.

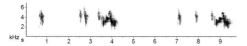

Song of Russet-capped Tesia recorded within breeding range of *T. e. everetti*, Flores. (K. D. Bishop)

There is often a brief song sequence within the calling sessions. This is a melodic, short, whistled three-syllable

sequence '*chwee-cheeeeweee-cheeeweereee*', that rises and falls between 2–7kHz, each sequence lasting for just over one second.

MOULT No details available.

HABITAT Occurs widely on Flores and Sumbawa where it frequents the remaining primary rain forest, as well as mature secondary growth, *Casuarina* woodland, degraded woodland with a shady understorey, scrub and cultivated areas. It is generally widespread and generally common, although less numerous in semi-deciduous and riverine forests (Coates *et al.* 1997).

BEHAVIOUR A very active warbler and its small size and darting actions make it difficult to follow in the l forest understorey. It usually keeps close to the ground amongst the tangle of vines, creepers, branches and ferns and often descends to the ground for forage amongst moss-covered rocks and boulders. It often feeds on the sides of moss-covered trees and will clamber up hanging vines into the lower canopy up to *c.* 25m (Coates *et al.* 1997), whereas other tesia species tend to forage lower.

Song is heard throughout the day and usually given from a perch close to the ground. When nervous or disturbed it frequently hops or bounces back and forth along a branch or hanging vine, continuously flicking its wings.

BREEDING HABITS Unknown. The breeding season is said to extend from May to July (Coates *et al.* 1997).

DISTRIBUTION Endemic to the Lesser Sundas in E Indonesia where it has long been known from the islands of Flores and Sumbawa. A third population was discovered in December 2000 on the small island of Adonara, east of Flores, during observations made at six sites during 14–18 December (Trainor 2002). Calling birds were recorded from scrubby gullies in candlenut plantations between 350–450m, and in fragments of moist deciduous forest from 450m to 700m on Ile Boleng. It was also present along the Wai Kenawe River. On Flores and Sumbawa it occupies a wider altitudinal range, from sea level to *c.* 2,200m on Flores, while on Sumbawa its range extends from 200m to 1,730m.

Russet-capped Tesia. Resident within breeding range.

MOVEMENTS Believed to be resident. No movements recorded.

DESCRIPTION *T. e. everetti*

Plumage – Adult fresh Forehead, crown and nape rich, warm russet-brown. Supercilium pale reddish brown, poorly defined from crown, sometimes absent. Lores warm russet-brown, slightly paler than crown. Eye-line poorly defined or absent. Ear-coverts pale russet-brown to rich buffy brown, some with faint paler shaft streaks. No eye-ring. Mantle, scapulars, rump, uppertail-coverts and tail dull olive-brown. Chin and upper throat dull white with slight greyish tinge, becoming greyer towards breast. Sides of neck ash-grey. Breast ash-grey with paler shaft streaks. Sides of breast and flanks mid slate-grey with slight brownish cast. Belly and undertail-coverts pale greyish white. Lesser, median and greater coverts, tertials and alula dull, uniform olive-brown as mantle. Primary coverts dark brown with dull olive-green fringes. Primaries and secondaries dull olive-brown with paler olive-green outer webs. Underwing-coverts dull grey.

Adult worn As fresh adult.

Juvenile Undescribed.

Bare Parts Upper mandible blackish. Lower mandible pale yellowish orange, unmarked. Tarsi, toes and claws dull straw.

IN HAND CHARACTERS

Measurements

Sexes combined:

Wing	50–54 (51.4; 5)
Tail	16–20 (18.5; 4)
Bill	15–17 (15.8; 5)
Tarsus	22.5–26 (24.5; 5)

Tail/wing ratio: 32–37% (36%; 4)
Bill width: 4.3–5.1 (4.6; 4)
Hind claw: 6.0–7.4 (6.7; 5)
Tail graduation: *c.* 2

Structure

Wing formula (n = 5):

p1/pc	p2	p3e	p4e	p5e	p6e	p7	p10
11–14	10–13	3–5	0–1	wp	wp	wp	3–5

Wing similar to Grey-bellied Tesia (Fig. 115); short and strongly rounded with large p1. Wing point at p5–7; p2 < ss tips; slight emargination on p3–6.

Tail extremely short, almost square; longer than in Javan Tesia.

Bill broad-based, rather flat, straight-sided; larger than in Javan Tesia.

Tarsi and toes long, as in Javan Tesia.

Weight No data available.

GEOGRAPHIC VARIATION

T. e. everetti (Flores, and possibly Adonara) Described above.

T. e. sumbawana (Sumbawa) Closely resembles the nominate race, but shows brownish grey rather than reddish sides to the head and a duller russet tone to the crown.

TAXONOMY AND SYSTEMATICS The taxonomic position of Russet-capped Tesia was uncertain for many years. Delacour (1942) included it in *Tesia* based on its very short tail and the slight downward curve to the long bill, which is broad and flattened at the base and has a ridged maxilla. Others including White & Bruce (1986) placed it in *Urosphena*, citing differences in morphology and habitat preference between it and the other tesia species. King (1989) convincingly demonstrated that vocal similarities and structural characters firmly place it within *Tesia*. Trainor (2002) considered that the Adonara population would probably be of the nominate race although no birds have been trapped or specimens collected to confirm this.

▲ Adult *T. e. everetti*, Flores, Indonesia, September. Tesias usually remain on or close to the forest floor and rarely appear in the open; the behaviour of this individual appears atypical but it is uncertain whether Russet-capped Tesia regularly behaves in this manner (Chris Gooddie).

Genus *Urosphena* Swinhoe, 1877

[Gr. *oura* tail; *sphen, sphenos* wedge]

Three very small species with extremely short tails comprising ten rectrices, a character shared with *Cettia* within which these species were formerly included. Their separation in the genus *Urosphena* is based on their exceptionally short tails and distinctive high-pitched songs that are thin, buzzing and insect-like, and often barely audible by the human ear. One species is a long-distance migrant, breeding in the Eastern Palearctic, the other two are resident in the mountains on Borneo and the Lesser Sundas. All frequent the ground and the lower storey in forest undergrowth. They are characterised by large, rounded heads, plump bodies, relatively long, fine bills, and strong legs. All show a striking head pattern with long and prominent pale supercilia and bold, contrasting, blackish eye-stripes. Their cup-shaped nests are built close to the ground.

TIMOR STUBTAIL
Urosphena subulata   Plate 37

Orthnocichla subulata Sharpe, 1884. *Notes Leyden Mus.*, 6: 179–180. Timor.

A little-known forest floor resident, endemic to just two or possibly three islands in the E Lesser Sundas. Polytypic, with two races recognised:
U. s. subulata (Sharpe, 1884). Timor and probably also this race on Wetar.
U. s. advena (Hartert, 1906). Babar.

IDENTIFICATION Length 8–9cm. Wing 53–58mm. Tail/wing *c.* 50%.
    A shy inhabitant of the forest floor where it typically appears as a small, 'tailless', dark brown or blackish bird. Its unobtrusive, mouse-like behaviour and barely audible song make this one of the most elusive of all warblers. Sexes alike.
Structure Appears tailless but the extremely short tail is hidden below the closed primary tips and rarely extends beyond. The resulting stunted appearance is augmented by the proportionately large, broad head with a low and flat, or slightly rounded, forehead and crown that barely rise above the bill base. A long and fine bill further exaggerates the apparent head size.
Plumage and bare parts Extended views may be needed to see plumage detail and its subdued tones can be difficult to appreciate on a poorly lit forest floor. A long, bold greyish or buffish supercilium extends from the bill base to the side of the nape. This is bordered above by a dull olive-brown crown, while the olive-brown eye-stripe adds to the contrasting appearance of the head. Below this, the pale ear-coverts and cheeks show slight brown mottling. The upperparts are uniform dull olive-brown in adults, but warmer and slightly brighter brown in young birds, and the closed wing and tail can sometimes appear slightly warmer and browner than the upperparts. The underparts are always difficult to see well but whitish flanks are usually visible. The whitish underparts may be visible when a bird stretches upwards, showing a dull greyish wash across the breast and faint diffuse striations along the flanks. Only the ventral region and undertail-coverts appear darker, being dull straw, but they usually appear much darker in dull light conditions.
    The bill is rather grey with a pinkish white lower mandible. The legs and feet are pale pinkish.

SIMILAR SPECIES No similar species occur within its range although the very different Sunda Bush Warbler is widespread on Timor. Other skulking, terrestrial and short-tailed species including Pygmy Wren-babbler and Lesser Shortwing are also resident on Timor but they are unlikely to be mistaken for Timor Stubtail.
Sunda Bush Warbler is the only resident warbler within the range of Timor Stubtail, where it occurs on Timor from sea level to at least 2,300m. It can be skulking and elusive like all *Cettia* species, but it generally occurs in more open situations than the stubtail, favouring scrub and bushes along the edges of roads and forest rides. It is an arboreal warbler and rarely forages on the ground. It has a short, fine bill and the tail extends conspicuously beyond the wing-tip. The supercilium is shorter, narrower and less conspicuous than Timor Stubtail and the upperparts are pale but drab greyish brown. Its melodic repeated '*suuueeeuuu*' song is quite unlike the very high-pitched whistle of Timor Stubtail.
Pygmy Wren-babbler is a most unlikely confusion species and is one of only two babblers found east of Wallace's Line. This minute and furtive tail-less bird of the forest floor occurs between 1,800m and 2,000m on Mount Mutis and so has a restricted region of overlap with Timor Stubtail. It appears dull and plain, with little contrast between the upperparts and underparts, and it also lacks a prominent supercilium. Juveniles show dark grey upperparts and a slightly streaked breast-band across white underparts.
Lesser Shortwing is another drab terrestrial species that overlaps widely with Timor Stubtail on Timor from 700m to 2,100m. Although it has a short tail and uniform brown upperparts, it lacks the prominent supercilium of the stubtail, and its characteristically rich song readily distinguishes it.

VOICE At 8–10kHz, the song approaches the upper frequency limit detectable by the human ear and will be inaudible to many. Each sequence is a thin, high-pitched monotone whistle lasting 0.8 to 1.1 seconds and repeated at intervals of *c.* 7 seconds. The song is thin and weak, often barely audible and thus easily missed, and its high frequency makes locating a singing bird particularly difficult as the song appears to surround the observer rather than emanating from a particular source. There are no introductory notes.

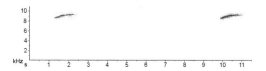

Song of Timor Stubtail, recorded within breeding range of *U. s. subulata*, West Timor, Indonesia. (K. D. Bishop)

Trainor *et al.* (2009) noted that the high-frequency whistle of this species varies between islands, and examination of these calls may help to clarify its taxonomy. No obvious additional calls are apparent on recordings of singing birds. It is possible that Timor Stubtail does not have a call or, alternatively, that the call is quiet, very brief or given at a frequency beyond the human audible range.

MOULT No data available.

HABITAT On Timor and Wetar, it frequents patches of primary forest as well as areas of mature secondary forest with an open understorey of fallen leaves in which to forage. If still present on Babar, it presumably occurs in similar situations, which Coates *et al.* (1997) term 'monsoon forest'. It is also found in hillside scrub on Timor (Coates *et al.* 1997).

BEHAVIOUR Like all *Urosphena* species, it invariably remains on or close to the ground, where its furtive and secretive behaviour makes it difficult to locate and even more difficult to follow. It typically forages for insects and spiders, moving in short hops and picking among leaf litter. It occasionally perches on tree roots, fallen trunks or low branches to sing, but with the legs tucked closely under the breast. It rarely, if ever, stands upright in the manner of a *Tesia*, even when agitated. It sometimes makes short flights of up to two metres (Coates *et al.* 1997).

BREEDING HABITS There is no published information on the breeding cycle, nest or eggs.

DISTRIBUTION Restricted to three islands in the E Lesser Sundas. The nominate race is resident on Timor where it is locally common from sea level to at least 1,900m (White & Bruce 1986; Coates *et al.* 1997). The race *advena* is known only from two specimens collected in 1905 on the island of Babar. It appears not to have been recorded there since, although suitable habitat still remains. A population was discovered on the island of Wetar in 1990 (Coates *et al.* 1997) and it has since been found on Atauro (Trainor & Soares 2004) and Roti (Trainor 2005).

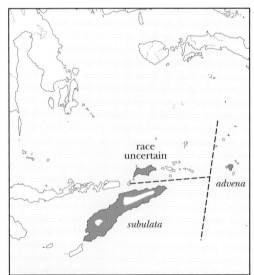

Timor Stubtail. Resident within breeding range.

MOVEMENTS Resident.

DESCRIPTION *U. s. subulata*
Plumage – Adult fresh Forehead and crown dull olive-brown, with darker fringes creating an indistinct scaly effect. Long, narrow, whitish supercilia meet above bill base and extend back to sides of nape, slightly duller and browner behind eye but retaining crisp definition between sides of crown and eye-lines. A well-defined blackish loral line below the supercilium reaches to the base of the bill. A broad, sharply defined, dull olive-brown eye-line extends behind the eye onto the side of nape. Ear-coverts white with distinct, dull brown mottling, becoming less distinct towards lower edge and cheeks. Eye-ring narrow, creamy white; appearing poorly defined against similarly coloured supercilium and ear-coverts. Nape, mantle, scapulars, rump and uppertail-coverts plain, drab, olive-brown. Tail feathers uniform dull rufous-brown. Chin, throat and belly white. Breast white with slight greyish wash, strengthening to a dull greyish brown smudge towards the bend of the wing. Lower sides of neck drab olive-brown interspersed with white, becoming mottled and merging with ear-coverts. Flanks white, washed dull greyish brown and faintly streaked, warming to dull straw on lower flanks and undertail-coverts.

Closed wing unmarked olive-brown, slightly warmer than mantle and scapulars. Lesser and median coverts dull rufescent brown. Greater coverts and tertials dull brown with diffuse and marginally brighter rufescent-brown fringes. Primary coverts and edges to secondaries and primaries dull, unmarked rufescent-brown. Primaries lack contrasting tips. Alula dull olive-brown with slightly paler fringe. Underwing-coverts mid grey to greyish white, similar to flanks.

Juvenile Crown and upperparts slightly warmer and brighter than in adult. Supercilium warm buff, lores and eye-line dark tan, so the head contrast is reduced compared with adult. Ear-coverts cream-buff with distinct warm brown mottling towards upper edges. Underparts warmer than adult with a dull pinkish brown wash on breast, becoming brighter and warmer brown near carpal bend. Flanks dull pinkish brown, colour deepening on lower flanks and undertail-coverts. Closed wing and tail uniform warm brown as mantle, generally warmer and browner than in adult.

Bare parts Upper mandible pale grey to pale brown, slightly paler towards tip. Lower mandible pinkish white, sometimes with indistinct grey shading near tip. Tarsi and toes pale pink to pinkish white. Iris very dark brown.

IN HAND CHARACTERS
Measurements

U. s. subulata (sexes combined, n = 3): *wing* 53–54 (53.3); *tail* 24–27 (26.0); *bill* 15.5–16.0 (15.7); *tarsus* 19.0–20.0 (19.5); bill width 3.1–3.2.
U. s. advena (sexes combined, n = 2): *wing* 57–58.

Structure

Wing formula (n = 3):

p1/pc	p2	p3e	p4e	p5e	p6(e)	p7	p10
12–14	11–13	3.5–4	0.5–1	wp	0–1	1.5–2	5–7

Wing similar to Bornean Stubtail (Fig. 116); short and strongly rounded; p1 rather large. Wing point p5 (6); p2 < ss tips; emargination on p3–5 , often slightly on p6.

Tail extremely short, almost square.

Bill stronger than in Asian Stubtail; longer than in Bornean Stubtail with more extended narrow tip.

Tarsi stronger than in Asian Stubtail or Bornean Stubtail.

Weight No data available.

GEOGRAPHIC VARIATION Two races are recognised. *U. s. advena* was described by Hartert (1906) from two specimens collected on Babar.

U. s. subulata (Timor and probably this race on Wetar) Described above.

U. s. advena (Babar) Differences from nominate race are slight and are possibly not consistent due to the small number of specimens available. Compared with the nominate form, specimens from Babar differ in having a slightly warmer rusty tone to the upperparts, a blackish upper mandible and a slightly longer wing.

TAXONOMY AND SYSTEMATICS It is not known whether the newly discovered populations on Wetar, Atauro and Roti should be assigned to one of the two recognised forms, an approach we have adopted here, or whether they represent one or more undescribed taxa.

▲ Adult, Timor, May (James Eaton/Birdtour Asia).

BORNEAN STUBTAIL
Urosphena whiteheadi   **Plate 37**

Orthnocichla whiteheadi **Sharpe, 1888**. *Ibis*, page 478. Mount Kinabalu, Borneo.

A poorly known and infrequently encountered endemic of N Borneo, restricted to submontane and montane forest. Monotypic.

IDENTIFICATION Length 8–9cm. Wing 47–55mm. Tail/wing 38–48%.

A small, dark terrestrial warbler with an extremely short tail, and a bold supercilium producing a striking head pattern. Sexes alike.

Structure Small and rounded, with the tail barely extending beyond the wing-tip. The head appears proportionately large and the broad crown distinctly long and flat, while the fine narrow bill appears too long for the head. This unusual structure combined with its short-hopping or shuffling gait, with the body held close to the ground and legs tucked closely under the breast, gives the impression of a small rodent scurrying through the leaf litter rather than a bird. It rarely, if ever adopts the upright posture typical of a *Tesia*. The wing is short and rounded, with an extremely long first primary extending well beyond the primary coverts and a very short primary projection, with the wing point formed by p5 or p6.

Plumage and bare parts A remarkable and attractive bird, often seen on or close to the forest floor in poor light conditions but whose plumage positively glows when illuminated by a shaft of sunlight. The combination of a long, conspicuous bright buff to golden-brown supercilium and contrasting black crown and black eye-stripe gives it a unique face pattern. The eye-stripe contrasts, in turn, with pale ear-coverts, which are white or light buff with narrow blackish tips. The entire upperparts including the closed wing and upper tail surface are deep sepia-brown or uniform rich sienna. Since it keeps close to the ground the underparts are often obscured and can be difficult to see well, but when a bird hops onto a low perch, the white or greyish white underparts show prominent dark feather fringes giving a conspicuous mottled appearance to the breast and upper flanks. The dull brown lower flanks and undertail-coverts are frequently hidden during foraging and may appear dark brown or blackish when visible.

The bill is black with a whitish tip and the base of the lower mandible is pale pink. The legs and feet are also pale pink.

SIMILAR SPECIES No species with a similar combination of characters occurs within the montane forests of its highly restricted range. Sunda Bush Warbler and Kinabalu Bush Warbler are larger and have much longer tails, and neither shows such a bright and conspicuous supercilium. A number of other ground-dwelling montane species occur in the damp gullies and ravines of N Borneo. These include White-browed Shortwing, Mountain Wren-babbler and Eye-browed Wren-babbler. None of which is likely to be confused with Bornean Stubtail, given reasonable views.

VOICE King (1989) characterised the songs of *Urosphena* species as a high-pitched monotone in the 8–10kHz range. This makes them difficult to hear and they are easily missed. However, each species has a characteristic delivery and, if audible, identification by song is straightforward. Bornean Stubtail has the briefest song of the three *Urosphena* species.

It is introduced with two sharp, thin, high-pitched '*pit-pit*' or '*tzi-tzi*' notes followed by an equally high-pitched '*tzeee*', each '*tzi-tzi-tzeee*' sequence lasting less than 0.75 seconds. It is often impossible to establish the direction of the sound and locate the singing bird.

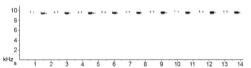

Song of Bornean Stubtail, Mount Kinabalu, Sabah, Malaysia, July. (Peter Kennerley)

The call is even more difficult to perceive, no more than a single high-pitched '*tzi*', occasionally repeated.

MOULT No data available.

HABITAT Moist sub-montane and montane forest above 500m, especially where the canopy is closed and light levels are low. It requires a poorly developed understorey with a thick layer of leaf litter. Its distribution within the forest is poorly understood, due to relative inaccessibility, but is apparently not uniform. It prefers dark, damp ravines and gently sloping banks and hillsides above streams, and appears to avoid drier, more level areas. It is much less common in higher montane forest, where it occurs in more open situations, but still requires sparse ground cover and a thick litter layer. It also occurs in secondary roadside forest and shifting-agriculture vegetation (Sheldon *et al.* 2001).

BEHAVIOUR A quiet and unobtrusive warbler of the forest floor and the lowest levels of the understorey, rarely perching more than 0.5m above ground and then only briefly. Occurs singly or occasionally in pairs. Foraging birds move slowly and deliberately through leaf litter with a short-hopping mouse-like gait, with the body held close to ground and the legs largely obscured by body feathering. It is easily overlooked as it is seldom vocal and even pairs rarely give contact calls. It is most often located by hearing the rustle of leaf litter. The bird is not particularly shy and will often ignore stationary observers, sometimes approaching to within 1m, but quickly disappearing into the undergrowth if disturbed. Active throughout most of the day in cool, shaded montane conditions.

BREEDING HABITS Little information. The only nest described was found in April 1982. It was a small cup constructed from reddish fibres, placed close to the ground on a mossy bank, and contained two eggs (Phillipps 1986; Jenkins *et al.* 1996).

DISTRIBUTION Confined to the mountains of NE Borneo, where it is locally distributed and uncommon. It ranges from Mount Kinabalu, Sabah (Malaysia), south locally through the Crocker Range to Gunung Liang Kubang and Barito Ulu in C Kalimantan, Indonesia. In Sarawak it occurs in the upper montane forest on Gunung Kalulong from 610m to 1,330m and Gunung Mulu above 1,200m. It appears to be absent from some apparently suitable peaks, including Gunung Penrissen and the hills in the Pueh Range. Recorded in submontane forest as low as 500m but is most numerous on Mount Kinabalu in primary forest above 900m and occurs there up to at least 2,600m (Davison, 1992) and to 3,150m in stunted upper montane forest (Smythies & Davison 1999).

MOVEMENTS Apparently resident.

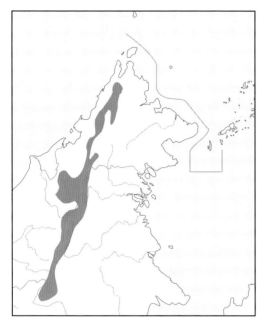

Bornean Stubtail. Resident within breeding range.

DESCRIPTION

Plumage – Adult fresh Forehead, crown and upper nape black, lower nape similar but with a faint brownish or maroon wash. Supercilia bright buff to golden-brown, usually meeting over the bill base; broad and each extending back over the ear-coverts, narrowing and tapering to a point on the side of the nape. Lores and broad eye-line black, sharply demarcated from supercilium; eye-lines expand towards rear of ear-coverts and extend onto the sides of the nape. Ear-coverts white to pale straw, typically mottled heavily with dark brown, most intensely towards rear edges. Eye-ring bright golden-buff above eye, merging with supercilium; whitish along lower edges, thus contrasting little with sides of head. Mantle and scapulars to rump and uppertail-coverts dark, deep sepia-brown to dull burnt sienna, narrow darker feather fringes forming indistinct scaling. Tail deep brown, matching upperparts. Chin and throat white, sides of throat with faint blackish mottling, more distinct as throat merges with lower ear-coverts and sides of neck. Centre of breast white with variable dark grey feather tips creating random mottling. Belly greyish white to dull yellowish cream. Sides of breast and flanks washed dark greyish brown. Undertail-coverts dark oily brown.

Upperwing-coverts deep sepia-brown to dull burnt sienna, with indistinct darker fringes, closely matching mantle colour. Tertials with broad fringes matching mantle and slightly darker centres. Primary coverts, secondaries and primaries dark brown, with broad edges matching mantle. Alula dull burnt sienna with narrow, paler fringe. Underwing-coverts dark greyish brown to slate-grey, very similar to flanks.

Adult worn Not known to differ from fresh adult.

Juvenile Undescribed.

Bare parts Upper mandible dark grey, usually with a small whitish tip. Lower mandible pink at base, becoming darker grey towards tip. Tarsi, toes and claws pale pink. Iris dark.

IN HAND CHARACTERS
Measurements

	Male	Female
Wing	52–55 (53.7; 7)	47–51 (49.7; 3)
Tail	21–23 (22.6; 7)	20–21 (20.7; 3)
Bill	14.0–15.3 (14.8; 6)	14.9–15.6 (15.2; 3)
Tarsus	19.2–20.4 (19.5; 7)	18.5–20 (19.5; 3)

Sexes combined:
Tail/wing ratio: 38–48% (42%; 10)
Bill width: 3.0–3.9 (3.5; 9)
Hind claw: 4.8–5.6 (5.2; 10)

Structure

Wing formula (n = 10):

p1/pc	p2	p3e	p4e	p5e	p6(e)	p7	p10
10–14	9–13	1–6	0–6	0–3	wp	0–2	4–6

Wing very short and strongly rounded; p1 rather large. Wing point p(5) 6; p2 < ss tips; emargination on p3–5, usually also p6.

Figure 116. Wing of Bornean Stubtail.

Tail extremely short; almost square.
Bill fine-tipped, but stouter than in Asian Stubtail.
Tarsi rather longer than in Asian Stubtail.
Recognition The only warbler on Borneo with an extremely short tail, a long bright buff to golden-brown supercilium and deep sepia-brown to blackish upperparts.
Weight No data available.

GEOGRAPHIC VARIATION Although there is slight individual variation, which may relate to individual variation, age or sex differences, there is no consistent plumage variation within the limited range.

TAXONOMY AND SYSTEMATICS No issues arising.

▲ Adult, Mount Kinabalu, Sabah, Malaysia, June (James Eaton/Birdtour Asia).

ASIAN STUBTAIL
Urosphena squameiceps   **Plate 37**

Tribura squameiceps Swinhoe, 1863. *Proc. Zool. Soc. London.* p. 292. Canton.

A small, short-tailed terrestrial warbler that breeds in the warm temperate regions of the eastern Palearctic and migrates to winter from S China to Indochina and Burma. Monotypic.

IDENTIFICATION Length 9–10cm. Wing 51–57mm. Tail/wing 50–59%.

A rather drab and nondescript, small, ground-dwelling warbler with a very short tail and a striking pale supercilium. It is the only *Urosphena* occurring in mainland Asia. Typically found foraging amongst leaf litter except when singing, when it perches on a branch to deliver a high-pitched stridulating song reminiscent of that of some *Locustella* and *Bradypterus* species. Sexes alike.

Structure Shows the combination of a large head, small body and short wings shared only with other *Urosphena* species. The large-headed appearance is exaggerated by a long, narrow bill and a flat broad crown showing little or no forehead. The neck seems almost non-existent and the body is small and rather dumpy. The wing is rounded with p1 extending up to 8mm beyond the primary coverts and the wing point is formed by p4–5. Unlike in the other two *Urosphena* species, the tail extends slightly beyond the tip of the closed wing, but being over 10mm shorter than the wing length, this structure places it well within the definition of the genus given by Delacour (1942). The legs are often hidden as the bird forages, or are only visible momentarily before being covered by the body feathering.

Plumage and bare parts Apart from the striking head pattern, the overall appearance is dull and lacks any distinctive features. The head shows a prominent creamy supercilium that extends onto the side of the nape and contrasts with a long, dark brown eye-stripe. The crown is warm brown with faintly darker feather tips creating a slightly scaled appearance. Above the supercilium, the borders to the crown contrast slightly with the slightly paler centre and help define the crown shape. Otherwise, the entire upperparts, including the closed wing and tail, are uniform warm brown and unmarked. It is often difficult to view the underparts on a bird foraging in leaf litter, but a perched bird shows a whitish chin and throat, while the breast and belly are washed pale greyish brown to peachy brown. The flanks and the undertail-coverts are usually a slightly brighter peachy brown.

The greyish brown bill shows a dull pink base below. The legs are conspicuous pale pink, when visible.

SIMILAR SPECIES No warblers within the breeding range of Asian Stubtail share similar plumage, structural and behavioural characters. The most likely confusion species are the superficially similar dull, uniform *Phylloscopus* warblers, among which Dusky Warbler is probably the closest in appearance. Northern Wren also shares certain structural and plumage similarities, but really is quite different from Asian Stubtail although it could, conceivably, be confused given brief views. On migration and in winter Asian Stubtail occurs alongside several superficially similar small, dark, ground-dwelling birds that frequent the recesses of the forest floor. Such potential confusion species include Pale-footed Bush Warbler, various wren-babblers (the

most similar being Eye-browed Wren-babbler) and two skulking shortwings, White-browed Shortwing and Lesser Shortwing. All are potential confusion species that can give just brief nondescript views as they disappear into the undergrowth, but all lack a shuffling gait when foraging and good prolonged views will reveal their true character. Separation from Dusky Warbler and Northern Wren is discussed below.

Dusky Warbler is a small, drab and skulking warbler that shares a similar dull and uniform plumage with Asian Stubtail and also has a long and conspicuous supercilium, but it has a much longer tail and relatively short bill. Although Dusky Warbler often forages amongst leaf litter, it adopts an upright posture on extended legs which are invariably visible. Its active progress through ground cover is quite different from the slower, shuffling movements of the stubtail and it regularly forages amongst bushes and tree branches, which Asian Stubtail rarely does. Furthermore, its repeated hard '*tak*' call is particularly distinctive and much harder than the quieter '*sit*' call of the stubtail.

Northern Wren has a long, fine bill, conspicuous supercilium, short tail, dumpy body and dull brown plumage like Asian Stubtail. But overall, it is darker, with a brown chin and throat, lightly barred flanks and patterned edges to the primaries and rectrices. It spends time foraging on the ground, but is rarely as skulking and shy as Asian Stubtail and is more likely to forage in full view at a higher level. It typically holds the tail cocked above the back, something the stubtail never does. It is readily separable by its far-carrying melodic song and its harsh '*teck*' and '*terrrrrr*' calls are louder and harder than any given by the stubtail.

VOICE The song is a thin, high-pitched monotone '*si-si-si-si-si-si-si-si-si-si-si-si-si-si-si-si-si-si-si-si-si-si-si-si-si*', delivered with a stridulating quality that separates it from others within its genus. Each song sequence lasts for between three and 11 seconds and comprises 7–8 '*si-si-si-si*' elements per second. It begins quietly and gradually increases in intensity and volume until abruptly stopping, commencing again after a break of several seconds.

The song is not dissimilar to those of some *Locustella* and *Bradypterus* warblers in both quality and duration. Compared with songs of the other two *Urosphena* species, that of Asian Stubtail has a slightly lower frequency, approximately 8kHz and well within the audible range of most observers. Song sequences last much longer than in the other *Urosphena* species and are separated by pauses of several seconds. The song may be obvious to observers attuned to its frequency but can easily be overlooked in woodland against a background of similar-sounding stridulations from small cicadas and crickets.

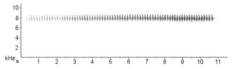

Song of Asian Stubtail, Tokyo, Japan, May. (Ueda 1998)

The call, given on the breeding and wintering grounds and by birds on migration, is a single short, harsh '*sit*', given erratically.

MOULT Moult is poorly documented, with no additional information to update the account of Dement'ev & Gladkov (1954). Adults have a complete moult on the breeding grounds in July and August. The tail and body moult commence when primary moult is well advanced. Juveniles also have a complete moult before leaving the breeding grounds, including the primaries, secondaries and tail. As in adults, moult of the primaries and secondaries precedes tail and body moult. Timing varies considerably, some birds having barely started to moult when others have largely completed, a disparity attributed to differing fledging times. Moult of juveniles is generally slightly later than in adults. Migrants trapped and examined in Hong Kong in October and November all appear in fresh, unworn plumage. Given a lack of data from wintering areas there is no evidence of a partial moult prior to northward migration, but it would be unsurprising if it occurs.

HABITAT In southern parts of the range (including Kyushu, Shikoku and Honshu), it breeds at medium elevation in deciduous and mixed woodland, on hill-slopes with steep gullies and in open glades with a heavy undergrowth of bamboo scrub, bushes and ferns. It is less numerous in northern areas and occurs at lower elevations, mainly in deciduous woodland and more open deciduous and mixed scrub, often in damp river valleys. It still requires thick undergrowth with ample leaf litter and fallen logs, often along rock-strewn gullies and stream beds.

Outside the breeding season, it favours drier, cooler, broadleaf evergreen and mixed deciduous woodland and is unusual in moist tropical forest. It occurs at or near sea level in more northern wintering areas, but in Indochina it tends to prefer cooler conditions at higher elevations. It invariably requires shaded and secluded primary or secondary woodland, or closed canopy scrubland with tangled undergrowth, fallen trees and damp ravines. It seems to prefer forest floor areas with a thick layer of dry litter, but this may reflect the relative ease with which observers can locate birds there from the sound of dry leaf movement. On migration, it is opportunistic and likely to utilise any area of coastal or inland woodland or scrub offering shade and undisturbed areas for feeding. It has been reported to occur in tall grass and marshes, but it is rare away from scrub and woodland.

BEHAVIOUR Skulking and elusive, frequenting the shady recesses of the forest floor. It hops quietly through leaf litter, often disappearing into a scrub thicket or brushwood tangle only to emerge unseen later. A bird will clamber higher into scrub or bushes occasionally and it will fly short distances into cover when alarmed. It is not a particularly shy species and will approach a stationary observer closely. It feeds almost exclusively on the ground, searching for small insects and spiders amongst fallen leaves and twigs, tree roots, brushwood, moss-covered rocks and dense scrub thickets. It moves in short jumps, keeping the long legs tucked well below the belly. It sometimes appears in more open situations, such as clear ground under bushes, in particular near pools, but it then behaves nervously and darts back into cover at the slightest disturbance.

Males begin to sing on arrival from late April in Japan and mid May onwards in the Russian Far East and continue until the end of June. Breeding adults may approach intruders giving alarm calls, particularly when with recently fledged young (Dement'ev & Gladkov 1954).

BREEDING HABITS In Japan, breeding lasts from late April until July. The nest is a loose open construction of moss, dead leaves and grasses. It is well hidden, placed on an embankment or a steep mossy slope among fallen logs, scattered leaf debris and overhanging ferns. A clutch of 5–7 eggs is laid in late May or early June and incubation lasts approximately 13 days. Both parents feed the young, which leave the nest 10–12 days after hatching. Single-brooded.

Ohara & Yamagishi (1984) and Ohara (1985) recorded nest helpers assisting a pair in Japan and speculate that cooperative breeding may occur regularly in this species.

DISTRIBUTION

Breeding A summer visitor to warmer temperate latitudes in the extreme E Palearctic, from S Ussuriland and adjacent regions of Heilongjiang, Jilin and Liaoning Provinces in NE China, south through the Korean peninsula. Also breeds on S Sakhalin and the southernmost Kuril Islands and south through the Japanese archipelago. On Hokkaido, Japan, it is generally common to sea level in lowland forest in the southwest, but rare in the north and east. It breeds widely at 400m to 1,600m throughout the hills of Honshu, Shikoku and Kyushu and on the island of Tsushima between South Korea and Honshu.

Non-breeding Winters widely throughout Taiwan and occasionally in Okinawa in southernmost Japan, from where there are records between late December and mid February (Brazil 1991). There is also a January record from the Yaeyama Islands. In southern China, it is widespread in small numbers in Guangdong Province and a common winter visitor to Hong Kong. It also winters in Hainan and Guangxi Provinces and south and west through N and C Vietnam, Laos and Thailand to the northern peninsular. The western limit of the wintering range appears to lie in Burma where it is relatively common in the Pegu Yomas, with other records from Mount Victoria, the southern Shan States and Tenasserim (Smythies 1968).

MOVEMENTS Birds usually depart from the northern breeding areas in September, while those breeding from Honshu southwards may remain in the breeding areas until October. Migrants move through the Korean peninsula and lowland Japan throughout September and often until mid October, when they frequently occur in coastal regions from which they are absent during the breeding season. In Japan, these include several of the Izu Islands south to Haha-jima, and the Ryukyu Islands south to Ishigaki-jima and Iriomote-jima.

It is a common migrant through the coastal provinces of eastern China from Hebei to Guangdong. In Hong Kong, it has been recorded from 2 October, but it remains rare until early November, when numbers begin to increase and peak towards the end of the month, then decline slightly in December. Wintering birds in Hong Kong cloud the migration picture but it usually remains fairly common until wintering birds begin to depart in mid February. There is often a slight increase in numbers as passage birds move through in late March and early April and it becomes very rare by the second week of April. Returning migrants reach the breeding areas in Honshu from early April onwards but northern breeders do not reach Hokkaido until early May.

Vagrancy It has not been recorded from India (Rasmussen & Anderton 2005) and is a vagrant to Nepal, with just one record from Dharan in January 1993 (Lewis 1993); this appears to represent the only record for the subcontinent. The only other report of vagrancy was a bird at Station Sibaliw, Panay, Philippines, on 9 October 1999 (Curio *et al.* 2001); an exceptionally early date at that latitude.

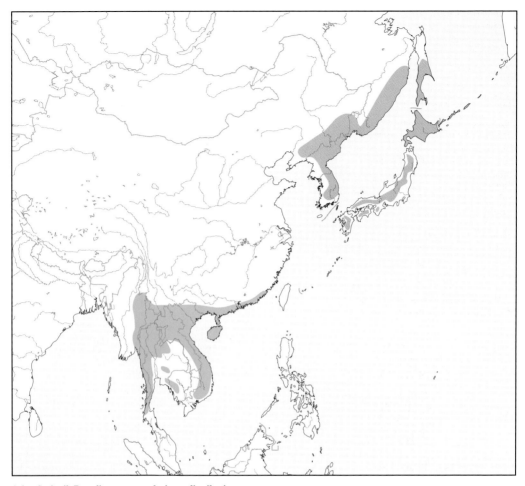

Asian Stubtail. Breeding range and winter distribution.

DESCRIPTION

Plumage – Adult fresh (September to December) Forehead, crown and nape warm brown with a faint olivaceous wash; crown feathers narrowly edged dark brown, producing a faintly scaly appearance. Sides of crown over and behind eye narrowly edged dark brown, forming a dark border above the supercilia. Supercilium cold buff, long, broad and conspicuous, from base of bill to side of nape, on some individuals almost meeting above bill; broadest in front of and above the eye, tapering slightly over the ear-coverts. Lores dark brown, forming a broad dark line between the bill base and the eye. A dark brown eye-line, sharply demarcated from the supercilium, extends from behind the eye to the side of the nape. Ear-coverts mottled dull brown and pale straw, paler towards lower edges. Upper edge of eye-ring cold buff, merging with supercilium, lower edge narrow, whitish and inconspicuous. Mantle and scapulars plain warm brown with faint olivaceous tinge. Rump and uppertail-coverts as mantle but with a more distinct olivaceous wash, uppertail-coverts often narrowly edged dark brown, appearing faintly scaly. Tail feathers warm brown with slightly brighter olivaceous fringes. Chin and throat white with variable creamy or buffy wash; feather tips slightly darker brown towards sides of throat, creating faint

barring or scaling, which merges with the mottling on the ear-coverts and the sides of the neck. Breast and belly white, washed faint greyish brown to pale peachy brown. Slightly darker feather tips on the sides of the upper breast, produce a faint scaly pattern, contiguous with that on the sides of the throat. Flanks dull greyish brown to tawny-brown. Undertail-coverts tawny-brown to brighter peachy brown.

Closed wing plain and featureless. Lesser and median coverts uniform warm brown, matching mantle colour. Greater coverts and tertials with broad, diffuse warm brown fringes similar to mantle colour and slightly darker centres. Primary coverts, secondaries and primaries dull brown with broad warm olivaceous-brown edges, slightly brighter than mantle. Alula warm brown with broad, slightly paler fringe. Underwing-coverts pale creamy buff to light sandy buff, slightly paler than flanks.

Adult worn Resembles fresh adult.

Juvenile Slightly warmer and brighter than adult, with stronger buffy suffusion to the underparts.

Bare parts Upper mandible dark greyish brown. Lower mandible dull pink at base, darkening to greyish brown at tip. Tarsi, toes and claws conspicuous pale pink. Iris dark brown; possible age-related changes have not been established.

IN HAND CHARACTERS
Measurements

	Male	Female
Wing	51–57 (54.4; 10)	51–57 (53.8; 10)
Tail	28–32 (29.9; 10)	27–32 (29.6; 10)
Bill	13.7–16.4 (14.8; 10)	13.6–15.8 (14.4; 10)
Tarsus	17.5–19.5 (18.6; 10)	17.3–19.4 (18.0; 9)

Sexes combined:
Tail/wing ratio: 50–59% (55%; 20)
Bill width: 2.6–3.3 (3.1; 20)
Hind claw: 5.0–6.1 (5.5; 10)
Tail graduation: 1–4 (2.1; 14)

Structure

Wing formula (n = 20):

p1/pc	p2	p3e	p4e	p5e	p6	p7	p10
4–8	7–9	0–3	wp	0–1	2.5–4	5–7	8–11

Wing rounded with small p1. Wing point p(3) 4–5; p2 = p7–9 (10); emargination on p3–5.

Figure 117. Wing of Asian Stubtail.

Tail very short, almost square.
Bill smallish and slender; concave-sided with very fine-tipped upper mandible.
Tarsi slender; toes and claws small and fine.

▲ Adult, South Korea, April. Appears proportionately longer legged than *Cettia*, enhanced by its conspicuous pale pink tarsus and feet (Robert Newlin).

Recognition An unmistakable brown-backed warbler with a prominent, long, buffy white supercilium and a very short tail.
Weight Hong Kong, 7.4–11.4g (8.9; 96) (HKRG unpublished data).

GEOGRAPHIC VARIATION See **Taxonomy and Systematics** below.

TAXONOMY AND SYSTEMATICS The race *U. s. ussuriana* was described by Seebohm from the Ussuri Valley in the Russian Far East. It closely resembles the nominate race but the upperparts were described as tending to be marginally brighter, the flanks more strongly washed dull brown and the breast warmly washed pale peachy brown. These differences are subtle and may not even be consistent across a large sample. A similar range of plumage variation can result from abrasion and age difference and brighter plumage tones may relate to fresh first-winter plumage of the nominate form. Here we follow Vaurie (1959) and Watson (1987) and treat *ussuriana* as a synonym of *squamiceps*.

▲ Adult, Hong Kong, November. A particularly distinctive, diminutive warbler with a proportionately large head and small body, and short tail. Shows characteristic narrow, dark fringes to crown feathers and less obvious fringes to mantle, and long, fine, pale tipped bill. This bird has lost all but one of its tail feathers, enhancing stub-tailed appearance (Michelle and Peter Wong).

▲ Adult, Taiwan, October. Note long, creamy white supercilium contrasting with dark brown eye-stripe (Liao Pen-shing).

Genus *Cettia* Bonaparte, 1834

[Fr. Francesco Cetti (1726–78) Italian mathematician and zoologist]

A genus of 17 nondescript species, characterised by the presence of ten rectrices rather than the 12 typically found in most warblers and other passerines. Their species diversity peaks in the Himalayas and mountains of western and southern China, but the genus also occurs in Taiwan, the Greater and Lesser Sundas and some islands of the southwest Pacific Ocean. Only Cetti's Warbler reaches Europe and the warmer regions of the temperate Western and Central Palearctic. Most species are resident or altitudinal migrants but Manchurian Bush Warbler is a long-distance migrant, as is the race *albiventris* of Cetti's Warbler, which breeds in central Asia and winters south to northwest India. Japanese Bush Warbler is a short-distance migrant within Japan.

The *Cettia* warblers are small to medium sized, the males of some species being considerably larger than the females. Most are plain and nondescript, appearing brownish above and pale below, and many show a prominent pale supercilium and dark eye-stripe. All are characterised by rather large domed heads, often with rather small bills, although those in the sub-genus *Vitia* have longer, slender bills. The wings are short and rounded with a well-developed first primary. The tails comprise ten broad, soft feathers with rounded tips and short undertail coverts. The rictal bristles are well developed.

Most *Cettia* typically inhabit forest undergrowth, thicket and scrub, often at high altitude, in some cases breeding above 3,000m, along and above the tree line. Their nests are rather bulky, often domed, and are situated low in a bush or among thick ground vegetation. The songs are often brief, but powerful and melodious, but those of Asian species are extraordinary long and complex.

Three groups or sub-genera have been recognised. Cetti's Warbler represents the only member of the sub-genus *Cettia*, and is distinguished from the Asian *Cettia* by its unique loud song and a preference for wetlands. All mainland Asian species are contained within the sub-genus *Horeites*. This comprises eleven species that inhabit the warmer temperate regions of the southeastern Palearctic and the higher mountain ranges in the Oriental region. The Himalayas and mountains of western China, with seven species, appear to represent the centre of radiation of this group, with outlying taxa reaching the mountains of Taiwan, Luzon in the Philippines, Borneo, and the Greater and Lesser Sundas.

The remaining group, within the sub-genus *Vitia*, consists of five species from the Lesser Sundas and tropical southwest Pacific, all of which appear to represent remnant populations of a once widespread ancestor. Of these, Fiji Bush Warbler and Shade Warbler were first described within the genus *Vitia*, while Palau Bush Warbler was placed within the unique genus *Psamathia*. Tanimbar Bush and Bougainville Bush Warblers, both described only recently and included in *Cettia*, share characters associated with *Vitia*. These five species differ from the Asian *Cettia* in having a proportionately longer, finer bill, a rather shorter tail, and more restricted sexual size dimorphism. Tanimbar Bush Warbler from the eastern Lesser Sundas exhibits greater sexual size dimorphism than the other species, and may represent a link between the Pacific *Vitia* and Asian *Horeites* species.

Orenstein & Pratt (1983) demonstrated similarities between the songs of the Pacific species. Moreover, their songs resemble some of the Asian *Cettia*, in particular those of Japanese Bush, Manchurian Bush and Brownish-flanked Bush Warblers. All have short and abrupt songs, commencing with a long, clear and unmodulated whistle followed by a concluding warble. The songs of Japanese Bush and Brownish-flanked Bush Warblers resemble those of the Pacific species more closely than they do most other Asian *Cettia*. Molecular analysis has shown a close relationship between the earlier known Pacific species and Bougainville Bush Warbler (LeCroy & Barker 2006), and indicates that these are, in turn, sister species of Manchurian Bush Warbler.

PALE-FOOTED BUSH WARBLER
Cettia pallidipes   Plate 37

Phylloscopus pallidipes Blandford, 1872. *J. Asiatic Soc. Bengal* 41(2): 162. Sikkim.

A resident or short-distance altitudinal migrant that breeds at low altitudes in the foothills of the Himalayas and in the lower hill ranges from NW India to S China and N Vietnam, with an isolated population in the Andaman Islands. Proportionately the shortest-tailed of all *Cettia* and originally included in *Urosphena*, but vocal and structural characters would place it in *Cettia*. Polytypic, with three races recognised:

C. p. pallidipes (Blandford, 1872). N India (N Uttarakhand) to Nepal and Bhutan.
C. p. osmastoni (Hartert, 1908). Andaman Islands.
C. p. laurentei (La Touche, 1921). E and C Burma to S China, N Thailand and N Vietnam.

IDENTIFICATION Length 11–12cm. Wing 46–56mm. Tail/wing 70–85%.

A small, short-tailed and nondescript dark brown *Cettia* with contrastingly pale underparts, a bold head pattern and strikingly pale legs. Unlike most *Cettia*, shows only limited sexual size dimorphism. Sexes alike.

Structure Appears stocky with a *Urosphena*-like structure, including a proportionately large head and small body, with little or no apparent neck. The head is distinctly rounded and domed, but with a better-defined forehead than shown by Asian Stubtail. The bill is quite short, but also fine and narrow, reminiscent of that of a *Phylloscopus* warbler. The wing is particularly short and rounded with a large first primary (p1) and closely bunched primary tips that extend no more than 5mm beyond the longest tertial and fall well short of the longest uppertail-covert.

The tail is shorter than in all other *Cettia* but proportionately longer than in Asian Stubtail and does not appear exceptionally short in the field; perhaps an illusion created by the short wings. It lacks the shuffling, ground-hugging gait that typifies *Urosphena* and the legs are usually visible as it hops around in low cover.

Plumage and bare parts Shows a bold and contrasting pale buff supercilium that extends from the bill base to the rear of the ear-coverts, where it flares slightly behind the eye. There is a sharply defined dark brown eye-stripe below this, while the ear-coverts are paler brown and faintly mottled. The entire upperparts from the crown to the uppertail-coverts, along with the closed wing and tail, are uniform and unmarked, varying slightly between dull olive-brown and dull rufous-brown. The underparts are always much paler than the upperparts, but vary racially and individually. In the nominate form, the underparts are silky white with a faint pinkish buff suffusion on the breast and a subdued greyish brown wash confined to the flanks and ventral region. The other two races, *laurentei* and *osmastoni*, show a variable brownish wash on the upper breast and lower flanks. This is greyish brown and more confined to the sides in *laurentei*, but warmer, darker and more extensive in *osmastoni*. Both these forms show a warm buffy wash on the undertail-coverts, whereas these are white, like the belly, in the nominate form.

The bill is dark grey with pale yellowish pink lower mandible, although this darkens slightly towards the tip. The legs are conspicuously pale pinkish white, paler than in any other *Cettia*.

SIMILAR SPECIES Pale-footed Bush Warbler resembles several similar nondescript warblers, including Asian Stubtail, several *Phylloscopus* species including Pale-legged Leaf-warbler, which shares similarly pale legs and a conspicuous contrasting supercilium, and several of the similar smaller *Cettia* warblers.

Asian Stubtail is a drab and extremely short-tailed warbler with a long, pale supercilium and contrasting face pattern similar to that of Pale-footed Bush Warbler. However, it usually shows fine dark fringes to the crown feathers, a diffuse darker shadow above the supercilium, and the supercilia meet above the base of the bill and extend to the sides of the nape. Structural differences, in particular the very short tail and longer, finer bill of Asian Stubtail, also separate it from Pale-footed Bush. It usually occurs on or close to the forest floor amongst leaf litter and moves in a series of short, low hops. In contrast, Pale-footed Bush Warbler usually forages in low cover, even within dense woodland, but not usually for prolonged periods on the ground. However, both are great skulkers and difficult to observe for long in dense undergrowth.

Pale-legged Leaf Warbler and **Sakhalin Leaf Warbler** are superficially similar to Pale-footed Bush Warbler, sharing a combination of fine, dark tipped bill, contrasting head pattern with a prominent supercilium, dull unmarked upperparts and pale pink legs. They differ in having dull olive-green upperparts, although the rump and occasionally the entire upperparts can take on an olive-brown colour.

When fresh, the closed wing shows two narrow wing-bars, a character never seen in Pale-footed Bush, but these become less conspicuous as they abrade and may eventually disappear. They also differ in structure and behaviour. It appears slim and delicate with a proportionately much longer tail giving an attenuated structure. They are constantly active, preferring lower bushes and light scrub in open woodland where they are relatively easy watch at length, quite unlike the more skulking Pale-footed Bush Warbler that tends to remain within deep cover. The call is a short, ringing metallic '*tink*', quite different from the quiet '*chit*' of Pale-footed Bush.

VOICE The short, explosive song comprises a series of clipped notes combined into a brief '*hweet-wee-chu-wee-chu-wee*', with a distinctive cheerful, chirpy character. The initial introductory '*hweet*' element is a short flat note and is followed immediately by the song. The second part of the song comprises a thin and high-pitched melody of clearly separated notes, rising in frequency between 3–8kHz to form a pleasant, sweet, undulating warble, '*wee-chu-wee-chu-wee*', performed quickly as a terminal flourish.

Each complete song sequence lasts for approximately one second and is repeated after a pause of two to five seconds.

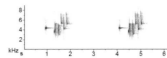

Song of Pale-footed Bush Warbler recorded within breeding range of *C. p. pallidipes*, Royal Chitwan National Park, Nepal. (Connop 1993)

The call is an occasional quiet '*chip*' or '*chit*'.

MOULT Details poorly known. Birds trapped on migration during October and November In Hong Kong show fresh, unworn plumage. It is likely that adults have a complete post-breeding moult, so it has not been possible to establish the age of the birds examined in Hong Kong. None have been examined between January and March so it is unclear whether a further moult takes place before breeding commences.

HABITAT In the Himalayan foothills, it shows a preference for dense scrub and tall rank grassland with scattered scrub in clearings and edges of secondary forest. It may occur in open woodland with scattered pines provided there is a dense scrub understorey. Stuart Baker (1924) noted it breeding from 1,200m to 2,150m, where cooler, drier conditions prevail and mentioned an exceptional record from the Rangbong Valley, Sikkim, at 2,750m. In Nepal, it breeds in the lowlands but has been recorded as high as 1,830m (Inskipp & Inskipp 1991; CI *in litt.*). There are frequent observations during the northern winter months from humid, lowland tropical Sal forest and grassland bordering the Gangetic Plain in Nepal and N India, suggesting it may be numerous there.

The breeding habitat of the race *laurentei* is not known to differ from that of the nominate form. Singing birds were recorded in N Thailand in April in tall herbage on an open, dry hillside at 1,380m (Round 1983). This habitat is now widespread in N Indochina and S China due to deforestation in the twentieth century. Where small patches of forest remain adjacent to encroaching grassland, this provides an ideal breeding situation. Habitat preferences on South Andaman Island are unknown.

BEHAVIOUR A shy and rarely seen inhabitant of the thickest scrub and grasslands, where it skulks among lower stems and branches. Only singing males reveal their presence, typically from thick cover but occasionally from an exposed perch. Outside the breeding season it becomes elusive and is rarely observed. Birds of the race *laurentei* breeding at lower elevations in the southern part of the range may remain on territories throughout the year, in particular in N Thailand and S Yunnan Province in China. These birds are occasionally heard in song during winter and territories are regularly occupied by singing males in Thailand by early April (Round 1983).

BREEDING HABITS Little data available. Nominate race birds return to the breeding grounds slightly later than *laurentei*. Breeding takes place in the Himalayan foothills during May and June (Stuart Baker 1924). The nest is a tidy domed structure placed close to the ground in a low dense bush or in thick bamboo. The outer layers are built from strips of coarse grass, the inner layers from finer grasses, the central cup being lined with a dense layer of feathers. The clutch is typically 3–4 eggs. Incubation and fledging periods are unknown.

DISTRIBUTION

C. p. pallidipes **Breeding** The nominate form is believed to be either resident or a short-distance altitudinal migrant in the Himalayan foothills. Records are few but sightings and specimens have established that its range extends from around Dehra Dun in N Uttarakhand, India, east to at least Bhutan. In Nepal it is fairly common at Royal Chitwan National Park (Inskipp & Inskipp 1991), but local and uncommon between 250m and 1,830m elsewhere (CI *in litt.*). In Bhutan, where Inskipp *et al.* (1999) considered it to be a rare to uncommon and local resident, it was noted by Spirenburg (2005) from the western and eastern valleys, most frequently from 1,400m to 2,000m, but with isolated records at 1,200m and 2,300m.

Non-breeding Outside the known breeding range, Rasmussen & Anderton (2005) noted its occurrence outside the breeding season from the Himalayan foothills, Assam Valley, Khasi Hills, Cachar and Manipur, but do not include Arunachal Pradesh within the winter range, despite reliable sight records. Rasmussen & Anderton commented that the only record from Meghalaya was a presumed wintering bird and that there are no documented breeding records (*contra* Stuart Baker 1924). They also comment that there are no definite records from Bangladesh. There is a report from the Eastern Ghats in Andhra Pradesh, S India, but it is uncertain whether this is an isolated occurrence or perhaps indicates an undocumented resident population.

C. p. laurentei **Breeding** This race occurs in N and C Burma including Maymyo, Shan States, Karen Hills and Karenni (Smithies 1968). Cheng (1987), however, recorded nominate *pallidipes* at Yingjiang, Luxi, near the Burmese border in western Yunnan Province, but it seems unlikely that this form would leapfrog the range of *laurentei* in Burma to reappear in Yunnan. Cheng also included Yunnan within the range of *laurentei*, noting occurrences in April in the southeast of the province, although this also seems unlikely and Cheng may have examined mislabelled specimens. The occurrence and probable resident status of the species in Yunnan was recently

confirmed by Hornskov (2000) who reported singing males at Jie Le, Ruili, near the border with Burma, in late November 2000 and again in mid March 2002. Further east, Carey *et al.* (2001) noted the species, presumably *laurentei*, as not uncommon in suitable habitat in western Guangxi Province. It is an uncommon resident up to 1,800m in NW Thailand (Lekagul & Round 1991) and also breeds in N Laos, N Vietnam and on the Da Lat Plateau in S Vietnam.

Non-breeding Outside the breeding season, there are reports of *laurentei* down to sea level in Hong Kong and Macau, which establish that dispersal to the south and east occurs in S China.

C. p. osmastoni Believed to be restricted to South Andaman Island in the Bay of Bengal. It is known only from Mount Harriet but may occur more widely, although but there are no recent records from anywhere on South Andaman Island.

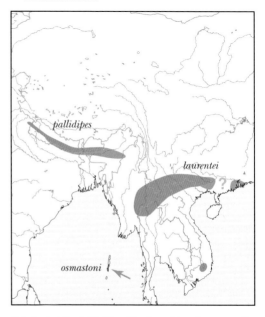

Pale-footed Bush Warbler. Mostly resident but some disperse to lower elevations outside the breeding season.

MOVEMENTS Poorly understood. Birds breeding at higher elevations in the Himalayas are apparently altitudinal migrants, appearing in lowland Nepal outside the breeding season. Skulking and silent birds in winter are elusive and easily overlooked and some may remain on breeding territories throughout the year. A series of late autumn records from Hong Kong (Carey *et al.* 2001) confirms that some birds migrate or disperse to warmer coastal regions and suggests that *laurentei* may be commoner in SE China outside the breeding season than current records indicate. Six of seven Hong Kong records were between 6 October and 19 November, suggesting passage migrants, with just one mid winter record, on 30 December. Five of the Hong Kong records relate to trapped birds from one small area of intensively-studied scrubland on a north-facing hillside at an elevation of approximately 350m, suggesting that it may be much commoner than this limited number of records infers. The remaining two were birds at sea level, trapped at the Mai Po Marshes Nature Reserve. There is just one other record of a bird from coastal S China, in Macau on 12 March 1907 (Vaughan & Jones 1913), which could have been wintering bird or a returning migrant.

DESCRIPTION *C. p. pallidipes*

Plumage – Adult fresh Forehead, crown and nape uniform olive-brown. Supercilium creamy buff; long and broad, extending from bill base, often ending squarely above rear of ear-coverts. Lores dark brown, sharply defined between bill base and eye. Behind eye, a well-defined dark brown eye-line extends the length of the supercilium. Ear-coverts white with pale pinkish buff tips producing faint mottling, most pronounced towards lower edges. Eye-ring dull cream, narrow and inconspicuous. Mantle and scapulars uniform olive-brown as crown but rump and uppertail-coverts marginally brighter rufous-brown, lacking olive tone. Tail feathers dull brown with indistinct, diffuse olive-brown fringes.

Chin, throat and belly silky white. Upper breast silky white with a faint creamy yellow or grey-buff wash, intensifying to pale peachy pink on the sides of the breast. Sides of throat faintly mottled peachy pink and merging with lower ear-coverts. Upper flanks pale peachy pink, darkening to pale grey-buff on lower flanks. Undertail-coverts white.

Lesser, median and greater coverts and tertials olive-brown, with broad, diffuse and indistinct fringes, marginally warmer than centres. Primary coverts, secondaries and primaries dull brown with tawny-brown edges and tips. Alula dark brown with slightly warmer, paler fringe. Underwing-coverts white.

Adult worn Closely similar to freshly moulted bird but slightly less warm.

Juvenile No specimens examined but said to be marginally warmer and browner than adult.

Bare parts Upper mandible dark grey with a narrow and indistinct horn cutting edge. Lower mandible pale horn to yellowish pink at base, darkening towards tip. Tarsi and toes fleshy pink; claws slightly paler. Iris dark brown.

IN HAND CHARACTERS
Measurements

C. p. pallidipes

	Male	Female
Wing	51–55 (53.8; 4)	46–52 (48.0; 4)
Tail	38–44 (41.5; 4)	36–40 (38.5; 4)
Bill	14, 14 (n = 2)	13–13.5 (13.3; 3)
Tarsus	18.5–20 (19.5; 4)	17.5–19.5 (18.8; 4)

Tail/wing ratio: 70–85% (78%; 19)
Bill width: 2.8–3.5 (3.2; 9)
Hind claw: 4.6–5.5 (5.0; 10)
Tail graduation: 3–6 (4.4; 11)

C. p. laurentei
Sexes combined (n = 3): *wing* 45–52; *tail* 40–41; *bill* 13.5–14.5; *tarsus* 18.5–19.0.

C. p. osmastoni
Sexes combined (n = 2): *wing* 52, 52; *tail* 40–41; *bill* 15, 15; *tarsus* 20.5 (n = 1).

Structure

C. p. pallidipes

Wing formula (n = 10):

p1/pc	p2	p3e	p4e	p5e	p6e	p7	p10
9–14	10–13	3–5	0–1	wp	0–0.5	1–2	4–6

Wing resembles Grey-sided Bush Warbler (Fig. 119); short and strongly rounded with fairly large p1. Wing point p(4) 5 (6); p2 < ss tips, p3 near p9; emargination on p3–6.

Tail short, slightly rounded, feathers broad-tipped.

Bill rather narrow, concave-sided with fine tip.

Tarsi, toes and claws slender.

Recognition A small short-tailed *Cettia*, plain olive-brown to rufous-brown above, with a prominent buff-toned supercilium, pale pinkish legs and white underparts (washed brownish in races *laurentei* and *osmastoni*). Tail/wing ratio is often < 80%, below the range for all other small *Cettia* except Hume's Bush and Yellow-bellied Bush Warblers.

Weight Thailand, (n = 2) 10.0g, 10.8g (PDR unpublished data); Hong Kong, 7.9–9.3g (8.5; 9) (HKRG unpublished data).

GEOGRAPHIC VARIATION The three races are probably geographically isolated and variation does not appear to be clinal.

C. p. pallidipes (NW India from Uttarakhand east to Nepal and Bhutan) Described above.

C. p. laurentei (E and C Burma to S China, N Thailand and N Vietnam) Upperparts slightly warmer than in nominate race and breast and flanks duller. The head pattern is bold and contrasting as in nominate birds, but the supercilium is slightly deeper buff. The crown, nape, mantle and rump are uniform warm rufescent-brown rather than olive-brown. The greater coverts and remiges are slightly duller mid brown with barely discernible rufescent fringes and the entire upperparts thus appear unmarked warm brown. The underparts are whitish but the breast shows a grey-brown wash that intensifies along the flanks. The undertail-coverts are warm buff or creamy buff, not white as in the nominate form.

C. p. osmastoni (South Andaman Island) Resembles the mainland races, but closer in appearance to *laurentei* than the nominate form. Differs from *laurentei* in having the ear-coverts warm tan faintly mottled with white, appearing as a paler patch on the side of the head. The upperparts are slightly warmer, richer and darker brown, with little or no contrast between the centres and fringes of the greater coverts and tertials. The breast shows a warmer, more extensive buff to ochre-brown wash that becomes dark greyish brown towards the lower flanks. The undertail-coverts are warm buff.

TAXONOMY AND SYSTEMATICS The small size and light delicate structure of Pale-footed Bush Warbler led Blandford (1872) to believe it to be a *Phylloscopus* warbler when he named it *Phylloscopus pallidipes*. Since it has only ten rectrices it was later transferred to the genus *Horeites* (= *Cettia*). When other races were described, Hartert (1908) included *osmastoni* within *Horeites*, but La Touche (1921) included *laurentei* within *Urosphena*. Pale-footed Bush Warbler clearly forms part of the *Cettia*/*Urosphena* complex. Its tail is proportionately shorter than in other *Cettia*, but longer than in the *Urosphena* species. Using a combination of song structure, wing/tail ratio and wing/tarsus ratio, King (1989) concluded that Pale-footed Bush Warbler belonged within *Cettia*.

▲ ▶ ▲ Adult *C. p. laurentei*, Hong Kong, January. A small, stocky *Cettia* that resembles Asian Stubtail but has distinctly longer tail, shorter, deeper based bill, and duller upperparts with a less contrasting supercilium and eye-stripe, while the strikingly pale pink legs separate it from others of the genus. Except when singing, usually keeps close to ground under dense cover, where it behaves like Asian Stubtail (Kelvin Yam).

SUNDA BUSH WARBLER
Cettia vulcania   Plate 38

Sylvia vulcania **Blyth, 1870**. *Ibis*, p. 170. Java

A common resident on the larger islands of SE Asia, where several isolated races are confined to 'islands' of upper montane forest. Recent phylogenetic studies by (Olsson *et al.* 2006) have shown that relationships within this species and Aberrant Bush Warbler are complex. Sunda Bush Warbler may comprise more than a single species. Treated here as a polytypic species with eight races recognised:

C. v. vulcania (Blyth, 1870). Java, Bali, Lombok, Sumbawa.
C. v. flaviventris (Salvadori, 1879). C and S Sumatra.
C. v. oreophila Sharpe, 1888. Mount Kinabalu, N Borneo.
C. v. everetti Hartert, 1898. Timor.
C. v. sepiaria Kloss, 1931. N Sumatra.
C. v. banksi Chasen, 1935. NW Borneo.
C. v. palawana Ripley & Rabor, 1962. Mount Mantalingajan, Palawan, Philippines.
C. v. kolichisi Johnstone & Darnell, 1997. Alor, Indonesia.

IDENTIFICATION Length 12–13cm. Wing 49–56mm. Tail/wing 92–108%.

A variable, medium-sized *Cettia* with plain brown or olive-brown upperparts and a well-marked head pattern. The underpart colour is quite variable between races, ranging from rich warm sepia to greyish brown or ash-grey in the Greater Sundas, to whitish with a pale brownish grey wash in the races resident in the Lesser Sundas. The distinctive song, which closely resembles that of Aberrant Bush Warbler, is a characteristic sound of the mountains on some of larger islands in SE Asia. Sexes similar; the male is slightly larger than the female but this is not obvious in the field.

Structure A typical neatly proportioned *Cettia* with a dumpy body, rather large rounded head and relatively long tail, similar in length to the body. The bill is short and fine, with a slightly decurved upper mandible. The tail is rounded rather than graduated, with ten relatively thin rectrices that usually appear loose and untidy. The wings are quite short, reaching only to the base of the tail and it shows a short primary projection with the tips closely bunched. When foraging the wings are often held loose at the sides of the body to reveal the rump and uppertail-coverts. It often adopts a perky, upright stance when excited.

Plumage and bare parts A drab and nondescript *Cettia* with a long, conspicuous supercilium, and a well-marked dark eye-stripe. The races inhabiting Sumatra, Java and Borneo in the Greater Sundas, show upperpart colour ranging from uniform drab olive-brown (Sumatra) to dull greyish brown, but with the edges to the primaries and secondaries appearing warmer, brighter than the upperparts and sometimes with a faint bronzed tinge (Borneo). The underparts are unmarked or almost so and paler than the upperparts. The chin and throat vary from pale cream to pale grey and the distinctly warmer breast and flanks range from rusty brown or peachy brown (Sumatra), to pale, faintly mottled greyish brown (Borneo). Colours intensify towards rich brown on the undertail-coverts in all races. See **Geographic Variation** for details of individual racial differences.

The bill is dark grey to blackish with a dull greyish pink base to the lower mandible, although this usually darkens at the sides towards the tip. The legs and feet are pale, varying from pale fleshy brown to greyish pink.

SIMILAR SPECIES No other *Cettia* occur within the insular range of Sunda Bush Warbler and there are no likely confusion species within its range. The very different Kinabalu Bush Warbler breeds in montane forest in N Sabah, Malaysia and occurs alongside Sunda Bush Warbler. The two species are quite different in plumage and structure. Their separation is discussed under that species.

VOICE The simple yet distinctive song is a melodic and slightly slurred fluty whistle, described as '*suuueeeuuu*', or '*cheehuueeoo*'. The initial whistled syllable being followed by a lazy undulation, rising slightly then falling in pitch within a frequency range of 2–4kHz. Each whistle lasts for just over one second and is repeated at intervals of six to eight seconds or more. There is, however, considerable inter-island and individual variation in frequency and duration.

Song of Sunda Bush Warbler, recorded within breeding range of *C. v. vulcania* Gunung Gedi, Java, Indonesia, August. (Pete Morris)

Song of Sunda Bush Warbler, recorded within breeding range of *C. v. oreophila* Mount Kinabalu, Sabah, Malaysia, July. (Peter Kennerley)

The call is a short, dry, rattling '*tzrrr, tzrrr*', two or more notes often repeated in quick succession, followed by a longer pause.

MOULT No published data.

HABITAT Closely associated with forest and dense undergrowth throughout its range. It typically occurs where there is a thick understorey of ferns and creepers, thick bamboo tangles and other rank vegetation. It often shows an affinity for forest clearings and is commonly encountered by roadsides where light has penetrated the forest to create a thick and dense undergrowth. It is restricted to the higher hills and only occurs in montane forest, although it extends into scrub at the tree line. On Mount Kinabalu, it ranges from 1,450m to 3,650m but is most frequently encountered from 2,600m to 3,000m in cool, moist, upper montane forest. It occurs to the highest summits on lower peaks in other parts of its range. The newly discovered population on Wetar is locally common in forest with a well-developed ground layer, and particularly favours degraded roadsides bordered by *Chromalaena odorata*, and also used clumps of sedges around springs (Trainor *et al.* 2009). In contrast to elsewhere in Asia, where it is strictly a montane species, on Timor and Wetar it occurs from sea level to the mountains.

BEHAVIOUR Generally keeps to dense undergrowth, hopping from perch to perch and feeding on or very close to the ground. However, at times it feeds openly in trees and shrubs several metres above the ground. Although it often goes undetected unless heard to call or sing, this is not a particularly skulking species and it can often be encountered feeding in scrub or low trees by a clearing or roadside. It nervously flicks its wings above its back when agitated, conspicuously flashing the whitish underwing-coverts. Males usually sing from an open perch up to 3m above the ground, but drop into low undergrowth once they stop singing.

BREEDING HABITS Little data is available and most information comes from Mount Kinabalu. Birds in breeding condition were reported there in February and July and mating was observed in late May (Smythies & Davison 1999). An empty nest discovered at 1,650m on Mount Kinabalu on 20 July consisted of a cup of dead grasses interwoven with live grass (Smythies & Davison 1999). No data is available on incubation and fledging periods.

DISTRIBUTION A wide-ranging species endemic to the Greater and Lesser Sundaic regions of Malaysia and Indonesia. Within the Greater Sundas, it breeds in montane forest on the upper slopes of the higher mountain ranges. Its isolation and sedentary nature has resulted in six endemic forms arising here, each restricted to either a mountain range or a single mountain massif. Two races in the eastern Lesser Sundas appear quite different from the other races and are each confined to a single island. Unlike the taxa occurring in the Greater Sundas, these two races occur at lower levels, reaching sea level on Timor.

C. v. vulcania is widespread in the mountains of Java and Bali between 1,500m and the tree line at 2,400m, and on neighbouring Lombok between 625m and 3,000m (Coates *et al.* 1997). In 1993, birds presumed to be of this race were discovered on Sumbawa between 1,500–1,850m on Gunung Tamora (Coates *et al.* 1997). This represents a slight eastwards range extension

C. v. flaviventris is endemic to stunted upper montane mossy forest at 2,100–3,400m in western and central Sumatra. It is recorded from the peaks of Gunung Talamau, Merapi, Singgalang and Kerinci in Barat Province and Gunung Dempu in Selatan Province (Marle & Voous 1988) and presumably occurs at similar elevations between these locations.

C. v. sepiaria breeds above 2,000m in the mountains of Aceh Province in N Sumatra, to the north of *flaviventris*.

C. v. oreophila is restricted to the submontane and montane forests on Mount Kinabalu in Sabah, Malaysia and possibly also on nearby Gunung Trus Madi. It is particularly numerous at 2,500–3,000m, but occurs widely from 1,400m to 3,700 m.

C. v. banksi is a widespread resident in the upland regions of northern Borneo, where it occurs throughout the Crocker Range in Sabah between 1,450m and 1,800m, except on Mount Kinabalu and Gunung Trus Madi, which is occupied by the race *oreophila*. It is common in the upper montane forest above 1,700m on Mount Mulu in Sarawak, Malaysia, to the south of the range of *oreophila*. To the southeast of Mount Mulu, another population that is probably also assignable to this form occurs in the uplands surrounding Mount Murud. In recent years, birds have been observed on Gunung Lunjut in the Kayan Mentarang Nature Reserve in Kalimantan, above 1,900m. It has been assumed that these birds are referable to *banksi*.

C. v. palawanae is confined to Mount Mantalingajan on Palawan, Philippines. It is only known from montane forest at *c.* 2,000m, in the summit region, although the extent of its altitudinal range is not established.

C. v. everetti is endemic to Timor, where it occurs from sea level to at least 2,300m, but mainly above 200m (Coates *et al.* 1997).

C. v. kolichisi is a recently discovered form, known to occur only from Alor where it occurs from 600–750m (Johnstone & Darnell 1997). Birds of an undetermined taxon were recently discovered on nearby Wetar, where it occurs from sea-level to the mountains (Trianor *et al.* 2009).

MOVEMENTS None documented. All island populations are believed resident and there is no evidence to suggest that any birds are migratory.

DESCRIPTION
C. v. vulcania
Plumage – Adult, fresh Forehead, crown and nape warm

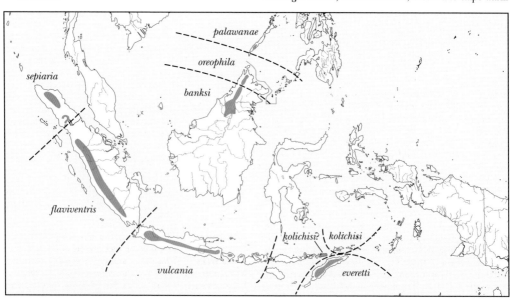

Sunda Bush Warbler. Resident within breeding range.

olive-brown. Supercilium dull creamy brown, long and narrow, from bill base to rear of ear-coverts, widening slightly over the eye. Loral line dark brown to blackish, well defined from the bill base to the eye. Eye-line well defined behind the eye, forming a distinct dark olive-brown line below the supercilium. Ear-coverts dull creamy white with olive-brown tips creating distinct mottling and merging with the eye-line to form a broad, diffuse smudge behind and below the eye. Lower cheeks tinged peachy brown and speckled olive-brown. Eye-ring narrow, creamy white, contrasting with darker ear-coverts. Mantle, scapulars, rump and uppertail-coverts unmarked warm olive-brown. Chin and throat white with a light rusty brown to peachy brown wash that intensifies towards the sides. Breast white with warm peachy buff wash that darkens near the carpal bend and extends below the ear-coverts to form a slightly paler mottled half-collar. Belly white, tinged peachy buff. Upper flanks suffused warm peachy buff, darkening to dull greyish brown on lower flanks, vent and undertail-coverts. Lesser and median coverts warm olive-brown, very similar to mantle. Greater coverts and tertials dull brown with rusty brown fringes, slightly warmer and brighter than mantle colour. Edges of primary coverts, secondaries and primaries dull rusty brown, tips of visible primaries showing no contrast with exposed webs. Alula dull with broad, diffuse rusty brown fringe. Tail feathers dark brown with dull rusty brown fringes. Underwing-coverts white to pale creamy yellow.

Adult worn Resembles fresh adult but slightly duller above and paler below. Supercilium slightly whiter and facial appearance more contrasting as warmer feather tips are lost. Crown and upperparts duller, with greyish brown tones more prominent. Underparts greyish white with a greyish brown wash on the sides of breast and flanks and most conspicuous towards the lower flanks and undertail-coverts. Wing-coverts, tertials and edges to primaries and secondaries and tail feathers dull brown, marginally warmer and brighter than upperparts.

Juvenile Young birds resemble adults but are dark olive-brown above with an ill-defined yellowish supercilium. Chin, throat, centre of breast and belly are yellow, while the sides of the breast and flanks are dark olive-buff.

Bare parts Upper mandible dark grey with pale pink cutting edge. Lower mandible dull greyish pink at base, darkening at sides towards tip. Tarsi and toes pale fleshy brown to greyish pink. Iris dull brown.

C. v. everetti

Plumage – Adult fresh Forehead, crown and nape light greyish brown, tinged olive. Supercilium white, tinged greyish, long and narrow, from the bill base to the rear of the ear-coverts. Lores marked a with distinct blackish line from the bill base to the eye. Eye-line appears as a black spot immediately behind eye, fading to pale olive-grey towards the rear of the ear-coverts. Ear-coverts white, tinged sandy brown to greyish brown; the darker grey tips usually creating faint mottling or speckling. Eye-ring inconspicuous, creamy white, merging with the supercilium and ear-coverts. Mantle and scapulars dull, pale greyish brown with slight olive wash. Rump and uppertail-coverts similar to mantle but olive wash often more pronounced. Chin and throat white with a faint greyish tinge towards sides, merging with the lower cheeks. Breast white with a delicate pale grey suffusion, warming and strengthening to pale peachy grey at the sides and extending to sides of neck below ear-coverts to form an indistinct half collar. Belly white. Upper flanks with pale grey suffusion, darkening to dull ash-brown on

the lower flanks and vent. Undertail-coverts pale creamy buff. Lesser and median coverts light greyish brown, similar in colour to mantle. Greater coverts and tertials dark grey with crisp narrow pale greyish tan fringes. Primary coverts, secondaries and primaries dark greyish brown, edged pale greyish tan. Visible primaries lack discernible pale tips. Alula inconspicuous, pale greyish brown. Tail feathers light brown, fringed pale greyish brown.

Adult worn Not known to differ from fresh adult.

Bare parts Upper mandible grey to greyish brown, paler than in nominate race, with pale pink cutting edge. Lower mandible pale greyish pink at base, darkening at the sides towards the tip. Tarsi and toes pale brownish pink to pale greyish pink, slightly paler than in nominate race. Iris dull brown.

IN HAND CHARACTERS
Measurements
C. v. vulcania, *C. v. flaviventris* and *C. v. oreophila* combined:

	Male	Female
Wing	50–56 (52.7; 6)	49–55 (51.7; 11)
Tail	51–57 (53.8; 6)	48–56 (51.7; 10)
Bill	14–15 (14.3; 6)	13.5–15 (14.0; 11)
Tarsus	22–25 (23.1; 6)	21.5–24.5 (23.0; 11)

Sexes combined:
Tail/wing ratio: 92–108% (101%; 17)
Bill width: 3.5–4.2 (3.8; 14)
Hind claw: 5.5–6.8 (6.1; 18)
Tail graduation: 11–12 (n = 3)
    Individual races, sexes combined; includes data from Johnson & Darnell (1997).
C. v. vulcania: wing 49–56 (53.1; 8); tail 45–57 (52.7; 7); bill 13.5–16 (14.3; 8); tarsus 22–25 (23.1; 8).
C. v. flaviventris: wing 50–55 (53.2; 6); tail 48–55 (51.8; 6); bill 13.5–14.5 (14.0; 6); tarsus 21.5–24.5 (22.9; 6).
C. v. oreophila: wing 49–53 (51.1; 6); tail 52–55 (52.7; 6); bill 14–15 (14.8; 6); tarsus 22–23 (23.5; 6).
C. v. everetti: wing 49–53 (50.8; 6); tail 48–53 (51.2; 5); bill 14–15 (14.6; 5); tarsus 21–22 (21.2; 5).
C. v. kolichisi: wing 45–49 (6).

Structure

C. v. vulcania

Wing formula (n = 5):

p1/pc	p2	p3e	p4e	p5e	p6e	p7(e)	p10
12–15	11–13	4–5	0–1.5	wp	wp	0.5–2	5–7

Wing resembles Brownish-flanked Bush Warbler (Fig. 118); strongly rounded with large p1 (c. 60% p2). Wing point p5–6; p2 < ss tips, p3 near ss tips; emargination on p3–6, sometimes also p7.
    Tail longish, graduated; feathers rather narrow.
    Bill rather small but strong, straight-sided.
    Tarsi long, rather slender, toes and claws weak.
Other races: *C. v. flaviventris* and *C. v. oreophila* are similar to *vulcania* in size and structure; *C. v. everetti* has a slimmer bill and shorter tarsus; *C. v. kolchisi* has a shorter wing than other races.
Weight No data available.

GEOGRAPHIC VARIATION Six races inhabit isolated 'islands' of upper montane forest within the Sundaic region and two are confined to islands in the Lesser Sundas. Substantial differences exist between some of these populations, mainly involving the tonal colour of the upperparts and, to a lesser extent, the underparts. Darker, more richly coloured races including nominate *vulcania*, *flaviventris*, *oreophila*, *sepiaria*, *banksi* and *palawanae* occur in the Greater Sundas and the adjacent islands of Lombok and Sumbawa. Within Sumatra and Borneo, populations separated by tracts of lowland forest show minor differences that merit sub-specific recognition, indicating that there is very little movement between them. In addition, Wells (1982) acknowledged that the vocalisations of the birds on Lombok are unknown and the bird had not been recorded there since its original discovery, while the population on Sumbawa had not then been discovered. In isolation, all these populations have evolved into distinct forms, separated by tracts of inhospitable humid lowland forest, which clearly represents a very real obstacle to movement and dispersal.

The races *everetti* and *kolichisi* are geographically isolated in a drier region of the Lesser Sundas. Their taxonomic position is uncertain and it is possible that they represent at least one distinct species. Johnstone & Darnell (1997) found that the song of *everetti* differs from that of nominate *vulcania* and also from that of *kolichisi*. They noted that the rectrices of these races are narrower than in the nominate form. The placement of *everetti* and *palawanae* within *vulcania* was considered provisional by Wells (1982).

C. v. vulcania (Java, Bali, Lombok and Sumbawa) Described above.

C. v. flaviventris (C and S Sumatra) Slightly darker and browner above than the nominate race, especially when fresh, with olive tones generally subdued or absent. The edges and fringes of the wing feathers are slightly warmer than the upperparts, appearing as a richer brown panel in the closed wing. The supercilium is darker and slightly narrower, washed pale rusty brown, and the side of the head is darker rufous-brown and appears less contrasting than in the nominate race. The underparts are strikingly darker, with the throat greyish brown and breast washed rich warm sepia, with the sides and flanks darker rufous-brown. However, the belly and ventral region are white with a faint buffy yellow wash.

C. v. sepiaria (N Sumatra) A poorly defined race, closely resembling *flaviventris*. Differs mainly in its overall slightly duller appearance.

C. v. oreophila (Mount Kinabalu, Sabah). Generally darker than the nominate race, lacking the warmer and richer tones above and the warmer wash to the underparts. When fresh, the supercilium is whitish, tipped olive-brown and particularly subdued behind the eye. The crown and upperparts vary from dull mahogany-brown to dull greyish brown and lack an olive tone. The fringes and edges to the wing feathers are warm chestnut, appearing brighter than the upperparts. The chin and throat are dull pale grey, darkening to grey-brown across the breast and onto the sides of the neck, becoming dark sepia-brown along the flanks and appearing darkest across the ventral region and on the undertail coverts.

C. v. banksi (Sabah and Sarawak) A poorly defined race that closely resembles *oreophila* but is slightly darker above.

C. v. palawanae (Mount Mantalingajan, Palawan) Closely resembles *oreophila* but the supercilium is pale olive-yellow rather than whitish and the upperparts are uniformly dark chestnut. The underparts differ in having a pale yellow-buff wash to the throat, centre of breast and belly, and a brighter, richer olive tone to the flanks and undertail-coverts.

C. v. everetti (Timor) Described above. Compared with the nominate form, the upperparts are slightly paler greyish brown with a slight olive wash. Much paler below. Breast white, washed pale grey and darkening to pale peachy grey at the sides. Supercilium conspicuous and whitish. Slightly smaller than the nominate race.

C. v. kolichisi (Alor) A small pale race that closely resembles *everetti*. It differs in its greyish brown crown, the lack of a pronounced olive tone to the upperparts, and the pale greyish brown edges and fringes to the wing-coverts, primaries and secondaries. The greyish white supercilium is poorly defined, but the dark greyish brown eyestripe gives a contrasting facial appearance. The underparts are dusky white but the sides of the breast and flanks are washed brownish grey as in *everetti*. Similar to *everetti* in size, but wing slightly shorter and bill slightly longer and thinner.

TAXONOMY AND SYSTEMATICS It has become increasingly likely that Sunda Bush Warbler actually consists of two or more species. For example, Wells (1982) considered that the placing of *palawanae* and *everetti* within *C. vulcania* was provisional and their true position had yet to be defined. Substantial individual variation and overlap exists both within and between these taxa. For example, birds breeding in the drier climate of the eastern Lesser Sundas may have developed a paler plumage in response to environmental or climatic factors. This may have resulted in these birds appearing quite different from those in the Greater Sundas but it is unclear whether this change is superficial, or reflected in fundamental genetic differences.

The taxonomic affinities of the recently discovered population on Wetar have yet to be established. Although Wetar lies adjacent to Alor where the race *kolichisi* is resident, it is uncertain whether these birds are the same as the Alor birds, or whether they represent an undescribed sub-species.

Until recently, most authorities (e.g. Vaurie 1959; Watson *et al.* 1986) considered Sunda Bush Warbler to be conspecific with or closely related to Brownish-flanked Bush Warbler. A recent investigation of phylogenetic relationships within *Cettia* by Olsson *et al.* (2006) has shown that Sunda Bush Warbler and Aberrant Bush Warbler are each other's closest relatives. Moreover, they established also that the taxa breeding in China (*intricata*) and Indochina (*oblita*), treated as races of Aberrant Bush Warbler, are more closely related to Sunda Bush Warbler than to Himalayan taxa included within Aberrant Bush Warbler. Based upon these findings, they concluded that the systematic arrangement of this group may require revision.

Olsson *et al.* (2006) suggested that this unusual distribution arose from an initial colonisation of the Sundaic Region by an ancestral form of Aberrant Bush Warbler from continental Asia. This was followed by a period of radiation throughout SE Asia, during which extensive areas were colonised. At some point, birds from southeast Asia which had diverged from the ancestral form recolonised continental Asia, leading to the present day distribution in China and Vietnam.

Although Olsson *et al.* (2006) adopted the inclusion of

the mainland taxa, *intricata* and *oblita*, within Sunda Bush Warbler, we consider that this arrangement sits awkwardly. Furthermore, *intricata* and *oblita* are largely inseparable from the allopatric Aberrant Bush Warbler of the E Himalayas although differences in song are helpful. Until the full extent and limits of variation are better understood, we have excluded *intricata* and *oblita* from Sunda Bush Warbler, which comprises the eight taxa discussed here. Further discussion on the position of *intricata* and *oblita* is given under Aberrant Bush Warbler.

▲ Adult *C. v. vulcania*, Java, March. Nominate race shows warm olive-brown upperparts, contrasting with unmarked pale cream chin and throat and warmer breast and flanks (Neville Kemp).

▲ Adult *C. v. oreophila*, Mount Kinabalu, Sabah, Malaysia, June. Generally darker than nominate race, with dull mahogany-brown upperparts and warm chestnut-brown fringes and edges to flight feathers. Underparts much darker than in nominate, ranging from grey-brown to sepia-brown, and showing less contrast with upperparts (David Bakewell).

ABERRANT BUSH WARBLER
Cettia flavolivacea   **Plate 38**

Neornis flavolivacea **Blyth, 1845.** *J. Asiatic Soc. Bengal* 14: 590. Nepal.

An altitudinal migrant that breeds fairly commonly across the southern Himalayas and into the mountains of W and SW China, Burma and N Indochina. It has traditionally been regarded as a single species comprising six or more races. Recent molecular studies have revealed a close phylogenetic relationship between Aberrant Bush and Sunda Bush Warbler, suggesting that Aberrant Bush Warbler (*sensu lato*) comprises two distinct species with differing phylogeny (Olsson *et al.* 2006). Racial differences within Aberrant Bush Warbler are poorly defined, and consequently much of the historical data cannot be assigned to a particular taxon. For clarity and simplicity, therefore, we have continued to treat Aberrant Bush Warbler as a single species, but whenever it has been possible to identify specific data, we have treated each lineage as distinct. Polytypic, with five races placed within two lineages.

Himalayan lineage

C. f. flavolivacea (Blyth, 1845). Himalayas from Uttarakhand to Arunachal Pradesh, India and Tibet (Xizang Autonomous Region).

C. f. weberi (Mayr, 1941). NE India (Nagaland, Mizoram, Manipur) and W Burma (Chin Hills).

C. f. stresemanni (Koelz, 1954). Meghalaya, NE India.

Chinese lineage

C. f. intricata (Hartert, 1909). N and E Burma, C China.

C. f. oblita (Mayr, 1941). N Laos, NW Vietnam.

IDENTIFICATION Length 12–13cm. Wing 51–58mm. Tail/wing 90–108%.

Perhaps the most readily recognisable of all the Himalayan *Cettia* and the only species within its range to show a combination of a strong yellow wash to the entire underparts and dull olive-brown upperparts. Sexes alike.

Structure Similar to other Himalayan *Cettia*, although slightly larger and proportionately longer-tailed than Brownish-flanked Bush, Hume's Bush and Yellow-bellied Bush Warblers. It has a typical rounded crown but a slightly more attenuated and less thickset and rounded body than Brownish-flanked Bush Warbler shows. The wing is exceptionally short and rounded, with a long first primary, while the outer primaries are closely bunched at the wing-tip to form a very short primary projection. The wing point is formed by p5, sometimes together with p4, and p3–7 are emarginated.

Plumage and bare parts This is a particularly distinctive *Cettia*, and often the most straightforward of the Himalayan species to identify. The chin and throat are bright, rich sulphur-yellow, the breast is similar but suffused dull olive-green and sullied darker fulvous-brown at the sides. The flanks are a darker olive and the lower underparts sullied but still largely yellowish in appearance. A narrow but conspicuous yellow supercilium extends from the bill to the rear of the ear-coverts, bordered below by a narrow, dark olive eye-stripe, while the ear-coverts are mottled yellow and brown. The upperparts are dull, oily olive-brown or drab brown with a light olive wash, although the rump and uppertail-coverts are slightly warmer and paler. The edges to the tertials, primaries, secondaries and tail feathers are tinged rufescent-brown and appear brighter than the upperparts.

The bill is dark grey to blackish, with a dull pink base to the lower mandible which darkens at the sides towards the tip. Tarsi and toes are pale flesh to plumbeous-pink.

SIMILAR SPECIES Juveniles of other *Cettia* species breeding within the range of Aberrant Bush Warbler can also show extensively yellowish underparts and many can approach the colour of Aberrant Bush Warbler, so care is required. Juvenile *Cettia* are most likely to be encountered between June and August. During this period, the separation of juveniles lurking within dense understorey will be difficult and identification will probably rely on accompanying adults. From September onwards, almost all juvenile *Cettia* will have moulted into a plumage that resembles the adult, leaving Aberrant Bush Warbler as the only species with extensively yellow-washed underparts. Note that on some races the yellow wash is subdued and the appearance can resemble Brownish-flanked Bush Warbler. Yellow-bellied Bush and Hume's Bush Warblers also show some yellow on the underparts, but this is invariably paler and restricted to the belly.

Yellow-bellied Bush and **Hume's Bush Warblers** are the only other *Cettia* occurring in continental Asia that show yellow underparts when adult, although there is individual variation and the yellow may be extremely subdued in some Hume's Bush Warblers. They differ from Aberrant Bush Warbler in their smaller size and much less conspicuous pale primrose-yellow underparts, lacking the deeper sulphur-yellow and olive-yellow tones of Aberrant Bush Warbler. In both species, the yellow tones are most apparent across the lower breast and belly, but become ochre-buff towards the sides of the upper breast, while the lower flanks and undertail-coverts are warm buff, washed with pale yellow. See also under Yellow-bellied Bush Warbler.

VOICE The song is a loud, rich and powerful melodic whistle with a slightly wavering quality. It often begins with several rapid but quiet '*thripp*' calls, although these are not always given at the start of each sequence.

Himalayan lineage The song of the nominate race comprises two components that merge seamlessly with each other. The first is a short series of flat, dry and slightly slurred '*titititi*' or '*drdrdrdr*' notes with a slight rattling quality, and this phrase is immediately followed by a liquid, plaintive whistle, variously described '*pueeeeuu*', *plueeeweew-ju*' or '*tueeeee-weeu*' rising in the '*eee*' and falling in the '*uu*' notes. Each complete song sequence can be described '*titititi-pueeeeuu*' or '*drdrdrdr-plueeeweew-ju*', within a frequency range of 2–5kHz. It lasts for *c.* 1.5 seconds and is repeated at intervals of about two seconds.

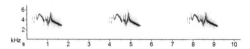

Song of Aberrant Bush Warbler, recorded within breeding range of *C. f. flavolivacea***, Nepal, May. (Connop 1993)**

Chinese lineage The song of *intricata* differs from that of nominate *flavolivacea* in its slightly more powerful and varied delivery, with a rising inflection from 3–7kHz. Unlike *flavolivacea*, it comprises a repetitive single slurred '*weedlededuweeeeeeez*', or '*plupleeapluuuuu–e*', initially rising in pitch, then decreasing slightly and finally increasing in frequency with an emphasis on the final '*eeez*' or '*–e*'. Each song sequence lasts approximately one second, followed by a pause of 3–4 seconds before being repeated.

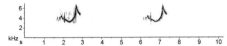

Song of Aberrant Bush Warbler, recorded within breeding range of *C. f. intricata*, Emei Shan, Sichuan Province, China, May. (Geoff Carey)

The most frequently heard call is an excited and quite buzzy, rapid and at times almost trilling '*trrrrrt, trrrrrt*', given erratically sometimes up to twice per second but often with longer pauses between. Also reported to give a dry and slightly slurred '*tsick*'. There are no known call differences between the two lineages.

MOULT No data available.

HABITAT Poorly known during the breeding season. Occurs in scrub and tall grass bordering broadleaf and evergreen forest, in overgrown clearings and sometimes in undergrowth and bamboo inside forest. Stuart Baker (1924) found it in thick scrub and long grass in pine, oak and rhododendron forests at elevations up to 3,500m. In winter, it descends to areas of scrub and long grass in foothills. Birds breeding in Assam occur in pine forest amongst the undergrowth of *Daphne* bushes.

BEHAVIOUR Shows typical skulking *Cettia* behaviour. Tends to frequent more open aspects within its habitat, appearing on the edge of clearings or along paths, where it hops nervously along the ground close to cover, continuously flicking its wings.

BREEDING HABITS Stuart Baker (1924) described the nest as built into a tuft of grass close to the ground. It is a domed structure of dried grass, lined with dried leaves and feathers. Nests with eggs have been recorded in June and August.

DISTRIBUTION Five very similar taxa breed across the southern slopes of the Himalayas from N Uttarakhand in NW India to W Burma and into the mountains of W China, with an isolated population in N Vietnam and N Laos. As discussed in **Taxonomy and Systematics**, the five taxa comprising Aberrant Bush Warbler form two distinct clades or lineages (Olsson *et al.* 2006), which has implications for all past specimen and sight records from NE India and SW China where the ranges may meet, particularly outside the breeding season.

Himalayan lineage

C. f. flavolivacea breeds throughout much of the southern Himalayas from Garhwal and Kumaon in Uttarakhand, NW India, east through Nepal and Sikkim to Bhutan and probably into W Arunachal Pradesh and north to the Qamdo district of Tibet (Xizang Autonomous Region). It is largely absent from W Nepal, but common east of the Kali Gandaki valley in C Nepal, breeding at 2,400–3,600m and descending to adjacent foothills between 1,830m and 915m outside the breeding season (Inskipp & Inskipp 1991). It is an uncommon altitudinal migrant in Bhutan, rare in the west but widespread in the east, where it occurs in summer between 1,800m and 3,400m (Spierenburg 2005). Outside the breeding season it descends to foothills between 600m and 2,400m, where it appears to be fairly widespread.

C. f. stresemanni is an altitudinal migrant that breeds in the hills to the south of the Brahmaputra River, where it is confined to Meghalaya and western Assam. It breeds from 1,200m to at least 2,100m, descending in winter to the foothills, usually below 1,000m.

C. f. weberi breeds from 1,100m to 2,900m in the hills of Nagaland, Manipur and eastern Mizoram in NE India, and in adjacent parts of NW Burma south to at least the region of Mount Victoria in the Chin Hills. Outside the breeding season, birds breeding at lower elevations are resident while those at higher elevations descend to winter below 1,000m.

Chinese lineage

C. f. intricata breeds widely in W China including N Yunnan and C and N Sichuan Provinces, northeast through the Qinling Mountains in S Shaanxi Province to SE Shanxi Province. It is believed to be a short-distance altitudinal migrant that descends to the foothills below the breeding range during the winter months.

C. f. oblita is restricted to N Laos and West Tonkin in N Vietnam. Reports of Aberrant Bush Warbler from NW Thailand (Lekagul & Round 1991), and from C and S Yunnan Province in China (JH *in litt.*), during the northern winter may refer to this form.

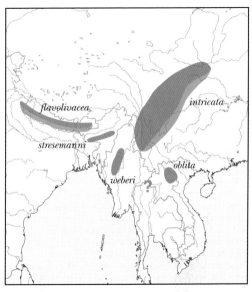

Aberrant Bush Warbler. Mostly resident but some disperse to lower elevations outside the breeding season.

MOVEMENTS An altitudinal migrant that leaves the higher breeding areas to winter in the foothills, where it has been recorded down to 600m in Bhutan. There are no documented movements between the wintering and breeding areas. Birds breeding at higher elevations in Sichuan Province descend to the lower slopes in winter, when they may form small flocks.

DESCRIPTION *C. f. flavolivacea*

Plumage – Adult fresh Forehead, crown and nape dull olive-brown. Supercilium yellowish olive, extending from bill base to rear of the ear-coverts; narrow above lores and broadest above eye and over ear-coverts, where it terminates abruptly. Loral line dark olive-green, well defined from bill base to eye. A distinct dark olive-green line behind the eye below supercilium. Ear-coverts dull olive with fine rich yellow streaking and flecking, almost uniform dull yellow below the eye. Eye-ring dull yellow, poorly defined. Mantle and scapulars dull oily olive-brown, contrasting with slightly warmer, richer brown rump and uppertail-coverts.

Chin and throat rich sulphur-yellow to ochre-yellow; breast similar but tinged dull olive-green, most intensely towards sides. Belly paler yellow, less rich, than throat, with diffuse white feathering towards centre. Flanks, ventral region and undertail-coverts yellow, suffused dull olive-green. Lesser, median, greater and primary coverts uniform dull, oily, olive-brown, similar to mantle. Entire upperparts thus appear plain and uniform. Tertials dull, oily, olive-brown with marginally warmer fringes. Edges of secondaries and primaries warm brown, slightly paler than mantle and lacking olive tones, tips showing no contrast with exposed webs. Alula uniform dull olive-brown. Tail feathers dark brown with dull rusty brown fringes. Underwing-coverts pale primrose-yellow, slightly paler than flanks.

Adult worn As fresh adult but yellow tones to underparts are subdued, with chin, throat and belly becoming dull brownish white to sandy brown, flanks and undertail-coverts pale sandy brown, lacking olive tones. Supercilium slightly paler, dull buffish white. Ear-coverts dull brown with fine white flecking. Top of head and upperparts remain dull olive-brown and rump and uppertail-coverts still retain slightly warmer brown appearance.

Juvenile Similar to adult but entire underparts are brighter yellow.

Bare parts Upper mandible dark grey with pale pink cutting edge. Lower mandible dull greyish pink at base, darkening at sides towards tip. Tarsi and toes variable, pale fleshy brown to greyish pink. Iris dull brown.

IN HAND CHARACTERS
Measurements

Himalayan lineage

C. f. flavolivacea

	Male	Female
Wing	52–58 (55.0; 8)	51–54 (52.7; 6)
Tail	49–56 (52.4; 8)	48–54 (50.7; 6)
Bill	13.5–14.5 (14.0; 7)	13.5–15 (14.3; 5)
Tarsus	22–24 (22.7; 7)	21.5–24 (22.8; 5)

Sexes combined:
Tail/wing ratio: 90–100% (95%; 33)
Bill width: 3.3–3.8 (3.5; 10)
Hind claw: 5.8–7.0 (6.5; 19)
Tail graduation: 11–14 (12.7; 9)
C. f. weberi (n = 5, unsexed): *wing* 48–54 (52.4); *tail* 53–57 (55.2); *bill* 13–14.5 (13.9); *tarsus* 21–23 (21.8). Tail relatively long, tail/wing ratio 100–108% (105%; 5).

Chinese lineage
C. f. intricata (n = 2): *wing* 51, 53; *tail* 48, 51; *bill* 13; *tarsus* 22.5–23.

Structure

C. f. flavolivacea

Wing formula (n = 5):

p1/pc	p2	p3e	p4e	p5e	p6e	p7e	p10
11–15	12–13	4–5	0–1	wp	wp	0.5–3	5–9

Wing resembles Brownish-flanked Bush Warbler (Fig. 118); strongly rounded with large p1 (*c.* 60% p2). Wing

point p5–6; p2 < ss tips, p3 = p8/9; emargination on p3–7.

Tail longish, graduated; feathers rather narrow.

Bill slender, but larger than in Yellow-bellied Bush Warbler.

Tarsi longish, stronger than in Yellow-bellied Bush Warbler.

Other races: *C. f. intricata* has a distinctly smaller bill. Wing as *flavolivacea*.

Recognition Shows a distinctive combination of olive-brown upperparts, narrow yellow supercilium and extensive yellow wash below. Distinguished from Yellow-bellied Bush Warbler by rich yellow throat and breast; also by longer tail and, typically, larger bill and tarsus measurements. Note several species of Himalayan *Cettia* have yellow underparts, particularly when in juvenile plumage, and are confusable with Aberrant Bush Warbler.

Ageing Impossible to age in the field once post-juvenile moult is complete. In the hand, only the presence of retained juvenile feathers will establish this age class.

Weight Thailand: 6.7–7.7g (7.3; 5) (PDR unpublished data).

GEOGRAPHIC VARIATION The five very similar races with overlapping characters fall into two lineages. The separation criteria of these remain largely unknown and they present a real identification challenge. It is uncertain whether silent birds in SW China and NE India can be safely separated and even trapped birds may not be distinguishable in the hand.

Himalayan lineage
C. f. flavolivacea (Himalayas from Uttarakhand to Arunachal Pradesh and SW China) Described above.
C. f. stresemanni (Meghalaya and W Assam) Differs only slightly from the nominate race. On average, it is usually marginally darker green and slightly browner above, with underparts slightly more sullied and the yellow tones slightly subdued. These differences are only detectable when in fresh plumage and it may not be possible to assign a particular individual to this race. Occasional individuals may lack yellow on underparts, which then appear dull olive-grey (although possibly these may be wintering birds of the taxon *intricata*).
C. f. weberi (Nagaland, Mizoram, Manipur to Chin Hills) Recognisably distinct from the two previous races. Slightly warmer and less olivaceous above than the nominate form, and somewhat similar to Brownish-flanked Bush Warbler. The underparts lack the richer ochre tones of the nominate form and appear slightly yellower and paler on the breast and belly, often with a light buff wash across the breast. The flanks are marginally browner or buffier.

Chinese lineage
C. f. intricata (N and E Burma, C China) Closely resembles *flavolivacea* and particularly *stresemanni*. Differs in its slightly darker and browner upperparts in which the olive tones are largely subdued, while the yellow tones to the underparts are paler and faded and the flanks are washed warmer buff. Resembles Brownish-flanked Bush but underparts show distinct yellow-ochre tone.
C. f. oblita (N Laos, NW Vietnam) This is a poorly defined form that may not be separable from *intricata*. On average, it is slightly brighter olive above than *intricata* with the yellow wash to the underparts appearing more distinct and flanks washed warmer buff. However, individual variation within *intricata* suggests that some may not be separable from *oblita*.

TAXONOMY AND SYSTEMATICS A recent molecular genetic study by Olsson *et al.* (2006) established that the taxa *intricata* and *oblita*, breeding in China and Vietnam respectively, are not the closest relatives of the Himalayan races of Aberrant Bush Warbler, but comprise a distinct lineage more closely related to Sunda Bush Warbler. Their research suggested that Sunda Bush Warbler originated from an ancestral form of Aberrant Bush Warbler in the Himalayas, which spread south into the Sundaic region, where what is now Sunda Bush Warbler became established. Secondary colonisation of the Asian mainland by an ancestral Sundaic form occurred at a later date, at a point when Sunda Bush Warbler had diverged sufficiently from Aberrant Bush Warbler to form a distinct species. The populations now occurring in N Vietnam and N Laos and C China are believed to be derived from this secondary colonisation event. These findings are acknowledged, but have not been fully adopted here and we continue to treat *intricata* and *oblita* as races of Aberrant Bush Warbler.

The races *intricata* and *oblita* so closely resemble those of the Himalayan lineage of Aberrant Bush Warbler in appearance that their separation may not be possible, particularly when dealing with silent birds in winter. Between the populations from Vietnam and China, there is minimal genetic divergence, *c.* 0.3% or less, indicating that gene flow is probably still occurring, or that they have only recently become separated (Olsson *et al.* 2006).

▲ Adult *C. f. weberi*, Burma, February. Upperparts slightly warmer, less olivaceous than nominate and similar to Brownish-flanked Bush Warbler. Underparts lack richer ochre tones, at best appearing slightly yellower and paler on breast and belly, often with light buff wash across breast (John and Jemi Holmes).

▲ Adult *C. f. intricata*, Sichuan, China, January. Differs from nominate *flavolivacea* and *stresemanni* by slightly darker and browner upperparts with olive tones, while yellow tones to underparts are subdued and faded, and flanks are washed warmer buff (Sid and Meggie Francis).

▲ Adult *C. f. intricata*, Sichuan, China, May. Note cleaner yellow tone to chin and throat, and rich sulphur-yellow to ochre-yellow underparts of this bird. Photographed within the breeding range of *intricata*, it is reminiscent of nominate *flavolivacea* (Nick Athanas).

BROWNISH-FLANKED BUSH WARBLER
Cettia fortipes   **Plate 39**

Horornis fortipes **Hodgson, 1845**. *Proc. Zool. Soc. London*, page 31. Nepal.

The most widespread of the *Cettia* in continental Asia. A short-distance altitudinal migrant breeding widely across the Himalayas from Pakistan to SW China and from the mountains and hills of C, S and SE China to Taiwan. Polytypic, with four races recognised:

C. f. fortipes (Hodgson, 1845). E Nepal to Bhutan, NE India, N Burma and adjacent SW China.

C. f. davidiana (Verreaux, 1871). C, S and SE China; also (presumably this race) N Laos and N Vietnam.

C. f. pallida (Brooks, 1872). NE Pakistan and Kashmir to W Nepal.

C. f. robustipes (Swinhoe, 1866). Taiwan.

IDENTIFICATION Length 11–12cm. Wing 47–60mm. Tail/wing 82–96%.

A mid sized *Cettia* with dingy brown plumage and a contrasting head pattern. Its song is highly distinctive and is the single best means of separating it from other *Cettia* species of similar appearance and structure. This song remains remarkably consistent throughout its range from the western Himalayas to Taiwan. Sexes alike.

Structure All races share a similar structure and posture, with a distinctly rounded crown, a plump, deep-bellied appearance to the body and a relatively long tail. The wings are short and rounded, with a large first primary (p1), the wing point is formed by p5–6 and the primary projection is short. The wings are typically held slightly spread and drooped along the sides of the body, making it difficult to establish the exact position of the longer primaries. The tail is slightly shorter than the wings and often held slightly cocked.

Plumage and bare parts This is a fairly drab and nondescript warbler but it shows some variation, with four races recognised. However, the effects of wear and lighting conditions can affect the appearance of individuals within the same taxon, making it difficult to assign a single bird to a particular race. All races are characterised by a fairly indistinct supercilium, invariably most conspicuous in front of the eye. This is bordered below by a short dark eye-stripe, again best defined in front of the eye and sometimes almost absent behind it. The crown, nape and mantle vary from uniform warm russet-brown to dull cold olive-brown, this variation being subject to age, plumage condition and race. All races show warm rusty brown outer webs to the primaries and secondaries that contrast with the darker and slightly drabber upperparts. The underparts show a greater degree of variation, ranging from brownish grey with pale buff flanks and breast sides in the nominate form to greyish white on the lower flanks in worn adults of the race *pallida*, which also shows the most marked contrast with the upperparts. This variation is discussed in greater detail under **Geographic Variation**.

The bill is dark grey with a pale yellowish pink lower mandible, darkening slightly towards the tip. The legs and feet are pale brownish pink.

SIMILAR SPECIES Brownish-flanked Bush Warbler occurs alongside a further six species of *Cettia*. Most are readily separable using a combination of plumage and structural characters, while vocal differences are diagnostic. Of the likely confusion species, Yellow-bellied Bush Warbler and Hume's Bush Warbler most closely resemble Brownish-flanked Bush Warbler. The remaining species all show well marked differences from Brownish-flanked Bush Warbler; the contrasting chestnut crown colour of Chestnut-crowned Bush Warbler and Grey-sided Bush Warbler; the yellow underparts and dull, oily olive-brown upperparts of Aberrant Bush Warbler; and the long pale supercilium, short tail and conspicuously pale pink legs of Pale-footed Bush Warbler.

Yellow-bellied Bush Warbler and **Hume's Bush Warbler** closely resemble each other and both share a similar structure with Brownish-flanked Bush Warbler. Their combined ranges overlap with Brownish-flanked from the C Himalayas east through the mountains of C and E China to Taiwan. Separation of adults of these species, particularly singing males, is straightforward when they are seen well. While plumage differences are diagnostic, it is differences in song that provide the best and most reliable means of identification. The explosive far carrying '*cheee wichew*' song of Brownish-flanked Bush Warbler lasts no more than two seconds. In contrast, the remarkable song of Yellow-bellied Bush can last for over half a minute, 'winding up' with up to 35 long, high pitched and ascending whistles, then transforming into a descending, slowing clicking trill. Hume's Bush Warbler has an equally distinctive but slightly less remarkable song consisting of a few discordant whistles followed by a slow wobbling trill, repeated several times with brief pauses.

The separation of silent birds relies on plumage characters. Adult Yellow-bellied and Hume's Bush Warblers appear distinctly paler than Brownish-flanked and show a warmer brown crown and slightly greyer nape and mantle, while the warm brown edges to their wing and tail feathers contrast with a colder mantle tone. In both species, the supercilium tends to be broader, longer and better defined than in Brownish-flanked, especially behind the eye, and the narrow dark eyestripe more conspicuous.

In the Himalayas, the yellow on the underparts of Hume's Bush Warbler is subdued or even absent. There is, however, usually a hint of yellow or warm buff along the flanks, quite different from the dull brown tones of nominate Brownish-flanked. Separation should be reasonably straightforward given good views. In China, Yellow-bellied Bush Warbler shows a distinctly yellowish wash to the underparts that adult Brownish-flanked always lacks. In SE China, however, Brownish-flanked of the race *davidiana* is paler above than nominate birds and more closely approaches the upperpart tones of Yellow-bellied Bush Warbler. On Taiwan, Brownish-flanked Bush Warbler of the race *robustipes* is particularly dull, showing little contrast between the upperparts and underparts, so separation here is relatively easy.

The separation of first-winter Yellow-bellied Bush and Brownish-flanked Bush Warblers presents an exceptionally difficult challenge, particularly in SE China. Here, some Yellow-bellied Bush Warblers appear to lack yellow tones, are warmer and browner above and closely resemble immature Brownish-flanked Bush Warblers. Even in the hand there are no consistent or diagnostic differences in biometrics or wing structure. For example, four birds trapped for ringing in Hong Kong and initially identified as Yellowish-bellied Bush Warblers later proved, following DNA investigation, to be Brownish-flanked Bush Warblers (PJL *in litt.*).

VOICE The song is a characteristic cheerful whistle followed immediately by a short, explosive song, comprising three or four short notes delivered rapidly, which form a terminal flourish. This distinctive and cheery song is similar and readily recognisable throughout the range. There are slight differences in the tone and pitch of the warbling element and also in the timing between each song burst, but this appears to reflect individual rather than geographic variation.

The song begins with a drawn-out whistle, sometimes with a slight wavering or stuttering quality. It is delivered at a frequency of 2–3kHz for between one and two seconds and slowly increases in volume. This leads immediately into a rapid warbling comprising two or three notes that rise and fall in pitch between 2–6kHz and lasting no more than one second. It is this second element of the song which has the characteristic 'explosive' character, described as '*wichew*' or '*wi-chew-eee*'. The full song, described as '*cheee wichew*' or '*eeeeee wi-chew-eee*' is repeated regularly at intervals of 10 to 30 seconds, occasionally more frequently, each repetition being similar to the previous sequence and retaining the explosive character. There is very little variation in song across the breeding range.

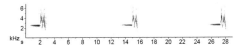

Song of Brownish-flanked Bush Warbler, recorded within breeding range of *C. f. fortipes*, Trongsa, Bhutan, April. (Peter Kennerley)

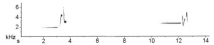

Song of Brownish-flanked Bush Warbler, recorded within breeding range of *C. f. davidiana*, Wu Yi Shan, Fujian Province, China, May. (Geoff Carey)

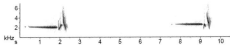

Song of Brownish-flanked Bush Warbler, recorded within breeding range of *C. f. robustipes*, An Ma Shan, Taiwan, April. (Peter Kennerley)

The call is a hard, short and clipped '*tak*' or '*chak*', repeated at regular intervals of 1–2 seconds by foraging birds. Calling frequency and intensity increases when several birds are together and excited, and may become almost continuous.

MOULT No data available but presumed not to differ from other Himalayan *Cettia*.

HABITAT When breeding, it inhabits the warm temperate regions of the lower Himalayas and subtropical regions in the hills and mountains of the Sino-Himalayan region. It occupies a wide range of thick scrub and dense undergrowth where the presence of scattered, open deciduous and evergreen woodland within breeding territories seems important. It also occurs regularly in similar situations within regenerating secondary woodland but appears to avoid primary and dense secondary forest where undergrowth is reduced.

Birds that winter at lower elevations occur on low hills and hillsides covered with dense grass and scattered bushes. The presence of scattered trees seems less important at this season, however, and birds are found in a wide range of scrub and grassland habitats.

BEHAVIOUR Shy and skulking, usually remaining low in thick cover where it can be extremely difficult to view, typically affording only brief glimpses. Feeding birds often descend to forage on the ground amongst leaf litter, hopping onto lower branches and moving through the lower layers of scrub in search of insects. Occasionally flies between bushes but rarely pauses to permit good views. It behaves in a typical *Cettia* manner, cocking its tail and drooping its wings along the flanks. Calls frequently, so following its progress though thick undergrowth is usually possible. It responds well to a taped rendition of the song and may then emerge from dense scrub to climb into view in the lower branches of a large bush or tree.

The start of the song period for resident birds is unknown. In Hong Kong, where it is primarily a scarce winter visitor, song is heard occasionally from early February and regularly from late February until departure to the higher hills in March. Song is regular in the breeding areas from mid March until at least mid June.

BREEDING HABITS Recorded as nesting in scrub under the open canopy of secondary forest. The nest is placed low down in a small bush or within thick undergrowth with vines. It is a deep cup built of grass blades and stems and lined with soft feathers. A semi-domed, or even a completely domed nest with an entrance at the side, is sometimes built. Usually-double brooded, with nesting beginning in May or early June and the second brood following in July or August. Little is known of its nesting habits. Four or five eggs are laid, but incubation and fledging periods are unknown.

DISTRIBUTION Brownish-flanked Bush Warbler breeds in the foothills of the mountain ranges and higher hills of S Asia, from the W Himalayas to E China and Taiwan. Those breeding at lower elevations and in warmer regions are resident throughout the year or disperse outside the breeding season, while those breeding at higher elevations descend to the foothills at the onset of cooler weather. Four races are recognised.

C. f. pallida Breeds in the lower W Himalayas between 1,800m and 3,000m. In NE Pakistan it is widely distributed from lower Swat through Indus Kohistan, Hazara and Azad Kashmir districts, and the Murree Hill range (Roberts 1992). In northern India, it breeds through Kashmir, Himachal Pradesh and Uttarakhand and reaches its eastern limit in W Nepal where it is considered rare (Inskipp & Inskipp 1991).

C. f. fortipes The nominate form breeds across the lower slopes of the Himalayas between 2,000m and 3,300m, from the Ilam district of eastern Nepal where it is locally fairly common (CI *in litt.*), through Bhutan between 1,400m and 2,800m and occasionally higher, and into Arunachal Pradesh. South of the Brahmaputra River it breeds at slightly lower elevations, between 1,200m and 2,000m, in the hills of the states of Meghalaya and Mizoram in NE India. There are no confirmed breeding records for Bangladesh (Rasmussen & Anderton 2005) but it has been reported from the Chittagong region. The breeding range also extends into NW Burma and adjacent regions of SW China in S Yunnan Province and Tibet (Xizang Autonomous Region). Outside the breeding season, this race descends to winter in the foothills, ranging between 1,400m and 2,135m in Nepal in December (CI *in litt.*) and it has been recorded as low as 600m in Bhutan (Spierenburg 2005).

C. f. davidiana Breeds in S and E China from SE Gansu and S Shaanxi Provinces, south through Sichuan to

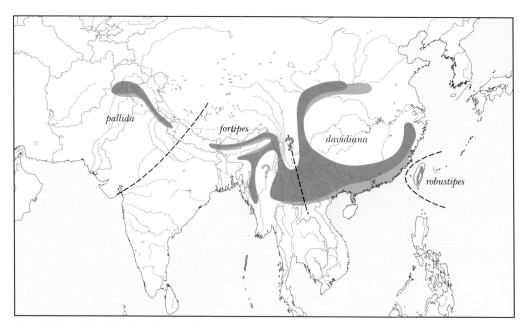

Brownish-flanked Bush Warbler. Mostly resident but some disperse to lower elevations outside the breeding season.

N Yunnan Province and locally in the higher hills throughout China south of the Yangtze River to Fujian and Guangdong Provinces (Cheng 1987). In recent years it has spread to coastal regions where it now breeds in the higher hills in Hong Kong. It is uncertain which race breeds in N Laos and the adjacent N Vietnamese provinces of West Tonkin and East Tonkin, but based on distribution in neighbouring Yunnan Province, this form would appear the most likely.

C. f. robustipes Restricted to the hills of Taiwan, where it breeds widely from 450m to at least 2,500m. It overlaps with Yellow-bellied Bush Warbler at higher elevations.

MOVEMENTS Due to its skulking and secretive behaviour, little is known of its post-breeding movements. Birds breeding at lower elevations in the Himalayas are believed to be resident but those breeding higher up are altitudinal migrants, but perhaps only descend to overwinter in scrub- and forest-covered foothills at the onset of colder weather.

In China, breeding territories in the hills are believed to be abandoned with the onset of cool weather and most birds descend to lower elevations, reaching sea level in Guangdong Province. In Hong Kong, this species is a scarce but regular winter visitor, with early occurrences from 22 October onwards, but the majority occur between November to February with notable influxes coinciding with the passage of cold fronts (Carey *et al.* 2001). Ringing recoveries show that some regularly overwinter in Hong Kong and year-on-year recaptures have demonstrated site fidelity of some returning individuals. Most depart Hong Kong from late February and records after mid March are unusual, the latest recorded date away from breeding areas being 4 April.

It is uncertain whether regular post-breeding dispersal occurs in Taiwan. Movements away from breeding areas have yet to be demonstrated and the warmer, damper winters

there leave much of the breeding range suitable for the survival of over-wintering birds.

DESCRIPTION *C. f. fortipes*
Plumage – Adult fresh Forehead and crown dark, rich brown with slight rusty wash. Supercilium whitish, from bill to rear of ear-coverts, well pronounced and palest, with a faint rusty wash above the eye, indistinct behind the eye. A broad, dark brown loral line extends from bill base to eye. Behind the eye, a dark brown eye-line widens slightly and merges with side of nape. Ear-coverts rich, warm chocolate-brown, with darker brown tips producing a slightly mottled effect. Upper edge of eye-ring whitish, merging with the supercilium; narrow lower edge also white, contrasting with brown ear-coverts. Nape, mantle, scapulars, rump and uppertail-coverts dark rich brown, usually lacking rusty tones. Tail feathers dark brown with warmer, richer fringes matching uppertail-coverts.

Chin and throat greyish white but with warm buff tips that obscure the paler feather bases. Throat sides and malar regions slightly darker, richer brown, merging with lower edges to ear-coverts. Breast washed rich buffy brown in centre, darkening to rusty brown on sides and on the neck below the ear-coverts. Belly pale creamy buff to yellowish buff, merging with the flanks and breast. Upper flanks dark buffy brown, darkening to rich rusty brown on lower flanks and across ventral region. Undertail-coverts rich sepia-brown, slightly darker than ventral region and similar in tone to uppertail-coverts.

Lesser and median coverts dark, rich brown with slightly paler rusty brown fringes. Primary and greater coverts and tertials with dark brown centres and paler rich brown fringes, slightly warmer than mantle colour. Secondaries and primaries with dark brown webs and paler rusty brown edges that form a paler panel in the closed wing, similar in colour to tertial and greater covert fringes. Alula dark brown with a warm brown fringe. Underwing-coverts white with a slight yellow tinge.

Adult worn Resembles fresh adult but generally paler. Contrasting head pattern remains similar. Upperparts slightly paler and greyer, but rump and uppertail-coverts retain slightly darker and richer tone, more rusty brown than tail. Closed wing similar to that of fresh adult, but brown fringes and edges slightly faded, wing-panel slightly more conspicuous, contrasting more with mantle.

Chin and throat white with creamy wash, paler than on fresh adult. Breast dull greyish brown, contrasting rather more with throat and belly, and appearing as a complete band, paler in centre, broadening and darkening towards sides. Buff tone to upper flanks paler and more pronounced than in fresh adult, darkening to dull brown on lower flanks and ventral region.

Juvenile Quite different from adult. Crown, lores, ear-coverts, nape, mantle, rump, uppertail-coverts, scapulars, wing-coverts, edges to flight feathers and tail uniform olive-brown. Chin to cheeks, throat, belly, undertail-coverts and flanks bright primrose-yellow. Breast primrose-yellow lightly washed olive-brown, much paler than upperparts.

Bare parts Upper mandible dark grey with fine pale yellowish or brownish cutting edge. Lower mandible pale yellow or dull flesh at base, darkening towards tip. Tarsi and toes brownish pink to greyish pink; claws slightly whiter. Iris warm hazel, it is not known whether colour changes with age.

IN HAND CHARACTERS
Measurements

C. f. fortipes

	Male	Female
Wing	54–58 (56.0; 22)	49–54 (51.6; 7)
Tail	47–54 (51.3; 19)	45–48 (46.2; 5)
Bill	13.5–15 (14.4; 18)	13.5–15 (14.2; 6)
Tarsus	21.5–23.5 (22.3; 13)	20–22 (20.9; 6)

Sexes combined:
Tail/wing: 85–96% (91%; 24)
Bill width: 3.1–3.8 (3.5; 14)
Hind claw: 5.8–6.8 (6.1; 11)
Tail graduation: 11–15 (13.3; 8)

C. f. davidiana

	Male	Female
Wing	54–60 (57.4; 36)	47–51 (49.1; 19)
Tail	48–54 (50.3; 30)	40–46 (42.6; 20)
Bill	13–14 (13.7; 48)	12–13.5 (12.9; 18)
Tarsus	21.5–23.5 (22.1; 26)	19–21 (20.3; 12)

Sexes combined:
Tail/wing: 82–96% (87%; 51)
Bill width: 3.0–3.5 (3.2; 13)
Hind claw: 5.0–6.7 (5.8; 11)
Tail graduation: 8–14 (10.4; 10)
C. f. pallida: wing, ♂ 54–59 (56.1; 21), ♀ 50–54 (51.3; 6); *tail*, ♂ 45–54 (50.2; 18), ♀ 45–50 (46.3; 6); *bill*, ♂ 13–14 (13.9; 19), ♀ 12.5–13.5 (12.9; 6); *tarsus*, ♂ 20.5–23 (21.7; 16), ♀ 20–20.5 (20.3; 4); bill width (sexes combined), 3.2–3.5 (3.3; 8); tail graduation 11–13 (12.2; 5).

Structure

C. f. fortipes

Wing formula (n = 10):

p1/pc	p2	p3e	p4e	p5e	p6e	p7(e)	p10
11–16	12–14	4–6	1–2.5	wp	wp	1–2	5–7

Wing short and strongly rounded with large p1; primaries rather pointed. Wing point p5–6; p2 < ss tips, p3 falls near p9; emargination on p3–6, sometimes slightly on p7.

Figure 118. Wing of Brownish-flanked Bush Warbler.

Tail medium length, graduated; ten feathers, narrow and rather pointed.

Bill quite strong, upper mandible with decurved tip.

Tarsi, toes and claws fairly strong.

Other races are similar in structure but their bills are smaller and lack the decurved tip.

Recognition Dull warm brown to olive-brown above with a poorly defined supercilium; brownish grey below (greyish white in race *pallida*). Averages slightly larger than Yellow-bellied Bush and Hume's Bush Warblers but measurements overlap. Lacks the striking supercilium of those species and the yellow-tinged underparts of Yellow-bellied Bush, and nominate *fortipes* is much darker above and below.

Ageing There are no reliable known characters for distinguishing young birds after post-juvenile moult. Iris and palate colour may differ between adult and immature birds.

Sexing Many could be sexed tentatively on size, those with wing > 56mm being males, wing < 54 females.

Weight Hong Kong, 6.9–9.4g (7.4; 73) (HKRG, unpublished data).

GEOGRAPHIC VARIATION There are four well-defined races.

C. f. fortipes (E Nepal to Bhutan, NE India, N Burma and adjacent SW China) Described above.

C. f. pallida (NE Pakistan and Kashmir to W Nepal) The palest and greyest race, breeding in the drier W Himalayas. Compared with other races in fresh plumage, the supercilium is paler and more conspicuous, especially over the lores and eye, fading to pale ash-grey over the ear-coverts. It shows a light ash-brown eye-stripe that contrasts with the supercilium and greyish white ear-coverts, and the head side appears rather paler and more contrasting than in other races. The upperparts are dull greyish brown with an olivaceous wash, much greyer and paler than in the nominate form, warmer tones on the rump and uppertail-coverts show the greater contrast. Some birds show a faint rufous wash on the crown. Dull warm brown edges to the wing-coverts, primaries and secondaries contrast with the colder upperparts. Below, a faint greyish brown wash across the breast contrasts with the white chin, throat and belly. The breast sides are rather greyer and darker, warming to dull fulvous-brown on the lower flanks, vent and undertail-coverts.

When worn, *pallida* shows greater variation. Most birds retain brown tones in the upperparts but the palest appear frosty grey on the crown, nape, mantle and scapulars, lacking almost all warmth, while the edges and fringes on the closed wing are cold brown, duller and colder than ever seen in other forms. The underparts are almost entirely white, with a faint grey wash restricted to the breast sides, flanks and undertail-coverts.

C. f. davidiana (C, S and SE China; presumably also N Laos and N Vietnam) Generally duller than the nominate form. The supercilium is dull buffy grey, diffuse and poorly defined, and the eye-stripe is dull greyish brown, paler and less crisp, the lower edge intergrading with slightly mottled, pale sandy grey ear-coverts. The head side appears paler, lacking the contrast and warmer brown tones of the nominate form. The crown is marginally warmer and contrasts slightly with the rest of the upperparts, which are warm greyish brown and lack rich, dark rusty tones. The warm chestnut-brown to dull rusty brown fringes and edges to the wing feathers are less richly coloured. The underparts are paler, more sandy than in the nominate form. The chin, throat and belly are white while the breast is washed pale sandy grey, becoming whitish in many worn spring birds. The breast sides show a darker grey-brown wash, which

extends below the ear-coverts to form a pale sandy grey half-collar. The flanks are paler, more sandy than those of the nominate form, but become warmer and slightly darker on the ventral region and undertail-coverts.

C. f. robustipes (Taiwan) Differs from other races by its overall drab appearance, with little contrast between the upperparts and underparts. The crown, nape and mantle are uniform dull, olive-brown, while the underparts are drab olive-brown, with a slight ochre suffusion, usually most conspicuous on the flanks and ventral region. The head shows a poorly marked supercilium, visible mainly in front of the eye and often absent behind it. The brighter, warm brown edges to the primaries, secondaries and tail feathers contrast slightly with the drab upperparts.

TAXONOMY AND SYSTEMATICS There is some variation within the Chinese race *davidiana*, with birds from N Yunnan and Sichuan Provinces showing a rather better defined head pattern than those from SE China, and also a slightly warmer crown, nape and mantle. Birds from the mountains of C China appear intermediate between the nominate form and those of SE China, which were previously described as the race *sinensis*. These eastern birds appear to represent the end of a cline of increasing colour saturation extending from the W Himalayas through the mountains of W China to the coastal hills of Guangdong and Fujian Provinces, and *sinensis* is usually treated as a synonym of *davidiana*.

◀ Adult *C. f. fortipes*, Arunachal Pradesh, India, April. Underpart colour variable, typically drab brownish-grey with pale buff flanks and breast sides when fresh, becoming greyish white when worn (Rajneesh Suvarna).

◀ Adult *C. f. pallida*, Uttarakhand, India, January. Palest and greyest race, with conspicuous whitish underparts and pale greyish brown flanks, breast, head and upperparts (Arun P. Singh).

▲ Adult *C. f. davidiana*, Sichuan, China, July. During the breeding season, appearance is generally duller than nominate race, and drabber than *davidiana* after complete moult. Note marginally warmer crown contrasting with grey-brown upperparts, and less richly coloured fringes and edges to the flight feathers (Liao Xiaodong).

▲ Adult *C. f. davidiana*, Hong Kong, January. After the complete moult, appearance of *davidiana* in SE China is quite different to breeding adult. Has warmer, less contrasting appearance with a rich buff suffusion to flanks and supercilium, appearing more uniform than breeding adult (Sam Chan).

▲ ▶ Adult *C. f. robustipes*, Nantou, Taiwan, May. Differs from other races by reduced contrast between upperparts and underparts, although when fresh usually shows slight ochre suffusion on flanks and ventral region. Slightly spread wing shows strongly rounded structure characteristic of many smaller *Cettia*, with long first primary, wing point formed by p5/p6 and emargination on p3–7 (Liao Pen-shing).

579

YELLOW-BELLIED BUSH WARBLER
Cettia acanthizoides Plate 39

Abrornis acanthizoides Verreaux, 1871. *Nouv. Arch. Mus. Hist. Nat. Paris* 6: 37. Mountains of western Tibet.

A diminutive *Cettia* that breeds in the higher hills and mountains of S, C and E China and Taiwan. Hume's Bush Warbler of the Himalayas was regarded until recently as conspecific with Yellow-bellied Bush Warbler, but studies of vocalisation and genetic divergence have established that two species are involved (Alström *et al.* 2007). Polytypic, with two races recognised:

C. a. acanthizoides (Verreaux 1871). C, S and E China.
C. a. concolor (Ogilvie-Grant, 1912). Taiwan.

IDENTIFICATION Length 10–11cm. Wing, male 53–56mm, female 47–49mm. Tail/wing 83–92%.

An attractive small and pale *Cettia* that occupies a specialised niche in mist-shrouded upper montane forest with a thick bamboo understorey, breeding up to the tree line and higher than most other *Cettia* species. It shows a well-marked head pattern and distinctive yellow-washed underparts. Although its plumage features are subtle, it possesses a most remarkable and unmistakable song. Sexes alike, but males are significantly larger than females and wing length provides a reliable means of separating them.

Structure This and Hume's Bush Warbler are the smallest *Cettia* species and they share structural features. These include a rounded appearance to the crown and the head, which appears large in relation to its small rounded body. The bill is slightly smaller and finer than in other E Asian *Cettia* species, including Hume's Bush Warbler. The closed wing shows a long first primary (p1), an extremely short primary projection, and the wing point falling below the tips of the longest uppertail-coverts. It often droops its wings along the sides of the body and holds the tail slightly raised, exaggerating its real length.

Plumage and bare parts Appears distinctly paler than most of the Asian *Cettia,* but only Hume's Bush Warbler is quite as pale as Yellow-bellied Bush, or possesses a similar combination of pale or slightly yellow-flushed underparts and pale greyish brown mantle.

The most distinctive and characteristic feature of Yellow-bellied Bush Warbler is the yellow wash to the breast, belly and flanks. This is usually a delicate primrose-yellow on the upper breast and belly, darkening to warm buffy yellow on the flanks. On some individuals this buffy colour can appear stronger, overwhelming the yellow on the lower flanks and undertail-coverts and showing little contrast with the closed wing. The chin and throat are usually greyish white, contrasting with the yellow upper breast. The head shows a well-marked whitish supercilium, often flushed primrose-yellow in front of the eye. This flares slightly over the eye, then diffuses and merges above the ear-coverts with the side of the crown. A dark eye-stripe is crisp and well defined in front of the eye but diffuses into the faintly mottled greyish brown ear-coverts behind. The upperparts are a distinctive pale brown, paler than in all other Asian *Cettia* except Hume's Bush. The crown and mantle are pale greyish brown with a slight olive tinge that contrasts with the still-paler mousy grey nape. The closed wing and tail appear warmer, richer and browner than the mantle with which they contrast and lack the olive wash.

The bill is dark horn with a pale yellowish base to the lower mandible, which darkens slightly on the side towards the tip. The legs and feet are pale brown.

SIMILAR SPECIES Appears distinctly paler than most of the Asian *Cettia*, the exception being Hume's Bush Warbler which it closely resembles, although separation of singing birds is straightforward and discussed below. Separation from other *Cettia* is usually based on a combination of subtle plumage characters, although these can be difficult to discern in gloomy montane forest undergrowth, together with differences in habitat and song.

Identification outside the breeding season requires great care. Brownish-flanked Bush Warbler, particularly frshly moulted birds in E China in autumn, can appear surprisingly similar to Yellow-bellied Bush Warbler. Aberrant Bush Warbler would seem an unlikely confusion species but a brief discussion is useful since it also has yellowish underparts.

Hume's Bush Warbler closely resembles Yellow-bellied Bush Warbler, sharing a similar combination of pale or slightly yellow-flushed underparts and a pale greyish brown mantle.

Although their ranges are largely allopatric, they may overlap in NE India and SW China, particularly outside the breeding season. Singing males are readily separable by their songs (see **Voice**). Otherwise, they share a similar diminutive size, structure and behaviour, but if seen well, the majority of Hume's Bush Warblers can be separated from most Yellow-bellied Bush. Hume's Bush Warbler tends to be slightly warmer and more richly coloured above, lacking the olive tinge typical of Yellow-bellied Bush. It appears more washed out below, with yellow tones subdued or completely absent and it never shows the stronger yellow wash to the breast, belly and flanks of Yellow-bellied Bush. There is limited overlap between some worn individuals. Care is required with identification of silent individuals in areas of possible range overlap, or outside the known range of either species.

Brownish-flanked Bush Warbler shares a similar structure and behaviour with Yellow-bellied Bush Warbler. It differs in its overall darker and browner appearance above and below, and in its distinctive song. Their separation is discussed in greater detail under Brownish-flanked Bush Warbler.

Aberrant Bush Warbler is distinctly larger and more bulky than Yellow-bellied Bush. Its movements through undergrowth are usually sluggish, laboured and clumsy, although, like Yellow-bellied, it continuously flicks its wings and usually holds the tail slightly cocked. The yellow underparts vary in both intensity and colour, from buffy yellow to olive-yellow, and become quite dark olive on the flanks, never approaching the pale primrose-yellow tone of Yellow-bellied Bush Warbler. The upperparts, including the flight feather edges, are olive with a slight yellowish green cast, considerably darker than those of Yellow-bellied Bush. Songs are diagnostic, that of Aberrant Bush being a short warble followed by a long, inflected '*pueeeeuu*' or '*tueeeee-weeu*' whistle.

VOICE The song is undoubtedly the most distinctive of any warbler. It begins with up to ten short, quiet, dry '*tret*' or '*trit*' calls given in rapid succession. These are immediately followed by a series of up to 35 drawn out high-pitched whistles as the bird gradually 'winds itself up', each whistle being given at a slightly higher pitch than the preceding one, beginning at *c.* 4kHz and increasing in frequency to *c.* 6kHz. This 'wind up' sequence lasts between 25 and 45 seconds, gradually increasing in pitch and volume as it approaches a climax when the bird appears not to be able to contain the 'pressure' any longer and cannot utter another note as each becomes ever more frantic. Unexpectedly, the 'wind-up' song stops, then immediately 'unwinds' into a descending trill composed of rapid clicks, slowing gradually so that each note becomes clearer and more distinct. The 'unwinding' sequence lasts for approximately 10–15 seconds and each complete song sequence lasts for approximately one minute. There is very little difference between the songs of mainland breeders and those on Taiwan.

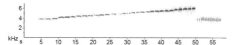

Song of Yellow-bellied Bush Warbler, recorded within breeding range of *C. a. concolor*, An Ma Shan, Taiwan, April. (Peter Kennerley)

The call is a quiet '*trit*', similar to the introductory notes of the song. A nervous or alarmed bird may give this call rapidly at short intervals and intermittently over long periods.

MOULT No data available.

HABITAT Throughout its range it breeds in open evergreen hill forest, typically comprising scattered pine, spruce, fir and hemlock with a dense understorey of dwarf bamboo. In the mountains of C and S China it breeds at higher elevations than other *Cettia*, but in the lower hills of E China, breeding occurs at lower elevations between 1,525m and 1,830m in Fujian Province (La Touche 1925–30). In C China and Taiwan it typically breeds above 2,500m, but it is absent from alpine habitat above 3,500m in C China where bamboo is lacking. Outside the breeding season, it is believed to descend to lower elevations close to the breeding area, and utilise dense mixed scrub undergrowth, within forest or along roadside forest edge. In Taiwan, birds remain above 2,000m in winter and possibly even the highest breeders are resident throughout the year provided the weather remains suitable. It is uncertain whether birds breeding in E China are resident or winter at lower elevations.

BEHAVIOUR Shows the skulking behaviour typical of a *Cettia*. Often responds to the call of Collared Owlet with a series of single alarm notes, moving to edges of scrub or venturing into the lower branches of trees and bushes. Otherwise, it can be difficult to observe except when singing. Males sing throughout the day during the breeding season and can be energetic and active as they perform circuits of the territory. It is not known whether they are vocal at night. The song is not given during the winter months.

BREEDING HABITS A nest examined in May was located in a thick patch of bamboo undergrowth and built close to the ground. It was constructed from coarse grasses and bamboo leaves, with a smaller inner cup of fine grass lined with feathers (La Touche 1925–30). Three or four eggs are laid in May or early June. No information is available on incubation or fledging periods. It is not known whether a second brood is reared.

DISTRIBUTION Yellow-bellied Bush Warbler breeds widely throughout the higher hills of C China and has two outlying populations with restricted ranges in E China and Taiwan. Two races are recognised.

C. a. acanthizoides The nominate form is believed to occur

exclusively in China, its range separated into two distinct regions. It breeds widely in the mountains of C China above 2,500m from the Qinling Mountains in Shaanxi Province south and west throughout the mountains of N and C Sichuan Province, and locally into the mountains of W Yunnan Province adjacent to NW Burma. It may extend into the mountains of N Burma, but this is unconfirmed. Smythies (1968) mentioned a single record from the southern Shan States, but this could refer to either this species or Hume's Bush Warbler. Recent visits to apparently suitable habitats in the mountains of W and N Burma have failed to locate either species.

A second population breeds locally on the highest hills in E and SE China, ranging from S Anhui Province south to at least the region of Huanggan Shan at 2,158m, in Wu Yi Shan National Park, N Fujian Province. Here the hills are much lower than in C China and since breeding occurs only above 1,850m its range in E China is patchy and fragmented.

C. a. concolor Endemic to Taiwan where it is restricted to the higher hills, its distribution associated with that of dwarf bamboo in cool montane forest. It occurs commonly throughout the mountains above 2,500m and remains fairly numerous up to at least 3,500m above the tree line where dwarf bamboo is abundant, provided there are scattered bushes within the territory.

Yellow-bellied Bush Warbler. Mostly resident but some disperse to lower elevations outside the breeding season

MOVEMENTS Presumably an altitudinal migrant through-out its range in C China where breeding areas become inhospitable during the cold winter months, but direct evidence is lacking. There are no reports from the lowlands of E China. Four birds trapped in Hong Kong were reported to be this species (Carey *et al.* 2001) but mtDNA of two birds showed them to be indistinguishable from that of Brownish-flanked Bush Warbler. Subsequent comparison of photographs and measurements of these and the other trapped birds showed that all four were very similar and

Yellow-bellied Bush Warbler has been removed from the Hong Kong list (Carey & Lockey 2009). This highlights the potential difficulties involved in identifying some individuals outside the breeding season and outside the known range (GJC & PJL *in litt.*).

In Taiwan, there is no direct evidence to support altitudinal migration and it is uncertain whether birds vacate the breeding grounds. The climate is milder than in C and W China and some, or perhaps all, remain in territories throughout the year, or only descend during the coldest winter weather. Winter records tend to be from known breeding sites but it has been noted down to *c.* 2,000m in December.

DESCRIPTION *C. a. acanthizoides*

Plumage – Adult fresh Forehead, fore-crown and crown pale rusty brown, tinged olive. Rear crown, side of neck and nape slightly paler, washed delicate mousy brown. Supercilium long, broad and conspicuous; white, with faint a primrose tinge in front of the eye and a primrose or ochre-buff suffusion behind it, extends from bill base to rear of ear-coverts, sharpest in front of eye, less distinct behind it, broadening and flaring slightly and merging with the crown and nape. A dark loral spot in front of eye often appears as a black triangle with its apex just reaching the bill base. There is a diffuse dull greyish eye-line behind the eye, its upper edge being sharply defined but the lower edge diffusing into the ear-coverts and barely discernible at the rear of the supercilium. Ear-coverts pale grey with darker grey-brown tips creating slight mottling. Eye-ring off-white, narrow, broken in front of and behind the eye, merging with supercilium and ear-coverts. Mantle and scapulars pale rusty brown with a delicate olive wash, similar in tone to crown. Rump and uppertail-coverts similar but usually tinged yellow. Tail feathers dull greyish with rich warm brown outer edges and tips.

Chin and throat white, feather tips washed greyish, lower throat and malar region often with a faint primrose-yellow suffusion. Sides of neck delicate mousy brown as nape. Yellow suffusion slightly more conspicuous on breast and belly and strengthening towards sides of breast and upper flanks, being pale yellow or richer buffy ochre adjacent to the wing bend. Lower flanks and undertail-coverts more saturated warm buff with a faint hint of yellow.

Closed wing plain and unmarked. Lesser and median coverts with broad pale rusty brown fringes and barely discernible darker centres. Greater coverts and tertials with fairly broad, pale, rusty brown fringes, merging with darker grey-brown centres. Secondaries and primaries dull grey without contrastingly paler tips, edges warm cinnamon-brown, slightly richer than greater covert and tertial fringes. Alula dark greyish with contrasting pale rusty brown fringe. Underwing-coverts white to pale primrose-yellow, paler than belly.

Adult worn Similar to freshly moulted bird, but crown and mantle sometimes slightly greyer, contrasting less with nape. Edges of primaries and secondaries usually less warm, showing little contrast with upperparts. Underparts variable; some with a distinct yellowish wash on centre of upper breast and belly, others greyish white with a buff wash confined to the lower flanks and undertail-coverts.

Juvenile Yellow underparts usually brighter but otherwise not known to differ from fresh adult.

Bare parts Upper mandible dark horn-brown with fine pinkish yellow cutting edge. Lower mandible yellowish pink at base, darkening towards tip. Tarsi and toes yellowish

brown to pinkish brown. Iris dark brown.

IN HAND CHARACTERS
Measurements

C. a. acanthizoides

	Male	Female
Wing	53–56 (54.3; 3)	47–49 (48.0; 3)
Tail	46–49 (47.3; 3)	40–43 (41.3; 3)
Bill	12 (12.0; 3)	11–11.5 (11.2; 3)
Tarsus	21–21.5(21.2; 3)	19.5 (19.5; 3)

Sexes combined:
Tail/wing ratio: 83–92% (87%; 9)
Bill width: 3.1–3.4 (3.3; 8)
Hind claw: 5.0–5.8 (5.5; 8)
Tail graduation: 7–10 (8.3; 7)
C. a. concolor (1 ♂, 2 ♀♀): *wing* 49–54; *tail* 42–49; *bill* 11.5–13; *tarsus* 20–21.5.

Comparison with Hume's Bush Warbler *C. brunnescens*

Average measurements, males only; from Alström *et al.* 2007:

	acanthizoides	*concolor*	*brunnescens*
Wing	52.8 (11)	51.6 (9)	53.3 (16)
Tail	47.3 (11)	47.2 (9)	46.9 (15)
Bill	13.0 (10)	13.4 (9)	13.4 (16)
Tarsus	21.1 (11)	21.1 (8)	21.7 (15)

Structure

C. a. acanthizoides

Wing resembles Hume's Bush Warbler and Brownish-flanked Bush Warbler (Fig. 118).

Tail as in Hume's Bush Warbler.

Bill small and slender; less fine-tipped than in Hume's Bush but distinctly shorter (in nominate *acanthizoides*).

Tarsi and toes slender, claws fine.

Recognition A small pale *Cettia* with a broad whitish supercilium, usually yellowish below. Warm-toned, pale greyish brown upperparts with a slight olive tinge and more distinctly yellow underparts distinguish most birds from the very similar Hume's Bush Warbler. Brownish-flanked Warbler (race *davidiana*) has similar measurements, but is browner, with the supercilium less pronounced and lacks yellow below. Aberrant Bush Warbler typically has a larger bill, olive-brown upperparts and richer yellow underparts.

Ageing Not usually possible after post-juvenile moult.

Weight 6g (del Hoyo *et al.* 2006).

GEOGRAPHIC VARIATION There are two races that closely resemble each other.

C. a. acanthizoides (C, S and E China) Described above.

C. a. concolor (Taiwan) Resembles the nominate form closely, showing only minor differences in colour tones. The upperparts are pale rusty brown, but the crown, nape and mantle are slightly warmer and darker than in the nominate form. Although the nape retains a greyish wash, it shows less contrast with the crown and mantle. The fringes of the greater-coverts and tertials and edges to the primaries and secondaries are browner and richer than those of the nominate form. The underparts of *concolor* show slight variation but most appear slightly brighter and richer than in the nominate form.

TAXONOMY AND SYSTEMATICS The taxon *brunnescens* was formerly included as a race of Yellow-bellied Bush Warbler, but differences in appearance and, in particular, vocalisations, enable singing males can be readily separated. Alström *et al.* (2007) provided further evidence to support their separation and *brunnescens* is now recognised as a distinct species, Hume's Bush Warbler. For further discussion, see comments under Hume's Bush Warbler.

Within nominate *acanthizoides*, (Alström *et al.* 2007) suggested that minor plumage differences between the populations of C and E China may be sufficiently marked to warrant recognition of an additional subspecies, but further study is required to determine this. Those breeding in E China appear slightly warmer brown on the upperparts and brighter yellow on the belly than birds from Sichuan

(Alström *et al.* 2007), but the effects of wear that could possibly affect their appearance have not yet been fully investigated.

The retention of *concolor* as a race of Yellow-bellied Bush Warbler is fully justified based on their similar calls and indistinguishable songs (Alström *et al.* 2007). The characteristic song of the Taiwan bird demonstrates both its affinity with its mainland neighbour and its distinction from Hume's Bush Warbler.

One outstanding issue remains to be resolved. The type specimen was described by Verreaux (1871) from the mountains of W Tibet which lie well outside the known range of this species, but much closer to that of the closely related *C. brunnescens*. Neither species is known to occur in W Tibet, where there is no known suitable habitat, making it a mystery how it came to be collected here. We have not been able to examine the type specimen and are unable to confirm that it actually is *acanthizoides*. If it should prove to be *brunnescens*, a change to the nomenclature of Yellow-bellied Bush Warbler may be required.

▲ Adult *C. a. acanthizoides*, China, May. Shows conspicuous yellow belly and flanks and greyer breast, contrasting with warm cinnamon-brown edges to remiges, and paler rusty-brown upperparts (Zhang Yong).

▲ Adult *C. a. acanthizoides*, Sichuan, China, May. This greyer bird is separated from allopatric Hume's Bush Warbler by slightly duller upperparts with olive tone, and by strikingly yellow underparts (Li Bin).

▲ Adult *C. a. concolor*, Taiwan, March. Slightly warmer and darker upperparts than the nominate form, particularly the crown, and richer brown fringes and edges to wing feathers (Chang Pei-wen).

▲ Adult *C. a. concolor*, Taiwan, March. Underparts of *concolor* show little variation; most appear slightly brighter than nominate (Chang Pei-wen).

HUME'S BUSH WARBLER
Cettia brunnescens   Plate 39

Horeites brunnescens **Hume, 1872**. *Ibis* p. 109. Near Darjeeling.

A small *Cettia* that breeds in the Himalayas in open forest and bamboo thicket up to and above the tree line, at higher elevations than most other *Cettia* species. It was originally described by Hume (1872) as a distinct species, but later subsumed within the wide-ranging Yellow-bellied Bush Warbler. Recent information on vocalisations and genetic divergence within the Yellow-bellied Bush Warbler complex (Alström *et al.* 2007) has established that *brunnescens* merits recognition at the species level. Monotypic.

IDENTIFICATION Length 10–11cm. Wing 47–56mm. Tail/wing 76–89%.
   A small, pale *Cettia* with a well-marked head pattern. It is readily located and recognised by its distinctive song. Sexes alike although males are larger than females, but there is limited overlap in wing length.
Structure One of the smallest *Cettia*, overlapping in size, shape and structure with the allopatric Yellow-bellied Bush Warbler. It has a rather plump or rounded body with short, rounded wings. The wings have a large first primary (p1) and a short primary projection with tightly bunched primaries that extends only fractionally beyond the longest tertial. It frequently droops its wings across the flanks, exposing the rump and uppertail-coverts. The tail is similar in length to the closed wing, but the short wings can make it appear distinctly longer, particularly when they are drooped and the uppertail-coverts are exposed. The tail is often slightly cocked.
Plumage and bare parts Paler than most *Cettia* with a subdued, faint yellowish wash to the flanks and upper breast sides, although this may be lost on some individuals. The head pattern is quite distinctive, with a fairly conspicuous pale supercilium and darker eyestripe. The supercilium is creamy white above the eye, tinged creamy buff towards the bill base. It usually broadens over the eye but narrows above the ear-coverts, merging with the crown sides and nape. The darker eyestripe shows greatest contrast in front of the eye where it forms a small triangular wedge, while behind, it becomes slightly paler, browner and more diffuse. The ear-coverts are lightly mottled although this is difficult to discern in the field. The pale rusty brown crown usually appears slightly warmer and richer than the greyer nape, giving it a distinctive appearance shared only with Yellow-bellied Bush Warbler. Otherwise, the upperparts, including the mantle, rump, uppertail-coverts and wing-coverts, are light warm brown, slightly paler than the crown, with no hint of olive, even when fresh. Most birds show cinnamon-brown edges to the secondaries, primaries and tail feathers, giving the closed wing a brighter appearance than the upperparts, while the tail is also brighter and contrasts with the duller uppertail-coverts. The underparts are pale grey and featureless. Most birds do show a faint yellowish wash on the sides of the upper breast and flanks. The lower flanks are suffused warm buff or buffy yellow and the undertail-coverts are pale apricot to warm buff, with yellow tones suppressed.
   The bill is dark brown with a pink or yellowish pink lower mandible, although this darkens slightly towards the tip. The legs and feet are yellowish brown to pinkish brown.

SIMILAR SPECIES Several small *Cettia* species that could be mistaken for Hume's Bush Warbler occur in the Himalayas. Of these, Yellow-bellied Bush Warbler and Brownish-flanked Bush Warbler are the closest in size, structure and overall appearance.
Yellow-bellied Bush Warbler differs from Hume's Bush Warbler in being slightly duller and less richly coloured above, but with an indistinct olive tone to the upperparts which Hume's Bush lacks. Below, the underparts are more strongly coloured than those of Hume's Bush, with yellow tones conspicuous and appearing warm yellow to rich buff on the lower flanks. They are best separated by their distinct and immediately recognisable songs. There are no known instances of mixed or intermediate songs. For more detail, see also under Yellow-bellied Bush Warbler.
Brownish-flanked Bush Warbler shares similar structure and behaviour with Hume's Bush Warbler. It differs in its overall darker appearance and distinctive song. For more detail see under Brownish-flanked Bush Warbler.

VOICE The song is quite different from that of Yellow-bellied Bush Warbler. It begins with a 'wind-up' sequence of three or four short, slightly discordant whistles, each at a slightly higher pitch than the previous, beginning at *c.* 4kHz and increasing in steps to reach 6kHz. Each whistle lasts for about two seconds, much longer than the 'wind-up' sequence given by Yellow-bellied Bush Warbler and sounds not dissimilar to a 'piping aboard ship' whistle. This 'wind-up' sequence switches abruptly to the 'unwinding' sequence before reaching a climax, during which a series of two to four short unmusical notes is delivered, alternating or descending in pitch between 3–5kHz and repeated seven to 12 times with a brief pause between each element. The entire song sequence lasts approximately 15 seconds and is followed by a brief pause of up to five seconds, before the entire sequence is repeated. Alström *et al.* (2007) describe a second song type, sometimes interspersed with the main song, consisting of one high-pitched, drawn-out note followed by a trembling trill.

Song of Hume's Bush Warbler, Pele La, Bhutan, April. (Peter Kennerley)

   The call is a short, rapid '*trrrt*', quite throaty and slightly lower pitched than that of Yellow-bellied Bush Warbler. It is often given in a rapid series at approximately two calls per second, especially when excited.

MOULT No data available, but probably does not differ from other Himalayan *Cettia* in timing, sequence and duration.

HABITAT During the breeding season, it occurs at higher elevations than most other Himalayan breeding *Cettia*, typically from 2,200m to 3,400m, showing only limited overlap with Grey-sided Bush Warbler. It inhabits similar habitats to those favoured by Yellow-bellied Bush Warbler in China and the presence of bamboo appears to be a prerequisite. It is most common in open fir forests with a dense bamboo understorey, while at higher elevations it occupies bamboo thickets with scattered bushes and limited tree cover. It occurs below 3,000m in cool broadleaf forest, but is less numerous here than in the higher fir forests. It occurs at lower elevations outside the breeding season and it is uncertain whether the preference for bamboo then remains. Birds then appear to occupy similar habitats to Yellow-bellied Bush Warbler.

BEHAVIOUR Not known to differ from Yellow-bellied Bush Warbler.

BREEDING HABITS Singing males return to breeding territories in Bhutan in April and remain until at least August (Spierenburg 2005). Very little is known of the breeding cycle. The nest is a domed structure, situated low down in a bush in forest. It is built of coarse grasses and contains a deep cup, densely lined with feathers. The eggs are laid in June.

DISTRIBUTION Ranges through the Himalayas from Himachal Pradesh east to Arunachal Pradesh in N India. The western limit lies in the mountains of Garhwal, where it is reportedly rare and localised. It is also apparently rare or absent from W Nepal, and is scarce and localised from 2,000m to 3,660m in C and E Nepal (Inskipp & Inskipp 1985; CI *in litt.*). To the east, it breeds in Sikkim and also Bhutan, where it is unreported from the west but relatively common on higher passes in the centre and east, including Pele La, Yutong La, Thrumsing La and Gayzamchu (Spierenburg 2005). It breeds in E India in the hills of Arunachal Pradesh and probably also in adjacent regions of SE Tibet (Xizang Autonomous Region), where Vaurie (1972) noted specimens collected between March and September. Although he included these under *C. acanthizoides*, Vaurie did not discuss their racial identity and it seems likely that they referred to Hume's Bush Warbler. The wintering range is poorly known. Birds breeding at higher elevations presumably descend to the foothills, but there are few records to confirm this. In fact, Spierenburg (2005) gave maximum altitudes of 3,000m in November and 700m in February, suggesting that some birds remain at higher elevations until forced to descend by cold weather. Contrary to Baker (1997), there is no evidence that it winters south of the Brahmaputra River in Assam (Rasmussen & Anderton 2005) and reports from Manipur and the Lushai Hills are unconfirmed. Inskipp & Inskipp (1985) know of no records in Nepal outside the breeding range.

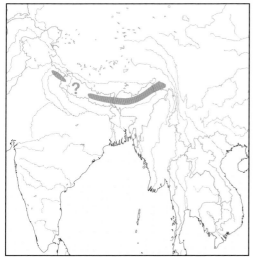

Hume's Bush Warbler. Mostly resident but some disperse to lower elevations outside the breeding season.

MOVEMENTS Believed to be an altitudinal migrant but there are few reports during the colder winter months. In Nepal, records from the Walung Ridge at 2,000m on 12 March and the northern slopes of Sheopuri at 2,590m on 30 March seem early for returning migrants and probably refer to wintering birds (Inskipp & Inskipp 1985).

DESCRIPTION
Plumage – Adult fresh Forehead and crown pale rusty brown. Rear crown, nape and sides of neck slightly paler, washed delicate mousy brown. Supercilium long, broad and conspicuous, from bill base to rear of ear-coverts; well defined in front of the eye, but broadening and flaring slightly towards the nape, merging with the crown and nape feathering; white with a faint creamy wash, this being most intense near the bill and nape. A black triangular loral spot extends from the front of the eye towards the bill base. Behind eye, a diffuse greyish eye-line, merging into the ear-coverts along lower edge and barely discernible at rear of supercilum. Ear-coverts pale brown with slightly darker grey-brown tips and whitish shafts creating a mottled appearance. Eye-ring off-white, narrow, broken in front of and behind the eye, merging with supercilium and ear-coverts. Mantle, scapulars, rump and uppertail-coverts rusty brown, similar in tone to the crown. Tail feathers dull grey-brown with rich, warm brown outer edges and tips. Chin, throat, malar region, breast and belly white, with slight greyish wash. Sides of upper breast and upper flanks often with faint yellowish suffusion. Lower flanks suffused warm buff or buffy yellow. Undertail-coverts more saturated, pale apricot to warm buff, yellow tones usually lacking.

Closed wing plain and unmarked. Lesser and median coverts with broad, pale rusty brown fringes and barely discernible darker centres. Greater coverts and tertials with fairly broad pale rusty brown fringes merging with larger, darker grey-brown centres. Primaries and secondaries dull grey, with outer webs edged warm cinnamon-brown, slightly richer than the fringes of the greater coverts and tertials and lacking contrasting paler tips. Alula with pale rusty brown fringes and contrasting darker centres. Underwing-coverts creamy white, sometimes with hint of yellow.
Adult worn Closely resembles fresh adult. In some, crown and mantle slightly greyer. Edges of primaries and secondaries usually less warm, contrasting less with upperparts.
Juvenile Brighter yellow below than adult. No other differences known.
Bare parts Upper mandible dark horn-brown with fine pink cutting edge. Lower mandible pink or yellowish pink at base, darkening towards tip. Tarsi and toes yellowish brown to pinkish brown. Iris warm brown.

IN HAND CHARACTERS
Measurements

	Male	Female
Wing	52–56 (53.7; 15)	49–54 (51.2; 6)
Tail	42–50 (44.8; 13)	39–46 (42.2; 6)
Bill	12–13.5 (12.9; 15)	12–14 (13.1; 6)
Tarsus	20.5–23 (21.5; 10)	20–21.5 (20.8; 5)

Sexes combined:
Tail/wing ratio: 76–89% (83%; 33)
Bill width: 3.1–3.4 (3.2; 15)

Hind claw: 5.0–6.7 (5.9; 11)
Tail graduation: 7–10 (8.8; 4)

Structure

Wing formula (n = 10):

p1/pc	p2	p3e	p4e	p5e	p6e	p7(e)	p10
10–12	9–13	3.5–5	0–1	wp	wp	0.5–1.5	4–7

Wing resembles Brownish-flanked Bush Warbler (Fig. 118); strongly rounded with large p1 (*c.* 60% p2). Wing point p5–6; p2 < ss tips, p3 falls near p9; emargination on p3–6, sometimes slightly on p7.

Tail rather short, rounded.

Bill small and slender with fine tip.

Tarsi and toes slender, claws quite long and fine.

Recognition A small pale *Cettia* with a broad whitish supercilium. The lack of an olive tone to upperparts, and the whitish underparts, should distinguish it from the similar Yellow-bellied Bush Warbler. Brownish-flanked Bush Warbler (race *fortipes*) is much darker and browner above and below. Measurements overlap extensively with these species. Aberrant Bush Warbler has a longer tail and a slightly larger bill than Hume's Bush and shows rich yellow underparts including the chin, throat and breast.

Ageing There are no known characters for distinguishing young birds after post-juvenile moult.

Weight No data available.

GEOGRAPHIC VARIATION None reported.

TAXONOMY AND SYSTEMATICS Hume's Bush Warbler was described as *Horeites brunnescens* by Hume (1872). It bears a close resemblance to Yellow-bellied Bush Warbler but Hume may not have been aware of the existence of this form, which was described from the mountains of W

Tibet only two years earlier. When specimens of both taxa became available for comparison, the similarities of their plumage and biometrics became apparent and the two were merged to form a single species, the name *acanthizoides* taking priority. This position remained largely unchallenged throughout the twentieth century, although a third taxon, *concolor*, resident on Taiwan, was subsequently recognised. However, major vocal differences became apparent when these taxa were studied on their Asian breeding grounds in the 1990s. Although nominate *acanthizoides* and *concolor* were found to share an identical song, that of *brunnescens* of the Himalayas was quite different. Playback experiments revealed that while the Chinese and Taiwan birds respond readily to each other's songs, neither responds to that of *brunnescens*. Similarly, *brunnescens* responds quickly to playback of its own song, but not to the songs of either nominate *acanthizoides* or *concolor*.

Alström *et al.* (2007) undertook a detailed investigation of the genetic, morphological and vocal characteristics of this group. They established that vocal differences between *brunnescens* and *acanthizoides/concolor* were considerably greater than found between several other sympatric warblers with no history of interbreeding and predicted that if they were to come into contact, the difference in song would act as a barrier to reproduction. In addition, examination of the cytochrome *b* tree suggested that *brunnescens* has been separated from *acanthizoides/concolor* for considerably longer than the latter two have been separated from each other. It was concluded that all three forms are valid, with *brunnescens* of the Himalayas better treated as a separate species, Hume's Bush Warbler, while *acanthizoides* of China and *concolor* of Taiwan should remain as races of Yellow-bellied Bush Warbler. Given the undoubted importance of voice in the establishment of boundaries between *Cettia* species in their dense undergrowth habitat, we have followed Alström *et al.* in recognising the specific status of *brunnescens*.

▲ Adult, Arunachal Pradesh, India, April. Lacks olive tone to mantle and distinctive yellow tone to underparts, at best showing faint yellowish wash to flanks and upper breast sides (Rajneesh Suvarna).

CHESTNUT-CROWNED BUSH WARBLER
Cettia major   **Plate 40**

Horeites major **Horsfield & Moore, 1854**. *Cat. Birds Mus. Hon. East India Co.* 1: 323. Nepal.

A relatively large *Cettia* breeding at higher elevations in the Himalayas and hills of NE India, east to C China. Polytypic, with two races recognised:
C. m. major (Horsfield & Moore, 1845). Himalayas to mountainous C China.
C. m. vafra (Koelz, 1954). Hills of NE India (Meghalaya, S Assam, Nagaland).

IDENTIFICATION Length 13cm. Wing 58–67mm. Tail/wing 65–85%.
   A particularly distinctive species, larger than all other Himalayan *Cettia*. It has a bold and contrasting head pattern with a warm chestnut-brown cap that contrasts with a strikingly pale supercilium and dark eye-stripe. Sexes alike.
Structure This is a large *Cettia*, similar in size to female Manchurian Bush Warbler. Like other mainland *Cettia*, it shows a short, thin bill and relatively large head with a long, slightly rounded or domed crown. The neck is short and thick so that the body appears quite small and rounded. It is distinctly larger and more bulky than the similarly plumaged Grey-sided Bush Warbler, with which it shares a similar structure, including a long first primary (p1) and short, rounded wings with the wing point formed by p5, leaving primaries closely bunched, and a short primary projection which exposes the longest uppertail-coverts. Proportionately short and rounded tail, often held slightly cocked, appear longer than it really is.
Plumage and bare parts The striking head pattern should be immediately apparent and contrasts with the otherwise drab appearance of this *Cettia*. The warm chestnut-brown crown extends from the bill base onto the lower nape where it meets the duller mantle. It may be duller and sometimes barely warmer than the upperparts on some individuals but it is usually a conspicuous feature. The long, pale buff supercilium is frequently suffused dull chestnut and poorly defined above the lores, but is bold and sharply defined over and behind the eye and over the ear-coverts, often flaring slightly onto the nape. A dark eyestripe adds to the bold head pattern which never appears as crisp or contrasting as that of Grey-sided Bush Warbler. The eyestripe is olive-brown behind the eye, and contrasts with the supercilium and paler brown ear coverts. On the loral region, it becomes less clearly defined dull chestnut, merging with the crown and supercilium so the chestnut of the crown merges with the lores in front of the eye.
   The upperparts are uniform drab grey-brown or olive-brown, although the rump and uppertail-coverts are slightly warmer and browner than the mantle and lack the olive tone. The edges of the primaries and secondaries are slightly warmer and paler, creating a warmer toned wing-panel in the closed wing.
   Underpart colour varies considerably. The chin and throat are white, usually washed delicate pale grey. This darkens to dull brown across the upper breast, usually with a darker greyer smudge on the breast sides. The flanks are usually dull grey-brown, showing little contrast with the closed wing, but are warm creamy brown to pale peachy brown in some pale birds. The belly is dull greyish white in dark birds, only slightly paler than the flanks, while in

pale birds it is creamy white. The undertail-coverts usually appear tawny-buff.
   The bill is dark grey with a yellowish pink base to the lower mandible and often slightly darker towards the tip. During the breeding season, it darkens to glossy black. Legs and feet dull flesh to pinkish brown.

SIMILAR SPECIES The breeding ranges of no fewer than six *Cettia* species overlap with that of Chestnut-crowned Bush Warbler in the Himalayas and mountains of C China. All are drab and skulking but each has its own character and distinctive song. Of these species, only Grey-sided Bush Warbler shares the combination of a conspicuous chestnut crown and contrasting bold supercilium, but it is considerably smaller and has a very different song. Their separation is discussed under that species.

VOICE The song is a cheerful melody comprising a series of six clear and distinct notes. It begins with a short two-note '*wi-wi*' introduction followed by a slight hesitation, then a rapid and pleasant cheery warbling '*whi-wee-whi-wee*' that rises and falls in pitch between 3–5kHz. Each complete '*wi-wi-whi-wee-whi-wee*' sequence lasts approximately 1.5 seconds and is repeated after a pause of up to three seconds.

Song of Chestnut-crowned Bush Warbler, recorded within breeding range of *C. m. major*, Emei Shan, Sichuan Province, China, May. (Per Alström)

   The call is a single thin but slightly harsh metallic and grating '*tzit*' or '*wzit*', repeated at intervals of two to three seconds.

MOULT Poorly understood. Adults have a complete post-breeding moult on the breeding grounds but it is not known whether further moult occurs before the start of the breeding cycle. Juveniles have a post-juvenile moult on the breeding grounds, presumed to be complete.

HABITAT In the Himalayas, it breeds in forests of fir and hemlock with a thick understorey of rhododendron and thorn scrub, from 3,300m to the tree line and beyond. Above the treeline, it breeds up to at least 4,000m in scrub and rhododendron thickets along sheltered gullies on steep hillsides. It breeds at slightly lower altitudes in China, where temperatures are cooler. On Emei Shan, Sichuan Province, it has been recorded singing as low as 1,800m although those birds could still have been on passage. It certainly breeds there in the extensive fir forests at 2,900m and most likely does so in windswept scrub habitat up to the summit area at 3,050m.
   Poorly known outside the breeding season. It has been recorded from lowland grasslands, swamps and reedbeds in the floodplains of the major rivers draining from the Himalayas into northern India. There are winter records from higher elevations, including the Kathmandu Valley at 1,500m, but these may refer to passage birds. There are no records in winter from China away from the immediate breeding areas.

BEHAVIOUR Typically shy, skulking and very elusive. Not known to differ from others within the genus.

BREEDING HABITS A nest from the Singalila Ridge, Sikkim, authenticated as belonging to this species (Stuart

Baker 1924), was described as a globular construction built in scrub at the edge of dense forest on a steep hillside. The outer layers were loosely built from grass and bamboo leaves, the inside formed from fine grasses and roots and lined with feathers (Ali & Ripley 1973). No information on incubation or fledging periods is available.

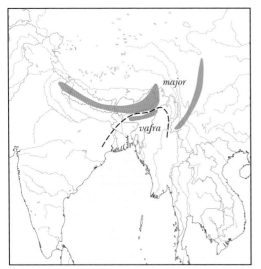

Chestnut-crowned Bush Warbler. Mostly resident but some disperse to lower elevations outside the breeding season.

DISTRIBUTION

C. m. major **Breeding** The nominate race breeds in the Himalayas and mountains of C China, where it occurs at higher elevations than other *Cettia*, ranging from 3,300m to 4,000m. It is patchily distributed and uncommon within its breeding range, with many apparently suitable regions unoccupied. In NW India, it breeds from the Garhwal and Kumaon districts of Uttarakhand. It appears to be scarce in Nepal, where breeding birds have been recorded in mid June from 3,550m to 3,680m in the upper Madi Khola Valley (Inskipp & Inskipp 1991), but it may be more widely distributed. In Bhutan it is largely absent from the W and C regions but it occurs more frequently in the extreme east (Spierenburg 2005) and has been recorded during the breeding season from 3,400m to 4,000m. The eastern limit of its Himalayan range lies in Arunachal Pradesh in NE India and it is also recorded from neighbouring regions in the Qamdo district of Tibet (Xizang Autonomous Region). It is uncertain whether it breeds in adjacent regions of China to the east but breeding in the high mountains of this remote region seems likely although there are no records. Breeding occurs throughout the mountains of SW and C China from W Yunnan Province, north to the Lijiang region and into S Sichuan Province north to the region of Sungpan, including the upper slopes of Emei Shan.

Non-breeding All birds are believed to descend to the lowlands outside the breeding season, although there is limited confirmatory evidence. In lowland Nepal, Inskipp & Inskipp (1991) note older records between October and April, as low as 200m at Royal Chitwan National Park and Koshi Barrage and there are records in January from the lower slopes of Phulchowki in the Kathmandu Valley. It has only been recorded once in Nepal since 1990 (CI *in litt.*), that being a bird at 3,100m at Khaptad National Park in the west on 12 May 1996, but few observations have been possible there during the breeding season, which coincides with the Southeast Monsoon. There are no recent wintering records from Chitwan where it was formerly regularly seen, albeit rarely, or from Koshi where it was always rare. Elsewhere, it has been recorded in March in the Dibru Saikhowa National Park in Assam, NE India, as low as 200m. It is not known from Burma (Smythies 1968) but Lekagul & Round (1991) include two winter records from N Thailand, indicating that some winter at considerable distances from the breeding areas.

C. m. vafra Breeds to the south of the Brahmaputra River in the hills of Meghalaya, southern Assam and Nagaland in NE India. Here it occurs at lower elevations, up to 1,800m, where most are believed to be resident, although some descend to lower in winter.

MOVEMENTS An altitudinal migrant that descends from breeding areas in the high mountains during the colder months. Its routes and migration timing are poorly known, with observations from wintering areas occasional and erratic.

Wintering birds remain in lowland Nepal up to April. Conditions in the breeding areas above 3,000m in Nepal and Bhutan are often inhospitable until early May. These high breeding territories are unlikely to be occupied before mid to late May.

DESCRIPTION *C. m. major*
Plumage – Adult fresh Forehead and crown unmarked warm chestnut. Pale rufous-buff supercilium poorly defined and indistinct in front of the eye, merging with side of crown and loral line but better defined above and behind the eye, where it broadens and extends to side of nape. Lores dull chestnut-brown, forming indistinct and diffuse line from bill base to eye and merging with lower edge of supercilium. Eye-line dull olive-brown, solid and sharply defined from supercilium, merging with side of nape. Ear-coverts pale cream, tipped dull olive-brown, heavily mottled, particularly towards upper edges. Eye-ring narrow, dull creamy white. Upper nape warm chestnut, merging into grey-brown lower nape, mantle and scapulars, usually with a faint olive wash. Rump and uppertail-coverts slightly warmer and browner than mantle, lacking olive tones. Tail feathers with broad, poorly defined, dull olive-brown fringes and marginally darker centres. Chin and throat to malar region white, usually with faint light grey wash, merging with lower edge of the ear-coverts. Breast whitish with a faint warm brown wash that intensifies to deeper greyish brown on side of breast and lower side of neck. Flanks dull oily brown, often tinged creamy brown to peachy brown, contrasting with pale creamy white belly; becoming more intense greyish brown on lower flanks. Undertail-coverts dull tawny-buff. Lesser and median coverts dull olive-brown with broad warm brown fringes. Greater and primary coverts and tertials dark greyish brown with fairly narrow, sharply defined warm brown fringes. Secondaries and primaries dark greyish brown, edged and narrowly tipped warm brown. Alula dark brown with narrow, warm brown fringe. Entire closed wing appears warm brown, contrasting with the dull olive-brown mantle. Underwing-coverts pale greyish white, paler than flanks.
Adult worn Very similar to fresh adult. Tends to lose olive tones from upperparts and bleaches slightly, but there is

much individual variation.

Juvenile Overall much darker than adult, and lacks chestnut-brown cap and warmer, paler tones. Crown and upperparts uniform dull greyish brown, with olivaceous wash. Supercilium dull olive-buff, darker and less contrasting than in adult. Loral line dark olive-brown. Eye-line dark olive-brown, sharply defined, reaching side of nape. Ear-coverts pale cream, tipped dark olive-brown, appearing heavily mottled as in adult, particularly towards upper edges. Eye-ring narrow and poorly defined, dull creamy white. Tail feathers dull olive-brown, edges showing little contrast with centres. Chin and throat to malar region white, with a faint greyish wash. Breast white with a greyish wash, darker at sides, sometimes appearing as a distinct breast-band. Flanks greyish, becoming dull greyish brown posteriorly and on undertail-coverts. Lesser and median coverts dark brown with narrow, cold brown fringes. Greater coverts and tertials dark brown with narrow, dull olive-straw fringes. Edges to primary coverts, secondaries and primaries dull brown, darker and lacking warm brown tones of adult. Slightly warmer than tertial fringes, but duller and colder than those of adult. Alula dark brown with narrow, dull brown fringe.

Bare parts Upper mandible glossy black during breeding season, dark grey at other times. Lower mandible glossy black with small yellowish pink base at start of breeding season, becoming yellowish pink at base later. Tarsi, toes and claws dull reddish flesh to dull pinkish brown. Iris hazel or deep brown in adult, colour of immature unknown.

IN HAND CHARACTERS
Measurements

C. m. major

	Male	Female
Wing	62–66 (64.4; 8)	60–63 (61.2; 5)
Tail	46–52 (49.9; 7)	44–52 (46.4; 5)
Bill	14–15 (14.7; 8)	14–15.5 (14.5; 5)
Tarsus	23.5–26 (24.6; 8)	22–24 (23.4; 5)

Sexes combined:
Tail/wing ratio: 65–85% (75%; 21)
Bill width: 2.9–3.3 (3.1; 9)
Hind claw: 5.0–7.0 (6.4; 10)
Tail graduation: 5–10 (6.8; 8)

Structure

Wing formula (n = 10):

p1/pc	p2	p3e	p4e	p5e	p6e	p7	p10
13–16	12–15	4–7	1–2	wp	0–2	1–3	6–8

Wing resembles Brownish-flanked Bush Warbler (Fig. 118) but lacks emargination on p7; strongly rounded with fairly large p1 (*c.* 40% p2). Wing point p5 (6); p2 < ss tips, p3 falls near p9; emargination on p3–6.

Tail rounded, relatively short; feathers broad and rounded.

Bill slender, concave-sided with fine tip.

Tarsi long and quite strong; toes and claws rather small.

Recognition A large *Cettia* with a warmly coloured crown and prominent pinkish buff supercilium. Distinguished from the similarly patterned Grey-sided Bush Warbler by its much larger dimensions. Also by the less sharply patterned face, the dark olive-toned mantle and the greyish brown wash to the upper breast and flanks.

Ageing Juveniles are readily distinguishable in late summer by differences in body plumage (see above) and from lack of feather wear. After post-juvenile moult, there is no established criterion for separating young birds from recently moulted adults.

Weight Thailand, (n = 1) 12.6g (PDR unpublished data).

GEOGRAPHIC VARIATION Two races recognised although the differences between them are poorly defined.

C. m. major (Himalayas from NW India to Sichuan and W Yunnan in C China) Described above.

C. m. vafra (Hills of Meghalaya, S Assam, Nagaland in NE India) Closely resembles the nominate form and differences are slight, but overall colour tones appear slightly more saturated. The chestnut crown is marginally brighter and extends slightly further onto the nape. The supercilium is usually slightly paler and the eye-stripe is marginally warmer reddish brown. The upperparts are slightly darker with the olive tone to the mantle and scapulars reduced. Below, the breast is rather more heavily washed greyish brown and the sides and flanks are darker, becoming deep warm brown on lower flanks and undertail-coverts.

TAXONOMY AND SYSTEMATICS No issues arising.

◄▲ Adult, Chiang Rai, Thailand, December. Shares chestnut crown with Grey-sided Bush Warbler but readily separated by uniform brown upperparts, often with faint olive wash, and distinctly larger size. Note how chestnut on side of crown bleeds into supercilium, so head appears browner and less contrasting than on Grey-sided Bush Warbler (Philip Round/The Wetland Trust).

GREY-SIDED BUSH WARBLER
Cettia brunnifrons   Plate 40

Prinia brunnifrons **Hodgson, 1845**. *Proc. Zool. Soc. London.* p. 29. Nepal.

A small and lively *Cettia*, fairly common and widespread throughout the upper montane forest of the Himalayas and mountains of C China, wintering in the adjacent foothills and lowlands. Polytypic, with three poorly defined races:

C. b. brunnifrons (Hodgson, 1845). Himalayas from C Nepal through Sikkim to Bhutan and perhaps NE India (Arunachal Pradesh).

C. b. whistleri (Ticehurst, 1923). NW Himalayas from extreme NE Pakistan (Kaghan valley) east through Kashmir to NW India (Uttarakhand).

C. b. umbratica (Stuart Baker, 1924). NE India (E Arunachal Pradesh) and NE Burma north and east into China (SE Tibet (Xizang Autonomous Region), SW Yunnan, W Sichuan and SE Gansu).

IDENTIFICATION Length 10–11cm. Wing 43–50mm. Tail/wing 82–96%.

Grey-sided Bush Warbler occurs alongside several similar small, short-billed *Cettia*. Its small size, distinctive head pattern with a warm chestnut cap and bold whitish supercilium, together with its highly distinctive and repetitive song, combine to give it a unique character. Only the larger Chestnut-crowned Bush Warbler shares a similar warm chestnut crown. Sexes alike.

Structure Comparable in size and structure with Brownish-flanked Bush Warbler and slightly larger than Hume's Bush Warbler and Yellow-bellied Bush Warbler. It shares with these species a thick-necked, plump-bodied appearance combined with a narrow, slightly rounded tail, rather shorter than the body length. The tail is often flicked upwards and held slightly cocked, a posture often adopted by singing males in spring. Although slightly rounded, the head rarely appears domed and may look distinctly flat-crowned. Combined with a well-defined supercilium this gives it a large-headed, broad-crowned appearance, perhaps exaggerated by the prominent chestnut crown. The dark grey bill appears particularly delicate, being small, narrow and distinctly tapered.

It is difficult to assess wing structure accurately as the primaries lack pale contrasting tips. The wing is rounded with a long first primary (p1) and, as with most of the smaller *Cettia*, primary projection between about one quarter and one third of the tertial length. The wing point, formed by p5–6, reaches only to the base of the tail, which exaggerates the plump appearance of the body and enhances the tail length.

Plumage and bare parts One of the easier *Cettia* to identify, but it can be frustratingly difficult to see well in thick undergrowth. It has a distinctive, bright and contrasting head appearance, with a chestnut forehead and crown, conspicuous long white supercilium and bold black eye stripe. Added to this are the white chin and throat and faintly mottled ear-coverts. Only Chestnut-crowned Bush Warbler, with a similar chestnut-brown crown, comes close in appearance but that species has a dull pinkish buff supercilium and the eyestripe is less crisp and blackish, so the head pattern appears less contrasting.

The body is relatively drab and nondescript. The upper-parts, including the closed wings, rump and tail, are uniform dull rufescent-brown with little or no suggestion of warmth.

Even the pale ash-grey wash on the breast and flanks, from which the species derives its name, is not particularly obvious unless seen well. Under most light conditions, the grey tones appear dark and show little or no contrast with the upperparts. Similarly, although there is a brownish olive wash to the ventral region and undertail-coverts, this often appears much darker in poor light and the whitish centre to the lower breast and belly can be difficult to discern.

The appearance of juveniles is poorly documented and as they differ significantly in appearance from adults, they are likely to be mistaken for other species. Compared with adults, they have a subdued head pattern with the supercilium less clearly defined, particularly behind the eye, and appearing greyish buff, slightly paler than the dull brownish olive crown and eye-stripe. The upperparts, including the mantle, rump and tail are uniform dull brownish olive, showing little contrast with the uniform, slightly paler dull ochreous-brown underparts.

In adults, the bill is dark grey with a pale yellow lower mandible that darkens slightly at the sides towards the tip. The legs and feet are pale, varying from brownish pink to greyish brown.

SIMILAR SPECIES

Chestnut-crowned Bush Warbler is the only *Cettia* that shares a combination of chestnut-brown cap, pale supercilium and dark eye-stripe, although this similarity is rather superficial. It is distinctly larger than Grey-sided Bush but this may be of little use in their field separation. By comparison, the supercilium and eye-stripe of Chestnut-crowned Bush are subdued and the head appears less contrasting. Whereas the supercilium is long, white and crisp in Grey-sided Bush, it is sullied dull pinkish buff in Chestnut-crowned Bush, with a rather diffuse upper border.

Other subtle plumage differences include the dull greyish brown wash to the upper breast and flanks of Chestnut-crowned Bush Warbler rather than clear ash-grey in Grey-sided Bush, and a dark olive toned mantle that differs from the dull rufescent-brown of Grey-sided Bush. These are useful supporting characters, but establishing identification from the appearance of the head is an essential first step. The songs are very different: see **Voice** below and discussion under Chestnut-crowned Bush Warbler.

VOICE The song comprises two distinct components, one following immediately after the other. These are so dissimilar that it is difficult to believe they are given by the same bird. The opening sequence begins with a loud, clear and cheery introductory '*wit chir-ee-chir-ee*' which is simple, pleasant and melodic, and varies in pitch from 3–8kHz. The initial '*wit*' note is clearly separated from the accompanying '*chir-ee-chir-ee*', in which the notes tend to slur into each other. This is immediately followed by two curious high-pitched squeaky or buzzing '*dzreeeuu-dzreeeuu*' phrases. The second part of the song has been likened to the sound of a child's toy having the air squeezed out of it.

Each complete song sequence '*wit chir-ee-chir-e dzreeeuu-dzreeeuu*' lasts approximately two seconds and is followed by a pause of two to five seconds before being repeated.

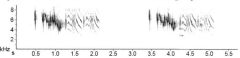

Song of Grey-sided Bush Warbler, recorded within breeding range of *C. b. brunnifrons*, Yutong La, Bhutan, April (Peter Kennerley)

Two distinctly different calls are given. That most frequently heard is assumed to be the main contact call. This comprises a three-note sequence '*chit-yuu-ee*' or '*chit-yuu-chit*' repeated about once per second. The other call is an occasional quiet, unassuming '*zit*', '*pzik*' or '*pzek*' with a distinctly buzzing quality, repeated once to twice per second. This is thought to be an alarm call.

MOULT No published information available but moult strategy is probably similar to that of closely related *Cettia* species. If so, juveniles undertake a complete moult in late summer before descending to wintering areas. Adults are believed to have a complete moult after breeding, followed by a pre-breeding body moult in spring.

HABITAT Breeds in the Himalayas at 2,700m to 4,000m, occurring throughout much of this range alongside and in similar habitats to Hume's Bush Warbler. Some breed above 4,000m in drier parts of the Himalayas and in Tibet (Xizang Autonomous Region). At lower levels, it inhabits relatively open glades and clearings in mature forest, often of fir, hemlock and rhododendrons, especially where sunlight promotes vigorous undergrowth. It also occurs where forest has been cleared for agriculture, leaving a mosaic of wooded patches, scrub-thickets, tangles of rank vegetation and dry-stone walls with a thick covering of vines, creepers and shrubs. At higher levels it frequents open, stunted moss forest with epiphytes and a dwarf bamboo understorey. Some even breed above the tree line in windswept bamboo grassland.

Outside the breeding season, it appears quite flexible in its requirements. It occurs in almost all types of habitat with thick cover including overgrown shrubland, dense grassland and dense rank undergrowth, mainly at 1,000–2,000m.

BEHAVIOUR Shy and retiring, spending much time deep within undergrowth. Outside the breeding season, it will occasionally appear in the open or fly a short-distance from one tangled scrub thicket to the next, but it invariably disappears quickly again into deep cover. Males are lively and energetic when breeding and regularly emerge from cover and sing from exposed perches close to the ground or on top of a low bush or thorn thicket, or even from rocks or stone walls. They rarely remain in view for long and frequently move through their territories while singing. They have been observed pursuing presumed females, both birds keeping low in thick cover as they fly from bush to bush, drooping and frequently vibrating their wings, presumably as part of the courtship display and a prelude to mating.

BREEDING HABITS Little known, with almost no new information since Stuart Baker (1924) published his account of this species. He described the nest as a an oval domed structure, built of grass, moss and lichen, lined with fine grass and feathers and placed in a low bush within forest or adjacent scrub thicket. The eggs are laid in May and the clutch size varies from three to five. Spierenburg (2005) noted a bird carrying nesting material on 3 May at 3,000m in Bhutan. It is unknown whether it is single- or double-brooded.

DISTRIBUTION Widespread and generally common throughout the montane forests of the Himalayas and into the mountains of W China.

Breeding

C. b. whistleri The western race *whistleri* breeds from the Neelum River region of Azad Kashmir and the Kaghan

Valley in extreme NE Pakistan, east through Indian Administered Kashmir to the Garhwal district of Uttarakhand in NW India and perhaps into the Kumaon district of Uttarakhand. There are few records from neighbouring W Nepal, however, and it is not believed to breed there regularly.

C. b. brunnifrons The nominate race breeds throughout the C Himalayas, from C Nepal east of the Kali Gandaki Valley through Sikkim to E Bhutan and perhaps into Arunachal Pradesh in NE India. Spierenburg (2005) considered this the commonest breeding *Cettia* in Bhutan, abundant throughout the alpine and temperate zones.

C. b. umbratica The breeding range of *umbratica* extends from E Arunachal Pradesh in NE India and NE Burma, north and east into China, where it has been recorded and presumably breeds in the mountains of SE Tibet (Xizang Autonomous Region) and Yunnan Province, north through the mountains of Sichuan to SE Gansu Province.

Non-breeding It is believed that most birds descend to lower elevations outside the breeding season, although some remain higher than Chestnut-crowned Bush Warbler. Winter distribution details are poorly understood but it appears to remain in the foothills and lowlands close to breeding areas. In Nepal, it winters mainly from 915m to 2,135m; being uncommon at lower levels but occurring occasionally down to 215m (Inskipp & Inskipp 1991). Similarly, in Bhutan, it is common in winter in dense undergrowth from 1,000m to 2,000m and occasionally occurs as low as 200m (Spierenburg 2005).

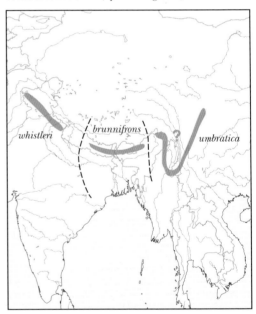

whistleri / brunnifrons / umbratica

Grey-sided Bush Warbler. Mostly resident but some disperse to lower elevations outside the breeding season.

MOVEMENTS Poorly documented. Although this species is regularly seen at elevations below the breeding sites, these are casual observations in presumed wintering areas. It is assumed that breeding areas are deserted during the cold winter months when birds descend to the foothills. They reach the lowlands in Nepal from September onwards but many appear to remain at higher elevations until later in the year when pushed down by cold weather. The only available data on the timing or duration of passage is from Spierenburg (2005), who noted passage between breeding and wintering areas in October and again in April, when it is common in Bhutan in regions where it does not breed. Numbers decline in these passage regions from the last week in April and singing birds are already back on high breeding territories in Bhutan and Nepal by mid April.

DESCRIPTION *C. b. brunnifrons*
Plumage – Adult fresh Forehead and crown unmarked warm chestnut, this usually extending onto the upper nape, but fading to dull rufescent-brown on lower nape. Supercilium white or creamy white, long, extending from bill base to rear of ear-coverts, sometimes to side of nape; well-defined above the lores and tapering slightly behind the eye, but clearly demarcated from side of crown and eye-line. Loral line blackish, well-defined, from bill base to front of eye. A dark brown eye-line, crisply defined along upper edge, extending behind the eye to rear of supercilium, flaring slightly and merging with nape. Ear-coverts pale greyish brown, with indistinct darker brown tips giving a mottled appearance. A narrow white eye-ring merges above eye with the supercilium, usually contrasting below eye with darker ear-coverts. Mantle and scapulars dull rufescent-brown. Rump and uppertail-coverts slightly darker than mantle, with warmer tones slightly suppressed but rarely absent. Tail feathers dark rufous-brown with little or no contrast between fringes and webs.

Chin and throat greyish white, sides of throat and malar regions often with faint darker feather tips, meeting faint mottling on lower ear-coverts. Entire breast washed ash-grey, palest in centre, darker near carpal bend and extending to form a pale grey crescent below the ear-coverts. Upper flanks washed ash-grey, darkening to brownish olive on lower flanks and undertail-coverts. Centre to belly white, washed pale greyish or creamy grey. Lesser and median coverts rufescent-brown, similar to mantle. Greater coverts and tertials dark brown with broad warm brown to rusty tan fringes, slightly warmer and brighter than mantle. Edges to primary coverts, secondaries and primaries narrowly edged warm rusty tan. Tips of primaries contrast little with exposed feather webs. Alula dark brown with a broad, crisp rusty tan fringe. Underwing-coverts pale grey to greyish white, similar to belly.
Adult worn Worn adult very similar to fresh bird, but may appear slightly darker and lacks rufescent wash above.
Juvenile Much darker than adult and lacks warmer and greyer tones. Supercilium well-defined but dull greyish olive and less contrasting than in adult. Lores and eye-line dull brownish olive, forming a well-defined dark line below the supercilium. Ear-coverts dull sandy brown with olive-brown tips, creating slight mottling. Narrow eye-ring dull sandy brown, contrasting little with either the supercilium or the ear-coverts. Crown, nape, mantle, scapulars, rump, uppertail-coverts and tail usually uniform dull brownish olive, occasionally appearing dull rufous-brown.

Chin and throat dull creamy brown, becoming dull sandy brown towards sides and merging with ear-coverts. Breast dull greyish brown, slightly paler than upperparts, darkening slightly towards sides. Flanks dull greyish brown, darkening to dull earth-brown towards lower flanks and onto undertail-coverts. Centre of belly paler brown with slight yellowish wash.

Lesser and median coverts dark brown with dull tan fringes, slightly warmer than mantle. Greater coverts and

tertials dark brown with poorly contrasting dull tan fringes. Primary coverts, secondaries and primaries narrowly edged dull tan. Alula dark brown with a narrow dull tan fringe.
Bare parts Upper mandible dark grey. Lower mandible pale yellow, darkening to grey near tip. Tarsi, toes and claws pale brownish pink to pale greyish brown. Iris dark brown in adults, colour in younger birds unknown.

IN HAND CHARACTERS
Measurements

C. b. brunnifrons

	Male	Female
Wing	44–50 (47.4; 26)	43–48 (45.5; 12)
Tail	39–46 (43.3: 21)	38–44 (40.3; 9)
Bill	11–12 (11.4; 25)	10.5–12 (11.3; 11)
Tarsus	17.5–19 (18.5; 14)	17.5–18.5 (18.1; 9)

Sexes combined:
Tail/wing ratio: 82–96% (91%; 33)
Bill width: 2.8–3.2 (3.1; 12)
Hind claw: 4.8–5.5 (5.3; 12)
Tail graduation: 10–18 (14.7; 9)
C. b. whistleri: measurements as for nominate race.

Structure

C. b. brunnifrons

Wing formula (n = 8):

p1/pc	p2	p3e	p4e	p5e	p6e	p7e	p10
10–12	9–11	2–4	0–1	wp	wp	0.5–1	4–6

Wing strongly rounded with large p1 (*c.* 60% p2). Wing point p(4) 5–6; p2 < ss tips, p3 falls near p9; emargination on p3–7.

Figure 119. Wing of Grey-sided Bush Warbler.

Tail medium, strongly graduated; feathers quite broad.
Bill small, straight and slender, laterally compressed with a fine tip.
Tarsi slender, claws fine.
Recognition A tiny warbler with a chestnut crown, bold white supercilium and pale grey underparts, plumage features which should separate adults easily from other small Himalayan *Cettia*. Duller, browner juveniles without the contrasting crown may however be more difficult to distinguish. Separated from much larger Chestnut-crowned Bush Warbler by measurements (wing < 58mm, bill usually < 14mm) and by paler underparts and more contrasting supercilium.
Weight ♂ 8–9g, ♀ 6–9g (del Hoyo *et al.* 2006).

GEOGRAPHIC VARIATION Three poorly defined races

are recognised. The differences between them appear to be clinal, with a tendency towards increasing colour saturation from west to east. These differences are small and probably inconsistent and apparent intergrades occur in collections.

C. b. brunnifrons (Himalayas from C Nepal to Bhutan and perhaps to Arunachal Pradesh, NE India) Described above. Many birds in Arunachal Pradesh appear intermediate between this form and the race *umbratica*.

C. b. whistleri (NW Himalayas from extreme NE Pakistan east to Uttarakhand, India) Closely resembles the nominate race but tends to be slightly paler, less intensely coloured, with a slightly paler chestnut crown. The rufescent wash to the mantle and scapulars is less noticeable and sometimes entirely absent. The edges and fringes to the wing feathers are slightly darker, warm brown rather than warm rusty tan and the lower flanks and undertail-coverts usually show a slightly warmer wash. Some appear to intergrade with the nominate form.

C. b. umbratica (E Arunachal Pradesh in NE India to NE Burma and C China) Birds in Arunachal Pradesh closely resemble the nominate form and probably represent an intergrade population. The characteristics of *umbratica* become better defined in birds breeding to the east in NE Burma and China, where they are slightly darker and browner above and lack the warmer tones to the rump and uppertail-coverts shown by the nominate form. The edges to the primaries and secondaries are duller and less obvious so the closed wing appears darker, less contrasting and similar in colour to the upperparts.

TAXONOMY AND SYSTEMATICS No issues arising.

▲ Adult *C. b. whistleri*, Uttarakhand, India, January. Closely resembles nominate, differing by slightly paler appearance, but many birds are not reliably separable. Note greyish underparts which separate it from Chestnut-crowned Bush Warbler (Arun P. Singh).

▲ Adult *C. b. umbratica*, Yunnan, China, November. Upperparts slightly darker and browner than nominate, and with browner, less contrasting edges to primaries and secondaries, similar in colour to the upperparts. This individual also lacks the bright chestnut cap and shows sullied grey underparts (John and Jemi Holmes).

MANCHURIAN BUSH WARBLER
Cettia canturians   Plate 41

Arundinax canturians **Swinhoe, 1860.** *Ibis* page 52. Amoy in winter, Shanghai in summer.

The largest *Cettia*, which breeds commonly in dense thickets and undergrowth in N and E China, the Korean Peninsula and adjacent regions of SE Russia and winters from Taiwan and S China to NW Thailand, Indochina and the N Philippines. Often treated as conspecific with Japanese Bush Warbler but distinct differences in plumage and pronounced sexual dimorphism between the sexes in Manchurian Bush Warbler suggest they are better treated as two species. Polytypic, with two races recognised:

C. c. canturians (Swinhoe, 1860). C and E China (S Gansu and Sichuan east to Jiangsu and W Zhejiang).

C. c. borealis (Campbell, 1892). NE China, SE Russia (S Ussuriland) and the Korean Peninsula.

IDENTIFICATION Length 15–18cm. Wing, male 71–82mm, female 57–66mm. Tail/wing 85–103%.

A distinctive, warmly coloured *Cettia* with a cinnamon-brown crown, warm brown upperparts and pale underparts. Sexes alike but males are the largest *Cettia* warblers and this species exhibits the most extreme sexual size dimorphism within the genus.

Structure Shows the characteristic dome-headed, short-winged and fairly long-tailed structure typical of all *Cettia*. The sexes are readily separable on size and structure. The wing length of the largest males can overlap that of the smallest female Oriental Reed Warbler, but it always lacks that species' bulk. Females are considerably smaller and overlap in size with other *Cettia* and the smaller *Acrocephalus*. The tarsus is particularly thick in the male and this is the only *Cettia* in which the sexes require different ring sizes. The wings are distinctly rounded with p1 extending well beyond the primary coverts and the wing point being formed by p5 in both sexes. It does, however, show a more substantial primary projection than most *Cettia*, with up to six tips visible. The relatively long and rounded tail has ten broad rounded feathers and a distinctive fan-like appearance when spread. The bill of the male is rather short but quite stout, the upper mandible being distinctly decurved towards the tip; that of the female is finer and less robust (Fig. 120).

Plumage and bare parts The nominate race shows a distinctive cinnamon-brown forehead and crown, which is slightly brighter than the warm brown upperparts, although these are brighter and more richly tinged in freshly moulted birds. The rump may appear slightly warmer and paler than the mantle and tail. The edges of the closed wing feathers are richer in tone than the upperparts, appearing cinnamon-brown and contrasting slightly with the warm brown upperparts. This contrast becomes more obvious on worn spring birds, in which the upperparts are paler and duller.

The head shows a long, pale supercilium that extends well behind the eye, contrasting with the crown and with a dark brown eyestripe. The ear-coverts appear pale and distinctly mottled. The underparts are dull white, lightly washed warm brown, especially on the breast sides and flanks. The unmarked undertail-coverts are warm buffy brown.

The bill is greyish brown with a dull pink base to the lower mandible, but darkens towards the tip. The legs are pale greyish pink.

SIMILAR SPECIES Several species superficially resemble Manchurian Bush Warbler within its range. Males may be momentarily mistaken for one of the larger *Acrocephalus* warblers, although this impression is soon dispelled. Even females are large compared with other resident or dispersive *Cettia* species occurring within the non-breeding range. Of these, the much smaller Brownish-flanked Bush Warbler overlaps with it in winter and Japanese Bush Warbler may do so in Taiwan or during passage along the east coast of China in spring.

Japanese Bush Warbler of the widespread race *cantans* is resident, dispersive or a short-distance migrant and quite rare outside its usual range in Japan and S South Korea. It is closely related to Manchurian Bush Warbler but its sexual size dimorphism is much less pronounced and the male is considerably smaller than male Manchurian Bush, closer in size to female Manchurian Bush. It always appears drab olive-brown above, including the crown, and lacks the warmer, brighter cinnamon-brown tone to the upperparts. Although it has a pale greyish supercilium, this is narrower and less conspicuous than that of Manchurian Bush. The bill is also longer and finer and almost black during the breeding season, unlike the heavier, stouter and conspicuously pale bill of Manchurian Bush.

Brownish-flanked Bush Warbler winters in similar shrubland habitat to that frequented by Manchurian Bush Warbler, particularly in S China. However, it is a diminutive bird, smaller and more delicately built than the smallest female Manchurian Bush. It is also duller, drabber and altogether more nondescript than its larger relative. The head is relatively plain, with a rather short supercilium and a short loral stripe. When fresh, the crown and the edges to the flight feathers and rectrices can appear warm rusty-brown, but the upperparts are always drab brown and the underparts usually brownish grey with buffish brown sides, more intensely washed than in Manchurian Bush Warbler.

VOICE The song comprises a short, fluty and rather liquid warbling '*lu-lu-lu-lu-lu-lu-wik-lu-ee*', with a slight wavering quality, resembling an accelerated version of the song of Japanese Bush Warbler. The introductory '*lu-lu-lu-lu-lu-lu*' sequence slowly increases in volume and intensity at a frequency of *c.* 1kHz, then increases in volume and frequency to fluctuate from 2–5kHz in the terminal '*wik-lu-ee*' element. This song was described by La Touche (1925–30) as a loud and melodious '*kolo-olo-olo-wichit-chit*',

    a   b   c

Figure 120. Comparison of head and bill shape of (a) male Manchurian Bush Warbler (b) female Manchurian Bush Warbler and (c) male Japanese Bush Warbler *C. d. cantans*.

which he considered somewhat short and monotonous. Each song sequence lasts approximately 1–2 seconds and is followed by a longer pause, typically from 3–7 seconds when in continuous song, but often longer if singing is sporadic. It is performed from within thick cover so there is often no indication that the bird is nearby until a surprisingly loud song burst is heard. The song is similar to that of Japanese Bush Warbler but never seems to include the characteristic '*ket-kyot*' phrase so characteristic of that species. Young birds in autumn have been heard to give a short song resembling the opening sequence of the adult song.

The song of *borealis* closely resembles that of the nominate form, but tends to begin with a shorter, louder and more varied introductory '*lu-lu-lu*' or '*lu-lu-wik-lu*' phrase and to have more notes in the terminal flourish. The entire song, '*lu-lu-lu-wik-lu-ee-wu-ee*' lasts for approximately one second. It is uncertain, however, whether this difference represents individual or regional variation, or whether it is consistent between the races.

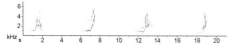

Song of Manchurian Bush Warbler, recorded within winter range of *C. c. canturians*, Hong Kong, China, March. (Geoff Carey)

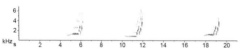

Song of Manchurian Bush Warbler, recorded within breeding range of *C. c. borealis*, Socheong Island, South Korea, May (Nial Moores/Birds Korea)

The call is a short, dry rattling '*trrrr*' or '*juuruht*', frequently repeated. A slightly shorter, rather quiet '*jat*' has been noted from the race *borealis*. It is not known to give the single '*chak*' call of Japanese Bush Warbler.

MOULT Little data available. Adults undergo a complete post-breeding moult on the breeding grounds prior to migration. The timing and duration of this are poorly understood, but moult is completed before arrival in wintering areas in late October. Young birds have a complete post-juvenile moult, also prior to autumn migration, replacing all wing and tail feathers as well as body plumage. As in the adult, the timing and duration of this moult are uncertain. Once completed, adults and first-year birds cannot be separated using plumage characters. Has partial pre-breeding moult in winter quarters shortly before spring migration in which body feathers are replaced.

HABITAT Requires thick, coarse vegetation at all times of year. It ranges from sea level to 700m and tends to be more numerous at higher elevations when breeding, but found mainly below 250m on migration and during the winter months. Breeds in shrub-covered hillsides, hedges, dense grassland and other patches of thick, rank vegetation, but avoids reedbeds. It uses a wider range of habitats at other times. In Hong Kong in winter, it is fairly numerous at sea level in coastal scrub and adjacent reedbeds, for example at the Mai Po Marshes Nature Reserve, where it frequents scrub-covered bunds with a few emergent trees and adjacent *Phragmites* beds standing in shallow water. This mix of habitats appears to suit its requirements particularly well and this site regularly attracts large numbers of migrants

and wintering birds, with a record 40, presumably migrants, recorded here on 15 November 1992 (Carey *et al.* 2001). Regular studies in higher, drier shrubland habitats in Hong Kong reveal that those areas are favoured during migration but few birds overwinter at those higher elevations.

In South Korea, the race *borealis* breeds in very dense scrub and *Salix koreensis* in broad river valleys.

BEHAVIOUR Known only from occasional and casual observations, even in regions where it is relatively abundant. It is always skulking and elusive throughout the year, but not particularly shy. Views outside the breeding season are often brief, but birds may emerge to feed on small insects on bare open ground, particularly on damp mud near stands of *Phragmites*, into which they disappear when disturbed. Others forage up to 2m from ground on the edges of bushes, sometimes remaining in intermittent view.

On return to breeding territories, from late March, males announce their presence with bouts of prolonged song. As in Japanese Bush Warbler, during the breeding season the throat of the male enlarges and the skin pulls tight, so that the entire gular region becomes inflated when singing, presumably as an aid to increasing the volume of the song. Males sing throughout the day until the females arrive, later in April, sometimes from the top of a bush but often from deep cover. Rival males may sing almost continuously, pausing only to catch insects. Song continues throughout the breeding season, up to the beginning of July, and can be heard from any thicket or scrub patch in the hills fringing the Yangtze valley. Young males may begin to sing on the breeding grounds in early August when the adults have departed (Kolthoff 1932). Song commences on the wintering grounds from mid February and is then heard regularly until departure.

BREEDING HABITS The most detailed account is given by Kolthoff (1932), of the nominate race in the Chinkiang (Zhenjiang) Mountains in Jiangsu Province along the Yangtze Valley. Pairs are not monogamous and males remain sexually active, with enlarged testes, until the young leave the nest, suggesting that opportunities for mating with additional females remain high throughout the breeding season. The nest is placed in a bush, most frequently *Pinus massoniana* or *Quercus dentata*, typically 1–1.5m above ground, close to the thickest part of the canopy. It is usually situated 200–300m from the closest singing male and never in the immediate vicinity of the song perch. The nest is a domed structure, roughly broad oval in shape, with an entrance hole in the side that often faces south. It is built from coarse, broad grasses and lined with fine grass stems and a few feathers. Nest building, incubation and feeding of the young are believed to be carried out exclusively by the female. The clutch of 3–5 eggs is laid in May or June. The earliest nest with eggs noted by Kolthoff (1932) was on 12 May and the latest on 24 June. Recently fledged young were recorded from 17 June onwards. Apparently single-brooded.

DISTRIBUTION Has a disjunct breeding distribution, the nominate race breeding in C and E China and the race *borealis* in NE China to the Russian Far East and the Korean Peninsula. The species appears to be absent from large parts of northern China between these two populations

Breeding

C. c. canturians In China, it breeds mainly north of the Yangtze River, with the southern limit closely following the Yangtze Valley, from northern Zhejiang and the

Shanghai region, north and west through the provinces of Jiangsu, Anhui, Hubei, Henan, Shanxi, southern Shaanxi and southern Gansu to NE Sichuan.

C. c. borealis Breeds in the northern and central regions of the Korean Peninsula south to Buyeo in Chungnam Province at *c.* 36°N (Kim 2008; Park 2008), although it is scarce towards the southern limit of its range, where it occurs sympatrically with Japanese Bush Warbler. For example, singing males were noted annually on the island of Eocheong, which lies off the west coast of South Korea, where Japanese Bush Warbler also breeds in small numbers (N. Moores *in litt.*). In the subalpine and hill regions on the peninsula it is replaced by Japanese Bush Warbler. Also breeds in NE China, in the eastern part of Liaoning, Jilin and Heilongjiang Provinces and into the Russian Far East in the Lake Khanka region. It probably also occurs in adjacent SE Ussuriland although this is not confirmed.

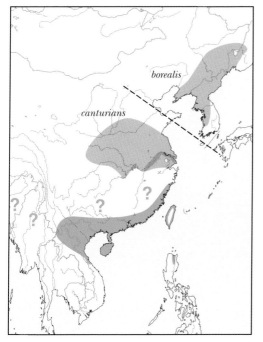

Manchurian Bush Warbler. Breeding range and winter distribution.

Non-breeding Separation of the two races outside the breeding season is confused due to uncertainty over their appearance. The nominate form winters throughout much of E China south of the Yangtze River, although some remain along the lower Yangtze Valley. Most migrate to the coastal provinces of Fujian, Guangdong, Guangxi and Hainan Island where it is common during the winter months. To the south and west, wintering birds reach Yunnan, N Vietnam, N Laos and occasionally extreme NW Thailand. What is believed to be the nominate form has also been recorded in NE India from the W Bengal daurs, the Cachar district in Assam and the Kashi Hills (Rasmussen & Anderton 2005) who also comment that it is probably an overlooked winter visitor to this region. It has not been reported from Burma but it seems likely to occur here.

The northern race *borealis* is believed to be a winter visitor to Taiwan where it is widespread below 1,000m. Small numbers also reach the N Philippines and there are reports from several locations in Luzon including Dalton Pass and Batan island (Dickinson *et al.* 1991). However, the racial identity of some of these specimens should be reviewed in light of a better understanding of their appearance. Birds of this race have not knowingly been encountered in Hong Kong, despite extensive ringing, so it is likely that SE China lies outside its normal wintering range.

MOVEMENTS Kolthoff (1932) reported the latest dates in the Yangtze Valley as 9 July for females and 11 July for males. After this, only juveniles were recorded, although these gradually departed during late July and early August and few were encountered after 15 August. However, an influx of birds appeared later in the season, during late September and October. As all were freshly moulted birds, it is uncertain whether they were first year or adults. The origin of these birds is also uncertain. These may have been birds of the nominate race that had bred further north, locally bred birds returning to the breeding area prior to southward migration, or birds of the race *borealis* on their way to wintering areas. Passage through China is largely undocumented. Ringing studies in Hong Kong have shown that the main passage, presumed to involve nominate race birds, begins during the first week in November, with just two September records and ten October occurrences since 1970 (Carey *et al.* 2001). Numbers increase rapidly throughout November and then decline in early December, with smaller numbers remaining until the end of February. Spring passage begins in early March, and continues until the end of the month, although most have departed by the end of the first week in April. The latest bird trapped at Mai Po was on 1 May 1993 (Carey *et al.* 2001).

Data on *borealis* is generally lacking. It is a migrant through the coastal provinces of E and N China including Fujian, Jiangsu, Shandong and Hebei. La Touche (1925–30) noted northbound migrants on Shaweishan, near Shanghai, during April and May, with some birds still passing through as late as the third week of the month. Return passage through Shaweishan was also quite late, between 10 October and 1 December.

Nial Moores (*in litt.*) considers *borealis* to be a fairly numerous migrant in South Korea, arriving in late March, with small numbers moving through until May. Southbound migrants occur mostly in October.

Birds that appear to be *borealis* occur occasionally In Japan and possibly overwinter there. They have been recorded in February from Izumi in Kagoshima Prefecture, Kyushu, and in March from Yonaguni island, the most southwesterly island in the Ryukyu Archipelago (YS *in litt.*).

DESCRIPTION *C. c. canturians*
Plumage – Adult fresh (August to November) Forehead and crown rather bright cinnamon-brown. Supercilium creamy white, long and conspicuous, extending from bill to rear of the ear-coverts, often reaching the nape; broadest in front of and over the eye, narrowing and tapering above the ear-coverts. Lores dark brown, forming a clearly defined line between bill base and eye. Eye-line equally prominent, dull earthy brown, sharply demarcated from supercilium and broadening slightly along its length to merge with the nape side. Ear-coverts pale cream with dark earth brown fringes creating distinct mottling, most obvious towards

upper edges. Eye-ring creamy white, narrow, upper edge merging with supercilium, lower part more conspicuous against darker ear-coverts. Nape, mantle and scapulars warm brown, tinged cinnamon, but much less strongly than on the crown. Rump and uppertail-coverts usually slightly warmer and brighter than mantle. Tail feathers dull brown with broad, diffuse cinnamon-brown or warm tawny-brown fringes, closely matching uppertail-coverts.

Chin and throat white, with faint creamy wash, intensifying towards the sides; very slightly mottled in malar regions, merging with the faintly mottled lower ear-coverts. Breast dull greyish white to pale creamy buff, sides suffused warm buffy brown. Upper flanks light buffy brown, becoming slightly darker and greyer on lower flanks. Belly white, sometimes with faint peachy or yellowish wash. Undertail-coverts plain warm buffy brown.

Lesser and median coverts tawny-brown with slightly brighter fringes. Greater coverts and tertials dark brown with broad cinnamon-brown to russet-brown fringes. Secondaries and primaries blackish, edged light cinnamon-brown, brighter and slightly warmer than mantle. Exposed primaries lack contrastingly paler tips. Primary coverts blackish, edged cinnamon-brown. Alula with a broad cinnamon-brown edge, similar to wing covert colour. Underwing-coverts white with a hint of grey, much paler than flanks.

Adult worn (December to February) Differs in coloration from fresh bird. Cinnamon tone retained on forehead and crown but less bright. Nape, mantle and scapulars paler and duller brown or tawny-brown. Fringes of lesser and median coverts usually as scapulars, those of greater coverts and tertials and edges of secondaries and primaries dull russet-brown. Underparts generally paler, with chin, throat and belly whitish and unmarked, breast pale greyish white with warmth restricted to smudge near carpal bend, flanks paler. Undertail-coverts slightly paler buff.

Juvenile Supercilium and throat saffron-yellow; rest of underparts washed pale yellow, suffused brownish on breast sides, and becoming gingery brown on lower flanks and undertail-coverts. Shows cinnamon tone on wing and tail feathers.

Bare parts Upper mandible dull greyish brown with narrow, dull pink cutting edge. Lower mandible dull pink at base, darkening to dull greyish brown towards tip. Tarsi, toes and claws pale greyish pink. Iris warmer and browner in older birds, greyish in immature birds.

IN HAND CHARACTERS
Measurements

C. c. canturians

	Male	Female
Wing	71–78 (74.4; 24)	57–64 (60.8; 14)
Tail	68–79 (72.8; 23)	53–63 (58.4; 13)
Bill	16–19 (17.6; 22)	14.5–16 (15.2; 13)
Tarsus	27–29.5 (28.0; 21)	22–24.5 (23.3; 13)

Tail/wing ratio: (sexes combined) 89–103% (97%; 37)
Bill width: ♂ 4.0–4.8 (4.4; 10), ♀ 3.4–4.0 (3.8; 10)
Hind claw: ♂ 7.8–9.2 (8.4; 10), ♀ 6.2–7.3 (6.9; 10)
Tail graduation: ♂ 13–17 (15.2; 10), ♀ 7–12 (10.4; 9)

Wing and tail of juvenile much shorter than adult.

C. c. borealis

	Male	Female
Wing	72–82 (74.8; 23)	61–66 (62.9; 10)
Tail	66–72 (69.2; 20)	55–61 (57.4; 9)
Bill	16.5–19 (17.6; 22)	15–16.5 (15.7; 8)
Tarsus	25.5–29.5 (27.8; 22)	22.5–24 (23.7; 8)

Tail/wing ratio: (sexes combined) 85–99% (92%; 30)
Similar in measurements to nominate *canturians* but tail/wing ratio apparently lower.

Structure

C. c. canturians

Wing formula (♂♂, n = 10):

p1/pc	p2	p3e	p4e	p5e	p6e	p7	p10
11–14	13–17	3–5	0–1	wp	0–1	3–4	10–12

Wing rounded with fairly large p1 (*c.* 40% p2). Wing point p(4) 5 (6); p2 < p10, p3 = p6/7–7/8; emarginated on p3–6, sometimes faintly on p7.

Figure 121. Wing of Manchurian Bush Warbler *C. c. borealis*.

Tail longish, markedly rounded; ten feathers, quite broad, narrowing towards tips.

Bill strong and deep, tip of culmen decurved; bill of female finer and more delicate (Fig. 120).

Tarsi stout; claws strong.

C. c. borealis: wing similar to nominate *canturians* (Fig. 121), but wing point p4–5, with p6 1–3 shorter and p10 11–15 shorter (in ♂).

Recognition A robust *Cettia* with olive-brown upperparts and a long pale supercilium. Confusable only with Japanese Bush Warbler (race *cantans*). Wing, tail and tarsus measurements of most males are well above the range of *cantans*, but those of females span the *cantans* range. Also separated from *cantans* by brighter plumage, contrasting cinnamon-brown crown and cleaner creamy white supercilium. Bill stouter than in *cantans* and pale rather than blackish.

Ageing Juveniles aged by yellow tinged supercilium and underparts, and by shorter wing and tail measurements. After complete post-juvenile moult, ageing is not possible using plumage characters. Palate colour may prove useful; yellowish in adults, pale pink in immature birds; also iris colour: brown in adults, greyish in immature birds (PJL unpublished data).

Weight

C. c. canturians: Hong Kong (winter), ♂ 18.5–27.6g (21.9; 132), ♀ 10.0–18.2g (13.2; 771) (HKRG unpublished data).

C. c. borealis: South Korea (breeding), ♂ 19–34.5g (25.5; 25), ♀ 13.3–15.9g (14.5; 11) (Park 2008).

GEOGRAPHIC VARIATION Two races occur, similar in size and structure, and both with marked size differences between males and females. Plumage differences between them are constant, with no intergrades documented.

C. c. canturians (C and E China) Described above.

C. c. borealis (NE China, SE Russia and the Korean Peninsula) During the breeding season the nape and mantle appear slightly colder and greyer than in the nominate form, although the forehead and usually the crown retain the warmer cinnamon-brown tone typical of that race. This contrasts with the distinctly greyer rear crown and nape, mantle and sides of the head. In addition, the edges of the primaries and secondaries, and the fringes to the greater coverts and tertials, are reddish brown and also contrast with the upperparts.

After the post-breeding or post-juvenile moult, the upperparts of *borealis* in fresh plumage appear uniform warm brown with only a slight greyish wash and so are slightly paler than in the nominate form but closely match those of worn nominate birds in spring. The entire underparts from the chin to the undertail-coverts are suffused uniform warm buff, more intensely coloured than the nominate race typically shows.

In late winter, worn *borealis* loses warmer tones to the underparts so that the chin, throat and belly are paler creamy white, while the breast typically shows a faint greyish brown wash, slightly paler than in worn nominate birds. Towards the lower flanks, this intensifies to a dull greyish brown smudge which contrasts with the pale buff undertail-coverts and white belly. The upperparts are slightly paler and greyer than in the nominate form and contrast with warmer wing edgings becomes more pronounced.

TAXONOMY AND SYSTEMATICS The taxa *canturians* and *borealis* were formerly treated as races of Japanese Bush Warbler. However, their significantly different plumage, structure and song, together with exceptionally marked sexual dimorphism, suggest strongly that these two races do not belong with this largely insular species.

It has been suggested that the plumage differences between *canturians* and *borealis* are sufficient to accord them separate species status. However, the reported differences may relate to comparison of fresh, bright *canturians* with worn, pale *borealis*. When birds in comparable plumages are compared, the differences become much less apparent and they are better treated as races of Manchurian Bush Warbler unless information to suggest otherwise becomes available.

▲ Adult *C. c. canturians*, Hong Kong, December. Absence of greyish tones to the brown upperparts suggest this is the nominate form. The rather delicate structure points to it being a female (Michelle and Peter Wong).

▲ Adult *C. c. canturians*, Hong Kong, December. This robust bird shows a proportionately larger and stouter bill and is probably a male. Overall warmth of plumage tones suggest this is the nominate race (Michelle and Peter Wong).

▲ Adult, Taiwan, November. The brown upperparts show a slight greyish cast suggesting that this is *borealis*. Establishing racial identity in autumn, particularly in regions where both races could occur, is usually not possible (Chang Pei-wen).

▲ Adult *C. c. borealis*, South Korea, October. Note greyish buff upperparts contrasting with chestnut-brown crown and closed wings. During the breeding season upperparts of the nominate race generally appear browner and more saturated (Robert Newlin).

JAPANESE BUSH WARBLER
Cettia diphone   Plate 41

Sylvia diphone **Kittlitz, 1830**. *Mém. Prés. Acad. Imp. Sci., St. Pétersbourg* 1: 237, pl. 14. Bonin Islands.

One of the most familiar Japanese birds, whose cheerful and distinctive song heralds the start of spring, although its preference for thickets and dense undergrowth means that it is seldom seen. Mainly resident or dispersive but those breeding in mountains descend to lower elevations in winter, and northern breeders migrate to S Japan. Formerly treated as conspecific with Manchurian Bush Warbler but morphological distinctions, the lesser sexual size dimorphism of Japanese Bush Warbler and the fact of sympatric breeding in South Korea, mean that they are better treated as two closely related but distinct species. Polytypic, with four races recognised.

C. d. diphone (Kittlitz, 1830). Islands of S Japan (S Izu Islands, Ogasawara Islands, Iwo Islands).

C. d. cantans (Temminck & Schlegel, 1847). Japan (Hokkaido, Honshu, Shikoku and Kyushu, together with N Izu Islands and N Ryukyu Islands) and S South Korea. Introduced on Hawaii.

C. d. restricta (Kuroda, 1923). Islands of SW Japan (Okinawa and adjacent Ryukyu Islands).

C. d. riukiuensis (Kuroda, 1925). Russia (S Sakhalin and S Kuril Islands).

IDENTIFICATION Length 14–16cm.
C. d. cantans: Wing, male 64–71mm, female 55–61mm. Tail/wing 93–102%.
C. d. diphone: Wing, male 56–60mm, female *c.* 50mm. Tail/wing 98–113%.

The widespread and most familiar race, *C. d. cantans*, which occurs throughout the main Japanese islands and S South Korea, is uniform drab olive-brown above with a fairly well marked supercilium and greyish white underparts. Although the bird is elusive, skulking and nondescript, its distinctive song is one of the characteristic sounds of the Japanese countryside and unlikely to be mistaken for any other species. Sexes alike but males are larger than females and sexual size dimorphism provides a reliable means of separating them.

Structure A robust *Cettia,* even the females being larger than the smaller Himalayan *Cettia.* Similar in size to female Manchurian Bush Warbler but considerably smaller than the male of that species. The wings are relatively long, reaching the longest undertail-covert tips, and distinctly rounded, with a long first primary (p1) extending well beyond the primary coverts. The wing point is formed by p4–6. The closed primaries form a tightly bunched wing point that extends one third to one half of the tertial length. The tail appears rather long, similar in length to the body, but typically rather loose, thin and dishevelled. The undertail-coverts are quite short, covering about one third of the tail length. The bill is short and fine, less robust and narrower at the base than in Manchurian Bush Warbler.

Plumage and bare parts Plumage varies considerably due to racial differences and the effects of wear. All races are nondescript but show a fairly conspicuous supercilium from the bill to the rear of the ear-coverts, and a well-defined eye-stripe. In the widespread race *cantans* and the slightly paler form *riukiuensis*, the upperparts and wing-coverts are dull brownish olive to greyish olive, showing little or no

contrast with the crown. The underparts are dull greyish white, palest on the belly centre. When worn, these races become distinctly greyer above and generally paler, but retain the warmer, browner edges to the wing feathers. Races restricted to the southern Japanese islands (nominate *diphone* and *restricta*) show contrast between the reddish-brown crown and browner upperparts. In nominate *diphone*, the forehead and crown are warm tan to warm brown and contrast with the slightly darker brown upperparts, which have only a slight rusty wash. There is a fairly conspicuous pale half-collar that extends from below the ear-coverts onto the sides of the nape. Birds of the S Ryukyu Islands are more warmly and richly coloured, with brown upperparts and a brighter cinnamon-brown crown, more closely resembling Manchurian Bush Warbler. All races show broad, brown, but diffuse edges to the tertials, and the secondaries and primaries are warmer than the upperparts, often appearing as a contrasting bronze-olive panel in the closed wing. The primaries lack obvious pale tips. See **Geographic Variation** for further details.

The bill is mostly blackish during the breeding season. At other seasons it is dark greyish brown with a yellowish pink base to the lower mandible, which darkens at the sides towards the tip. The legs and feet are dull reddish brown although paler yellowish brown on some, perhaps immature birds.

SIMILAR SPECIES Several species of drab, brownish and largely nondescript warblers in NE Asia could potentially be confused with Japanese Bush Warbler, but all are separable with care. These include several brown and largely unmarked *Phylloscopus* warblers, with Dusky, Radde's, Yellow-streaked and Pale-legged Leaf Warblers being the closest in appearance and size, although none particularly resembles Japanese Bush. All are smaller than Japanese Bush and share the characteristic slim *Phylloscopus* structure and restless, nervous behaviour. All four are fairly skulking species that feed close to the ground and call regularly; each species has a diagnostic call that is quite different from the harsh '*tzhik, tzhik*' cal of Japanese Bush. Furthermore, all are quite rare or unknown within the range of Japanese Bush Warbler so confusion here is unlikely.

Although three of the *Locustella* warblers that breed in Japan share brown and largely unmarked upperparts, their structure is quite different so this should preclude confusion. Middendorff's Grasshopper and Styan's Grasshopper Warblers feature the characteristic *Locustella* structure of a long, thin bill, sloping forehead, long wings, deep undertail-coverts, broad and graduated tail, horizontal structure and ground-hugging behaviour, quite distinct from the rounded, dumpy structure of Japanese Bush Warbler with its rounded wings, short undertail-coverts and slightly rounded tail. The even larger Gray's Grasshopper Warbler shares similar structural characters with the other *Locustella* warblers but is separable on size alone.

Of the unstreaked *Acrocephalus*, only two species occur regularly within the range of Japanese Bush Warbler; the significantly larger, paler and reed-dwelling Oriental Reed Warbler and the slightly smaller Black-browed Reed Warbler, with its characteristic blackish band above a conspicuous pale supercilium. Both have very different *Acrocephalus*-like songs and neither of these species presents a risk of confusion if seen well or heard singing.

Manchurian Bush Warbler most closely resembles Japanese Bush Warbler in structure, but is strikingly different in appearance from Japanese Bush Warbler and should not present any problems, despite formerly being treated as a race of this species. Although Japanese Bush Warbler is variable, the migrant races *cantans* and *riukiuensis* most likely to occur alongside Manchurian Bush Warbler, are quite unlike that species. Male Manchurian Bush is much larger than male Japanese Bush, while the female overlaps with it in size and structure. Manchurian Bush is warmer and paler brown on the upperparts and lacks olive tones in the plumage. The crown is cinnamon-tinged and it has a broader and more conspicuous supercilium and cleaner whitish or creamy white underparts. It also has a stouter and paler bill, unlike the fine and largely dark bill of Japanese Bush. Care is required with the southern resident forms of Japanese Bush Warbler, particularly the race *restricta*, which is warmer and browner than the migrant forms and has a brighter rufescent-brown crown. But these southern races are unlikely to come into contact with Manchurian Bush Warbler. The songs of these species are quite similar, with comparable structure, frequency and pace of delivery. In Japan, where Manchurian Bush is a vagrant, this will rarely present a problem, but in South Korea, where both species breed, care is required when separating by song alone.

VOICE The song comprises a melodic, drawn-out wavering whistle '*wuuuuuuuweeuuweechu*' or '*weeewuweeeeuuweechu*' lasting between two and three seconds and repeated continuously for several minutes at intervals of five to ten seconds. The initial introductory whistle rises slightly in volume and intensity at a frequency of *c.* 2kHz for approximately one to two seconds before breaking into the melodic and tuneful '*uuweechu*' element that forms the terminal flourish within a frequency range of 2–5kHz, lasting approximately one second. The song of the race *riukiuensis* is identical to that of *C. d. cantans*, but it is uncertain whether songs (or calls) of the southern breeding forms differ. Nial Moores (*in litt.*) has noted considerable individual variation between males sound-recorded in South Korea, but little change within the song of an individual throughout the breeding season.

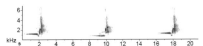

Song of Japanese Bush Warbler of undetermined race, possibly *C. d. restricta* or *C. d. riukiuensis*, Okinawa, Japan, March (Ueda 1998)

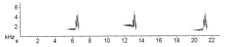

Song of Japanese Bush Warbler, recorded within breeding range of *C. d. cantans*, Gageo Island, South Korea, March (Nial Moores/Birds Korea)

Japanese Bush Warbler has an extremely noisy and demonstrative repeated '*kek-kow*' alarm call which can last for just a few seconds or continue unbroken for several minutes. It comprises a series of rapidly delivered paired notes that form a distinct element and alternate between 2kHz and 3kHz. Typically two or three pairs of notes are given per second, but this delivery can speed up or slow down. As the bird considers the threat to have abated, it reduces both the pace and intensity of the call until it comes to a stop.

The contact call is a harsh '*tzhik, tzhik*', repeated at intervals of approximately one second. There is no call resembling the slurred churring call characteristic of Manchurian Bush Warbler.

MOULT Limited data is available. Adults of the race *cantans* have a complete post-breeding moult in late summer but there is no information available on its timing or duration. Juveniles also have a complete moult shortly after fledging. After these moults adults and first year birds are inseparable on plumage features (YS *in litt.*). It is unclear whether there is a further moult in winter or spring. Data on other races is lacking.

HABITAT The race *cantans* is common in thick rank and coarse vegetation throughout much of Japan. During the breeding season it is found in damp thickets, dense grasslands, scrub and undergrowth in woodland and forests, from the lower hills to the alpine zone above 3,000m in central Honshu. In Hokkaido it breeds at or close to sea level (Brazil 1991). For nesting it favours areas with a dense understorey of dwarf bamboo *Sasa kurilensis* (Hadena & Okabe 1970). Birds wintering in S Japan occur in similar overgrown rank habitats, but also in *Phragmites* reedbeds and urban parks and gardens.

In South Korea, *cantans* breeds in the hills in mixed woodland with low evergreen scrub and the bamboos *Pseudosasa japonica* and *Phyllostachys pubescens*, while in the higher subalpine region it favours areas with *Rhododendron schlippenbachii* and thick shrubs.

Introduced birds in Hawaii favour dense undergrowth with grasses and bamboo and also occur in the upper native forest, particularly on the steeper slopes.

Birds of the nominate race in the Ogasawara and the race *restricta* in the southern Ryukyu Islands are found in similar dense rank undergrowth in scrub and subtropical woodland, where they are resident and believed to maintain territories throughout the year.

BEHAVIOUR Not known to differ from that of Manchurian Bush Warbler. Usually silent during the winter months although calling birds might be heard at any time. Males in lowland wintering areas give occasional bursts of song from February onwards. It is extremely vocal when on its breeding territories. It usually sings from an exposed perch above the understorey, or when moving through bushes, continuously moving the tail up and down while singing and often doing so in full view several metres above ground (Hadena & Okabe 1970). During the breeding season, the throat of the male enlarges and the skin pulls tight, so that the entire gular region becomes enlarged when singing, presumably serving to increase the song volume. This is otherwise an elusive and skulking species that can be difficult to find in dense undergrowth. It is believed to be entirely insectivorous throughout the year.

BREEDING HABITS Singing begins from January onwards in the lowlands of Kyushu in S Japan and from mid March in C Honshu, but not until May in the mountains of Honshu and on Hokkaido. The first eggs are laid in March in Kyushu, but progressively later to the north. Northern breeders are believed to be single-brooded, but southern breeders may be double-brooded since singing continues until late August or early September. The nest is a domed structure built up to a metre above ground in low scrub or dwarf bamboo. A clutch of 4–6 eggs is laid and incubation takes 16 days, followed by a fledging period of a further 14 days (Hadena & Okabe 1970; Brazil 1991).

DISTRIBUTION
Breeding
C. d. cantans The most widespread form, breeding throughout the main Japanese islands from Hokkaido south throughout Honshu and Shikoku to southern Kyushu. It also breeds on several offshore island including Sado, Tsushima, the Goto and Danjo Islands in the Sea of Japan, the northern Izu Islands south to Aogashima and the N Ryukyu Islands, including Tanegashima and Yakushima and (almost certainly this race) on Amami-oshima. In South Korea it breeds on the island of Cheju-do, to the south of the Korean Peninsula, where birds were described as *C. d. takahashii*, a form now considered synonymous with *cantans*. It has recently been established that this race also breeds locally in the hills and mountains of S South Korea, north to Birobong peak in Sobaeksan National Park at *c.* 37°N (Kim 2008; Park 2008).

It is believed that northern breeding birds and those breeding at higher elevations are migratory while those breeding at lower elevations in the southern part of the range in Japan, north to the low hills of central Honshu, are sedentary or disperse outside the breeding season. This race was introduced into the Hawaiian Islands in 1929 where it has flourished and is now widespread in Oahu. It has subsequently become established on Kauai, Molokai, Lanai and Maui.

C. d. riukiuensis Breeds on S Sakhalin and on the southernmost Kuril Islands, including Etorofu and Kunashiri, in Russia. It also breeds on Rishiri-to, an island off the northwest tip of N Hokkaido, Japan.

C. d. diphone Resident on small subtropical islands in the Pacific to the south of the main Japanese Islands. It breeds in the southernmost Izu Islands, from Torishima south to include Muko-jima, Chichi-jima and Haha-jima in the Ogasawara Islands. Further south, in the Iwo Islands, it occurs and presumably breeds on Hirashima, Kita-iwo-jima and Iwo-jima.

C. d. restricta Formerly considered endemic to the island of Minami-daito-jima, which lies to the east of the Ryukyu Archipelago (Nansei Shoto), but now believed to be extinct here. It has recently been established that birds resident and breeding in the S Ryukyu Islands, including Okinawa, Kume-jima and south and west to Ishigaki-jima and Iriomote-jima, are inseparable from descriptions (all specimens having been destroyed) of *restricta* from Minami-daito-jima (Kajita *et al.* 2002). Here we have adopted these findings and consider the resident taxon breeding in the S Ryukyu Islands to be the race *restricta*. It is recognised that *restricta* may well be extinct and these birds may represent a very closely related but undescribed taxon (YS *in litt.*). It is, however, certain that these southern breeders are very different to the paler birds breeding on the northern islands of the Nansei Shoto, including Amami-Oshima.

Non-breeding The non-breeding ranges are uncertain. The extent of overlap between *cantans* and *riukiuensis* is unclear, and also whether these races occur alongside *restricta* in the S Ryukyu Islands. Northern breeding *cantans* and *riukiuensis*, and *cantans* from the colder regions of Japan, move to the lowlands from C Honshu southwards, where they overlap with resident birds. At this season, such is the extent of confusion that migratory birds from Sakhalin and the Kuril islands (formerly named *sakhalinensis*) are now known to be *riukiuensis*, a form previously believed to breed in the

Ryukyu Islands but now known to be only a winter visitor. During the winter months, *riukiuensis* ranges throughout the Ryukyu Archipelago and occurs alongside resident birds, including *restricta* on Okinawa and presumed *cantans* on Amami-Oshima. Small numbers also winter in Taiwan, but it is not known to winter in China.

Japanese Bush Warbler. Breeding range and winter distribution. Races *cantans* and/or *riukiuensis* winter throughout Ryukyu Islands and lowland Taiwan.

MOVEMENTS Birds breeding in Sakhalin, the Kuril Islands, Hokkaido, northern Honshu and the mountains of C Honshu vacate the breeding grounds from early October to winter in milder regions of C and S Japan. Those breeding in the mountainous regions of Honshu are believed to descend and disperse widely throughout the coastal lowlands. Northern breeders, however, are migrants that winter in S Japan, including the Ryukyu Islands. It is unknown where Korean breeding birds spend the winter but there are no reports from South Korea during the winter months.

Between 1988 and 2001, Komatsu *et al.* (2004) studied the migration of Japanese Bush Warbler at Niigata City, on the coast of the Sea of Japan, where it occurs only as a migrant. Recovery data showed that this coastline is an important flyway for birds originating from Hokkaido. It is believed most of these over-winter on the main Japanese islands, the furthest recovery being from Shimane Prefecture in SW Honshu, 710km from Niigata. Spring migration occurred throughout April and May, with males passing 10–14 days before females, and forming about 40% of the catch of almost 2,000 birds. Autumn passage occurred throughout October and November. In autumn overall numbers were four times higher than in spring, with males now accounting for over 50%, and no observed timing difference between males and females.

Japanese Bush Warbler is rare outside Japan and South Korea. Although Cheng (1987) included Taiwan within the winter range of *cantans*, its occurrence here appears to be irregular and erratic. La Touche (1925–30) collected six individuals on Shaweishan, off the coast of eastern China, which he ascribed to *C. d. riukiuensis* (= northern breeding *C. d. sakhalinensis*). Four occurred between 24 and 27 April, the others on 9 March and 1 December. As all were migrants, the relatively late dates of the spring occurrences of the four April birds suggests these would be northern breeders. Territories in S Japan are occupied throughout the year. Migratory birds begin to return to breeding territories in southern Honshu from late March onwards, with those further north during April or early May.

DESCRIPTION

C. d. diphone

Plumage – Adult fresh Forehead, crown and centre of nape warm tan to warm brown with a slight rusty wash. Supercilium from bill base to rear of ear-coverts, broadest above the lores where warm tan, slightly paler than the crown, tapering behind eye and fading to dull brownish cream over the ear-coverts, sometimes reaching side of nape. Lores dark brown, forming well-defined line between bill base and eye. Eye-line paler, greyish brown, extending to side of nape. Ear-coverts pale creamy brown, paler towards lower edges, tipped dark brown to produce distinct mottling. Eye-ring dull cream, narrow and poorly defined. Side of nape tinged greyish, merging with similarly coloured eye-line. Mantle and scapulars to uppertail-coverts uniform warm brown with a rusty wash, slightly darker than crown but marginally brighter on rump and uppertail-coverts.

Chin, throat and belly white, washed greyish buff or creamy buff, side of throat usually contrasting sharply with ear-coverts. Breast white, washed greyish brown, becoming darker greyish brown on sides and on pale half-collar below ear-coverts. Flanks dull greyish brown, slightly warmer buffy-grey or pale peachy grey posteriorly and merging with pale buff undertail-coverts. Lesser and median coverts with broad, warm tan fringes and indistinctly darker centres. Greater coverts and tertials with broad, warm rusty brown fringes merging with the more conspicuous darker centres. Primary coverts, secondaries, primaries and alula dull brown, with broad rusty brown edges. Primary tips dull rusty-brown contrasting slightly with the exposed brown webs. Tail feathers dark brown, broadly edged warm tan. Underwing-coverts white with a faint grey wash.

Adult worn Colder, greyer and paler than fresh plumage, without warm brown tones. Supercilium largely white; ear-coverts cold greyish brown with faint whitish streaks. Crown, nape and upperparts pale greyish brown with warmer rusty tones retained only on rump and uppertail-coverts and sometimes on the edges of the tail feathers. Fringes of greater coverts and tertials and edges of primary coverts, primaries and secondaries pale greyish brown. Underparts whiter, with the grey wash restricted to side of breast. Pale half-collar below ear-coverts usually still conspicuous. Undertail-coverts pale creamy buff, occasionally almost white.

Juvenile/First-winter Resembles fresh adult but underparts lightly washed pale yellow.

Bare parts Upper mandible pale straw with a narrow, pink to yellowish pink cutting edge. Lower mandible dull pink to yellowish pink. Tarsi and toes pale reddish brown, usually lacking darker plumbeous tones; claws vary from blackish to pale pink. Iris dull reddish brown, dull greyish brown in immature birds.

C. d. cantans

Plumage – Adult fresh (August to November) Distinctly darker than nominate *diphone*, with strong olive tones apparent on both upperparts and underparts.

Forehead, crown and nape uniform, dull brownish olive. Supercilium pale grey to pale greyish olive, narrow and indistinct above lores but broadening over the eye and more conspicuous over the ear-coverts and onto side of nape. Lores dark greyish olive, forming well-defined line from the bill base to the eye. Eye-line dull olive-brown to greyish olive, sharply demarcated from supercilium but merging below into the upper ear-coverts. Eye-ring dull cream and conspicuous, lower edge contrasting with darker ear-coverts. Ear-coverts dull greyish olive with white feather bases, appearing faintly mottled. Side of nape shows little contrast with ear-coverts, thus usually no suggestion of a paler half-collar. Mantle and scapulars dull brownish olive, concolorous with crown; rump and uppertail-coverts similar, but slightly warmer and lacking the greyer tinge sometimes seen in the mantle.

Chin, throat, breast, flanks, lower belly and undertail-coverts greyish white with pale yellow tips and broad, olive-brown to oily brown diffuse sub-terminal fringes giving a dull, sullied and uniform appearance to underparts. Centre of belly slightly paler, dull creamy brown. Lesser, median, greater and primary coverts and alula uniform dull brownish olive, similar to or slightly warmer than mantle. Edges of tertials, secondaries and primaries dull brown to warm tan, usually perceptibly warmer and brighter than the feather centres and lacking the olive tones of the upperparts. Tail uniform brown, slightly warmer than uppertail-coverts. Underwing-coverts creamy white, usually tinged yellow, slightly paler than flanks.

Adult worn (January to March) Paler and greyer with olive tones reduced. Supercilium pale grey but less prominent, lacking clear definition in front of eye. Loral stripe dull brown, still well-defined, but eye-line reduced to a dull greyish brown smudge immediately behind eye. Ear-coverts pale grey, less mottled, but with pale shaft streaks often apparent. Crown, nape, mantle and scapulars pale greyish brown; rump and uppertail-coverts retain darker loose yellow tips, becoming warmer olive tones, similar in colour to the tail. Underparts pale greyish white, with warmth restricted to pale sandy grey lower flanks. Sides of breast pale grey, in some extending below ear-coverts to form a pale greyish white half-collar. Fringes of lesser, median, greater and primary coverts variable, sometimes pale greyish brown as mantle, sometimes retaining warmer tones. Broad fringes to tertials and edges to primaries and secondaries warm tan, so that closed wing appears warmer and browner than upperparts and contrasts with pale underparts.

Juvenile Differs conspicuously from adult. Supercilium and ear-coverts pale sulphur-yellow, with ear-coverts mottled pale olive-brown. Lores, eye-line, crown, nape, mantle and scapulars uniform pale olive-brown. Fringes to wing-coverts and edges of secondaries and primaries as fresh adult. Chin and upper throat pale primrose-yellow, unmarked. Lower throat, breast, belly and undertail-coverts pale sulphur-yellow, usually with faint brownish mottling on sides of breast, intensifying towards carpal bend and along lower flanks.

Bare parts Upper mandible pale brown to greyish brown with a narrow, pink to yellowish pink cutting edge. Lower mandible dull pink to yellowish pink at base, darkening towards tip. In spring, bill blackish including base, but cutting edge usually remains pale, appearing as a narrow pale line. Tarsi and toes pale reddish brown to yellowish brown, usually lacking darker plumbeous tones; claws vary from blackish and pale pink. Iris dull reddish brown in adults, dull greyish brown in immature birds.

IN HAND CHARACTERS
Measurements

C. d. cantans

	Male	Female
Wing	64–71 (66.9; 37)	55–61 (56.8; 10)
Tail	61–69 (64.7; 37)	53–60 (55.3; 10)
Bill	14.5–17 (16.0; 35)	13.5–15 (14.3; 9)
Tarsus	24–27 (25.1; 36)	21–23 (22.2; 10)

Bill width: ♂ 3.8–4.5 (4.2; 12), ♀ 3.6–4.2 (4.0; 10)
Tail graduation: ♂ 8–12 (9.9; 12), ♀ 7–10 (8.3; 6)
Sexes combined:
Tail/wing ratio: 93–102% (97%; 47)
Hind claw: 5.6–8.0 (6.5; 21)

Juvenile wing *c.* 15% shorter than in adult, tail *c.* 20% shorter.

C. d. riukiuensis: *wing*, ♂ 67–71 (69.0; 5), ♀ 56–58 (57.1; 8); *tail*, ♂ 64–67 (65.2; 5), ♀ 52–59 (54.8; 6); *bill*, ♂ 15.5–16.5 (15.9; 5), ♀ 14–15.5 (14.6; 6); *tarsus*, ♂ 25–27 (25.9; 4), ♀ 22–23 (22.8; 5).

C. d. diphone (6 ♂♂, 2 ♀♀): *wing*, ♂ 56–60 (57.8), ♀ 49, 50; *tail*, ♂ 60–64 (62.3), ♀ 49, 54; *bill*, ♂ 17–18 (17.6), ♀ 17, 17; *tarsus*, ♂ 24–25 (24.2), ♀ 22.5, 23.5.

Sexes combined: tail/wing ratio 98–113% (107%; 8); bill width 3.8–4.2 (4.0; 6); hind claw 5.0–6.5 (5.7; 7); tail graduation 10–12 (11.2; 6).

C. d. restricta (Live measurements from Kajita *et al.* 2002): *wing* (unflattened), ♂ 60–66 (62.6; 39), ♀ 52–56 (53.5; 12); *tail*, ♂ 62–71 (66.0; 37), ♀ 53–58 (55.2; 12); *bill*, ♂ 18–20 (19.0; 12), ♀ 16.5–17.5 (16.6; 8); *tarsus*, ♂ 25–27 (25.9; 50), ♀ 22–23.5 (22.8; 13).

Structure

C. d. cantans

Wing formula (n = 6):

p1/pc	p2	p3e	p4e	p5e	p6e	p7	p10
12–14	12–15	3–5	0–0.5	wp	0.5–1.5	3–5	10–12.5

Wing rounded with fairly large p1 (40–50% p2). Wing point (p4) p5; p2 = p10 or ≤ ss tips, p3 = p6/7–7; emargination on p3–6, sometimes faintly on p7.

Figure 122. Wing of Japanese Bush Warbler *C. d. cantans*.

Tail longish, markedly rounded; feathers narrower than

in Manchurian Bush Warbler.

Bill strong but concave-sided with narrow tip; narrower, less stout than in Manchurian Bush Warbler (Fig. 120).

Tarsi, toes and claws quite strong.

C. d. diphone
Wing formula (male, n = 6).

p1/pc	p2	p3e	p4e	p5e	p6e	p7(e)	p10
10–13	12–13	2.5–4	0–0.5	wp	0–0.5	2–4	9–11

Wing slightly more rounded than in *cantans*, with wing point p4–6 and p3 = p6/7–7/8; p7 usually emarginated. Tail/wing ratio higher than in *cantans* and bill longer, with straighter (less concave) sides and broader tip.

C. d. riukiuensis: structure as in *cantans*, wing point p4–5, p3 = p6/7.

C. d. restricta: structure as in *diphone* with relatively long tail and bill. Wing point at p(4) 5–6; p3 = p7/8 (Kajita *et al.* 2001).

Recognition A largish *Cettia*, race *cantans* with uniform olive-brown upperparts. Easily confusable with female Manchurian Bush Warbler but distinguished by lack of contrasting warm crown and by more subdued greyish supercilium. Bill blackish (paler in Manchurian Bush).

Ageing Juveniles with yellow underparts readily distinguishable. Ageing is difficult after post-juvenile moult, but skull ossification and iris colour can be useful. The iris is reddish brown in older adults, but greyish brown throughout the first winter and spring. Skull ossification in young birds is incomplete up to November, sometimes as late as January (YS *in litt.*).

Sexing Sexual size difference less pronounced than in Manchurian Bush Warbler but both wing length and tail length show a bimodal distribution. In race *cantans*, Abe (1984) considered that birds with wing above 62mm were males, those with wing below 61mm females.

Weight
C. d. cantans: Japan, ♂ 14–18.5g (15.7; 32), ♀ 10–12.6g (11.3; 9) (Hasegawa 1977); South Korea, ♂ 15.1–26.6g (20.7; 27), ♀ 9.0–13.2g (12.3; 27) (Park 2008).
C. d. riukiuensis: Ryukyu Islands, ♂ 14–19.7g (16; 65), ♀ 9.5–12.3g (11.0; 52) (Kajita *et al.* 2002).
C. d. restricta: Ryukyu Islands, ♂ 15–20.9g (17.9; 39), ♀ 10.0–13.9g (11.9; 10) (Kajita *et al.* 2002).

GEOGRAPHIC VARIATION Involves structure as well as plumage tone. The two northern migratory races differ from each other in coloration only. The resident island races are more warmly coloured on the upperparts, particularly on the crown, and also differ from the northern birds in both size and structure.

C. d. cantans (Main islands of Japan, N Izu and N Ryukyu Islands, S South Korea. Introduced on Hawaii) Described above.

C. d. riukiuensis (S Sakhalin and S Kuril Islands, Russia) A pale race with distinctive greyish olive upperparts. The crown, nape, mantle and scapulars are slightly paler than in *cantans*, lacking strong olive-brown tones and show enhanced contrast with warmer brown edges and fringes on the closed wing. The supercilium is paler and slightly more conspicuous than in other races, the eye-stripe darker and more contrasting. The underparts are whiter than in *cantans*, with only a faint grey tinge across the breast, pale grey flanks and dull creamy undertail-coverts. During the breeding season the upperparts become progressively paler and greyer as plumage abrades. Calls and song are indistinguishable from those of *cantans*.

C. d. diphone (Southern Izu Islands, Ogasawara Islands, Iwo Islands, S Japan) Described above. Uniform warm brown upperparts with a warm brown to warm tan crown, often with a slight rusty wash. Compared with *cantans* it is warmer and paler, with a longer and paler bill, shorter wing, proportionately longer tail and paler legs.

C. d. restricta (Okinawa and adjacent Ryukyu Islands, SW Japan) Extinct at the type locality but birds on some of the S Ryukyu Islands resemble the description of this form. The warmest and most richly coloured of the four races, with warm rusty brown upperparts, a cinnamon-brown crown and rich brown edges to the secondaries and primaries. The supercilium is light sandy-buff, the ear-coverts, breast and flanks washed sandy buff and the belly white. Like the nominate race, it shows a relatively long, deep bill and a short wing.

TAXONOMY AND SYSTEMATICS The taxonomy and nomenclature of Japanese Bush Warbler have a complex history. Here we recognise four races within *C. diphone* although some authorities still recognise up to seven. Two large migratory taxa that occur on the Asian mainland, *canturians* and *borealis*, were formerly treated as races of Japanese Bush Warbler. Plumage and vocal differences combined with exceptional sexual dimorphism suggest that they should be grouped together as a separate species, Manchurian Bush Warbler, distinct from Japanese Bush Warbler, and this treatment has been adopted here. DNA studies provide support for this treatment. Hamao *et al.* (2008) compared the cytochrome *b* gene of Manchurian Bush Warbler of the race *borealis* and Japanese Bush Warbler of the race *cantans*, and estimated a nucleotide difference of 2.4%.

Nominate *diphone* and *cantans* differ significantly in plumage, structure and measurements. There is no overlap in wing length between the same sexes of these races; *diphone* is shorter winged and proportionately much longer tailed. These races are unlikely to come into contact at any season, *diphone* being restricted to small, oceanic sub-tropical islands south of Honshu where *cantans* is entirely absent, even as a vagrant. As yet, the phylogenetic relationship between these taxa has not been investigated. With such significant morphological differences between them, they may merit full species status, but we await the support of DNA evidence.

A third race, *riukiuensis*, was believed to be resident in the Ryukyu Islands until recently. However, Kajita *et al.* (2002) demonstrated that these birds were winter visitors. Furthermore, they proved to be identical to *sakhalinensis*, a migrant form breeding in S Sakhalin and the S Kuril Islands. Apparent slight differences between *riukiuensis* and *sakhalinensis* could be accounted for by wear and body moult. Y. Shigeta (*in litt.*) has found only slight mtDNA differences (0.5% bp substitutions) between *riukiuensis* (= *sakhalinensis*) and *cantans*, demonstrating the close relationship between these taxa. As the taxon *riukiuensis* was described earlier, it has nomenclatural priority over *sakhalinensis*, which now becomes a junior synonym. It was also confirmed that birds occupying the island of Cheju Do, south of the Korean peninsula and once described as the endemic race *C. d. takahashii*, showed the same DNA sequence as *cantans* from the main Japanese islands (YS *in litt.*). This race is treated as a synonym of *cantans*.

The fourth race *restricta*, formerly believed to be restricted to Minami-Daito-jima in the S Ryukyu Islands, was considered extinct and the only specimens were destroyed during the Second World War. However, Kajita *et al.* (2002) established that two forms of Japanese Bush Warbler occur on Okinawa. One is a winter visitor with a drab greyish olive appearance and referable to *riukiuensis* (see above). The other is a resident form with a richer, rusty brown appearance. These rusty brown birds match descriptions of *restricta* in appearance and measurements. However, *restricta* is extinct at its type locality and without reference to the lost type specimen it remains uncertain whether the extant S Ryukyu breeders really are *restricta*, or whether they represent an undescribed taxon. Birds resembling *restricta* have now been recorded from Okinawa and Kume-jima (YS *in litt.*). It seems likely that birds breeding on islands to the south of Okinawa are also referable to this race.

DNA studies have shown that Japanese Bush Warbler groups with Luzon Bush Warbler and the *Cettia* species of the SW Pacific, rather than with those from the Himalayas and W China (LeCroy & Barker 2006).

▲ ▶ Adult *C. d. diphone*, Haha-jima, Japan, June. Differs from *cantans* by conspicuous whitish supercilium, warmer brown upperparts, dingy white underparts, and paler legs and feet. Structural differences from *cantans* include longer and paler bill, shorter wings and proportionately longer tail (Pete Morris).

◀ Adult *C. d. cantans*, Honshu, Japan, February. The most widespread and familiar race. Note dull greyish olive upper-parts and wing-coverts showing little contrast with crown, but contrasting bronze-olive edges to secondaries and primaries form contrasting closed wing (Akiko Hidaka).

▲ ▼ Adult probably *C. d. riukiuensis*, Yehliu, Taiwan, December. Closely resembles *cantans* but with paler, contrasting supercilium and slightly paler greyish-olive to brownish-olive upperparts contrasting with browner primary fringes. Underparts slightly paler than *cantans*, whitish with faint grey tinge to breast and flanks, and dull cream undertail-coverts (Liao Pen-shing).

LUZON BUSH WARBLER
Cettia seebohmi   Plate 42

Cettia seebohmi Ogilvie-Grant, 1894. *Ibis* 6(6): 507. Northern Luzon.

A poorly known *Cettia* restricted to the scrub and grass-covered hills of NW Luzon in the Philippines. Monotypic.

IDENTIFICATION Length 12cm. Wing 50–58mm. Tail/wing 105–132%.

A dark and warmly coloured warbler with rufous-brown upperparts, slightly warmer crown and wing, whitish supercilium and greyish white underparts. Has a proportionately long tail. Highly skulking but readily located by its song. Sexes alike and similar in size.

Structure A medium-sized *Cettia* showing the characteristic rounded head, domed crown and small, dumpy body of the genus. The short, rounded wing shows only about three projecting primaries but these lack paler fringes and the tips are difficult to discern. The first primary (p1) extends far beyond the primary coverts and the wing point is formed by p5. It has a particularly long tail for a *Cettia*, slightly longer than the body and with a loose and filamentous structure, even when fresh, giving it the distinctly ragged appearance suggestive of a *Prinia*.

Plumage and bare parts Its overall drab and nondescript appearance resembles that of other small *Cettia*, although it shows a contrasting appearance to the head, which shows a warm brown crown, conspicuous greyish white supercilium extending from the bill base to the ear-coverts, a dark brown eye-stripe and faintly mottled ear-coverts. The upperparts are dark rufous-brown offset by a slightly warmer panel in the wing and paler brown rump and tail. The underparts are paler, with the whitish throat merging into the duller, greyish white to brownish grey lower breast and belly. The flanks are slightly darker and distinctly browner than the breast, becoming dull cinnamon-brown on the lower flanks and undertail-coverts.

The bill is dark grey or blackish with a pink lower mandible that darkens slightly towards the tip. The legs and feet are dull greyish pink.

SIMILAR SPECIES Several drab and nondescript warblers occur within the range of Luzon Bush Warbler and could be considered potential confusion species. Of these, Benguet Bush Warbler occurs in similar habitat and is a great skulker. Long-tailed Bush Warbler also occurs in Luzon, but is much darker and a bird of montane forest. Several nondescript migrant warblers from NE Asia also reach Luzon, some only on passage, while others wintering here. However, only two of the migrants occurring regularly in N Luzon could present identification issues; Manchurian Bush Warbler and Middendorff's Grasshopper Warbler, and both are quite different.

Benguet Bush Warbler has a more restricted distribution on Luzon than Luzon Bush Warbler but shares similar habitat preferences. It appears to be extremely rare and localised but is almost certainly overlooked and more numerous than the few records suggest. This is an extreme skulker, only likely to be seen when singing from an exposed grass stem or low bush, in rather similar circumstances to Luzon Bush Warbler. When not singing, Benguet Bush Warbler has a characteristic horizontal stance with an elongated body, long and deep undertail-coverts and a proportionately long and robust tail that should be apparent on a stationary

singing bird. It is distinctly larger than Luzon Bush Warbler and usually conveys this impression well when sitting upright and singing. Its overall appearance is dull russet-brown, but with dull greyish brown underparts that appear even drabber than those of Luzon Bush Warbler. It usually shows a necklace of small spots across the lower throat which Luzon Bush lacks. The undertail-coverts are dull cinnamon-brown to russet-brown, but are marked with pale tips.

Long-tailed Bush Warbler is also resident in N Luzon but is a bird of moist montane forest and most unlikely to occur alongside Luzon Bush Warbler in grassland and scrub.

Manchurian Bush Warbler occurs widely but sparingly in N Luzon from November to March, but usually at lower elevations. The male is considerably larger than Luzon Bush Warbler and could not be confused. Even females are slightly larger and more robust and with distinctly longer wings and a shorter tail, creating the impression of a more neatly proportioned bird. Manchurian Bush is a much paler bird with a long creamy white supercilium, distinctive cinnamon-brown crown, warm olive-brown to paler sandy brown upperparts, and paler, cleaner underparts.

Middendorff's Grasshopper Warbler is distinctly larger and paler than Luzon Bush and has a strikingly different structure with a horizontal stance, long primary projection, long undertail-coverts and a heavily graduated tail. Plumage differences include white tips to the outer rectrices, a warm tawny-brown rump contrasting with the duller, faintly mottled mantle, and whitish underparts. Moreover it winters mainly in lowland wetlands and would only occur in the hills within the range of Luzon Bush Warbler during migration.

VOICE Song closely resembles that of Brownish-flanked Bush Warbler but is slightly faster, richer and more pleasant to the ear. It commences with a long and slightly slurred or wavering introductory whistle '*tuuudwuuuudwuudwuu*' or '*doo-doooor*', that slowly increases in volume for approximately one second. This is followed immediately by a rich and fluty rhythmic sequence, rising and falling slightly in pitch and described as '*hee-yuee-yuee*' or '*dor-por-dee-dor-dee*'. The first two notes are delivered slowly, the second one being rather more drawn out, then rising and falling in pitch between 2–6kHz to form a climax of five or six loud, explosive notes that often slur into one another. The entire song sequence is rendered '*tuuuwuuwuuwuu-hee-yuee-yuee* or *doo-dooooor-dor-por-dee-dor-dee*' and lasts about two seconds before being repeated at intervals of between two and 15 seconds.

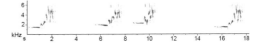

Song of Luzon Bush Warbler, Mount Polis, Luzon, Philippines. (Peter Morris)

The call is a single sharp '*checkk*' or '*chick*', given repeatedly.

MOULT Details unknown.

HABITAT Ranges from 800m to at least 2,100m and probably occurs to the highest summits in suitable habitat. It is likely to be encountered in any extensive area of dense vegetation, including thickets, scrub growth, tall rank grasses and reeds. It avoids heavily forested areas but does occur in rank understorey in open deciduous forest and, especially, in open pine forest.

BEHAVIOUR Poorly known but probably differs little from that of other *Cettia*. This species does not appear to have been studied and is always difficult to observe. Typically remains concealed within thick cover but males perch prominently in grassland or on the sides of bushes when singing.

BREEDING HABITS No details are available and the nest and eggs are unknown. Adults with enlarged gonads have been recorded in April and fledged juveniles noted in May and June.

DISTRIBUTION Confined to the highlands of N Luzon in the Philippines, where its distribution suggests that it is a relict montane species. Originally discovered at 1,800m in the highlands of Lepanto, but has since been found to be widespread and locally common above 800m throughout Benguet Province south to Pangasinan and north to Balbalsang in Kalinga Province (D. Allen *in litt.*). It has also occurred at Dalton Pass and Mount Puguis, suggesting it may be more widespread than records suggest.

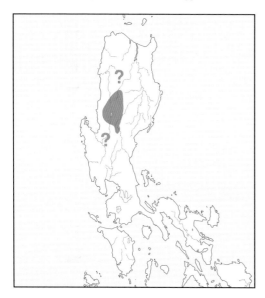

Luzon Bush Warbler. Resident within breeding range.

MOVEMENTS No seasonal or altitudinal movements have been reported, although birds caught at Dalton Pass may have been dispersing.

DESCRIPTION

Plumage – Adult fresh Forehead, crown and nape warm rufescent-brown. Supercilium pale greyish white and well defined from the bill base to eye, becoming warm brown behind the eye but more diffuse above the ear-coverts and merging with side of crown and nape. Lores with well defined, broad blackish line reaching to the bill base; eye-line less clearly defined, dull brown, becoming warmer and flecked light fawn to grey towards the rear where it merges with upper ear-coverts. Ear-coverts dull brown, with pale greyish white tips creating paler mottling. Eye-ring narrow, whitish and indistinct, merging with the supercilium and ear-coverts. Mantle and scapulars dull rufous-brown, mantle feathering long, fluffy and filamentous, often overlying the rump, uppertail-coverts and tertials. Rump and uppertail-coverts rufous-brown, slightly warmer than mantle. Tail

feathers with a loose, filamentous structure, with rufescent-brown centres, merging with darker brown fringes.

Chin and throat white with a slight greyish wash, merging with the more extensive light grey wash on breast and belly. Sides of breast light grey with diffuse darker striations extending to the sides of the neck and upper flanks. Upper flanks light grey, darkening to dull cinnamon-brown on the lower flanks, ventral region and undertail-coverts.

Lesser and median coverts as mantle and scapulars. Greater coverts and tertials dark brown with broad, rufous-brown fringes, appearing distinctly warmer than upperparts. Edges to secondaries and primaries warm rufous-brown. Together with the greater coverts and tertials, they form a contrastingly warmer panel on the closed wing. Inner edges of inner primaries and secondaries with a narrow buff-peach line from near bases to within 10mm of the tips, but absent on outer three primaries. Alula dull brown with an indistinct narrow rufous-brown fringe. Underwing-coverts white with a trace of grey, much paler than flanks.

Adult worn Resembles fresh adult.

Juvenile Not described.

Bare parts Upper mandible dark grey to black with a dull pink cutting edge. Lower mandible warm pink at base, slightly darker at tip. Tarsi, toes and claws dull greyish pink or flesh coloured, although colour may change with age.

IN HAND CHARACTERS

Measurements

Sexes combined:

Wing	50–58 (53.6; 7)
Tail	59–67 (62.2; 7)
Bill	15.5–17 (16.1; 16)
Tarsus	21.5–23.5 (22.8; 7)

Tail/wing ratio: 105–132% (117%; 7)
Bill width: 3.7–4.4 (4.1; 6)
Hind claw: 6.4–7.0 (6.7; 7)
Tail graduation: 15–22 (18.5; 6)

Structure Wing similar to Brownish-flanked Bush Warbler (Fig. 118) but more strongly rounded with large p1 (12–14mm > pc). Wing point p5–7; p2 and p3 < p10, p4 = p8/9; emargination on p3–6, sometimes slightly on p7.

Tail rather long, strongly graduated; ten feathers, narrow, loose and filamentous.

Bill stout but concave-sided with narrow tip.

Tarsi strong.

Weight Range 11.0–13.8g (12.2; 7) (Dunning 2007).

GEOGRAPHIC VARIATION None recorded.

TAXONOMY AND SYSTEMATICS Originally described as a distinct species *Cettia seebohmi*, but treated for many years as a race of Japanese Bush Warbler, from which it differs in both structure and appearance. Hamao *et al.* (2008) found that the basic song structure of Luzon Bush and Japanese Bush Warblers was similar, a monotone whistle followed by variably modulated warbles. But they discovered significant differences in their sonograms which led them to conclude that these should be treated as two distinct species. They also compared mtDNA seqences from Luzon Bush Warbler and other *Cettia* taxa, and found that it formed a monophyletic grouping with Japanese Bush and Bougainville Bush Warblers.

▲ ◀ Adult, Dalton Pass, Luzon, October. Underpart colour shows considerable variation. Some, like this individual, are dull greyish brown, others show paler dingy white underparts and supercilium. Note proportionately long tail for a *Cettia* (Philip Round/The Wetland Trust).

PALAU BUSH WARBLER
Cettia annae   Plate 42

Psamathia annae Hartlaub & Finsch, 1868. *Proc. Zool. Soc. London.* p. 5, pl. 2. Pulau Islands.

A resident of scrub and forest undergrowth confined to five islands in the Palau Archipelago in the remote SW Pacific, where it is the only warbler. Monotypic.

IDENTIFICATION Length 14–15cm. Wing 51–79mm. Tail/wing *c.* 90%.

A rather nondescript large *Cettia* with yellowish underparts, a conspicuous pale supercilium and a dark eye-stripe. Sexes alike although males are significantly larger than females.

Structure Similar in structure to other *Cettia* of the SW Pacific, but distinctly larger than both Fiji Bush Warbler and Shade Warbler. Like those species, it is distinctly round-headed with a robust body. However, it differs in having a disproportionately short tail, particularly when compared with species occurring in continental Asia, and a distinctive long bill that is uncharacteristic of *Cettia*. As with many resident species, the wing is distinctly rounded with a long first primary (p1) and a short primary projection. The wing point is formed by p5, occasionally together with p4 and p6, although these are usually slightly shorter.

Plumage and bare parts The upperparts are uniform drab olive-brown, but typically appear blackish within the dense scrub it inhabits. The most striking plumage feature is the long pale olive-yellow supercilium that usually extends to the rear of the ear-coverts and contrasts with the olive-brown crown and nape. Below this, the dark eye-stripe contrasts with the pale supercilium and also with the lightly mottled, pale olive-yellow ear-coverts. The underparts are pale olive-yellow, often with slight mottling formed by narrow feather fringes. This intensifies to form a slightly darker wash across the upper breast, becoming yellowish buff or warm buff on the lower flanks and undertail-coverts.

The bill is pale grey with a dull pink lower mandible that usually darkens towards the tip.

The legs and feet are dull pink.

SIMILAR SPECIES Very few passerines occur in the Palau Archipelago where it is the only warbler. Giant White-eye is the only potential confusion species.

Giant White-eye shares drab olive-brown upperparts, slightly paler underparts and a yellowish supercilium with Palau Bush Warbler. It differs in both structure and behaviour. It is a bulkier bird, with a shorter, thicker bill, much shorter tail and dark legs, unlike the dull pink legs of Palau Bush Warbler. It exhibits typical inquisitive, boisterous, white-eye behaviour and is more likely to occur in the mid storey to upper forest canopy than in the dense undergrowth preferred by Palau Bush Warbler. Its distinctive song has a mechanical character and is accompanied by a rhythmic rattling or clicking sound, quite different to that of Palau Bush Warbler (see **Voice** below).

VOICE The simple song is a characteristic bird sound of Palau and comprises a slow, slightly discordant and variably pitched whistle lasting approximately one second and gradually increasing in volume. This is not dissimilar to the introductory whistle of the song of Brownish-flanked Bush Warbler but slightly lower in pitch. Each whistle is followed by a pause of about two seconds before being repeated,

usually at a slightly higher or lower frequency than before, within a frequency range of 1–2kHz.

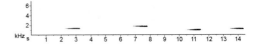

Song of Palau Bush Warbler, Palau Archipelago, July. (McPherson Natural History Unit)

The call is a series of chattering, low, flat, '*thack thack*' notes given in rapid succession (Pratt *et al.* 1987). Harsh scolding calls given by a bird on Koror (M. Hale *in litt.*) were perhaps this chatter call.

MOULT No information available.

HABITAT Believed to occur in all types of forest and scrub throughout the islands. On Koror, it occurs on gentle slopes in dense primary and mature secondary forest, usually in slightly more open situations with low tangled vegetation; also in tangled scrub by the shore.

BEHAVIOUR A skulking species that usually keeps close to the ground, being more frequently heard than seen. Occasionally comes to the edge of vegetation, but typically it remains deep within cover, occasionally darting mouse-like between clumps of thick scrub. Its behaviour is not known to differ from that of Fiji Bush Warbler. Song may be given throughout the year. On Koror, it was regularly heard throughout the day in February (M. Hale *in litt.*).

BREEDING HABITS No data available.

DISTRIBUTION Confined to the islands of Babelthuap, Koror, Garakayo, Peleliu and Ngabad in the Palau Archipelago, where it is common and widespread in suitable habitat.

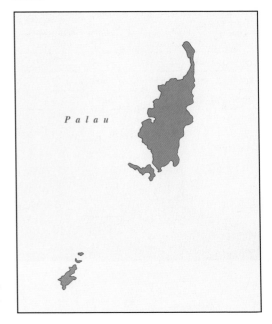

Palau Bush Warbler. Resident within breeding range.

MOVEMENTS Believed to be resident and no inter-island movements have been recorded.

DESCRIPTION

Plumage – Adult fresh Forehead and crown dull olive-brown. Supercilium long and narrow, pale olive-yellow, extending from bill base to side of nape. Loral spot dark brown, reaching to the bill base. A dull olive-brown eye-line, often flecked olive-yellow, extends behind the eye to beyond ear-coverts. Ear-coverts pale olive-yellow with olive-brown tips producing distinct mottling. Eye-ring concolorous with supercilium and upper ear-coverts. Nape, mantle and scapulars to uppertail-coverts dull olive-brown and unmarked, concolorous with crown. Tail feathers dark brown with dull olive-brown fringes and tips. Chin and throat pale olive-yellow, slightly mottled with brown across the malar region and merging with the ear-coverts. Upper breast slightly duller than throat, often with a faint greyish brown wash. Sides of breast and upper flanks with faint olive-brown striations, becoming more conspicuous on sides of neck, which merge with mottled ear-coverts. Lower breast and flanks rich yellowish buff, becoming darker warm buff on ventral region and undertail-coverts.

Lesser and median coverts dull olive-brown as mantle. Greater coverts and tertials dark brown with broad, diffuse olive-brown fringes matching upperparts. Secondaries and primaries with olive-brown edges, slightly warmer and brighter than upperparts. Alula darker brown than rest of wing, with an indistinct narrow olive-brown outer fringe. Underwing-coverts pale yellow, similar to throat.

Adult worn Not known to differ from the fresh adult.

Juvenile Undescribed.

Bare parts Upper mandible pale grey with narrow, dull pink cutting edge. Lower mandible dull, sometimes showing slight darkening towards tip. Tarsi and toes dull pink; claws slightly darker. Iris dark, colour perhaps varying with age.

IN HAND CHARACTERS
Measurements

	Male	Female
Wing	71–79 (74.8; 6)	61–75 (66.7; 7)
Tail	61–68 (63.5; 6)	52–63 (57.2; 5)
Bill	21–23 (21.7; 5)	20–22 (21.0; 7)
Tarsus	27–30 (29.0; 6)	26.5–30 (28.2; 7)

(Rozendaal 1987)

Unsexed (n = 3): bill width 4.2–4.5; hind claw 6.8–8.0; tail graduation 13–14.

Structure

Wing formula (n = 3):

p1/pc	p2	p3e	p4e	p5e	p6e	p7(e)	p10
21	14–18	3–4	0–2	wp	0–2	2–5	10–11

Wing strongly rounded with large p1 (> 60% p2). Wing point p(4) 5 (6); p2 < ss tips; emargination on p3–6, slightly on p7.

Figure 123. Wing of Palau Bush Warbler.

Tail medium, graduated, feathers quite narrow.
Bill long, narrow but deep and strong.
Tarsi long and robust, claws strong.

Weight No data available.

GEOGRAPHIC VARIATION None recorded.

TAXONOMY AND SYSTEMATICS Previously placed in the monotypic genus *Psamathia* but now included in *Cettia*, together with the closely related Fiji Bush Warbler and Shade Warbler, both of which were formerly included in the genus *Vitia*. Based upon similarities in song structure, egg colour and external morphology, Orenstein & Pratt (1983) concluded that *Psamathia* and *Vitia* are closely related to *Cettia* and that their inclusion within *Cettia* is justified. Although Palau Bush Warbler most closely resembles Luzon Bush Warbler, while Fiji Bush Warbler and Shade Warbler appear morphologically closer to Japanese Bush Warbler, they reject the idea of multiple colonisation of the region. They propose that the tropical Pacific *Cettia* are derived from a common ancestor and represent relicts of a widespread ancestral *Cettia* species that was once widespread throughout the Indo-Pacific region. See further comments under Bougainville Bush Warbler.

▲ ▶ Adult, Babeldoab Island, Palau, January (Jon Hornbuckle).

SHADE WARBLER
Cettia parens   Plate 42

Vitia parens **Mayr, 1935**. *Amer. Mus. Novit.*, No. 820: 4. San Cristobal, Solomon Islands.

A poorly known *Cettia* endemic to San Cristobal in the Solomon Islands. Monotypic.

IDENTIFICATION Length 11–12cm. Wing 49–62mm. Tail/wing 80–85%.

A drab and nondescript *Cettia* with dull chestnut-brown upperparts and a slightly paler cinnamon-buff supercilium. Unlikely to be mistaken for any other species on San Cristobal, where the distinctly paler San Cristobal Leaf Warbler is the only other warbler. Sexes similar, but male larger than female.

Structure A relatively bulky *Cettia* showing distinct sexual size dimorphism, the wing of the smallest males being larger than that of the largest females. Being sedentary, it has short and rounded wings with a very large first primary (p1). Also shows long legs and a relatively long slender bill. It is proportionately shorter-tailed than Palau Bush Warbler, similar in size to Fiji Bush Warbler but smaller than Bougainville Bush Warbler.

Plumage and bare parts The entire upperparts are uniform dull chestnut-brown apart from the long cinnamon-buff supercilium and a darker eye-line below this. On some birds, the edges to the flight feathers appear slightly warmer and brighter cinnamon-brown than the upperparts and form a contrasting brighter panel in the closed wing. Warmer toned individuals may appear rusty brown on the crown and nape, slightly brighter than on the mantle. The chin and throat are pale cinnamon-buff, contrastingly paler than the dull cinnamon-brown breast and belly. The lower abdomen and undertail-coverts are a darker, richer cinnamon-brown.

The bill is dark grey with a dull pink lower mandible. The legs and feet are dull pinkish brown.

SIMILAR SPECIES None on San Cristobal. See Bougainville Bush Warbler for distinctions from that species.

VOICE The song is similar in character to that of Palau Bush Warbler. It begins with a clear whistle that leads into a short undulating, tuneful warble; '*wuuuuuuuu duu-dee-wee*', within a frequency range of 1.5–4.5kHz. Sometimes the introductory whistle briefly wavers or is interrupted before continuing, and the undulating warble may contain between three and five elements; '*wuu-tuu-wuuuuuuuu wee-duu-wee-du*'.

The call is a short, harsh, '*trzzzr*', rapidly repeated.

MOULT No information available.

HABITAT Restricted to remnant pockets of subtropical moist forest, where it occurs in thick undergrowth.

BEHAVIOUR Little known. Said to be shy and skulking, foraging on the ground and amongst undergrowth. The frequently heard song suggests that it is common where it occurs. It is delivered from 2–3m above the ground within dense cover (del Hoyo *et al.* 2006).

BREEDING HABITS Nestlings have been reported in early December (del Hoyo *et al.* 2006).

DISTRIBUTION Restricted to San Cristobal (Makira) in the Solomon Islands. Its former range is uncertain

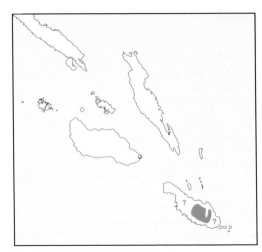

Shade Warbler. Resident within breeding range.

since much of the lowland forest there has been removed by logging. It remains common where primary forest remains, typically above 600m, including on the ridge above Hauta.

MOVEMENTS Believed to be resident. There are no records away from San Cristobal.

DESCRIPTION
Plumage – Adult fresh Forehead, crown and nape warm rusty brown, with indistinct dark brown fringes giving crown a faintly scaly appearance. Supercilium cinnamon-buff, extending from bill base to rear of ear-coverts; widest over the eye, tapering over ear-coverts and becoming less well defined. A dark brown loral stripe below the supercilium, extending from bill base to eye. A dark brown eye-stripe behind the eye, narrower and less well defined towards nape. Ear-coverts dull brownish buff, mottled dark brown. Eye-ring dull brownish buff, poorly defined. Mantle and scapulars uniform dull chestnut-brown, slightly darker than the crown. Rump and uppertail-coverts slightly warmer cinnamon-brown. Tail uniform dull cinnamon-brown in centre, darkening slightly towards the edges. Chin and throat whitish washed cinnamon-buff. Upper breast and belly light cinnamon-brown, slightly darker than throat, gradually darkening onto lower breast. Sides of breast and flanks deep cinnamon-buff to cinnamon-brown, usually with indistinct darker striations that extend to the sides of the neck. Lower belly and undertail-coverts richly washed deep cinnamon-brown. Lesser and median coverts dull chestnut-brown, similar to mantle and nape. Greater coverts with darker centres merging with narrow cinnamon-brown fringes, these being perceptibly warmer than upperparts. Alula, tertials, secondaries and primaries with cinnamon-brown fringes to outer webs, forming a warmer panel on the closed wing that contrasts slightly with the upperparts. Underwing-coverts drab yellowish brown.
Adult worn Not known to differ in appearance from fresh adult.
Juvenile Differs from adult in having crown and upperparts more olive-brown, and a poorly defined supercilium. Chin and throat washed yellowish. Breast, belly and flanks olivaceous-grey, becoming browner on lower belly and undertail-coverts.

Bare parts Upper mandible dark grey with pale pink cutting edge. Lower mandible dull pink and unmarked. Tarsi, toes and claws dull pinkish brown. Iris dull brown, colour perhaps varying with age.

IN HAND CHARACTERS
Measurements

	Male	Female
Wing	59–62 (60.1; 3)	49–55 (53.0; 4)
Tail	49, 50 (2)	43–47 (44.8; 3)
Bill	18.5–19 (18.8; 3)	17.0–18.5 (17.5; 4)
Tarsus	26 (26.0; 3)	23–26 (23.7; 4)

(Rozendaal 1987)

Structure Wing resembles Palau Bush Warbler (Fig. 123); short and strongly rounded with large p1 (>60% p2); wing point p5–6; p2 < ss tips, p3 near p10.

Tail short, tip rounded, feathers rather narrow.
Bill quite long, strong and deep.
Tarsi long but quite slender, toes and claws long.

Weight ♂ 18.5–19.0g (18.8; 3), 2 ♀♀,14.0g, 14.0g (Rozendaal 1987).

GEOGRAPHIC VARIATION None recorded.

TAXONOMY AND SYSTEMATICS Originally placed in the genus *Vitia* but Orenstein & Pratt (1983) demonstrated that song structure, egg colour and external morphology are similar to *Cettia* and concluded that there was no justification for retaining *Vitia*, which is now subsumed within *Cettia*. Shade Warbler forms part of a grouping of tropical *Cettia* species, together with Palau Bush and Fiji Bush Warblers (Orenstein & Pratt 1983), to which the recently discovered Tanimbar Bush Warbler of Yamdena (Rozendaal 1987) and Bougainville Bush Warbler of Bougainville (LeCroy & Barker 2006) can probably be added.

By comparing plumage coloration and pattern and morphometric analysis together with molecular studies, LeCroy & Barker (2006) confirmed the suspected close relationship between the SW Pacific *Cettia* and established that all are derived from an ancestral species originating from NE Asia and closely related to Japanese Bush Warbler, which forms a sister clade with these species. See further comments under Bougainville Bush Warbler.

▲ Adult, San Cristobal (Makira), Solomon Islands, June (Jon Hornbuckle).

FIJI BUSH WARBLER
Cettia ruficapilla   Plate 42

Vitia ruficapilla Ramsay, **1876**. *Proc. Linn. Soc. New South Wales.* 1:42. Kandavu, Fiji.

A resident *Cettia* endemic to Fiji, where it is fairly common and widespread. Polytypic, with four races, each restricted to a single island within the archipelago:
C. r. ruficapilla (Ramsay 1876). Kandavu, S Fiji.
C. r. badiceps (Finsch, 1876). Viti Levu, C Fiji.
C. r. castaneoptera (Mayr, 1935). Vanua Levu, N Fiji.
C. r. funebris (Mayr, 1935). Taveuni, NE Fiji.

IDENTIFICATION Length 12–13cm. Wing 53–61mm. Tail/wing *c.* 90–95%.

A dark, skulking *Cettia* with a warmly coloured head and a whitish throat and upper breast. Its presence is usually revealed by a distinctive duetting song, which is one of the characteristic bird sounds heard throughout Fiji and as likely to be heard in farmyards and cultivated areas as in secondary forest. Sexes similar but separable by size, the wing length of the smallest males exceeding that of the largest females.

Structure Shows the rather domed head, round dumpy body and well-rounded tail typical of SW Pacific *Cettia*. The wing is short and rounded, with a large first primary (p1) and tightly bunched primary tips that project only slightly beyond the secondaries. The bill is proportionately longer than in the continental Asian *Cettia* species and appears thinner but this feature is infrequently seen well, for the bird typically appears as a dark rodent-like shape darting between adjacent patches of thick scrub.

Plumage and bare parts All races show a warm chestnut crown and duller but still obviously warm brown upperparts, including the wings and tail. Below, the chin and throat are white and the breast and flanks dull greyish brown, often with indistinct striations on the sides of the upper breast and upper flanks. In the nominate race, the ear-coverts are also warm chestnut and the supercilium and eye-stripe poorly defined, giving the head a warm but otherwise rather plain appearance. In other races, a paler supercilium is more conspicuous.

The bill is light horn above and dull yellowish pink below. The legs and feet are dull brown, usually with a slight pinkish or plumbeous tinge.

SIMILAR SPECIES No similar species occur in Fiji, although confusion is possible with the recently rediscovered Long-legged Warbler, which is known from just two islands, Viti Levu and Vanua Levu, and is the only other warbler found in Fiji.

Long-legged Warbler is extremely rare and poorly known and was believed extinct until its rediscovery in the Wabu Forest Reserve on Viti Levu in 2003. If seen well, separation from the race *badiceps* of Viti Levu and *castaneoptera* of Vanua Levu should be straightforward. It shows a long and conspicuous bright buff supercilium and a warm brown crown and upperparts, quite distinct from the darker, browner upperparts, contrasting warm chestnut cap and paler underparts of Fiji Bush Warbler. As its name suggests, it has long legs, proportionately much longer than those of Fiji Bush Warbler.

VOICE The full song consists of a duet with one bird, presumably the male, delivering the opening sequence, followed closely by a dry double call from the second bird.

The smooth continuity and flow of the song make it difficult to believe that two birds are involved (Watling 2001).

The opening sequence of the male comprises a long quavering whistle on a single note, followed by a short phrase of between two and five elements; '*feee-e-e-fiddle-dee-dee*' delivered at a higher pitch than the whistle. This is followed immediately by a sharp double '*tsic-tslc*' possibly given by the female. The long whistle varies in pitch between individuals but the double phrase is more or less stereotyped throughout the population. An abbreviated song is occasionally given.

The call is unknown.

MOULT No information available.

HABITAT Frequents a wide variety of habitats on Kandavu, Vitu Levu and Vanua Levu, including suburban gardens, cultivated and agricultural land, scrub and undergrowth in secondary forest and remnant primary forest. The requirement common to all habitat types appears to be thick, dense scrub, in which it breeds. Occurs mainly from 100m to 1200m, although the race *badiceps* breeds down to sea level on Viti Levu.

On Taveuni, the race *funebris* is apparently restricted to undisturbed primary forest and is absent from the gardens, cultivated lands and dense secondary scrub occupied on other islands

BEHAVIOUR Poorly known. Typically skulks in dense low undergrowth and is more frequently heard than seen. It rarely appears in the open but occasionally flits between adjacent bushes, usually keeping close to the ground. It appears to be insectivorous, gleaning food items from leaves and stems, or foraging on the ground amongst leaf litter. It occasionally joins mixed-species flocks.

BREEDING HABITS Breeding has been recorded in every month from October to February, suggesting a preference for the wet season, which coincides with the northern winter. However, breeding behaviour has also been noted in June (Watling 2001), and the lack of data may conceal a year-long breeding season. The nest is a large, untidy domed structure with the entrance hole on one side. The clutch

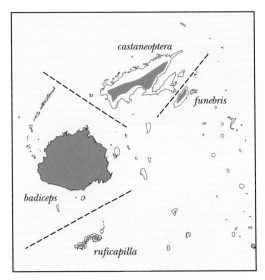

Fiji Bush Warbler. Resident within breeding range.

comprises two eggs (Watling 2001). Details of incubation and fledging are unknown.

DISTRIBUTION Restricted to the Fiji Archipelago in the SW Pacific Ocean where it occurs on four islands, each supporting an endemic race.
C. r. ruficapilla Kandavu.
C. r. badiceps Vitu Levu.
C. r. castaneoptera Vanua Levu.
C. r. funebris Taveuni.

It is common and widespread throughout these islands, although less numerous on Taveuni where the resident race is less catholic in its habitat preferences.

MOVEMENTS Believed to be resident, with no inter-island movements recorded.

DESCRIPTION *C. r. ruficapilla*
Plumage – Adult fresh Forehead, crown and nape warm chestnut, forming a bright cap. Supercilium warm chestnut-buff, long and narrow, extending from bill base to side of nape, contrasting little with the crown. A small chestnut-brown loral spot in front of eye and an indistinct narrow dull cinnamon-brown eye-line, most obvious immediately behind eye, fading and merging with ear-coverts. Ear-coverts warm chestnut-buff, faintly mottled warm buff, similar in colour to supercilium and crown. Eye-ring narrow, chestnut-buff and indistinct. Mantle and scapulars warm brown, occasionally with a slight olive wash, contrasting with the brighter crown. Rump, uppertail-coverts and tail warmer rufescent-brown and unmarked.

Chin and throat white with a slight greyish or occasionally faint chestnut wash. Upper breast white, with a more conspicuous greyish wash, often with indistinct striations that extend to sides of upper breast, sides of neck and upper flanks. Flanks dull greyish brown, becoming warmer and browner posteriorly. Belly white with a slight greyish wash. Vent and undertail-coverts warm rufescent brown.

Lesser and median coverts warm brown, similar to mantle colour. Greater coverts and tertials dark brown with broad warm brown fringes. Edges of secondaries and primaries warm brown; these together with greater coverts and tertial fringes give the closed wing a warmer, brighter appearance than the upperparts. Alula dull brown with a faint narrow grey fringe. Underwing-coverts pale greyish white, much paler than flanks.
Juvenile Undescribed.
Bare parts Upper mandible light horn with narrow pinkish cutting edge and tip. Lower mandible dull yellowish pink and unmarked. Tarsi and toes dull pinkish brown to dark plumbeous brown; claws slightly darker than toes. Iris dark brown, colour perhaps varying with age.

IN HAND CHARACTERS
Measurements

C. r. ruficapilla

	Male	Female
Wing	57–61 (59.4; 9)	53–55 (53.7; 8)
Tail	52.5–58 (55.8; 9)	48–51 (49.5; 7)
Bill	18–20 (19.0; 9)	18–19 (18.3; 6)
Tarsus	24.5–26 (25.1; 9)	23–24 (23.5; 7)

(Rozendaal 1987)

C. r. badiceps

	Male	Female
Wing	57–61 (58.2; 12)	50–56.5 (52.5; 6)
Tail	52–58.5 (55.5; 11)	48–49.5 (48.4; 5)
Bill	17–19 (18.0; 12)	16–18.5 (16.8; 6)
Tarsus	25–25.5 (24.8; 12)	21–24 (22.6; 5)

(Rozendaal 1987)

Sexes combined (races *ruficapilla* and *badius*):
Tail/wing ratio: 92–94% (93%; 3)
Bill width: 4.2–4.4 (n = 3)
Hind claw: 6.2–6.8 (6.6; 5)
Other races (from Rozendaal 1987):
C. r. castaneoptera: wing, ♂ 57–63 (60.2; 10), ♀ 54–60 (55.9; 5); *tail*,♂ 54.5–62 (58.8; 10), ♀ 54–55 (54.8; 4); *bill*, ♂ 17.5–20 (19.0; 10), ♀ 17.5–19 (18.6; 4); *tarsus*, ♂ 24.5–27 (25.4; 10), ♀ 24–25 (24.7; 5).
C. r. funebris: wing, ♂ 61–65 (62.7; 9), ♀ 55, 57 (2); *tail*, ♂ 50–60 (56.9; 9), ♀ 49 (1); *bill*, ♂ 18–19.5 (18.7; 9), ♀19 (2); *tarsus*, ♂ 25–27 (26.4; 9), 25, 25.5 (2).

Structure Wing resembles Palau Bush Warbler (Fig. 123); short and rounded with large p1 (*c.* 50% p2). Wing point p5–6; p2 < ss tips, p3 = p9/10; emargination on p3–6.
Tail medium length, graduated, ten rather narrow feathers.
Bill longish, strong, but quite narrow.
Tarsi long and strong, claws strong.
Weight Race unknown: 9.0–15.5g (12.7; 18) (Langham 1987).

GEOGRAPHIC VARIATION The four races closely resemble each other and variation between them is slight, these relating to differences in size, prominence of the supercilium and colour of the ear-coverts.
C. r. ruficapilla (Kandavu) Described above.
C. r. badiceps (Viti Levu) Head pattern more contrasting than in nominate race. Crown warm chestnut but ear-coverts are mottled greyish and white. The supercilium is more conspicuous, appearing creamy white and contrasting with the narrow blackish eye-stripe. Upperparts typically dull olive-brown.
C. r. castaneoptera (Vanua Levu) Similar to *badiceps* but upperparts are browner, less olive. The supercilium is washed slightly with buff, especially in front of the eye. Slightly larger than *badiceps*.
C. r. funebris (Taveuni) Ear-coverts brighter chestnut than in nominate race and the supercilium is paler and slightly more conspicuous. Upperparts slightly darker. The largest race.

TAXONOMY AND SYSTEMATICS When described, Fiji Bush Warbler was placed in a genus *Vitia*, together with the closely related Shade Warbler, but it is now included with *Cettia* on the basis of its voice, morphology and egg colour.

It forms part of a species group of five closely related *Cettia* occurring in the SW Pacific, the others being Shade Warbler, Bougainville Bush Warbler from the Solomon Islands, Palau Bush Warbler from the Caroline Islands and Tanimbar Bush Warbler from Tanimbar in the eastern Lesser Sundas. Orenstein & Pratt (1983) and LeCroy & Barker (2006) discussed the likely origins of this group and their relationship with *Cettia* from the Asian mainland. Both concluded that this group is most closely related to Japanese

Bush Warbler and these five species represent remnant, relict populations of a once wide-ranging ancestral taxon that occupied much of this region. See Bougainville Bush Warbler for further discussion.

▲ Adult *C. r. ruficapilla*, Kandavu, Fiji, November (Paul Noakes).

TANIMBAR BUSH WARBLER
Cettia carolinae   **Plate 42**

Cettia carolinae Rozendaal, 1987. *Zool. Meded. Leiden.* 61: 177–202. Yamdena, Tanimbar Islands, Indonesia.

Endemic to the island of Yamdena in the eastern Lesser Sundas, Indonesia, where it was discovered in 1985. Considered NEAR THREATENED by Birdlife International due to its highly restricted range on a single small island and it may have declined as a result of habitat loss in parts of its range. Monotypic.

IDENTIFICATION Length 11–13cm. Wing 59–71mm. Tail/wing *c.* 65–70%.

A medium sized, short-tailed *Cettia* with a rufous cap and a well-marked supercilium. This is the only warbler resident on Yamdena. Sexes alike but males are significantly larger than females.

Structure Compared with the continental Asian *Cettia*, Tanimbar Bush Warbler shows a disproportionately long bill, longer wings and a relatively short tail. This distinctive structure, combined with its typically horizontal stance and distinctive habit of slightly raising the tail while continuously flicking the wings, gives it a character unique among the birds of the Tanimbar Islands. The wing is rounded with a large first primary (p1) and wing point formed by p4–6.

Plumage and bare parts Generally nondescript and drab although the head shows a long, dull cinnamon-buff supercilium, bordered below by a well-defined dark brown eye-stripe and above by a rufous-brown crown. The ear-coverts are dull grey and faintly mottled. The upperparts including the tail appear unmarked dull warm brown, but the fringes to the greater coverts, tertials and secondaries can produce an obvious warmer panel in the closed wing. The underparts lack any distinctive features but the greyish white chin, throat, upper breast and belly usually contrast with the duller olive-grey breast sides and browner flanks.

Bill blackish with a dull greyish pink lower mandible, which darkens towards the tip. The legs and feet are dull pinkish flesh.

SIMILAR SPECIES There are no similar species resident on Yamdena and Rufous-sided Fairy-warbler is the only remotely similar species, but this is a tiny bird of the mid to upper storey where it picks insects from leaves, quite unlike the skulking and elusive Tanimbar Bush Warbler.

Several species of migrant warbler from N Asia could conceivably reach Tanimbar, at least as vagrants. Of these, only the significantly larger Gray's Grasshopper Warbler is known to occur regularly in the eastern Lesser Sundas.

Compared with other *Cettia* resident in the Indo-Pacific region, which would never naturally occur alongside, Tanimbar Bush Warbler most closely resembles Fiji Bush Warbler, in particular the races *badiceps* and *castaneoptera*. It differs in being slightly duller and less contrasting, with warmer, slightly paler, rufous-brown upperparts, a paler ventral region, duller grey-brown flanks and a dull rufous crown only slightly brighter than the mantle. Its geographically closest relative is Sunda Bush Warbler of the race *C. v. everetti* which is resident on Timor. This differs from Tanimbar Bush Warbler in its smaller size and much shorter bill, pale greyish brown upperparts and white underparts, with only a faint greyish wash on the breast and throat sides.

VOICE The song consists of a long, drawn-out and pene-trating whistle, '*tuuuuuuuuuu*', rising slightly in volume and pitch between 2–3kHz, followed by a pleasing terminal flourish, described as a melodic '*chir-rup*' or '*chir-rip*'. Each complete '*tuuuuuuuuuuu-chirrup*' song sequence lasts just over a second and is followed by a pause of 5 to 15 seconds before being repeated. The whistle sometimes has a slight wavering quality, '*tuu-tuu-tuuuu*' and the terminal flourish usually differs slightly in pitch from one sequence to the next. This 'whistle-warble' song was noted as being very similar to that of Fiji Bush Warbler and uttered at the same frequency of approximately 2kHz (Rozendaal 1987). The song is also quite similar in structure and tone to that of Brownish-flanked Bush Warbler.

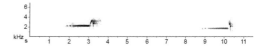

Song of Tanimbar Bush Warbler, Yamdena, Tanimbar, Lesser Sundas, Indonesia. (K. D. Bishop)

The call is a quiet '*cherr*' or '*chuck*', given singly or as a series of notes.

MOULT No information available.

HABITAT Frequents undergrowth in primary monsoon forest, secondary forest, regenerating scrub, forest edge and roadside bamboo thickets (Rozendaal 1987). Also found in dense forest edge understorey and selectively logged semi-evergreen forest, as well as in tall, closed forest in the centre of Yamdena (Bishop & Brickle 1998).

BEHAVIOUR Highly skulking and elusive, which undoubt-edly accounts for its late discovery in an ornithologically explored region. It typically skulks in dense undergrowth, keeping within a metre of the forest floor. It has a habit of clinging to tree trunks, tangled lianas, saplings and rattans. The song is usually delivered from deep within cover although Rozendaal (1987) mentioned an individual singing while moving through dense bamboo up to 5m above the ground.

BREEDING HABITS Unknown.

Tanimbar Bush Warbler. Resident within breeding range.

DISTRIBUTION Known only from the southern part of Yamdena, an island in the Tanimbar group in the E Lesser Sundas. It was found at two locations by Rozendaal (1987); northwest of Bomaki and on the limestone escarpment behind Loroulung, but it is thought to be more widespread. Subsequently, Bishop & Brickle (1998) found it to be particularly vocal during the wet season and reported its song as a characteristic sound of the forest, implying that it is widespread and common. Further studies are required.

MOVEMENTS Believed to be resident. Unrecorded away from Yamdena.

DESCRIPTION

Plumage – Adult fresh Forehead, crown and nape rufous-brown. Supercilium long and conspicuous, from bill base to rear of the ear-coverts, broadening slightly over and immediately behind the eye; dull cinnamon-buff, usually with a slight greyish wash, most noticeable behind eye. Lores and eye-line dark brown, forming a sharply defined line below supercilium, extending to rear of ear-coverts and merging with side of neck. Ear-coverts faintly mottled grey and brown, appearing paler than eye-line. Paler eye-ring narrow and inconspicuous. Mantle, scapulars, rump and uppertail-coverts warm brown, duller than crown. Tail dull brown, slightly warmer towards the edges. Chin, throat and centre of upper breast white with a greyish wash, gradually merging with the dull grey sides of breast and flanks, these often with a cold brown wash. Centre of belly white. Vent and undertail-coverts dull cream.

Lesser and median coverts warm brown, matching mantle colour. Greater coverts, alula and tertials with broad rufous-brown fringes that merge with darker brown centres. Secondaries and primaries dull grey-brown, edged rufous-brown. Underwing-coverts white.

Adult worn Not known to differ from the fresh adult.

Juvenile Not described.

Bare parts Upper mandible blackish with a dull pink cutting edge and tip. Lower mandible dull greyish pink with a diffusely darker distal third. Tarsi and toes dull pinkish flesh to bluish horn; claw colour similar. Iris dark brown.

IN HAND CHARACTERS

Measurements

	Male	Female
Wing	68–71 (69.0; 4)	59–61 (60.0; 3)
Tail	45–49 (47.5; 4)	39, 41 (2)
Bill	20 (20.0; 4)	19 (19.0; 3)
Tarsus	22–25 (23.8; 4)	21–24 (22.3; 3)

(Rozendaal 1987)

Sexes combined (Rozendaal 1987):
Tail/wing ratio: 65–70%
Bill width: 4.3–5.1
Tail graduation: 6–7

Structure

Wing formula (Rozendaal 1987):

p1/pc*	p2	p3	p4e	p5e	p6e	p7	p10
12–19.5	10.5–12	2–3	wp	0–0.5	0.5	1.5–5	9–10

*p1/pc ♂ 15.5–19, ♀ 12–14.5 (S. van der Mije, R. Dekker *in litt.*).

Wing resembles Palau Bush Warbler (Fig. 123); rounded with large p1. Wing point p4(5–6); p2 < ss tips, p3 near p7; emargination on p4–6.

Tail short and rounded, feathers rather narrow.

Bill long and strong.

Weight ♂ 18.6–20.6g (19.5; 4), ♀ 13.5–15.0g (14.3; 3) (Rozendaal 1987).

GEOGRAPHIC VARIATION None recorded.

TAXONOMY AND SYSTEMATICS Undiscovered *Cettia* populations had been anticipated in the Lesser Sundas, but it was expected that these would show characters of the wide-ranging Sunda Bush Warbler, which breeds throughout the Greater Sundas, east to Lombok and also on Timor. However, Tanimbar Bush Warbler differs significantly from the Sunda Bush Warbler complex in size, structure and plumage and appears not to be closely related. Although it occurs geographically closer to the *everetti* race of Sunda Bush Warbler on Timor, Rozendaal considered it to represent a link between the *Cettia* of continental Asia and the SW Pacific *Cettia* grouping including Fiji Bush Warbler, Palau Bush Warbler and Shade Warbler.

Its plumage characters are closest to Fiji Bush Warbler, in particular to races *badiceps* and *castaneoptera*. Structural features suggesting a link with the SW Pacific *Cettia* rather than with the Sunda Bush Warbler complex include the long bill and relatively long wing. The low tail/wing ratio, however, distinguishes Tanimbar Bush Warbler from these species. Furthermore, it exhibits a greater degree of sexual size dimorphism than either Sunda Bush Warbler or Fiji Bush Warbler. The songs of Tanimbar Bush and Fiji Bush Warblers are similar and differ significantly from that of Sunda Bush Warbler, which is consistent across all its populations including that on Timor.

▲ Adult, Yamdena, Lesser Sundas, Indonesia, July (Jon Hornbuckle).

BOUGAINVILLE BUSH WARBLER
Cettia haddeni   Plate 42

Cettia haddeni LeCroy & Barker, 2006. *American Museum Novitates* 3511, 1–20. Crown Prince Range, Bougainville, Solomon Islands.

A recently described *Cettia* from Bougainville Island, Papua New Guinea. Its song was familiar to inhabitants of the montane forests, who named it Odedi, but it has been heard by only a small number of visiting researchers. Currently known from just three specimens, collected in 2000 and 2001. Considered NEAR THREATENED by Birdlife International because it is poorly known and it may be declining due to introduced predators and habitat degradation. Monotypic.

IDENTIFICATION Length c. 13cm. Wing 60–66mm. Tail/wing *c.* 65%.

A rather large, dark and featureless *Cettia* endemic to Bougainville. Highly skulking, making location and identification dependent on recognising its distinctive clear whistled song. Sexes believed to be alike.

Structure A large, heavy *Cettia* with a proportionately short tail and a strongly rounded wing, with a long first primary (p1) and the wing point formed by p5 and p6. For a *Cettia*, the bill is long and heavy with a broad base and the legs and toes are large and robust. It is not known whether it exhibits the sexual size dimorphism found in other SW Pacific *Cettia*. LeCroy & Barker (2006) consider this may be the case but their assessment is based on just three specimens.

Plumage and bare parts The head is particularly drab, with a dull chestnut-brown crown showing little contrast with the slightly paler, warm brown sides and there is no suggestion of a paler supercilium or eye-ring. A diffuse eye-stripe only slightly darker than the surrounding feathering extends across the lores and behind the eye. The upperparts, including the mantle, uppertail-coverts and wing-coverts are featureless dark brown. The flight feather edges and tail are similar but slightly tinged with chestnut. The breast and belly are dark grey and appear diffusely dark-mottled and contrast with the paler chin and throat.

The bill is dark brown with a yellowish base, becoming darker towards the tip. The legs are pale yellow-straw.

SIMILAR SPECIES Unlikely to be mistaken for any other species within its restricted range. As it is so poorly known, it is useful to discuss differences with other similar southwest Pacific *Cettia*. Shade Warbler, its geographically closest relative resident on Makira Island, Solomon Islands, and Fiji Bush Warbler, are both smaller with narrower bills and less robust legs, but are proportionately longer-tailed. Shade Warbler is less dark, more olive above and tinged yellowish below. Of the races of Fiji Bush Warbler, *funebris* from Taveuni Island is most similar to Bougainville Bush Warbler, but shows a more contrasting warm chestnut head, a distinct pale supercilium and a more extensively whitish throat and breast. Palau Bush Warbler is slightly larger than Bougainville Bush Warbler and has a longer tail and wing, but a narrower bill. It shows quite different olive and yellow tones to the plumage and a bolder, more contrasting face pattern. The recently discovered Tanimbar Bush Warbler of the eastern Lesser Sundas is broadly similar in overall appearance but shows a well-marked head pattern. It overlaps with Bougainville Bush Warbler in a number of measurements but its legs are smaller and the bill narrower.

VOICE Commences with a short attenuated whistle at *c.* 2kHz, quickly followed by a one- or two-note phrase rising to *c.* 4kHz; '*twuuuu-wuuu-weee*', repeated at intervals of 3–4 seconds. This phrase has a similar quality to that of other Pacific *Cettia* but the introductory whistle is shorter.

The call is unknown.

MOULT An immature collected on 11 August 2001 was in body and wing moult. Two adults collected in January 2000 and September 2000 showed no suggestion of moult (LeCroy & Barker 2006).

HABITAT Dense undergrowth in montane forest. Beehler (1983) heard the song of what is now known to be Bougainville Bush Warbler in ridge forest NE of Panguna. Despite surveying nearby montane plateau forest where he camped for five days he was unable to locate it there, leading him to suggest that it may be restricted to forested ridges on montane woodland.

BEHAVIOUR Shy and skulking and almost nothing is known of its behaviour. The three known specimens came from birds trapped using mist-nets. Diamond (1975) suggested that it is shy, territorial and solitary. The song is delivered from deep cover, close to the ground and not from an open perch.

BREEDING HABITS Unknown.

DISTRIBUTION Known only from the Crown Prince Mountains on Bougainville, North Solomons Province, Papua New Guinea, where resident between 1,000–1,400m (Diamond 1975; LeCroy & Barker 2006). On the basis of the frequency with which he heard the song on Mount Balbi, between 1,140m and 1,340m, Diamond (1975) considered it to be not uncommon in those forests. The montane regions of the island have been largely inaccessible since 1980 and its true distribution may prove to be more extensive are there is suitable habitat above 1,000m along the entire mountainous spine of the island.

DESCRIPTION
Plumage – Adult Forehead and crown dark chestnut-brown with slightly paler shaft streaks. No supercilium. A narrow, diffuse darker brown line runs across the lores and behind the eye. No contrasting eye-ring. Ear-coverts warm reddish brown with paler shaft streaks. Feathering around bill base slightly warmer, richer tan-brown. Nape washed dark chestnut, darkening and merging posteriorly with the plain unmarked dark brown mantle and scapulars. Rump and uppertail-coverts similar in colour to the mantle. Upper surface of tail dark brown, closely matching the mantle colour; underside uniform dark brown. Chin and throat pale greyish white, unmarked. Rest of underparts, including breast, belly and upper flanks, grey, with exposed blackish feather bases giving a diffuse mottled appearance; darkest towards the carpal bend and palest towards the centre of the belly. Lower flanks dark brownish olive. Undertail-coverts dark brown, unmarked. Upperwing-coverts, alula and tertials plain dull brown with warmer chestnut-brown fringes. Primaries and secondaries narrowly edged reddish brown.
Immature LeCroy & Barker (2006) described an immature bird, aged from its largely unossified skull, as being very similar in appearance to the adult.
Bare parts Upper mandible dark brown. Lower mandible yellowish at base, becoming dark brown towards the tip. Tarsi yellowish ochre, browner at the front; toes slightly yellower; claws pale straw, slightly paler than toes. Iris dark brown.

IN HAND CHARACTERS

Measurements *Wing* (1 ♂, 2 unsexed) 60–66; *tail* (1 ♂, 1 unsexed) 43; *bill* (1 ♂, 2 unsexed) 19.0; *tarsus* (1 ♂, 2 unsexed) 26.5, 29, 29; bill width 7–8 (n = 3) (LeCroy & Barker 2006).

Structure Wing strongly rounded with large p1 (*c.* 60% p2). Formula (holotype): wing point p5–6; p2 19mm shorter, p3 9mm shorter, p4 1mm shorter (LeCroy & Barker 2006).

Tail of ten feathers, relatively short, graduated.

Bill strong, very broad at base.

Tarsi and toes comparatively long and strong.

Recognition Larger bodied and heavier than Luzon Bush Warbler, which is similar in wing length but has a proportionately longer tail. Compared to other *Cettia* species of the SW Pacific, distinctly larger than Shade Warbler and slightly larger than Fiji Bush Warbler. Slightly smaller than Palau Bush Warbler on all measurements except tarsus and bill width.

Weight ♂ (n = 1) 25g.

GEOGRAPHIC VARIATION None recorded.

TAXONOMY AND SYSTEMATICS With ten rectrices, Bougainville Bush Warbler clearly belongs within *Cettia and* is probably most closely related to the three species on other islands in the SW Pacific, Palau Bush Warbler,

Shade Warbler and Fiji Bush Warbler. LeCroy & Barker (2006) studied this relationship in depth and also that of Tanimbar Bush Warbler, Luzon Bush Warbler and Japanese Bush Warbler.

Although Shade Warbler from Makira Island in the Solomon Islands occurs geographically closer to Bougainville, it is quite distinct from Bougainville Bush Warbler. Closest in appearance and overall structure is Fiji Bush Warbler of the form *C. r. funebris* from Taneuni. In addition, Tanimbar Bush Warbler from Yamdena in the Lesser Sundas closely resembles Bougainville Bush Warbler, which it also approaches on a number of key measurements.

A phylogenetic study by LeCroy & Barker (2006) revealed that Bougainville Bush Warbler belongs within a monophyletic group of island forms that includes Palau Bush Warbler, Shade Warbler and Fiji Bush Warbler. They established that DNA of these *Cettia* differed from Bougainville Bush Warbler by approximately 4% leading them to conclude that it is at least as distinct from the other SW Pacific *Cettia* as they are from each other. This SW Pacific group was found to form a sister clade with Japanese Bush Warbler, suggesting that they were derived from a common ancestor that originated in NE Asia, and supporting an earlier suggestion by Orenstein & Pratt (1983).

▲ ▶ Adult, Panguna, Bougainville, July (Ashley Banwell).

CETTI'S WARBLER
Cettia cetti   **Plate 40**

Sylvia cetti Temminck, 1820. *Man. Ornith.*, ed 2(1): 194. Sardinia.

The only European *Cettia*. It occurs in damp, bushy and waterside habitats across warm temperate latitudes from S England and NW Africa to the E Mediterranean, the Black Sea and Central Asia. European populations are resident or dispersive but most Asian breeders are migratory, wintering in the Middle East and south to Pakistan. Polytypic, with three races recognised:

C. c. cetti (Temminck, 1820). W and S Europe to the W Black Sea coasts; also NW Africa.

C. c. orientalis Tristram, 1867. Crimea, Turkey and the Levant to the Caucasus and NW Iran.

C. c. albiventris Severtzov, 1873. Central Asia from Caspian Sea east to W China (Xinjiang Uygur Autonomous Region) and south to N Afghanistan.

IDENTIFICATION Length 13–15cm. Wing, male 58–72mm, female 52–66mm. Tail/wing 88–102%.

A medium-sized nondescript warbler with uniform dark rufous-brown upperparts and well-rounded wings and tail. Its behaviour is essentially skulking and it usually betrays its presence by a short burst of distinctive 'explosive' song. It is quite unlike any other European warbler and the only member of this wide-ranging but primarily Asian genus to occur in the Western Palearctic. Sexes similar but separable on size, males being much larger than females.

Structure The nominate race in Europe is similar in body size to Eurasian Reed Warbler but is more robust, with a dumpy body and a proportionately larger head with a distinctly rounded crown and a rather short, fine bill. Wing length of males averages about 10% larger than females. The short and distinctly rounded wings show tightly bunched primaries with no more than five or, occasionally, six tips visible in the wing point, which is formed by p4–5. The first primary (p1) is quite long and extends well beyond the primary coverts. The second is relatively short. It has a proportionately long and distinctly rounded tail that is frequently flicked upwards above the back or held slightly cocked, and it is often spread in flight, when it appears particularly conspicuous. Together, these characters create the impression of a relatively long-tailed, robust warbler that is enhanced by the short wings and rather short undertail-coverts. The legs are quite stout.

Plumage Plain, dark and nondescript. The nominate form appears particularly dark rufescent-brown, but those breeding in the Middle East and Central Asia are distinctly paler both above and below. European birds have the entire upperparts, including wings and tail, uniform dark rufous-brown, offset only by a narrow greyish supercilium and a slightly darker eye-stripe, that contrast with the crown and ear-coverts, and a broken narrow whitish eye-ring that is most conspicuous below the eye. The wings show no contrast with the mantle or scapulars. The primaries lack pale tips, making their spacing and projection difficult to discern in the field. The underparts are drab, unmarked and equally featureless, although the chin and throat are white with a slight greyish wash and the belly is pale greyish white. Below the throat, the breast and upper flanks darken to brownish grey, then darken further to dull rufescent-brown or sepia-brown on the lower flanks. The undertail-coverts are drab grey-brown, colder than the flanks and narrowly

tipped pale grey. Young birds do not differ significantly from adults and are often inseparable after the first autumn moult is completed.

The bill is dark grey with a dull pink lower mandible that usually darkens slightly at the sides towards the tip. The legs and feet are brownish pink during the breeding season but slightly paler and without the brown tone throughout the rest of the year, although this colouring may refer to immature birds.

SIMILAR SPECIES Unlikely to be confused with any other species in Europe, where no other warbler shares the combination of dark rufous-brown upperparts, drab brownish to greyish underparts and pale grey tips to the grey-brown undertail-coverts. This appearance, together with the long, broad tail and combined with its characteristic and readily recognisable song makes confusion most unlikely. Within its Asian range, the paler appearance of the races *orientalis* and, in particular, *albiventris* approaches that of several similarly sized unstreaked *Acrocephalus* and *Locustella* species. Although closer in overall appearance, no species in either genus shares a similar head and body profile, and the wing structure with the long first primary. All races throughout the range have the characteristic explosive song.

VOICE The daytime song is a loud series of clearly defined notes that starts and finishes abruptly and lasts between two and five seconds. In delivery and quality it is quite unlike that of any other European bird. There is considerable individual and regional variation, but each bird gives a stereotyped song, which it seems to keep for life and which is individually recognisable.

The song commences with an introductory explosive '*tchi*' or '*chuit*' that is followed immediately by a rapid series of '*chuee*' or '*piti*' notes, usually between six and 15 of these are given. In S England, the typical song is variously described as '*chuit chuee-chuee-chuee-chuee-chuee*', or '*chee chewee-chewee-chewee-chewee*', or '*chee cheweechoo-weechoo-weechoo-wee*' or similar variations, within a frequency range of 3–8kHz. In southern France, a slightly different song is given as '*ti tipitipitpi ti-pi ti-pi*', with a slight pause between the main song and the last two notes, which are sometimes repeated a second time. The main song may be followed by a series of '*chip*' calls. During peak song periods, particularly at dawn, males normally deliver one to two songs per minute as they move around the territory (D. T. Ireland in Cramp 1992). An interval of one to four minutes or longer is typical at other times.

Territorial males also have a nocturnal song that begins in the early hours and continues until dawn. It is delivered from a fixed song perch and with greater frequency than the daytime song. Burton (1979) recorded 32 bursts within seven minutes, while Henderson (1979) and Ireland (1984) found a maximum frequency of 10–12 song bursts per minute around 03:00 hours. This song is briefer and less varied and rich than daytime song, described as '*pwit pit-i-chew-it-chew-it*' (J. Craggs-Hall in Cramp 1992). It elicits no response from other males and is thought to advertise the territory to unmated females. It is given in England by both single and mated males. In autumn and winter, a quieter less energetic sub-song is given with reduced frequency.

In the Caucasus and Central Asia, the songs of *orientalis* and *albiventris* differ slightly from that of nominate *cetti* in Western Europe but they are similar in structure and delivery and remain easily recognisable.

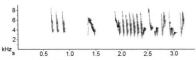

Song of Cetti's Warbler, recorded within breeding range of *C. c. cetti*, Spain, April. (Sample 2003)

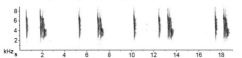

Nocturnal song of Cetti's Warbler, recorded within breeding range of *C. c. cetti*, Lesvos, Greece, May. (Sample 2003)

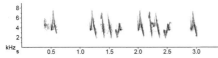

Song of Cetti's Warbler, recorded within breeding range of *C. c. albiventris*, Ili River, Kazakhstan, May. (Peter Kennerley)

The usual contact call, given by both sexes, is a staccato '*chip*' or '*tschiek*', usually given singly, but sometimes strung together in a series. This lacks the whiplash quality of the similar calls of Savi's and River Warblers. In addition, the female occasionally gives a quiet '*huit*' or '*wheet*' in presence of the male. A loud clicking or ticking '*tsuk-tsuk-tsuk*' is given in alarm and also a rattling call described as '*t-k-t-k-t-k-t-k*', like the winding of a mechanical clock. Another rattle-like call, similar to that of a Northern Wren but slower and slightly higher-pitched, can be heard throughout the year. In *albiventris*, Dement'ev & Gladkov (1954) describe a '*tich-ich-ich-ich*' call from alarmed birds.

MOULT In Europe, adults have a complete post-breeding moult. This takes place from mid June in S Europe, but from mid July or later in NW Europe. Wing feather replacement follows the typical passerine sequence but the tail feathers may be dropped and replaced simultaneously (Ginn & Melville 1983). Individual duration is approximately 60 days, so moult is complete from mid August in southern populations but not until early to mid September in NW Europe. Some birds undergo a partial pre-breeding moult in March and April. The extent of this is variable but it usually involves the head and body feathering and some wing-coverts and occasionally some tail feathers and tertials (Ginn & Melville 1983).

In SW Europe, post-juvenile moult occurs between late June and September and is extensive, involving the head and body feathers, lesser and median coverts, inner greater coverts and some tertials. Occasionally, all the greater coverts and a variable number of inner primaries and secondaries are also replaced. In NW Europe, the extent of post-juvenile moult is less clear-cut. Some young birds, perhaps from early broods, also replace all the body feathering between mid July and mid September. Others, however, appear to develop their first-winter body and head plumage by adding to, rather than replacing, the juvenile feathering, also between mid July and mid September.

Moult in the eastern races, *orientalis* and *albiventris*, is poorly understood. According to Dement'ev & Gladkov (1954) *orientalis*, which is resident or a short-distance migrant in the Middle East, has a complete post-breeding moult, although said not to have begun by mid August, when adults are still feeding young and the plumage is

heavily abraded. This is followed by a partial pre-breeding body moult. For example, birds examined at Kumbashi, on the Caspian Sea coast of Azerbaijan, were said to have a 'vigorous' partial moult between mid March and early April (Dement'ev & Gladkov 1954).

The Central Asian race *albiventris* has also been reported to have a complete moult after breeding (e.g. Williamson 1968). In E Kazakhstan, however, adults are still in old plumage in September and October (AG *in litt.*), and presumably moult in the winter quarters after migration.

HABITAT In W and S Europe it breeds in a wide variety of damp habitats, including swamps, marshes, reedbeds, watercourses and lake margins and always requires low, thick scrub and bushes nearby. It generally breeds close to water but peripheral or overspill populations will use adjacent habitats such as damp woodland, hedgerows, dry scrub, cereal fields and dry reeds. Territories may include wet reedbeds, but patches of scrub or bushes are required to provide areas for foraging. Stands of pure *Phragmites* over water are generally avoided. It is most numerous in the warmer regions around the Mediterranean, breeding from sea level up to 1,450m in Spain and as high as 2,100m in the Haut Atlas, Morocco.

The eastern races *orientalis* and *albiventris* are less restricted to wetlands than their European counterparts. In Central Asia, it breeds most frequently in meadows with scattered bushes, hedgerows, orchards, dense scrub and herbage. It is not uncommon in arid semi-deserts with scattered low scrub provided there is a damp watercourse or irrigation channel nearby. Breeding takes place along mountain streams in the hills above Samarkand to at least 1,550m, while in Kazakhstan it breeds in the lower Tien Shan Mountains to at least 750m. Migrants are not restricted to wetlands and can occur in most habitats up to 1,200m.

BEHAVIOUR A classic skulking species that is difficult to observe well, although it is not particularly shy. It usually forages within thick cover near the water's edge, collecting small insects and aquatic invertebrates on or near the ground and gleaning prey from leaves, twigs and branches. It also extracts insects from broken reed stems. It feeds in the open occasionally, particularly in winter, hopping about on mud or vegetation. When disturbed near the nest, it adopts an alarm posture with head lowered, tail cocked and wings drooped along the flanks and flicked nervously. It frequently gives a short alarm call or burst of song before flying to a more distant perch and singing again.

Males occupy large territories and tend to sing throughout the year except during moult and during cold spells in winter. Territories are often linear, following streams or other watercourses, with singing birds about 50–100m apart in favoured areas. In Kazakhstan, they are more widely spaced, up to 500m apart (Dement'ev & Gladkov 1954). Territories are defended vigorously and rival males may be attacked and expelled if song fails to deter them. In extreme cases, intruding males are vigorously pursued in flight low over reeds and scrub and such chases may last for several minutes.

Song is rarely heard during mid winter but its frequency increases from late winter and peaks during the early breeding season. It is most frequent in England from late March to May, when it can be heard throughout the day, but especially at and after dawn and at dusk. It is delivered from regularly used song posts (often 100–250m apart) as the bird moves around its territory, typically with a long pause between each burst. The singing bird frequently sits upright with head thrown back and tail slightly lowered. Breeding males produce a nocturnal song, during which they give more frequent bursts from the same song post. They often begin this in the early morning hours, but revert to daytime song at dawn (D. T. Ireland in Cramp 1992).

BREEDING HABITS Some males are monogamous but the majority are polygynous. Of 125 territorial males in a study at Radipole, S England, just 22 were monogamous, while 70 were polygamous, the remainder remaining unmated or with status unknown (D. T. Ireland in Cramp 1992). Of the polygynous males, 42 attracted two females, 22 attracted three and six mated with four. The pair-bond is never strong, the male associating little with the female, yet the same bond is often renewed in successive years. Males take little or no part in nest building, incubation or raising the young. When the first female starts incubation, the male continues to attract additional females. Within the male's large territory, females appear to establish smaller, discrete breeding territories (Bibby 1982) and will defend these against other females mated with the same male (D. T. Ireland in Cramp 1992).

In W Europe, nest building begins in May. Eggs are laid from early June but mainly during mid to late June. The nest is built by the female alone, usually with the male in close attendance and singing frequently. It is placed in thick vegetation close to water, typically 0.3–0.45m above ground, usually supported by stems of reed *Phragmites* or nettle *Urtica*, or by smaller twigs of tangled scrub. It is an untidy construction of leaves and stems, lined with feathers, hair and other fine material, The usual clutch is 4–5 eggs. Incubation by the female lasts 16–17 days. Fledging takes a further 14–16 days, the young being fed by both parents. After fledging, males accompany females and young within the breeding territory for about 15–20 days until they disperse. Females are usually single-brooded. Some may raise a second brood but this tends to be less successful than the first.

The breeding behaviour of *orientalis* and *albiventris* is not known to differ from the nominate race. In Kazakhstan, *albiventris* begins singing on its return to breeding sites from late March onwards. Gavrilov & Gavrilov (2005) describe the nest of *albiventris* as built from grass and leaves and lined with thin grass and occasionally hair. A clutch of 4–5 eggs is laid in May to early June. Singing ceases in late July to mid August.

DISTRIBUTION Breeds throughout the warmer regions of W and S Europe to C Asia. Most in Europe and North Africa are resident or dispersive but those breeding in the colder regions of western and C Asia migrate to warmer regions outside the breeding season.

C. c. cetti The nominate race is largely resident in the lowlands of North Africa in Morocco, Algeria and Tunisia and throughout the northern Mediterranean from Portugal and Spain east through Italy and the Balkans to Greece. Warmer winters in NW Europe in the late twentieth century have enabled expansion into this formerly inhospitable region but it remains largely absent from the Black Sea coast, where freezing winter temperatures in Bulgaria and Romania prevent settlement in this otherwise suitable region. It is reported to breed in the Crimean region of Ukraine (Dement'ev & Gladkov 1954) but is said to be a summer visitor, arriving in the second half of April (see **Movements**).

The northern breeding limit in France during the nineteenth century lay in Pyrénées Atlantiques and Provence. Slow expansion to the north, west and

southeast began early in the twentieth century. It had reached Anjou by 1924 and the Loire basin by 1927. It accelerated in the mid 1950s through the low-lying marshy regions of NW France to reach northern Bretagne by 1960 and the English Channel coast in 1961 (Cramp 1992). It has subsequently continued into most suitable low-lying regions of southern, western and northern France. A secondary expansion through SE France reached Switzerland, where breeding occurred annually from 1975 to 1984.

Breeding was first established in Belgium in 1964 and in Germany in 1975, but the colder winters of northern continental Europe have prevented permanent colonisation. Birds reached the S Netherlands during the 1970s and numbers increased to a peak of approximately 60 singing males in 1977 (van den Berg & Bosman 1999). But they declined sharply after a severe winter in 1978 and although breeding continued to 1983, the species became rare, with just 49 records from the country from 1986 to 2001 (van der Vliet *et al.* 2002) and no subsequent sign of recolonisation. The first record from Jersey in the Channel Islands in October 1960 (Long 1961) was followed by three singing males in November 1967 (Long 1968), but breeding was not established until 1973.

Colonisation of S England followed a similar pattern, with the first record in Hampshire in March–April 1961, followed by another in East Sussex in October 1962. The first singing male was located in 1967, followed by a series of scattered singing birds from 1971 onwards and confirmed breeding in the Stour Valley in Kent, in 1973. A succession of mainly mild winters then allowed continued expansion, with only occasional setbacks, notably during 1978 and 1985/86. The population increased rapidly in England and S Wales in the early years of the twenty-first century, from nearly 700 pairs or singing males in 2000 (Ogilvie *et al.* 2002) to over 1,300 by 2005 (Holling *et al.* 2008). It is mostly concentrated within the warmer southern coastal counties, although East Anglia now holds a substantial population and the limit of regular breeding extends north to Anglesey in N Wales. Small numbers also occur in inland counties north to C England.

C. c. orientalis This larger paler form breeds in W Asia. The western limit lies in Turkey, but birds showing characters of *orientalis* breed in Lesvos, Greece, and apparent intergrades with the nominate form have been reported further west. The breeding range follows the southern coast of the Black Sea and extends into the lower slopes of the Caucasus Mountains in Azerbaijan, S Georgia and Armenia up to 1,900m. Only *orientalis* appears to breed in the Caucasus but it is unclear whether it extends north and east into S Russia or whether birds breeding along the Terek and Volga Rivers are *albiventris*, as stated by Dement'ev & Gladkov (1954). Gavrilov & Gavrilov (2005) include the entire Caspian region within the range of *orientalis* and extend its range east across N Kazakhstan through the Astana region to Rozhdestvenka (*c.* 77°E). South of the Caucasus and Caspian Sea, *orientalis* breeds in Cyprus, Syria, Lebanon and N Israel, then east through Jordan, Iraq and N Iran, and along the Amu Darya through southernmost Uzbekistan and neighbouring parts of Turkmenistan.

It appears that *orientalis* is either resident or a short-distance migrant within the Middle East, This is not surprising as the climate in this region is mild throughout the year and only birds breeding at higher elevations in the Taurus and Caucasus Mountains, and in N Kazakhstan and adjacent regions of Russia, vacate the breeding areas. Some descend to lower elevations while others migrate to winter in the Middle East. In Turkey, birds descend from the Taurus Mountains to winter in the south and west of the country and birds breeding in the Caucasus descend to the foothills by November, returning as the snow line recedes (Cramp 1992), although it is scarce, or overlooked, in Armenia during the winter months.

***C. c. albiventris* Breeding** As a breeding bird, this race occurs in Uzbekistan, S and E Kazakhstan and westernmost China. With the advent of irrigation in the twentieth century, it has spread into formerly unsuitable arid regions in C Asia, where it requires little more than a water-filled channel and a few overhanging bushes. The ranges of *orientalis* and *albiventris* now approach and may possibly overlap in Turkmenistan and Uzbekistan in the region of the Aral Sea and the Amu Darya.

Dement'ev & Gladkov (1954) extended the western limit of *albiventris* to include the Terek River where it enters the Caspian Sea and comment that it is common in the delta of the Volga River and along the Ural River to Orenburg and Orsk. Elsewhere, the breeding range of *albiventris* includes much of S and C Kazakhstan, from the northern end of the Aral Sea, along the length of the Syr Darya and into Uzbekistan, south to the region of Samarkand, where it is numerous in

wetlands surrounding the city and along tree-lined streams in the surrounding hills up to at least 1,550m. In Kazakhstan, it is particularly common in wetlands along the southern edge of Lake Balkash, in the Alakol Depression and along the Ili River, and is widespread around Almaty, including the lower slopes of the eastern Tien Shan. To the east and north, breeding extends to the Zaysan Depression, the region of Ust-Kamenogorsk and the foothills of the southern Altai.

In China it breeds in suitable wetlands in the extreme west of the Xinjiang Uygur Autonomous Region, along the southern foothills of the Tien Shan and in wetlands and along rivers in the Takla Makan Desert, including the Kashi region. It is common along the Ili River and in the foothills of the Altai Mountains.

Non-breeding This race is mainly migratory, but some southern breeders remain on or close to the breeding areas throughout the year. Small numbers regularly winter north to the upper Amu Darya and are more often noted in southernmost Kazakhstan, east to Almaty, now that milder winters have become more frequent (AG pers. comm., V. Kovshar pers. comm.). It winters widely in S Iran and S Afghanistan and is scarce and local from October onwards in the lowlands of Pakistan, where wintering is centred on Baluchistan and the North West Frontier Province, some birds reaching the Indus plain in the Punjab and Sind Province. It has been recorded as a vagrant in NW India, with scattered records south and east to Bharatpur in Rajasthan.

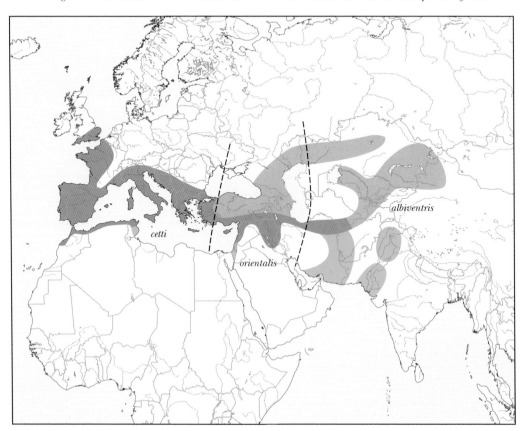

Cetti's Warbler. Breeding range and winter distribution.

MOVEMENTS The W European population is largely resident, but post-breeding dispersal occurs during September and early October, both north and south from the breeding areas. Birds are more widespread in the Mediterranean region during the winter months (Cramp 1992). There is limited evidence of migration along the Atlantic coast of France in late August and early September but no indication that European birds reach North Africa, where increased numbers wintering in the lowlands are believed to originate from local breeding populations in the Atlas Mountains (Cramp 1992).

Ringing recoveries in NW Europe show that northerly dispersal involves juvenile birds almost entirely, with reported movements from Belgium to the Netherlands and E England, and from the Channel Islands to S England. The occurrence of vagrants, for example at Cape Clear in S Ireland, over 600km northwest of the nearest breeding area, demonstrates that longer-distance dispersal is possible. Elsewhere in Europe, vagrants have been recorded from Scotland, Sweden and Poland.

The situation is less clear in SE Europe. Part of this population migrates to winter outside the breeding range, in particular in the Middle East. Passage occurs across the S Aegean Sea where the species is a regular prey item of Eleonora's Falcon. The origin of these birds is unknown since European birds are believed to be largely resident but they could be from the Black Sea, or from colder regions of Turkey. In Israel, dispersing birds appear from September onwards, but the main passage is in October and November, when migrants of both *orientalis* and the nominate race augment the local population. Wintering birds remain until late February. Return passage through Eilat shows two peaks, one in late February and early March, the second in late April and early May (Shirihai 1996), suggesting that two populations pass through. Two sight records of vagrants in Egypt are probably referable to *orientalis*. Small numbers showing the characters of *albiventris* have been trapped on migration and during winter in Israel, particularly at Eilat.

Little is known of movements within C Asia, where *albiventris* is almost entirely migratory. It leaves the Orenburg region in late August but some linger in the Volga delta until November. To the east, departure occurs between the end of September and late November. Migrants pass through the Syr Darya region from mid September with some still present to mid November, but all move when ice forms on the lakes.

The first birds return to breeding sites in mid March, when these are still under a covering of ice and snow, but southern breeders arrive in numbers by early April. Northern birds breeding near Orenburg (presumably *orientalis*) do not appear until mid May.

DESCRIPTION *C. c. cetti*

Plumage – Adult fresh Forehead to nape plain dark rufous-brown. Supercilium dull greyish white to ash-grey, quite short and narrow, appearing broadest and most contrasting between the bill base and the eye. It is less distinct behind the eye, tapering and merging with the side of the crown before the rear of the ear-coverts. Loral spot variable, usually restricted to a dark brown spot in front of the eye but sometimes extending to the bill base to form a complete loral line. A dull rufous-brown eye-line is well-defined immediately behind the eye but diffuses into the upper ear-coverts and rear of supercilium. Ear-coverts pale greyish white to ash-grey, with narrow rufous-brown tips creating indistinct mottling, especially towards the upper edges. Eye-ring narrow, greyish white above eye, merging with supercilium; whiter below the eye, usually contrasting slightly with the grey ear-coverts. Mantle and scapulars dark rufous-brown and unmarked, concolorous with crown. Rump and uppertail-coverts similar to mantle but usually slightly brighter. Tail dark brown with broad, diffuse rufous-brown fringes, slightly darker than the uppertail-coverts. Chin and throat white with a faint greyish wash. Sides of throat slightly greyer, merging with lower ear-coverts. Breast white, washed light brownish grey, becoming darker ash-grey towards the sides, often linked to a greyish half-collar on the lower sides of the neck. Upper flanks with a light brownish grey wash, darkening to dull sepia-brown on the lower flanks. Undertail-coverts dull, cold sepia-brown with narrow greyish white tips. Belly paler than breast and flanks, typically white with a pale greyish or creamy wash. Lesser, median and primary coverts dark rufous-brown, lacking darker centres. Greater coverts and tertials with broad, dark rufous-brown fringes, similar to the mantle colour. Secondaries and primaries blackish brown, narrowly edged dark rufous-brown. Primary tips dull rufous-brown, lacking contrast with the blackish brown webs. Alula with a broad, diffuse, dull rufous brown fringe and a slightly darker centre. Underwing-coverts light grey-brown.

Adult worn Similar to freshly moulted bird but individually variable. Supercilium sometimes reduced to a narrow, pale greyish line from the bill base, fading rapidly behind the eye. Upperparts slightly drabber, dull rufous-brown to dull greyish brown, particularly on the crown and nape; the more rufous rump and uppertail-coverts become slightly more contrasting. Chin, throat and belly usually whiter, and breast and flanks paler. Sepia-brown undertail-coverts may lose pale tips. Webs of rectrices and flight feathers browner.

First-winter As fresh adult but with slightly browner rectrices and flight feathers.

Juvenile Differs from fresh adult by more uniform appearance to head, which lacks distinct supercilium but shows conspicuous pale eye-ring. Upperparts often duller and slightly less rufous. Webs of rectrices and flight feathers dark brown, less blackish. Underparts slightly colder, more extensively washed ash-grey, and flanks often paler and browner, lacking grey tones..

Bare parts Upper mandible dark grey-brown to dull plumbeous-grey. Lower mandible dull pink to pinkish-yellow at base, becoming dark bluish grey towards tip. Tarsi pale pink, pinkish flesh or pinkish brown; toes sometimes slightly browner feet; soles dusky yellow to pale flesh. Iris dull sepia-brown to blackish brown in adults; dull grey-brown to dark brown in immature birds.

IN HAND CHARACTERS

Measurements

C. c. cetti

	Male	Female
Wing	58–66 (61.9; 54)	52–59 (54.6; 26)
Tail	54–63 (58.7; 50)	48–57 (51.4; 25)
Bill	13–15.5 (14.4; 51)	13–14.5 (13.6; 26)
Tarsus	20–23.5 (21.9; 45)	18.5–21 (19.7; 25)

(Ages combined. Includes data from Cramp 1992)

Bill width: ♂ 3.2–3.8 (3.5; 15), ♀ 3.0–3.4 (3.2; 8)
Hind claw: ♂ 6.2–7.2 (6.6; 14), ♀ 4.9–6.2 (5.6; 8)
Sexes combined:
Tail/wing ratio: 89–102% (95%; 27)
Tail graduation: 8–14 (10.3; 24)

C. c. orientalis: *wing*, ♂ 61–70 (64.4; 18), ♀ 58–59 (58.5; 4); *tail*, ♂ 57–64 (60.7; 16), ♀ 51–57 (54.5; 4); *bill*, ♂ 13–15 (14.4; 14), ♀ 13–14 (13.5; 4); *tarsus*, ♂ 21–24 (22.0; 13), ♀ 29–21 (20.5; 4). Larger than nominate *cetti*.

C. c. albiventris: *wing*, ♂ 65–72 (68.9; 16), ♀ 60–66 (63.5; 6); *tail*, ♂ 59–71 (66.7; 16), ♀ 59–65 (60.5; 4); *bill*, ♂ 15–16 (15.6; 14), ♀ 14–15 (14.7; 6); *tarsus*, ♂ 21–24 (22.8; 10), ♀ 20–22.5 (21.3; 6). The largest race.

Structure

C. c. cetti

Wing formula (Cramp 1992):

p1/pc	p2	p3e	p4e	p5e	p6(e)	p7	p10
9–12	6–12	0.5–3	wp	wp	0–2	1.5–4	5.5–9

Wing rounded with rather large p1 (*c.* 50% p2). Wing point p4–5 (6); p2 = ≤ p10, p3 = p6–7; emargination on p3–5, often slightly on p6, occasionally p7.

Figure 124. Wing of Cetti's Warbler *C. c. cetti*.

Tail graduated; ten rather broad rounded feathers.
Bill rather short, narrow and concave-sided, tip of culmen slightly decurved.
Tarsi and toes strong; claws short, fine, slightly decurved.

Other races: similar in structure to nominate *cetti*.

Recognition A stocky *Cettia* with rich, rufescent-brown upperparts, grey-tinged underparts and pinkish legs. Readily distinguished from all other European warblers by the rounded wing with large p1 and short p2, and by ten (not 12) rectrices.

Ageing In late summer, adults show worn primaries and tail feathers and are readily separable from juveniles in fresh, unworn plumage. In SW Europe, from September onwards, young birds are partially moulted and show a moult limit in the greater coverts between newer inner and older outer feathers and sometimes also a contrast between newer inner and older outer primaries. They are thus distinguishable from adults in which the entire plumage is freshly moulted.

In NW Europe, birds in wing moult in early autumn are adults. From mid August onwards, separation of moulted adults and juveniles becomes difficult. Adults show fresh darker flight feathers and tail feathers, the latter with broad tips. In young birds these are unmoulted and slightly browner and paler. The tail feathers are less broad than in adults, usually with slightly worn tips. These differences

are slight and only useful with experience, and some birds cannot be reliably aged. Palate colour appears to provide a useful character, being yellow in young birds and pale pink in adults. Otherwise skull ossification provides a reliable means of ageing until October at least.

Weight

C. c. cetti: ♂ usually 13–17g, ♀ 10–13g, with little overlap between sexes; in Camargue, France, ♂ 12.8–18.5g (15.2; 467), ♀ 8.5–14.5g (11.5; 873).

C. c. albiventris: ♂ 14.4–16.8g (15.4; 8), ♀ 11.8–13.0g (12.0; 5) (Cramp 1992); In SE Kazakhstan, unsexed 9.7–19.9g (14.1; 172) (AG unpublished data).

GEOGRAPHIC VARIATION Clinal, with smaller darker birds resident in W Europe and larger paler birds breeding in C Asia. There is considerable intergradation in the populations of E Europe and W Asia and racial boundaries are not well established. Only the most distinctive western and eastern birds are racially identifiable with certainty.

C. c. cetti (W and S Europe to the W Black Sea coasts; also NW Africa) Described above. The darkest and smallest form. Some birds from NW Africa and the Balearic Islands are almost as pale as *orientalis*, while others from the Balkans, Crete and Turkey resemble the nominate form but overlap with the larger *orientalis* on measurements (Cramp 1992).

C. c. orientalis (Crimea, S Russia, Turkey, Cyprus and the Levant to the Caucasus and NW Iran) Distinctly larger and paler than the nominate race, with a longer, paler and better marked supercilium that tapers and merges with the crown towards the rear of the ear-coverts. Entire upperparts, including crown, mantle, uppertail-coverts, tail, wing covert and tertial fringes warmer and paler rufous-brown than nominate, while chestnut-brown edges to primaries and secondaries create a warm panel in the closed wing that contrasts with the upperparts. Underparts paler than nominate with a white centre to the belly and lower breast and only a light greyish wash on the sides of the neck and breast and along flanks, becoming pale greyish brown towards the ventral region. Undertail-coverts pale grey-brown, the tips to the longest feathers being slightly broader and paler than in the nominate race.

C. c. albiventris (S Russia and C Asia east to W China) Slightly larger but strikingly paler than *orientalis*. Supercilium paler and greyer than in nominate race and usually distinct to the rear the of the ear-coverts. Upperparts, including edges to the closed wing feathers, light tan, paler than in *orientalis*, and lacking the darker rufous and chestnut tones; considerably paler than in the nominate race. Sides of neck and breast lightly washed pale grey, merging with the similarly coloured ear-coverts. Underparts cleaner and paler than the other races, with the chin, throat, breast, belly and flanks uniformly washed with a delicate pale grey. Ventral region pale brown, wrapping around from the uppertail-coverts. Undertail-coverts whitish with a faint brown tinge and broader (but less contrasting) white tips.

TAXONOMY AND SYSTEMATICS Birds breeding in W and C Turkey appear intermediate between the nominate form and *orientalis* and have been described as *sericea*. But differences from the nominate form appear slight, variable and inconsistent. Here we treat *sericea* as a synonym of *C. c. cetti*.

▲ Adult *C. c. cetti*, Tuscany, Italy, October. The darkest race. Often adopts characteristic posture with tail slightly raised, and wings spread across flanks revealing rounded structure (Daniele Occhiato).

▲ Adult *C. c. orientalis*, Armenia, May. Differs from nominate form by paler, less richly toned appearance. (Peter Kennerley).

▲ ▶ Juvenile *C. c. cetti*, Suffolk, England, July. Overall appearance drabber, more dingy than adult, with duller, greyer underparts that often show a slight creamy yellow tinge to centre of upper breast. Head is plainer with subdued supercilium which enhances whitish eye-ring (James Kennerley).

▲ ▶ Adult *C. c. albiventris*, Uzbekistan, June. Paler than *orientalis* with light tan edges to the primaries and secondaries contrasting with the greyish brown mantle. Supercilium and underparts whitish with delicate pale grey wash, paler than other races. Note whitish undertail-coverts, tinged pale brown. Bill appears unusually fine (Paul Leader).

APPENDIX 1

SOURCES OF ORIGINAL DESCRIPTIONS, TYPE LOCALITIES AND SYNONYMS

Many new forms were described and named as species by nineteenth and early twentieth century explorer-naturalists. Several different scientific names were sometimes given to what would eventually prove to be the same taxon. It was left to museum taxonomists to clear up this confusion, which they did with great vigour in the first half of the twentieth century. However, many good species were lost in the rush to subsume a proliferation of new taxa within the smallest number of species. Taxonomists, museum workers and field observers have since attempted to reverse some of the more glaring errors, but others doubtless still remain. We have attempted to bring some of the synonyms together here and hope this will help to clarify the confusing historical picture. Synonyms of current scientific names are indented in the list below and are in smaller font.

Locustellidae

Genus *Bradypterus*

Swainson, 1837. *Nat. Hist. Class Birds* 2: 241. *Bradypterus* in index, page 379.

Bradypterus baboecala (Vieillot, 1817)

Bradypterus baboecala baboecala
Sylvia baboecala Vieillot, 1817. *Nouv. Dict. Hist. Nat.* nouv. éd. 11: 172. Based upon 'La Caqueteuse' of Levaillant 1802, *Hist. Nat. Oiseaux Afrique* 3, page 61, plate 121, figure 1. Knysna district, Cape Province.

> *Bradypterus baboecala brachyptera*
> Sylvia brachyptera Vieillot, 1817. *Nouv. Dict. Hist. Nat.* nouv. éd. 11: 206. Based upon 'La Pavaneur' of Levaillant 1802, *Hist. Nat. Oiseaux Afrique* 3, page 65, plate 122, figures 1–2. Plettenberg Bay, Cape Province.

Bradypterus baboecala abyssinicus
Lusciniola abyssinica Blundell & Lovat, 1899. *Bull. Brit. Orn. Club* 10: 19. Chercher, Abyssinia.

Bradypterus baboecala centralis
Bradypterus brachypterus centralis Neumann, 1908. *Bull. Brit. Orn. Club* 21: 55. Between Mkingo (=Mukingo) and Muhera, Rwanda.

Bradypterus baboecala msiri
Bradypterus msiri Neave, 1909. *Bull. Brit. Orn. Club* 25: 25. Bunkeya River, Lufira valley, Katanga (=Shaba), Congo Free State.

> *Bradypterus baboecala bedfordi*
> Bradypterus bedfordi Ogilvie-Grant, 1912. *Ibis*, page 382. Mababe Flats, north of Lake Ngami, Bechuanaland. 2,900 feet.

Bradypterus baboecala elgonensis
Bradypterus elgonensis Madarász, 1912. *Orn. Monatsber.* 20: 175. Buchungu, Mount Elgon.

Bradypterus baboecala transvaalensis
Bradypterus transvaalensis Roberts, 1919. *Ann. Transvaal Mus.* 6: 116. Wakkerstroom, Transvaal.

Bradypterus baboecala benguellensis
Bradypterus brachypterus benguellensis Bannerman, 1927. *Bull. Brit. Orn. Club* 47: 147. Chicuma, Benguela, western Angola. 5,400 feet.

Bradypterus baboecala tongensis
Bradypterus brachypterus tongensis Roberts, 1931. *Ann. Transvaal Mus.* 14: 241. Kosi Bay, northern Zululand.

Bradypterus baboecala moreaui
Bradypterus brachypterus moreaui Sclater, 1931. *Bull. Brit. Orn. Club* 52: 57. Amani, Usambara district, Tanganyika. 3,000 feet.

Bradypterus baboecala chadensis
Bradypterus brachypterus chadensis Bannerman, 1936. *Bull. Brit. Orn. Club* 57: 43. Lake Chad.

Bradypterus baboecala sudanensis
Bradypterus baboecala sudanensis Grant & Mackworth-Praed, 1941. *Bull. Brit. Orn. Club* 61: 25. White Nile, southern Sudan.

Bradypterus carpalis Chapin, 1916

Bradypterus carpalis
Bradypterus carpalis Chapin, 1916. *Bull. Amer. Mus. Nat. Hist.* 35: 27, figure 4. Faradje, upper Uele district, Belgian Congo.

Bradypterus graueri Neumann, 1908

Bradypterus graueri
Bradypterus graueri Neumann, 1908. *Bull. Brit. Orn. Club* 21: 56. Western Kivu Volcanoes, Belgian Congo. 2,200 meters.

Bradypterus grandis Ogilvie-Grant, 1917

Bradypterus grandis
Bradypterus grandis Ogilvie-Grant, 1917. *Ibis*, page 78. Bitye, Ja (=Dja) River, southern Cameroon.

Bradypterus alfredi Hartlaub, 1890

Bradypterus alfredi alfredi
Bradypterus alfredi Hartlaub, 1890. *J. Ornithol.* 38: 152. Njangalo (=Nyangabo). Northeastern Congo Free State.

> *Bradypterus alfredi albicrissalis*
> Bradypterus alfredi albicrissalis Neumann, 1914. *Orn. Monatsber.* 22: 10. Mubuku valley, eastern Ruwenzori, Uganda.

Bradypterus alfredi kungwensis
Bradypterus alfredi kungwensis Moreau, 1942. *Bull. Brit. Orn. Club* 62: 42. Ujamba, Mount Kungwe (=Nkungwe), Tanganyika. 7,600 feet.

Bradypterus barratti Sharpe, 1876

Bradypterus barratti barratti
Bradypterus barratti Sharpe, 1876. *Ibis*, page 53.
Neighbourhood of Mac Mac goldfields, Lydenburg
district, Transvaal.

Bradypterus barratti godfreyi
Caffrillas barratti godfreyi Roberts, 1922. *Ann. Transvaal
Mus.* 8: 234. Pirie, Cape Province.

Bradypterus barratti wilsoni
Bradypterus (Caffrillas) barratti wilsoni Roberts, 1933. *Ann.
Transvaal Mus.* 15: 271. Kloof, Natal.

Bradypterus barratti priesti
Bradypterus (Caffrillas) barratti priesti Benson, 1946.
Ostrich 17: 197. Vumba, near Umtali, southern
Rhodesia. 5,500 feet.

Bradypterus barratti cathkinensis
Bradypterus barratti cathkinensis Vincent, 1948. *Bull.
Brit. Orn. Club* 69: 18. Near Cathkin Peak and the
Mahlabachaneng Pass, Giant's Castle Game Reserve,
Natal. 7,000 feet.

Bradypterus barratti major
Caffrillas barratti major Roberts, 1922. *Ann. Transvaal
Mus.* 8: 234. Wakkerstroom, Transvaal.

Bradypterus barratti lysis
Bradypterus barratti lysis Parker, 1962. *Bull. Brit. Orn. Club*
82: 122. New name for *Caffrillas barratti major* Roberts,
1922. Preoccupied by *Dumeticola major* Brooks, 1872.
Wakkerstroom, Transvaal.

Bradypterus sylvaticus Sundevall, 1860

Bradypterus sylvaticus sylvaticus
Bradypterus sylvaticus Sundevall, 1860. In: Grill, *Svenska
Vetenskaps-Akad.* Handlingar, Stockholm, ser. 2(10): 30.
Knysna.

Bradypterus sylvaticus pondoensis
Bradypterus pondoensis Haagner, 1909. *J. South African
Orn. Union* 5: 90. Port St Johns, 'West Pondoland'.

Bradypterus cinnamomeus (Rüppell, 1840)

Bradypterus cinnamomeus cinnamomeus
Sylvia (Salicaria) cinnamomea Rüppell, 1840. *Neue
Wirbelthiere Fauna Abyssinien, Vögel*, page 111, plate
42, figure 1. (labeled *Curruca (Sylvia) cinnamomea*.
Entschetqab, Semien Province, Abyssinia.

Bradypterus cinnamomeus rufoflavidus
Bradypterus rufoflavidus Reichenow & Neumann, 1895.
Orn. Monatsber. 3: 75. Kifinika Hut, Mount Kilimanjaro.
3,000 meters.

Bradypterus cinnamomeus salvadorii
Bradypterus salvadorii Neumann, 1900. *J. Ornithol.* 48: 304.
Gurui (=Mount Hanang), Tanganyika. 3,400 meters.

Bradypterus cinnamomeus pallidior
Bradypterus cinnamomeus pallidior Neumann, 1914. *Orn.
Monatsber.* 22: 10. Forest west of Baraka, Kivu, Belgian
Congo.

Bradypterus cinnamomeus chyuluensis
Bradypterus cinnamomeus chyuluensis van Someren, 1939.
J. East Africa Uganda Nat. Hist. Soc. 14: 92. Chyulu Range,
Kenya. 7,000 feet.

Bradypterus cinnamomeus macdonaldi
Sathrocercus cinnamomeus macdonaldi Grant & Mackworth-
Praed, 1941. *Bull. Brit. Orn. Club* 61: 26. Gumaro stream,
3 miles west of Gore, Wallaga area, western Abyssinia.

Bradypterus cinnamomeus nyassae
Bradypterus nyassae Shelley, 1893. *Ibis*, page 16. Mlanje
(=Lichenya) plateau, Nyasaland. 6,000 feet.

Bradypterus cinnamomeus mildbreadi
Bradypterus mildbreadi Reichenow, 1908. *Orn. Monatsber.*
16: 161. Ronssaro (=Ruwenzori), Kenya. 4,000 meters.

Bradypterus cinnamomeus cavei
Bradypterus cinnamomeus cavei Macdonald, 1939. *Bull.
Brit. Orn. Club* 60: 9. Kipia, Imatong Mountains, Sudan.
8,800 feet.

Bradypterus bangwaensis Delacour, 1943

Bradypterus bangwaensis
Bradypterus cinnamomeus bangwaensis Delacour, 1943. *Ibis*,
85: 39. New name for *Bradypterus casteneus* Reichenow,
1900, preoccupied by *Turdinus castaneus* Büttikofer,
1893. Bango Mountains and Bangwa, Cameroon.

Bradypterus bangwaensis castaneus
Bradypterus castaneus Reichenow, 1900. *Orn. Monatsber.* 8:
6. Bangwa, northwestern Cameroon.

Bradypterus lopezi (Alexander, 1903)

Bradypterus lopezi lopezi
Phlexis lopezi Alexander, 1903. *Bull. Brit. Orn. Club* 13: 48.
Moka, Fernando Po.

Bradypterus lopezi barakae
Bradypterus barakae Sharpe, 1906. *Ibis*, page 546. New
name for *Phlexis rufescens* Sharpe, 1902, preoccupied by
Bradypterus rufescens Sharpe & Bouvier, 1876. Ruwenzori
Mountains.

Bradypterus lopezi rufescens
Phlexis rufescens Sharpe, 1902. *Bull. Brit. Orn. Club* 13: 9.
Ruwenzori Mountains.

Bradypterus lopezi camerunensis
Bradypterus camerunensis Alexander, 1909. *Bull. Brit. Orn.
Club* 25: 19. Mount Cameroon. 7,000 feet.

Bradypterus lopezi youngi
Bradypterus mariae youngi Serle, 1949. *Bull. Brit. Orn. Club*
69: 54. Mount Cameroon. 5,400 feet.

Bradypterus lopezi mariae
Bradypterus mariae Madarász, 1905. *Annales Hist.-Nat.
Mus. Nat. Hungarici* 3: 401. Kibosho, Tanganyika.

Bradypterus lopezi fraterculus
Bradypterus babaeculus fraterculus Mearns, 1913. *Smithsonian
Misc. Coll.* 61(20): 3. Escarpment, Kenya. 7,390 feet.

Bradypterus lopezi sjöstedti
Bradypterus sjöstedti Neumann, 1914. *Orn. Monatsber.* 22:
9. Meru, Tanganyika.

Bradypterus lopezi altumi
Bradypterus altumi van Someren, 1919. *Bull. Brit. Orn.
Club* 40: 22. Molo forest, Kenya.

Bradypterus lopezi mitoni
Bradypterus altumi mitoni van Someren, 1931. *J. East Africa
Uganda Nat. Hist. Soc.* 37: 195. Lumi River, Taveta, Kenya.

Bradypterus lopezi usambarae
Bradypterus usambarae Reichenow, 1917. *J. Ornithol.* 65:
391. Usambara, Tanganyika.

Bradypterus lopezi roehli
Bradypterus roehli Grote, 1920. *Orn. Monatsber.* 28: 7.
Mlalo, near Wilhelmstal (=Lushoto), western Usambara,
Tanganyika.

Bradypterus lopezi granti
Bradypterus usambarae granti Benson, 1939. *Bull. Brit. Orn.
Club* 59: 110. Mount Mlanje, Lichenya plateau, Nyasaland.

Bradypterus lopezi ufipae
Sathrocercus cinnamomeus ufipae Grant & Mackworth-Praed, 1941. *Bull. Brit. Orn. Club* 62: 30. Mbisi (=Mbizi), Sumbawanga, Ufipa plateau, southwestern Tanganyika. 8,000 feet.

Bradypterus lopezi boultoni
Bradypterus mariae boultoni Chapin, 1948. *Ann. Carnegie Mus.* 31: 1. Northwestern Mombolo highland, western Angola. 5,000 feet.

Bradypterus lopezi manengubae
Bradypterus mariae manengubae Searle, 1949. *Bull Brit. Orn. Club* 69: 55. Manenguba. 6,500 feet.

Bradypterus thoracicus (Blyth, 1845)

Bradypterus thoracicus thoracicus
Dumeticola thoracica Blyth, 1845. *J. Asiatic Soc. Bengal* 14: 584. Nepal.

> **Bradypterus thoracicus saturata**
> Tribura thoracica saturata Yen, 1933. *Orn. Monatsber.* 41: 16. Yao Shan, Kwangsi, China.

Bradypterus thoracicus przevalskii
Dumeticola thoracica przevalskii Sushkin, 1925. *Proc. Boston Soc. Nat. Hist.* 38(1): 41. Dshachar mountains, upper Hwang Ho, eastern Tsinghai, China.

Bradypterus thoracicus kashmirensis
Dumeticola thoracica kashmirensis Sushkin, 1925. *Proc. Boston Soc. Nat. Hist.* 38(1): 42. Northwestern Himalaya.

Bradypterus davidi (La Touche, 1923)

Bradypterus davidi davidi
Tribura thoracica davidi La Touche, 1923. *Bull. Brit. Orn. Club* 43: 168. Chinwangtao, northeastern Chihli, China.

Bradypterus davidi suschkini
Dumeticola thoracica suschkini Stegmann, 1929. *J. Ornithol.* 77: 249. Source of the Manyk, affluent of the Lebed, northeastern Altai.

> **Bradypterus davidi shanensis**
> Tribura thoracica shanensis Ticehurst, 1941. *Ibis*, page 318. Maymyo, upper Burma.

Bradypterus major (Brooks, 1871)

Bradypterus major major
Dumeticola major Brooks, 1871. *J. Asiatic Soc. Bengal* 41(2): 77. Kashmir

Bradypterus major innae
Tribura major innae Portenko 1955, *Trudy Zool. Inst. Akad. Nauk, SSSR* 18: 504. Achang, northern slope, Russian Range, Astin Tagh, (Kun Lun). Sinkiang.

Bradypterus tacsanowskius (Swinhoe, 1871)

Bradypterus tacsanowskius
Locustella tacsanowskia Swinhoe, 1871. *Proc. Zool. Soc. London*, page 355. Transbaikalia.

> **Bradypterus tacsanowskius netrix**
> Tribura major netrix Stresemann, 1931. *Orn. Monatsber.* 39: 105. Yŭo-schŭi-tsuăn, Sining, eastern Tsinghai, China.

> **Bradypterus tacsanowskius chui**
> Tribura tacsanowskia chui Yen, 1933. *Orn. Monatsber.* 41: 15. Yao Shan, Kwangsi, China.

Bradypterus luteoventris (Hodgson, 1845)

Bradypterus luteoventris
Tribura luteoventris Hodgson, 1845. *Proc. Zool. Soc. London*, page 30. Nepal.

Bradypterus luteoventris ticehursti
Bradypterus luteoventris ticehursti Deignan, 1943. *Proc. Biol. Soc. Washington* 56: 71. Northern Siam.

Bradypterus luteoventris saturatus
Tribura luteoventris saturatus Ticehurst, 1941. *Ibis*, page 318. Thayetmyo-Minbu border, southern Chin Hills, Burma. 5,000 feet.

Bradypterus mandelli (Brooks, 1875)

Bradypterus mandelli mandelli
Dumeticola mandelli Brooks, 1875. *Stray Feathers* 3(4): 284–287. Sikkim.

Bradypterus mandelli melanorhynchus
Lusciniola melanorhyncha Rickett, 1898. *Bull. Brit. Orn. Club* 8: 10. Kuatun, northwestern Fohkien, China.

Bradypterus mandelli idoneus
Tribura idonea Riley, 1940. *Proc. Biol. Soc. Washington* 53: 48. Camly, west of Dalat, southern Annam, Vietnam.

Bradypterus montis (Hartert, 1896)

Bradypterus montis
Stasiasticus montis Hartert, 1896. *Novit. Zool.* 3: 540. Mount Arjuno, eastern Java.

Bradypterus timorensis Mayr, 1944

Bradypterus timorensis
Bradypterus montis timorensis Mayr, 1944. The birds of Timor and Sumba. *Bull. Amer. Mus. Nat. Hist.* 83(2): 158. Mount Mutis, western Timor.

Bradypterus seebohmi (Ogilvie-Grant, 1895)

Bradypterus seebohmi
Lusciniola seebohmi Ogilvie-Grant, 1895. *Bull. Brit. Orn. Club* 4: 40. Lepanto Mountains, northern Luzon, Philippines.

Bradypterus alishanensis Rasmussen, Round, Dickinson & Rozendaal, 2000

Bradypterus alishanensis
Bradyptereus alishanensis Rasmussen, Round, Dickinson & Rozendaal, 2000. *Auk* 117(2): 279–289. Taiwan.

Bradypterus caudatus (Ogilvie-Grant, 1895)

Bradypterus caudatus caudatus
Pseudotharrhaleus caudatus Ogilvie-Grant, 1895. *Bull. Brit. Orn. Club* 4: 40. Lepanto Mountains, northern Luzon, Philippines.

Bradypterus caudatus unicolor
Pseudotharrhaleus unicolor Hartert, 1904. *Bull. Brit. Orn. Club* 14: 74. Mount Apo, south Mindanao, Philippines.

Bradypterus caudatus malindangensis
Pseudotharrhaleus malindangensis Mearns, 1909. *Proc. U.S. Nat. Mus.* 36: 441. Mount Malindang, Mindanao, Philippines.

Bradypterus accentor (Sharpe, 1888)

Bradypterus accentor
Androphilus accentor Sharpe, 1888. *Ibis*, page 390, plate 9, figure 2. Mount Kinabalu, Sabah, Borneo.

Bradypterus castaneus (Büttikofer, 1893)

Bradypterus castaneus castaneus
Turdinus castaneus Büttikofer, 1893. *Notes Leyden Mus.* 15: 260–261. Minahassa, northern Celebes.

> **Bradypterus castaneus everetti**
> Androphilus everetti Hartert, 1896. *Novit. Zool.* 3: 69. Bonthain Peak, southern Celebes.

Bradypterus castaneus disturbans
Androphilus disturbans Hartert, 1900. *Novit. Zool.* 7: 238.
Mount Mada, Buru, southern Moluccas.

Bradypterus castaneus musculus
Androphilus disturbans musculus Stresemann, 1914. *Novit.*
Zool. 21: 136, plate 4, figure 3. Mount Pinaia, central
Ceram, southern Moluccas.

Genus *Elaphrornis*
Legge, 1879. *Birds of Ceylon*, page 514.

Elaphrornis palliseri (Blyth, 1851)
Elaphrornis palliseri
Brachypteryx palliseri Blyth, 1851. *J. Asiatic Soc. Bengal* 20:
178. Ceylon. Above 3,500 feet.

Genus *Locustella*
Kaup, 1829. *Skizzirte Entwickelungs-Geschichte Europäisch.* **Thierwelt, page 115.**

Locustella luscinioides (Savi, 1824)
Locustella luscinioides luscinioides
Sylvia Luscinioides Savi, 1824. *Nuovo Giornale de'Letterati*
7(14): 341. Pisa.

Locustella luscinioides fusca
Cettia fusca Severtsov, 1873. *Izvestiia Imp. Obshchestva*
Liubitelei Estest. Antrop. Etnogr., Moscow 8(2) 1872: 131.
Arys', Chimkent, southern Kazakhstan.

Locustella luscinioides sarmatica
Locustella luscinioides sarmatica Kazakov, 1973. *Zool.*
Zhurnal 52: 616. Lower course of the River Don, Rostov-
on-Don.

Locustella fluviatilis (Wolf, 1810)
Locustella fluviatilis
Sylvia fluviatilis Wolf, 1810. In: Meyer & Wolf,
Taschenbuch Deutschen Vögelkunde 1: 229. Danube,
Austria.

Locustella fluviatilis obscura
Locustella fluviatilis obscura Tschusi, 1912. *Ornith. Jahrb.*
23: 216. Liman b. Bosn. Gradiska.

Locustella naevia (Boddaert, 1783)
Locustella naevia naevia
Motacilla naevia Boddaert, 1783. *Table Planches Enlum,*
page 35. (Based upon Brisson, 1760, *Ornith.* 3: 389–390
and *La Fauvette tachetée* of Daubenton 1765–81, *Planches*
Enlum., plate 581, figure 3). Bologna, Italy.

Locustella naevia straminea
Locustella straminea Seebohm, 1881. *Cat. Birds Brit. Mus.*
5: 117, ex *Acridiornis straminea*, Severtsov, 1873, *Izvestiia*
Imp. Obshchestva Liubitelei Estest. Antrop. Etnogr., Moscow,
8(2): 66, *nomen nudum.* Etawah, India.

Locustella naevia mongolica
Locustella naevia mongolica Sushkin, 1925. *Proc. Boston*
Soc. Nat. Hist. 38(1): 48. Temir-su River, near Zaïsansk,
eastern Kazakhstan.

Locustella naevia obscurior
Locustella naevia obscurior Buturlin, 1929. *Sistem. Zametki*
Ptitzah Sever. Kavkaza, page 22. Mikhailovskaia Colony,
northern Caucasus.

Locustella lanceolata (Temminck, 1840)
Locustella lanceolata lanceolata
Sylvia lanceolata Temminck, 1840. *Man. Ornith.*, ed. 2(4):
614, 'Mayence,' error for Russia.

Locustella lanceolata minuta
Locustella minuta Swinhoe, 1863. *Proc. Zool. Soc. London,*
page 93–94. Amoy, China.
Locustella lanceolata subsignata
Locustella subsignata Hume, 1873. *Stray Feathers*, pages
409–410. Port Blair, Andaman Islands.

Locustella lanceolata hendersonii
Locustella lanceolata hendersonii Cassin, 1858. *Proc. Acad.*
Nat. Sci. Philadelphia 10: 191–196. Hakodadi, Island of
Jesso, Japan.
Locustella lanceolata macropus
Locustella macropus Swinhoe, 1863. *Proc. Zool. Soc. London*
page 93. Amoy, China.
Locustella lanceolata gigantea
Locustella lanceolata gigantea Johansen, 1954. *J. Ornithol.*
95: 92. Shaweishan island, eastern China.

Locustella certhiola (Pallas, 1811)
Locustella certhiola certhiola
Motacilla Certhiola Pallas, 1811. *Zoographia Rosso-Asiat.* 1:
509, '*in regionem ultra Baicalem*' [mountainous region
between Onon and Borzya in eastern Transbaikalia],
fide Meise, 1934, *Abh. Ber. Mus. Tierkunde Völkerkunde*
Dresden, 18(2): 39.

Locustella certhiola rubescens
Locustella rubescens Blyth, 1845. *J. Asiatic Soc. Bengal* 14:
582. Calcutta.

Locustella certhiola minor
Locustella minor David & Oustalet, 1877. *Oiseaux de la*
Chine, page 250. Peking.

Locustella certhiola centralasiae
Locustella certhiola centralasiae Sushkin, 1925. *Proc. Boston*
Soc. Nat. Hist. 38(1): 46. Kara-ussu, Hangai Mountains,
northwestern Mongolia.

Locustella certhiola sparsimstriata
Locustella certhiola sparsimstriata Meise, 1934. *Abh. Ber.*
Mus. Tierkunde Völkerkunde Dresden 18(2): 39. Bjelowa,
Kemerovskaya region, western Siberia.

Locustella ochotensis (Middendorff, 1853)
Locustella ochotensis ochotensis
Sylvia (*Locustella*) *Ochotensis* Middendorff, 1853. *Reise*
Sibiriens 2(2): 185–186, plate 16, figures 7–8. Udskoe
Ostrog, lower Uda River, Udskaya Gulf, Okhotsk Sea.

Locustella ochotensis japonica
Lusciniopsis japonica Cassin, 1858. *Proc. Acad. Science Philadelphia*, pages 191–196. Hakodadi, Islands of Jesso, Japan.

Locustella ochotensis subcerthiola
Locustella subcerthiola Swinhoe, 1874. *Ibis*, page 154. Hakodadi (= Hakodate), Japan, and Kamtschatka. Restricted to Kamchatka by Dickinson *et al.*, 2001, *Zool. Verhand* 335: 225–226. Syntype: BMNH 1898.9.1.1323 male collected about 1843 by I. G. Voznesenskiy [ex Seebohm Coll.].

> **Locustella ochotensis blakistoni**
> *Arundinax blakistoni* Swinhoe, 1876. *Ibis*, page 332. Hakodadi, northern Japan.

Locustella pleskei **Taczanowski, 1890**

Locustella pleskei
Locustella pleskei Taczanowski, 1889. *Proc. Zool. Soc. London*, page 620. Tchimulpa, Korea.

Locustella pleskei styani
Locustella styani La Touche, 1905. *Bull. Brit. Orn. Club* 16: 21. Foochow and Swatow.

Locustella fasciolata (Gray, 1861)

Locustella fasciolata fasciolata
Acrocephalus fasciolatus Gray, 1861. *Proc. Zool. Soc. London*, page 349. Batchian, Moluccas.

Locustella fasciolata amnicola
Locustella amnicola Stepanyan, 1972. *Zool. Zh.* 51(3): 1896–1897. Sakhalin, southern Kuril Islands and Hokkaido.

Locustella pryeri (Seebohm, 1884)

Locustella pryeri pryeri
Megalurus pryeri Seebohm, 1884. *Ibis*, page 40. Tokio, not very far from Yokohama.

Locustella pryeri sinensis
Lusciniola pryeri sinensis Witherby, 1912. *Bull. Brit. Orn. Club* 31: 11. Hankow.

Acrocephalidae

Genus *Acrocephalus*

Naumann & Naumann, 1811. *Naturge-schichte Land-Wasser-Vögel Nördlichen Deutschlands*, **Nachtrag, page 199.**

Acrocephalus melanopogon (Temminck, 1823)

Acrocephalus melanopogon melanopogon
Sylvia melanopogon Temminck, 1823. In: Temminck & Laugier, *Planches Color, livr.* 41, plate 245, figure. 2. 'campagnes prés de Rome'.

Acrocephalus melanopogon mimicus
Lusciniola mimica Madarász, 1903. *Vorläufiges Neuen Rohrsänger*, page 3. Tedzhen, Transcaspia and eastern Persia.

Acrocephalus melanopogon albiventris
Lusciniola melanopogon albiventris Kazakov, 1974. *Vestnik Zool.* 2: 16. Lower Chelbas River, near Kanevskaya, Krasnodar region, Sea of Azov.

Acrocephalus schoenobaenus (Linnaeus, 1758)

Acrocephalus schoenobaenus
Motacilla Schoenobaenus Linnaeus, 1758. *Syst. Nat.*, *ed.* 10: 184. Southern Sweden.

Acrocephalus paludicola (Vieillot, 1817)

Acrocephalus paludicola
Sylvia paludicola Vieillot, 1817. *Nouv. Dict. d'Hist. Nat., nouv. éd.*, 11: 202. Lorraine and Picardy.

Acrocephalus sorghophilus (Swinhoe, 1863)

Acrocephalus sorghophilus
Calamodyta sorghophila Swinhoe, 1863. *Proc. Zool. Soc. London* page 92. Amoy, Fohkien, China.

Acrocephalus bistrigiceps **Swinhoe, 1860**

Acrocephalus bistrigiceps
Acrocephalus bistrigiceps Swinhoe, 1860. *Ibis* page 51. Amoy, Fohkien, China.

Acrocephalus tangorum **La Touche, 1912**

Acrocephalus tangorum
Acrocephalus tangorum La Touche, 1912. *Bull. Brit. Orn. Club* 31: 10. Chinwangtao, northeastern Chihli, China.

Acrocephalus concinens (Swinhoe, 1870)

Acrocephalus concinens concinens
Calamoherpe concinens Swinhoe, 1870. *Proc. Zool. Soc. London* page 432. Peking.

Acrocephalus concinens haringtoni
Acrocephalus agricola haringtoni Witherby, 1920. *Bull. Brit. Orn. Club* 41: 26. Buttakundi, Kagan valley, Hazara district, Pakistan.

> **Acrocephalus concinens hokrae**
> *Acrocephalus concinens hokrae* Whistler, 1930. *Bull. Brit. Orn. Club* 50: 71–72. Hokra jheel, Kashmir. 5,000 feet.

Acrocephalus concinens stevensi
Acrocephalus concinens stevensi Stuart Baker, 1922. *Bull. Brit. Orn. Club* 43: 16. Hessamara, northern Lakhimpur, eastern Assam.

Acrocephalus agricola (Jerdon, 1845)

Acrocephalus agricola agricola
Sylvia (acrocephalus) agricola Jerdon, 1845, *Madras J. Lit. Sci.* 13(2): 131. Neighbourhood of Nellore, Madras.

> **Acrocephalus agricola capistrata**
> *Salicaria capistrata* Severtsov, 1872. *Izvestiia Imp. Obshchestva Liubitelei Estest. Antrop. Etnogr.* Moscow 8(2), page 127. Turkestan.

> **Acrocephalus agricola brevipennis**
> *Salicaria brevipennis* Severtsov, 1872. *Izvestiia Imp. Obshchestva Liubitelei Estest. Antrop. Etnogr.* Moscow 8(2), page 127. Karatau Mountains and western foothills of the Tien Shan.

Acrocephalus agricola septimus
Acrocephalus agricola septima Gavrilenko, 1954. *Nauk Zap. Poltavsk. Derzhav. Pedagog. Inst.* 7: 53. 'Magna Palus' in Parva Perestshepina, Poltava region.

Acrocephalus dumetorum **Blyth, 1849**

Acrocephalus dumetorum
Acrocephalus dumetorum Blyth, 1849. *J. Asiatic Soc. Bengal* 18: 815. India.

Acrocephalus dumetorum turanicus
Acrocephalus dumetorum turanicus Zarudnyi, 1911. *J. Ornithol.* p238. Tedzhen.

Acrocephalus orinus Hume, 1871

Acrocephalus orinus
Acrocephalus orinus Oberholser, 1905. *Proc. U.S. Nat. Mus.*, 28, p 899. Near Rampur, Sutlej Valley, Punjab Himalayas.

Acrocephalus macrorhynchus
Acrocephalus macrorhynchus Hume, 1871. *Ibis*, p 31. Not far from Rampoor, Sutlej valley, Himachal Pradesh, India.

Acrocephalus palustris (Bechstein, 1798)

Acrocephalus palustris
Motacilla s. Sylvia palustris Bechstein, 1798. In: Latham's *Allgemeine Uebersicht der Vögel* 3: 545. Germany.

Acrocephalus palustris laricus
Acrocephalus palustris laricus Portenko, 1955. *Trudy Zool. Inst. Akad. Nauk, SSSR.* 18: 504. Demavend, northern Iran.

Acrocephalus scirpaceus (Hermann, 1804)

Acrocephalus scirpaceus scirpaceus
Turdus scirpaceus Hermann, 1804. *Observ. Zool.* page 202. Alsace.

Acrocephalus scirpaceus fuscus
Curruca fusca Hemprich & Ehrenberg, 1833. *Symb. Phys. Avium Decas I, fol. cc.* Northern Arabia.

Acrocephalus scirpaceus avicenniae
Acrocephalus baeticatus avicenniae Ash, Pearson, Nikolaus & Colston, 1989. *Bull. Brit. Orn. Club* 109: 36–43. Coastal Sudan, Eritrea and northwest Somalia.

Acrocephalus baeticatus (Vieillot, 1817)

Acrocephalus baeticatus baeticatus
Sylvia baeticatus Vieillot, 1817. *Nouv. Dict. Hist. Nat.*, nouv. éd. 11: 195; based on 'L'Isabelle' of Levaillant, 1802, *Hist.Nat. Oiseaux Afrique* 3: 63, plate 121, figure 2. Knysna district, Cape Province.

Acrocephalus baeticatus cinnamomeus
Acrocephalus cinnamomeus Reichenow, 1908. *Orn. Monatsber.* 16: 161. North shore of Lake Albert Edward (= Lake Edward).

Acrocephalus baeticatus minor
Acrocephalus boeticatus minor Lynes, 1923. *Bull. Brit. Orn. Club* 43: 96. Zalingei, Darfur, Sudan. 3,000 feet.

Acrocephalus baeticatus nyong
Acrocephalus baeticatus nyong Bannerman, 1936. *Bull. Brit. Orn. Club* 57: 9. Akonolinga, Nyong River, Cameroon.

Acrocephalus baeticatus hopsoni
Acrocephalus baeticatus hopsoni Fry, Williamson & Ferguson-Lees, 1974. *Ibis* 116: 340–346. Malamfatori, Lake Chad, Nigeria.

Acrocephalus baeticatus fraterculus
Acrocephalus cinnamomeus fraterculus Clancey, 1975. *Arnoldia* (*Rhodesia*) 7(20): 12. Bela Vista, Maputo, Rhodesia.

Acrocephalus baeticatus suahelicus
Acrocephalus baeticatus suahelicus Grote, 1926. *Orn. Monatsber.* 34: 145. Zanzibar.

Acrocephalus baeticatus hallae
Acrocephalus boeticatus hallae White, 1960. *Bull. Brit. Orn. Club* 80: 21. Brandberg, southwest Africa.

Acrocephalus baeticatus guiersi
Acrocephalus baeticatus guiersi Colston & Morel, 1984.

Bull. Brit. Orn. Club 104: 4. Lake Guiers, near Richard Toll, Senegal.

Acrocephalus brevipennis (Keulemans, 1866)

Acrocephalus brevipennis
Calamodyta brevipennis Keulemans, 1866. *Nederlandsch. Tijdschrift. Dierkunde* 3: 368. São Nicolau, Brava, São Tiago, Cape Verde Islands.

Acrocephalus gracilirostris (Hartlaub, 1864)

Acrocephalus gracilirostris gracilirostris
Calamoherpe gracilirostris Hartlaub, 1864. In: Gurney, *Ibis*, page 348. Natal.

Acrocephalus gracilirostris leptorhynchus
Turdirostris leptorhyncha Reichenow, 1879. *Ornith. Centralblatt* 4: 155. Tschara, mouth of the Tana River, Kenya.

Acrocephalus gracilirostris zuluensis
Calamocichla zuluensis Neumann, 1908. *Bull. Brit. Orn. Club* 21: 96. Eshowe, Zululand, Natal.

Acrocephalus gracilirostris palustris
Calamocichla palustris Reichenow, 1917. *J. Ornithol.* 65: 391. Ndjiri Swamp, Masailand, Tanganyika. (Preoccupied by *Sylvia palustris* Bechstein, 1803)

Acrocephalus gracilirostris parvus
Phyllostrephus parvus Fischer & Reichenow, 1884. *J. Ornithol.* 32: 262. Murentat, near Lake Naivasha, Kenya.

Acrocephalus gracilirostris macrorhynchus
Bradypterus macrorhynchus Jackson, 1910. *Bull. Brit. Orn. Club* 27: 8. Polosat, Laikipia, Kenya. 7,500 feet.

Acrocephalus gracilirostris jacksoni
Calamocichla jacksoni Neumann, 1901. *Orn. Monatsber.* 9: 185. Entebbe, Uganda.

Acrocephalus gracilirostris nuerensis
Calamocichla leptorhyncha nuerensis Lynes, 1914. *Bull. Brit. Orn. Club* 33: 130. Upper White Nile, Sudan, between Lake No and the Sobat River.

Acrocephalus gracilirostris cunenensis
Calamocichla cunenensis Hartert, 1903. *Bull. Brit. Orn. Club* 13: 62. Cunene river, southern Angola.

Acrocephalus gracilirostris neglectus
Calamocichla neglecta Alexander, 1908. *Bull. Brit. Orn. Club* 23: 33. Lake Chad.

Acrocephalus gracilirostris tsanae
Calamoecetor leptorhyncha tsanae Bannerman, 1937. *Bull. Brit. Orn. Club* 57: 71. Achera Mariam, north shore of Lake Tsana (=Tana), Abyssinia. 6,000 feet.

Acrocephalus gracilirostris winterbottomi
Calamaecetor leptorhyncha winterbottomi White, 1947. *Bull. Brit. Orn. Club* 68: 34. Manyinga River, Macondo district, Angola.

Acrocephalus rufescens (Sharpe & Bouvier, 1876)

Acrocephalus rufescens rufescens
Bradypterus rufescens Sharpe & Bouvier, 1876. *Bull. Soc. Zool. France* 1: 307. Landana, Cabinda.

Acrocephalus rufescens plebeius
Calamocichla plebeja Reichenow, 1893. *Orn. Monastber.* 1: 178. Jaunde (=Yaounde), Cameroon.

Acrocephalus rufescens poensis
Calamocichla poensis Alexander, 1903. *Bull. Brit. Orn. Club* 13: 37. Bilelipi, Fernando Po.

Acrocephalus rufescens ansorgei
Calamocichla ansorgei Hartert, 1906. *Bull. Brit. Orn. Club*

16: 52. Duque de Braganza, northern Angola.

Acrocephalus rufescens niloticus
Calamocichla ansorgei nilotica Neumann, 1908. *Novit. Zool.* 15: 246. Wadelai, northwestern Uganda.

Acrocephalus rufescens foxi
Calamocichla foxi Sclater, 1927. *Bull. Brit. Orn. Club* 47: 118. Lake Maraye, Kigezi district, southwestern Uganda.

Acrocephalus rufescens chadensis
Calamocichla chadensis Alexander, 1907. *Bull. Brit. Orn. Club* 19: 63. Wunnda, Lake Chad.

Acrocephalus rufescens senegalensis
Acrocephalus rufescens senegalensis Colston & Morel, 1985. *Bull. Brit. Orn. Club* 104: 3–5. Senegal.

Acrocephalus newtoni (Hartlaub, 1863)

Acrocephalus newtoni
Calamoherpe newtoni Hartlaub, 1863. *Proc. Zool. Soc. London*, page 165. Near Soamandrikazay, Madagascar.

Acrocephalus sechellensis (Oustalet, 1877)

Acrocephalus sechellensis
Ellisia sechellensis Oustalet, 1877. *Bull. Soc. Philomath. Paris*, sér. 7(1): 103. Marianne Island, Seychelles.

Acrocephalus rodericanus (Newton, 1865)

Acrocephalus rodericanus
Drymoeca rodericana Newton, 1865. *Proc. Zool. Soc. London*, page 47, Plate 1, figure 3. Rodrigues Island.

Acrocephalus griseldis (Hartlaub, 1891)

Acrocephalus griseldis
Calamoherpe griseldis Hartlaub, 1891. *Abhandl. Naturwissen. Vereine Bremen*, 12 (1893): 7. Nguru, Kilosa district, Tanganyika Territory.

Acrocephalus griseldis babylonicus
Acrocephalus babylonicus Ticehurst, 1920. *Bull. Brit. Orn. Club* 41: 12–13. Basra, lower Mesopotamia.

Acrocephalus arundinaceus (Linnaeus, 1758)

Acrocephalus arundinaceus arundinaceus
Turdus arundinaceus Linnaeus, 1758. *Syst. Nat.* ed. 10: 170. Danzig.

Acrocephalus arundinaceus zarudnyi
Acrocephalus arundinaceus zarudnyi Hartert, 1907. *Bull. Brit. Orn. Club* 21: 26. Djarkent, Turkistan.

Acrocephalus orientalis (Temminck & Schlegel, 1847)

Acrocephalus orientalis
Salicaria turdina orientalis Temminck & Schlegel, 1847. In: Siebold, *Fauna Japonica, Aves*, page 50, plate 20. Japan.

Acrocephalus orientalis magnirostris
Acrocephalus magnirostris Swinhoe, 1860. *Ibis* page 51. Amoy in winter, Shanghai in summer.

Acrocephalus orientalis melvillensis
Acrocephalus australis melvillensis Mathews, 1912. *Austral Avian Rec.* 1: 77. Melville Island, Northern Territory, Australia.

Acrocephalus stentoreus (Hemprich & Ehrenberg, 1833)

Acrocephalus stentoreus stentoreus
Curruca stentorea Hemprich & Ehrenberg, 1833. *Symb. Phys. Avium Decas I, fol. bb.* Damietta, lower Egypt.

Acrocephalus stentoreus brunnescens
Agrobates brunnescens Jerdon, 1839. *Madras J. Lit. Sci.* 10: 269. Carnatic, near Trichinopoly.

Acrocephalus stentoreus meridionalis
Calamodyta meridionalis Legge, 1875. *Stray Feathers* 3: 369. Jaffna, Ceylon.

Acrocephalus stentoreus celebensis
Acrocephalus celebensis Heinroth, 1903. *J. Ornithol.* 51: 125. Makasar, Celebes.

Acrocephalus stentoreus amyae
Acrocephalus stentoreus amyae Stuart Baker, 1922. *Bull. Brit. Orn. Club* 43: 17. Hessamara, northern Lakhimpur, eastern Assam.

Acrocephalus stentoreus lentecaptus
Acrocephalus stentoreus lentecaptus Hartert, 1924. *Treubia* 6: 21. Ampenan, northern Lombok.

Acrocephalus stentoreus sumbae
Acrocephalus stentoreus sumbae Hartert, 1924. *Treubia* 6: 21. Nangamesi Bay, Waingapu, Sumba.

Acrocephalus stentoreus toxopei
Acrocephalus stentoreus toxopei Hartert, 1924. *Treubia* 6: 20. Kayeli, Buru.

Acrocephalus stentoreus meyeri
Acrocephalus meyeri Stresemann, 1924. *Orn. Monatsber.* 32: 168. Toriu River, Gazelle Peninsula, New Britain.

Acrocephalus stentoreus cervinus
Acrocephalus cervinus De Vis, 1897. *Ibis* Series 7(11): 386. Boirave, Orangerie Bay, southeastern New Guinea.

Acrocephalus stentoreus siebersi
Acrocephalus stentoreus siebersi Salomonsen, 1928. *Orn. Monatsber.* 36: 119. Tjibaroesa, western Java.

Acrocephalus stentoreus harterti
Acrocephalus stentoreus harterti Salomonsen, 1928. *Orn. Monatsber.* 36: 119. Laguna de Bay, Luzon, Philippines.

Acrocephalus stentoreus levantinus
Acrocephalus stentoreus levantina Roselaar, 1994. *Dutch Birding* 16: 237–239. Northern Israel.

Acrocephalus australis (Gould 1838)

Acrocephalus australis australis
Calamoherpe australis Gould 1838. In: Lewin, *Nat. Hist. Birds New South Wales.* Parramatta, New South Wales, Australia.

Acrocephalus australis mellori
Acrocephalus australis mellori Mathews, 1912. *Novit. Zool.* 18: 342. Mannam, South Australia.

Acrocephalus australis inexpectatus
Acrocephalus australis inexpectatus Mathews, 1912. *Austral Avian Rec.* 1: 92. Parramatta, New South Wales, Australia.

Acrocephalus australis gouldi
Acrocephalus gouldi Dubois, 1901. *Synop. Avium*, page 369. (New name for *Calamoherpe longirostris*, preoccupied by *Turdus longirostris* Gmelin, 1789). Australia, west and south.

Acrocephalus australis longirostris
Calamoherpe longirostris Gould, 1845. *Proc. Zool. Soc. London*, page 20. King George Sound, Western Australia.

Acrocephalus australis carterae
Acrocephalus australis carterae Mathews, 1912. *Novit. Zool.* 18: 343. Point Torment, west Kimberley, northwestern Australia.

Acrocephalus familiaris (Rothschild, 1892)

Acrocephalus familiaris familiaris
Tatare familiaris Rothschild, 1892. *Ann. Mag. Nat. Hist.* ser. 6(10): 109. Laysan, Leeward Hawaiian Chain.
EXTINCT

Acrocephalus familiaris kingi
Conopoderas kingi Wetmore, 1924. *Condor* 26: 177. Nihoa Island, Hawaii.

Acrocephalus kerearako Holyoak, 1974

Acrocephalus kerearako kerearako
Acrocephalus vaughani kerearako Holyoak, 1974. *Bull. Brit. Orn. Club* 94: 149. Mangaia, Cook Islands.

Acrocephalus kerearako kaoko
Acrocephalus vaughani kaoko Holyoak, 1974. *Bull. Brit. Orn. Club* 94: 150. Mitiaro, Cook Islands.

Acrocephalus vaughani (Sharpe, 1900)

Acrocephalus vaughani
Tatare vaughani Sharpe, 1900. *Bull. Brit. Orn. Club* 11: 2. Pitcairn Island.

Acrocephalus taiti Ogilvie-Grant, 1913

Acrocephalus taiti
Acrocephalus taiti Ogilvie-Grant, 1913. *Bull. Brit. Orn. Club* 31: 58. Henderson Island.

Acrocephalus rimitarae (Murphy & Mathews, 1929)

Acrocephalus rimitarae
Conopoderas vaughani rimitarae Murphy & Mathews, 1929. *Amer. Mus. Novit.* 350: 20. Rimitara, Tubuai Islands.

Acrocephalus aequinoctialis (Latham, 1790)

Acrocephalus aequinoctialis aequinoctialis
Sylvia aequinoctialis Latham, 1790. *Index Ornith.*, page 533. Christmas Island, Line Islands.

Acrocephalus aequinoctialis pistor
Acrocephalus pistor Tristram, 1883. *Ibis* 1 Ser. 5: 44–45. Fanning Island, Line Islands.

Acrocephalus mendanae Tristram, 1883

Acrocephalus mendanae mendanae
Acrocephalus mendanae Tristram, 1883. *Ibis*, page 43, plate 1. Hiva Oa, Marquesas Islands.

Acrocephalus mendanae dido
Conopoderas caffra dido Murphy & Mathews, 1928. *Amer. Mus. Novit.* 337: 16. Ua Pu, Marquesas Islands.

Acrocephalus mendanae consobrina
Conopoderas caffra consobrina Murphy & Mathews, 1928. *Amer. Mus. Novit.* 337: 13. Motu One (Motane Island), Marquesas Islands.

Acrocephalus mendanae fatuhivae
Conopoderas caffra fatuhivae Murphy & Mathews, 1928. *Amer. Mus. Novit.* 337: 14. Fatu Hiva, Marquesas Islands.

Acrocephalus percernis (Wetmore, 1919)

Acrocephalus percernis percernis
Conopoderas percernis Wetmore, 1919. *Bull. Mus. Comp. Zool.* 63: 213. Nuku Hiva, Marquesas Islands.

Acrocephalus percernis idae
Conopoderas caffra idae Murphy & Mathews, 1928. *Amer. Mus. Novit.* 337: 15. Huahuna, Marquesas Islands.

Acrocephalus percernis aquilonis
Conopoderas caffra aquilonis Murphy & Mathews, 1928. *Amer. Mus. Novit.* 337: 17. Eiao, Marquesas Islands.

Acrocephalus percernis postremus
Conopoderas caffra postrema Murphy & Mathews, 1928. *Amer. Mus. Novit.* 337: 17. Hatutu, Marquesas Islands.

Acrocephalus caffer (Sparrman, 1786)

Acrocephalus caffer caffer
Sitta caffra Sparrman, 1786. *Mus. Carlsonianum,* fasc.1, No. 4, plate 4. Tahiti, Society Islands.

Acrocephalus caffer longirostris
Turdus longirostris Gmelin, 1789. *Syst. Nat.* 1: 823. Moorea, Society Islands. **EXTINCT**

Acrocephalus caffer musae
Oriolus musae Forster, 1844. *Descr. Anim. Ed. Licht.*, p63. Raiatea, Society Islands. **EXTINCT**

Acrocephalus caffer garretti
Acrocephalus caffer garretti Holyoak & Thibault, 1978. *Bull. Brit. Orn. Club* 98: 122–127. Huahine, Society Islands. **EXTINCT**

Acrocephalus atyphus (Wetmore, 1919)

Acrocephalus atyphus atyphus
Conopoderas atypha Wetmore, 1919. *Bull. Mus. Comp. Zool.* 63: 206. Fakarava, Tuamotu Archipelago.

> *Acrocephalus atyphus crypta*
> *Conopoderas atypha crypta* Wetmore, 1919. *Bull. Mus. Comp. Zool.* 63: 209. Makemo, Tuamotu Archipelago.
> *Acrocephalus atyphus agassizi*
> *Conopoderas atypha agassizi* Wetmore, 1919. *Bull. Mus. Comp. Zool.* 63: 210. Apataki, Tuamotu Archipelago.
> *Acrocephalus atyphus nesiarcha*
> *Conopoderas atypha nesiarcha* Wetmore, 1919. *Bull. Mus. Comp. Zool.* 63: 210. Rangiroa, Tuamotu Archipelago.

Acrocephalus atyphus ravus
Conopoderas atypha rava Wetmore, 1919. *Bull. Mus. Comp. Zool.* 63: 208. Pinaki, Tuamotu Archipelago.

Acrocephalus atyphus eremus
Conopoderas atypha erema Wetmore, 1919. *Bull. Mus. Comp. Zool.* 63: 211. Makatea, Tuamotu Archipelago.

Acrocephalus atyphus flavidus
Conopoderas atypha flavida Murphy & Mathews, 1929. *Amer. Mus. Novit.* 350: 16. Napuka, Tuamotu Archipelago. **EXTINCT?**

Acrocephalus atyphus palmarum
Conopoderas atypha palmarum Murphy & Mathews, 1929. *Amer. Mus. Novit.* 350: 12. Anaa, Tuamotu Archipelago.

Acrocephalus atyphus niauensis
Conopoderas atypha niauensis Murphy & Mathews, 1929. *Amer. Mus. Novit.* 350: 13. Niau, Tuamotu Archipelago.

Acrocephalus luscinius (Quoy & Gaimard, 1830)

Acrocephalus luscinius luscinius
Thryothorus luscinius Quoy & Gaimard, 1830. In: Dumont, d'Urville, *Voyage Astrolabe, Zool.* 1: 202. Guam.

> *Acrocephalus luscinius mariannae*
> *Acrocephalus mariannae* Tristram, 1883. *Ibis*, page 45. Guam.
> *Acrocephalus luscinius hivae*
> *Conopoderas luscinia hivae* Yamashina, 1942. *Bull. Biogeogr. Soc. Japan* 12: 81. Saipan.

Acrocephalus luscinius nijoi
Conopoderas luscinia nijoi Yamashina, 1940. *Tori* 10: 674. Agiguan, Marianas Islands.

Acrocephalus luscinius yamashinae
Conopoderas yamashinae Takatsukasa, 1931. *Dôbutsu.*
Zasshi 43: 485. Pagan, Marianas Islands. **EXTINCT**

Acrocephalus luscinius astrolabii
Acrocephalus luscinia astrolabii Holyoak & Thibault, 1978.
Bull. Brit. Orn. Club 98: 122–127. 'Mangareva' in error,
possibly Yap, Caroline Islands. **EXTINCT**

Acrocephalus syrinx (Kittlitz, 1833)

Acrocephalus syrinx
Sylvia syrinx Kittlitz, 1835. *Mém. Acad. Imp. Sci. St*
Pétersbourg 2: 6, plate 8. Lugunor and Uleei, Caroline
Islands, Micronesia.

Acrocephalus rehsei (Finsch, 1883)

Acrocephalus rehsei
Calamoherpe rehsei Finsch, 1883. *Ibis*, page 143. Nawodo,
Nauru, Micronesia.

Genus *Hippolais*

Conrad, 1827. *Neue Alpina* 2: 77.

Hippolais icterina (Vieillot, 1817)

Hippolais icterina
Sylvia icterina Vieillot, 1817. *Nouv. Dict. d'Hist. Nat., nouv.*
éd. 11: 194. Nancy, France.

Hippolais icterina alaris
Hippolais icterina alaris Stresemann, 1928. *Jour. Ornith.* 76:
375. Kuramabad, Gilan, northern Iran.

Hippolais polyglotta (Vieillot, 1817)

Hippolais polyglotta
Sylvia polyglotta Vieillot, 1817. *Nouv. Dict. d'Hist. Nat.,*
nouv. éd. 11: 200. France.

Hippolais olivetorum (Strickland, 1837)

Hippolais olivetorum
Salicaria olivetorum Strickland, 1837. In: Gould, *Birds of*
Europe, vol 2, plate 107. Zante, Ionian Islands.

Hippolais languida (Hemprich & Ehrenberg, 1833)

Hippolais languida
Curruca languida Hemprich & Ehrenberg, 1833. *Symb.*
Phys. Avium Decas I, fol. cc. Syria.

Hippolais languida magnirostris
Sylvia magnirostris Severtsov, 1873. *Izvestiia Imp. Obshchestva*
Liubitelei Estest. Antrop. Etnogr., Moscow 8(2): 123. Karatau
Mountains and western foothills of the Tien Shan.

Genus *Iduna*

Keyserling & Blasius, 1840. *Wirbelthiere Europa's*, page 58.

Iduna pallida (Hemprich & Ehrenberg, 183)

Iduna pallida pallida
Curruca pallida Hemprich & Ehrenberg, 1833. *Symb.*
Phys. Avium, fol. bb. The Nile in Egypt and Nubia.

Iduna pallida elaeica
Salicaria elaeica Lindermayer, 1843. *Isis von Oken, col.*
343. Greece.

Iduna pallida tamariceti
Salicaria tamariceti Severtsov, 1873. *Izvestiia Imp.*
Obshchestva Liubitelei Estest. Antrop. Etnogr., Moscow 8(2):
131. Syr-Dar'ya.

Iduna pallida turcestanica
Hippolais pallida turcestanica Zarudny, 1915. *Materialy*
Poznaniu Fauny Flory Ross. Imp., Sect. Zool. 14: 95. Kunya
Kuduka, Kyzylkum.

Iduna pallida reiseri
Hypolais pallida reiseri Hilgert, 1908. *Falco* 4: 3. Biskra,
southern Algeria.

Iduna pallida laeneni
Hippolais pallida laeneni Niethammer, 1955. *Bonner Zool.*
Beitr. 6: 66. Bol, on east shore of Lake Chad.

Iduna pallida alulensis
Hippolais pallida alulensis Ash, Pearson & Bensch, 2005.
Ibis 147: 841–843. Alula, northeast Somalia.

Iduna opaca (Cabanis, 1850)

Iduna opaca
Hypolais opaca Cabanis, 1851. *Museum Heineanum* 1: 36.
Senegal.

Iduna rama (Sykes, 1832)

Iduna rama
Sylvia rama Sykes, 1832. *Proc. Zool. Soc. London*, page 89.
Dukhun, India.

Iduna caligata (Lichtenstein, 1823)

Iduna caligata
Sylvia caligata Lichtenstein, 1823. In: Eversmann, *Reise*
von Orenburg nach Buchara, page 128. Ilek River, near
Orenburg.

Iduna caligata scita
Sylvia scita Eversmann, 1842. Addendum to Pallas, 1811.
Zoographia Rosso-Asiat. 3, page 12. Ural Mountains.

Iduna caligata obsoleta
Salicaria obsoleta Severtsov, 1873. Turk. Jevotn, page 63.
Moscow.

Iduna caligata annectens
Hippolais rama annectens Sushkin, 1925. *List Distribution*
Birds, Russian Altai, page 75. Kosh-Agach, southeastern
Altai.

Iduna natalensis (Smith, 1847)

Iduna natalensis natalensis
Chloropeta natalensis Smith, 1847. *Illus. Zool. South Africa,*
Aves, plate 112, figure 2. Near Port Natal (Durban), Natal.

Iduna natalensis icterina
Chloropeta icterina Sundevall, 1850. *Öfversigt K. Vetenskaps-*
Akad. Förhandlingar, Stockholm 7: 105. Near Durban, Natal.

Iduna natalensis massaica
Chloropeta massaica Fischer & Reichenow, 1884. *J.*

Ornithol. 32: 54. Tschaga, base of Mount Kilimanjaro, Tanganyika.

Iduna natalensis umbriniceps
Chloropeta natalensis umbriniceps Neumann, 1902. *Orn. Monatsber.* 10: 10. Malo, Omo River, Abyssinia.

Iduna natalensis storeyi
Chloropeta storeyi Ogilvie-Grant, 1906. *Bull. Brit. Orn. Club* 19: 32. Chedaro, Nairobi River, Kenya.

Iduna natalensis major
Chloropeta natalensis major Hartert, 1904. *Bull. Brit. Orn. Club* 14: 73. Canhoca, northern Angola.

Iduna natalensis batesi
Chloropeta batesi Sharpe, 1905. *Ibis*, page 468. Ja River, southern Cameroon.

Iduna similis (Richmond, 1897)

Iduna similis
Chloropeta similis Richmond, 1897. *Auk* 14: 163. Mount Kilimanjaro, Tanganyika. 10,000 feet.

Iduna similis kenya
Chloropeta kenya Sharpe, 1901. *Bull. Brit. Orn. Club* 12: 35. Mount Kenya.

Iduna similis schubotzi
Chloropeta schubotzi Reichenow, 1908. *Orn. Monatsber.* 16: 119. Lugege Forest, Rwanda.

Genus *Phragamaticola*

Phragamaticola Jerdon, 1845. Second Supplement to the Catalogue of the birds of Southern India. *Madras J. Lit. Sci.* 13: 129.

Phragamaticola aedon (Pallas, 1776)

Phragamaticola aedon aedon
Muscicapa Aëdon Pallas, 1776. *Reise Verschiedene Provinzen Russischen Reichs* 3: 695. Dauria.

Phragamaticola aedon stegmanni
Acrocephalus aedon stegmanni Watson, 1985. *Bull. Brit.*

Orn. Club 105: 79. (New name for *Phragamaticola aëdon rufescens*, preoccupied by *Bradypterus rufescens* Sharpe & Bouvier, 1876).

Phragamaticola aedon rufescens
Phragamaticola aëdon rufescens Stegmann, 1929. *J. Ornithol.* 77: 250. Eastern Amurland.

Genus *Calamonastides*

Grant & Mackworth-Praed, 1940. *Bull. Brit. Orn. Club* 60: 91–92.

Calamonastides gracilirostris (Ogilvie-Grant, 1906)

Calamonastides gracilirostris gracilirostris
Chloropeta gracilirostris Ogilvie-Grant, 1906. *Bull. Brit Orn. Club* 19: 33. Southeastern slopes of Ruwenzori mountains, Uganda, 3,400 feet.

Calamonastides gracilirostris bensoni
Chloropeta gracilirostris bensoni Amadon, 1954. *Ostrich* 25: 141. Mouth of Luapula River, Lake Mweru, northern Rhodesia.

Calamonastides gracilirostris bredoi
Chloropeta gracilirostris bredoi Schouteden, 1955. *Ann. Mus. Roy. Congo Belge, Tervuren*, sér. 4: 330. Nkole, on Lake Mweru, border of Zaire and Zambia.

Genus *Nesillas*

Oberholser, 1899. *Proc. Acad. Nat. Sci. Philadelphia*, page 211.

Nesillas typica (Hartlaub, 1860)

Nesillas typica typica
Ellisia typica Hartlaub 1860. *J. Ornithol.* 8: 92. Madagascar.

Nesillas typica monticola
Nesillas typica monticola Hartert & Lavaunden, 1931. *Bull. Brit. Orn. Club* 51: 56. Mount Tsaratanana, Madagascar, altitude c. 2,750 meters.

Nesillas typica ellisii
Drymoica ellisii Schagel & Pollen, 1868. In: Pollen & van Dam, *Recherches Faune Madagascar* pt. 2, page 91, pl. 28, fig. 2. Madagascar.

Nesillas typica longicaudata
Ellisia longicaudata Newton, 1877. *Proc. Zool. Soc. London*, page 299. Anjouan, Comoro Islands.

Nesillas typica obscura
Nesillas typica obscura Delacour 1931. *Oiseau* 1: 476. Namoroka, Madagascar.

Nesillas typica moheliensis
Nesillas typica moheliensis Benson, 1960. *Ibis* 103: 81. Bandamale, Moheli, Comoro Islands, altitude 500 meters.

Nesillas lantzii (Crandidier, 1867)

Nesillas lantzii
Ellisia Lantzii Crandidier, 1867. *Rev. Mag. Zool. Paris*, sér. 2, 19: 86. West coast of Madagascar.

Nesillas brevicaudata (Milne-Edwards & Oustalet, 1888)

Nesillas brevicaudata
Ellisia brevicaudata Milne-Edwards & Oustalet, 1888. *Nouv. Archives Mus. Nat Hist. Paris*, sér 2, 10: 249. Grand Comoro Island.

Nesillas mariae Benson 1960

Nesillas mariae
Nesillas mariae Benson 1960. *Ibis* 103: 81. Bandamale, Moheli, Comoro Islands, altitude 500 meters.

Nesillas aldabranus Benson & Penny, 1968

Nesillas aldabranus
Nesillas aldabranus Benson & Penny, 1968. *Bull. Brit.*

Orn. Club 88: 102. Middle Island, north coast of Aldabra Atoll. **EXTINCT**

Cettiidae

Genus *Oligura*

Hodgson, 1844. In Gray, J. E. (ed.), *Zool. Misc.* Page 82.

Oligura castaneocoronata (Burton, 1836)

Oligura castaneocoronata castaneocoronata
Sylvia? castaneo-coronata Burton, 1836. *Proc. Zool. Soc. London* (1835), page 152. No locality (= Himalayas).

Oligura castaneocoronata regia
Tesia castaneocoronata regia Koelz, 1954. Contrib. Inst. Regional Exploration, no. 1, page 11. Blue Mountain, Lushai, (=Mizo) Hills, Mizoram, India.

Oligura castaneocoronata ripleyi
Oligura castaneo-coronata ripleyi Deignan, 1951. *Postilla, Yale Peabody Mus. Nat. Hist.*, no. 7, page 3. Likiang Mountains, Yunnan Province, China.

Oligura castaneocoronata abadiei
Tesia castaneo-coronata abadiei Delacour & Jabouille, 1930. *Oiseau* 11: 405. Chapa (Tonkin), altitude 1,600 meters, Northern Vietnam.

Genus *Tesia*

Hodgson, 1837. *J. Asiatic Soc. Bengal* 6: 101.

Tesia cyaniventer Hodgson, 1837

Tesia cyaniventer
Tesia cyaniventer Hodgson, 1837. *J. Asiatic Soc. Bengal* 6: 101. Nepal.

Tesia cyaniventer superciliaris
Tesia cyaniventer superciliaris La Touche 1921. *Bull. Brit. Orn. Club* 42: 18. Mengtsz, southeastern Yunnan.

Tesia olivea (McClelland, 1840)

Tesia olivea olivea
Saxicola? olivea McClelland, 1840. *Proc. Zool. Soc. London* (1839), page 161. Assam.

Tesia olivea chiangmaiensis
Tesia olivea chiangmaiensis Renner *et al.* 2008. *J. Ornithol.* 149: 439–450. Chiang Mai Province of northern Thailand.

Tesia superciliaris (Bonaparte, 1850)

Tesia superciliaris
Microura superciliaris Bonaparte, 1850. *Consp. Gen. Avium* 1: 258. Java

Tesia everetti (Hartert, 1879)

Tesia everetti everetti
Orthnocichla everetti Hartert, 1879. *Novit. Zool.* 4: 170. Flores.

Tesia everetti sumbawana
Orthnocichla everetti sumbawana Rensch, 1928. *Orn. Monatsber.* 36: 48. Batoe Doelang (= Batudulang), Sumbawa, altitude 800–1,000 meters.

Genus *Urosphena*

Swinhoe, 1877. *Ibis* Series 4(2): 203–205, pl. 4.

Urosphena subulata (Sharpe, 1884)

Urosphena subulata subulata
Orthnocichla subulata Sharpe, 1884. *Notes Leyden Mus.* 6: 179–180. Timor.

Urosphena subulata advena
Orthnocichla subulata advena Hartert, 1906. *Novit. Zool.* 13: 298. Tepa, Babber Island = Babar.

Urosphena whiteheadi (Sharpe, 1888)

Urosphena whiteheadi
Orthnocichla whiteheadi Sharpe, 1888. *Ibis*, page 478. Mount Kinabalu, Borneo.

Urosphena squamiceps (Swinhoe, 1863)

Urosphena squamiceps squamiceps
Tribura squameiceps Swinhoe, 1863. *Proc. Zool. Soc. London*, page 292. Canton.

Urosphena squamiceps ussuriana
Cettia ussurianus Seebohm, 1881. *Cat. Birds Brit. Mus.* 5: 143. Ussuri Valley.

Genus *Cettia*

Bonaparte, 1834. *Icon. Fauna Ital.*, 1. Text to pl. 29, fig. 3.

Cettia pallidipes (Blandford, 1872)

Cettia pallidipes pallidipes
Phylloscopus pallidipes Blandford, 1872. *J. Asiatic Soc. Bengal* 41(2): 162. Sikkim.

Cettia pallidipes osmastoni
Horeites pallidipes osmastoni Hartert, 1908. *Bull. Brit. Orn. Club* 21: 107. Andaman Islands.

Cettia pallidipes laurentei
Urosphena laurentei La Touche, 1921. *Bull. Brit. Orn. Club*
42: 30. Southeast Yunnan.

Cettia vulcania (Blyth, 1870)

Cettia vulcania vulcania
Sylvia vulcania Blyth, 1870. Ibis, page 170. Java.

Cettia vulcania montana
Sylvia montana Horsfield, 1821. *Trans. Linn. Soc. London*
13: 156. Java.

Cettia vulcania flaviventris
Brachypteryx flaviventris Salvadori, 1879. *Ann. Mus. Civ.
Stor. Nat. Genova* 14: 226. Mount Singalang, Bella Vista,
western Sumatra.

Cettia vulcania sumatrana
Cettia sumatrana Ogilvie-Grant, 1916. *Bull. Brit. Orn. Club*
36: 66. Korinchi, Sumatra. 10,000 feet.

Cettia vulcania oreophila
Cettia oreophila Sharpe, 1888. *Ibis,* page 387. Mount
Kinabalu, northern Borneo.

Cettia vulcania everetti
Cettia everetti Hartert, 1898. *Novit. Zool.* 5: 113. Atapupa,
Timor.

Cettia vulcania sepiaria
Cettia montana sepiaria Kloss, 1931. *Treubia* 13: 352.
Pajatoengkalan, Pangmoh, Acheen, northern Sumatra.
2,000 meters.

Cettia vulcania banksi
Cettia montana banksi Chasen, 1935. *Orn. Monatsber.*
43: 147. Mount Mulu, northern Sarawak, Borneo.
2,200–2,600 meters.

Cettia vulcania palawana
Cettia montana palawana Ripley & Rabor, 1962. *Postilla*
73: 10. Mount Mantalingajan, Palawan, Philippines.
6,700 feet.

Cettia vulcania kolichisi
Cettia vulcana kolichisi Johnstone & Darnell, 1997.
The Western Australian Naturalist 21(3): 145–151. Alor,
Indonesia.

Cettia flavolivacea (Blyth, 1845)

Cettia flavolivacea flavolivacea
Neornis flavolivacea Blyth, 1845. *J. Asiatic Soc. Bengal* 14:
590. Nepal.

Cettia flavolivacea intricata
Horeites flavolivacea intricatus Hartert, 1909. *Vögel Pal. Fauna,*
page 533. Tai-pai Shan, Tsin-ling Range, Shensi, China.

Cettia flavolivacea grahami
Antiornis grahami Riley, 1926. *Proc. Biol. Soc. Washington,*
39: 55. O-mei Shan, Szechwan, China. 3,500 feet.

Cettia flavolivacea dulcivox
Horeites pallidus dulcivox Stresemann, 1924. *Abh.
Ber. Mus. Tierk. Völkerk, Dresden* 16(2): 16. Washan,
Szechwan.

Cettia flavolivacea weberi
Horeites flavolivacea weberi Mayr, 1941. *Ibis,* page 244.
Mount Victoria, Chin hills, Burma.

Cettia flavolivacea alexanderi
Horeites flavolivacea alexanderi Ripley, 1951. *Postilla* 6: 6.
60 miles east of Kohima, Naga Hills, India.

Cettia flavolivacea oblita
Horeites flavolivacea oblita Mayr, 1941. *Ibis,* page 245.
Chapa, Tonkin.

Cettia flavolivacea stresemanni
Neornis flavolivaceus stresemanni Koelz, 1954. *Contrib. Inst.
Regional Exploration* 1: 17. Mawryngkneng, Khasi Hills,
Meghalaya, India.

Cettia flavolivacea circumspectus
Neornis flavolivaceus circumspectus Koelz, 1954. *Contrib.
Inst. Regional Exploration* 1: 18. Mawphlang, Khasi Hills,
Meghalaya, India.

Cettia fortipes (Hodgson, 1845)

Cettia fortipes fortipes
Horornis fortipes Hodgson, 1845. *Proc. Zool. Soc. London,*
page 31. Nepal.

Cettia fortipes manis
Homochlamys fortipes manis. Koelz, 1954. *Contrib. Inst. Regional
Exploration* 1: 18. Mawphlang, Khasi Hills, Meghalaya, India.

Cettia fortipes mizorum
Homochlamys fortipes mizorum. Koelz, 1954. *Contrib. Inst.
Regional Exploration* 1: 18. Sangau, Lushai Hills, Mizoram,
India.

Cettia fortipes robustipes
Horeites robustipes Swinhoe, 1866. *Ibis,* page 398.
Formosa.

Cettia fortipes davidiana
Arundinax davidiana Verreaux, 1870. *Nouv. Arch. Mus.
Hist. Nat. Paris* 6: 37. Muping, Szechwan.

Cettia fortipes sinensis
Cettia sinensis La Touche, 1898. *Bull. Brit. Orn. Club* 7: 37.
Fohkien.

Cettia fortipes dulcivox
Horeites pallidus dulcivox Stresemann, 1924. *Abh. Ber. Mus.
Tierkunde Völkerkunde Dresden* 16(2): 16. Wa Shan, Szechwan.

Cettia fortipes pallida
Horeites pallidus Brooks, 1872 *Jour. Asiat. Soc. Bengal*
41(2): 78. Kashmir.

Cettia acanthizoides (Verreaux, 1870)

Cettia acanthizoides acanthizoides
Abrornis acanthizoides Verreaux, 1870. *Bull. Nouv. Arch.
Mus. Hist. Nat. Paris* 6: 37. Mountains of Chinese Tibet.

Cettia acanthizoides inconspicuus
Horeites robustipes inconspicuus Stresemann, 1924. *Abh.
Ber. Mus. Tierkunde, Völkerkunde Dresden* 16(2): 18.
Wanxian, Szechwan.

Cettia acanthizoides concolor
Horeites acanthizoides concolor Ogilvie-Grant, 1912. *Bull.
Brit. Orn. Club* 29: 107. Mt. Arizan (Ali Shan), Formosa.

Cettia brunnescens (Hume, 1872)

Cettia brunnescens
Horeites brunnescens Hume, 1872. *Ibis* page 109. Near
Darjeeling.

Cettia major (Horsfield & Moore, 1845)

Cettia major major
Horeites major Horsfield & Moore, 1854. *Cat. Birds Mus.
Hon. East India Co.* 1: 323. Nepal.

Cettia major vafra
Homochlamys major vafra Koelz, 1954. *Contrib. Inst.
Regional Exploration* 1: 18. Phulbari, Garo Hills, Assam.

Cettia brunnifrons (Hodgson, 1845)

Cettia brunnifrons brunnifrons
Prinia brunnifrons Hodgson, 1845. *Proc. Zool. Soc. London,*
page 29. Nepal.

Cettia brunnifrons whistleri
Horeites brunnifrons whistleri Ticehurst, 1923. *Bull. Brit. Orn. Club* 44: 28. Simla.

Cettia brunnifrons umbratica
Horeites brunnifrons umbraticus Stuart Baker, 1924. *Bull. Brit. Orn. Club* 44: 63. Shweli-Salwin Divide, west-central Yunnan.

> *Cettia brunnifrons muroides*
> *Horeites brunnifrons muroides* Koelz, 1954. *Contrib. Inst. Regional Exploration* 1: 18. Bamanigaon, Assam.

Cettia canturians (Swinhoe, 1860)

Cettia canturians canturians
Arundinax canturians Swinhoe, 1860. *Ibis* page 52. Amoy in winter, Shanghai in summer.

> *Cettia canturians minuta*
> *Cettia cantans minuta* Seebohm, 1881. *Cat. Birds Brit. Mus.* Vol. V. page 140.

Cettia canturians borealis
Cettia minuta borealis Campbell, 1892. *Ibis* page 235. Chemulpo, Korea.

Cettia diphone (Kittlitz, 1830)

Cettia diphone diphone
Sylvia diphone Kittlitz, 1830. *Mém. Prés. Acad. Imp. Sci., St Pétersbourg* 1: 237, plate. 14. Bonin Islands (Ogasawara-shoto).

> *Cettia diphone iwootoensis*
> *Horeites diphone iwootoensis.* Momiyama, 1927. *Bull. Brit. Orn. Club* 47: 146. Motoyama, Volcano Islands.
> *Cettia diphone ponafidinicus*
> *Horeites diphone ponafidinicus.* Momiyama, 1930. *Bull. Biogeogr. Soc. Japan,* 1: 175. Tori-shima, Seven Islands of Izu.

Cettia diphone cantans
Salicaria cantans Temminck & Schlegel, 1847. In: Siebold, *Fauna Japonica*, Aves page 51, pl. 19. Japan.

> *Cettia diphone takahashii*
> *Horornis cantans takahashii* Momiyama, 1927. *Annot. Ornith. Orient.* 1: 37. Cheju Do.
> *Cettia diphone ijimae*
> *Horornis cantans ijimae* Kuroda, 1922. *Annot. Zool. Japon.* 10: 117. Miyake-jima, Seven Islands of Izu.

Cettia diphone restricta
Horornis cantans restricta. Kuroda, 1923. *Bull. Brit. Orn. Club* 43: 122. Minami-daito-jima, Borodino Islands, east of the Ryu Kyu Islands. **EXTINCT?**

Cettia diphone riukiuensis
Horornis cantans riukiuensis. Kuroda, 1925. *Avifauna Riu Kiu Islands*, page 69. Sonai, Iriomote-jima, southern Ryu Kyu Islands.

> *Cettia diphone sakhalinensis*
> *Horornis cantans sakhalinensis.* Yamashina, 1927. *Dôbutsu. Zasshi* 39: 281. Nayoro, Sakhalin.
> *Cettia diphone viridis*
> *Horeites diphone viridis.* Portenko, 1955. *Trudy Zool. Inst. Akad. Nauk, SSSR.* 18: 505. Kunashir, southern Kurils.

Cettia seebohmi Ogilvie-Grant, 1894

Cettia seebohmi
Cettia seebohmi Ogilvie-Grant, 1894. *Ibis* 6(6): 507. Northern Luzon.

Cettia annae (Hartlaub & Finsch, 1868)

Cettia annae
Psamathia annae Hartlaub & Finsch, 1868. *Proc. Zool. Soc. London,* page 5, plate 2. Pulau Islands.

Cettia parens (Mayr, 1935)

Cettia parens
Vitia parens Mayr, 1935. *Amer. Mus. Novit.* 820: 4. San Cristobal Island, Solomon Islands.

Cettia ruficapilla (Ramsay, 1875)

Cettia ruficapilla ruficapilla
Vitia ruficapilla Ramsay, 1875. *Proc. Linn. Soc. New South Wales.* 1: 42. Kandavu, Fiji.

Cettia ruficapilla badiceps
Drymochaera badiceps Finsch, 1876. *Proc. Zool. Soc. London,* page 20. Vitu Levu, Fiji.

Cettia ruficapilla castaneoptera
Vitia ruficapilla castaneoptera Mayr, 1935. *Amer. Mus. Novit.* 820: 5. Vanua Levu, Fiji.

Cettia ruficapilla funebris
Vitia ruficapilla funebris Mayr, 1935. *Amer. Mus. Novit.* 820: 5. Taveuni, Fiji.

Cettia carolinae Rozendaal, 1987

Cettia carolinae
Cettia carolinae Rozendaal, 1987. *Zool. Meded. Leiden* 61: 177–202. Yamdena, Tanimbar Islands, Indonesia.

Cettia haddeni LeCroy & Barker, 2006

Cettia haddeni
Cettia haddeni LeCroy & Barker, 2006. *Amer. Mus. Novit.* 3511: 1–20. Crown Prince Range, Bougainville, Solomon Islands.

Cettia cetti (Temminck, 1820)

Cettia cetti cetti
Sylvia cetti Temminck, 1820. *Man. Ornith.,* ed 2(1): 194. Sardinia.

> *Cettia cetti schiebeli*
> *Cettia cetti schiebeli* Rokitansky, 1934. *Falco* 30: 6. Lake Lentini, Sicily.
> *Cettia cetti whitakeri*
> *Cettia cetti whitakeri* Orlando, 1937. *Riv. Ital. Ornitologia* Ser 2, 7: 213. Sardinia.

Cettia cetti orientalis
Cettia (Potamodus) orientalis Tristram, 1867. *Ibis,* page 79. Palestine.

Cettia cetti albiventris
Cettia albiventris Severtsov, 1873. *Izvestiia Imp. Obshchestva Liubitelei Estest. Antrop. Etnogr.,* Moscow 8(2): 131. Karatau Mountains, Kazakhstan.

> *Cettia cetti cettioides*
> *Cettia cettioides* Hume, 1873. *Stray Feathers* 1: 194. Sind.

APPENDIX 2

LIVE WING LENGTHS OF SELECTED PALEARCTIC MIGRANT SPECIES

Status is defined as follows: B – at or near the breeding area; P – on passage, autumn and/or spring; W – on the wintering area.

Primary generation is defined as: J – juvenile, A – adult (includes immature birds with fresh primaries after complete post-juvenile moult); C – combined juvenile and adult.

Primary condition describes the wear to the outermost primaries, defined as: N – new, unworn or fresh; O – old and distinctly abraded; N** – new outer primaries grown in recent partial moult, old inner primaries retained.

Wing length is the maximum straightened value except where marked with an asterix *, which refers to natural, unstraightened wing length, the standard method used in Japan.

Data for both sexes is combined unless otherwise stated.

Species	Race	Location and month	Status	Primaries generation	Primaries condition	Sex	Wing length range	Wing length mean	Wing length SD	Wing length n	Source
Baikal Bush Warbler	suschkini	Thailand, Nov-May	W	A	N		48-55	52.9	1.5	33	PDR
Chinese Bush Warbler		Thailand, Nov-Jan	W	A	N		52-57	55.1	1.6	7	PDR
Savi's Warbler	luscinioides	France, Aug	B, P	J	N		61-74	68.9	2.4	70	PP
	luscinioides	France, Apr-Aug	B, P	A	O, N**, N		63-75	68.9	2.2	87	PP
	luscinioides	Hungary	B	J	N		62-75	69.7	2.6	125	C
	luscinioides	Hungary	B	A	O		68-74	70.1	?	18	C
	fusca	C and SE Kazakhstan, Jul-Sep	B, P	J	N		67-74	70.9	1.5	58	AG
	fusca	C and SE Kazakhstan, Apr-Sep	B, P	A	O		66-75	71.5	2.5	21	AG
River Warbler		SE Kenya, Nov-Dec	P	J	N		67-82	75.0	2.1	4650	NRG
		SE Kenya, Nov-Dec	P	A	N**		67-82	75.5	2.1	2172	NRG
		SE Kenya, Apr	P	A	N		73-82	77.8	2.2	19	DJP
Grasshopper Warbler	naevia	S England, Jul-Sep	B	J	N		58-69	64.0	1.5	3201	SJRR
	naevia	S England, Aug-Sep	B	A	O		69-67	62.8	1.7	239	SJRR
	obscurior	Armenia, May	B	A	O		63-64	63.5		2	PRK
	straminea	SE Kazakhstan, Aug-Oct	B	J	N		56-64	60.1	2.0	81	AG
	straminea	SE Kazakhstan, May-Sep	B	A	O		55-62	58.3	1.6	48	AG
Lanceolated Warbler		Thailand, Sep-Apr	W	C	O, N		54-59	55.5	1.4	17	PDR
		Hong Kong, Sep-Nov	P	C	N,O, N**		53-61	55.9	1.9	34	HKRG
Pallas's Grasshopper Warbler	centralasiae	E Kazakhstan, Aug	B	J	N		61-68	64.2	2.1	25	GN/DJP
	all races	Hong Kong, Sep-Oct	P	J	N		56-69	62.4	2.6	131	HKRG
	all races	Hong Kong, Sep-Oct	P	A	O, N**		58-69	62.3	2.6	30	HKRG
	all races	Thailand, Sep-Apr	P, W	C	O, N		57-73	65.8	3.7	75	PDR

Species	Race	Location and month	Status	Primaries generation	Primaries condition	Sex	Wing length range	Wing length mean	Wing length SD	Wing length n	Source
Middendorff's Grasshopper Warbler	ochotensis	Japan, Jun-Sep	B	C	N, O		62-72*	65.5*	2.7	23	TM
	subcerthiola	Talan Is. Russia, July	B	C	N, O	M	74			1	PRK
						F	72			1	
Styan's Grasshopper Warbler		Hong Kong, Oct-Apr	W	C	N, N**		64-75	69.0	2.8	28	HKRG
Gray's Grasshopper Warbler	amnicola	Japan, Jul-Sep	B	J	N		71-79*	74.2*	2.5	17	TM
Japanese Swamp Warbler	pryeri	Japan, Jul-Sep	B	J	N	M	49-52*	50.5*		8	S
	pryeri	Japan, Jul-Sep	B	J	N	F	46-48*	47.3*		5	S
	pryeri	Japan, May-Oct	B	A	O, N	M	51-56*	53.3*	1.0	15	S
	pryeri	Japan, May-Oct	B	A	O, N	F	47-51*	48.8*	1.4	17	S
Moustached Warbler	melanopogon	SE Spain, Apr-Jul	B	C	O, N		50-60	54.4	2.0	300	PVG
	mimicus	Azerbaijan, Aug	B	J	N		57-61	59.3	1.4	40	GN/ DJP
	mimicus	Azerbaijan, Aug	B	A	N		59-63	62.0	1.3	13	GN/ DJP
	mimicus	SE Kazakhstan, Jun-Sep	B	J	N		56-70	62.2	1.6	596	AG
	mimicus	SE Kazakhstan, Apr-Aug	B	A	O		56-66	62.0	2.1	57	AG
Sedge Warbler		E England, Jul-Sep	B	J	N		60-71	65.2	1.6	4381	DJP
		Belgium, Jun-Sep	B	J	N		59-71	65.2	1.6	13512	KBIN
		Belgium, Apr-Sep	B	A	O	M	62-71	66.4	1.5	166	KBIN
		Belgium, Apr-Sep	B	A	O	F	60-68	64.2	1.5	183	KBIN
		SE Ukraine, Aug-Sep	P	J	N		63-71	66.4	1.7	144	GN
		SE Ukraine, Aug-Sep	P	A	O		65-71	67.7	1.7	143	GN
		C. Arabia, Apr	P	A	N		63-72	67.1	1.7	52	GN/ JSA
		S Uganda, Dec-Apr	W	A	N		63-73	68.2	1.7	239	DJP
		C Kenya, Mar-May	P	A	N		62-72	67.9	1.8	640	DJP
		SE Kenya, Nov-Dec	P	C	O		62-71	66.7	1.7	182	NRG
		SE Kenya, Apr	P	A	N		63-75	68.9	2.0	145	DJP
Aquatic Warbler		Belgium, Jul-Sep	P	J	N		59-68	63.9	1.4	603	KBIN
		Belgium, Jul-Sep	P	A	O		58-64	61.9	1.5	57	KBIN
Streaked Reed Warbler		Philippines, Jan-May	W	C	O, N		55-59	56.6	1.1	13	M&L
Black-browed Reed Warbler		Hong Kong, Oct-May	P	A	N, O		49-62	55.6	1.9	1655	HKRG
		Thailand, Oct-May	W	A	N, O		50-60	55.1	1.8	361	PDR
Manchurian Reed Warbler		Hong Kong, Oct-May	P	C	N, O		51-57	54.4	1.4	25	HKRG
		Thailand, Oct-Apr	W	C	N, O		52-58	54.5	1.4	113	PDR
Blunt-winged Warbler	concinens	Hong Kong, Oct-Apr	W	A	N, O		53-57	55.2	1.2	10	HKRG
	concinens	Thailand, Nov-Apr	W	A	N, O		50-59	54.9	1.6	45	PDR

Species	Race	Location and month	Status	Primaries generation	Primaries condition	Sex	Wing length range	Wing length mean	Wing length SD	Wing length n	Source
Paddyfield Warbler	*septima*	SE Ukraine, Aug	B	J	N		53-63	58.2	1.6	360	GN
	septima	SE Ukraine, Aug	B	A	O		55-60	57.1	1.2	21	GN
	agricola	SE Kazakhstan, Jul-Aug	B	J	N		52-64	58.9	1.7	1907	AG
	agricola	SE Kazakhstan, May-Aug	B	A	O		54-62	58.0	1.6	413	AG
	agricola	Hong Kong, Oct-Apr	P, W	A	N		56-60	57.9	1.1	9	HKRG
Blyth's Reed Warbler		SE Kazakhstan, Jul-Oct	B, P	J	N		58-69	63.5	1.7	1025	AG
		SE Kazakhstan, May-Sep	B, P	A	O		58-69	62.9	1.8	652	AG
Marsh Warbler		Belgium, Jul-Sep	B	J	N		64-75	69.3	1.6	6014	KBIN
		Belgium, May-Aug	B	A	N,O	M	67-75	70.8	1.6	243	KBIN
		Belgium, May-Aug	B	A	N,O	F	65-73	69.0	1.5	203	KBIN
		Oman, May	P	A	N		64-73	68.8	1.6	284	GN/ JSA
		SE Kenya, Nov-Dec	P	J	O		62-75	68.1	1.7	8882	NRG
		SE Kenya, Nov-Dec	P	A	O		62-75	68.2	1.7	5408	NRG
		SE Kenya, Apr	P	A	N		65-73	69.5	1.9	80	DJP
Eurasian Reed Warbler	*scirpaceus*	E England, Jul-Oct	B	J	N		59-71	65.3	1.5	3886	DJP
	scirpaceus	E England, Jul-Aug	B	A	O		62-70	65.9	1.5	659	DJP
	scirpaceus	Belgium, Jul-Oct	B	J	N		59-72	65.6	1.7	26118	KBIN
	scirpaceus	Belgium, May-Sep	B	A	O	M	63-72	67.0	1.5	1170	KBIN
	scirpaceus	Belgium, May-Sep	B	A	O	F	60-72	65.0	1.5	1227	KBIN
	scirpaceus	NE Spain, Jun-Jul	B	J	N		59-66	62.1	1.4	143	JCF
	scirpaceus	NE Spain, Jun-Jul	B	A	O	M	62-65	64.1	1.0	22	JCF
	scirpaceus	NE Spain, Jun-Jul	B	A	O	F	59-65	62.3	1.2	76	JCF
	scirpaceus	S Spain, Jun-Aug	B	J	N		57-67	61.3	2.0	285	GOES
	scirpaceus	S Spain, Jun-Jul	B	A	O		60-68	63.2	1.8	141	GOES
	scirpaceus	C Sweden, Jun-Jul	B	J	N		60-72	66.6		3779	BN/SB
	scirpaceus	C Sweden, Jun-Jul	B	A	O		62-72	67.6		1011	BN/SB
	scirpaceus	SE Ukraine, Aug	B	J	N		64-70	66.8	1.6	101	GN
	small resident '*scirpaceus*'	NW Morocco, Sep	B	J	N		55-66	60.4	1.7	67	PP
	fuscus	SE Kazakhstan, Aug	B	J	N		64-74	68.5	1.8	693	GN/ DJP
	fuscus	SE Kazakhstan, Aug	B	A	O		67-72	69.2	1.4	26	GN/ DJP
	fuscus	SW Arabia, Apr-May	P	A	N		62-74	68.2	1.9	152	GN/ JSA
	fuscus	S Uganda, Oct-Jan	W	C	O		63-70	66.9	1.6	76	DJP
	typical *fuscus*	S Uganda, Dec-Apr	W	A	N		64-73	68.5	1.7	131	DJP
	warmer *fuscus*	S Uganda, Dec-Apr	W	A	N		64-72	68.3	1.7	50	DJP
	fuscus	C Kenya, Dec-Apr	P, W	A	N		64-76	68.3	2.1	604	DJP
	fuscus	SE Kenya, Nov-Dec	P	C	O		63-74	69.4	1.9	148	NRG
	fuscus	SE Kenya, Nov-Dec	P	A	N		67-74	71.3	1.8	26	NRG

Species	Race	Location and month	Status	Primaries generation	Primaries condition	Sex	Wing length range	Wing length mean	Wing length SD	Wing length n	Source
Eurasian Reed Warbler (cont.)	includes some 'smaller' *fuscus*	C Arabia, Apr-May	P, B	A	N, O		58-74	66.2	2.8	322	GN/ JSA
Basra Reed Warbler		C Arabia, Apr-May	P	A	N		79-87	82.5	2.3	23	GN/ JSA
		SE Kenya, Nov-Dec	P	J	O		73-87	79.5	2.7	184	NRG
		SE Kenya, Nov-Dec	P	A	O		76-88	80.7	3.8	25	NRG
		SE Kenya, Nov-Dec	P	A	N		76-90	83.1	2.4	1201	NRG
Great Reed Warbler	*arundinaceus*	Sweden, Jul-Sep	B	J	N		90-104	96.7	2.6	106	SB
	arundinaceus	Sweden, May-Aug	B	A	O	M	97-106	101.1	1.8	217	SB
	arundinaceus	Sweden, May-Aug	B	A	O	F	92-101	96.8	1.8	239	SB
	arundinaceus	NE Spain, May-Aug	B	A	O		89-97	92.5	1.9	31	JCF
	arundinaceus	SE Ukraine, Aug	B	J	N		90-103	95.4	2.6	208	GN
	arundinaceus	SE Ukraine, Aug	B	A	O		93-103	96.2	2.3	20	GN
	both races	C Arabia, Apr-May	P	A	O		90-103	96.8	2.9	90	GN/ JSA
	both races	NE Sudan, Aug-Sep	P	J	N		89-102	95.1	2.7	148	GN/ DJP
	both races	NE Sudan, Aug-Sep	P	A	O		88-102	94.5	2.9	192	GN/ DJP
	both races	C Kenya, Apr	P	A	N		90-104	96.0	2.9	114	DJP
	both races	SE Kenya, Nov-Dec	P	A	N		89-102	97.1	3.0	115	NRG
	both races	SE Kenya, Apr	P	A	N		90-103	97.2	3.6	23	DJP
	zarudnyi	SE Kazakhstan, Jul-Sep	B	J	N		87-104	95.4	2.8	2109	AG
	zarudnyi	SE Kazakhstan, May-Aug	B	A	O		88-105	96.3	2.9	387	AG
Oriental Reed Warbler		Hong Kong, Aug-Nov	P	A	N		73-97	83.7	3.6	3561	HKRG
		Hong Kong, Mar-May	P	A	O		76-98	87.0	4.4	1004	HKRG
		Thailand, Sep-May	W	A	N,O		73-91	83.0	3.3	479	PDR
		Singapore, Sep-Apr	W	A	N,O		76-89	82.3	2.7	116	PRK
Clamorous Reed Warbler	*brunnescens*	SE Kazakhstan, May	B	A	O		85-101	92.5	3.0	241	AG
Icterine Warbler		Crimea, Aug	P	J	N		74-82	77.9	1.9	76	GN/ DJP
		Crimea, Aug	P	A	O		74-82	78.5	2.0	26	GN/ DJP
Melodious Warbler		NE Spain, Jun-Sep	B	J	N		62-67	64.1	1.3	44	JCF
		NE Spain, Apr-Sep	B	A	N, O		61-69	65.6	1.8	92	JCF
		S Spain, Jun-Sep	B	J	N		60-69	63.9	2.0	79	GOES
		S Spain, Apr-Aug	B	A	N,O		62-71	65.6	2.0	97	GOES
Olive-tree Warbler		SE Kenya, Nov-Dec	P	J	O		72-93	83.9	2.6	727	NRG
		SE Kenya, Nov-Dec	P	A	O		76-93	85.9	2.5	608	NRG
Upcher's Warbler		Oman, Apr-May	P	A	N		72-81	76.9	2.0	90	GN/JSA
		SE Kenya, Nov-Dec	W	C	O		67-82	75.7	2.4	646	NRG
		SE Kenya, Nov-Dec	W	A	N		69-82	77.3	2.7	38	NRG

Species	Race	Location and month	Status	Primaries generation	Primaries condition	Sex	Wing length range	Wing length mean	Wing length SD	Wing length n	Source
Eastern Olivaceous Warbler	elaeica	C. Arabia, Apr-May	P	A	N		61-73	66.1	2.0	313	GN/JSA
	elaeica	SW Arabia, Apr-May	P	A	N		62-71	66.7	1.9	133	GN/JSA
	elaeica	NE Sudan, Aug-Sep	P	J	N		60-71	65.3	1.6	620	GN/DJP
	elaeica	NE Sudan, Aug-Sep	P	A	O		60-70	65.9	1.8	291	GN/DJP
	elaeica	SE Kenya, Nov-Dec	W	C	O		60-72	65.9	1.8	1074	NRG
	elaeica	SE Kenya, Nov-Dec	W	A	N		62-72	66.8	2.0	69	NRG
	pallida	N Sudan, Aug-Sep	P, W	J	N		59-64	61.7	1.4	68	GN/JSA
	pallida	N Sudan, Aug-Sep	P, W	A	O		59-66	62.7	1.6	32	GN/JSA
	reiseri	Gambia, Jan-Feb	W	A	N		62-65	63.9	0.9	14	RR
Western Olivaceous Warbler		S Spain, Jun-Sep	B	J	N		63-71	67.2	1.7	55	GOES
		S Spain, May-Aug	B	A	O		64-73	69.7	1.9	74	GOES
		Gambia, Jan-Feb	W	A	N		65-72	68.7	1.9	17	RR
Sykes's Warbler		Kazakhstan, Jul-Sep	B	J	N		59-64	61.4	1.2	23	AG
		Kazakhstan, May-Jul	B	A	O		59-67	61.5	1.8	47	AG
Booted Warbler		Kazakhstan, Jul-Sep	B	J	N		57-67	61.4	2.0	63	AG
		Kazakhstan, May-Aug	B	A	O		57-66	61.0	2.2	37	AG
Thick-billed Warbler	both races	Thailand, Oct-May	W	A	N, O		72-85	78.2	2.3	60	PDR
	both races	Hong Kong, Aug-Nov	P	A	N		74-81	78.5	2.1	31	HKRG
Asian Stubtail		Hong Kong, Oct-May	W	A	N,O		49-61	55.8	1.8	97	HKRG
Manchurian Bush Warbler	canturians	Hong Kong, Oct-May	W	A	N,O	M	71-80	75.0	1.9	134	HKRG
	canturians	Hong Kong, Oct-May	W	A	N,O	F	57-69	61.7	1.5	767	HKRG
Cetti's Warbler	cetti	NE Spain, all year	B	J	N,O	M	59-65	61.4	1.2	444	JCF
	cetti	NE Spain, all year	B	A	N,O	M	59-66	62.6	1.5	207	JCF
	cetti	NE Spain, all year	B	J	N,O	F	51-59	54.6	1.5	546	JCF
	cetti	NE Spain, all year	B	A	N,O	F	53-61	56.0	1.1	142	JCF
	cetti	E England, Jul-Oct	B	C	N	M	61-65	63.3	1.0	36	DJP
	cetti	E England, Jul-Oct	B	C	N	F	53-59	57.3	1.2	108	DJP
	albiventris	SE Kazakhstan, Jun-Oct	B	J	N		57-74	64.3	3.8	130	AG
	albiventris	SE Kazakhstan, Mar-Oct	B	A	N, O		58-74	64.6	4.2	74	AG

Initials in the text refer to the following sources. **Individuals**: JSA – J. S. Ash; SB – S. Bensch; JCF – J. C. Fernández-Ordóñez; PVG – P. V. Garcia; AG – A. Gavrilov; PRK – P. R. Kennerley; TM – T. Matsuo; BN – B. Neilson; GN – G. Nikolaus; DJP – D. J. Pearson; PP – P. Provost; RR – R. Riddington; PDR – P. D. Round; SJRR – S. J. R. Rumsey. **Organisations**: GOES – Grupo Ornitológico del Estrecho; HKRG – Hong Kong Ringing Group; KBIN – Belgian Ringing Scheme/N. Roothaert; NRG – Ngulia Ringing Group. **References**: C – Cramp (1992); M&L – McClure & Leelavit (1972); S – Shigeta (1988).

APPENDIX 3

PRINCIPAL MEASUREMENTS FROM MUSEUM SPECIMENS

Measurements taken by the authors; all from specimens at the Natural History Museum, Tring, UK, except where indicated by an asterisk.

APPENDIX 3A. WING AND TAIL MEASUREMENTS

Except in *C. cetti*, all birds included were judged to have adult primaries and tail feathers.

GENUS/ SPECIES	RACE/LOCALITY	WING				TAIL			
		range	mean	SD	n	range	mean	SD	n
Bradypterus									
baboecala	*baboecala*	58–62	59.7	1.6	15	61–74	66.0	3.2	15
baboecala	*transvaalensis*	58-63	61.0	1.8	6	64–71	69.7	3.5	6
baboecala	*tongensis*	53–60	57.3	1.6	23	59–65	62.2	2.0	19
baboecala	*msiri*	54–61	58.5	3.1	4	67–74	69.8	3.1	4
baboecala	*centralis* (Cameroon)	54–57	55.5	1.1	8	60	60.0		3
baboecala	*elgonensis**	53–58	56.4	1.7	11	60–64	64.4	1.4	7
baboecala	*abyssinicus*	56–60	57.6	1.5	5				
baboecala	*sudanensis*	50–55	53.0	1.6	7				
*carpalis**		66–71	68.4	1.6	7	66–75	68.4	3.8	7
graueri		61			1	72			1
grandis		67			1	76			1
alfredi	*kungwensis*	59–62	60.3	1.5	4	53–58	56.3	2.9	3
barratti	*priesti*	61–66	63.0	1.7	9	62–71	65.9	3.2	9
barratti	*barratti*	62–65	63.6	1.5	5	63–68	66.2	2.2	5
barratti	*godfreyi*	60–67	64.2	2.5	6	67–72	69.3	1.6	6
sylvaticus		56–63	59.8	2.5	6	49–60	55.3	3.7	6
cinnamomeus	*cinnamomeus*	58–66	62.7	2.1	29	63–74	69.3	3.0	12
cinnamomeus	*cavei*	58–65	62.4	2.0	11	63–69	64.4	2.1	8
cinnamomeus	*mildbreadi*	58–64	60.3	2.2	11				
cinnamomeus	*nyassae*	60–67	63.5	2.4	12	66–78	72.5	4.5	11
bangwaensis		60–66	63.4	1.7	19	57–67	62.4	2.7	19
lopezi	*mariae*	58–65	62.0	2.2	19	55–65	62.1	3.4	19
lopezi	*usambarae*	61–65	62.4	1.4	17	57–70	62.5	4.1	13
lopezi	*granti*	60–65	61.9	1.5	11	59–68	62.7	2.6	9
lopezi	*ufipae*	64–70	66.7	1.7	9	66–74	70.3	2.9	8
lopezi	*boultoni*	62	62.0		2	64–68	66.0		2
lopezi	*camerunensis*	54–60	57.2	1.3	15	54–61	56.5	2.6	6
lopezi	*lopezi*	58–62	59.6	1.8	5	53–64	58.8	4.2	5
lopezi	*barakae*	56–60	57.8	1.5	5	58–70	64.8	5.0	5
thoracicus	*thoracicus*	51–59	54.6	2.0	26	41–52	48.0	3.1	23
thoracicus	*przevalskii*	53–57	54.8	1.7	4	48–50	49.0		2
thoracicus	*kashmirensis*	55–57	56.2	1.1	5	45–50	47.8	2.6	5
davidi		51–55	53.0		2	44			1
major		54–62	59.0	1.9	48	54–66	58.8	2.6	46
tacsanowskius		53–60	55.7	2.0	25	51–61	55.4	3.0	23
luteoventris		49–57	52.9	1.7	55	51–62	56.8	2.3	54

GENUS/ SPECIES	RACE/LOCALITY	WING				TAIL			
		range	mean	SD	n	range	mean	SD	n
mandelli	*mandelli*	51–58	53.4	2.1	21	55–65	59.7	2.8	17
mandelli	*melanorhynchus*	49–53	50.8	1.5	6	49–61	55.2	4.5	5
mandelli	*idoneus*	51			1				
*montis**		52–56	53.9	1.3	14	53–61	58.5	2.6	13
caudatus	*caudatus*	62			1	88			1
caudatus	*unicolor*	61–62	61.5		2	71	71.0		2
accentor		58–61	59.4	1.1	5	55–61	58.0	2.1	5
castaneus	*castaneus*	54–58	56.0		2	50–57	53.5		2
castaneus	*disturbans*	60			1				
Elaphrornis									
palliseri		58–64	61.1	1.9	19	58–68	62.8	2.9	18
Locustella									
luscinioides	*luscinioides*	65–74	70.4	2.4	28	54–61	56.9	2.0	25
luscinioides	*fusca*	68–72	70.0	1.3	8	57–60	57.7	1.4	7
fluviatilis		68–79	75.2	2.5	26	52–59	55.4	2.1	26
naevia	*naevia*	61–65	63.6	1.2	22	51–58	53.8	2.1	22
naevia	*straminea*	55–61	58.9	1.8	33	46–56	51.2	2.9	30
lanceolata		54–61	57.3	1.8	33	40–47	43.2	1.8	28
certhiola	*certhiola*	60–71	65.0	2.8	17	41–53	48.7	1.9	17
certhiola	*minor*	57–67	61.6	2.6	21	43–49	46.3	1.9	20
certhiola	*rubescens*	61–66	63.7	2.0	17	45–55	49.5	2.7	17
certhiola	*sparsimstriata*	65–72	69.1	2.4	8	50–54	52.1	2.1	8
certhiola	*centralasiae*	60–71	64.8	3.0	21	43–51	48.0	2.8	21
ochotensis		64–77	70.5	2.9	49	49–58	53.9	2.7	35
pleskei		68–75	71.0	3.1	4	56–65	60.5	3.9	4
fasciolata	*fasciolata*	78–86	81.3	2.4	15	64–71	68.1	2.2	14
fasciolata	*amnicola*	81–87	83.7		3	65–68	66.0		3
pryeri	*pryeri*	52–54	53.0		2	48–50	49.5		2
pryeri	*sinensis*	58–59	58.5		2	46–59	53.3	1.8	4
Acrocephalus									
melanopogon	*melanopogon* (Spain)	53–58	55.1	1.4	11	44–50	46.6	1.5	11
melanopogon	*melanopogon* (E Mediterranean)	57–63	58.7	1.5	22	47–54	49.5	1.9	20
melanopogon	*mimicus*	57–67	62.6	1.9	58	48–58	52.8	2.3	58
schoenobaenus	(W and C Europe)	62–69	66.0	1.7	82	44–52	47.3	2.0	81
schoenobaenus	(Siberia)	66–72	68.5	1.4	22	46–51	47.9	1.3	17
paludicola		59–64	62.2	1.8	19	44–49	46.5	1.4	20
sorghophilus		57–59	57.7		3	45–48	46.7		3
bistrigiceps		52–60	55.4	2.1	77	42–52	46.2	2.6	26
tangorum		52–57	54.7	1.6	12	49–55	51.6	2.6	10
concinens	*concinens*	52–58	55.1	1.8	14	49–55	52.6	2.2	14
concinens	*haringtoni*	54–59	57.2	1.3	29	53–58	56.1	2.0	20
concinens	*stevensi*	53–57	54.8	1.3	21	50–56	53.7	1.6	18
agricola		54–62	57.7	1.7	76	47–58	52.5	2.4	73
dumetorum		59–65	62.4	1.5	132	46–54	49.9	1.9	129
orinus		60–61	60.5		2	53–54	53.5		2
palustris		64–72	68.4	1.7	43	47–55	51.3	1.9	43
scirpaceus	*scirpaceus* (UK)	63–69	65.4	1.7	32	48–55	51.1	1.8	29
scirpaceus	*fuscus**	65–72	67.6	1.8	37	49–57	52.6	2.0	20

GENUS/ SPECIES	RACE/LOCALITY	WING				TAIL			
		range	mean	SD	n	range	mean	SD	n
scirpaceus	avicenniae*	56–62	58.8	1.3	20	45–51	48.1	1.7	19
baeticatus	baeticatus	56–63	59.7	1.6	38	44–53	49.6	2.3	34
baeticatus	hallae	57–63	59.0	2.2	10	45–53	47.6	2.5	9
baeticatus	suahelicus	56–63	59.1	1.9	15	46–52	48.9	1.7	15
baeticatus	cinnamomeus (C and E Africa)*	51–57	54.4	1.4	30	39–48	44.5	2.0	29
baeticatus	cinnamomeus (L. Chad)	55–59	56.0	1.7	5	42–49	45.2	2.6	5
baeticatus	guiersi	56–60	58.0	1.4	5	45–50	47.2	2.2	3
brevipennis		62–69	66.3	1.6	11	58–65	61.6	2.3	11
gracilirostris	gracilirostris	72–81	75.7	2.3	22	65–74	69.9	2.8	16
gracilirostris	cununensis	68–77	72.1	3.1	7				
gracilirostris	leptorhynchus	59–68	64.9	2.0	40	55–60	58.0	1.8	16
gracilirostris	winterbottomi	67–74	69.3		3				
gracilirostris	parva (Tanzania)	65–70	67.3	1.7	10	58–64	61.0	2.6	7
gracilirostris	parva (Kenya highlands)*	67–78	72.6	3.3	28	60–74	68.4	5.3	7
gracilirostris	jacksoni	61–70	64.8	2.7	12	55–64	58.1	2.7	10
gracilirostris	tsanae	70–76	72.3	2.6	6				
gracilirostris	neglecta	62–68	64.7	2.3	6	58–61	59.7	1.5	3
rufescens	rufescens	67–76	73.1	2.7	29	64–78	69.8	3.8	19
rufescens	ansorgei	72–82	77.3	2.7	31	72–80	75.0	2.2	24
newtoni		64–73	68.4	2.6	14	70–78	73.1	2.3	14
sechellensis		65–74	67.8	3.7	6	51–60	56.8	3.9	6
rodericanus		60–65	63.3	2.0	7	63–74	70.6	2.8	5
griseldis		78–84	82.1	2.2	9	56–64	61.9	2.5	9
arundinaceus	arundinaceus	90–101	95.7	2.7	65	68–80	73.8	2.6	65
arundinaceus	zarudnyi	92–104	97.1	2.9	31	68–81	74.3	3.2	31
orientalis		76–90	83.1	3.7	51	60–76	67.4	3.6	51
stentoreus	stentoreus	74–84	79.9	2.9	28	65–81	71.2	3.4	28
stentoreus	brunnescens (C Asia/India)	78–95	86.9	3.4	81	66–84	74.6	4.1	79
stentoreus	brunnescens (Red Sea/ Arabian Sea)*	79–86	82.4	3.2	8	69–82	76.4	4.1	8
stentoreus	amyae	81–90	85.9	2.9	10	68–78	73.7	3.7	9
stentoreus	meridionalis	77–84	81.3	2.5	16	65–74	68.1	2.4	14
stentoreus	harterti	74–75	74.7		3	68–71	69.7	1.5	3
stentoreus	siebersi*	71–77	74.4	2.5	7	62–67	64.3	1.8	7
stentoreus	lentecaptus	73–81	76.8	3.9	4	61–73	67.0	5.0	4
stentoreus	sumbae	65–71	68.2	1.7	13	55–64	60.5		13
australis	australis	70–78	73.5	2.2	15	57–67	61.4	2.4	13
australis	gouldi	71–78	75.6	2.5	11	62–71	65.1	2.9	11
familiaris	familiaris*	60–64	61.8	2.9	4	53–61	58.0	3.8	4
familiaris	kingi*	62–65	63.3		3	60–63	61.5		2
kererako	kererako*	77–80	78.3	1.3	4	75–80	77.5	2.6	4
kererako	kaoko	83			1				
vaughani*		75–84	79.6	2.7	11	65–76	69.4	4.1	10
taiti*		80–83	81.0		3	78–80	79.3		3
aequatorialis	aequatorialis*	71–79	75.0		2	69			1
caffer	caffer*	94–103	98.2	3.4	6	75–85	80.8	3.5	6
mendanae	mendanae*	98–102	100.4	1.5	7	80–86	83.8	2.7	5

GENUS/ SPECIES	RACE/LOCALITY	WING				TAIL			
		range	mean	SD	n	range	mean	SD	n
mendanae	*fatuhivae**	94–97	95.5	1.1	6	77–84	79.0	2.8	6
percernis	*percernis**	99–104	102.1	1.9	8	81–91	85.5	2.8	8
percernis	*aquilonis**	91–95	93.0		2	82–85	83.5		2
percernis	*idae**	83–90	86.5		2	75–78	76.5		2
atyphus	*atyphus**	91			1	91			1
atyphus	*ravus**	82–89	87.0	3.4	4	69–74	70.0	2.9	4
atyphus	*eremus**	88–93	90.5		2	75–80	77.5		2
luscinius	*luscinius**	85–91	87.3	2.9	4	73–76	74.3		3
syrinx		75–81	77.8	1.6	12	63–72	67.2	2.3	12
Hippolais									
icterina		76–83	78.8	1.7	48	48–54	51.6	1.8	45
polyglotta		61–70	66.1	2.2	88	46–54	49.4	1.8	88
olivetorum		81–90	86.1	2.4	24	59–69	64.4	2.8	24
languida		71–80	75.8	2.3	35	55–63	58.9	1.8	35
Iduna									
pallida	*elaeica*	62–71	66.8	1.8	113	45–54	50.3	1.9	109
pallida	*pallida*	61–67	63.7	2.0	38	47–54	50.2	1.9	38
pallida	*reiseri*	65			1	52–54	53.0		2
pallida	*laeneni*	59–64	61.6	2.2	11	47–52	49.9	2.0	11
pallida	*alulensis**	58–62	60.5	1.9	4	47–50	49.0	1.4	4
opaca		65–73	69.2	2.0	26	52–60	55.7	1.9	28
rama		58–65	61.2	1.5	100	46–56	51.8	1.8	99
caligata		56–65	60.2	1.8	90	42–49	46.3	1.5	89
natalensis	*massaica*	58–67	62.3	2.1	35	51–62	56.3	2.5	21
natalensis	*natalensis*	56–65	61.4	2.0	27	53–62	56.6	2.3	21
natalensis	*major*	61–70	65.3	2.8	11	52–59	56.1	2.1	11
natalensis	*batesi*	57–61	59.1	1.3	20	51–58	53.5	2.0	19
similis		55–64	58.8	2.0	33	48–60	56.3	3.5	20
Phragamaticola									
aedon	*aedon*	78–86	80.3	2.3	82	76–90	81.3	3.3	80
aedon	*stegmanni*	73–79	76.5	2.2	15	70–81	76.5	3.1	15
Calamonastides									
gracilirostris	*gracilirostris**	58–62	60.0		2	62			1
gracilirostris	*bensoni*	59			1	58			1
Nesillas									
typica	*typica*	58–70	64.5	3.3	27	67–93	81.9	6.8	26
typica	*ellisii*	57–67	61.3	2.8	43	67–85	75.7	5.1	43
typica	*obscura*	59–72	68.1	4.4	10	67–83	79.6	5.0	10
typica	*longicaudata*	59–70	63.6	4.4	5	67–78	72.8	4.3	5
typica	*moheliensis*	63			1	74			1
lantzii		57–67	62.3	3.1	12	68–84	76.9	4.7	11
brevicaudata		62–68	64.7	2.1	9	61–67	64.3	2.2	7
mariae		64			1	64			1
Oligura									
castaneocoronata	*castaneocoronata*	46–53	49.5	2.0	33	20–27	23.3	2.1	29
castaneocoronata	*abadiei*	48–52	49.7		3	24–25	24.7		3
Tesia									
cyaniventer		45–53	49.7	1.9	51	15–19	16.9	1.3	20
olivea		42–52	47.0	2.1	30	13–19	16.2	1.7	22

GENUS/ SPECIES	RACE/LOCALITY	WING				TAIL			
		range	mean	SD	n	range	mean	SD	n
superciliaris		47–51	48.6	1.5	5				
everetti		50–54	51.4	1.7	5	16–20	18.5	1.7	4
Urosphena									
subulata		53–54	53.3		3	24–27	25.7		3
whiteheadi		47–55	52.5	2.4	10	20–26	22.0	1.1	10
squamiceps		51–57	54.1	1.9	20	27–33	29.7	1.5	20
Cettia									
pallidipes	*pallidipes*	46–56	51.9	3.3	19	36–43	40.9	2.5	19
pallidipes	*laurentei*	45–52	48.3		3	40–41	40.7		3
pallidipes	*osmastoni*	52	52.0		2	40–41	40.5		2
vulcania	*vulcania*	50–56	53.5	2.3	6	51–57	54.8	2.7	5
vulcania	*flaviventris*	50–55	53.2	2.0	6	48–55	51.8	2.3	6
vulcania	*oreophila*	49–53	51.1	1.5	6	50–55	52.7	2.0	6
vulcania	*everetti*	50			1	50			1
flavolivacea	*flavolivacea*	51–58	54.7	2.2	33	48–55	52.2	2.3	33
flavolivacea	*stresemanni*	50–53	51.5		2				
flavolivacea	*weberi*	48–54	52.4	2.5	5	53–57	55.2	1.8	5
flavolivacea	*intricata*	53			1	51			1
fortipes	*fortipes*	49–58	54.9	2.3	29	45–54	50.3	2.6	24
fortipes	*pallida*	50–59	55.0	2.5	27	45–54	49.3	2.9	24
fortipes	*davidiana*	47–60	54.6	3.5	56	41–54	47.2	4.1	50
acanthizoides	*acanthizoides*	47–56	51.0	3.0	10	40–49	44.7	3.3	9
acanthizoides	*concolor*	49–54	51.3		3	42–49	44.7		3
brunnescens		48–56	52.4	2.3	33	39–50	43.9	2.6	33
major		60–66	62.8	2.3	21	40–51	47.4	3.7	20
brunnifrons	*brunnifrons*	43–50	46.8	1.8	38	38–46	42.4	2.7	30
brunnifrons	*whistleri*	43–47	44.6	1.3	11	40–45	41.9	1.5	9
canturians	*canturians* (male)	71–78	74.4	1.8	24	68–79	72.8	2.9	23
canturians	*canturians* (female)	57–64	60.8	1.9	14	53–63	58.4	2.4	13
canturians	*borealis* (male)	72–82	74.8	2.5	23	66–72	69.2	2.6	20
canturians	*borealis* (female)	61–66	62.9	1.5	10	55–61	57.4	1.9	9
diphone	*cantans* (male)	64–71	66.9	1.7	37	61–69	64.7	2.0	37
diphone	*cantans* (female)	55–61	56.8	2.2	10	53–60	55.3	2.1	10
diphone	*riukiuensis* (male)	67–71	69.0	1.9	5	64–67	65.2	1.1	5
diphone	*riukiuensis* (female)	56–58	57.1	0.8	8	52–59	54.8	1.8	6
diphone	*diphone* (male)	56–60	57.8	1.3	6	60–64	62.3	1.4	6
diphone	*diphone* (female)	49–50	49.5		2	49–54	51.5		2
seebohmi		50–58	53.6	3.2	7	59–67	62.3	3.8	7
annae		68–77	71.7	4.7	3	60–67	63.0	3.6	3
cetti	*cetti*	52–65	59.2	4.2	27	47–63	56.0	4.7	27
cetti	*cetti* (male)	59–65	62.0	1.8	17	55–63	59.1	2.4	17
cetti	*cetti* (female)	52–57	54.3	1.4	10	47–53	50.7	2.4	10
cetti	*orientalis*	58–70	63.3	3.2	22	51–64	59.5	3.4	20
cetti	*albiventris*	60–72	67.5	3.5	22	59–71	65.5	3.8	20

APPENDIX 3B. BILL AND TARSUS MEASUREMENTS

GENUS/ SPECIES	RACE/LOCALITY	BILL				TARSUS			
		range	mean	SD	n	range	mean	SD	n
Bradypterus									
baboecala	baboecala	15.0–17.5	16.0	0.8	15	21.0–24.0	22.8	0.9	15
baboecala	elgonensis*	14.0–15.5	14.5	0.6	8	20.0–21.5	21.0	0.6	7
carpalis*		17.0–18.5	17.6	0.5	6	26.0–28.0	27.3	1.2	3
graueri		16.0			1	24.0			1
grandis		16.5			1	25.0			1
alfredi	kungwensis	16.5–18.0	17.0	0.7	4	21.0–24.0	22.8	1.3	4
barratti	priesti	15.0–16.0	15.3	0.4	9	22.0–24.0	23.2	0.6	9
barratti	barratti	14.5–16.0	15.7	0.7	5	22.0–23.0	22.5	0.6	4
barratti	godfreyi	15.0–16.0	15.4	0.4	6	21.5–23.0	22.4	0.6	6
sylvaticus		15.0–16.0	15.4	0.5	6	20.0–20.5	20.2	0.3	6
cinnamomeus	cinnamomeus	14.0–15.5	14.8	0.6	12	23.0–25.0	24.0	0.5	12
cinnamomeus	nyassae	14.5–15.5	15.1	0.3	10				
bangwaensis		15.0–17.0	16.0	0.6	18	23.5–26.0	24.9	0.7	18
lopezi	mariae	14.5–16.5	15.5	0.6	18	23.5–26.0	24.7	0.7	18
lopezi	ufipae	15.5–18.0	16.8	0.8	9	24.5–26.0	25.4	0.7	9
lopezi	camerunensis	14.5–16.0	15.4	0.5	19	21.5–24.0	22.9	0.8	19
lopezi	barakae	13.5–15.0	14.3	0.5	6	22.0–22.5	22.3	0.3	5
thoracicus	thoracicus	12.0–14.0	13.1	0.5	22	19.0–21.0	20.2	0.7	19
thoracicus	przevalskii	13.0	13.0		2	20	20.0		2
thoracicus	kashmirensis	13.0–14.5	14.0	0.7	4	19.0–20.5	19.9	0.6	5
davidi		12.5–12.7	12.6		2	19.0–19.5	19.3		2
major		16.5–19.0	17.5	0.6	44	21.0–23.5	22.1	0.7	43
tacsanowskius		13.0–15.0	13.8	0.7	22	18.0–20.0	19.1	0.6	25
luteoventris		12.5–14.0	13.3	0.5	53	18.0–20.0	19.2	0.7	46
mandelli	mandelli	13.0–15.0	13.9	0.5	15	17.5–19.5	18.6	0.6	18
mandelli	melanorhynchus	12.5–14.0	13.2	0.5	6	17.5–19.5	18.2	0.8	6
montis*		13.5–15.0	14.4	0.6	14	19.5–22.0	20.7	0.6	14
caudatus	caudatus	16.5			1	26.0			1
caudatus	unicolor	17.3			1	26.0	26.0		2
accentor		15.0–16.0	15.6	0.4	5	22.0–23.5	23.0	0.7	5
castaneus	castaneus	16.0–17.0	16.5		2	25.0–26.0	25.5		2
castaneus	disturbans	17.0			1	25.0			1
Elaphrornis									
palliseri		16.5–18.5	18.0	0.6	16	24.0–27.0	25.7	0.9	18
Locustella									
luscinioides	luscinioides	14.5–16.5	15.6	0.6	25	20.0–23.0	21.5	0.7	26
luscinioides	fusca	15.5–17.0	15.8	0.5	8	20.5–22.0	21.4	0.6	7
fluviatilis		15.0–17.0	15.7	0.6	26	20.0–22.5	22.0	0.7	25
naevia	naevia	12.5–15.0	14.1	0.6	21	19.5–21.0	20.1	0.6	20
naevia	straminea	13.0–15.5	13.8	0.6	33	17.5–19.5	18.8	0.6	26
lanceolata		12.5–14.0	13.2	0.4	27	18.0–20.0	18.8	0.5	28
certhiola	certhiola	14.0–16.0	15.1	0.5	17	20.0–23.0	21.3	0.9	18
certhiola	minor	13.5–15.5	14.7	0.6	21	19.5–22.0	20.8	0.8	18
certhiola	rubescens	14.5–16.0	15.3	0.5	16	21.0–23.0	21.6	0.6	17
certhiola	sparsimstriata	15.0–16.0	15.5	0.4	8	21.5–23.0	22.6	0.6	7
certhiola	centralasiae	14.0–16.0	14.8	0.8	21	19.5–23.0	21.4	0.9	21

GENUS/ SPECIES	RACE/LOCALITY	BILL				TARSUS			
		range	mean	SD	n	range	mean	SD	n
ochotensis		15.5–18.5	17.0	0.7	47	22.0–25.5	23.7	0.9	29
pleskei		18.5–19.5	19.1	0.5	4	23.5–25.0	24.3	0.7	4
fasciolata	*fasciolata*	19.0–22.0	20.7	0.9	14	26.0–29.0	27.6	0.7	15
fasciolata	*amnicola*	20.5–21.5	21.0	0.5	3	28.0	28.0		3
pryeri	*pryeri*	11.5–12.5	12.0		2	19.0–19.5	19.3		2
pryeri	*sinensis*	11.5–13.0	12.6	0.6	5	18.5–20.0	19.2	0.6	5
Acrocephalus									
melanopogon	*melanopogon* (Spain)	13.5–15.5	14.6	0.6	10	19.5–20.5	19.9	0.3	11
melanopogon	*melanopogon* (E Mediterranean)	14.5–16.5	15.3	0.6	18	20.0–21.5	20.6	0.4	14
melanopogon	*mimicus*	14.5–16.5	15.6	0.5	53	20.0–23.0	21.3	0.6	48
schoenobaenus	(W/C Europe)	13.0–15.5	14.7	0.6	64	20.0–23.0	21.1	0.6	62
schoenobaenus	(Siberia)	14.0–16.0	14.8	0.6	16	20.5–22.5	21.6	0.5	15
paludicola		13.0–14.0	13.4	0.4	18	19.0–21.5	20.3	0.7	19
sorghophilus		13.5–15.0	14.3	0.8	3	20.0–21.0	20.5	0.5	3
bistrigiceps		13.5–15.0	14.2	0.5	25	20.0–22.0	20.9	0.6	23
tangorum		14.5–16.0	15.3	0.6	12	21.0–22.5	21.6	0.5	12
concinens	*concinens*	15.0–16.0	15.7	0.4	12	21.0–22.0	21.8	0.5	8
concinens	*haringtoni*	14.5–15.5	14.9	0.3	18	21.0–23.0	22.1	0.6	19
concinens	*stevensi*	15.0–16.5	15.6	0.4	17	20.5–22.0	21.6	0.8	4
agricola		13.0–16.0	14.8	0.6	75	20.0–23.0	21.7	0.7	60
dumetorum		15.5–18.5	17.1	0.7	123	20.5–23.5	22.1	0.7	56
palustris		14.5–17.0	15.8	0.6	47	21.0–23.5	22.4	0.7	43
scirpaceus	*scirpaceus* (UK)	15.5–18.0	16.9	0.7	24	21.5–23.5	22.4	0.6	31
scirpaceus	*fuscus**	17.0–19.0	17.7	0.6	20	21.0–24.0	22.8	0.9	19
scirpaceus	*avicenniae**	15.0–17.0	15.8	0.6	19	19.5–22.5	20.7	0.7	19
baeticatus	*baeticatus*	15.5–17.5	16.5	0.6	30	21.5–23.5	22.5	0.5	22
baeticatus	*hallae*	16.0–17.0	16.8	0.4	6	22.0–23.0	22.3	0.4	6
baeticatus	*suahelicus*	17.0–18.5	17.5	0.5	15	21.0–23.0	21.8	0.8	10
baeticatus	*cinnamomeus* (C and E Africa)*	15.0–17.0	15.8	0.5	27	20.0–22.0	21.2	0.7	21
baeticatus	*cinnamomeus* (L. Chad)	16.0–16.5	16.1	0.2	5	20.5–21.5	20.9	0.5	5
baeticatus	*guiersi*	15.5–16.5	16.0	0.5	5	21.0–22.0	21.4	0.6	5
brevipennis		19.5–21.0	20.2	0.5	18	25.5–27.0	26.5	0.6	18
gracilirostris	*gracilirostris*	19.0–21.0	20.0	0.7	15	27.0–30.0	28.4	0.7	16
gracilirostris	*leptorhynchus*	18.0–20.5	19.2	0.9	16	25.0–20.7	26.1	0.9	14
gracilirostris	*parva* (Kenya highlands)*	18.5–20.0	19.5	0.7	7	28.0–29.0	28.6	0.5	7
gracilirostris	*jacksoni*	17.5–19.5	18.4	0.6	9	25.0–26.0	25.8	0.4	9
rufescens	*rufescens*	20.0–23.0	21.5	0.9	18	28.0–31.0	29.5	0.9	18
rufescens	*ansorgei*	20.0–23.5	22.0	0.9	23	28.0–33.0	30.7	1.3	24
newtoni		18.0–20.0	18.6	0.7	14	24.0–28.0	25.8	1.2	15
sechellensis		17.5–18.5	18.0	0.3	6	24.0–27.5	25.2	1.3	6
rodericanus		17.5–18.5	18.0	0.3	7	22.5–24.5	23.3	0.8	7
griseldis		20.0–23.0	21.4	0.9	9	24.5–26.5	25.2	0.7	8
arundinaceus	*arundinaceus*	20.5–24.0	22.8	0.9	65	27.0–31.0	29.1	1.0	65
arundinaceus	*zarudnyi*	21.0–24.5	23.5	0.9	29	27.0–32.0	29.7	1.3	29
orientalis		21.0–24.5	22.4	0.8	50	26.5–31.0	28.2	1.0	48
stentoreus	*stentoreus*	24.0–27.5	25.5	0.8	27	26.0–30.0	28.0	1.2	27

GENUS/ SPECIES	RACE/LOCALITY	BILL				TARSUS			
		range	mean	SD	n	range	mean	SD	n
stentoreus	brunnescens (C Asia/ India)	23.0–26.0	24.6	1.0	69	24.0–30.5	28.5	1.3	70
stentoreus	brunnescens(Red Sea/ Arabian Sea)*	24.0–26.0	24.8	0.7	8	25.5–28.5	27.1	1.1	8
stentoreus	amyae	23.0–26.0	24.9	1.0	10	28.5–30.0	29.3	0.6	10
stentoreus	meridionalis	23.0–26.0	24.6	1.0	15	27.0–30.5	28.3	1.2	13
stentoreus	harterti	19.0–21.0	20.2	1.0	3	26.0–27.0	26.5	0.5	3
stentoreus	siebersi*	19.0–23.0	21.3	1.4	7	26.0–29.0	27.6	1.3	7
stentoreus	lentecaptus	22.0–24.0	23.6	1.1	4	24.0–27.0	26.3	1.5	4
stentoreus	sumbae	19.0–21.0	20.5	0.7	13	24.5–26.0	25.0	0.6	13
australis	australis	19.0–21.0	20.1	0.7	14	23.0–26.0	24.9	0.9	13
australis	gouldi	19.5–22.0	21.2	1.0	11	24.0–27.0	25.7	0.9	11
familiaris	familiaris*	18.0–19.0	18.6	0.5	4	20.5–23.5	22.0	1.22	4
familiaris	kingi*	18.5–19.5	19.0		3	23.5–24.5	24.2		3
kerearako	kerearako*	22.0			1	27.0–28.0	27.8	0.5	4
kerearako	kaoko	21.5			1	27.0			1
vaughani*		19.5–22.0	20.6	0.9	9	28.5–32.5	30.0	1.3	11
taiti*		17.0–19.5	18.3		3	26–29	28.0		3
aequatorialis	aequatorialis*	20.5–21.5	21.0		2	25–26	25.5		2
caffer	caffer*	31.0–39.0	34.3	2.7	6	31.5–35.0	32.3	1.3	6
mendanae	mendanae*	28.0–33.0	31.7	2.0	7	30.0–33.0	31.6	1.3	7
mendanae	fatuhivae*	30.0–35.0	32.1	1.7	7	30.0–34.0	31.7	1.3	7
percernis	percernis*	27.5–32.0	30.5	1.4	8	28.5–33.0	30.4	1.4	7
percernis	aquilonis*	26.5–27.5	27.0		2	27.5–30.0	28.8		2
percernis	idae*	24.5–26.5	25.5		2	25			1
atyphus	atyphus*	27.0–27.5	27.2		3	29.5–30.5	30.2		3
atyphus	ravus*	27.0–28.0	27.4	0.5	4	28.5–31.5	29.9	1.3	4
atyphus	eremus*	28.5–32.0	30.3		2	27.0–30.5	29.8		2
luscinius	luscinius*	35.0–36.0	35.4	0.5	4	30.0–34.0	31.9	1.8	4
syrinx		24.0–27.5	25.6	1.3	11	26.0–29.0	27.2	1.0	12
Hippolais									
icterina		15.0–17.5	16.6	0.6	45	19.5–22.0	20.8	0.7	44
polyglotta		14.0–17.0	15.8	0.8	85	19.5–22.0	20.4	0.6	79
olivetorum		18.5–21.0	19.6	0.6	23	22.5–24.5	23.3	0.6	24
languida		17.0–20.0	18.2	0.7	32	20.0–23.0	22.1	0.7	32
Iduna									
pallida	elaeica	14.5–17.5	16.3	0.8	100	19.0–22.0	21.0	0.7	82
pallida	pallida	14.5–17.0	15.8	0.6	48	20.0–22.0	21.1	0.6	38
pallida	reiseri	15.5			1	20.0			1
pallida	laeneni	14.5–16.0	15.3	0.5	8	19.0–21.5	20.0	0.6	11
pallida	alulensis*	15.0–16.0	15.4	0.5	4	20.0–21.0	20.4	0.48	4
opaca		16.5–19.0	17.9	0.6	32	21.5–24.0	22.8	0.6	30
rama		14.0–17.0	15.3	0.6	99	19.5–22.0	20.5	0.6	54
caligata		12.5–15.0	13.6	0.7	84	18.5–21.0	19.9	0.6	73
natalensis	massaica	14.5–16.0	15.4	0.5	20	20.5–22.0	21.0	0.5	21
natalensis	natalensis	14.0–16.5	15.5	0.8	12	19.0–22.0	21.2	0.9	12
natalensis	major	15.0–16.5	16.0	0.5	11	21.0–23.0	22.0	0.7	11
natalensis	batesi	15.0–16.5	15.5	0.8	12	19.5–21.0	20.5	0.9	12
similis		13.5–16.0	15.4	0.7	20	21.5–23.0	22.5	0.5	20

GENUS/ SPECIES	RACE/LOCALITY	BILL				TARSUS			
		range	mean	SD	n	range	mean	SD	n
Phragamaticola									
aedon	*aedon*	17.5–20.5	19.0	0.7	80	27.0–30.0	27.8	1.0	50
aedon	*stegmanni*	17.5–19.5	18.4	0.6	14	26.5–29.0	27.4	0.8	15
Calamonastides									
gracilirostris	*gracilirostris**	14.0–16.5	15.3		2	21.0–23.0	22.0		2
gracilirostris	*bensoni*	16.0			1	20.0			1
Nesillas									
typica	*typica*	14.5–17.0	15.6	0.9	25	23.0–26.5	24.9	1.1	22
typica	*ellisii*	14.5–17.0	16.1	0.7	42	22.5–27.0	25.0	1.1	36
typica	*obscura*	16.0–18.0	17.5	0.8	10	24.0–27.0	25.2	1.1	10
typica	*longicaudata*	16.5–18.0	17.2	0.7	5	23.0–27.0	24.6	1.5	5
typica	*moheliensis*	17.0			1	25.0			1
lantzii		14.5–16.5	15.6	0.7	12	21.5–25.0	23.2	1.2	12
brevicaudata		16.0–18.0	16.9	0.8	7	23.0–27.0	25.3	1.5	7
mariae		16.0			1	23.0			1
Oligura									
castaneocoronata	*castaneocoronata*	11.5–13.5	12.3	0.5	31	20.5–23.5	22.1	0.8	28
castaneocoronata	*abadiei*	12.0–12.5	12.2		3	22.0–23.0	22.3		3
Tesia									
cyaniventer		13.5–15.5	14.5	0.6	51	21.5–25.0	23.4	0.8	45
olivea		12.0–15.0	13.9	0.8	27	19.5–24.0	22.0	0.9	28
superciliaris		14.0–15.0	14.5	0.4	5	22.5–25.5	24.3	1.4	5
everetti		15.0–17.0	15.8	0.9	5	22.5–26.0	24.5	1.3	5
Urosphena									
subulata		15.5–16.0	15.7	0.2	3	19.0–20.0	19.5		3
whiteheadi		14.0–15.5	15.0	0.5	9	18.5–20.5	19.5	0.5	10
squamiceps		13.5–16.5	14.7	0.8	20	17.5–19.5	18.3	0.7	19
Cettia									
pallidipes	*pallidipes*	13.0–14.5	13.7	0.5	16	17.5–20.0	19.3	0.7	18
pallidipes	*laurentei*	13.5–14.5	14.0		2	18.5–19.0	18.8		3
pallidipes	*osmastoni*					20.5			1
vulcania	*vulcania*	13.5–14.5	13.9	0.4	6	23.0–25.0	23.5	0.8	6
vulcania	*flaviventris*	13.5–14.5	14.0	0.3	6	21.5–24.5	22.9	1.0	6
vulcania	*oreophila*	14.0–15.0	14.8	0.4	6	22.0–23.0	22.6	0.4	6
vulcania	*everetti*	14.0			1	21.0			1
flavolivacea	*flavolivacea*	13.0–15.0	13.9	0.6	30	21.0–24.0	22.2	0.9	30
flavolivacea	*stresemanni*	14.0	14.0		2	21.5–23.0	22.3		2
flavolivacea	*weberi*	13.0–14.5	13.9	0.6	5	21.0–23.0	21.8	0.8	5
flavolivacea	*intricata*	13.0			1	22.5–23.0	22.8		2
fortipes	*fortipes*	13.5–15.0	14.4	0.5	24	20.0–23.5	21.9	0.9	19
fortipes	*pallida*	12.5–14.0	13.3	0.5	24	20.0–23.0	21.4	1.0	20
fortipes	*davidiana*	12.5–14.0	13.4	0.6	48	19.0–23.5	21.6	1.1	38
acanthizoides	*acanthizoides*	11.0–12.5	11.8	0.5	10	19.0–21.5	20.1	0.8	10
acanthizoides	*concolor*	11.5–13.0	12.3		2	20.0–21.5	20.7		3
brunnescens		12.0–14.0	12.9	0.5	33	20.0–23.0	21.2	0.7	26
major		13.0–15.5	14.4	0.7	21	22.0–26.0	24.2	0.9	21
brunnifrons	*brunnifrons*	10.5–12.0	11.4	0.5	37	17.5–19.0	18.4	0.5	23
brunnifrons	*whistleri*	10.5–12.0	11.5	0.5	12	17.5–18.5	18.0	0.2	10

GENUS/ SPECIES	RACE/LOCALITY	BILL				TARSUS			
		range	mean	SD	n	range	mean	SD	n
canturians	*canturians* (male)	16.0–19.0	17.6	0.7	22	27.5–29.5	28.0	0.7	21
canturians	*canturians* (female)	14.5–16.0	15.2	0.6	13	22.5–24.5	23.3	0.6	13
canturians	*borealis* (male)	16.5–19.0	17.6	0.6	22	25.5–29.5	27.8	1.0	22
canturians	*borealis* (female)	15.0–16.5	15.7	0.5	8	22.5–24.5	23.7	0.5	8
diphone	*cantans* (male)	14.5–17.0	16.0	0.6	35	24.0–26.5	25.1	0.7	36
diphone	*cantans* (female)	13.5–15.0	14.3	0.4	9	21.5–23.0	22.2	0.6	10
diphone	*riukiuensis* (male)	15.5–16.5	15.9	0.4	5	25.0–27.0	25.9	1.0	4
diphone	*riukiuensis* (female)	14.0–15.5	14.6	0.7	6	22.0–23.0	22.8	0.5	5
diphone	*diphone* (male)	17.0–18.0	17.6	0.5	6	24.0–25.0	24.2	0.4	6
diphone	*diphone* (female)	17.0	17.0		2	22.5–23.5	23.0		2
seebohmi		15.5–17.0	16.2	0.1	6	21.5–23.5	22.6	0.7	7
annae		20.5–22.5	21.7	1.2	3	26.0–29.0	27.7	1.4	3
cetti	*cetti*	13.0–15.5	14.0	0.8	26	19.0–23.0	21.0	1.2	26
cetti	*cetti* (male)	13.0–15.5	14.3	0.8	16	20.5–23.0	21.8	0.8	17
cetti	*cetti* (female)	13.0–14.5	13.5	0.5	10	19.0–20.0	19.7	0.4	9
cetti	*orientalis*	13.0–15.5	14.2	0.7	18	20.0–23.5	21.7	1.1	17
cetti	*albiventris*	14.0–16.0	15.4	0.6	20	20.5–24.0	22.2	1.2	16

APPENDIX 4

ORIGINS, MIGRATION STATUS AND MOULT STRATEGIES

Origin is given as P – Palearctic, A – Afrotropical, O – Oriental, Au – Australasian and Oc – Oceanic; migration status as R – resident, S – short-distance migrant, L – long-distance migrant or A – altitudinal migrant. Species may fall into more than one category, minor categories being given in parentheses.

Summaries of moult strategy are given for Palearctic migrants, based on the notation of Svensson (1992). Moults are specified as Complete (C), or partial (p). Their timing is given as Summer – S (July–August), Autumn – A (September–December) or Winter – W (January–April), using lower case for partial moults. S refers to moult at or near the breeding area while A and W will refer to moult in a non-breeding area. Moult suspended and divided between two periods is indicated by a dash (as in S–A). A species may employ more than one strategy. Less frequent strategies are shown in parentheses, unusual strategies in square brackets. Uncertainty about a moult timing is indicated by ?.

Genus/Species	Origin	Migration status	Moult in Palearctic species	
			adult	first year
Bradypterus				
Little Rush Warbler	A	R		
White-winged Swamp Warbler	A	R		
Grauer's Swamp Warbler	A	R		
Dja River Warbler	A	R		
Bamboo Warbler	A	R		
Barratt's Warbler	A	R		
Knysna Scrub Warbler	A	R		
Cinnamon Bracken Warbler	A	R		
Bangwa Forest Warbler	A	R		
Evergreen Forest Warbler	A	R		
Spotted Bush Warber	P (O)	A		
Baikal Bush Warbler	P	L	sp? ap? WC	sp WC
Long-billed Bush Warbler	P	A		
Chinese Bush Warbler	P	L	AC wp?	sp? AC wp?
Brown Bush Warbler	O	R A		
Russet Bush Warbler	O	R A		
Javan Bush Warbler	O	R		
Timor Bush Warbler	O	R		
Benguet Bush Warbler	O	R		
Taiwan Bush Warbler	O	R A		
Long-tailed Bush Warbler	O	R		
Kinabalu Bush Warbler	O	R		
Chestnut-backed Bush Warbler	O	R		
Elaphrornis				
Ceylon Bush Warbler	O	R		
Locustella				
Savi's Warbler	P	L	SC wp, or S-AC, or sp AC	AC, or A-WC
River Warbler	P	L	ap WC	WC
Western Grasshopper Warbler	P	L	sp AC, or [SC]	AC, or (A-WC?)
Lanceolated Warbler	P	L	sp WC	sp WC
Pallas's Grasshopper Warbler	P	L	sp WC	WC
Middendorff's Grasshopper Warbler	P	L	sp WC	WC
Styan's Grasshopper Warbler	P	L	sp WC	WC
Gray's Grasshopper Warbler	P	L	sp WC	WC

Genus/Species	Origin	Migration status	Moult in Palearctic species	
			adult	first year
Japanese Swamp Warbler	P	R S	SC	SC
Acrocephalus				
Moustached Warbler	P	R S L	SC wp, or S-AC wp, or AC wp	
Sedge Warbler	P	L	(sp) AC wp, or sp WC, or sp A-WC	AC wp, or A-WC, or WC
Aquatic Warbler	P	L	sp AC wp	AC wp
Streaked Reed Warbler	P	L	WC	WC
Black-browed Reed Warbler	P	L	SC	SC
Manchurian Reed Warbler	P	L	AC (wp)	AC (wp)
Blunt-winged Warbler	P	R S L	SC	SC
Paddyfield Warbler	P	L	sp AC wp	sp AC wp
Blyth's Reed Warbler	P	L	(sp) AC wp	sp AC wp
Large-billed Reed Warbler	P	S? L	AC	AC
Marsh Warbler	P	L	ap WC	(sp) (ap) WC
Eurasian Reed Warbler	P (A)	L (S) (R)	sp AC, or sp WC, or (SC)	sp AC, or sp WC, or (SC)
African Reed Warbler	A	R S		
Cape Verde Warbler	A	R		
Lesser Swamp Warbler	A	R		
Greater Swamp Warbler	A	R		
Madagascar Swamp Warbler	A	R		
Seychelles Warbler	A	R		
Rodrigues Warbler	A	R		
Basra Reed Warbler	P	L	sp AC wp, or sp A-WC, or sp WC	sp AC wp, or sp A-WC, or sp WC
Great Reed Warbler	P	L	sp AC wp, or sp WC, or [SC wp]	sp AC wp, or sp WC
Oriental Reed Warbler	P	L	SC wp	SC wp
Clamorous Reed Warbler	P O Au	R S L	SC, or AC	SC, or sp AC
Australian Reed Warbler	Au	R S		
Millerbird	Oc	R		
Cook Islands Warbler	Oc	R		
Pitcairn Island Warbler	Oc	R		
Henderson Island Warbler	Oc	R		
Rimatara Warbler	Oc	R		
Kiritimati Warbler	Oc	R		
Southern Marquesan Warbler	Oc	R		
Northern Marquesan Warbler	Oc	R		
Tahiti Warbler	Oc	R		
Tuamotu Warbler	Oc	R		
Nightingale Warbler	Oc	R		
Caroline Islands Warbler	Oc	R		
Nauru Warbler	Oc	R		
Hippolais				
Icterine Warbler	P	L	(sp) WC	WC
Melodious Warbler	P	L	AC wp	AC wp
Olive-tree Warbler	P	L	ap WC	sp (ap) WC
Upcher's Warbler	P	L	AC, or A-WC	sp AC, or sp A-WC

Genus/Species	Origin	Migration status	Moult in Palearctic species	
			adult	first year
Iduna				
Eastern Olivaceous Warbler	P (A)	R S L	sp AC, or sp A-WC	sp AC, or sp A-WC
Western Olivaceous Warbler	P	L	sp AC	sp AC
Sykes's Warbler	P	L (S)	sp AC (wp)	sp AC (wp)
Booted Warbler	P	L	sp AC wp	sp AC wp
Dark-capped Yellow Warbler	A	R		
Mountain Yellow Warbler	A	R		
Phragamaticola				
Thick-billed Warbler	P	L	SC	SC
Calamonastides				
Papyrus Yellow Warbler	A	R		
Nesillas				
Madagascar Brush Warbler	A	R		
Lantz's Brush Warbler	A	R		
Grande Comore Brush Warbler	A	R		
Moheli Brush Warbler	A	R		
Aldabra Brush Warbler	A	R		
Oligura				
Chestnut-headed Tesia	O (P)	R A		
Tesia				
Grey-bellied Tesia	O	R A		
Slaty-bellied Tesia	O	R A		
Javan Tesia	O	R		
Russet-capped Tesia	O	R		
Urosphena				
Timor Stubtail	Au	R		
Bornean Stubtail	O	R		
Asian Stubtail	P	L	SC	SC
Cettia				
Pale-footed Bush Warbler	O	R A		
Sunda Bush Warbler	O	R		
Aberrant Bush Warbler	O (P)	R A		
Brownish-flanked Bush Warbler	O (P)	R A		
Yellow-bellied Bush Warbler	O (P)	R A		
Hume's Bush Warbler	O (P)	R A		
Chestnut-crowned Bush Warbler	O (P)	R A		
Grey-sided Bush Warbler	O (P)	R A		
Manchurian Bush Warbler	P (O)	S L	SC	SC
Japanese Bush Warbler	P (O)	R S	SC	SC
Luzon Bush Warbler	O	R		
Palau Bush Warbler	Oc	R		
Shade Warbler	Au	R		
Fiji Bush Warbler	Oc	R		
Tanimbar Bush Warbler	Au	R		
Bougainville Bush Warbler	Au	R		
Cetti's Warbler	P	R S L	SC (wp), or (AC?)	sp (wp), or (sp AC?)

APPENDIX 5

COMPARATIVE FIELD CHARACTERS OF SIMILAR SPECIES

Appendix 5.1. Plumage and structural comparison of adult Spotted Bush Warbler *Bradypterus thoracicus* **and Baikal Bush Warbler** *Bradypterus davidi* **during the breeding season.**

Character	Spotted Bush Warbler	Baikal Bush Warbler
Size and structure	averages slightly larger than Baikal Bush	smallest *Bradypterus*, proportionately shorter-tailed than Spotted Bush
Bill	black	black
Legs	deep plumbeous-pink	fleshy pink
Crown	dark reddish brown, slightly warmer than mantle	slightly darker than mantle with marginally darker feather tips, creating faintly scaled appearance
Supercilium	narrow, dull grey, less prominent and greyer than Baikal Bush, most conspicuous in front of eye, contrasting with distinct, dark loral line	buffy white, broadest above lores, bordered by short dark eye-stripe, typically a dark spot immediately in front of and behind eye
Ear-coverts	dark grey, merging with dark grey side to neck, giving head a distinctly grey appearance	dull brown, contrast little with crown and upperparts, head browner and paler than Spotted Bush
Mantle	dark russet-brown, typically warmer, darker and richer brown than Baikal Bush	uniform dull reddish brown
Rump	dark russet-brown	paler warm sandy brown, contrasting with mantle and uppertail-coverts
Tail	dark russet-brown	dull reddish brown
Tertials	russet-brown fringes and slightly darker centres, appearing uniform with mantle	dull brown with broad warm reddish brown fringes, slightly warmer than mantle
Chin and throat	white with black spotting on lower throat, variable in extent and contrast	whitish, with rows of small blackish spots forming conspicuous necklace across lower throat
Breast	dark ash-grey to paler dull mouse-brown, with conspicuous black spots on throat and upper breast, these being variable in extent but usually smaller and rounder than breast spots of Baikal Bush, typically appearing as a well-defined necklace across upper breast, but not as extensive as shown by Baikal Bush	pale greyish brown, darkening to warm buffy brown towards sides, never as dark or grey as Spotted Bush Warbler, blackish spots larger than on throat and bleeding into diffuse blackish striations on upper breast
Flanks	grey to dark fulvous-brown	warmer buffy brown
Undertail-coverts	dark fulvous-brown with conspicuous broad pale tips	warm buffy brown with conspicuous broad pale tips, creating a series of pale and dark bands; extensive pale tips sometimes almost obscure darker brown bases, so that undertail-coverts appear almost whitish

Appendix 5.2. Plumage and structural comparison of adult Long-billed Bush Warbler *Bradypterus major*, **Chinese Bush Warbler** *Bradypterus tacsanowskius*, **Brown Bush Warbler** *Bradypterus luteoventris* **and Russet Bush Warbler** *Bradypterus mandelli* **during the breeding season.**

Character	Long-billed Bush Warbler	Chinese Bush Warbler	Brown Bush Warbler	Russet Bush Warbler
Size and structure	largest of the six continental Asian *Bradypterus*			
Bill	dark grey with fleshy pink, lower mandible, darker towards tip	entirely black in male, female with pale yellowish pink lower mandible, slightly darker towards tip	black with pinkish yellow lower mandible, sometimes with slightly darker sides towards tip	entirely black
Legs	deep yellowish pink	dull pink	pinkish grey to plumbeous-grey	dull plumbeous-pink
Overall appearance	dull mousy brown with conspicuous whitish supercilium and contrasting chestnut edged tail and wings	drab and nondescript, with greyish olive-brown upperparts and pale ochre-tinged underparts	most warmly toned upperparts of the continental Asian *Bradypterus*	darkest of the six continental Asian *Bradypterus*, with dull russet-brown upperparts and flanks, and conspicuously pale tipped undertail-coverts
Crown	dull mouse-brown	uniform greyish brown	uniform warm brown	uniform, dull russet-brown
Supercilium	whitish, long, narrow but clearly defined, from fore-crown to rear of ear-coverts	restricted to pale loral wedge merging above and below eye with pale eye-ring	faint and diffuse, not reaching behind rear of eye, often absent	faint greyish white, not reaching behind eye
Ear-coverts	cold brown flecked white, appearing finely mottled or streaked	grey-brown	warm brown, slightly darker than crown	dull rusty brown
Mantle	dull mouse-brown	uniform greyish brown	uniform warm brown	uniform, dull russet-brown
Tail	dark brown with dull mousy brown fringes	slightly warmer brown than upperparts, lacking greyish tone, with darker brown shafts	slightly darker than upperparts with distinctly darker feather shafts	dark brown with broad, diffuse rusty brown fringes
Chin and throat	white, with variable gorget of greyish brown spots across lower edge of throat, almost absent on some birds, extending onto upper breast on others	white, often with indistinct diffuse gorget of small spots across lower throat, usually not extending onto upper breast, absent on some birds	creamy white, unmarked	white, with small faint spots extending onto the lower edge of throat
Breast	washed light peachy buff, usually unmarked	buffy brown to pale sandy grey with a slight yellowish or ochre-tinge, unmarked	warm sandy brown, paler than mantle, unmarked	grey with gorget of blackish spots extending across upper breast
Flanks	warm buff to olive-buff	grey-brown, darkening to warmer brown	warm tan	uniform, dull russet-brown
Undertail-coverts	warm buff to olive-buff, lacking contrasting pale tips	warm brown, slightly darker than flanks with diffuse but distinctly paler creamy white tips	warm fulvous-brown to greyish brown, lacking contrasting pale tips	dark greyish brown with broad buffy white to greyish white tips

Appendix 5.3. Plumage and structural comparison of adult Grasshopper Warbler *Locustella naevia* and Lanceolated Warbler *Locustella lanceolata* during the breeding season.

Character	Grasshopper Warbler	Lanceolated Warbler
Size	slightly larger than Lanceolated	smallest *Locustella*
Bill	longer	short
Tail	longer	short
Mantle	darker centres encircled with olive-brown fringes, producing a mottled appearance	darker centres extend to feather tips, creating a streaked effect
Rump and uppertail-coverts	poorly defined dark feather centres, bleeding into fringes	obvious dark feather centres contrasting with fringes
Tertials	broader olive-brown fringes bleeding into dull brown centres, lacks crisp contrast	well-defined narrow fringes, and blackish centres; contrast crisp
Flanks	often unstreaked; if streaking present, broad and diffuse	long, thin, crisp streaks extend along flanks; rarely absent
Breast	spotting usually restricted to gorget on lower throat, occasionally extending as bib onto upper breast	well-defined streaking forms pectoral band across breast
Undertail-coverts	pale buffy brown with diffuse, dark centres to all feathers extending to feather bases	pale buff to warm tan, generally slightly darker than flanks, with short, well defined blackish spot or streak in centre, not extending to feather bases; the longest often unmarked

Appendix 5.4. Plumage and structural comparison of adult Pallas's Grasshopper Warbler *Locustella certhiola*, Middendorff's Grasshopper Warbler *Locustella ochotensis* and Styan's Grasshopper Warbler *Locustella pleskei* during the breeding season.

Character	Pallas's Grasshopper Warbler, race *certhiola*	Middendorff's Grasshopper Warbler	Styan's Grasshopper Warbler
Size and structure	generally smallest of the three species in this group	wing length overlaps with both species	averages largest of this group, with proportionately longest tail
Bill	proportionately shortest, dark brown or blackish with pink lower mandible, darker at sides towards tip	structure falls between other two species, dark grey with greyish pink lower mandible, darkening along sides towards tip	proportionately longest, dark grey or blackish with a paler greyish pink to yellowish pink lower mandible, some are unmarked, other with darker shading along sides
Legs	dull pink to pinkish brown	reddish brown to greyish pink	fleshy pink with a slight grey or brown cast
Crown	blackish with dull ash-grey fringes creating strongly streaked appearance	uniform greyish brown	uniform dull olivaceous grey
Supercilium	whitish or pale sandy grey, long and broad, extending to rear of ear-coverts	pale grey-buff, extending to rear of ear-coverts, most prominent in front of the eye, becoming less distinct, more diffuse towards the nape	dull greyish brown, extending to rear of ear-coverts but usually broadest in front of and over eye

Character	Pallas's Grasshopper Warbler, race *certhiola*	Middendorff's Grasshopper Warbler	Styan's Grasshopper Warbler
Mantle	feathers blackish with rusty brown fringes forming contrasting lines	warm olive-brown to dull tawny-brown, often with slightly darker, indistinct and diffuse streaking forming vague lines, especially on worn birds in late summer	uniform grey-brown, usually unmarked but occasionally with very faint slightly darker striations
Rump and uppertail-coverts	warm chestnut-brown, rump plain or with faint darker spots, uppertail-coverts usually with large, crisp blackish spot in centre	dull tawny-brown, unmarked	dull olive-brown, unmarked, slightly paler, less greyish than mantle
Tail feathers	warm rusty brown with narrow blackish centres and broad whitish tips to all except central pair	greyish brown with broad tawny-brown fringes and conspicuous broad whitish tips, these narrowest or absent on central pair	grey-brown with broad, diffuse olive-brown fringes, outer four pairs with narrow creamy white or pale buff tips, lacking or much restricted on inner two pairs
Tertials	blackish with crisp rusty brown fringe to outer web, often with white notch by shaft on inner web on all tertials	olive-brown with wide, warm brown fringes, similar to mantle colour, some with pale sandy brown or whitish notch on inner web on inner two feathers	narrow, olivaceous-brown fringes similar to mantle colour and slightly darker centres, usually lack whitish notch on inner web
Chin and throat	white, unmarked or with small blackish spots scattered across lower throat	white, with diffuse pale olive-buff breast-band	whitish or pale greyish brown
Breast	creamy white	white, washed pale olive-buff forming diffuse breast-band	pale greyish brown, becoming darker greyish brown on side of upper breast
Flanks	dark sandy brown	pale olive-brown to pale buff	light creamy buff, darkening slightly towards ventral region
Edges of closed wing feathers	rusty brown, similar to mantle and tertial fringes	warm olive-brown, similar to mantle	olive-brown, slightly warmer than mantle
Outer web of p2	narrowly edged white	narrowly edged white	usually matches other primaries, sometimes slightly paler, never whitish
Undertail-coverts	pale sandy-brown to creamy white with large diffuse indistinct whitish tips	pale creamy buff to warm olive-buff, usually with broad, indistinct whitish tips	typically creamy brown, occasionally rich buff, with paler tips and contrasting dark brown shaft streaks

Appendix 5.5. Plumage and structural comparison of adult Manchurian Reed Warbler *Acrocephalus tangorum*, Blunt-winged Warbler *Acrocephalus concinens* and Paddyfield Warbler *Acrocephalus agricola* during the breeding season.

Character	Manchurian Reed Warbler	Blunt-winged Warbler	Paddyfield Warbler
Size and structure	primary projection ≤ 50% of exposed tertial length; tail slightly longer than other species with narrower and more pointed rectrices	has shortest primary projection of Asian Acrocephalus, typically 35–45% of exposed tertial length	primary projection ≤ 50% of exposed tertial length
Bill	longer, deeper and broader based than Paddyfield, dark grey with pinkish orange lower mandible, becoming dusky tip towards tip, usually more extensive than Paddyfield	fairly long and deep-based, appearing stout, dark grey with pinkish lower mandible, usually with greyish sides	smallest and finest in structure, dark brown to blackish with pale flesh lower mandible, darker at sides towards tip
Legs	orange-brown to reddish brown	dull straw to brownish flesh	variable, pale grey-brown to pinkish brown
Overall appearance	generally paler than Paddyfield, with conspicuous pale supercilium contrasting with darker eye-stripe	drab and nondescript, lacks conspicuous supercilium of other two species	overall cinnamon-brown appearance with conspicuous pale supercilium
Crown	dull rufous-brown fading to pale sandy brown, with conspicuous dark brown band bordering side	uniform warm brown	grey-brown, slightly duller than mantle, with darker dull brown band bordering side, contrasting with supercilium
Supercilium	pale cream, long and conspicuous, extending to rear of ear-covert and contrasting with dark lores and eye-stripe	diffuse and poorly defined, most conspicuous in front of eye, often not extending beyond rear edge of eye	pale cream, extending to rear of ear-coverts, flaring slightly behind eye, contrasting with diffuse eye-stripe
Ear-coverts	pale sandy grey with fine whitish feather shafts	warm brown	pale sandy buff, lightly mottled, giving paler appearance to side of head and extending as half-collar onto side of neck
Mantle	dull rufous-brown fading to pale sandy brown	uniform warm brown, with slight greyish cast when worn	dull cinnamon-brown
Rump and uppertail-coverts	rufous-brown, contrasting with paler mantle	slightly warmer than mantle	cinnamon-brown, slightly warmer than mantle
Tail	warm sandy brown with darker feather shafts	warm brown with darker feather shafts	dull grey-brown with faded mouse brown fringes and edgings
Tertials	broad, mid brown centres and sandy brown fringes	earthy brown with sandy-brown fringes similar to upperparts	dark brown centres with contrasting cinnamon-brown to sandy brown fringes
Breast	lightly washed fulvous brown	light sandy brown	pale buffy brown
Flanks	lightly washed fulvous brown to washed-out buff, slightly darker than breast	darker and richer brown than breast	pale buffy brown, similar to breast

Appendix 5.6. Plumage and structural comparison of adult Blyth's Reed Warbler *Acrocephalus dumetorum*, **Marsh Warbler** *Acrocephalus palustris* **and Eurasian Reed Warbler** *Acrocephalus scirpaceus* **during the breeding season.**

Character	Blyth's Reed Warbler	Marsh Warbler	Eurasian Reed Warbler, race *fuscus*, typical morph
Size and structure	wing distinctly more rounded than Marsh and Eurasian Reed with a shorter primary projection, typically 50–60% of tertial length	has longest wing with primary projection 80–90% of tertial length	wing length similar to Marsh but primary projection averages shorter, typically 70–80% of tertial length
Bill	dark grey with dull yellow to pale pinkish lower mandible, usually darkening on sides towards tip; similar in length to Eurasian Reed but slightly broader based, thus appearing more substantial	dark olive-brown with pale pinkish or yellowish flesh lower mandible; slightly shorter and broader based than in Eurasian Reed	dark greyish brown with pale flesh brown to yellowish flesh lower mandible, usually darkening slightly at sides towards tip; relatively long and narrow
Legs	rather dark, dull reddish brown to pinkish grey, never pale brown	usually distinctive pale brown or pinkish straw	variable, mid brown or flesh-brown, tend to be darker than Marsh although there is overlap
Crown	light greyish olive-brown	olive-brown, tinged greenish	pale olive-brown with indistinct greyish cast
Supercilium	creamy buff, typically bulges in front of eye giving a bland appearance to head, usually poorly defined and less conspicuous behind eye although more prominent here than shown by other species	creamy buff, well marked above lores and merging with creamy eye-ring, indistinct or absent behind eye, contrasts with dark olive-brown triangle in front of eye	pale buff, distinct in front of eye but barely extends beyond eye, contrasts with dark loral triangle immediately in front of eye
Mantle	drab greyish olive-brown	pale uniform olive-brown, usually with distinct greenish or ochreous tinge	pale olive-brown, tinged more ochreous, less greenish
Rump and uppertail-coverts	uniform with mantle	uniform with mantle	tawny-brown, warmer than mantle
Tail	dark greyish brown with slightly browner outer edges and tips	dark grey-brown, narrowly edged olive-brown, outermost usually with fine whitish fringe around distal inner edge and tip	usually with whitish fringes to tips of t4–6, extending broadly around distal edge of inner web on t6
Tertials	rather uniform greyish brown with barely discernible brownish fringe	blackish brown, outer edges and tips with sharply defined broad, bright olive-brown or greenish brown fringes	dark grey-brown, outer edges and tips with broad olive-brown fringes, slightly warmer than mantle, not sharply defined
Breast	greyish white or silvery white	washed yellowish olive-brown	buffy white
Edges of closed wing feathers	greyish brown with barely discernable brownish fringe, usually lacks pale primary tips in breeding season	narrow olive-brown edges similar to mantle, primaries with prominent narrow greyish white tips in spring	edged light olive-brown, often shows pale primary tips in spring

Appendix 5.7. Plumage and structural comparison of adult Basra Reed Warbler *Acrocephalus griseldis*, **Great Reed Warbler** *Acrocephalus arundinaceus*, **Oriental Reed Warbler** *Acrocephalus orientalis* **and Clamorous Reed Warbler** *Acrocephalus stentoreus* **during the breeding season.**

Character	Basra Reed Warbler	Great Reed Warbler	Oriental Reed Warbler	Clamorous Reed Warbler race *brunmescens*
Size and structure	smallest of this group, with proportionately shorter tail, primary projection *c.* 80% of tertial length	largest Palearctic *Acrocephalus*, approximately 15% larger than Basra Reed, primary projection 80–90%	closely resembles Great Reed but slightly smaller, primaries project *c.* 75%, intermediate between Great Reed and Clamorous Reed	slimmer than Great Reed, proportionately shorter-winged than other large Palearctic *Acrocephalus*, with shortest primary projection, typically 50–70%
Bill	proportionately longest, finest bill of this group	wide and stout bill, rather thrush-like	as Great Reed	slimmer and less 'thrush-like' than Great Reed, with a gradual decurvature along length of upper mandible
Legs	dark grey, adults with a slight brown tinge; less stout than Great Reed	typically pale, grey-brown to pale brown or pinkish brown, stout and robust	dull plumbeous-grey, usually slightly darker than Great Reed	plumbeous-grey to greyish brown, usually darker than Great Reed and Oriental Reed
Crown	cold olive-brown	warm olive-brown with greyish tinge	dull greyish brown	olive-brown with greyish tinge
Supercilium	long whitish and conspicuous, narrower than Great Reed Warbler, more prominent than shown by smaller unstreaked European *Acrocephalus*	conspicuous pale creamy buff super-cilium broadest in front of eye and extending to rear of ear-coverts, contrasting with greyish brown loral line	as Great Reed	less bold and contrasting than that of Great Reed Warbler
Mantle	olive-brown, colder than Great Reed	warm olive-brown	warm olive-brown, as Great Reed	uniform olive-brown with slight greyish cast
Rump and uppertail-coverts	slightly paler and warmer than mantle	cinnamon-brown, warmer and brighter than mantle and tail	slightly warmer and paler than mantle	usually warmer olive-brown contrasting with slightly greyer mantle and tail
Tail	dark brown, conspicuously darker than uppertail-coverts, tips of t4–6 narrowly fringed brownish white	greyish olive-brown, narrowly edged warm buff, slightly darker than upperparts, t6 with diffuse buffy white fringe around tip	similar to mantle, with paler, more conspicuous tips to all tail feathers than in Great Reed	mouse-brown with slightly browner narrow edges to mantle, and buff tips, but lacks contrast of Great Reed and Oriental Reed
Tertials	dull brown, outer web with broad olive-brown fringe and tip	dull brown, with broad olive-brown outer fringes poorly demarcated	dark grey-brown with broad diffuse olive-brown fringes	narrow fringe paler than mantle, centre contrasting with darker feather shaft
Chin and throat	white, faintly tinged creamy buff	creamy white, with faint, narrow greyish throat streaks, occasionally extending to upper breast	dull creamy white, streaks on throat tend to be sharper and more boldly defined than on Great Reed	whitish, unstreaked

Character	Basra Reed Warbler	Great Reed Warbler	Oriental Reed Warbler	Clamorous Reed Warbler race *brunnescens*
Breast	white washed creamy buff, sides suffused cold olive-brown, always unstreaked	washed pale tawny buff, occasionally with faint greyish streaking on upper breast	washed pale tawny buff; streaking on upper breast more extensive, sharper and more boldly defined than on Great Reed	whitish, washed pale fulvous-brown towards sides, becoming greyer with wear
Flanks	washed pale buff	warm tawny buff	pale straw, warmer and richer on lower flanks	darkest of this group, light fulvous-brown darkening to tawny-brown on lower flanks, contrasting with paler undertail-coverts

Appendix 5.8. Plumage and structural comparison of adult Icterine Warbler Hippolais icterina and Melodious Warbler *Hippolais polyglotta* during the breeding season.

Character	Icterine Warbler	Melodious Warbler
Size and structure	size between Eastern Olivaceous and Olive-tree, primary projection similar to exposed tertial length with 7–8 primary tips visible	slightly smaller than Icterine, with shorter primary projection between half and two-thirds of exposed tertial length, and 6–7 primary tips visible, although these are already worn by late spring
Tail movements	occasionally flicks tail	tends to flick tail more frequently than Icterine
Legs	dark olive-grey, slaty or blue-grey	horn-brown to grey-brown or dark grey, often slightly browner than Icterine, but some overlap
Overall appearance	bright green-and-yellow warbler with conspicuous pale wing-panel	closely resembles Icterine but usually lacks paler wing-panel
Crown	bright greenish olive-brown	olive-brown, tinged greenish
Mantle	light olive-green to greenish olive-brown	as Icterine but usually slightly duller and browner
Tail	greyish black, feathers narrowly edged pale yellow, t6 similar in length to t1	dark brown, feathers narrowly edged pale olive-yellow, t6 with paler grey-brown outer web and slightly shorter than t1
Tertials	outer webs broadly edged pale yellow to whitish, forming part of pale wing-panel	outer webs broadly edged pale yellowish olive to buff-brown
Breast and belly	lemon-yellow	marginally richer yellow than Icterine, some with slight brownish cast to breast
Flanks	lemon-yellow with slight olive tinge	yellow, suffused olive-brown
Edges of the closed wing feathers	conspicuous pale wing panel formed by pale yellow to whitish edges to secondaries, which contrast with blackish webs of flight feathers	usually match wing colour, occasionally with broad yellowish olive to buff-brown edges to secondaries that form distinct pale wing-panel, rarely as conspicuous as Icterine

Appendix 5.9. Plumage and structural comparison of adult Olive-tree Warbler *Hippolais olivetorum* and Upcher's Warbler *Hippolais languida* during the breeding season.

Character	Olive-tree Warbler	Upcher's Warbler
Size and structure	largest of the *Hippolais* with proportionately long wings, primary projection 80–100% length of exposed tertial length, and 7–8 well-spaced primary tips usually visible	distinctly smaller than Olive-tree with shorter primary projection, c. 70% length of exposed tertials (slightly longer than in *elaeica* Eastern Olivaceous), with 6–7 pale primary tips visible when fresh
Tail movements	dips tail in a random, shrike-like manner	moves tail up and down and from side to side, slowly and deliberately, often partially spread
Bill	strong and straight, with fairly deep base, and appears both long and quite heavy	fairly broad-based but slim, slightly longer than Eastern Olivaceous but with similarly drooping tip
Legs	robust, dark grey	Finer than Olive-tree, greyish tinged brown or flesh
Overall appearance	darker, with hooded appearance and conspicuous pale wing-panel	paler than Olive-tree, with more conspicuous supercilium and darker tail, pale wing-panel less obvious
Supercilium	diffuse greyish white, most conspicuous above lores, extending only to rear edge of eye where it merges with narrow white eye-ring; pale grey lores tend to merge with the supercilium to create a rather bland and open-faced expression	longer, paler supercilium than Olive-tree, extending behind eye and contrasting with darker lores, giving head a crisper appearance
Mantle	drab brownish grey with olive tinge	uniform light brownish grey, paler than Olive-tree
Tail	uniform dark grey-brown, similar to mantle, outermost rectrices broadly edged greyish white, tip and distal part of inner web of t4–6 (and sometimes t3) with white fringe	grey-brown towards base, becoming blackish brown towards tip, with prominent white edge to outermost and broad white tips and inner web margins to t4–6
Tertials	dark grey-brown, innermost fringed grey-buff, outermost more broadly fringed buffy white	dark grey-brown with broad light grey-brown fringes
Breast and belly	off-white with greyish wash, and creamy tinge to belly	largely white, unmarked
Flanks	washed grey	washed grey-buff
Edges of the closed wing feathers	wings slightly darker and browner than the mantle and scapulars, with conspicuous pale panel formed by buffy white edges to secondaries and outer tertial, and tips to greater coverts	shows pale wing-panel but as paler secondary edges are narrower than Olive-tree, so tends to appear less prominent, and is readily lost during breeding season

Appendix 5.10. Plumage and structural comparison of adult Eastern Olivaceous Warbler *Iduna pallida*, Western Olivaceous Warbler *Iduna opaca*, Sykes's Warbler *Iduna rama* and Booted Warbler *Iduna caligata* during the breeding season.

Character	Eastern Olivaceous Warbler race *elaeica*	Western Olivaceous Warbler	Sykes's Warbler	Booted Warbler
Size and structure	slightly larger than Sykes's and can appear heavier bodied, larger headed, and longer winged, with primaries projecting ≥ 50% of exposed tertial length	slightly larger than Eastern Olivaceous with proportionately longer tail; primary projection c. 50%	wing shorter and tail longer than in Eastern Olivaceous; primary projection ≥ 30% with no more than five pale primary tips visible	smallest *Iduna*, with compact structure, rounded crown and small, fine bill; primary projection ≥ 35%, slightly longer than in Sykes's; shorter-tailed than Sykes's
Tail movements	diagnostic regular, continuous tail dipping	no tail movements	Flicks, cocks and spreads tail in all directions in a nervous manner, accompanied by wing flicking	randomly flicks wings and tail, but usually does not fan and cock tail as Sykes's
Bill	quite long and rather heavier looking, upper mandible showing distinct decurvature towards tip, lower mandible entirely pale	larger, deeper and broader than in Eastern Olivaceous, often shows slight convex outer edges, lower mandible entirely pale	quite long, straight-sided, slightly smaller and thinner than Eastern Olivaceous with upper mandible relatively straight towards tip; lower mandible pale pinkish, unmarked or some-times with faint dark smudge behind tip, not extensive as in Booted	fine, *Phylloscopus*-like, with concave sides and narrower base than Sykes's; pale lower mandible with dark smudge at tip, more extensive than in Sykes's
Legs	dark grey to greyish flesh	grey-brown or greyish flesh	browner and paler than Eastern Olivaceous, similar to Booted but usually with darker feet and tarso-tibial joint	pinkish or light brown, some with grey or blue-grey tinge, generally indistinct
Overall appearance	Greyish brown overall, usually showing pale panel in closed wing	slightly warmer, less greyish than Eastern Olivaceous; lacks pale edgings to wing feathers and prominent whitish tail tip markings	pale brown, plainest and drabbest of these species; closed wing uniform, head less patterned and contrasting than Booted	small brown warbler with a fairly obvious supercilium, sometimes appearing no larger than a Chiffchaff
Crown	uniform grey-brown, tinged olive, lacking dark sides to crown	light brown with greyish tinge	slightly darker line above supercilium, over lores only	diffuse line usually evident above supercilium in front of eye, occasionally extending behind it
Supercilium	creamy buff, narrow but quite well marked in front of eye, merging with pale lores, poorly defined behind eye	pale buff, rather narrow and poorly defined, shows little contrast with the crown; supercilium poorly defined, head appearance typically bland	most prominent in front of eye and contrasts with dark loral spot, rarely extends beyond eye	most conspicuous, typically extending well beyond eye and contrasting with slightly darker eye-stripe
Mantle	grey-brown with slight olive tinge	light brown, lacking greyish tone of Eastern Olivaceous, with no hint of olive tinge	uniform pale greyish brown, lacking olive tones	dull brown to olive-brown, becoming paler sandy brown with wear

Character	Eastern Olivaceous Warbler race *elaeica*	Western Olivaceous Warbler	Sykes's Warbler	Booted Warbler
Tail	outer web of t6 usually much paler than inner web, but both with distal white fringe; white distal fringes on inner webs of other feathers narrow and variable, often on t5 only, sometimes on all feathers including t1	outer web of t6 with narrow brownish white edge and whitish fringe at tip, broadest on inner web and usually merging into greyish brown web	t6 with whitish outer edge, bordered whitish around tip and on distal part of inner web, t5 tipped whitish, more conspicuously than in Booted	t6 with narrow pale buff or greyish white outer edge which broadens and extends around tip and onto distal part of the inner web; t5 usually with pale tip, extending onto inner web, narrower and less conspicuous than Sykes's
Tertials	dull greyish brown with broad paler sandy grey fringes	greyish brown with paler, buffier fringes	little or no contrast between the tertial centres and fringes, colour as upperparts	darker-centred than in Sykes's, so paler edges better-defined and more contrasting
Breast and belly	white with slight greyish wash	off-white	off-white to silvery white with, at best, only a faint buff tinge	warm buff on breast, becoming off-white on belly
Flanks	washed dull grey-buff, slightly warmer than upperparts	washed pale buff	dull brownish white to pale greyish brown	suffused warm buff to rufous-buff
Edges of closed wing feathers	sandy buff edges and tips to secondaries, creating faint pale panel in closed wing and pale line across bunched secondary tips	plain and uniform with upperparts, lacking contrasting pale panel in closed wing typical of Eastern Olivaceous	edged greyish brown, lacking contrast with upperparts	greyish brown, secondaries edged warm brown, primaries finely edged warm buff, and with narrow pale greyish fringes and tips

Appendix 5.11. Plumage and structural comparison of adult Brownish-flanked Bush Warbler *Cettia fortipes*, Yellow-bellied Bush Warbler *Cettia acanthizoides* and Hume's Bush Warbler *Cettia brunnescens* during the breeding season.

Character	Brownish-flanked Bush Warbler race *fortipes*	Yellow-bellied Bush Warbler	Hume's Bush Warbler
Size	small, male slightly larger than female	very small, male slightly larger than female	very small, male slightly larger than female
Bill	averages stouter and heavier with decurved tip	shorter and less fine-tipped than Hume's Bush	averages longer with narrower tip
Crown	dark, rich brown with slight rusty wash	pale rusty brown, tinged olive	pale rusty brown lacking olive tone
Supercilium	fairly indistinct, most conspicuous in front of and above eye	long and conspicuous, often faintly tinged primrose in front of eye where well defined; behind eye broadening, flaring and merging with crown and nape	long and conspicuous, creamy white above eye, creamy buff towards bill base
Mantle	dark rich brown, usually lacking rusty tone	pale rusty brown with delicate olive wash	light warm brown, slightly warmer than Yellow-bellied Bush and lacking an olive tinge
Breast and belly	washed rich buffy brown	often conspicuous primrose-yellow	yellow tones subdued or completely absent
Flanks	dark buffy brown, darkening to rich rusty brown on lower flanks	warm buff with faint hint of yellow	warm buff sometimes with a slight buffy yellow wash
Undertail-coverts	rich sepia-brown	warm buff with faint hint of yellow	pale apricot to warm buff, with yellow tones entirely suppressed

Appendix 5.12. Plumage and structural comparison of adult Manchurian Bush Warbler *Cettia canturians* and Japanese Bush Warbler *Cettia diphone* during the breeding season.

Character	Manchurian Bush Warbler race *canturians*	Manchurian Bush Warbler race *borealis*	Japanese Bush Warbler race *cantans*
Size	largest *Cettia*, male much larger than female	largest *Cettia*, male much larger than female	Smaller than Manchurian Bush, sexual size dimorphism less pronounced
Bill	lower mandible pale, bill of male heavier, stouter than female	lower mandible pale, bill of male heavier, stouter than female	almost entirely black in breeding season, structure longer and finer, bill structure of sexes similar
Crown	cinnamon-brown, limited contrast with warm-tinged cinnamon brown nape and side of head	cinnamon-brown, contrast with greyer rear crown, nape and side of the head usually striking	drab olive-brown, similar to nape and mantle, lacks contrast
Supercilium	long, pale, conspicuous	long, pale, conspicuous	pale greyish, narrower and less conspicuous
Mantle	warm brown, tinged cinnamon, but much less strongly than on crown	slightly paler and greyer than nominate *canturians*	drab olive-brown
Tail	broad, diffuse cinnamon-brown or warm tawny-brown fringes, similar to uppertail-coverts	as nominate *canturians*	uniform brown, slightly warmer than uppertail-coverts
Tertials	dark brown with broad cinnamon-brown to russet-brown fringes	as nominate *canturians*	dull brown to warm tan, lacking olive tones of upperparts
Breast	creamy white, lightly washed warm brown	creamy white with faint greyish brown wash	drab greyish white
Flanks	light buffy brown, becoming slightly darker and greyer on lower flanks	dull greyish brown	drab greyish white
Edges of closed wing feathers	cinnamon-brown, richer than upperparts, but usually lacks striking contrast	cinnamon-brown, richer than upperparts and contrast usually striking	dull brown to warm tan, lacking olive tones of upperparts

APPENDIX 6

SCIENTIFIC NAMES OF OTHER BIRD SPECIES MENTIONED IN THE TEXT

Asian Desert Warbler *Sylvia nana*

Bagobo Babbler *Leonardina woodi*

Barn Swallow *Hirundo rustica*

Barred Warbler *Sylvia nisoria*

Bearded Tit *Panurus biarmicus*

Blackbird *Turdus merula*

Blackcap *Sylvia atricapilla*

Black Kite *Milvus migrans*

Black-tailed Hawfinch *Eophona migratoria*

Bluethroat *Luscinia svecica*

Blue Tit *Parus caeruleus*

Bristle-thighed Curlew *Numenius tahitiensis*

Broad-tailed Warbler *Schoenicola brevirostris*

Brown Shrike *Lanius cristatus*

Chaffinch *Fringilla coelebs*

Collared Owlet *Glaucidium brodiei*

Coal Tit *Parus ater*

Common Blackbird *Turdus merula*

Common Chiffchaff *Phylloscopus collybita*

Common Myna *Acridotheres tristis*

Common Nightingale *Luscinia megarhynchos*

Common Redshank *Tringa totanus*

Common Redstart *Phoenicurus phoenicurus*

Common Sandpiper *Actitis hypoleucos*

Common Stonechat *Saxicola torquata*

Common Tern *Sterna hirundo*

Common Whitethroat *Sylvia communis*

Corn Bunting *Emberiza calandra*

Dusky Warbler *Phylloscopus fuscatus*

Eleonora's Falcon *Falco eleonorae*

Eye-browed Wren-babbler *Napothera epilepidota*

Garden Warbler *Sylvia borin*

Giant White-eye *Megazosterops palauensis*

Great Tit *Parus major*

Great Spotted Woodpecker *Dendrocopos major*

Grey Emutail *Amphilais seebohmi*

Hermit Thrush *Catharus guttatus*

Lesser Shortwing *Brachypteryx leucophrys*

Lesser Whitethroat *Sylvia curruca*

Linnet *Carduelis cannabina*

Long-billed White-eye *Rukia longirostra*

Long-legged Warbler *Trichocichla rufa*

Long-tailed Tit *Aegithalos caudatus*

Mountain Wren-babbler *Napothera crassa*

Nihoa Finch *Telespiza ultima*

Northern Wren *Troglodytes troglodytes*

Pale-legged Leaf-warbler *Phylloscopus tenellipes*

Pygmy Wren-babbler *Pnoepyga pusilla*

Radde's Warbler *Phylloscopus schwarzi*

Red-wattled Lapwing *Hoplopterus indicus*

Rufous-sided Fairy-warbler *Gerygone dorsalis*

San Cristobal Leaf Warbler *Phylloscopus makirensis*

Sardinian Warbler *Sylvia melanocephala*

Siberian Rubythroat *Luscinia calliope*

Song Thrush *Turdus philomelos*

Sooty Tern *Onychoprion fuscatus*

Spotted Flycatcher *Muscicapa striata*

Tahiti Monarch *Pomarea nigra*

Thamnornis Warbler *Thamnornis chloropetoides*

Victorin's Warbler *Cryptilles victorini*

White-browed Shortwing *Brachypteryx montana*

Willow Warbler *Phylloscopus trochilus*

Wood Lark *Lullula arborea*

Yellow-streaked Warbler *Phylloscopus armandii*

Zitting Cisticola *Cisticola juncidis*

APPENDIX 7
RECENT DEVELOPMENTS TO 2010

As this project entered its concluding stages in late 2009, the results of fieldwork from the last 12 months gradually reached us. Including these new findings within the body of the text at such a late stage was largely unrealistic, although wherever possible the publishers have encouraged us to do so. This update presents a brief summary of discoveries that were received too late to include in full. Researchers made a surprising number of unexpected discoveries in this period, demonstrating that interest in these groups remains high and shows no sign of abating. In addition, Per Alström has kindly provided us with an insight into unpublished work on the systematics of Locustellidae and Cettiidae, based upon comparison of mitochondrial and nuclear gene sequences. This has revealed some unexpected phylogenetic relationships, which are expected to impact upon the way we view these genera and the species included within them for many years to come.

Latest discoveries

• In April 2009, Frank Rheindt encountered a singing *Bradypterus* in dense, dwarf montane forest on Taliabu, an island in the Moluccas, at an elevation of 1,050–1,100m. Although no *Bradypterus* has previously been recorded from Taliabu, Chestnut-backed Bush Warbler breeds on nearby Sulawesi to the west, and on the islands of Seram and Buru to the southeast. As yet, the bird has not been seen well, it has not been trapped and no photographs have been taken, so details of its appearance remain scant – 'brown with a well-developed strong white supercilium'. The song is described as being reminiscent of Russet Bush Warbler (Rheindt 2010). However, a sonogram of a recording made by Bram Demeulemeester and Dominique Verbelen in November 2009 shows the song has an energy peak at *c.* 7kHz, much higher than the taxa within the Russet Bush/Javan Bush/Timor Bush Warbler complex, and closer in frequency to the songs of Long-tailed Bush Warbler at *c.* 7kHz and Chestnut-backed Bush Warbler, which peaks at 7–8kHz. The true genetic affinity of this *Bradypterus* will need to be resolved by molecular methods, including comparison with Chestnut-backed Bush Warbler on Sulawesi, Seram and Buru – which may represent three distinct species – as well as Javan and Timor Bush Warblers.

• IIn June 2008, breeding grounds of Large-billed Reed Warbler were located by Rob Timmins in the Wakhan Corridor region of NE Afghanistan. A subsequent survey in June 2009 revealed a substantial population in scrubby thickets along high altitude streams and river valleys of the Upper Amu Darya, and 19 adult birds were trapped (Timmins *et al.* 2009). Birds were also found in July 2009 at three nearby sites in SE Tajikistan, where eight adults were trapped and breeding was confirmed (Ayé *et al.* 2010). More surveys in similar habitats in the Tien Shan, Pamirs and Himalayas are expected to reveal further populations.

• In September 2009, Pascal Provost and Hamid Rguibi-Idrissi encountered a small unstreaked *Acrocephalus* in reedbeds at Larache, NW Morocco, which differed in size, structure and appearance from migratory Eurasian Reed Warblers breeding in Europe and passing through the same reedbeds. Although the presence of a resident 'reed warbler' was already known, what was not appreciated was just how distinct it was, and it probably merits recognition as an undescribed taxon (Jiguet *et al.* 2010). In appearance, it is superficially similar to Eurasian Reed Warbler although freshly moulted birds are washed buff, particularly on the throat and flanks, but on some individuals this extends to cover the entire underparts and the head, including the supercilium. Other differences include darker legs and feet with contrastingly brighter yellow soles, a dark smudge on the lower mandible and a dark grey orbital ring. These birds are significantly smaller than even Spanish breeding Eurasian Reed Warblers. Furthermore, adults have complete rapid moult in September, shedding up to five primaries, five secondaries and all the rectrices simultaneously. Biometrics place it between Eurasian Reed Warbler and the *guiersi* race of African Reed Warbler in Senegal, but wing structure is closer to that of Eurasian Reed. It has been suggested that these birds may represent a link between Eurasian Reed and African Reed Warblers (Jiguet *et al.* 2010), which some authorities consider to be representatives of a single species. Feather and blood samples have been collected for DNA analysis, and the results of these investigations are expected in the near future.

• In parallel with the above discovery in Morocco, Hering *et al.* (2010) describe the breeding of African Reed Warblers at two sites in Libya – the first record of this species from the Western Palearctic. Initially discovered in 2007/08, their identity was established in 2008 when birds breeding near the coast in Benghazi, Cyrenaica, were trapped and found to have a rounded wing structure. Suspicion that these were African Reed Warblers was confirmed by DNA analysis. In 2009, at a site at Al Oardah in the Fezzan region of the Libyan desert, approximately 30 singing males were discovered. Genetic analysis of one bird confirmed this to be African Reed Warbler. Birds heard at other sites may also have been this species, although Eurasian Reed Warblers were also found on migration.

While searching other breeding sites for African Reed Warblers in 2009/10, Hering *et al.* found *Acrocephalus* breeding in the Ain Safi headwaters near the Siwah Oasis in western Egypt, close to the border with Libya. Preliminary DNA analysis has shown these birds to be closest to Eurasian Reed Warbler of the race *avicenniae*, a surprising discovery as this taxon is only known from mangroves fringing the Red Sea coastline, with the closest breeding site being in Saudi Arabia, some 1,400km distant. Other reed warblers also thought to be of the same genetic type were found 150km to the west, on a salt lake at Al Jagbub Oasis in Libya. All these *Acrocephalus* had a short wing length, between 55–65mm, within the range of African Reed Warbler and also similar to that of the Moroccan birds described by Jiguet *et al.* (2010). Hering *et al.* concluded that the *Acrocephalus* breeding in northern and western Libya are African Reed Warblers, while those in eastern Libya and Egypt are better assigned to Eurasian Reed Warbler. Furthermore, they speculate that the birds breeding in the Maghreb region of Morocco and Algeria may also eventually prove to be African Reed Warblers.

• The rediscovery of Timor Bush Warbler on Timor-Leste in December 2009 by Colin Trainor came as a complete surprise, as much of the likely suitable habitat, including the type locality, had been surveyed on many occasions. It was found to be fairly common in tall grassland in the Hatu Builico valley between 1,720m–2,050m below Mount Ramelau, even occurring close to human habitation. Even more surprising was the discovery of another population on neighbouring Alor by Philippe Verbelen in September 2009, an island where there had not been any previous records of *Bradypterus*. This bird is distinct from the Timor bird and will be described as a new subspecies of Timor Bush Warbler (Verbelen & Trainor in prep.).

Likely revisions to the systematics of the Locustellidae and Cettiidae

Per Alström and colleagues have been investigating relationships within Locustellidae (Alström *et al.* in sub.) and Cettiidae (Alström *et al.* in prep.). Although not yet published, Per has kindly provided a short summary of the most interesting discoveries that relate to the species included here. Although we have not been able to take account of these latest findings within the body of this book, inclusion of this brief summary of likely revisions is appropriate, as it appears highly likely that they will become widely adopted in the future.

Taxonomic and systematic implications for Locustellidae at genus level

Alström *et al.* (in sub.) have established that not a single one of the polytypic genera included in Locustellidae (except for *Schoenicola*, for which only one of the two species has been analysed so far) is monophyletic. They will recommend that a number of taxonomic changes should be adopted, based on the Locustellidae multi-gene phylogeny (Fig. 125). Their findings and recommendations are expected to include the following:

• The position of the taxon *pryeri*, previously included in *Megalurus*, is confirmed within *Locustella*. It had previously been placed within *Locustella* on morphology (Morioka & Shigeta, 1993), and on analysis of the mitochondrial ND2 gene (Drovetski *et al.* 2004), and this treatment was adopted here. However, the suggestion by Bairlein *et al.* (2006) that the two subspecies *L. p. pryeri* and *L. p. sinensis* might deserve specific rank is not supported.

• Asian *Bradypterus* are more closely related to *Locustella* than to African *Bradypterus*.

• All the Asian species of *Bradypterus* should be included with *Locustella* within clade A (Fig. 125).

• The name *Bradypterus* should be restricted to African species (which includes *B. baboecala*, the type species of the genus) (Fig. 125).

• The monotypic genus *Dromaeocercus* should be synonymised with *Bradypterus* in clade B (Fig. 125).

• *Schoenicola* is provisionally retained as a genus, pending further studies of its affinities based on additional loci.

• The genera *Cincloramphus* and *Eremiornis* are synonymised with *Megalurus*. This is a preliminary standpoint, which takes into account the phylogenetic uncertainty (conflicting data regarding the position of *M. palustris*) and a desire to maintain taxonomic stability.

As yet, Alström *et al.* (in sub.) have not sampled the genera *Amphilais* (monotypic, Madagascar), *Megalurulus* (four species, Melanesia), *Buettikoferella* (monotypic, Timor), and *Chaetornis* (monotypic, Indian subcontinent), all of which have been suggested to be closely related to *Megalurus*. Furthermore, *Elaphrornis* (monotypic, Sri Lanka), which has previously been placed in *Bradypterus* (e.g. Bairlein *et al.* 2006), has not yet been sampled. Future studies will show whether these assumptions are correct, though in any event they are unlikely to affect the taxonomic changes proposed in Alström *et al.* (in sub.).

Taxonomic and systematic implications for Locustellidae at species level

According to Alström *et al.* (in sub.), several taxa currently treated as conspecific appear to be sufficiently divergent in cytochrome *b* to merit species status, although the authors stress that this needs to be corroborated by independent data. Cases within the Locustellidae include the following:

• Little Rush Warbler *Bradypterus baboecala tongensis/ B. b. transvaalensis* (from South Africa) differs from *B. b. centralis* (from Nigeria) and *B. b. elgonensis* (Kenya) by 7.5–7.7% (mean 7.6%). Furthermore, they are not recovered as sisters.

• Evergreen Forest Warbler *Bradypterus lopezi mariae* (from Tanzania) and *B. l. usambarae* (from Mozambique) differ from *B. l. ufipae* (from Zambia) by 3.6%.

• A sample of Brown Bush Warbler *B. luteoventris* from western Burma differed from two Thai/Vietnamese samples by 2.6%; an unexpectedly large difference in a monotypic species, suggesting that these may merit treatment as subspecies.

• Gray's Grasshopper Warbler *Locustella fasciolata fasciolata* and *L. f. amnicola* differ by 3.9–4.4% (mean 4.1%); (also remarked upon by Drovetski *et al.* 2004).

Conversely, divergence between some closely related taxa currently treated as species falls within the variation typically found between races of recognised polytypic species. The status of these species will need to be investigated further. These include:

- Differences between Russet Bush Warbler *Bradypterus mandelli* and Javan Bush Warbler *B. montis* were unexpectedly small (1.3–1.6%, mean 1.5%). This is particularly surprising when their geographic isolation is considered, although their vocalisations are quite similar. These species have previously been treated as conspecific (e.g. Watson *et al.* 1986), but were split based on minor differences in morphology and song by Dickinson *et al.* (2000). Furthermore, samples of the monotypic *B. montis* from Java and Bali revealed a 0.9% difference. It is hoped that samples from the vocally similar species on Timor (and Alor) will become available for comparison in the near future.

- Differences between Styan's Grasshopper Warbler *Locustella pleskei* and Middendorff's Grasshopper Warbler *L. ochotensis* were unexpectedly small (0.9–1.2%, mean 1.0%). Similar slight differences were also found in the mitochondrial ND2 gene by Drovetski *et al.* (2004).

Figure 125. Phylogenetic tree of the Locustellidae showing the current taxonomy, and the new taxonomy proposed by Alström *et al.* (in sub.), based upon comparison of mitochondrial and nuclear gene sequences. Relationships with insufficient statistical support are indicated with an asterisk (*).

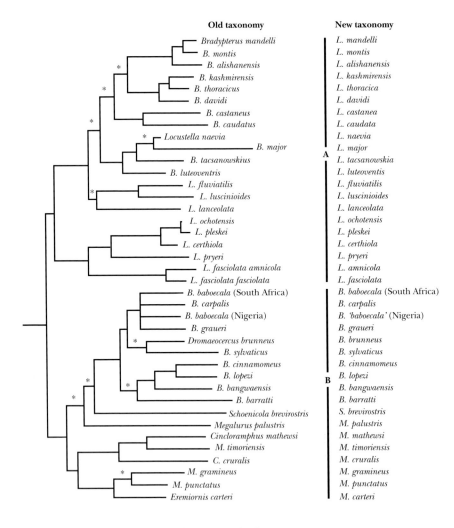

Taxonomic and systematic implications for Cettiidae at genus level

Alström *et al.* (2006) demonstrated that *Cettia* is non-monophyletic, meaning that relationships between species presently included within *Cettia* will require revision. They established that *Tesia*, *Tickellia*, and Mountain Tailorbird *Orthotomus cucullatus* (which has ten rectrices) are nested within *Cettia*. Research into relationships within Cettiidae has not progressed to the same extent as with Acrocephalidae and Locustellidae.

▲ Adult Spotted Bush Warbler, *Bradypterus thoracicus przevalskii*. China, July (Fang Gu Yun).

BIBLIOGRAPHY

Aalto, T. & Dernjatin, P. 2006. Small *Hippolais* warblers revisited – Booted and Sykes's Warblers. *Alula* 12: 2–8.

Abdulali, H. 1965. The birds of the Andaman and Nicobar islands. *J. Bombay Nat. Hist. Soc.* 61: 483–571.

Abe, N. 1984. [The wing length as a sexing criterion of *Cettia diphone cantans* in the autumn routine ringing.] *J. Yamashina Inst. Ornithol.* 16: 151–158. (Japanese, English summary)

Abella, J. C., Mejías, J. F., Barragán, A. & Sánchez, P. 1997. El Carricero Agrícola *Acrocephalus agricola*. *Garcilla* 100: 26–27.

Adam, R. G. & Meek, E. R. 1994. Did Marsh Warblers *Acrocephalus palustris* breed in Orkney in 1993? *Orkney Bird Report* (1993): 73–76.

Adriaens, P., Demeulemeester, M. & Vantieghem, S. 1995. [Booted Warbler *Hippolais caligata* in Zeebrugge on 15/09/1994.] *Mergus* 9: 103–107. (Dutch, English summary)

Aebischer, A. & Meyer, D. 1998. Brutbiologie des Rohrschwirls *Locustella luscinioides* am Neuenburgersee. *Orn. Beob.* 95(3): 177–202.

Aebischer, A. & Meyer, D. 1999. Breeding biology of Savi's Warbler *Locustella luscinioides* at Lake Neuchatel. *J. Field. Orn.* 70(2): 287.

Aebischer, A., Perrin, N., Kreig, M., Studer, J. & Meyer, D. R. 1996. The role of territory choice, mate choice and arrival date on breeding success in the Savi's Warbler *Locustella luscinioides*. *J. Avian Biol.* 27(2): 143–152.

Afanasieva, G. A. 1993. [Geographical peculiarities of some indices in young *Acrocephalus scirpaceus* Herm.] In: [*Materials of the Meeting 'Species and its productivity within range'*.] Pp. 79–80, Table 1. Gidrometeoizdat Press, St Petersburg. (Russian)

Afanasiev, V. T. 1998. [The Aquatic Warbler (*Acrocephalus paludicola*) in the Desna River valley]. *Ornitologiya* 28: 237. Moscow Univ. Press. (Russian)

Aidley, D. J. & Wilkinson, R. 1987a. Moult of some Palaearctic warblers in northern Nigeria. *Bird Study* 34: 219–225.

Aidley, D. J. & Wilkinson, R. 1987b. The annual cycle of six *Acrocephalus* warblers in a Nigerian reed-bed. *Bird Study* 34: 226–234.

Åkesson, S. 1991. Secretary Bird *Sagittarius serpentarius* feeding on Marsh Warblers *Acrocephalus palustris* in Tsavo, Kenya. *Scopus* 15: 46–47.

Åkesson, S. 1993. Effect of geomagnetic field on orientation of the Marsh Warbler, *Acrocephalus palustris*, in Sweden and Kenya. *Anim. Behav.* 46: 1157–1167.

Åkesson, S., Walinder, G., Karlsson, L. & Ehnbom, S. 2001. Reed Warbler orientation: initiation of nocturnal migratory flights in relation to visibility of celestial cues at dusk. *Anim. Behav.* 61: 181–189.

Åkesson, S., Walinder, G., Karlsson, L. & Ehnbom, S. 2002. Nocturnal migratory flight initiation in Reed Warblers *Acrocephalus scirpaceus*: effect of wind on orientation and timing of migration. *J. Avian Biol.* 33(4): 349–357.

Alexander, H. G. 1955. Field-notes on some Asian Leaf-Warblers - II. *Brit. Birds* 48: 349–356.

Ali, S. & Ripley, S. D. 1973. *Handbook of the Birds of India and Pakistan together with those of Bangladesh, Nepal, Bhutan and Sri Lanka*. Vol. 8. Oxford University Press, Bombay.

Al-Saghier, O. & Porter, R. F. 1997. The first Grasshopper Warbler *Locustella naevia* in Yemen. *Sandgrouse* 19(2): 150.

Alker, P. 1995. The River Warbler in Greater Manchester. *Birding World* 8: 216–217.

Alker, P. J. & Redfern, C. P. F. 1996. Double brooding and polygyny in Sedge Warblers *Acrocephalus schoenobaenus* breeding in north-west England. *Bird Study* 43(3): 356–363.

Allen, N. 2004. *Southern Bird* 20: 14.

Alonzo-Pasicolan, S. 1992. The bird-catchers of Dalton Pass. *Bull. Oriental Bird Club* 15: 33–36.

Alström, P. 1989. Bestämning av träksångare *Locustella lanceolata*. *Vår Fågelvärld* 48: 335–346.

Alström, P. & Olsson, U. 1992. More on Pallas's Grasshopper Warbler. *Birding World* 5: 118–119.

Alström, P., Ericson, P. G. P., Olsson, U. & Sundberg, P. 2006. Phylogeny and classification of the avian superfamily Sylvioidea. *Molecular Phylogenetics and Evolution* 38: 381–397.

Alström, P., Fregin, S., Norman, J. A., Zuccon, D., Ericso, P. G. P., Christidis, L. & Olsson, U. (in sub.). Comparison of methods for inferring gene trees and species phylogenies using multilocus sequence data in a taxonomically densely sampled avian family (Locustellidae).

Alström, P., Olsson, U., Rasmussen, P. C., Yao, C. T., Ericson, P. G. P. & Sundberg, P. 2007. Morphological, vocal and genetic divergence in the *Cettia acanthizoides* complex (Aves: Cettiidae). *Zool. J. Linn. Soc.* 149: 437–452.

Alström, P., Olsson, U. & Round, P. D. 1991. The taxonomic status of *Acrocephalus agricola tangorum*. *Forktail* 6: 3–13.

Alström, P., Olsson, U. & Round, P. D. 1994. Bestimmung der kleinen fernöstlichen Rohrsänger *Acrocephalus*. *Limicola* 8: 121–131.

Alström, P., Rasmussen, P. C., Olsson, U. & Sundberg, P. 2008. Species delimitation based on multiple criteria: the Spotted Bush Warbler *Bradypterus thoracicus* complex (Aves: Megaluridae). *Zool. J. Linn. Soc.* 154: 291–307.

Alström, P., Ripley, S. D. & Rasmussen, P. C. 1993. Re-evaluation of the taxonomic status of *Phylloscopus subaffinis arcanus*. *Bull. Brit. Orn. Club* 113: 207–209.

Amadon, D. 1954. A new race of *Chloropeta gracilirostris* Ogilvie-Grant. *Ostrich* 25: 140–141.

Ananian, V. & Busuttil, S. 2002. The first breeding records of Citrine Wagtail *Motacilla citreola* and Savi's Warbler *Locustella luscinioides* in Armenia. *Sandgrouse* 24(1): 52–53.

Ananian, V., Busuttil, S. & Finn, M. 2002. Recent observations of some rare breeding birds in Armenia. *Sandgrouse* 24(1): 46–48.

Andersen, E. M., Schlawe, C. & Lorenz, S. 2008. First record of Lanceolated Warbler breeding in North America. *Western Birds* 39: 2–7.

Andrew, D. G. 1997. The earlier breeding records of Icterine Warbler in England. *Brit. Birds* 90: 187–189.

Andrews, I. J. 1994. Cetti's Warbler in Edinburgh: a new bird for Scotland. *Scottish Birds* 17: 176–177.

Anon. 1979. Rare birds in southern Africa: Knysna Scrub Warbler *Bradypterus sylvaticus* (Sundevall). *Afr. Wildl.* 33(4): 53.

Anon. 1997. European News. *Brit. Birds* 90: 79–93.

Anon. 2000. British Ornithologist's Union Records Committee: 26th Report (October 1999). *Ibis* 142: 177–179.

Aneselin, A. & Meire, P. M. 1989. Habitat selection of Sedge Warbler and Reed Warbler in small reedbeds. *Ann. Soc. Roy. Zool. Belgium* 119: 121–136.

Antonov, A. I. 2003. [New data on the avifauna of mid and lower Amur River]. *J. Berkut.* 12: 47–49. (Russian)

Antonov, A. 2004. Smaller Eastern Olivaceous Warbler *Hippolais pallida elaeica* nests suffer less predation than larger ones. *Acta Ornitologica* 39: 87–92.

Appert, O. 1972. Beobachtungen über Thamnornis und die übrigen Sylviidae der Mangokygegend in Südwest-Madagaskar. *J. Ornithol.* 113: 76–85.

Aquatic Warbler Conservation Team. 1999. World population, trends and conservation status of the Aquatic Warbler *Acrocephalus paludicola*. *Vogelwelt* 120: 65–85.

Arbogast, B. S., Edwards, S. V., Wakeley, J., Beerli, P. & Slowinski, J. B. 2002. Estimating divergence times from molecular data on phylogenetic and population genetic timescales. *Annual Review of Ecology and Systematics* 33: 707–740.

Arinaitwe, J. 1996. Grauer's Bush Warbler *Bradypterus graueri*. *East Africa Nat. Hist. Soc. Bull.* 26: 14–15.

Arnason, B. 1989. Melodious Warbler *Hippolais polyglotta* new in Iceland. *Bliki* 8: 50.

Arnason, B. & Brynjólfsson, B. 2000. [Blyth's Reed Warbler *Acrocephalus dumetorum*: new to Iceland]. *Bliki* 21: 59–60. (Icelandic, English summary)

Arnaud, M. 1961. Six mois d'observations ornithologiques à Hassi Messoud (Octobre 1959–Avril 1960). *Oiseau et R.F.O.* 31: 140–152.

Ash, J. S. 1960. Leg colouration of Reed Warblers. *Brit. Birds* 53: 359.

Ash, J. S. 1977. Four species new to Ethiopa and other notes. *Bull. Brit. Orn. Club* 97: 4–9.

Ash, J. S. 1978a. Ethiopia as a presumed wintering area for the eastern Grasshopper Warbler. *Locustella naevia straminea. Bull. Brit. Orn. Club* 98: 22–24.

Ash, J. S. 1978b. A Basra Reed Warbler *Acrocephalus griseldis* in Mozambique. *Bull. Brit. Orn. Club* 98: 29–30.

Ash, J. S. 1980. Migrational status of Palaearctic birds in Ethiopia. *Proc. Pan-Afr. Orn. Congr.* 4: 199–208.

Ash, J. S. 1983. Over fifty additions to the Somali list including two hybrids, together with notes from Ethiopa and Kenya. *Scopus* 7: 54–79.

Ash, J. S. & Atkins, J. 2009. *Birds of Ethiopia and Eritrea.* Christopher Helm, London.

Ash, J. S. & Miskell, J. E. 1981. Basra Reed Warblers *Acrocephalus griseldis* overwintering in Somalia. *Scopus* 5: 81–82.

Ash, J. S. & Miskell, J. E. 1983. Birds of Somalia, their habitat, status and distribution. *Scopus.* Special Supplement No. 1.

Ash, J. S. & Miskell, J. E. 1998. *Birds of Somalia.* Pica Press, Mountfield.

Ash, J. S. & Pearson, D. J. 2002. *Hippolais* warblers apparently breeding on the north Somalia coast. *Bull. Brit. Orn. Club.* 122: 222–228.

Ash, J. S. & Watson, G. E. 1974. *Locustella naevia* in Ethiopia. *Bull. Brit. Orn. Club* 94: 39–40.

Ash, J. S., Coverdale, M. A. C. & Gullick, T. M. 1991. Comments on status and distribution of birds in western Uganda. *Scopus* 15: 24–29.

Ash, J. S., Dowsett, R. J. & Dowsett-Lemaire, F. 1989. New ornithological distributional records from eastern Nigeria. *Tauraco Research Report* No.1: 13–27.

Ash, J. S., Pearson, D. J. & Bensch, S. 2005. A new race of Olivaceous Warbler *Hippolais pallida* in Somalia. *Ibis* 147: 841–843.

Ash, J. S., Pearson, D. J., Nikolaus, G. & Colston, P. R. 1989. The mangrove reed warbler of the Red Sea and Gulf of Aden coasts, with description of a new subspecies of the African Reed Warbler *Acrocephalus baeticatus. Bull. Brit. Orn. Club* 109: 36–43.

Aspinall, S. 1996. *The status and conservation of the breeding birds of the United Arab Emirates.* Hobby Publications, Dubai.

Atienza, J. C., Pinilla, J. & Justribo, J. H. 2001. Migration and conservation of the Aquatic Warbler *Acrocephalus paludicola* in Spain. *Ardeola* 48: 197–208.

Atkin, K., Townsend, A. D., Pyman, G. A., Swaine, C. M. & Davis, P. 1965. Some comments on the problems of separating Reed and Marsh Warblers. *Brit. Birds* 58: 181–188.

Austin, O. L. 1948. The birds of Korea. *Bull. Mus. Comp. Zool.* 101: 1–301.

Austin, O. L. & Kuroda, N. 1951. The birds of Japan, their status and distribution. *Bull. Mus. Comp. Zool.* 109: 279–637.

Axell, H. E. & Jobson, G. J. 1972. Savi's Warblers breeding in Suffolk. *Brit. Birds* 65: 229–232.

Ayé, R. 2006. Basra Reed Warblers in Iran in May 2004, with notes on vocalization. *Dutch Birding* 28: 304–306.

Ayé, R., Hertwig, S. T. & Schweizer, M. 2010. Discovery of a breeding area of the enigmatic Large-billed Reed Warbler *Acrocephalus orinus. J. Avian Biol.* 41: 452–459.

Backhurst, G. C. & Pearson, D. J. 1976. Savi's Warbler in Tsavo, an addition to the Kenya list. *East Africa Nat. Hist. Soc. Bull.* 1976: 21–22.

Backhurst, G. C. & Pearson, D. J. 1977. Southward migration at Ngulia, Tsavo, Kenya, 1976/77. *Scopus* 1: 12–17.

Backhurst, G. C. & Pearson, D. J. 1978. Southward migration at Ngulia, Tsavo, Kenya, 1977/78. *Scopus* 2: 42–47.

Backhurst, G. C. & Pearson, D. J. 1979. Southward migration at Ngulia, Tsavo, Kenya, 1978/79. *Scopus* 3: 19–25.

Backhurst, G. C. & Pearson, D. J. 1984. The timing of the southward night migration of Palaearctic birds over Ngulia, southeast Kenya. *Proc. Pan-African Ornithol. Congr.* 5: 361–369.

Backhurst, G. C. & Pearson, D. J. 1993. Ringing and migration at Ngulia, Tsavo, autumn 1991. *Scopus* 15: 172–177.

Baha el Din, M. & Baha el Din, S. 1995. Status of Upcher's Warbler *Hippolais languida* in Egypt. *Bull. Ornithol. Soc. Middle East* 35: 22–24.

Baha el Din, S. & Riad, A. 1992. Booted Warbler in Egypt in September 1991. *Dutch Birding* 14: 176–177.

Baha el Din, S., Baha el Din, M. & Bensch, S. 2010. Mangrove Olivaceous Warblers in Egypt – new to the Western Palearctic. *Birding World* 23: 215–217.

Baird, J. 1963. On ageing birds by skull ossification. *Ring* 37: 253–255.

Bairlein, F., Alström, P., Aymí, R., Clement, P., Dyrcz, A., Gargallo, G., Hawkins, A. F. A., Madge, S. C., Pearson, D. J. & Svensson, L. 2006. Family Sylviidae (Old World warblers). Pp. 492–709. In: del Hoyo, J., Elliott, A. & Christie, D. A. (eds.). *Handbook of the Birds of the World.* Vol. 11. Lynx Edicions, Barcelona.

Bakaev, S. 1976. [Breeding of Sykes's Warbler *Hippolas caligata rama* (*Aves, Sylviidae*) in the lower reaches of the Zerafshan River]. *Vestnik Zoologii* 11(6): 31–35. (Russian)

Baker, J. K. 1988. Identification of Pallas's Grasshopper Warbler. *Brit. Birds* 81: 645–646.

Baker, K. 1997. *Warblers of Europe, Asia and North Africa.* Christopher Helm/A&C Black, London.

Baker, R. H. 1951. *The Avifauna of Micronesia, Its Origin, Evolution and Distribution.* Vol. 3(1): 1–359. University of Kansas Publications.

Bakus, G. J. 1967. Changes to the avifauna of Fanning Island, central Pacific, between 1924 and 1963. *Condor* 69: 207–209.

Balachandran, S. 1999. Blyth's Reed Warbler *Acrocephalus dumetorum* feeding on nectar. *J. Bombay Nat. Hist. Soc.* 96(3): 473–474.

Balatskiy, N. N. 1995. [A systematic review of the family Sylviidae (*Passeriformes, Aves*) from the Northern Palearctic]. *Russian J. Ornithol.* 4(1/2): 33–44. (Russian)

van Balen, S. & Prentice, C. 1997. Birds of the Negara River Basin, South Kalimantan, Indonesia. *Kukila* 9: 81–107.

Ballard, J. W. O. & Whitlock, M. C. 2004. The incomplete natural history of mitochondria. *Molec. Ecol.* 13: 729–744.

Bannerman, D. A. & Bannerman, W. M. 1968. *History of the Birds of the Cape Verde Islands. Birds of the Atlantic Islands.* Vol. 4. Oliver & Boyd, Edinburgh.

Banwell, A. 1985. Grasshopper Warbler mistaken for Savi's Warbler. *Brit. Birds* 78: 197.

Baral, H. S. 1996. A checklist of birds recorded during *Birdquest* lowland tour, February 1996. Unpublished.

Baral, H. S. 2000. *Birds of Koshi.* Department of National Parks and Wildlife, Kathmandu.

Baral, H. S., Giri, T., Choudhary, B. & Som, G. C. 2004. Moustached Warbler *Acrocephalus melanopogon*: first record for Nepal. *Forktail* 20: 93.

Barbier, P. G. R. 1971. Grasshopper Warbler or Pallas's Grasshopper Warbler in Dorset? *Brit. Birds* 64: 198.

Bardin, A. V. 1998. [Two records of *Hippolais caligata* in the Leningrad Region]. *Russian J. Ornithol.* Express issue 47: 16–17. (Russian)

Barhoum, D. N. & Burns. K. J. 2002. Phylogenetic relationships of the Wrentit based on mitochondrial cytochrome *b* sequences. *Condor* 104: 740–749.

Barnes, K. N. (ed.). 2000. *The Eskom Red Data Book of birds of South Africa, Lesotho and Swaziland.* Birdlife South Africa, Johannesburg.

Barratt, K. 1998. The status of the Marsh Warbler in Essex. *Essex Bird Report* 1997: 159–166.

Barrett, G., Silcocks, A., Barry, S., Cunningham, R. & Poulter, R. 2003. *The New Atlas of Australian Birds.* RAOU, Hawthorne East, Victoria.

Barua, M. & Sharma, P. 2005. The birds of Nameri National Park, Assam, India. *Forktail* 21: 15–26.

Basciutti, P., Negra, O. & Spina, F. 1997. Autumn migration strategies of the Sedge Warbler *Acrocephalus schoenobaenus* in northern Italy. *Ringing & Migration* 18: 59–67.

Bates, R. S. P. & Lowther, E. N. H. 1952. *Breeding Birds of Kashmir.* Oxford University Press, Bombay.

Baumanis, Ya. A. 1983. [*Blyth's Reed Warbler: Territorial distribution and number.*] Pp. 154–155. Zinatne Press, Riga. (Russian)

Baxter, P. 2001. Racial identification of the Olivaceous Warbler at Collieston. *Birding Scotland* 4: 13–14.

Bayly, N. J. & Rumsey, S. J. R. 2007. Grasshopper Warbler *Locustella naevia* autumn migration – findings from a study in southeast Britain. *Ringing & Migration* 23(3): 147–155.

Beaman, M. 1994. *Palearctic Birds - A Checklist of the Birds of Europe, North Africa, and Asia north of the foothills of the Himalayas.* Harrier publications, Stonyhurst.

Beaman, M. & Madge, S. 1999. *The Handbook of Bird Identification for Europe and the Western Palearctic.* Christopher Helm, London.

Beaman, M. & Woodcock, M. 1978. Head-pattern of *Hippolais* Warblers. *Brit. Birds* 71: 546.

Becker, P. & Lutgens, H. 1976. Sumpfrohrsänger (*Acrocephalus palustris*) in Sudwest Afrika. *Madoqua* 9: 41–44.

Becker, P. H. 1990. Song of the Grasshopper Warbler *Locustella naevia* in acoustic isolation. *Vogelwarte* 35: 257–267.

Beddall-Smith, J. 1919. Evidence towards double-broodedness of the Reed Warbler. *Brit. Birds* 12: 278–279.

Beehler, B. 1983. Thoughts on an ornithological mystery from Bougainville Island, Papua New Guinea. *Emu* 83: 114–115.

Beier, J. 1981. Untersuchungen an Drossel- und Teichrohrsänger (*Acrocephalus arundinaceus, A. scirpaceus*): Bestandsentwicklung, Brutbiologie, Ökologie. *J. Ornithol.* 122: 209–230.

Beier, J., Leisler, B. & Wink, M. 1997. [A Great Reed x Reed Warbler (*Acrocephalus arundinaceus* x *Acrocephalus scirpaceus*) hybrid and its parentage]. *J. Ornithol.* 138: 51–60. (German, English summary)

Bell, B. & Bell, D. 1998. Pitcairn paradise preserved. *World Birdwatch* 20: 8–11.

Bell, B. D., Borowiec, M., McConkey, K. R. & Ranoszek, E. 1997. Settlement, breeding success and song repertoires of monogamous and polygynous Sedge Warblers (*Acrocephalus schoenobaenus*). *Vogelwarte* 39: 87–94.

Bell, D. G. 1960. An encounter with a Grasshopper Warbler. *Bird Notes* 29: 109–110.

Bell, D. G. 1979. Paddyfield Warbler in Cleveland. *Brit. Birds* 72: 348–351.

Belousov, E. M. 1981. [Identification of *Hippolais pallida* and *Hippolais rama* (Aves, Sylviidae)]. *Zool. Zhurnal* 60(7): 1112–1114. (Russian)

van Bemmel-Lieneman, N. & van Bemmel, A. C. V. 1940. De vogels van het Tenggergebergte. *Trop. Nat.* 29: 93–101.

van Bemmelen, R. S. A. & Groenendijk, D. 2004. Masters of Mystery: Savi's Warbler. *Dutch Birding* 26: 53–56.

van Bemmelen, R. S. A. & Groenendijk, D. 2004. Masters of Mystery: Booted Warbler. *Dutch Birding* 26: 328–332.

Bennun, L. A. 1986. Montane birds of the Bwindi (Impenetrable) Forest. *Scopus* 10: 87–91.

Bensch, S. & Hasselquist, D. 1991. Territorial infidelity in the polygynous Great Reed Warbler *Acrocephalus arundinaceus*: the effect of variation in territory attractiveness. *J. Anim. Ecol.* 60: 857–871.

Bensch, S. & Hasselquist, D. 1992. Evidence for active female choice in a polygynous Great Reed Warbler. *Anim. Behav.* 44: 301–311.

Bensch, S. & Nielsen, B. 1999. Autumn migration speed of juvenile Reed and Sedge Warblers in relation to date and fat loads. *Condor* 101: 153–156.

Bensch, S. & Pearson, D. 2002. The Large-billed Reed Warbler *Acrocephalus orinus* revisited. *Ibis* 144: 259–267.

Bensch, S., Eriksson, N. & Hasselquist, D. 1987. [Studies of the ecology of the Great Reed Warbler at Lake Kvismaren]. *Vår Fågelvärld* 46: 89–92. (Swedish, English summary)

Bensch, S., Hasselquist, D., Hedenström, A. & Ottoson, U. 1991. Rapid moult among palaearctic passerines in West Africa - an adaption to the oncoming dry season? *Ibis* 133: 47–52.

Benson, C. W. 1939. On the status of the genus *Bradypterus* in Nyasaland, including a new race, *Bradypterus usambarae granti*.

Bull. Brit. Orn. Club 59: 108–113.

Benson, C. W. 1960. The birds of the Comoro islands: results of the British Ornithologists' Union centenary expedition 1958. *Ibis* 103b: 5–106.

Benson, C. W. 1978. Misidentification of a Marsh Warbler in Malawi. *Scopus* 2(4): 99.

Benson, C. W. & Irwin, M. P. S. 1965. The River Warbler *Locustella fluviatilis* (Wolf) in Barotseland, south-western Zambia. *Bull. Brit. Orn. Club* 85: 116.

Benson, C. W. & Penny, M. J. 1968. A new species of warbler from the Aldabra Atoll. *Bull. Brit. Orn. Club* 88: 102–108.

Benson, C. W., Brooke, R. K., Dowsett, R. J. & Irwin, M. P. S. 1971. *The Birds of Zambia.* Collins, London.

Benson, C. W., Brooke, R. K. & Traylor, M. A. 1978. Multiple original spellings of *Bradypterus* Swainson, 1837. *Bull. Brit. Orn. Club* 98: 4–5.

Benson, C. W., Colebrook-Robjent, J. F. R. & Williams, A. 1977. Contribution à l'ornithologie de Madagascar. *Oiseau et RFO* 47: 41–64.

Beresford, P., Barker, F. K., Ryan, P. G. & Crowe, T. M. 2005. African endemics span the tree of songbirds (Passeri): molecular systematics of several evolutionary 'enigmas'. *Proc. Royal Soc. B.* 272: 849–858.

Berezovikov, N. N. 2004. [Attempted nest robbing of *Acrocephalus dumetorum* by Siberian Chipmunk *Eutamias sibiricus*]. *Russian J. Ornithol.* Express issue 263: 537–538. (Russian)

van den Berg, A. B. 1984. Voorkomen van Krekelzanger in Nederland. [Occurrence of River Warbler in the Netherlands] *Dutch Birding* 6: 105–107. (Dutch, English summary)

van den Berg, A. B. 1989a. Mystery Photographs 32: Olivaceous Warbler. *Dutch Birding* 11: 116–117.

van den Berg, A. B. 1989b. [Booted Warbler at Bloemendaal in September 1988.] *Dutch Birding* 11: 123–126. (Dutch, English summary)

van den Berg, A. B. & Bosman, C. A. W. 1988. Paddyfield Warbler, *Acrocephalus agricola*, at Van Gölü, eastern Turkey. *Zool. Middle East.* 2: 16–18.

van den Berg, A. B. & Bosman, C. A. W. 1999. *Rare birds of the Netherlands.* Pica Press, Mountfield.

van den Berg, A. B. & van Spanje, T. 2003. [Unusual Icterine Warbler] *Dutch Birding* 25: 355–356. (Dutch, English summary)

van den Berg, A. B. & Symens, P. 1992. Occurrence and identification of Basra Reed Warbler in Saudi Arabia. *Dutch Birding* 14: 41–48.

van den Berg, A. & The Sound Approach. 2005. Olivaceous warblers in the western Mediterranean and their identification. *Dutch Birding* 27: 302–307.

Berg, M. L., Beintema, N. H., Welbergen, J. A. & Komdeur, J. 2005. Singing as a handicap: the effects of food availability and weather on song output in the Australian Reed Warbler *Acrocephalus australis*. *J. Avian Biol.* 36: 102–109.

Berg, M. L., Beintema, N. H., Welbergen, J. A. & Komdeur, J. 2006. The functional significance of multiple nest-building in the Australian Reed Warbler *Acrocephalus australis*. *Ibis* 148: 396–404.

Berger, A. J. 1972. *Hawaiian Birdlife.* University Press of Hawaii.

Berger, A. J. 1975. The Japanese Bush Warbler on Oahu. *Elepaio* 36: 19–21.

Berlijn, M. 1995. Identification of Styan's Grasshopper Warbler in Ussuriland. *Dutch Birding* 17: 161.

Berlioz, J. 1929. Les caractères de la faune avienne de Polynésie. *L'Oiseau et la Revue Francaise d'Ornithologie* 10: 581–590.

Berruti, A., Taylor, P. J. & Vernon, C. J. 1993. Morphometrics and distribution of the Knysna Warbler *Bradypterus sylvaticus* Sundevall and Barratt's Warbler *B. barratti* Sharpe. *Durban Mus. Nov.* 18: 29–36.

Bertault, Y. & Fremont, J.-Y. 1993. First observation of a possible Basra Reed Warbler in Turkey. *Bull. Ornithol. Soc. Middle East* 31: 18–20.

van Beusekom, R. F. J. 1995. [Melodious Warbler breeding in Flevoland in 1990.] *Dutch Birding* 17: 240–244. (Dutch, English summary)

Beven, G. 1974. Studies of less familiar birds 173. Icterine Warbler. *Brit. Birds* 67: 370–376.

Bibby, C. J. 1978. Some breeding statistics of Reed and Sedge Warblers. *Bird Study* 25: 207–222.

Bibby, C. J. 1980. Another mystery photograph: Moustached or Sedge Warbler? *Brit. Birds* 73: 367–370.

Bibby, C. J. 1982a. Studies of west Palearctic birds 184. Moustached Warbler. *Brit. Birds* 75: 346–359.

Bibby, C. J. 1982b. Polygyny and breeding ecology of the Cetti's Warbler *Cettia cetti*. *Ibis* 124: 288–301.

Bibby, C. J. & Green, R. E. 1981. Autumn migration strategies of Reed and Sedge Warblers. *Ornis Scand.* 12: 1–12.

Bibby, C. J. & Thomas, D. K. 1984. Sexual dimorphism in size, moult and movements of Cetti's Warbler *Cettia cetti*. *Bird Study* 31: 28–34.

Bibby, C. J. & Thomas, D. K. 1985. Breeding and diets of the Reed Warbler at a rich and a poor site. *Bird Study* 32: 19–31.

Bibby, C. J., Green, R. E., Pepler, G. R. M. & Pepler, P. A. 1976. Sedge Warbler migration and Reed Aphids. *Brit. Birds* 69: 384–399.

Bijnens, L., Stevens, J., Janssens, L. & Louette, M. 1987. Community structure of Grand Comoro land birds with special reference to the ecology of congeneric species. *Rev. Zool. Afr.* 101: 221–232.

Bil, W. 1987. [Many Aquatic Warblers near Makkum in summer of 1986.] *Dutch Birding* 9: 176. (Dutch, English summary)

Billett, D. F. 1952. Double nest of reed warbler. *Brit. Birds* 45: 366–367.

Birdlife International. 2000. *Threatened Birds of the World.* Lynx Edicions and Birdlife International, Barcelona and Cambridge.

Birdlife International. 2001. *Threatened Birds of Asia: the Birdlife International Red Data Book.* Birdlife International, Cambridge.

Birdlife International. 2004. *Threatened birds of the world 2004.* CD-ROM version. Birdlife International, Cambridge.

Biserov, M. F. & Medvedeva, E. A. 2002. [*Bradypterus thoracicus* in the region of Bureinskiy mountain ridge]. *Russian J. Ornithol.* Express issue 179: 219–222. (Russian)

Bishop, D. & Brickle, N. W. 1999. An annotated checklist of the birds of the Tanimbar Islands. *Kukila* 10: 115–150.

Blagosklonov, K. N. 1967. [Breeding biology of *Hippolais rama* in the lower reaches of the Amu Darya.] *Russian J. Ornithol.* 2(1): 77–85. (Russian)

Blakers, M., Davies, S. J. J. F. & Reilly, P. N. 1984. *The atlas of Australian birds.* Melbourne University Press, Carlton, Victoria.

Blankert, H. 1981. [Occurrence of Melodious Warbler in Benelux.] *Dutch Birding* 3: 25–26. (Dutch, English summary)

Bocheński, Z. & Kuoenierczyk, P. 2003. Nesting of the *Acrocephalus* warblers. *Acta Zool. Cracoviensia* 46(2): 97–195).

Bochkareva, E.N. & Ivanitskiy, V.V. 2006. [The song orgranization in the Moustached Warbler *Acrocephalus melanopogon*]. Page 89. In: Kurochkin, E. N. (ed.). [*Ornithological studies in Northern Eurasia*]. Abstracts of XII Int. Orn. Conference of Northern Eurasia, Stavropol, 31 January–5 February 2006. Stavropol University Press, Stavropol. (Russian)

Boddy, M. 1980. Booted Warbler at Theddlethorpe dunes, 12th October 1980. *Lincolnshire Bird Report 1980.* 1980: 36.

Bolshakov, C., Bulyuk, V. & Chernetsov, N. 2003. Spring nocturnal migration of Reed Warblers *Acrocephalus scirpaceus*: departure, landing and body condition. *Ibis* 145: 106–112.

Bonham, P. F. & Robertson, J. C. M. 1975. The spread of Cetti's Warbler in north-west Europe. *Brit. Birds* 68: 393–408.

Boon, L. Finding Paddyfield Warblers in Bulgaria. *Birding World* 7: 444–445.

Borghesio, L., Ndang'ang'a, K., Nalyanya, N., Kahinda, M. & Laiolo, P. 2004. Some interesting bird observations from Northern Kenya. *Scopus* 24: 33–39.

Borowiec, M. 1992. [Breeding ecology of the Sedge warbler *Acrocephalus schoenobaenus* near Wroclaw - a preliminary report.] *Remiz* 1: 12–14. (Polish, English summary)

Borowiec, M. & Lontkowski, J. 1988. Polygyny in the Sedge Warbler *Acrocephalus schoenobaenus*. *Vogelwelt* 109: 222–226.

Borrow, N. & Demey, R. 2001. *Birds of Western Africa.* Christopher Helm, A&C Black, London.

Bos, E. & van der Burg, E. 1983. [Melodious Warbler on De Maasvvlakte in May 1982.] *Dutch Birding* 5: 20–21. (Dutch, English summary)

Boston, F. M. 1956. Savi's Warbler in Cambridgeshire. *Brit. Birds* 49: 326–327.

Boswell, J. 1967. The song of Pallas's Grasshopper Warbler. *Brit. Birds* 60: 523–524.

Boswell, J. 1968. The song of Blyth's Reed Warbler. *Brit. Birds* 61: 34–35.

Boswell, J. 1985. Song of Grasshopper Warbler. *Brit. Birds* 78: 198.

Bourne, W. R. P. 1960. Olivaceous Warbler in Dorset. *Brit. Birds* 53: 312–313.

Bourne, W. R. P. & David, A. L. F. 1983. Henderson Island and its birds. *Notornis* 30: 233–252.

Bowey, K. 1995. Apparent female Moustached Warbler singing. *Brit. Birds* 88: 113.

Bowey, K. 1999. Sedge warblers nesting in Rape crops. *Brit. Birds* 92: 371.

Bowler, J. & Taylor, J. 1989. An annotated checklist of the birds of Manusela National Park, Seram. Birds recorded on the Operation Raleigh Expedition. *Kukila* 4(1–2): 3–29.

Boyd, A. W. 1916. Early nesting of Reed-Warbler in Cheshire. *Brit. Birds* 9: 121.

Boyd, A. W. 1933. Notes on the nesting of the Reed-Warbler. *Brit. Birds* 26: 222–223.

Boyd, A. W. 1939. Reed-Warbler's nest of sheep's wool. *Brit. Birds* 32: 83.

Boyd, M. 1989. Mystery photographs 140: Aquatic Warbler. *Brit. Birds* 82: 68–69.

Bradshaw, C. 1997. Identification of pale Paddyfield Warblers. *Brit. Birds* 90: 142–147.

Bradshaw, C. 2000a. The occurrence of Moustached Warbler in Britain. *Brit. Birds* 93: 29–38.

Bradshaw, C. 2000b. Separating *Acrocephalus* and *Hippolais* Warblers. *Brit. Birds* 93: 277.

Bradshaw, C. 2001. Blyth's Reed Warbler: problems and pitfalls. *Brit. Birds* 94: 236–245.

Bradshaw, C. & Steele, J. 1995. Mystery Photographs 195: Booted Warbler. *Brit. Birds* 88: 561–564.

Bradshaw, C. & Steele, J. 1997. Mystery Warblers in Tselinograd. *Brit Birds* 90: 155–158.

Bräger, S. & Berndt, R. K. 1993. [Population trend of the Savi's Warbler (*Locustella luscinioides*) in Schleswig-Holstein, FRG, between 1951–1990.] *Corax* 15: 270–273. (German, English summary)

Brandt, J. H. 1962. Nests and eggs of the birds of the Truk Islands. *Condor* 64: 416–437.

Brazil, M. A. 1991. *The birds of Japan.* Christopher Helm, London.

Brazil, M. A. 1992. The Birds of Shuangtaiziheko National Nature Reserve, Liaoning Province, P. R. China. *Forktail* 7: 91–124.

Breek, C. J. & van den Berg, A. B. 1992. [Blyth's Reed Warbler at Lelystad in June 1990.] *Dutch Birding* 14: 121–126. (Dutch, English summary)

Breek, C. J., Ebels, E. B. & Mauer, K. A. 2006. Sykes' Spotvogel bij Almere-Haven in oktober 1986. *Dutch Birding* 28: 219–224. (Dutch, English summary)

Breek, K. 1987. Vangst van een Kleine Spotvogel in het Kromsloot-park in oktober 1986. *Grauwe Gans* 3: 8–13.

van den Brink, B. & Loske, K.-H. 1990. Botswana and Namibia as regular wintering quarters for European Reed Warblers? *Ostrich* 61: 146–147.

Britton, P. L. 1970. The immature plumages of two African warblers. *Bull. Brit. Orn. Club* 90: 26–28.

Britton, P. L. 1978. Seasonality, density and diversity of birds of a papyrus swamp in western Kenya. *Ibis* 120: 450–466.

Britton, P. L. (ed.). 1980. *Birds of East Africa.* East Africa Natural History Society, Nairobi.

Britton, P. L. & Britton, H. A. 1977. An April fall of Palaearctic migrants at Ngulia. *Scopus* 1: 109–111.

Britton, P. L. & Harper, J. F. 1969. Some new distributional records for Kenya. *Bull. Brit. Orn. Club.* 89: 162–165.

Britton, D., Grant, P. J. & Harvey, W. G. 1980. Identification of Blyth's Reed and Paddyfield Warbler. *Brit. Birds* 73: 589.

Bronskov, A. I., Molodan, G. N. & Govyadov, A. V. 1989. [Breeding passerines in natural systems of Donetsk district] *All-Union Wildlife Inventory and Census Workshop.* Abstracts, Part III. Ufa: 26–28. (Russian)

Brooke, M. de L. & Hartley, I. R. 1995. Nesting Henderson Reed-Warblers (*Acrocephalus vaughani taiti*) studied by DNA fingerprinting: unrelated coalitions in a stable habitat? *Auk* 112: 77–86.

Brooke, R. K. 1966. Distribution and breeding notes on the birds of the central frontier of Rhodesia and Mozambique. *Ann. Natal Mus.* 18(2): 429–453.

Brooks, D. J., Evans, M. I., Martins, R. P. & Porter, R. F. 1987. The status of birds in North Yemen and the records of the OSME Expedition in autumn 1985. *Sandgrouse* 9: 4–66.

Brooks, W. E. 1875. Notes on a new *Dumeticola*, and on *Tribura luteoventris*, Hodgson, and *Dumeticola affinis*, Hodgson. *Stray Feathers* 3: 284–287.

Brooks, W. E. 1880. Ornithological observations in Sikkim, the Punjab and Sind. *Stray Feathers* 8: 464–489.

Brosset. A. 1984. Oiseaux migrateurs européen hivernant dans la partie Guinéen du Mont Nimba. *Alauda* 52: 81–101.

Brown, L. H. & Britton, P. L. 1980. *The Breeding Seasons of East African Birds.* The East Africa Natural History Society, Nairobi.

Brown, P. E. 1946. Preliminary Observations on a colony of Reed-Warblers. *Brit. Birds* 39: 290–308.

Brown, P. E. & Davis, M. G. 1949. *Reed Warblers. An introduction to their breeding-biology and behaviour.* Foy Publications, East Molesey.

Broyd, S. J. 1983. Supercilium of Pallas's Grasshopper Warbler. *Brit. Birds* 76: 89–90.

Bruner, P. L. 1972. *Field Guide to the Birds of French Polynesia.* Pacific Scientific Information Center, Honolulu.

Bruner, P. L. 1974. Behaviour, ecology and taxonomic ststus of three southeastern Pacific Warblers of the genus *Acrocephalus.* Unpublished thesis. Louisiana State University, Baton Rouge.

Brunov, V. V. 1977. [New find of *Bradypterus thoracicus*]. *Ornitologiya* 13: 188–189. (Russian)

Buchanan, K. 1903. Nesting Notes from Kashmir. *J. Bombay Nat. Hist. Soc.* 15: 131–133.

Buchanan, K. L. & Catchpole, C. K. 2000. Extra-pair paternity in the socially monogamous Sedge Warbler *Acrocephalus schoenobaenus* as revealed by multilocus DNA fingerprinting. *Ibis* 142: 12–20.

Bulyuk, V. & Chernetsov, N. 2000. Two migratory flights of Sedge Warblers (*Acrocephalus schoenobaenus*) from Finland to Estonia. *Ornis Svecica* 10: 79–83.

Bundy, G. & Warr, E. F. 1980. A checklist of the birds of the Arabian Gulf States. *Sandgrouse* 1: 4–49.

Burton, J. F. 1979. Continuous nocturnal singing by Cetti's Warbler. *Brit. Birds* 72: 184–185.

Burton, J. F. & Johnson, E. D. H. 1984. Insect, amphibian or bird? *Brit. Birds* 77: 87–104.

Burua, M. & Sharma, P. 1999. Birds of Kaziranga National Park, India. *Forktail* 15: 47–60.

Busche, G. 1989. [Methodological study on the calculation of breeding bird numbers in large areas, illustrated by the case of the Marsh Warbler *Acrocephalus palustris* in W-Schleswig-Holstein.] *Vogelwelt* 110: 209–220. (German, English summary)

Bushell, C. I. 1984. Head pattern of Booted Warbler. *Brit. Birds* 77: 366.

Busse, P. 1984. Key to sexing and ageing of European Passerines. *Beitr. zur Naturkunde Niedersachsens* 37: 1–224.

Bussmann, C. 1979. Ökologische Sonderung der Rohrsänger Südfrankreichs aufgrund von Nahrungsstudien. *Vogelwarte* 30: 84–101.

Butchart, S. H. M. & Stattersfield, A. S. 2004. *Threatened birds of the world 2004.* CD-ROM. Birdlife International, Cambridge.

Buttle. C. 1995. The Olivaceous Warbler in Suffolk. *Birding World* 8: 293–294.

Butterfield, D. 1988. Paddyfield Warbler in Suffolk. *Birding World* 1: 203–205.

Butterfield, D. 2000a. The Blyth's Reed Warbler in Highland. *Birding World* 13: 277–278.

Butterfield, D. 2000b. The Blyth's Reed Warbler at Nigg Ferry in June 2000. *Birding Scotland* 3: 127–128.

de By, R. A. 1990. Migration of Aquatic Warbler in western Europe. *Dutch Birding* 12: 165–181.

Cade, M. 1999. The Olivaceous Warbler in Dorset. *Birding World* 12: 284–285.

Cade, M. 2000. The Sykes's Warbler in Dorset. *Birding World* 13: 274–276.

Cai, Q. K. (ed.). 1987. [*The birds of Beijing*] Beijing Press, Beijing. (Chinese)

Caldwell, H. R. & Caldwell, J. C. 1931. *South China Birds.* Hester May Vanderburgh, Shanghai.

Callion, J., White, N. & Holloway, D. 1990. Grasshopper Warblers raising two and three broods in Cumbria. *Brit. Birds* 83: 506–508.

Calvert, M. 1981. Reed Warbler nest survival during exceptional rainfall. *Cheshire Bird Report* 1981: 70–71.

Calvert, M. 1983a. Height and support of Reed Warbler nests. *The Naturalist* 108: 105–106.

Calvert, M. 1983b. Reed Warbler nests and instances of re-use for further breeding attempts. *The North Western Naturalist* 1983: 8–10.

Calvert, M. 1984. Cheshire Reed Warblers and Weather. *North Western Naturalist* 1984: 17–20.

Calvert, M. 1987. Early nesting by Reed Warblers. *BTO News* 151: 3.

Calvert, M. 1998. Effect of weather on Reed Warbler nests. *CAWOS Bird News* 40: 16.

Calvert, M. 1997. Reed Warbler Chronicle. Diary of the 1997 breeding season at Rostherne Mere NNR. *CAWOS Bird News* 36: 7–9.

Calvert, M. 1999. Rostherne Mere reedbeds and their relevance as nesting areas for Reed Warblers – some observations at September 1999. *Rostherne Mere NNR Natural History Report* 1999: 34–36.

Calvert, M. 2000. Earlier arrival and nesting by Reed Warblers at a site in north Cheshire. *North Western Naturalist* 1(3): 11–12.

Calvert, M. 2001. Nesting of Reed Warblers within hawthorn hedge. *CAWOS Bird News* 48: 18.

Calvert, M. 2003. Dispersal of young Reed Warblers from a breeding site in north Cheshire. *North Western Naturalist* 4(3): 3–5.

Calvert, M. 2005. Apparent loss of pigmentation in an aged Reed Warbler. *Brit. Birds* 98: 101–102.

Calvert, M. 2005. *Reed Warblers at Rostherne Mere.* English Nature, Shrewsbury.

Calvert, M. & Cook, K. 2005. Abnormal Reed Warbler chicks. *Brit. Birds* 98: 433.

Cantello, J. 1984. Identification of singing Reed and Marsh Warblers by mouth colour. *Brit. Birds* 77: 214–215.

Cantello, J. 1988. Icterine & Melodious Warbler identification. *Birding World* 1: 403.

Cantera, J. P. & Desnos, A. 1994. [Early date for a Sedge Warbler *Acrocephalus schoenobaenus* in Corsica.] *Alauda* 62: 141. (French)

Cantos, F. J. & Tellería, J. L. 1994. Stopover site fidelity of four migrant warblers in the Iberian Peninsula. *J. Avian Biol.* 25: 131–134.

Carey, G. & Lockey, H. (eds.). 2009. *The Hong Kong Bird Report 2003–04.* Hong Kong Bird Watching Society Limited, Hong Kong.

Carey, G. J., Chalmers, M. L., Diskin, D. A., Kennerley, P. R., Leader, P. J., Leven, M. R., Lewthwaite, R. W., Melville, D. S.,

Turnbull, M. & Young, L. 2001. *The Avifauna of Hong Kong*. Hong Kong Bird Watching Society, Hong Kong.

Carlson, K. 1980. Another mystery photograph: Moustached or Sedge Warbler? *Brit. Birds* 73: 538–539.

Carr, P. 1996. Variation in winter moult strategies evident in Sedge Warblers passing through the Akamas, Cyprus in spring 1995. *Akamas Cyprusa report of bird migration spring 1995*: 52–56.

Carswell, M. 1986. Birds of the Kampala Area. *Scopus*. Special Supplement No. 3.

Carter, C. 1998. Identification of large *Acrocephalus* warblers at Candaba Swamp, Luzon, Philippines. *Bull. Oriental Bird Club* 27: 52–54.

Cassin, J. 1858. Catalogue of birds collected by A. A. Henderson, M. D., US Navy, at Hakodadi, Islands of Jesso, Japan, with notes and description of new species. *Proc. Acad. Science Philadelphia*, Pp: 191–196.

Castell, P. 1996. Description of the nestlings of Olive-tree Warbler *Hippolais olivetorum*. *Sandgrouse* 18(2): 68.

Castell, P. 1999a. Clamorous Reed Warbler *Acrocephalus stentoreus* apparently predating nest of Booted Warbler *Hippolais rama* in the United Arab Emirates. *Sandgrouse* 21(2): 177–178.

Castell, P. 1999b. The nest and nestlings of Cape Verde Cane Warbler *Acrocephalus brevipennis*. *Bull. African Bird Club* 6: 100.

Castell, P. 2001. Clamorous Reed Warblers *Acrocephalus stentoreus* nesting in maize. *Bull. African Bird Club* 8: 56.

Castell, P. & Kirwan, G. M. 2005. Will the real Sykes's Warbler please stand up? Breeding data support specific status for *Hippolais rama* and *H. caligata*, with comments on the Arabian population of 'booted warbler' *Sandgrouse* 27(1): 30–36.

Catchpole, C. K. 1967. Sex determination by wing length in a population of Reed and Sedge Warblers. *Attenborough Ringing Group Report* 1: 16–21.

Catchpole, C. K. 1970. *Some aspects of behavioural ecology in two* Acrocephalus *species*. PhD. thesis, University of Nottingham.

Catchpole, C. K. 1971. Polygamy in reed warblers. *Brit. Birds*. 64: 232–233.

Catchpole, C. K. 1972. A comparative study of territory in the Reed Warbler *Acrocephalus scirpaceus* and Sedge Warbler *A. schoenobaenus*. *J. Zool. Lond.* 166: 213–231.

Catchpole, C. K. 1973a. The functions of advertising song in the Sedge Warbler and the Reed Warbler. *Behaviour* 46: 300–320.

Catchpole, C. K. 1973b. Conditions for co-existence in sympatric breeding populations of *Acrocephalus* warblers. *J. Anim. Ecol.* 43: 363–380.

Catchpole, C. K. 1974. Habitat selection and breeding success in the Reed Warbler (*Acrocephalus scirpaceus*). *J. Anim. Ecol.* 43: 363–380.

Catchpole, C. K. 1977. Aggressive responses of male Sedge Warblers (*Acrocephalus schoenobaenus*) to playback of species song and sympatric song, before and after pairing. *Anim. Behav.* 25: 489–496.

Catchpole, C. K. 1978. Interspecific territorialism and competition in *Acrocephalus* warblers as revealed by playback experiments in areas of sympatry and allopatry. *Anim. Behav.* 26: 1072–1080.

Catchpole, C. K. 1980. Sexual selection and the evolution of complex songs among European warblers of the genus *Acrocephalus*. *Behaviour* 74: 149–166.

Catchpole, C. K. 1983. Variation in the song of the Great Reed Warbler *Acrocephalus arundinaceus* in relation to mate attraction and territorial defence. *Anim. Behav.* 31: 1217–1225.

Catchpole, C. K. 1986a. Interspecific territorialism in Reed Warblers: a local effect revealed by playback experiments. *Anim. Behav.* 34: 299–300.

Catchpole, C. K. 1986b. Song repertoires and reproductive success in the Great Reed Warbler *Acrocephalus arundinaceus*. *Behav. Ecol. Sociobiol.* 19: 439–445.

Catchpole, C. K. & Komdeur, J. 1993. The song of the Seychelles Warbler *Acrocephalus sechellensis*, an island endemic. *Ibis* 135: 190–195.

Catchpole, C. K. & Leisler, B. 1989. Variation in the song of the Aquatic Warbler in response to playback of different song structures. *Behaviour* 108: 125–138.

Catchpole, C. K., Leisler, B. & Winkler, H. 1985. Polygyny in the Great Reed Warbler *Acrocephalus arundinaceus*: a possible case

of deception. *Behav. Ecol. Sociobiol.* 16: 285–291.

Cederroth, C. 2000. Sällsynta fåglar i Sverige 1999. SOF 2000. *Fågelåret* 1999. Stockholm.

Chadwick, P. 1984. Aquatic Warbler and streaked Sedge Warbler. *Brit. Birds* 77: 378.

Chalmers, M. L. 1986. *Annotated checklist of the birds of Hong Kong*. 4th edition. Hong Kong Bird Watching Society, Hong Kong.

Chalmers, M. L. 1988. Blunt-winged Warbler *Acrocephalus concinens*. Unpublished manuscript.

Chapin, J. P. 1953. Birds of the Belgian Congo. *Bull. Amer. Mus. Nat. Hist.* 75A, part 3.

Chapin, R. T. 1973. Observations on *Bradypterus carpalis* and *Bradypterus graueri*. *Bull. Brit. Orn. Club* 93: 167–170.

Chapman, M. S. 1979. Identification of Booted Warbler. *Brit. Birds* 72: 437–438.

Charlwood, R. H. & Harber, D. D. 1965. The original misidentification of the Hampshire Cetti's Warbler. *Brit. Birds* 58: 225–227.

Cheke, A. S. 1987. Observations on the surviving endemic birds of Rodrigues. In: Diamond, A. W. (ed.). *Studies of Mascarene Island Birds*: 364–402. Cambridge University Press, Cambridge.

Cheke, A. S. & Diamond, A. W. 1986. Birds on Moheli and Grande Comore (Comoro Islands) in February 1975. *Bull. Brit. Orn. Club* 106(4): 138–148.

Cheng, T. H. 1987. *A Synopsis of the Avifauna of China*. Science Press. Beijing.

Cheng, T. H., Tan, Y. K., Liang, C. Y. & Chang, C. F. 1963. [Studies of birds of Mount Omei and their vertical distribution.] *Acta Zoologica Sinica* 15(2): 317–335. (Chinese)

Chernetsov, N. 1996. Preliminary hypotheses on migration of the Sedge Warbler *Acrocephalus schoenobaenus* in the eastern Baltic. *Vogelwarte* 38: 201–210.

Chernetsov, N. 1999. Timing of spring migration, body condition, and fat score in local and passage populations of the Reed Warbler *Acrocephalus scirpaceus* on the Courish Spit. *Avian Ecol. Behav.* 2: 75–88.

Chernyshov, V. M. 2006. [Peculiarities of the age composition of breeding pairs in populations of Blyth's Reed Warbler and Tree Sparrow.] Page 567. In: Kurochkin, E. N. (ed.). [*Ornithological studies in Northern Eurasia*]. Abstracts of XII Int. Orn. Conference of Northern Eurasia, Stavropol, 31 January – 5 February 2006. Stavropol University Press, Stavropol. (Russian)

Choudhary, H. 1997. Additional sightings! *Danphe* 6(1): 2–3.

Christian, F. W. 1920. List of Mangaia Island birds. *J. Polynesian Soc.* 29: 87.

Christmas, S. E. 1978. The Sedge Warbler population of Holywell Meadow, Oxford. *Report of the Oxford Ornithological Society on the Birds of Oxfordshire for 1977*: 34–36.

Christmas, S. E., Christmas, T. J. & Sherwood, R. G. 1978. Reed and Sedge Warbler migration in Yugoslavia. *Ringing & Migration* 2: 10–14.

Christy, P. 1994. La redecouverte de la fauvette du Dja au Gabon. *Canopee* 2: 7.

Christy, P. & Clarke, W. 1994. *Guide des oiseaux de la Réserve de la Lopé*. ECOFAC, Gabon, Libreville.

Chytil, J. 1998. Savi's Warbler imitating Bearded Tit and Water Rail. *Brit. Birds* 91: 200–201.

Ciach, M. 2005. Reed Warbler with abnormal body-feathers. *Brit. Birds* 98: 433–434.

Cibois, A., Thibault, J-C. & Pasquet, E. 2007. Uniform phenotype conceals double colonization by reed-warblers of a remote Pacific archipelago. *J. Biogeogr.* 34(7): 1150–1166.

Cibois, A., Thibault, J-C. & Pasquet, E. 2008. Systematics of the extinct reed warblers *Acrocephalus* of the Society Islands of eastern Polynesia. *Ibis* 150: 365–376.

Clafton, F. R. 1968. Grasshopper Warbler resembling Pallas's Grasshopper Warbler. *Brit. Birds* 61: 269–270.

Clancey, P. A. 1955a. Comments on geographical variation in the Knysna Scrub-Warbler *Bradypterus sylvaticus* Sundevall of South Africa. *Bull. Brit. Orn. Club* 75: 26–28.

Clancey, P. A. 1955b. A review of the races of Barratt's Scrub-Warbler *Bradypterus barratti* Sharpe of South Africa. *Bull. Brit. Orn. Club* 75: 38–44.

681

Clancey, P. A. 1961. The Reed Warbler *Acrocephalus scirpaceus* in Natal, a species new to the South African list. *Ostrich* 32: 143–144.

Clancey, P. A. 1964. *Birds of Natal and Zululand*. Oliver & Boyd, Edinburgh & London.

Clancey, P. A. 1975a. On the species limits of *Acrocephalus baeticatus* (Vieillot) (Aves: Sylviidae) of Ethiopian Africa. *Arnoldia* 7: 1–14.

Clancey, P. A. 1975b. The Great Reed Warbler *Acrocephalus arundinaceus* (Linnaeus) in the South African sub-region. *Durban Mus. Nov.* 10: 231–235.

Clancey, P. A. 1975c. Variation in *Acrocephalus palustris* (Bechstein). *Durban Mus. Nov.* 10: 235–238.

Clancey, P. A. 1976. The austral African races of the Rush Warbler *Bradypterus baboecala* (Vieillot). *Durban Mus. Nov.* 11: 120–128.

Clancey, P. A. (ed.). 1980. *SAOS Checklist of Southern African Birds*. Southern African Ornithological Society, Johannesburg

Clancey, P. A. 1985. *The Rare Birds of Southern Africa*. Winchester, Johannesburg.

Clancey, P. A. 1989. The Natal Record of the European Reed Warbler. *Ostrich* 60: 91.

Clancey, P. A. 1994. Further comment on *Acrocephalus baeticatus* and *A. cinnamomeus* of the Afrotropics. *Honeyguide* 40: 262–267.

Clancey, P. A. & Wolters, H. E. 1962. *Bradypterus barratti major* (Roberts) 1922 pre-occupied by *Bradypterus major* (Brooks) 1872. *Bull. Brit. Orn. Club* 82: 174.

Clapp, R. B. & King, W. B. 1975. Status of Kokikokiko *Acrocephalus aequinoctialis*. *Bull. Brit. Orn Club* 95: 2–3.

Clarke, A. 1983. *Philippines: March - May '83*. Unpublished manuscript.

Clarke, R. 2006. Three new birds for Australia. *Birding World* 19: 82.

Clements, J. F. 2000. *Birds of the World: a checklist*. 5th edition. Ibis Publishing Co. Vista.

Coates, B. J. 1990. *The Birds of Papua New Guinea, including the Bismark Archipelago and Bougainville*. Vol. 2. Dove Publications, Australia.

Coates, B. J., Bishop, K. D. & Gardner, D. 1997. *A Guide to the Birds of Wallacea: Sulawesi, the Moluccas and Lesser Sunda islands, Indonesia*. Dove Publications, Australia.

Cofta, T. 1996a. [Identification of *Locustella* warblers appearing in Europe.] *Notatki Ornithol.* 37: 113–140. (Polish, English summary)

Cofta, T. 1996b. [First record of the Pallas's Grasshopper Warbler (*Locustella certhiola*) in Poland.] *Notatki Ornithol.* 37: 143–146. (Polish, English summary)

Colenut, S. & Vinicombe, K. 1993. Mystery photographs 186: Melodious Warbler. *Brit. Birds* 86: 139–142.

Collar, N. J. & Andrew, P. 1988. *Birds to Watch. The ICBP World Check List of Threatened Birds*. Technical Publication No. 8. ICBP, Cambridge.

Collar, N. J. & Stuart, S. N. 1985. *Threatened birds of Africa and related islands: the ICBP/IUCN Red Data Book*. Part 1: 524–528. ICBP, Cambridge.

Collar, N. J., Aldrin, N., Mallari, D. & Tabaranza, B. R. Jr. 1999. *Threatened birds of the Philippines*. Haribon Foundation/Birdlife International. Makati.

Collar, N. J., Crosby, M. J. & Stattersfield, A. J. 1994. *Birds to Watch 2: the world list of threatened birds*. Birdlife Conservation Series 4. Birdlife International, Cambridge, UK.

Collyer, A. A., Beadman, J. & Hill, T. H. 1984. Similarity between songs of two *Locustella* warblers and stridulation of Roesel's bush-cricket. *Brit. Birds* 77: 112–115.

Colston, P. R. & Holyoak, D. T. 1970. A specimen of *Locustella luscinioides* from Western Arabia in the collection of the British Museum. (Nat. Hist.). *Bull. Brit. Orn. Club*. 90: 47.

Colston, P. R. & Morel, G. J. 1984. A new subspecies of the African Reed Warbler *Acrocephalus baeticatus* from Senegal. *Bull. Brit. Orn. Club*. 104: 3–5.

Conant, S. 1983. Ecological requirements of the Nihoa Millerbird and the Nihoa Finch, including an analysis of management options for the millerbird. Unpublished report, U.S. Fish and Wildlife Service, Honolulu, Hawaii.

Conant, S. 1984. Plumage color changes in a Nihoa Millerbird (*Acrocephalus familiaris*). *Condor* 86: 212.

Conant, S. & Morin, M. 2001. Why isn't the Nihoa Millerbird extinct? *Stud. Avian Biol.* 22: 338–346.

Conant, S., Collins, M. S., Ralph, C. J. & Scott, J. M. 1981. Effects of observers using different methods upon the total population estimates of two resident island birds. Pp 373–381 In: Ralph, C. J. & Scott, J. M. eds. (1981). *Estimating the number of terrestrial birds*. Studies in Avian Biology 6.

Condor, P. J. 1953. Olivaceous Warbler on Skokholm. *Brit. Birds* 46: 191–192.

Cooper, D., Cooper, J. & Fairbank, R. 2002. The Sykes's Warbler in East Sussex. *Birding World* 15: 378–380.

Cope, D. 1992. Tail-dipping Icterine Warblers. *Birding World* 5: 447.

Corso, A. 2000. Tail movements by *Hippolais* warblers. *Birding World* 13: 508.

Corso, A. 2004. The first Upcher's Warbler *Hippolais languida* in Cyprus. *Sandgrouse* 26(1): 67.

Cottridge, D., Giri, T. & Kightley, C. 1994. *Birds recorded in Nepal, Limosa Holidays tour 13th–25th February 1994*. Unpublished.

Courtney-Haines, L. M. 1991. *A Cabinet of Reed-Warblers. A Monograph Dealing with the Acrocephaline Warblers of the World*. Surrey, Beatty & sons, Chipping Norton, Australia.

Craig, R. J. 1992. Territoriality, habitat use, and ecological distinctness of an endangered Pacific Island reed warbler. *J. Field Ornithol.* 63(4): 436–444.

Craig, R. J. 1996. Seasonal population surveys and natural history of a Micronesian bird community. *Wilson Bull.* 108: 246–267.

Cramp, S. (ed.). 1992. *The Birds of the Western Palearctic* Vol. 6. Oxford University Press, Oxford.

Crespo, J., Alba. E. & Garrido, M. 1988. Tongue spots of nestling Olivaceous Warblers. *Brit. Birds* 81: 470–471.

Crockett, P. 2001. Olivaceous Warbler at Collieston, NE Scotland, September 2000. *Birding Scotland* 4: 11–12.

Crudas, J. & Devlin, T. R. E. 1967. Ageing of Reed Warblers: Use of tongue spots as a criterion. *4th Report Rye Meads Ringing Group*.

Crumbie, M. 1986. Observations to clarify the status of the Reef Heron (*Egretta gularis*), Little Green Heron (*Butorides striatus*) and Clamorous Warbler (*Acrocephalus stentoreus*) in Abu Dhabi Island, 1985, with additional notes. *Bull. Emirates Nat. Hist. Group* 28: 10–26.

Curio, E., Hornbuckle, J., de Soye, Y., Aston, P. & Lastimoza, L. L. 2001. New bird records for the island of Panay, Philippines, including the first record of the Asian Stubtail *Urosphena squamiceps* for the Philippines. *Bull. Brit. Orn. Club* 121(3): 183–197.

Da Prato, E. S. 1980. Bittern-like posture of juvenile Sedge Warblers. *Brit. Birds* 73: 314–315.

Dal Molin, A., Équipe de la réserve de la Mazière, 2009. Capture d'une Locustelle de Pallas *Locustella certhiola* dans le Lot-et-Garonne en 2008. *Ornithos* 16(3): 207.

Dally, A. 2003. Saharan Olivaceous Warbler in Morocco. *Birding World* 16: 475.

David, A. & Oustalet, E. 1877. *Oiseaux de Chine*. Libraire de l'Académie de Médecine, Paris.

Davidson, P. 2001. A further twelve new species for Cambodia. *Cambodia Bird News* 7: 26–35.

Davies, C. 2001. The European Bird Report: Passerines. *Brit. Birds* 94: 419–430.

Davies, N. B. & Green, R. E. 1976. The development and ecological significance of feeding techniques in the Reed Warbler *Acrocephalus scirpaceus*. *Anim. Behav.* 24: 213–229.

Davis, P. 1958. Lanceolated Warbler at Fair Isle. *Brit. Birds* 51: 243–244.

Davis, P. 1960. Booted Warbler at Fair Isle: the problem of identification. *Brit. Birds* 53: 123–125.

Davis, P. 1961. Lanceolated Warblers at Fair Isle and the problem of identification. *Brit. Birds* 54: 142–145.

Davis, P. 1962. River Warbler on Fair Isle: a bird new to Britain. *Brit. Birds* 55: 137–138.

Davis, P. 1965. Some comments on the problems of separating Reed and Marsh Warblers. *Brit. Birds* 58: 184–188.

Davis, P. 1994. River Warbler reacting to mowing machine. *Brit. Birds* 87: 91.

Davison, G. W. H. 1992. *Birds of Mount Kinabalu, Borneo.* Natural History Publications (Borneo), Kota Kinabalu.

Dean, A. R. 1984. Icterine and Melodious Warblers in southwest Britain. *Brit. Birds* 77: 116–117.

Dean, T. 1993. Grasshopper Warbler reeling in response to electric drill. *Brit. Birds* 86: 20.

Dean, W. R. J. 2002. *The Birds of Angola.* British Ornithologists' Union Checklist No. 18. BOU, Tring.

Dee, T. J. 1986. *The Endemic Birds of Madagascar.* ICBP, Cambridge.

Deignan, H. G. 1945. The Birds of Northern Thailand. *US Natl. Mus. Bull.* 186. 616 pp.

Deignan, H. G. 1963. Checklist of the Birds of Thailand. *US Natl. Mus. Bull.* 226: 1–263.

De Juana, E. 2006. *Aves raras de España.* Lynx Edicions, Barcelona.

Delacour, J. 1942. The bush-warblers of the genera *Cettia* and *Bradypterus*, with notes on allied genera and species (part 1) *Ibis* 84: 509–519.

Delacour, J. 1943. The bush-warblers of the genera *Cettia* and *Bradypterus*, with notes on allied genera and species (part 2). *Ibis* 85: 27–40.

Delacour, J. 1947. The name of the Javanese Bush Warbler. *Auk* 64: 129.

Delacour, J. 1952. The specific grouping of the bush warblers *Bradypterus luteoventris, Bradypterus montis* and *Bradypterus seebohmi. Ibis* 94: 362–363.

Delapré, J.-P., Guilpain, J.-M., Isaac, B., Philippe, D. & Troffigué, A. 2005. Observation d'une Hypolaïs du Sahara le 22 avril 2004 dans les jardins de l'auberge Derkaoua, près d'Erfoud dans l'Est marocain. *Go-South Bull.* 2: 31–33.

Dement'ev, G. P. & Gladkov, N. A. (eds.). 1954 (translated 1968). *Birds of the Soviet Union.* Vol. 6. Israel Program for Scientific Translations, Jerusalem.

Deng, H. & Zhang, X. 1990. Standard metabolic rate in several species of passerine birds in alpine meadow. *Acta Zoologica Sinica* 36: 373–384.

Dennis, R. H. 1973. River Warbler on Fair Isle. *Brit. Birds* 66: 312–313.

Densley, M. 1982. Identification of Pallas's Grasshopper Warbler. *Brit. Birds* 75: 133–134.

Depuy, A. 1969. Catalogue Ornithologique du Sahara Algerien. *L'Oiseau et la Revue Francaise d'Ornithologie* 39: 225–241.

Depuy, A. & Johnson, E. D. H. 1967. Capture d'une locustelle fluviatile (*Locustella fluviatilis*) au Sahara algérien. *L'Oiseau et la Revue Francaise d'Ornithologie* 37: 143.

Dernjatin, P. & Andersen, M. W. 2006. Central Asian *Hippolais* Warblers. *Alula* 12(4): 146–153.

Devillers, P. & Dowsett-Lemaire, F. 1978. African Reed Warblers (*Acrocephalus baeticatus*) in Khouar (Niger). *Gerfaut* 68: 211–213.

Diamond, A. W. 1980. Seasonality, population structure and breeding ecology of the Seychelles Brush Warbler *Acrocephalus sechellensis. Proc. Pan-African Ornithol. Congr.* 5: 253–266.

Diamond, J. M. 1974. Colonisation of exploded volcanic islands by birds: the supertramp strategy. *Science* 184: 803–806.

Diamond, J. 1975. Distributional ecology and habits of some Bougainville birds (Solomon Islands). *Condor* 77: 14–23.

Dickinson, E. C. (ed.). 2003. *The Howard and Moore complete checklist of the birds of the world.* (Revised and enlarged 3rd edition). Christopher Helm, London.

Dickinson, E. C. & Gregory, S. M. S. 2006. Systematic notes on Asian birds. 55. A re-examination of the date of publication of Jerdon's Second Supplement to the Catalogue of the Birds of southern India. *Zool. Med. Leiden* 80: 169–178.

Dickinson, E. C., Kennedy, R. S. & Parkes, K. C. 1991. *The Birds of the Philippines: an annotated checklist.* British Ornithologists' Union, Checklist No. 12. BOU, Tring.

Dickinson, E. C., Morioka, H. & Walters, M. 2001. Systematic notes on Asian birds. 19. Type material from Japan in The Natural History Museum, Tring, U.K. *Zool. Verhandelingen* 335: 215–227.

Dickinson, E. C., Rasmussen, P. C., Round, P. D. & Rozendaal, F. G. 1998. Reinstatement of *Bradypterus seebohmi* to the Indian avifauna, and revalidation of an earlier name. *Ostrich* 69: 399.

Dickinson, E. C., Rasmussen, P. C., Round, P. D. & Rozendaal, F. G. 2000. Systematic notes on Asian birds 1. A review of the russet bush-warbler *Bradypterus seebohmi. Zool. Verhandelingen* 331: 11–64.

Dierschke, J. 1994. River and Savi's Warbler identification. *Birding World* 7: 287.

Dierschke, V., Stühmer, F. & Stühmer, T. 1996. Records of Booted Warbler *Hippolais caligata* in north-eastern Turkey. *Sandgrouse* 18(2): 66–67.

Diesselhorst, G. 1965. Winter habitat of *Acrocephalus dumetorum* Blyth *Bull. Brit. Orn. Club.* 85: 111.

Dijkstra, S. 1997. Population dynamics and space use of the Seychelles Warbler (*Acrocephalus sechellensis*) on the plateau area of Aride island, a saturated environment. Unpublished dissertation, University of Groningen.

Dittberner, H. & Dittberner, W. 1985. Schlagschwirl-Männchen (*Locustella fluviatilis*) zieht die Brut alleine auf. *Orn. Mitt.* 37: 212–214.

Dittberner, H. & Dittberner, W. 1986. Zum werzug des Schlagschwirls *Locustella fluviatilis* aus dem europaischen Brutareal. *Verhandlungen Orn. Ges. Bayern* 24: 277–284.

Dolgushin, I. A., Korelov, M. N., Kuz'mina, M. A., Gavrilov, E. I., Kovshar, A. F. & Borodikhin, I. F. 1972. [*Birds of Kazakhstan.* Vol 4.] Alma-Ata. (Russian)

Donald, P. F., de Ponte Machado, M., Pitta Groz, M. J., Taylor, R., Wells, C. E., Marlow, T. & Hille, S. 2004. Status of the Cape Verde Cane Warbler *Acrocephalus brevipennis* on São Nicolau, with notes on song, breeding behaviour and threats. *Malimbus* 26: 34–37.

Dorsch, H. 1979. Möglichkeiten der Unterscheidung von Teich- und Sumpfrohrsänger anhand morphologischer Merkmale. *Falke* 26: 405–419.

Dorsch, H. 1981. Morphologische Maße von Sumpf- und Teichrohrsänger (*Acrocephalus palustris* [Bechst.] und *A. scirpaceus* [Herm.]). *Zool. Abh. Mus. Tierk. Dresden* 37: 33–66.

Dorsch, H. 1983. Bewertung verschiedener Merkmale zur sicheren Unterscheidung von Teich- und Sumpfrohrsänger (*Acrocephalus scirpaceus, A. palustris*) mit einer praktischen Bestimmungshilfe. *Ber. Vogelwarte Hiddensee* 4: 111–120.

Dowsett, R. J. 1969. Breeding biology of the Olivaceous Warbler *Hippolais pallida laeneni. Bull. Nigerian Ornithol. Soc.* 6: 107–108.

Dowsett, R. J. 1972. The River Warbler *Locustella fluviatilis* in Africa. *Zambia Mus. Jour.* 3: 69–79.

Dowsett, R. J. 1975. Sight record of an Olive-tree Warbler near Mambova. *Bull. Zambian Ornithol. Soc.* 7: 19–20.

Dowsett, R. J. 1985. Site-fidelity and survival rates of some montane forest birds in Malawi, south-central Africa. *Biotropica* 17: 145–154.

Dowsett, R. J. & Lemaire, F. 1976. The problem of the African Reed Warbler (*Acrocephalus baeticatus*) in Zambia. *Bull. Zambian Ornithol. Soc.* 8: 62–63.

Dowsett, R. J. & Dowsett-Lemaire, F. 1980. The systematic status of some Zambian birds. *Gerfaut* 70: 151–199.

Dowsett, R. J. & Dowsett-Lemaire, F. 1984. Breeding and moult cycles of some montane forest birds in south-central Africa. *Revue d'ecologie (La Terre et La Vie)* 39: 89–111.

Dowsett, R. J. & Dowsett-Lemaire, F. 1993. *Comments on the taxonomy of some Afrotropical bird species.* Pp. 323–389. In: Dowsett, R. J. & Dowsett-Lemaire, F. (eds.). *A contribution to the distribution and taxonomy of Afrotropical and Malagasy birds.* (Tauraco Research Report No. 5). Tauraco Press, Liège, Belgium.

Dowsett, R. J. & Dowsett-Lemaire, F. 2000. Lobeke Faunal Reserve. *Bird Conserv. Internatn.* 10: 69–87.

Dowsett, R. J. & Forbes-Watson, A. D. 1993. *Checklist of the Birds of the Afrotropical and Malagasy Regions.* Tauraco Press, Belgium.

Dowsett, R. J. & Moore, A. 1997. Swamp warblers *Acrocephalus gracilirostris* and *Acrocephalus rufescens* at Lake Chad, Nigeria. *Bull. Brit. Orn. Club* 117: 48–51.

Dowsett, R. J. & Stjernstedt, R. 1979. The *Bradypterus cinnamomeus-mariae* complex in central Africa. *Bull. Brit. Orn. Club.* 99: 86–94.

Dowsett, R. J., Aspinwall, D. R. & Dowsett-Lemaire, F. 2008. *The Birds of Zambia.* Tauraco Press & Aves a. s. b. l., Liege, Belgium.

Dowsett, R. J., Aspinwall, D. R. & Leonard, P. M. 1999. Further additions to the avifauna of Zambia. *Bull. Brit. Orn. Club* Vol. 119: 94–103.

Dowsett, R. J., Backhurst, G. C. & Oatley, T. B. 1988. Afrotropical ringing recoveries of Palearctic migrants. 1. Passerines (*Turdidae* to *Oeiolidae*). *Tauraco* 1: 29–63.

Dowsett-Lemaire, F. 1978. Annual turnover in a Belgian population of Marsh Warblers, *Acrocephalus palustris. Gerfaut* 68: 519–532.

Dowsett-Lemaire, F. 1979a. The sexual bond in the Marsh Warbler, *Acrocephalus palustris. Gerfaut* 69: 3–12.

Dowsett-Lemaire, F. 1979b. The imitative range of the song of the Marsh Warbler *Acrocephalus palustris* with special reference to imitations of African birds. *Ibis* 121: 453–468.

Dowsett-Lemaire, F. 1981a. Eco-ethological aspects of breeding in the Marsh Warbler. *Rev. Ecol.* 35: 437–491.

Dowsett-Lemaire, F. 1981b. The transition period from juvenile to adult song in the European Marsh Warbler. *Ostrich* 52: 253–255.

Dowsett-Lemaire, F. 1983. Ecological and territorial requirements of montane forest birds on the Nyika Plateau, south-central Africa. *Le Gerfaut* 73: 345–378.

Dowsett-Lemaire, F. 1989. Ecological and biogeographical aspects of forest bird communities in Malawi. *Scopus* 13: 1–80.

Dowsett-Lemaire, F. 1990. Eco-ethology, distribution and status of Nyungwe Forest birds, Rwanda. In: Dowsett, R. J. (ed.). *Enquête faunistique et floristique dans la Forêt de Nyungwe, Rwanda.* Tauraco Press, Ely.

Dowsett-Lemaire, F. 1994. The song of the Seychelles Warbler *Acrocephalus sechellensis* and its African relatives. *Ibis* 136: 489–491.

Dowsett-Lemaire, F. & Dowsett, R. J. 1979. Reed and Marsh Warbler identification. *Brit. Birds* 72: 190–191.

Dowsett-Lemaire, F. & Dowsett, R. J. 1987a. European Reed and Marsh Warblers in Africa: migration patterns, moult and habitat. *Ostrich* 58: 65–85.

Dowsett-Lemaire, F. & Dowsett, R. J. 1987b. European and African Reed Warblers, *Acrocephalus scircapeus* and *A. baeticatus*; vocal and other evidence for a single species. *Bull. Brit. Orn. Club.* 107: 74–85.

Dowsett-Lemaire, F. & Dowsett, R. J. 1989. *Zoogeography and taxonomic relationships of the Cameroon Afromontane region.* Tauraco Research Report No.1: 48–56.

Dowsett-Lemaire, F. & Dowsett, R. J. 1998. *Surveys of Oku Mt and other IBAs in NW Province (Cameroon), February–March 1998.* Birdlife International, Cambridge.

Dowsett-Lemaire, F. & Dowsett, R. J. 2000. Birds of the Lobéké Faunal Reserve, Cameroon, and its regional importance for conservation. *Bird Conserv. Internatn.* 10: 67–87.

Dowsett-Lemaire, F. & Dowsett, R. J. 2006. *The Birds of Malawi.* Tauraco Press & Aves a. s. b. l., Liege, Belgium.

Drovetski, S. V., Zink, R. M., Fadeev, I. V., Nesterov, E. V., Koblik, A., Red'kin, Y. A. & Rohwer, S. 2004. Mitochondrial phylogeny of *Locustella* and related genera. *J. Avian Biol.* 35: 105–110.

Duckels, A. S. 1970. Late singing Grasshopper Warblers. *Brit. Birds* 63: 343.

Duckworth, J. W. 1990. *Parental care in the Reed Warbler.* Unpublished DPhil thesis, University of Cambridge, Cambridge, UK.

Duckworth, J. W. 1991. Responses of breeding Reed Warblers *Acrocephalus scirpaceus* to mounts of Sparrowhawk *Accipiter nisus*, Cuckoo *Cuculus canorus* and Jay *Garrulus glandarius. Ibis* 133: 68–74.

Duckworth, J. W., Davidson, P., Evans, T. D., Round, P. D. & Timmins, R.J. 2002. Birds records from Laos, principally the Upper Lao/Thai Mekong and Xiangkhouang Province, in 1998–2000. *Forktail* 18: 11–44.

Duckworth, J. W., Tizard, R. J., Timmins, R. J., Thewlis, R. M., Robichaud, W. G. & Evans, T. D. 1998. Bird records from Laos, October 1994–August 1995. *Forktail* 13: 33–68.

Dubois, P. J. 1983. Status of Paddyfield Warbler in Romania. *Brit. Birds* 76: 585.

Dubois, P.J., Le Maréchal, P., Olioso, G. & Yésou, P. 2000. *Inventaire des oiseaux de France.* Nathan, Paris.

Duff, A. 1980. Another mystery photograph: Moustached Warbler or Sedge Warbler? *Brit. Birds* 73: 370.

Dunn, P. 2001. The putative Caspian Reed Warbler in North Yorkshire. *Birding World* 14: 329–332.

Dunning, J. B. (ed.). 2007. *CRC Handbook of Avian Body Masses.* 2nd edition. CRC Press, Boca Raton, Florida.

Duquet, M. 1994. [Identification of little *Acrocephalus* warblers.] *Ornithos* 1: 36–40. (French, English summary)

Duquet, M. 1996. [Aquatic Warbler pitfall.] *Ornithos* 3: 136–137. (French, English summary)

Dürr, T., Sohns, G. & Wawrzyniak H. 1995. [Analysis of ringing recoveries of Savi's Warblers *Locustella luscinioides* ringed in eastern Germany.] *Vogelwelt* 116: 317–325. (German, English summary)

Dyadicheva, E. A. 1996. [Status of population and nesting conditions of the Paddyfield Warbler]. *Berkut* 5(2): 163–166. (Russian)

Dybbro, T. 1978. [Gray's Grasshopper Warbler in Denmark.] *Oversigt over Danmarksfugle 1978.* Copenhagen. (Danish)

Dymond, J. N., Fraser, P. A. & Gantlett, S. J. M. 1989. *Rare birds in Britain and Ireland.* Poyser, Calton.

Dyrcz, A. 1974. Factors affecting the growth rate of nestling Great Reed Warblers and Reed Warblers at Milicz, Poland. *Ibis* 116: 330–339.

Dyrcz, A. 1977. Polygamy and breeding success among Great Reed Warblers *Acrocephalus arundinaceus* at Milicz, Poland. *Ibis* 119: 73–77.

Dyrcz, A. 1980. Breeding ecology of Great Reed Warbler *Acrocephalus arundinaceus* and Reed Warbler *A. scirpaceus* at fish-ponds in SW Poland and lakes in NW Switzerland. *Acta Ornithol.* 18: 307–334.

Dyrcz, A. 1981. Breeding ecology of Great Reed Warbler *Acrocephalus arundinaceus* and Reed Warbler *A. scirpaceus* at fish-ponds in SW Poland and lakes in NW Switzerland. *Acta Ornithol.* 18: 307–334.

Dyrcz, A. 1986. Factors affecting facultative polygyny and breeding results in the Great Reed Warbler (*Acrocephalus arundinaceus*). *J. Ornithol.* 127: 447–461.

Dyrcz, A. 1989. Polygyny in the Aquatic Warbler *Acrocephalus paludicola. Ibis* 131: 298–300.

Dyrcz, A. 1992. [Ringing recoveries of the Aquatic Warbler (*Acrocephalus paludicola*) from the Biebrza marshes at the region of English Channel.] *Notatki Ornithol.* 33: 336–337. (Polish, English summary)

Dyrcz, A. 1993. Biometrical differences between sexes in the breeding population of Aquatic Warbler *Acrocephalus paludicola. Ringing & Migration* 14: 149–151.

Dyrcz, A. 1995. Breeding biology and ecology of different European and Asiatic populations of the Great Reed Warbler *Acrocephalus arundinaceus. Japanese J. Ornithol.* 44(3) 123–142.

Drycz, A. & Czeraszkiewicz, R. 1993. [The abundance, threats and means of protection of the breeding population of the Aquatic Warbler (*Acrocephalus paludicola*) in Poland.] *Notatki Ornithol.* 34: 231–246. (Polish, English summary)

Dyrcz, A. & Zdunek, W. 1993a. Breeding ecology of the Aquatic Warbler *Acrocephalus paludicola* on the Biebrza marshes, northeast Poland. *Ibis* 135: 181–189.

Dyrcz, A. & Zdunek, W. 1993b. Breeding statistics of the Aquatic Warbler *Acrocephalus paludicola* on the Biebrza marshes, northeast Poland. *J. Ornithol.* 134: 317–323.

Dyrcz, A., Borowiec, M. & Czapulak, A. 1994. Nestling growth and mating system in four *Acrocephalus* species. *Vogelwarte* 37: 179–182.

Dyrcz, A., Okulewicz, J., Witkowski, J., Jesionowski, J., Nawrocki, P. & Winiecki, A. 1984. [Birds of fens in Biebrza marshes. Faunistic approach]. *Acta Ornithol.* 20: 1–108. [Polish, English summary]

Dyrcz, A., Sauer-Gürth, H., Tkadlec, E. & Wink, M. 2004. Offspring sex ratio variation in relation to brood size and mortality in a promiscuous species: the Aquatic Warbler *Acrocephalus paludicola*. *Ibis* 146: 269–280.

Dyrcz, A., Wink, M., Backhaus, A., Zdunek, W., Leisler, W. & Schulze-Hagen, K. 2002. Correlates of multiple paternity in the Aquatic Warbler (*Acrocephalus paludicola*). *J. Ornithol.* 143: 430–439.

Eames, J. C., Steinheimer, F. D. & Bansok, R. 2002. A collection of birds from the Cardamom Mountains, Cambodia, including a new subspecies of *Arborophila cambodiana*. *Forktail* 18: 67–86.

Eck, S. 1994. Die geographisch-morphologische Vikarianz der grossen palaearktischen Rohrsänger (Aves: Passeriformes: Sylviidae: *Acrocephalus [arundinaceus]*). *Zool. Abh. Mus. Tierk. Dresden* 48: 161–168.

van Eerde, K. A. 1999. [Hybrid Sedge x European Reed Warbler at Makkum in August 1997.] *Dutch Birding* 21: 34–37. (Dutch, English summary)

Efimov, S. V. 2006. [The post-nesting movements of the *Acrocephalus* warblers on fish-rearing ponds of Upper Don.] Page 201. In: Kurochkin, E. N. (ed.). [*Ornithological studies in Northern Eurasia*]. Abstracts of XII Int. Orn. Conference of Northern Eurasia, Stavropol, 31 January – 5 February 2006. Stavropol University Press, Stavropol. (Russian)

Eguchi, K., Fujimaki, Y., Kawaji, N., Morioka, H., Urano, E. & Yanagisawa, N. 2000. *Check-list of Japanese Birds*. 6th revised edition. Ornithological Society of Japan, Tokyo.

Eikenaar, C., Berg, M. L. & Komdeur, J. 2003. Experimental evidence for the influence of food availability on hatching asynchrony and incubation attendence in the Australian Reed Warbler. *J. Avian Biol.* 34: 419–427.

Eischer, K. 1995. The Thick-billed Warbler in Finland. *Birding World* 8: 10–11.

Eisentraut, M. 1973. Die Wirbeltiere Fauna von Fernando Poo und Westcamerun. *Bonner Zoologische Monographien* 3: 1-427.

Eising, C. M., Komdeur, J., Buys, J., Reemer, M. & Richardson, D. S. 2001. Islands in a desert: breeding ecology of the African Reed Warbler *Acrocephalus baeticatus* in Namibia. *Ibis* 143: 482–493.

Elgood, J. H. 1994. *The Birds of Nigeria*. British Ornithologists' Union, Checklist No. 4. 2nd edition. BOU, London.

Elgood, J. H., Sharland, R. E. & Ward, P. 1966. Palaearctic migrants in Nigeria. *Ibis* 108: 84–116.

Ellis, P., Jackson, W. & Suddaby, D. 1994. The Blyth's Reed Warbler in Shetland. *Birding World* 7: 227–230.

Elts, J., Kuresoo, A., Leibak, E., Leito, A., Lilleleht, V., Luigujõe, L., Lõhmus, A., Mägi, E. & Ots, M. 2003. Eesti lindude staatus, pesitsusaegne ja talvine arvukus 1998–2002. *Hirundo* 16: 58–83. (Estonian, English summary)

Engbring, J., Ramsey, F. L. & Wildman, V. J. 1982. *Micronesian forest bird survey, 1982: Saipan, Tainan, Agiguan and Rota*. US Fish and Wildlife Service, Honolulu.

Érard, C. 1961. *Acrocephalus paludicola* (Vieill.) a niché en France. *Alauda* 29: 193–195.

Ericson, P. G. P., Anderson, C. L., Britton, T., Elzanowski, A., Johansson, U. S., Källersjö, M., Ohlson, J. I., Parsons, T. J., Zuccon, D. & Mayr, G. 2006. Diversification of Neoaves: integration of molecular sequence data and fossils. *Biol. Let.* 2: 543–547.

Eriksson, K. 1969. On occurrence and ecology of Blyth's Reed Warbler (*Acrocephalus dumetorum*) and Marsh Warbler (*A. palustris*) in Finland. *Ornis Fennica* 46: 157–170.

Escott, C. J. & Holmes, D. A. 1980. The avifauna of Sulawesi, Indonesia: faunistic notes and additions. *Bull. Brit. Orn. Club* 100: 189–194.

Etchécopar, R. D. & Hüe, F. 1983. *Les Oiseaux de Chine: Passereaux*. Editions Boubée, Paris.

Evans, L. G. R. 1997. Aquatic Warblers in Autumn 1997. *Rare Birds* 3: 227.

Evans, T. D. & Timmins, R. J. 1998. Bird records from Laos during January–July 1994. *Forktail* 13: 69–96.

Ezaki, Y. 1984. Notes on the moult of the Eastern Great Reed Warbler *Acrocephalus arundinaceus orientalis* in the breeding grounds. *J. Yamashina Inst. Ornithol.* 16: 88–91.

Ezaki, Y. 1987. Male time budgets and recovery of singing after pairing in polygamous Great Reed Warblers. *Jap. J. Ornithol.* 36: 1–11.

Ezaki, Y. 1990. Female choice and the causes and adaptations of polygyny in Great Reed Warblers. *J. Anim. Ecol.* 59: 103–119.

Ezaki, Y. 1992. Importance of communal foraging grounds outside the reed marsh for breeding Great Reed Warblers. *Ecol. Research* 7: 63–70.

Ezaki, Y. 1993. Habitat, ecology and social organisation of the Great Reed Warbler *Acrocephalus arundinaceus* during the breeding season. *Physiol. Ecol. Japan* 29: 29–42.

Ezaki, Y. 1995. Establishment and maintenance of the breeding territory in the polygynous Great Reed Warbler. *Ecol. Research* 10: 359–368.

Faber, M. 1992. [Moustached Warbler (*Acrocephalus melanopogon*) – a new species to the avifauna of Poland.] *Notatki Ornithol.* 33: 159–163. (Polish, English summary)

Fadhel, O. 2007. Days in Iraq with the Basra Reed Warbler *Acrocephalus griseldis*. *Sandgrouse* 29(1): 95–97.

Faivre, B., Secondi, J., Ferry, C., Chastragnat, L. & Cezilly, F. 1999. Morphological variation and the recent evolution of wing length in the Icterine Warbler: a case of unidirectional introgression? *J. Avian Biol.* 30: 152–158.

Fayad, V. C. & Fayad, C. C. 1977. A Grasshopper Warbler *Locustella naevia* from Kenya. *Scopus* 1: 84–86.

Fedorov, V. A. 1996. [Ecology of the Marsh Warbler *Acrocephalus palustris* and Blyth's Reed Warbler *Acrocephalus dumetorum* in southwestern part of the Pskov Region.] *Russian J. Ornithol.* 5: 11–33. (Russian, English summary)

Fedorov, V. A. 1996. [Formation of territorial links in some *Acrocephalus* species.] *Russian J. Ornithol.* Express issue 1: 8–12. (Russian)

Fedorov, V. A. 1997. [Repeated use of nests by *Acrocephalus arundinaceus* and *A. scirpaceus*.] *Russian J. Ornithol.* Express issue 24: 9–13. (Russian)

Fedorov, V. A. & Mukhin, A. L. 1998. [Post-juvenile moult of *Acrocephalus scirpaceus*]. *Russian J. Ornithol.* Express issue 39: 3–7. (Russian)

Fennell, C. M. & King, B. F. 1964. New occurrences and recent distributional records of Korean birds. *Condor* 66: 239–246.

Ferguson-Lees, I. J. 1954a. Photographic studies of some less familiar birds. LIV. Moustached Warbler. *Brit. Birds* 47: 15–16.

Ferguson-Lees, I. J. 1954b. Photographic studies of some less familiar birds. LVI. Icterine Warbler. *Brit. Birds* 47: 121–123.

Ferguson-Lees, I. J. 1964. Studies of less familiar birds 129. Cetti's Warbler. *Brit. Birds* 57: 357–359.

Ferguson-Lees, I. J., England, M. D. & Peach, A. N. H. 1965. Studies of some less familiar birds 131. Melodious Warbler. *Brit. Birds* 58: 9–10.

Ferry, C. & Deschaintre, A. 1966. *Hippolais icterina* et *polyglotta* dans leur zone de sympatrie. *Abstr. Int. Orn. Congr.* 14: 57–58.

Fessl, B. & Hoi, H. 2000. Song complexity and song structure in the Moustached Warbler *Acrocephalus melanopogon*. *J. Avian Biol.* 31: 144–150.

Fessl, B., Kleindorfer, S. & Hoi, H. 1996. Extra pair parental behaviour: evidence for an alternative mating strategy in the Moustached Warbler *Acrocephalus melanopogon*. *J. Avian Biol.* 27: 88–91.

Field, G. D. 1973. Subalpine and Grasshopper Warblers in Sierra Leone. *Bull. Brit. Orn. Club* 93: 101–103.

Finsch, O. 1877. On a small collection of birds from the Marquesas Islands. *Proc. Zool. Soc. London*: 407–410.

Finsch, O. 1883. On a new Reed-Warbler from the island of Nawodo, or Pleasant Island, in the Western Pacific. *Ibis* (5)1: 142–144.

Fisher, H. H. 1940. The occurrence of vestigal claws on the wings of birds. *Amer. Midland Nat.* 23: 234–243.

Fischer, S. & Haupt, H. 1994. [Settling patterns and movements of East-German Great Reed Warblers (*Acrocephalus arundinaceus*) – an analysis of ringing recoveries of the Hiddensee bird ringing station.] *Vogelwarte* 37: 183–189. (German, English summary)

Fischer, S., Frommolt, K.-H. & Tembrock, G. 1996. [Variability of song in the Great Reed Warbler *Acrocephalus arundinaceus*.] *J. Ornithol.* 137: 503–513. (German, English summary)

Flade, M. 1999. *Report on the Aquatic Warbler expedition to Western Siberia, 4–19 June 1999*. Aquatic Warbler Conservation Team.

Fleischer, R. C., McIntosh, C. E. & Tarr, C. L. 1998. Evolution on a volcanic conveyor belt: using phylogeographic reconstructions and K-Ar-based ages of the Hawaiian Islands to estimate molecular evolutionary rates. *Molec. Ecol.* 7: 533–545.

Fleischer, R. C., Slikas, B., Beadell, J., Atkins, C., McIntosh, C. E. & Conant, S. 2007. Genetic variability and taxonomic status of the Nihoa and Laysan Millerbirds. *Condor* 109: 954–962.

Flint, V. E., Boehme, R. L., Kostin, Y. V. & Kuznetsov, A. A. 1984. *A Field Guide to the Birds of the USSR.* Princeton University Press, Princeton, New Jersey.

Flumm, D. S. 1984. Identification pitfalls: Aquatic Warbler. *Brit. Birds* 77: 377–378.

Flumm, D. S. & Lord, N. A. G. 1978. The identification of a Paddyfield Warbler. *Brit. Birds* 71: 95–101.

Fogden, M. P. L. 1965. Borneo Bird Notes, 1963–65. *Sarawak Mus. J.* 12: 395–413.

Fogden, M. P. L. 1972. Premigratory dehydration in the Reed Warbler (*Acrocephalus scirpaceus*) and water as a factor limiting migratory range. *Ibis* 114: 548–552.

Fontaine, B. 2003. Is Dja River Warbler *Bradypterus grandis* really globally threatened? *Bull. African Bird Club* 10: 28–29.

Forster, J. R. 1844. *Descriptiones animalium...* Lichtenstein, Berlin.

Fouquet, M., Girard, O., Hirschfeld, E., Lonthowski, J., Skakuj, M. & Stawarczyk, T. 1997. New for the UAE: River Warbler *Locustella fluviatilis*, Kittlitz's Plover *Charadrius pecuarius* and Lesser Noddy *Anous tenuirostris*. *Emirates Bird Report* 19: 120–122.

Fraser, M. W. 1986. Icterine Warbler and Red-backed Shrikes in the Cape of Good Hope Nature Reserve. *Promerops* 172: 11.

Fraser, M. & McMahon, L. 1995. European Marsh Warblers on the Cape Peninsula. *Safring News* 24: 75–76.

Fraser, P. A., Lansdown, P. G. & Rogers, M. J. 1999. Report on Scarce Migrant Birds in Britain in 1996. *Brit. Birds* 92: 3–25.

Fregin, S., Haase, M., Olsson, U. & Alström, P. 2009. Multi-locus phylogeny of the family Acrocephalidae (Aves: Passeriformes) – The traditional taxonomy overthrown. *Molecular Phylogenetics and Evolution* 52: 866–878.

Friedmann, H. & Williams, J. G. 1968. Notable records of rare or little-known birds from western Uganda. *Rev. Zool. Bot. Afr.* 77: 11–36.

Fry, C. H. 1977. Taxonomy of the *Acrocephalus baeticatus* complex of African Marsh Warblers. *Nigerian Field* 42: 134–137.

Fry, C. H. 1990. Foraging behaviour and identification of Upcher's Warbler. *Brit. Birds* 83: 217–221.

Fry, C. H., Ash, J. S. & Ferguson-Lees, I. J. 1970. Spring weights of some Palaearctic migrants at Lake Chad. *Ibis* 112: 58–82.

Fry, C. H., Britton, P. L. & Horne, J. F. M. 1974. Lake Rudolf and the Palaearctic exodus from East Africa. *Ibis* 116: 44–51.

Fry, C. H., Williamson, K. & Ferguson-Lees, I. J. 1974. A new subspecies of *Acrocephalus baeticatus* from Lake Chad and a taxonomic appraisal of *Acrocephalus dumetorum*. *Ibis* 116: 340–346.

Fu, T. S., Gao, W. & Song, Y. I. 1984. [*Birds of the Changbai Mountains*]. Northeast Normal University Press. (Chinese)

Fujimaki, Y., Higuchi, H., Yanagisawa, N., Sato, F., Komaru, M., Umeki, M., Alekseev, S. A., Lobkov, E. G., Ladygin, A. V. & Banin, D. A. 1991. [Birds of the eastern Kamchatka peninsula.] *Strix* 10: 219–228. (Japanese, English summary)

Fujita, G. & Nagata, H. 1997. Preferable habitat characteristics of male Japanese Marsh Warblers *Megalurus pryeri* in breeding season at Hotoke-numa reclaimed area, Northern Japan. *J. Yamashina Inst. Ornithol.* 29: 43–49.

Fujita, K., Fujita, G., Tomioka, T., Yamamoto, Y. & Higuchi, H. 2005. [Estimated population sizes of Owston's Varied Tits and Taczanowski's Grasshopper Warblers, before and after the volcanic eruption of Miyake Island, the Izu Islands, Japan]. *Strix* 23: 105–114. (Japanese, English summary)

Furusawa, I. 1947. The observation of the Short-tailed Bush Warbler. *Tori* 1947: 6–11.

Galea, R. 2002. Savi's Warbler *Locustella luscinioides* moulting while on migration. *Il-Merill* 30: 37.

Gallagher, M. J. 1960. Bird notes from Christmas Island, Pacific Ocean. *Ibis* 102: 489–502.

Gallagher, M. & Woodcock, M. W. 1980. *The Birds of Oman.* Quartet Books, London.

Galsworthy, A. J. 1991. Separation of first-winter Pallas's Grasshopper Warbler from Lanceolated Warbler. *Hong Kong Bird Report* 1990: 155–164.

Gamova, T. V. 2006. [The change of parameters of vocalization of the Black-browed Reed Warbler *Acrocephalus bistrigiceps* in nesting period.] Page 131. In: Kurochkin, E. N. (ed.). [*Ornithological studies in Northern Eurasia*]. Abstracts of XII Int. Orn. Conference of Northern Eurasia, Stavropol, 31 January – 5 February 2006. Stavropol University Press, Stavropol. (Russian)

Gamova, T. V. & Surmach, S. G. 2006. [On organization of the mating interrelations in the Black-browed Reed Warbler *Acrocephalus bistrigiceps*.] Pp. 133–134. In: Kurochkin, E. N. (ed.). [*Ornithological studies in Northern Eurasia*]. Abstracts of XII Int. Orn. Conference of Northern Eurasia, Stavropol, 31 January – 5 February 2006. Stavropol University Press, Stavropol. (Russian)

Gan, X.-J., Zhang, K.-J., Tang, S.-M., Li, B. & Ma, Z.-J. 2006. [Three new records of birds in Shanghai: *Locustella pleskei* (Pleskei's Warbler), *Megalurus pryeri* (Japanese Swamp Warbler) and *Acrocephalus concinens* (Blunt-winged Paddyfield Warbler)]. *Fudan Journal* 45(3): 417–420. (Chinese)

Gantlett, S. J. M. 1979. Head Pattern of *Hippolais* warblers. *Brit. Birds* 72: 82.

Gantlett, S. J. M. 1993. Photo-forum: Clamorous Reed Warbler. *Birding World* 6: 250–251.

Gantlett, S. J. M. 2003. 2002: the Western Palearctic Year. *Birding World* 16: 23–41.

Gantlett, S. J. M. 2004. 2003: the Western Palearctic Year. *Birding World* 17: 19–43.

Gargallo, G. 1995. Further evidence for additional pre-nuptial moult in Melodious Warblers (*Hippolais polyglotta*). *Vogelwarte* 38: 96–99.

Gargallo, G. 1997. Ageing Cetti's Warbler *Cettia cetti* by means of plumage characteristics. *Ringing & Migration* 18: 14–17.

Gaston, A. J. 1976. The moult of Blyth's Reed Warbler *Acrocephalus dumetorum* with notes on the moult of other Palearctic warblers in India. *Ibis* 118: 247–251.

Gavrilenko, M. I. 1954. [Paddyfield Warbler (*Acrocephalus agricola septima* subsp. nova) and Reed Warbler (*Acrocephalus scirpaceus scirpaceus* Herm.) in Poltavshchina. Their biology, distribution and taxonomy]. *Nauk zap. Poltavsk. derzh. ped. in-tu, prirodn.* Ser. (7): 53–62. (Ukrainian)

Gavrilov, E. & Gavrilov, A. 2005. *The Birds of Kazakhstan.* Tethys Ornithological Research Vol. 2. Almaty, Kazakhstan.

Gavris, G. G. 1992. [A new record of Paddyfield Warbler in Poltava Region]. *Vestnik zoologii* 2: 85. (Russian)

Gaymer, R., Blackmann, R. A. A., Dawson, P. G., Penny, M. & Penny, C. M. 1969. The endemic birds of Seychelles. *Ibis* 111: 157–176.

Gelang, M., Cibois, A., Pasquet, E., Olsson, U., Alström, P. & Ericson, P. G. P. 2009. Phylogeny of babblers (Aves, Passeriformes): major lineages, family limits and classification. *Zool. Scripta* 38: 235–236.

George, P. V. 1961. On the Indian Great Reed Warbler *Acrocephalus stentoreus* breeding in Kerala. *J. Bombay Nat. Hist. Soc.* 58: 797.

George, P. V. & Mathew, I. P. 1965. The Pallas's Grasshopper Warbler *Locustella certhiola rubescens* Blyth, from South India. *J. Bombay Nat. Hist. Soc.* 62(2): 304.

Gilbert, D. C. 1986. Effect of migrant Icterine Warbler on local breeding warblers. *Brit. Birds* 79: 405–406.

Gillham, E. H. & Homes, R. C. 1952. Moustached Warbler in Kent. *Brit. Birds* 45: 412–413.

Ginn, H. B. & Melville, D. S. 1983. *Moult in Birds.* British Trust for Ornithology, Guide No. 19. BTO, Tring.

Giri, T. & Choudhary, H. 1997. Additional sightings! *Danphe* 6(2): 7.

Giri, T. & Choudhary, H. 2003. Additional sightings! *Danphe* 12(1–2): 3.

Gladwin, T. W. 1963. Increases in weights of *Acrocephali*. *Bird Migr.* 2: 319–324.

Glass, P. O. 1987. *Nightingale Reed-warbler surveys and inventories.* Pp

154–157 in: Commonwealth of the Northern Mariana Islands, Div. Fish Wildl. Progress Report Oct. 1, 1982 to Sep. 30, 1987.

Gloe, P. & Lensch, A. 1993. [A new singing site of Aquatic Warbler, *Acrocephalus paludicola*, in western Schleswig-Holstein.] *Corax* 15: 160–162. (German, English summary)

Glue, D. E. 1990. Breeding biology of the Grasshopper Warbler in Britain. *Brit. Birds* 83: 131–145.

Gluschenko, Yu. N. 1981. [*Nesting birds of the Khanka Lowlands.*] In: Litvinenko, N. M. (ed.). [*Rare birds of the Far East.*] Pp 25–33. Far East Science Centre, Academy of Sciences, Moscow. (Russian).

Gluschenko, Yu. N. 1989. [Paddyfield Warbler *Acrocephalus agricola tangorum* La Touche, 1912.] In: Ler, P.A. *et al.* (eds.). [Rare vertebrates of the Soviet Far East and their protection]. Pp 158–159. Leningrad: Nauka. (Russian)

Glutz von Blotzheim, U. N. & Bauer, K. M. (eds.). 1991. *Handbuch der Vögel Mitteleuropas.* Vol 12/I & 12/II: Passeriformes (3 Teil). Sylviidae. AULA-Verlag, Wiesbaden. (German)

Goc, M. [First record of the Paddyfield Warbler (*Acrocephalus agricola*) in Poland.] *Notatki Ornithol.* 37: 323–325. (Polish, English summary)

Godwin-Austin, H. 1870. Second list of birds obtained in the Khasi and North Cachar hill ranges including the Garo Hills and country at their base in the Mymensingh and Sylhet districts. *J. Asiatic Soc. Bengal* 39(2): 264–275.

Golley, M. & Millington, R. 1996. Identification of Blyth's Reed Warbler in the field. *Birding World* 9: 351–353.

Goodman, S. M. & Meininger, P. L. 1989. *The birds of Egypt.* Oxford University Press, Oxford.

Goodman, S. M., Pidgeon, M., Hawkins, A. F. A. & Schulenburg, T. S. 1997. *The Birds of southeastern Madagascar.* Fieldiana Zoology (New Series) 87: 132 pp.

Goodman, S. M., Tello, G. G. & Langrand, O. 2000. Patterns of morphological and molecular variation in *Acrocephalus newtoni* on Madagascar. *Ostrich* 71: 367–370.

Gore, M. E. J. & Won, P. O. 1971. *The Birds of Korea.* Royal Asiatic Society, Seoul.

Gorman, G. 2002. Aquatic Warbler. *Alula* 8(2): 62–65.

Gräffe, E. 1873. Vogelbälge aus Huahine. *J. Mus. Godeffroy, Hamburg* 1: 48–51.

Grahn, J. F. 2004. River Warblers with songs similar to that of Grasshopper Warbler. *Brit. Birds* 97: 196–197.

Grant, C. H. B. & Mackworth-Praed, C. W. 1940. A new genus of African swamp warbler. *Bull. Brit. Orn. Club* 60: 91–92.

Grant, P. J. 1978. Head pattern of Icterine and Melodious Warblers. *Brit. Birds* 71: 132.

Grant, P.J. 1980. Identification of two first-winter Marsh Warblers. *Brit. Birds* 73: 186–189.

Grant, P. J. 1983a. Identification pitfalls and assessment problems 2: Savi's Warbler. *Brit. Birds* 76: 78–80.

Grant, P. J. 1983b. Mystery photographs 74: Savi's Warbler. *Brit. Birds* 76: 81–82.

Grant, P. J. 1986. Mystery photographs 114: River Warbler. *Brit. Birds* 79: 283–284.

Grant, P. J. 1988. The Welches Dam *Acrocephalus* warbler. *Birding World* 1: 49.

Grant, P. J. & Colston, P. R. 1979. Head-pattern of *Hippolais* warblers. *Brit. Birds* 72: 436–437.

Grant, P. J. & Medhurst, H. P. 1982. The Wandlebury warbler. *Brit. Birds* 75: 183–185.

Grantham, M. 2007. Worried about missing a rare Acro? *Ringer's Bulletin* 12(1): 6–7.

Graves, G. R. 1992. The endemic land birds of Henderson Island, southeastern Polynesia: notes on natural history and conservation. *Wilson Bull.* 104: 32–43.

Gray, G. R. 1860. List of Birds collected by Mr. Wallace at the Molucca Islands, with descriptions of new species. *Proc. Zool. Soc. London,* 341–366.

Greaves, C. 1989. Marsh Warblers – trapping in Dhofar. *Oman Bird News* 5: 3.

Green, R. E. 1976. Adult survival rates for Reed and Sedge Warblers. *Wicken Fen Group Report* 8: 23–26.

Green, R. E. & Davis, N. B. 1972. Feeding ecology of Reed and Sedge Warblers. *Wicken Fen Group Report* 4: 8–14.

Gregory-Smith, R. 1993. Eastern Palearctic migrants to South-East Asia and Australia. *Adjutant* 23: 41–46.

Grieve, A. 1992. First record of Thick-billed Warbler *Acrocephalus aedon* in Egypt. *Sandgrouse* 14: 123–124.

Grimes, L. G. 1976. The duets of *Laniarius atroflavus, Cisticola discolor* and *Bradypterus barratti. Bull. Brit. Orn. Club* 96: 113–120.

Grimes, L. G. 1987. *The Birds of Ghana.* British Ornithologists' Union, Checklist No. 9. BOU, London.

Grimmett, R. 1989. Red Data Bird: Aquatic Warbler. *World Birdwatch* 11(2): 5.

Grimmett, R. & Taylor, H. 1992. Recent observations from Xinjiang Autonomous Region, China, 16 June to 5 July 1988. *Forktail* 7: 139–143.

Grimmett, R., Inskipp, C. & Inskipp, T. 1998. *Birds of the Indian Subcontinent.* Christopher Helm, London.

Grinkevich, V. & Mukhin, A. 2006. [How we can explain small natal dispersion during wide post-nesting movements in the Reed Warbler *Acrocephalus scirpaceus*?] Page 157. In: Kurochkin, E. N. (ed.). [*Ornithological studies in Northern Eurasia*]. Abstracts of XII Int. Orn. Conference of Northern Eurasia, Stavropol, 31 January – 5 February 2006. Stavropol University Press, Stavropol. (Russian)

Gynther, I. C. 1994. Clamorous Reed-Warblers feeding in the canopy of eucalypts. *Sunbird* 24: 61–65.

Gyurácz, J. & Bank, L. 1995. Study of autumn migration and wing shape of Sedge Warbler (*Acrocephalus schoenobaenus*) in Southern Hungary. *Ornis Hungarica* 5: 23–32.

Gyurácz, J. & Csörgő, T. 1994. Autumn migration dynamics of the Sedge Warbler (*Acrocephalus schoenobaenus*) in Hungary. *Ornis Hungarica* 4: 31–37.

Hachisuka, M. & Udagawa, T. 1951. Contributions to the Ornithology of Formosa, Part II. *Quarterly J. Taiwan Mus.* 4(1/2): 1–180.

Hackett, S. J., Kimball, R. T., Reddy, S., Bowie, R. C. K., Braun, E. L., Braun, M. J., Chojnowski, J. L., Cox, W. A., Han, K.-L., Harshman, J., Huddleston, C. J., Marks, B. D., Miglia, K. J., Moore, W. S., Sheldon, F. H., Steadman, D. W., Witt, C. C. & Yuri, W. 2008. A phylogenomic study of birds reveals their evolutionary history. *Science* 320: 1763–1768.

Hadden, D. 1981. *Birds of the North Solomons.* Wau Ecology Institute Handbook No. 8. Wau Ecology Institute, Wau, Papua New Guinea.

Hadden, D. 2004. *Birds and bird lore of Bougainville and the North Solomons. Alderley, Queensland.* Dove Publications, Australia.

Hadena, K. & Okabe, T. 1970. The life history of *Cettia diphone.* 1. Breeding ecology. *Misc. rep. of the Yamashina Inst. for Ornithol.* 6: 131–140.

Hagemeijer, W. J. M. & Blair, M. J. (eds.). 1997. *The EBCC Atlas of European Breeding Birds: Their Distribution and Abundance.* Poyser, London.

Hall, B. P. & Moreau, R. E. 1970. *An atlas of speciation in African passerine birds.* British Museum (Natural History), London.

Hall, S. 1996. The timing of post-juvenile moult and fuel deposition in relation to the onset of autumn migration in Reed Warblers *Acrocephalus scirpaceus* and Sedge Warblers *Acrocephalus schoenobaenus. Ornis Svecica* 6: 89–96.

Hamao, S. 1992. [Lack of pair-bond: A polygynous mating system of the Japanese Bush Warbler *Cettia diphone.*] *Jap. J. Ornithol.* 40: 51–65. (Japanese, English summary)

Hamao, S. 1993. [Individual identification of male Japanese Bush Warblers *Cettia diphone* by song.] *Jap. J. Ornithol.* 41: 1–7. (Japanese, English summary)

Hamao, S. 2000. Cost of mate guarding in the Black-browed Reed Warbler, *Acrocephalus bistrigiceps*: when do males stop guarding their mates? *J. Yamashina Inst. Ornithol.* 32: 1–12.

Hamao. S. 2001. *Male reproductive tactics in the Black-browed Reed Warblers, Acrocephalus bistrigiceps: Cost and benefit of mate attraction.* PhD. thesis, Rikkyo University, Japan.

Hamao, S. 2003. Reduction of cost of polygyny by nest predation in the Black-browed Reed Warbler. *Ornithol. Sci.* 2: 113–118.

Hamao, S. 2008. Singing strategies among male Black-browed Reed Warblers *Acrocephalus bistrigiceps* during the post-fertile period of their mates. *Ibis* 150: 388–394.

Hamao, S. & Eda-Fujiwara, H. 2004. Vocal mimicry by the Black-browed Reed Warbler *Acrocephalus bistrigiceps*: objective identification of mimetic sounds. *Ibis* 146: 61–68.

Hamao, S. & Saito, D. S. 2005. Extrapair fertilizations in the Black-browed Reed Warbler (*Acrocephalus bistrigiceps*): effects of mating status and nesting cycle of cuckolded and cuckolder males. *Auk* 122: 1086–1096.

Hamao, S. & Ueda, K. 1998. Nest sharing by polygynously mated females in the Black-browed Reed Warbler. *Ibis* 140: 176–178.

Hamao, S. & Ueda, K. 1999. Reduced territory size of an island subspecies of bush warbler *Cettia diphone*. *Jap. J. Ornithol.* 47: 57–60.

Hamao, S. & Ueda, K. 2000. Simplified song in an island population of the bush warbler *Cettia diphone*. *J. Ethol.* 18: 53–57.

Hamao, S., Matsubara, H., Kajita, M. & Mitamura, A. 2001. A record of a male Bush Warbler feeding its fledglings. *Strix* 19: 187–189. (Japanese, English summary)

Hamao, S., Veluz, M. J. S., Saitoh, T. & Nishiumi, I. 2008. Phylogenetic relationship and song differences between closely related bush warblers (*Cettia seebohmi* and *C. diphone*). *Wilson Bull* 120(2): 268–276.

Hambler, C., Hambler, K. & Newing, J. M. 1985. Some observations on *Nesillas aldabranus*, the endangered Brush Warbler of Aldabra Atoll, with hypotheses on its distribution. *Atoll Res. Bull.* 290: 1–21.

Haneda, K. & Teranishi, K. 1968. Life history of the Eastern Great Reed Warbler (*Acrocephalus arundinaceus orientalis*). 2. Polygyny and territory. *Jap. J. Ecol.* 18: 204–212.

Hanmer, D. B. 1979. A trapping study of Palaearctic passerines at Nchalo, southern Malawi. *Scopus* 3: 81–92.

Hanmer, D. B. 1988. Moult in the Cape Reed and African Marsh Warblers *Acrocephalus gracilirostris* and *A. baeticatus*. *Proc. 6th Pan-African Ornithol. Congr.*: 331–337.

Hanmer, D. B. 1989. Migrant Palaearctic passerines at Nchalo, Malawi. *Safring News* 15: 19–28.

Hansson, B., Gavrilov, E. & Gavrilov, A. 2003. Hybridisation between Great Reed Warblers *Acrocephalus arundinaceus* and Clamorous Reed Warblers *A. stentoreus*: morphological and molecular evidence. *Avian Science* 3(2–3): 145–151.

Harber, D.D. 1964. Cetti's Warbler in Sussex. *Brit. Birds* 57: 366.

Harpum, J. 1978. Olive-tree Warbler at Dodoma, central Tanzania. *Scopus* 2: 24–25.

Harrap, S. 1988a. Identification of Icterine and Melodious Warblers. *Birding World* 1: 273–277.

Harrap, S. 1988b. Identification of Olivaceous and Booted Warblers. *Birding World* 1: 312–315.

Harrap, S. 1989a. Identification of Booted Warbler. *Birding World* 2: 294–295.

Harrap, S. 1989b. Marsh Warbler identification. *Birding World* 2: 369–370.

Harrap, S. 1990. Hinweise zur Unterscheidung der Spötter *Hippolais* im Freiland. *Limicola* 4: 49–73.

Harrap, S. 1994. Little-known Oriental bird: Kinabalu Friendly Warbler *Bradypterus accentor*. *Bull. Oriental Bird Club* 20: 24–27.

Harrap, S. & Lewington, I. 1990. Identification of *Hippolais* warblers. *Birding World* 3: 268–272.

Harrap, S. & Quinn, D. 1989. The difficulties of Reed, Marsh and Blyth's Reed Warbler identification. *Birding World* 2: 318–324.

Harris, A. 1990. Mystery photographs 159: Cetti's Warbler. *Brit. Birds* 83: 408–410.

Harris, A., Shirihai, H. & Christie, D. A. 1995. *The Macmillan birder's guide to European and Middle Eastern birds*. Macmillan, London.

Harris, A., Tucker, L. & Vinicombe, K. 1989. *The Macmillan Field Guide to Bird Identification*. Macmillan, London.

Harrison, C. 1982. *An atlas of the birds of the western Palaearctic*. Collins, London.

Harrison, J. A., Allan, D. G., Underhill, L. G., Herremans, M., Tree, A. J., Parker, V. & Brown, C. J. (eds.). 1997. *The Atlas of Southern African Birds including Botswana, Lesotho, Namibia, South*

Africa, Swaziland and Zimbabwe. Vol. 2. Passerines. Birdlife South Africa, Johannesburg.

Harrison, J. M. 1958. River Warbler in Switzerland. *Bull. Brit. Orn. Club* 78: 126.

Harrison, R. 1984. Sedge Warbler feeding on ground. *Brit. Birds* 77: 115–116.

Harrio, M. 1986. Vaaleakultarinta *Hippolais pallida* foistamiseen Suomessa-hyrin vaikea tuntea. *Lintumies* 21: 159–162.

Harrop, H. R., Mavor, R. & Ellis, P. M. 2008. Olive-tree Warbler in Shetland: new to Britain. *Brit. Birds* 101: 82–88.

Hartert, E. 1897. Descriptions of seven new species of bird and one new subspecies from Flores, and of one new subspecies from Djampea. All collected by Mr. Alfred Everett. *Novit. Zool.* 4: 170–172.

Hartert, E. 1908. *Horeites pallidipes osmastoni*. *Bull. Brit. Orn. Club* 21: 107–108.

Hartert, E. J. O. 1924. *Treubia* 6: 20–25.

Hartert, E. & Steinbacher, F. 1932–1938. *Die Vögel der paläarktischen Fauna*, Ergänzungsband. Friedländer, Berlin.

Harvey, P. 2001. The Thick-billed Warbler on Shetland. *Birding World* 14: 372–373.

Harvey, P. & Bradshaw, C. 1999. Booted Warblers with long supercilia: the 1976 Fair Isle bird. *Brit. Birds* 92: 477–479.

Harvey, P. & Shaw, K. 1998. Blyth's Reed Warbler on Fair Isle in September 1996. *Birding Scotland* 2: 14–17.

Harvey, P. & Shaw, K. 2001. Thick-billed Warbler on Out Skerries. *Birding Scotland* 4: 154–158.

Harvey, P. V. & Small, B. J. 2007. From the Rarities Committee's files: Eastern Grasshopper Warbler – are there any confirmed British records? *Brit. Birds* 100: 658–664.

Harvey, P., Harrop, H., Ellis, P. & Mavor, R. 2006. The Olive-tree Warbler on Shetland – a new British bird. *Birding World* 19: 378–387.

Harvey, W. G. 1977. Cetti's Warblers in east Kent in 1975. *Brit. Birds* 70: 89–96.

Harvey, W. G. 1980. Nocturnal singing by Cetti's Warblers. *Brit. Birds* 73: 193.

Harvey, W. G. 1990. *Birds of Bangladesh*. University Press Ltd. Dhaka.

Harvey, W. G. & Porter, R. F. 1986. Mystery photographs 116: Blyth's Reed Warbler. *Brit. Birds* 79: 392–396.

Harvey, W. G., Porter, R. F. & Tucker, L. 1984. Field identification of Blyth's Reed Warbler. *Brit. Birds* 77: 393–411.

Hasselquist, D. 1994. Male attractiveness, mating tactics and realised fitness in the polygynous Great Reed Warbler. Ph. D. thesis. Lund University, Sweden.

Hasselquist, D. 1998. Polygyny in Great Reed Warblers: a long-term study of factors contributing to male fitness. *Ecology* 79: 2376–2390.

Hasselquist, D. & Bensch, S. 1991. Trade-off between mate guarding and attraction in the polygynous Great Reed Warbler. *Behav. Ecol. Sociobiol.* 28: 187–193.

Hasselquist, D., Bensch, S. & Ottosson, U. 1993. Diurnal song pattern in the Great Reed Warbler *Acrocephalus arundinaceus*. *Ornis Svecica* 3: 125–136.

Hasselquist, D., Bensch, S. & von Schantz, T. 1995. Low frequency of extrapair paternity in the polygynous Great Reed Warbler, *Acrocephalus arundinaceus*. *Behav. Ecol.* 6: 27–38.

van der Have, T. M. & van den Berk, V. M. 1995. Paddyfield Warbler in Göksü delta, southern Turkey, in September 1991. *Dutch Birding* 17: 20–21.

Haverschimdt, F. R. 1949. The clutch of the Reed-Warbler. *Brit. Birds* 42: 293.

Hazevoet, C. J. 1986. Especialidades de Cabo Verde. *Dutch Birding* 8: 134–139.

Hazevoet, C. J. 1993. On the history and type specimens of the Cape Verde Cane Warbler *Acrocephalus brevipennis* (Keulemans, 1866) (Aves, Sylviidae). *Bijragen tot. de Dierkunde* 62: 249–253.

Hazevoet, C. J. 1995. *The birds of the Cape Verde Islands*. British Ornithologists' Union, Checklist No. 13. BOU, Tring.

Hazevoet, C. J. 1999. Notes on birds from the Cape Verde

Islands in the collection of the Centro de Zoologia, Lisbon, with comments on taxonomy and distribution. *Bull. Brit. Orn. Club* 119: 25–31.

Hazevoet, C. J., Monteiro, L. R. & Radcliffe, N. 1999. Rediscovery of the Cape Verde Cane Warbler *Acrocephalus brevipennis* on São Nicolau in February 1998. *Bull. Brit. Orn. Club* 119(1): 68–71.

Hedenström, A., Bensch, S., Hasselquist, D., Lockwood, M. & Ottosson, U. 1993. Migration, stopover and moult of the Great Reed Warbler *Acrocephelus arundinaceus* in Ghana, West Africa. *Ibis* 135: 177–180.

Hedenström, A., Bensch, S., Hasselquist, D. & Ottosson, U. 1990. Observations of Palaearctic migrants rare to Ghana. *Bull. Brit. Orn. Club* 110: 194–197.

Heinroth, O. & Heinroth, M. 1924–26. *Die Vögel Mitteleuropas.* Vol. 1, p 315. Berlin.

Heise, G. 1970. Zur Brutbiologie des Seggenrohrsängers (*Acrocephalus paludicola*) *J. Ornithol.* 111: 54–67.

Helbig, A. J. & Seibold, I. 1999. Molecular Phylogeny of Palearctic-African *Acrocephalus* and *Hippolais* Warblers (Aves: Sylviidae). *Molecular Phylogenetics and Evolution* 11(2): 246–260.

Helbig, A. J., Seibold, I., Martens, J. & Wink, M. 1995. Genetic differentiation and phylogenetic relationships of Bonelli's Warbler *Phylloscopus bonelli* and Green Warbler *P. nitidus*. *J. Avian Biol.* 26: 139–153.

Hemmingsen, A. M. & Guildal, J. A. 1968. Observations on birds in north eastern China, especially the migration at Pei-Tai-Ho Beach. Part 2. *Spolia Zool. Mus. Haun. Copenhagen.* No. 28.

Henderson, A. C. B. 1979. Continuous nocturnal singing by Cetti's Warbler. *Brit. Birds* 72: 185.

Henry, C. 1972. Notes sur la reproduction et la biologie de la Locustella tachetée et de la Locustelle luscinioide. *L'Oiseau et la Revue Francaise d'Ornithologie* 42: 52–60.

Henry, G. M. 1971. *A guide to the birds of Ceylon.* Oxford University Press, Colombo.

Heredia, B. 1993. The status and conservation of Aquatic Warbler. *Birding World* 6: 294–295.

Heredia, B. 1993. The status and conservation of Aquatic Warbler. *Birding World* 6: 294–295.

Heredia, B. 1996. Action plan for the Aquatic Warbler (*Acrocephalus paludicola*) in Europe. In: Heredia, B., Rose, L. & Painter, M. (eds.). *Globally threatened birds in Europe: action plans.* Pp 327–338. Council of Europe, Strasbourg, and Birdlife International, Cambridge.

Hering, J. & Fuchs, E. 2009. The Cape Verde Warbler: distribution, density, habitat and breeding biology on the island of Fogo. *Brit. Birds* 102: 17–24.

Hering, J. & Hering H. 2005. Discovery of the Cape Verde Warbler *Acrocephalus brevipennis* on Fogo, Cape Verde Islands. *Bull. African Bird Club* 12: 147–149.

Hering, J., Brehme, S., Fuchs, E, & Winkler, H. 2010. Zimtrohrsänger *Acrocephalus baeticatus* und 'Mangroverohrsänger' *A. scirpaceus avicenniae* erstmals in der Paläarktis – Irritierendis aus den Schilfröhrichten Nordafrikas. *Limicola* 23: 202–232.

Herremans, M. 1976. Grootgrondbezit bij de Cetti's zanger *Cettia cetti*. *Wielwaal* 42: 369–371.

Herremans, M. 1990. Body-moult and migration overlap in Reed Warblers (*Acrocephalus scirpaceus*) trapped during nocturnal migration. *Gerfaut* 80: 149–158.

Herremans, M. 1992. New records of European Reed Warbler *Acrocephalus scirpaceus* from Botswana. *Babbler* 24: 10–13.

Herremans, M. 1994. Major concentration of River Warblers *Locustella fluviatilis* wintering in northern Botswana. *Bull. Brit. Orn. Club* 114: 24–26.

Herremans, M. 1998. Strategies, punctualities of arrival and ranges of migrants in the Kalahari basin, Botswana. *Ibis* 140: 585–590.

Herroelen, P. 1962. De timaar de Waterrietzanger – *Acrocephalus paludicola* L. – in België. *Giervalk* 52: 641–643.

Herroelen, P. 1991. [Migration of Aquatic Warblers in western Europe.] *Dutch Birding* 13: 65–66. Dutch, English summary)

Heunks, E. 1999. [Leucistic Great Reed Warbler near Tienhoven in June 1998.] *Dutch Birding* 21: 100. (Dutch, English summary)

Hickey, C. M., Capitolo, P. & Walker, B. 1996. First record of a Lanceolated Warbler in California. *Western Birds* 27: 197–201.

Higgins, P. J., Peter, J. M. & Cowley, S. J. (eds.). 2006. *Handbook of Australian, New Zealand and Antarctic Birds. Vol. 7: Boatbill to Starlings.* Oxford University Press, Melbourne.

Hill, B. J. 1993. Cetti's Warbler flycatching. *Brit. Birds* 86: 571.

Hinde, R. A. & Thom, A. S. 1947. The breeding of the Moustached Warbler in Cambridgeshire. *Brit. Birds* 40: 98–104.

Hirschfeld, E. 1994a. On the status of Booted Warbler *Hippolais caligata* in the United Arab Emirates. *Emirates Bird Report* 18: 100–104.

Hirschfeld, E. 1994b. First Blyth's Reed Warblers *Acrocephalus dumetorum* in the United Arab Emirates. *Emirates Bird Report* 18: 113–115.

Hirschfeld, E. & Stawarczyk, T. 1991. First record of Paddyfield Warbler *Acrocephalus agricola* in Bahrain. *Sandgrouse* 13: 110–112.

Hockey, P. A. R., Dean, W. R. J. & Ryan, P. G. (eds.). 2005. *Roberts Birds of Southern Africa*, 7th ed. New Holland, Cape Town.

Hoddinott, D. J. 1998. River Warbler *Locustella fluviatilis* at Nata Lodge, [Botswana]. *Babbler* 34: 33.

Hodgson, C. J. 1984. Sound of Grasshopper Warbler and woodcrickets. *Brit. Birds* 77: 328.

Hoffman, H. J. 1949. Probable singing by female Grasshopper Warbler. *Brit. Birds* 42: 58–59.

Hoffman, H. J. 1950. Domed nest of Grasshopper Warbler. *Brit. Birds* 43: 119.

Hofmeyer, J. H., Hofmeyer, P. K., Broekhuysen, G. J. & Stanford, W. 1961. The nest of the Knysna Scrub Warbler (*Bradypterus sylvaticus*) and some notes on parental behaviour. *Ostrich* 32: 177–180.

Hogg, P., Dare, P. J. & Rintoul, V. 1984. Palaearctic migrants in the central Sudan. *Ibis* 126: 307–331.

Hoi, H. & Ille, R. 1996. Trade-offs of territory choice in male and female Marsh Warblers. *Auk* 113: 243–246.

Hoi, H. & Ille, R. 1997. Does insect sampling reflect food availability in Marsh Warblers *Acrocephalus palustris*? – a reply to Schulze-Hagen and Dowsett-Lemaire. *Ibis* 139: 699–701.

Hoi, H., Eichler, T. & Dittami, J. 1991. Territorial spacing and interspecific competition in three species of reed warblers. *Oecologia* 87: 443–448.

Hoi, H., Kleindorfer, S., Ille, R. & Dittami, J. 1995. Prey abundance and male parental behaviour in *Acrocephalus* warblers. *Ibis* 137: 490–496.

Holling, M. & the Rare Breeding Birds Panel. Rare breeding birds in the United Kingdom in 2005. *Brit. Birds* 101: 276–316.

Hollom, P. A. D., Porter, R. F., Christensen, S. & Willis, I. 1988. *Birds of the Middle East & North Africa.* Poyser, Calton.

Hollyer, J. N. 1975. The Cetti's Warbler in Kent. *Kent Bird Report* 22: 84–95.

Hollyer, J. N. 1978. Tail-cocking by Moustached Warblers. *Brit. Birds* 71: 422.

Holmbring, J.-A. 1973. The Great Reed Warbler *Acrocephalus arundinaceus* in Sweden in 1971 and a review of its earlier status. *Vår Fågelvärld* 32: 23–31.

Holmes, D. A. 1997. Kalimantan Bird Report – 2. *Kukila* 9: 141–169.

Holmes, D. & Nash, S. 1989. *The birds of Java and Bali.* Singapore.

Holmes, P. R. 1986. The avifauna of the Sura River Valley, Ladakh. *Forktail* 2: 21–41.

Holyoak, D. T. 1973. Notes on the birds of Rangiroa, Tuamotu Archipelago, and surrounding ocean. *Bull. Brit. Orn. Club* 93: 26–32.

Holyoak, D. T. 1974a. Undescribed land birds from the Cook Islands, Pacific Ocean. *Bull. Brit. Orn. Club* 94: 145–150.

Holyoak, D. T. 1974b. Les oiseaux des Iles de la Societe (Part 2). *L'Oiseau et la Revue Francaise d'Ornithologie* 44(2). 152–184.

Holyoak, D. T. 1975. Les oiseaux des Iles Marquèses (suite et fin). *L'Oiseau et la Revue Francaise d'Ornithologie* 45: 341–366.

Holyoak, D. T. 1978. Variable albinism of flight feathers as an adaptation for recognition of individual birds in some Polynesian populations of *Acrocephalus* warblers. *Ardea* 66: 112–117.

Holyoak, D. T. 1979. Notes on the birds of Viti Levu and Taveuni, Fiji. *Emu* 79: 7–18.

Holyoak, D. T. 1981. *Guide to Cook Island Birds*. D.T. Holyoak, privately published.

Holyoak, D. T. & Thibault, J. C. 1977. Habitats, morphologie et inter-actions ecologiques des oiseaux insectivores de Polynesie orientale. *L'Oiseau et la Revue Française d'Ornithologie* 47: 115–146.

Holyoak, D. T. & Thibault, J. C. 1978. Undescribed *Acrocephalus* Warblers from Pacific Ocean Islands. *Bull. Brit. Orn. Club* 98: 122–127.

Holyoak, D. T. & Thibault, J. C. 1984. Contribution à l'étude des oiseaux de Polynésie orientale. *Mém. Mus. Hist. Nat., Paris (sér. A), Zool.* 127: 1–209.

Honza, M. & Literák, I. 1997. Spatial distribution of four *Acrocephalus* warblers in reedbeds during the post-breeding migration. *Ringing & Migration* 18: 79–83.

Honza, M., Literak, I., Pavelka, J. & Formanek, J. 2000. Postbreeding occurrence of the Marsh Warbler *Acrocephalus palustris* in reedbed areas of the Czech Republic and its migration to Africa. *Ökol. Vögel* 22: 119–129.

Honza, M., Moksnes, E., Roskaft, E. & Øien, I. J. 1999. Effect of Great Reed Warbler *Acrocephalus arundinaceus* on the reproductive tactics of the Reed Warbler *A. scirpaceus*. *Ibis* 141: 489–493.

Hoogerwerf, A. 1937. Nestelende karekieten (*Acrocephalus stentoreus siebersi*) bij Batavia. *Trop. Nat.* 26: 157–160.

Horne, J. F. M. 1987. Vocalisations of the endemic land-birds of the Mascarenes Islands. In: Diamond, A. W. (ed.). *Studies of Mascarene Island Birds*. Pp: 101–150. Cambridge University Press, Cambridge.

Hornskov, J. 1991. Some bird observations at Laoye Shan, east Qinghai province, China. *Hong Kong Bird Report* 1990: 179–182.

Hornskov, J. 1995. Recent observations of birds in the Philippine Archipelago. *Forktail* 11: 1–10.

Hornskov, J. 2000. *Yunnan & Beijing, China: 12 November – 10 December 2000*. Unpublished manuscript.

Hornskov, J. 2002. *Birds seen in Yunnan, China, 26 Feb – 24 Mar 2002*. Unpublished manuscript.

Hornskov, J. 2004. *Birds at Beidaihe, Spring 2003*. Unpublished manuscript.

Hottola, P. 1988. Dumarin alula. *Lintumies* 23: 26–27.

Hottola, P. 1992. Pallas's Grasshopper Warbler identification. *Birding World* 4: 436.

Hottola, P. 1993. Alula colour of Blyth's Reed Warbler in spring. *Dutch Birding* 15: 71–72.

del Hoyo, J., Elliot, A. & Christie, D. A. (eds.). 2006 *Handbook of the Birds of the World*. Vol 11. Old World Flycatchers to Old World Warblers. Lynx Edicions, Barcelona.

Hudson, N. and the Rarities Committee. Report on rare birds in Great Britain in 2008. *Brit. Birds* 102: 528–601.

Hûe, F. & Etchécopar, R. D. 1970. *Les oiseaux du Proche et du Moyen Orient de la Méditerranée aux contreforts de l'Himalaya*. Boubée & Cie. Paris.

Hulten, M. 1959. Beitrag zur kenntnis des Feldschwirls (*Locustella naevia*). *Regulus* 39: 95–117.

Hume, A. 1869. [Letter addressing BOU meeting and making first mention of *Phyllopneuste macrorhyncha*.] *Ibis* (2)5: 355–357.

Hume, A. 1871. Stray notes on Ornithology in India. No.VI: on certain new or unrecorded birds. *Ibis* (3)1: 23–38.

Hustler, K. 1995. First breeding record, incubation period and density of the Greater Swamp Warbler in Zimbabwe. *Honeyguide* 41: 161–163.

Ille, R. & Hoi, H. 1995. Factors influencing fledging survival in the Marsh Warbler *Acrocephalus palustris*: food and vegetation density. *Ibis* 137: 586–588.

Ilyichev, V. D. (ed.). 1976. *Opredelanie pola I vozrasta vorobinykh ptits fauny SSSR*. Moscow.

Ingram, C. 1909. The birds of Manchuria. *Ibis* (9)3: 422–469.

Ingram, C. 1926. Ouessant Ornithology and other Notes on French Birds. *Ibis* (12)2: 247–269.

Ingram, C. 1930. Note discussing occurrence of Gray's Grasshopper Warbler on Ouessant. *Bull. Brit. Orn. Club* 50: 4.

Inskipp, C. & Inskipp, T. 1991. *A Guide to the Birds of Nepal*. 2nd edition. Croom Helm, Beckenham.

Inskipp, C. & Inskipp, T. P. 1993. Birds recorded during a visit to Bhutan in autumn 1991. *Forktail* 8: 97–112.

Inskipp, C. & Inskipp, T. 1993. Birds recorded during a visit to Bhutan in spring 1993. *Forktail* 9: 121–143.

Inskipp, C., Inskipp, T. & Grimmett, R. 1999. *Birds of Bhutan*. Christopher Helm, London.

Inskipp, T., Lindsey, N. & Duckworth, W. 1996. *An annotated checklist of the birds of the Oriental Region*. Oriental Bird Club, Sandy.

Insley, H. & Boswell, R. C. 1978. The timing of arrivals of Reed and Sedge Warblers at South Coast ringing sites during autumn passage. *Ringing & Migration* 2: 1–9.

Iovchenko, N. P. 1999. Modern status and ecology peculiarities of the Booted Warbler (*Hippolais caligata*) on the northwest border of the distribution area. *Ring* 21(1): 90.

Ireland, D. T. 1984. Nocturnal singing by Cetti's Warblers. *Brit. Birds* 77: 212.

Ireson, G. M., Moule, G. W. H., Crudass, J. & Devlin, T. R. E. 1965. The problems of separating Reed and Marsh Warblers. *Brit. Birds* 58: 473–478.

Irwin, M. P. S. 1981. *The Birds of Zimbabwe*. Quest Publishing, Harare.

Irwin, M. P. S. & Turner, D. A. 2001. A contribution to the systematics of the Papyrus Yellow Warbler *Chloropeta gracilirostris*. *Honeyguide* 47: 201–203.

Isenmann, P. 1977. Wo überwintert der Seggenrohrsänger? *Beitr. Vogelkd.* 25: 366–367.

Ishizawa, J. & Nakamura, T. 1964. [Studies on the migration of Gray's Grasshopper Warbler.1. Distribution and migration in Japan and the vicinity]. *Misc. Rep. Yamashina Inst. Ornithol.* 4: 63–70. (Japanese, English summary)

Jackson, W. T. & Stone, D. A. 1983. Great Reed Warbler attacking Reed Warbler. *Brit. Birds* 76: 456.

Jander, G. 1983. Zum Gesang des Feldrohrsängers. *Falke* 30: 272–277.

Jännes, H. 1987. [Identification and distribution of Paddyfield Warbler *Acrocephalus agricola*.] *Lintumies* 22: 166–169. (Finnish, English summary)

Jännes, H. 1995. [Thick-billed Warbler.] *Alula* 1: 18–20. (Finnish, English summary)

Jenni, L. & Winkler, R. 1994. *Moult and ageing of European Passerines*. Academic Press, London.

Jennings, M. C. 1987. New breeding species: *Columba arquatrix* and *Acrocephalus scirpaceus*. Phoenix 4: 1–2.

Jiguet, F. 2003. Saharan Olivaceous Warbler. *Birding World* 16: 392.

Jiguet, F. 2005. More on Saharan Olivaceous Warbler. *Birding World* 18: 262–263.

Jiguet, F. & CAF. 2006. En direct de la CAF. Décisions prises par la Commission de l'Avifaune Française en 2004–2005. *Ornithos* 13(4): 244–257.

Jiguet, F., Rguibi-Idrissi, H. & Provost, P. 2010. Undescribed reed warbler breeding in Morocco. *Dutch Birding* 32: 29–36.

Jilka, A. & Leisler, B. 1974. The relationship between the frequency spectrum of the territorial song of three reed warbler species (*Acrocephalus schoenobaenus*, *A. scirpaceus*, *A. arundinaceus*) and the respective habitats. *J. Ornithol.* 115: 192–212.

Jobling, J. A. 2009. *Helm Dictionary of Scientific Bird Names*. Christopher Helm, London.

Jobson, G. J. 1971. Savi's Warbler breeding in Suffolk. *Suffolk Bird Report* 1970: 23–24.

Joiris, C. 1975. The origin of British Aquatic Warblers. *Brit. Birds* 68: 519.

Johansen, H. 1928. [Nest und Eier von *Locustella fasciolata* Gray]. *Uragus* 6(1): 22–24. (Russian)

Johansen, H. 1954. Die Vogelfauna Westsibiriens. *J. Ornithol.* 95: 64–110.

Johansen, H. 1961. Revised list of the birds of the Commander Islands. *Auk* 78: 44–56.

Johansson, U. S., Fjeldså, J. & Bowie, R. C. K. 2008. Phylogenetic relationships within Passerida (Aves: Passeriformes): A review and a new molecular phylogeny based on three nuclear intron markers. *Molecular Phylogenetics and Evolution* 48, 858–876.

Johns, G. C. & Avise, J. C. 1998. A comparative summary of genetic distances in the vertebrates from the mitochondrial cytochrome b gene. *Molecular Biology and Evolution* 15: 1481–1490.

Johnstone, R. & Dunlop, G. 2003. An Eastern Cetti's Warbler in East Sussex – a new British Bird. *Birding World* 16: 338–339.

Johnstone, R. E. & Darnell, J. C. 1997. Description of a new subspecies of bush-warbler of the genus *Cettia* from Alor Island, Indonesia. *The Western Australian Naturalist* 21(3): 145–151.

Johnstone, R. E. & Storr, G. M. 2004. *Handbook of Western Australian Birds.* Vol. 2.. Western Austalia Museum, Perth.

de Jong, J. 1985. [Paddyfield Warbler at Makkum in October 1984.] *Dutch Birding* 7: 140–141. (Dutch, English summary)

Jønsson, K. A. & Fjeldså, J. 2006. A phylogenetic supertree of oscine passerine birds (Aves: Passeri). *Zool. Scripta* 35: 149–186.

Jonsson, L. 1992. *Birds of Europe with North Africa and the Middle East.* Christopher Helm/A&C Black, London.

Joyner, S. 2001. The Pallas's Grasshopper Warbler in Norfolk. *Birding World* 14: 382–384.

Julliard, R., Bargain, B., Dubos, A. & Jiguet, F. 2006. Identifying autumn migration routes for the globally threatened Aquatic Warbler *Acrocephalus paludicola.* *Ibis* 148: 735–743.

Jupp, D. 1998. Booted Warbler – first for Suffolk. *Suffolk Birds* 46: 172–173.

Kagawa, T. 1989. [Interspecific relationship between two sympatric warblers, Great Reed Warbler *Acrocephalus arundinaceus* and Schrenck's Reed Warbler *A. bistrigiceps.*] *Jap. J. Ornithol.* 37: 129–144. (Japanese, English summary)

Kaiser, A. 1993. A new multicategory classification of subcutaneous fat deposits of songbirds. *J. Field Ornithol.* 64: 246–255.

Kajita, M. 2002. [Biogeographical intraspecific phylogeny of the Bush Warbler.] *Iden* 56: 42–46. (Japanese)

Kajita, M., Mano, T. & Sato, F. 2002. Two forms of Bush Warbler *Cettia diphone* occur on Okinawajima Island: Re-evaluation of *C. d. riukiuensis* and *C. d. restricta* by multivariate analyses. *J. Yamashina Inst.Ornithol.* 33: 148–167.

Kalyakin, M. V. 1996. *Aquatic Warbler in Russia.* Unpublished report for BirdLife/Vogelbescherming Nederland, Moscow.

Kalyakin, M. V., Babenko, V. G. & Nechaev, V. A. 1993. [On the systematic relationship between Pallas's Grasshopper Warbler (*Locustella certhiola*) and Middendorff's Grasshopper Warbler (*L. ochotensis*)]. *Sbor. Trud. Zool. Muz. MGU [Arch. Zool. Mus. Moscow State University]* 30: 164–182. (Russian)

Kalyakin, M. V., Flade, M., Gissing, B., Koerners, S., Kloskovskii, J., Kozulin, A. V., Kroguletc, J., Morozov, V. V., Soloviev, S. A. & Winters, S. 2000. [*Avifaunal records in Omsk Region*] Pp 92–94. Materiali k rasprostraneniyu ptits na Urale, v Priural'e i Zapadnoi Sibiri Ekaterinburg. (Russian)

Kapanen, M. 1996a. Booted Warbler – a modest conquerer. *Alula* 2(2): 84–88.

Kapanen, M. 1996b. Finnish Birds No. 3. Blyth's Reed Warbler – Viitakerttunen. *Alula* 3: 134–135.

Karlsson. L., Perrson, K. & Walinder, G. 1988. Ålderbestämning av rörsångare *Acrocephalus scirpaceus* med hjälp av irisfärg, tarsfärg och tungfläckar. *Vår Fågelvärld* 47: 141–146. (Swedish, English summary)

Kawaji, N. & Abe, J. 1988. Records of the Pallas's Grasshopper Warbler *Locustella certhiola* from Japan. *J. Yamashina Inst. Ornithol.* 20: 107–110.

Kazakov, B. A. 1973. [Distribution and systematic status of *Locustella luscinioides* (Sylviiae, aves) in the south-east European part of the range]. *Zool. Zhurnal* 52(4): 616–618 (Russian, English summary)

Kazakov, B. A. 1974. [Distribution and taxonomic status of the warbler Lusciniola melanopogon Temm., in the European section of the USSR]. *Vestnik Zool.* 2: 15–19. (Russian, English summary)

Keast, A. 1976. Adaptive morphology and biogeography relative to the evolution and classification of the Australian and Pacific warblers. *Proc. 16th Int. Ornithol. Congr.*: 519–529.

Keith, S. & Vernon, C. 1966. Notes on African warblers of the genus *Chloropeta* Smith. *Bull. Brit. Orn. Club* 86: 115–120.

Kelsey, M. G. 1985. Mouth and gape colours of singing Marsh and Reed Warblers. *Brit. Birds* 78: 297–298.

Kelsey, M. G. 1989. A comparison of the song and territorial behaviour of a long-distance migrant, the Marsh Warbler *Acrocephalus palustris*, in summer and winter. *Ibis* 131: 403–414.

Kelsey, M. G., Green, G. H., Garnett, M. C. & Hayman, P. V. 1989. Marsh Warblers in Britain. *Brit. Birds* 82: 239–256.

Kelsey, M. G., Pearson, D. J. & Backhurst, G. C. 1989. Age differences in the timing and biometrics of migrating Marsh Warblers in Kenya. *Ringing & Migration* 10: 41–17.

Kennedy, R. J. 1978. Mortality and site faithfulness of warblers. *Bird-ringing in South West Lancashire.* 1977: 43–44.

Kennedy, R. S., Gonzales, P. C., Dickinson, E. C., Miranda, H. C. & Fisher, T. H. 2000. *A Guide to the Birds of the Philippines.* Oxford University Press, Oxford.

Kennerley, P. R. 1987. Survey of the birds of Poyang Lake Nature Reserve, Jiangxi Province, China 29 December 1985 – 4 January 1986. *Hong Kong Bird Report* 1984/1985: 97–111.

Kennerley, P. R. 1989. A record of a *Bradypterus* warbler probably breeding in Bali. *Kukila* 4: 155–157.

Kennerley, P. R. 1992. Paddyfield Warbler at Mai Po: the first record for Hong Kong. *Hong Kong Bird Report* 1991: 123–126.

Kennerley, P. R. & Leader, P. J. 1992. The identification, status and distribution of small *Acrocephalus* warblers in eastern China. *Hong Kong Bird Report* 1991: 143–187.

Kennerley, P. R. & Leader, P. J. 1993. Identification of Middendorff's and Styan's Grasshopper Warblers. *Dutch Birding* 15: 241–248.

Kennerley, P. R. & Leader, P. J. 1993. Russet Bush Warbler and Brown Bush Warbler: two species new to Hong Kong. *Hong Kong Bird Report* 1992: 114–130.

Kennerley, P. R. & Prŷs-Jones, R. P. 2006. Occurrences of Gray's Grasshopper Warbler in Europe, including a further case of Meinertzhagen fraud. *Brit. Birds* 99: 506–516.

Kemp, J. 1990. Grasshopper not Savi's. *Birding World* 3: 286–287.

Kikkert, J.-E. 1996. DB Actueel: Struikrietzanger te Walem. *Dutch Birding* 18: 155–156.

Kikkert, J.-E. 1997. [Blyth's Reed Warbler at Walem in June–July 1996.] *Dutch Birding* 19: 273–276. (Dutch, English summary)

Kikkert, J.-E. 1997. Struikrietzanger te Walem in juni 1995. *Limb Vogels* 8: 79–81.

Kilburn, M. 1998. Overseas Reports: Xinjiang Autonomous Region, 7–27 June 1998. *Hong Kong Bird Watching Society Bull.* 169: 18–23.

Kim, S. J. 2008. Distribution and Song Characteristic of Japanese Bush Warbler *Cettia diphone borealis* in the central part of Korea. *Korea National Parks Service: 2008 Annual report on migratory researches*: 133–147.

Kim, C. H. & Isao, N. 2004. Observation of new species recorded in South Korea. http://www.birdskorea.org/Birds/Miscellaneous/ BK-BM-Locustella-on-Ulleungdo.shtml

King, B. 1966. *List of bird skins and specimens collected in Thailand from 1 March 1964 to 30 June 1966 under MAPS programme.* Centre for Thai National Reference Collections, Bangkok.

King, B. 1989. The avian genera *Tesia* and *Urosphena.* *Bull. Brit. Orn. Club* 109: 162–166.

King, B. 1968. Late autumn song of Grasshopper Warbler. *Brit. Birds* 61: 136.

King, J. E. 1955. Annotated list of birds observed on Christmas Island, October to December 1953. *Pacific Science* 9: 42–48.

King, J. R. 1994. Initiation of remige moult by first-year Great Reed Warblers *Acrocephalus arundinaceus arundinaceus* in Europe. *Ringing & Migration* 15: 123–126.

King, J. R. 1996. Moult of Oriental Great Reed Warbler. *Dutch Birding* 18: 82.

King, J. 1998. Redefining *Acrocephalus* and *Hippolais.* *Birding World* 11: 42.

Kinnear, N. B. 1929. On the birds collected by Mr H. Stevens in northern Tonkin in 1923–1924, with notes by the collector, Part II. *Ibis* (12)5: 292–344.

Kirby, H. Jr. 1925. The birds of Fanning Island, central Pacific Ocean. Condor 27: 185–196.

Kirwan, G. 1992. A record of Aquatic Warbler from Turkey. *Bull. Ornithol. Soc. Middle East* 28: 18–19.

Kirwan, G. 1994. A record of Booted Warbler *Hippolais caligata* from Turkey. *Bull. Ornithol. Soc. Middle East* 33: 7–9.

Kirwan, G. & Martins, R. P. 2000. Turkey Bird Report. 1992–1996. *Sandgrouse* 22: 13–25.

Kirwan, G. M., Boyla, K., Castell, P., Demirci, B., Özen, M., Welch, H. & Marlow, T. 2008. *The Birds of Turkey.* Christopher Helm, London.

Kitson, A. R. 1980. Further Notes from Mongolia. *Brit. Birds* 73: 398–401.

Kleindorfer, S., Hoi, H. & Fessl, B. 1996. Alarm calls and chick reactions in the Moustached Warbler, *Acrocephalus melanopogon*. *Anim. Behav.* 51: 1199–1206.

Kloskowski, J. & Krogulec, J. 1999. Habitat selection of Aquatic Warbler *Acrocephalus paludicola* in Poland: consequences for conservation of the breeding areas. *Vogelwelt* 120: 113–120.

Kloubec, B. & Čapek, M. 2005. Seasonal and diel budgets of song: a study of Savi's Warbler (*Locustella luscinioides*). *J. Ornithol.* 146: 206–214.

Knysh, M. P. 1994. [Vagrant Blyth's Reed Warblers in northeast Ukraine.] *Berkut* 3(2): 102. (Ukrainian)

Knysh, M. P. 1997. [Record of Blyth's Reed Warbler in northeast Ukraine.] *Berkut* 6(1/2): 32. (Ukrainian)

Knysh, N. P. 1999. [Nesting ecology of the Marsh Warbler in the forest-steppe region of Sumy Region.] *Berkut* 8(1): 57–70. (Ukrainian)

Knysh, N. P. 2001. [Breeding peculiarities of the Marsh Warbler in the Sumy Region in 1999]. *Berkut* 10(1): 102–104. (Ukrainian)

Kobayashi, K. 1932. [On the breeding of *Locustella fasciolata* (Gray)]. *Tori* 7: 297–300. (Japanese)

Kobayashi, Y. & Oyama, N. 2003. A trend in the breeding population of the Japanese Marsh Warbler along the lower Iwaki River. *Strix* 21: 29–34. (Japanese, English summary)

Kocher, T. D., Thomas, W. K. & Meyer, A., Edwards, F., Pääbo S., Villablanca, F. X. & Wilson, A. C. 1989. Dynamics of mitochondrial DNA evolution in animals: amplification and sequencing with conserved primers. *Proc. Nat. Acad. Sci. USA* 86: 6196–6200.

Koelz, W. 1939. Notes on the birds of Zanskar and Purig, with appendices giving new records for Ladakh, Rupshu and Kulu. *Pap. Michigan Acad. Sci.* 25: 297–322.

Kok, D. & van Duivendijk, N. 1998. Masters of Mystery: Caspian Reed Warbler. *Dutch Birding* 20: 36–40.

Kok, D. & van Duivendijk, N. 1999. Masters of Mystery: Upcher's Warbler. *Dutch Birding* 21: 167–171.

Kolthoff, K. 1932. Studies of birds in the Chinese provinces of Kiangsu and Anhwei, 1921–1922. *Goteborgs Kungl. Vetenak. Vitterh. Samh-Handl.* 5 Foljden, ser B. 3: 1–190.

Komatsu, Y., Satoh, H., Fujisawa, M. & Chiba, A. 2004. Some aspects of seasonal migration of the Bush Warbler *Cettia diphone* at Niigata City on the coast of central Japan, as revealed by banding. *J. Yamashina Inst. Ornithol.* 36: 28–36.

Komdeur, J. 1991. *Cooperative breeding in the Seychelles Warbler.* Ph.D. thesis, University of Cambridge.

Komdeur, J. 1992. Importance of habitat saturation and territory quality for evolution of cooperative breeding in the Seychelles Warbler. *Nature* 358: 493–495.

Komdeur, J. 1994a. Experimental evidence for helping and hindering by previous offspring in the co-operative breeding Seychelles Warbler *Acrocephalus sechellensis*. *Behav. Ecol. Sociobiol.* 34: 175–186.

Komdeur, J. 1994b. Conserving the Seychelles Warbler *Acrocephalus sechellensis* by translocation from Cousin Island to the islands of Aride and Cousine. *Biol. Conserv.* 76: 143–152.

Komdeur, J. 1994c. The effect of kinship on helping in the co-operative breeding Seychelles Warbler *Acrocephalus sechellensis*. *Proc. R. Soc. London* 256: 47–52.

Komdeur, J. 1996a. Facultative sex ratio bias in the offspring of Seychelles Warblers. *Proc. R. Soc. London* 263: 661.

Komdeur, J. 1996b. Influence of helping and breeding experience on reproductive performance in the Seychelles Warbler: a translocation experiment. *Behav. Ecol.* 7: 326–333.

Komdeur, J. 1996c. Seasonal timing of reproduction in a tropical bird, the Seychelles Warbler: a field experiment using translocation. *J. Biol. Rhythms* 11: 333–346.

Komdeur, J. 1998. Long-term fitness benefits of egg sex modification by the Seychelles Warbler. *Ecol. Lett.* 1: 56–62.

Komdeur, J. 2003. Daughters on request: about helpers and egg sexes in the Seychelles Warbler. *Proc. R. Soc. London* 270: 3–11.

Komdeur, J. & Kats, R. H. K. 1999. Predation risk affects trade-off between nest guarding and foraging in Seychelles Warblers. *Behav. Ecol.* 10: 630–640.

Komdeur, J., Bullock, I. D. & Rands, M. R. W. 1991. Conserving the Seychelles Warbler by translocation: a transfer from Cousin Island to Aride Island. *Bird Conserv. Internatn.* 1: 179–188.

Komdeur, J., Daan, S., Tinbergen, J. & Mateman, C. 1997. Extreme adaptive modification in sex ratio of the Seychelles Warbler's eggs. *Nature* 385: 522–525.

Komdeur, J., Huffstadt, A., Prast, W., Castle, G., Mileto, R. & Wattel, J. 1995. Transfer experiments of Seychelles Warblers to new islands: changes to dispersal and helping behaviour. *Anim. Behav.* 49: 695–708.

Komdeur, J., Magrath, M. J. L. & Krackow, S. 2002. Pre-ovulation control of hatchling sex ratio in the Seychelles Warbler. *Proc. R. Soc. London* 269: 1067–1072.

Komdeur, J., Piersma, T., Kraaijeveld, K., Kraaijeveld-Smit, F. & Richardson, D. S. 2004. Why Seychelles Warblers fail to recolonize nearby islands: unwilling or unable to fly there? *Ibis* 146: 298–302.

Komen, J. 1988. Identity crisis: African Reed, European Reed and European Marsh Warblers. *Bokmakerie* 40: 106–110.

Komen, J. 1989. European Reed Warbler records. *Ostrich* 60: 91–93.

Komen, J. 1990. Distribution of Greater Swamp Warbler in southern Africa. *Lanioturdus* 25: 55–56.

Komen, J. & Myer, E. 1988. European Reed Warblers in Namibia. *Ostrich* 59: 142–143.

Koridon, J. A. F. 1967. Eerste vondst van de Veldrietzanger (*Acrocephalus agricola*) in Nederland. *Limosa* 40: 185.

Koskimies, P. 1980. Breeding biology of Blyth's Reed Warbler *Acrocephalus dumetorum* in SE Finland. *Ornis Fennica* 57: 26–32.

Koskimies, P. 1984. Polygyny in Blyth's Reed Warbler. *Ann. Zool. Fennici* 21: 239–242.

Koskimies, P. & Saurola, P. 1985. Autumn migration strategies of the Sedge Warbler *Acrocephalus schoenobaenus* in Finland: a preliminary report. *Ornis Fennica* 62: 145–152.

Kosonen, L. 1983. Todennäköinen vita-ja luhtakerttusen risteymä *Acrocephalus dumetorum* x *palustris* Tampereella. *Lintuviesti* 8: 210–213. (Finnish, English summary)

Kotyukov, Yu. V. 1998. [Discovery of *Hippolais caligata* and *Phylloscopus trochiloides* breeding in the south-eastern part of Meshchera]. *Russian J. Ornithol.* Express issue 37: 3–6. (Russian)

Kotyukov, Yu. V. & Sorokin, A. G. 1998. [A record of *Hippolais icterina* in the north of Khanty-Mansi Autonomous District]. *Russian J. Ornithol.* Express issue 35: 22. (Russian)

Kovács, G. & Végvári, Z. 1999. Population size and habitat of the Aquatic Warbler *Acrocephalus paludicola* in Hungary. *Vogelwelt* 120: 121–126.

Kovalenko, A. V. 2003. [Feeding by *Acrocephalus scirpaceus* on young Marsh (Laughing) Frogs *Rana ridibunda*.] *Russian J. Ornithol.* Express issue 245: 1360–1361. (Russian)

Kovshar, A. F. 1972. [*Birds of Kazakhstan*, Vol 4]. Alma-Ata. (Russian)

Kozulin, A. & Flade, M. 1999. Breeding habitat, abundance and threat status of the Aquatic Warbler *Acrocephalus paludicola* in Belarus. *Vogelwelt* 120: 97–111.

Kozulin, A., Vergeichik, L. & Stepanovich, Y. 2004. Factors affecting fluctuations of the Aquatic Warbler *Acrocephalus paludicola* population of Byelarussian mires. *Acta Ornithol.* 39: 35–44.

Krishna Raju, K. S. R., Shekar, P. B. & Selvin, P. J. 1972. Movement of Blyth's Reed Warbler (*Acrocephalus dumetorum* Blyth) through Point Calimere. *J. Bombay Nat. Hist. Soc.* 69: 186–187.

Krivitskiy, I. A. 2000. *Cettia cetti*. In: [*Birds of the USSR*. Sylviidae]. Pp: 170. Publ. House of Kharkov National University, Kharkov. (Russian)

Kumar, S. 2005. Molecular clocks: four decades of evolution. *Nature Reviews Genetics* 6: 654–662.

Kumerloeve, H. 1978. Tail-cocking by Moustached Warblers. *Brit. Birds* 71: 89–90.

Kurlavicius, P. 1991. Rare and new bird species in Lithuania: this centuary. *Acta Ornithol. Litu* 4: 81–95.

Kuroda, N. 1938. On a melanistic example of *Tribura luteoventris* Hodgson from Formosa. *Tori* 10: 3–9.

Kvartalnov, P. V. 2006. [The Black-browed Reed Warbler: individual breeding strategy.] Page 257. In: Kurochkin, E. N. (ed.). [*Ornithological studies in Northern Eurasia*]. Abstracts of XII Int. Orn. Conference of Northern Eurasia, Stavropol, 31 January – 5 February 2006. Stavropol University Press, Stavropol. (Russian)

La Touche, J. D. D. 1899. Notes on the birds of north-west Fohkien. *Ibis* (7)5: 169–210.

La Touche, J. D. D. 1912a. *Acrocephalus tangorum*. *Bull. Brit. Orn. Club* 31: 10–11.

La Touche, J. D. D. 1912b. A list of the species of birds collected and observed in the island of Shaweishan. *Bull. Brit. Orn. Club* 29: 124–160.

La Touche, J. D. D. 1914. On the spring migration at Chinwangtao in north-east Chihli. *Ibis* (10)2: 560–586.

La Touche, J. D. D. 1920. Notes on the birds of north-east Chihli, in north China. *Ibis* (11)2: 629–671.

La Touche, J. D. D. 1921a. Notes on the birds of north-east Chihli in north China. Part III. *Ibis* (11)3: 3–48.

La Touche, J. D. D. 1921b. *Urosphena laurentei*. *Bull. Brit. Orn. Club* 42: 30–31.

La Touche, J. D. D. 1923. Description of *Tribura thoracica davidi*. *Bull. Brit. Orn. Club* 43: 168–169.

La Touche, J. D. D. 1925–30. *A handbook of the birds of eastern China*. Vol. 1. Taylor and Francis, London.

Lacan, F. & Mougin, J.-L. 1974. Les oiseaux des Iles Gambier et de quelques atolls orientaux de l'archipel des Tuamotu (Océan Pacifique). *L'Oiseau et la Revue Francaise d'Ornithologie* 44: 193–280.

Laird, W. 1992. Plumage variation of Clamorous Reed Warblers in Israel. *Brit. Birds* 85: 83–85.

Lamarche, B. 1981. Liste commentee des oiseaux du Mali. *Malimbus* 3: 73–102.

Langham, N. P. E. 1987. Morphometrics and moult in Fijian passerines. *New Zealand J. Zool.* 14: 463–475.

Langrand, O. 1990. *Guide to the Birds of Madagascar*. Yale University Press, New Haven & London.

Lansdown, P. 1992. Mystery photographs 177: Great Reed Warbler. *Brit. Birds* 85: 249–250.

Lavauden, L. 1937. Supplément to Milne-Edwards, A. & Grandidier, A. *Histoire Physique, Naturelle et Politique de Madagascar*. Vol. 12. Historie Naturelle des Oiseaux. Societé d'Éditions Géographiques, Maritimes et Coloniales, Paris.

Le Sueur, F. 1980. Some Cetti's Warbler breeding observations. *Bird Study* 27: 249–253.

Leader, P. J. 1992. Blunt-winged Warbler: a new species for Hong Kong. *Hong Kong Bird Report* 1991: 120–122.

Leader, P. J. 1994. Middendorff's Grasshopper Warbler: the first record for Hong Kong. *Hong Kong Bird Report* 1993: 123–131.

Leader, P. J. 1995. Booted Warbler: the first record for Hong Kong. *Hong Kong Bird Report* 1994: 118–122.

Leader, P. J. 1998a. The winter status and conservation of Styan's Grasshopper Warbler. *Hong Kong Bird Report* 1996: 158–161.

Leader, P. J. 1998b. Little-known Oriental bird: Pleske's Warbler *Locustella pleskei*. *Bull. Oriental Bird Club* 28: 49–51.

Leader, P. J. & Lewthwaite, R. W. 1996. Manchurian Reed Warbler: the first records for Hong Kong. *Hong Kong Bird Report* 1995: 119–122.

LeCroy, M. & Barker, K. 2006. A New Species of Bush-Warbler from Bougainville Island and a Monophyletic Origin for Southwest Pacific *Cettia*. *Amer. Mus. Novit.* 3511: 1–20.

Lees, J., Brown, P. & Gray, M. 2002. The Sykes's Warbler on Orkney. *Birding World* 15: 375–377.

van Leeuwen, H. 1929. Beitrag zur Kenntnis der Avifauna der Mittel-Javanischen Vulkane Sumbing und Sindoro. *Treubia* 10: 439–446.

Legge, W. V. 1880. *A History of the Birds of Ceylon*. Taylor and Francis, London.

Leibak, E., Lilleleht, V. & Veromann, H. (eds.). 1994. *The Birds of Estonia: status, distribution and numbers*. Estonian Academy Publishers, Tallinn.

Leisler, B. 1971. Artmerkmale am Fuß adulter Teich- und Sumpfrohränger (*Acrocephalus scirpaceus, A. palustris*) und ihre Funktion. *J. Ornithol.* 113: 366–373.

Leisler, B. 1972a. Die Mauser des Mariskensängers (*Acrocephalus melanopogon*) als ökologisches Problem. *J. Ornithol.* 113: 191–206.

Leisler, B. 1972b. Artmerkmale am Fuß adulter Teich- und Sumpfrohrsänger und ihre Funktion. *J. Ornithol.* 113: 366–372.

Leisler, B. 1973. Die Jahresverbreitung des Mariskensängers (*Acrocephalus melanopogon*) nach Beobachtungen und Ringfunden. *Vogelwarte* 27: 24–39.

Leisler, B. 1975. Die Bedeutung der Fussmorphologie für die ökologische Sonderung Mitteleuropäischer Rohrsänger (*Acrocephalus*) und Schwirle (*Locustella*). *J. Ornithol.* 116: 117–153.

Leisler, B. 1977a. Observations on the moult of the Great Reed Warbler *Acrocephalus arundinaceus*. *Ibis* 119: 204–206.

Leisler, B. 1977b. Die ökologische Bedeutung der Lokomotion mitteleuropäischer Schwirle (*Locustella*). *Egretta* 20: 1–25.

Leisler, B. 1985. Öko-ethologische Voraussetzungen für die Entwicklung von Polygamie bei Rohrsängern (*Acrocephalus*). *J. Ornithol.* 126: 357–381.

Leisler, B. & Catchpole, C. K. 1992. The evolution of polygamy in European reed warblers of the genus *Acrocephalus*: a comparative approach. *Ethol. Ecol. Evol.* 4: 225–243.

Leisler, B. & Winkler, H. 1979. Zur Unterscheidung von Teich- und Sumpfrohrsänger. *Vogelwarte* 30: 44–48.

Leisler, B., Heidrich, P., Schulze-Hagen, K. & Wink, M. 1997. Taxonomy and phylogeny of reed warblers (genus *Acrocephalus*) based on mtDNA sequences and morphology. *J. Ornithol.* 138: 469–496.

Leisler, B., Ley, H.-W. & Winkler, H. 1989. Habitat, behaviour and morphology of *Acrocephalus* warblers: an integrated analysis. *Ornis Scand.* 20: 181–186.

Leivo, M. & Dernjatin, P. 2000. Booted Warbler. In: Kazakhstan - The Land of the Pallas's Sandgrouse. *Alula* 6: 53–54.

Lekagul, B. & Round, P. D. 1991. *A Guide to the Birds of Thailand*. Bangkok.

Lemaire, F. 1974. Le chant de la Rousserolle verderolle (*Acrocephalus palustris*): étendu du répertoire imitatif, construction rhythmique et musicalité. *Gerfaut* 68: 3–28.

Lemaire, F. 1975. Dialectical variations in the imitative song of the Marsh Warbler (*Acrocephalus palustris*) in western and eastern Belgium. *Gerfaut* 65: 95–106.

Lemaire, F. 1977. Mixed song, interspecific competition and hybridisation in Reed and Marsh Warblers. *Behaviour* 63: 215–240.

Leonard, P. M. & Beel, C. 1996. White-winged Warbler *Bradypterus carpalis* – new to Zambia. *Newsletter of the Zambian Orn. Soc.* 26: 139–140.

Leonard, P. & Beel, C. 1999. Two new resident birds in northern Zambia. *Bull. African Bird Club* 6: 56–57.

Lewington, I. 1988. The Welches Dam *Acrocephalus* warbler, *Birding World* 1: 180–181

Lewington, I., Alström, P. & Colston, P. 1991. *A field guide to the rare birds of Britain and Europe*. HarperCollins, London.

Lewis, A. 1993. Asian Stubtail *Urosphena squameiceps*: a new species for Nepal and the Indian subcontinent. *Forktail* 9: 155.

Lewis, I. 1996. The Aquatic Warbler in Dorset. *Dorset Birds* 1995: 145–149.

Lewthwaite, R. W. 1996. Forest birds of Southeast China: observations during 1984–1996. *Hong Kong Bird Report* 1995: 150–203.

Lewthwaite, R. W., Kilburn, E. M. S., Ming, M. & Hackett, J. A.

1998. *Report on a birding trip to Xinjiang, China, 7–26 June 1998.* Unpublished manuscript.

Leven, M. R. 1994. Yellow-bellied Bush Warbler in Hong Kong. *Hong Kong Bird Report* 1993: 212–214.

Lightbody, J. P. 1987. Female choice in Middendorff's Grasshopper-Warbler. *Auk* 104: 549–550.

Lindblom, K. 2008. Booted Warbler and Lanceolated Warbler in Finland. *Alula* 14(2): 84–90.

Lindholm, A. & Aalto, T. 2005. The calls of Sykes's and Booted Warblers. *Birding World* 18: 395–396.

Lindholm, A., Bensch, S., Dowsett-Lemaire, F., Forsten, A. & Kärkkäinen, H. 2007. Hybrid Marsh x Blyth's Reed Warbler with mixed song in Finland in June 2003. *Dutch Birding* 29: 223–231.

Lister, M. D. 1952. Notes on Blyth's Reed Warbler in India. *Brit. Birds* 45: 328–329.

Lloyd, P. 1998. Sex ratios in Seychelles Warblers. *Africa – Birds and birding* 3: 16.

Loippo, M. 2002. Birding sites on the eastern shore of Lake Ladoga. *Alula* 8(4): 140–146.

Long, R. 1961. Cetti's Warbler in the Channel Islands. *Brit. Birds* 54: 208.

Long, R. 1964. Exceptional longevity in Reed Warblers. *Brit. Birds* 57: 128–129.

Long, R. 1968. Cetti's Warblers in the Channel Islands. *Brit. Birds* 61: 174–175.

Long, R. 1971. Longevity in Reed Warblers. *Brit. Birds* 64: 462.

Long, R. 1975. Mortality of Reed Warblers in Jersey. *Ringing & Migration* 1: 28–32.

Long, R. C. & Benson, C. W. 1960. The River Warbler *Locustella fluviatilis* (Wolf) in Nyasaland. *Bull. Brit. Orn. Club* 80: 52.

van Loon, A. J. 1990. Siberian *Locustella* Warblers. *Dutch Birding* 12: 195–197.

van Loon, A. J. & Keijl, G. O. 2001. Blyth's Reed Warbler at Nieuwegein in June–July 1998. *Dutch Birding* 23: 83–85.

Loskot, V. M. 2002. On the type specimens of *Locustella ochotensis* (Middendorff, 1853) in the collection of the Zoological Institute, St. Petersburg (Aves: Sylviidae). *Zoosyst. Rossica* 11(1): 239–242.

Loskot, V. M. & Sokolov, E. P. 1993. Taxonomy of the mainland and insular Lanceolated Warblers, *Locustella lanceolata* (Temminck) (Aves: Sylviidae). *Zoosyst. Rossica* 2: 189–200.

Louette, M. 2004. *Oiseaux.* pp 91–196. In: Louette, M., Meirte, D. & Jacqué, R. (eds.). *La faune terrestre de l'archipel des Comores.* Musée Royal de l'Afrique centrale, Tervuren, Belgium.

Louette, M., Herremans, M., Bijnens, L. & Janssens, L. 1988. Taxonomy and evolution in the brush warblers *Nesillas* on the Comoro Islands. *Tauraco* 1: 110–129.

Lu, C. H. & Li, F. 1997. [New bird record for Heilongjiang – Japanese Swamp Warbler.] *Sichuan J. Zool.* 16: 104. (Chinese)

Ludlow, F. 1951. The birds of Kongbo and Pome, south-east Tibet. *Ibis* 93: 547–578.

Ludlow, F. & Kinnear, N. B. 1937. The birds of Bhutan and adjacent territories of Sikkim and Tibet. Part 2. *Ibis* Series 14, Vol. 1, Part 2: 249–293.

Luoto, H., Lindholm, A., Lindroos, T. & Rauste, A. 2002. Rare birds in Finland in 2000. *Alula* 8(1): 2–19.

Luschi, P. & del Seppia, C. 1996. Song-type function during territorial encounters in male Cetti's Warblers *Cettia cetti. Ibis* 138: 479–484.

Lynes, H. 1925. On the birds of northern and central Darfur, with notes on the west-central Kordofan and north Nuba provinces of British Sudan (Part IV). *Ibis* 68: 344–416.

Lysaght, A. M. 1959. Some eighteenth century bird paintings in the library of Sir Joseph Banks (1743–1820). *Bull. Brit. Mus. Nat. Hist.* Hist. ser. 1(6): 253–371.

Lysenkov, E. V., Spiridonov, S. N. & Lapshin, A. S. 2004. [Notes on the nesting biology of *Hippolais caligata* in Mordovia.] *Russian J. Ornithol.* Express issue 268: 702–705. (Russian)

Macdonald, J. D. 1948. Breeding of Olivaceous Warbler in the Sudan. *Bull. Brit. Orn. Club* 69: 17.

MacKinnon, J. & Phillipps, K. 1993. *A field guide to the birds of Borneo, Sumatra, Java and Bali.* Oxford University Press, Oxford.

Mackowicz, R. 1989. Breeding biology of the River Warbler (Wolf 1810) in north-eastern Poland. *Acta Zool. Crakov* 32: 331–437.

Maclean, I., Musina, J., Nalianya, N., Mahood, S., Martin, R. & Byuaruhanga, A. 2003. Systematics, distribution and vocalisations of Papyrus Yellow Warbler *Chloropeta gracilirostris. Bull. African Bird Club* 10: 94–100.

MacLeod, J. G. R. & Broekhuysen, G. J. 1951. The nest and eggs of the Victorin's Scrub-Warbler. *Ostrich* 22: 44.

MacLeod, J. G. R., Stanford, N. R. & Broekhuysen, G. J. 1958. Notes on the parental behaviour of the Victorin's Warbler *Bradypterus victorini* Sundevall. *Ostrich* 29: 71–73.

Madge, S. C. 1984. Mystery photographs 85: Gray's Grasshopper Warbler. *Brit. Birds* 77: 17–20.

Madge, S. C. 1987. Mystery photographs 126: Clamorous Reed Warbler. *Brit. Birds* 80: 280–282.

Madge, S. C. 1992. Identification of Moustached Warbler. *Birding World* 5: 299–303.

Mädlow, W. 1992. Ein Buschrohrsänger *Acrocephalus dumetorum* in Berlin. *Limicola* 6: 292–296.

Mambetzhumaev, A. M. 1993. [Breeding biology of the southern Booted Warbler (*Hippolais rama*) in the Lower Amu-Darya River]. *Russian J. Ornithol.* 2(1): 77–85. (Russian, English summary)

Mann, C. F. 1987. Notable bird observations from Brunei, Borneo. *Forktail* 3: 51–56.

Mann, C. F. 2008. *The Birds of Borneo: an annotated checklist.* British Ornithologists' Union, Checklist No. 23. BOU, Peterborough.

Manns, D. J. 1979. Cetti's Warbler displaying in open. *Brit. Birds* 72: 184.

Manson, A. J. 1985. Results of a ringing programme at Muruwati. Farm, Mazowe. *Honeyguide* 31: 203–211.

Manson, C. & Manson, A. 1976. Notes on ortstreue amongst Palaearctic warblers in Rhodesia. *Honeyguide* 86: 40–41.

Manzi, R., Pavan, G. & Frugis, S. 1988. Variation in the song of Cetti's Warbler (*Cettia cetti* Temm): A preliminary study. *Monit. Zool. Ital.* 22: 287–298.

Maragna, P. & Pesente, M. 1997. Complete moult confirmed in a Great Reed Warbler *Acrocephalus arundinaceus* population breeding in northern Italy. *Ringing & Migration* 18: 57–58.

Markitan, L. V. 2006. [Peculiarities of the territorial structure of many-species community of *Acrocephalus* spp. warblers in Eastern Priazovie (the Azov Sea region)]. Page 326. In: Kurochkin, E. N. (ed.). [*Ornithological studies in Northern Eurasia*]. Abstracts of XII Int. Orn. Conference of Northern Eurasia, Stavropol, 31 January – 5 February 2006. Stavropol University Press, Stavropol. (Russian)

van Marle, J. G. & Voous, K. H. 1988. *The birds of Sumatra.* British Ornithologists' Union, Checklist No. 10. BOU, Tring.

Marova, I. M., Valchuk, O. P., Kvartalynov, P. V. & Ivanitskij, V. V. 2005. On the taxonomic position and evolutionary interrelations of the Thick-billed Warbler, *Phragmaticola aedon* (based on ecological an ethological data). *Alauda* 73: 308.

Marsh, P. 1982. Grey-and-white juvenile Reed Warbler. *Brit. Birds* 75: 35–36.

Marshall, B. & Tulloch, R. J. 1973. Thick-billed Warbler in Shetland. *Scottish Birds* 7: 262–263.

Marshall, J. T. 1949. The endemic avifauna of Saipan, Tinian, Guam and Palau. *Condor* 51: 200–221.

Martin, R. & Martin, E. 1993. European Marsh Warbler in the southwestern Cape. *Promerops* 208: 12.

Martin, R., Martin, J., Martin, E., Neatherway, P., Neatherway, M, & Tyler, D. 1982. A note on the distribution of the Knysna Scrub-Warbler in the South Western Cape Province. *Bokmakierie* 34: 13.

Martins, R. P. 1989. Turkey Bird Report 1982–6. *Sandgrouse* 11: 1–41.

Martinez, I. 1984. [Complete moult of Great Reed Warbler *Acrocephalus a. arundinaceus* L. at the Ebro Delta.] *Bull. del Grup Català d'anellament* 3: 29–31. (Spanish)

Márton, K., Gergó, H. & Tibor, C. 2000. The postnuptial moult of Savi's Warbler (*Locustella luscinioides*). *Ornis Hungarica* 10: 99–110.

Masibalavu, V. T. & Dutson, G. 2006. *Important Bird Areas in Fiji: Conserving Fiji's natural heritage*. BirdLife International, Cambridge, UK.

Mather, J. R. & Burns, D. M. 1971. Grasshopper Warbler or Pallas's Grasshopper Warbler in Dorset? *Brit. Birds* 64: 197–198.

Matyukhin, A. V., Matyukhin, A. A. & Shevchenko, V. L. 1991. [New records of Paddyfield Warbler in the Ural'sk region.] *Mat.10 Vsesoyuz.orn. Konf.* (Vitebsk) Part. 2 Posters, Book 2: 64–65. *Navuka i tekhnika, Minsk.* (Russian)

Mauer, K. 1979. [Captures of Aquatic Warbler *Acrocephalus palustris* on Putten in 1970–73. *Dutch Birding* 1: 122. (Dutch, English summary)

Mayr, E. 1935. Birds collected during the Whitney South Sea Expedition. Part XXX. Descriptions of twenty-five new species and sub-species. *Amer. Mus. Novit.* 820: 1–6.

Mayr, E. 1936. Birds collected during the Whitney South Sea Expedition. Part XXXI. Descriptions of twenty-five species and sub-species. *Amer. Mus. Novit.* 828: 1–19.

Mayr, E. 1940. The origin and the history of the bird fauna of Polynesia. *Proc. 6th Pac. Sci. Congress* 4: 197–216.

Mayr, E. 1942. Birds collected during the Whitney South Sea Expedition. XLVIII. Notes on the Polynesian species of *Aplonis*. *Amer. Mus. Novit.* 1166.

Mayr, E. 1944. The birds of Timor and Sumba. *Bull. Amer. Mus. Nat. Hist.* 83(2): 123–194.

Mayr, E. 1948. Geographic variation in the Reed Warbler. *Emu* 47: 205–210.

Mayr, E. & Cottrell, G. W. 1986. *Checklist of Birds of the World*, Vol XI. Museum of Comparative Zoology, Cambridge, Mass.

Mayr, E. & Vuilleumier, F. 1983. New species of birds described from 1966 to 1975. *J. Ornithol.* 124: 217–232.

McAdams, D. G. 1994. Paddyfield Warbler in County Cork. *Irish Birds* 5: 192–195.

McAdams, D, & Jännes, H. 2000. Odd one out. *Birdwatch* 99: 26–30.

McCanch, N. 1975. Juvenile Grasshopper Warbler without tongue-spots. *Ringing & Migration* 1: 56.

McClure, H. E. 1974. *Migration and survival of the birds of Asia*. U. S. Army Medical Component, SEATO Medical Research Laboratory, Bangkok.

McClure, H. E. & Leelavit, P. 1972. *Birds banded in Asia during the MAPS Program, by locality, from 1963 through 1971.* Report No. FE-315-7. US Army Research and Development Group, Far East.

McKean, J. L. 1983. Some notes on the occurrence of the Great Reed Warbler *Acrocephalus arundinaceus* in the Northern Territory. *N. Territ. Nat.* 6: 3–8.

McKean, J. L. 1984. The occurrence in Australia of Gray's Grasshopper Warbler *Locustella fasciolata*. *The Australian Birdwatcher* 10 (5): 171–172.

Mead, C. J. 1965. The Sussex Cetti's Warbler and the value of fault-bars as a means for ageing birds. *Brit. Birds* 58: 227–228.

Mead, C. J. 1977. The wing-formulae of some live warblers from Portugal. *Ringing & Migration* 1: 178–183.

Mead, C. J. & Watmough, B. R. 1976. Suspended moult of Trans-Saharan migrants in Iberia. *Bird Study* 23: 187–196.

Meadows, B. S. 1999. The African Reed Warbler in mangroves at Yanbu al Sinaiyah. *Phoenix* 16: 18–19.

Medway, Lord, & Wells, D. R. 1976. *The Birds of the Malay Peninsula*. Vol. 5: Conclusion and Survey of Every Species. Witherby, London.

Meek, E. R. & Adam, R. G. 1997. Marsh Warblers breeding in Orkney: first Scottish breeding record. *Brit. Birds* 90: 230.

Meek, E. R. & Little, B. 1979. Paddyfield Warbler in Northumberland. *Brit. Birds* 72: 352–357.

Meek, E. R., Adam, R. G. & Hadasch, J. 1998. Marsh Warblers breeding in Orkney in 1993: a first for Scotland. *Scottish Birds* 19: 170–171.

Mees, G. F. 1971. Systematic and faunistic remarks on birds from Borneo and Java, with new records. *Zool. Meded. Leiden* 45(21): 225–244.

Mees, G. F. 1991. Bemerkungen über *Acrocephalus caffer* (Sparrman) in der Tahiti-Gruppe (Aves, Sylviidae). *Proc. Kon. Akad. v. Wetensch.* 94: 243–256.

Meeus, H. & Vermeyen, R. 1982. Song of Melodious Warbler. *Dutch Birding* 4: 59–60.

Meinertzhagen, R. 1930. *Nicoll's birds of Egypt* Vol. 1. Hugh Rees Ltd., London.

Meinertzhagen, R. 1948. The Birds of Ushant. *Ibis* 90: 553–567.

Meinertzhagen, R. 1950. The record of the Moustached Warbler breeding in Great Britain. *Bull. Brit. Orn. Club* 70: 54–55.

Meininger, P. L., Sorensen, U. G. & Atta, G. A. M. 1986. Breeding birds on the lakes in the Nile Delta, Egypt. *Sandgrouse* 7: 1–20.

Meise, W. 1938. Ueber *Locustella ochotensis* und *certhiola*. *Orn. Monatsber.* 46: 168–173.

Melling, T. 2006. Time to get rid of the Moustache: a review of British records of Moustached Warbler. *Brit. Birds* 99: 465–478.

Mellor, M. 1981. Tail-cocking by Sedge Warbler. *Brit. Birds* 74: 444.

Melville, D. S. 1987. Three species new to Hong Kong and (eastern) China: Blyth's Reed Warbler. *Hong Kong Bird Report.* 1986: 58–68.

Melville, D. S. 1988. Does the Great Reed Warbler *Acrocephalus arundinaceus orientalis* breed in Hong Kong? *Hong Kong Bird Report* 1987: 76–84.

Melville, D. S. 1990. Yellow-bellied Bush Warbler: a species new to Hong Kong. *Hong Kong Bird Report* 1989: 96–98.

Melville, D. S. 1991. Notes on birds of Shuangtaizihekou National Nature reserve, Liaoning Province, China. *Hong Kong Bird Report* 1990: 167–171.

Melville, D. S. & Leven, M. R. 1999. Report on bird ringing in Hong Kong in 1997. *Hong Kong Bird Report* 1997: 100–113.

Melville, D. S. & Round, P. D. 1984. Weights and gonad condition of some Thai birds. *Bull. Brit. Orn. Club* 104: 127–138.

Melville, D. S., Galsworthy, A. C. & Leader, P. J. 1991. Pale-footed Bush Warbler: a species new to Hong Kong. *Hong Kong Bird Report* 1990: 111–116.

Merom, K., McCleery, R. & Yom-Tov, Y. 1999. Age-related changes in wing length and body mass in the Reed Warbler *Acrocephalus scirpaceus* and Clamorous Reed Warbler *A. stentoreus*. *Bird Study* 46: 249–255.

Merom, K., Quader, S. & Yom-Tov, Y. 2005. The winter fattening model: a test at low latitude using the Clamorous Reed Warbler. *Ibis* 147: 680–687.

Mester, H. 1967. Über den Zug des Seggenrohrsängers. *Anthus* 4: 1–6.

Mey, E. 1997. Records of Blunt-winged Warbler *Acrocephalus concinens* in central Vietnam. *Forktail* 12: 166–167.

Meyer de Schauensee. R. 1984. *The Birds of China*. Smithsonian Institution Press, Washington.

Millington, R. 1998. *Locustella* warblers in autumn 1998. *Birding World* 11: 387–389.

Milder, S. L. & Schreiber, R. W. 1982. Notes on the nesting behavior of *Acrocephalus aequinoctialis*. *Bull. Brit. Orn. Club* 102: 20–22.

Milder, S. L. & Schreiber, R. W. 1989. The vocalisations of the Christmas Island Warbler *Acrocephalus aequinoctialis*, an island endemic. *Ibis* 131: 99–111.

Milne-Edwards, A. & Crandidier, A. 1881. *Historie Physique, Naturelle et Politique de Madagascar*, Vol. 12. Historie Naturelle des Oiseaux 1. Impremerie Nationale, Paris.

Milon, P., Petter, J. J. & Randrianasolo, G. 1973. *Faune de Madagascar*. Vol. 35. Oiseaux. ORSROM & CNRS, Tananarive & Paris.

Milsom, T. P. 1982. Edge effect in breeding Reed Warblers in North Humberside. *Bird Study* 29: 167–168.

Mitchell, A. 1998. Lanceolated Warbler – first for Suffolk. *Suffolk Birds* 47: 148–149.

Mobakken, G. 2000. Marsh Warblers breeding on Utsira. *Brit. Birds* 93: 279.

Monnet, C., Thibault, J. & Varney, A. 1993. Stability and changes during the twentieth century in the breeding landbirds of Tahiti (Polynesia). *Bird Conserv. Internatn* 3: 261–280.

Moreau, R. E. 1972. *The Palaearctic-African Bird Migration Systems.* Academic Press, London.

Morel, G. & Roux, F. 1966. Les migrateurs palearctiques au Senegal. *La Terre et La Vie* 113: 143–176.

Morel, M.-Y. 1987. *Acrocephalus scirpaceus* et *Acrocephalus beaticatus* dans la region de Richard-Toll (Sénegal). *Malimbus* 9: 47–55.

Morgan, J. 1998. Wing formula of Reed Warblers *Acrocephalus scirpaceus* from Israel – a cautionary note. *Ringing & Migration* 19: 57–58.

Morin, M. S., Conant, S. & Conant, P. 1997. Laysan and Nihoa Millerbird (*Acrocephalus familiaris*). No. 302. In: Poole, A. & Gill, F. (eds.). *The birds of North America.* Academy of Natural Sciences, Philadephia and the American Ornithologists' Union, Washington, D.C.

Morioka, H. & Shigeta, Y. 1993. Generic allocation of the Japanese Marsh Warbler *Megalurus pryeri* (Aves: Sylvidae). *Bull. Nat. Sci. Mus. Tokyo*, Ser. A, 19(1): 37–43.

Morris, P. & Hawkins, F. 1998. *Birds of Madagascar. A photographic guide.* Pica Press, Sussex.

Mosher, S. M. & Fancy, S. G. 2002. Description of nests, eggs, and nestlings of the endangered Nightingale Reed-Warbler on Saipan, Micronesia. *Wilson Bull.* 114: 1–10.

Moskvitin, S. S. & Anan'ina, T. A. 1990. [Behavioural rhythm and time budget of Blyth's Reed Warbler (*Acrocephalus dumetorum*) when feeding nestlings.] *Sovremennaya ornitologiya* 1990: 172–178. (Russian)

Mountford, G. R. 1951. Studies of some species rarely photographed XXX: the Great Reed Warbler. *Brit. Birds* 44: 195–197.

Murphy, R. C. & Mathews, G. M. 1928. Birds collected during the Whitney South Sea Expedition. V. *Amer. Mus. Novit.* 337: 9–18.

Murphy, R. C. & Mathews, G. M. 1929. Birds collected during the Whitney South Sea Expedition. VI. *Amer. Mus. Novit.* 350: 1–21.

Murray, A. & Osborn, K. 1999. Lanceolated Warbler in Scotland. *Birding Scotland* 2: 100–101.

Müller, H. E. J. 1981. Altersbestimmung, Mauser und einige biometrische Daten von Rohrschwirlen. *Der Falke* 28: 258–265.

Mwambu, P. 1999. Some aspects of the conservation biology of Grauer's Rush (Swamp) Warbler (*Bradypterus graueri* Neumann, 1908). MSc. Thesis, Makerere University, Kampala, Uganda.

Nadler, T. & Ihle, U. 1988. Beobachtungen am Feldrohrsänger *Acrocephalus agricola* in Bulgarien. *Limicola* 2: 205–217.

Nadtochiy, A. S. & Kushnarev, I. O. 1994. [Nesting ecology of *Acrocephalus* Warblers along the middle reaches of the Severskiy Donet River.] *Kharkov* 2: 47–49. (Russian)

Nagata, H. 1986. Female choice in Middendorff's Grasshopper Warbler (*Locustella ochotensis*) *Auk* 103: 694–700.

Nagata, H. 1993. The structure of a local population and dispersal pattern in the Styan's Grasshopper Warbler, *Locustella pleskei. Ecol. Research* 8: 1–9.

Nagata, H. 1997. [Present status of Japanese Marsh Warbler (*Megalurus pryeri*) and its conservation.] *J. Yamashina Inst. Ornithol.* 29: 27–42. (Japanese, English summary)

Nagata, H. & Yoshida, H. 1997. Some notes on the wintering ecology of Japanese Marsh Warblers, *Megalurus pryeri*, at two sites around Lake Kasumigaura. *J. Yamashina Inst. Ornithol.* 29: 50–56.

Nagata, H., Ueda, K. & Kominami, Y. 2003. [The population growth of the Japanese Marsh Warbler along the Lower Tone River.] *Strix* 21: 15–28. (Japanese, English summary)

Nakamichi, R. & Ueda, K. 2003. [Recent status and habitat preference of the Japanese Marsh Warbler at Hotoke-numa marsh, northern Honshu, Japan.] *Strix* 21: 5–14. (Japanese, English summary)

Nakamura, T. & Ishizawa, J. 1965. [Studies on the migration of *Locustella fasciolata*. II. Duration of migration, flock formation and physiology.] *Misc. Rep. Yamashina Inst. Ornithol.* 4: 217–219. (Japanese, English summary)

Nankinov, D. N. 1992. Ringing of *Acrocephalus* reed warblers in Bulgaria: a preliminary report. *Ring* 14: 101–109.

Nankinov, D. N. 2000. Range expansion and current breeding distribution of River Warbler *Locustella fluviatilis* in Bulgaria. *Sandgrouse* 22: 50–54.

Nasirwa, O. & Njoroge, P. 1997. *Papyrus-endemic birds in the fringing swamps of Lake Victoria, western Kenya.* Ornithology 28. Research Reports of the Centre for Biodiversity, National Museums of Kenya.

Naumov, R. L. & Kislenko, G. S. 1965. [The nesting of the Lanceolated and Pallas's Grasshopper Warblers in the Krasnoyarsk region.] *Ornitologiya* 7: 83–86. (Russian)

de Naurois, R. 1985. Sur la reproduction de la Rousserolle *Calamocichla rufescens* ssp dans la region des Niayes (Senegasl Nord-Occidental). *Alauda* 53: 182–185.

Naylor, A. K. & Green, R. E. 1976. Timing of fledging and passage of Reed Warblers. *Wicken Fen Group Report* 8: 15–18.

Nazarenko, A. A., Surmach, S. G. & Morozova, E. P. 2003. [Further nest locatings of the Spotted Bush Warbler *Tribura (thoracica) davidi* in Ussuriland.] *Russian J. Ornithol.* Vol. 12: 1241–1245. (Russian)

Nazarov, Y. N. & Shibaev, Y. V. 1983. [On the breeding biology and taxonomic status of the Pleskei's Grasshopper Warbler *L. pleskei* Tacz., new for the USSR.] *Trudy Zool. Inst. Leningrad.* 116: 72–78. (Russian)

Nechaev, V. A. 1969. [*Birds of the Kuril Islands.*] Leningrad: Akademia Nauk SSSR, Sibirskoe Otdelenie. (Russian).

Nechaev, V. A. 1979. [Middendorff's Grasshopper Warbler *Locustella ochotensis* on the islands of Sakhalin and Moneron (biology, systematics).] In: [*Biology of birds in the southern Far East of the USSR.*] Vladivostok. (Russian)

Nechaev, V. A. & Gorchakov, G. A. 1997. [Breeding by *Acrocephalus agricola tangorum* on the coast of the Sea of Japan.] *Russian J. Ornithol.* Express issue 23: 7–9. (Russian)

Neal, G. 1996. *The birds of Spurn, a comprehensive checklist.* Spurn Bird Observatory.

Neto, J. M. 2004. *Breeding Ecology, Moult and Migration of Savi's Warblers* Locustella luscinioides*, in Portugal.* DPhil thesis, University of Oxford.

Neto, J. M. & Gosler, A. G. 2006. Post-juvenile and post-breeding moult of Savi's Warblers *Locustella luscinioides* in Portugal. *Ibis* 148: 39–49.

Neto, J. M., Newton, J., Gosler, A. G. & Perrins, C. M. 2006. Using stable isotope analysis to determine the winter moult extent in migratory birds: the complex moult of Savi's Warbler *Locustella luscinioides. J. Avian Biol.* 37: 117–124.

Neufeldt, I. 1967. Studies of less familiar birds 144. Thick-billed Warbler. *Brit. Birds* 60: 239–243.

Neufeldt, I. 1970. Biology of the Short-tailed and Short-winged Bush Warblers as evidence of their generic independence. *Abs. XV Congr. Inter. Orn.* The Hague: 164–165.

Neufeldt, I. 1971. Der Kurzflügelsänger, *Horeites diphone* (Kittlitz). *Der Falke* 18: 364–375.

Neufeldt, I. A. & Nechaev, V. A. 1978. [Gray's Grasshopper Warbler *Locustella fasciolata* (Gray)]. *Trudy Zool. Inst. Akad. Nauk SSSR*, 76: 61–93. (Russian)

Neufeldt, I. A. & Netschajew, W. A. 1977. Vergleichencle untersuchungen an kontinentalen und insulären Reisenschwirler, *Locustella fasciolata* (Gray). *Mitt. Zool. Mus. Berlin* 53 (Suppl.) 1: 91–116.

Newall, R. G. 1989. '*Locustella*' locomotion. *Brit. Birds* 82: 331.

Newton, I. 1995. Relationship between breeding and wintering ranges in Palaearctic-African migrants. *Ibis* 137: 241–249.

Nicoll, M. J. 1904. Ornithological journal of a voyage around the world in the 'Valhalla'. *Ibis* (8)4: 32–67.

Nicolson, E. M. & Ferguson-Lees, I. J. 1962. 'The Hastings Rarities' *Brit. Birds* 55: 229–384.

Nielsen, B. & Bensch, S. 1995. Post–fledging movements of juvenile Reed Warblers *Acrocephalus scirpaceus* and Sedge Warblers *Acrocephalus schoenobaenus. Ornis Svecica* 5: 125–131.

Nightingale, T. & Hill, M. 1993. *Birds of Bahrain.* Immel, London.

Nikolaus, G. 1979. The first record of the Basra Reed Warbler in the Sudan. *Scopus* 3: 103–104.

Nikolaus, G. 1982. Further notes on some birds new to south Sudan. *Scopus* 6: 1–4.

Nikolaus, G. 1983. An important ringing site on the Sudan Red Sea coast, *Scopus* 7: 15–18.

Nikolaus, G. 1984. Further notes on birds new or little known in the Sudan. *Scopus* 8: 38–42.

Nikolaus, G. 1987. Distribution Atlas of Sudan's Birds with notes on habitat and status. *Bonner Zoologische Monographien* 25: 1–322.

Nikolaus, G. 1989. Birds of South Sudan. *Scopus*. Special Supplement No. 3: 1–24.

Nikolaus, G. 1990. Shrikes Laniidae feeding on Marsh Warblers *Acrocephalus palustris* during migration. *Scopus* 14: 26–28.

Nikolaus, G. 1993. Second Marsh Warbler Study (in Oman). *Oman Bird News* 14: 17–18.

Nikolaus, G. & Pearson, D. J. 1982. Autumn passage of Marsh Warblers *Acrocephalus palustris* and Sprossers *Luscinia luscinia* on the Sudan Red Sea coast. *Scopus* 6: 17–19.

Nikolaus, G. & Pearson, D. J. 1991. The seasonal separation of primary and secondary moult in Palaearctic passerine migrants on the Sudan coast. *Ringing & Migration* 12: 46–47.

Nimnuan, S. & Round, P. D. 2008. Letter to the Editor. *BirdingASIA* 9: 10.

Nisbet, I. C. T. 1960. Weights of birds caught at night at a Malayan radio tower. *Ibis* 110: 352–354.

Nisbet, I. C. T. 1967. Migration and moult in Pallas's Grasshopper Warbler. *Bird Study* 14: 96–103.

Nisbet, I. C. T. & Medway, Lord. 1972. Dispersion, population ecology and migration of Eastern Great Reed Warblers *Acrocephalus orientalis*, wintering in Malaysia. *Ibis* 114: 451–494.

Nishide, T. 1975. Survey of Japanese Marsh Warbler *Melalurus pryeri* in Hachiro-gata reclaimed land, Akita Pref. *J. Yamashina Inst. Ornithol.* 7: 681–696.

Nishide, T. 1993. [The ecology of Japanese Marsh Warblers (*Megalarus pryeri*) in Hachiro-gata reclaimed land: Population dynamics and the factors of the dynamics.] *Strix* 12: 41–52. (Japanese, English summary)

Nissardi, S., Masala, M. A., Zucca, C. & Murgia, P. F. 1995. [First observation for Italy of Paddyfield Warbler *Acrocephalus agricola* and wintering in Stagno Molentargius (CA).] *Avocetta* 19: 93. (Italian)

Normaja, J. 1994. Plumage variation in River Warblers. *Birding World* 7: 192–195.

Normaja, J. 2000. Melodious Warbler. *Alula* 6: 62–65.

Norris, A. S. 1977. Unusual song of Grasshopper Warbler. *Brit. Birds* 70: 502–503.

Ogilvie, M. & the Rare Breeding Birds Panel. 2002. Rare breeding birds in the United Kingdom in 2000. *Brit. Birds* 95: 542–582.

Ogilvie-Grant, W. R. 1913. On a small collection of birds from Henderson Island, South Pacific. *Ibis* (10) 1: 343–350.

Ogilvie-Grant, W. R. & Whitehead, J. 1895. On the birds of the Philippine islands. Part V. The Highlands of the Province of Lepanto, North Luzon. *Ibis* (7) 1: 433–472.

Ohara, H. 1985. A helper at the nest of the Short-tailed Bush Warbler *Cettia squamiceps*. *J. Yamashina Inst. Ornith.* 17: 67–73.

Ohara, H. & Yamagishi, S. 1984. The first record of helping at the nest in the Short-tailed Bush Warbler *Cettia squamiceps*. *Tori* 33: 39–41.

Olsen, K. M. 1991. Sjældne fugle i Danmark og Grønland i 1989. *Dan Ornithol. Foren Tidsskr.* 85: 20–34.

Olsson, U., Alström, P., Gelang, M., Ericson, P. G. P. & Sunberg, P. 2006. Phylogeography of Indonesian and Sino-Himalayan region bush-warblers (*Cettia*, Aves). *Molecular Phylogenetics and Evolution* 41: 556–565.

Opaev, A. S., Marova, I. M. & Ivanitskiy, V. V. 2006. [Divergence of the social systems of Great Reed Warbler *Acrocephalus a.arundinaceus*, Eastern *A. a. orientalis* and Turkestanian *A.stentoreus* Warblers.] Page 401. In: Kurochkin, E. N. (ed.). [*Ornithological studies in Northern Eurasia*]. Abstracts of XII Int. Orn. Conference of Northern Eurasia, Stavropol, 31 January – 5 February 2006. Stavropol University Press, Stavropol. (Russian)

Oreel, G. J. 1981. Tail-cocking by Moustached Warblers. *Brit. Birds* 74: 446.

Orenstein, R. I. & Pratt, H. D. 1983. The relationships and evolution of the Southwest Pacific genera *Vitia* and *Psamathia* (Sylviinae). *Wilson Bull.* 95 (2): 184–198.

Ormerod, S. J. 1990. Time of passage, habitat use and mass change of *Acrocephalus* warblers in a South Wales reedswamp. *Ringing & Migration* 11: 1–11.

Orr, B. & Scott, C. 1998. Melodious Warblers in Scotland. *Birding Scotland* 1: 127–129.

Osborn, K. 1987. Mottling on upperparts of a Paddyfield Warbler. *Brit. Birds* 80: 634–635.

Osborn, K. 1993. The Shetland *Hippolais* warbler. *Birding World* 6: 437–438.

Osborn, K. & Donald, C. 1995. Blyth's Reed Warbler identification. *Birding World* 8: 77.

Osborn, K., Reid, J. & Reeves, S. 1998. Pallas's Grasshopper Warblers on Shetland in autumn 1997. *Birding Scotland* 1: 14–17.

Osieck, E. 1979. [Capture of Melodious Warbler *Hippolais polyglotta* in the Netherlands.] *Dutch Birding* 1: 73–74. (Dutch, English summary)

Osieck, E. 1981. Observations of Melodious Warbler in 1960 and 1968 wrongly accepted. *Dutch Birding* 3: 23–25.

Osmaston, B. B. 1926. Birds nesting in the Dras and Sura Valleys. *J. Bombay Nat. Hist. Soc.* 31: 186–196.

Osmaston, B. B. 1930. A tour in further Kashmir. *J. Bombay Nat. Hist. Soc.* 36: 108–134.

Osmaston, B. B. 1932. Some Andaman Birds. *J. Bombay Nat. Hist. Soc.* 35: 891–893.

Ottosson, U., Bensch, S., Svensson, L. & Waldenström, J. 2005. Differentiation and phylogeny of the Olivaceous Warbler *Hippolais pallida* species complex. *J. Ornithol.* 146: 127–136.

Oudebeek, W. H. P. 1988. [Paddyfield Warbler at Zuidland in September 1987.] *Dutch Birding* 11: 29–30. (Dutch, English summary)

Owen, R. P. 1977. A checklist of the birds of Micronesia. *Micronesica* 13: 65–81.

Ozawa, K. 1964. [The grasshopper-warblers, *Locustella lanceolata* and *L. ochotensis*, obtained at sea in the central Japan Sea.] *Misc. Rep. Yamashina Inst. Ornithol.* 21: 55–57. (Japanese, English summary)

Page, D. 2001. Separating *Acrocephalus* and *Hippolais* Warblers. *Brit. Birds* 94: 44.

Page, D. & Greaves, P. K. 1983. Identification of Pallas's Grasshopper Warbler. *Brit. Birds* 76: 88.

Pain, D. J., Green, R. E., Giessing, B., Kozulin, A., Poluda, A., Ottosson, U., Flade, M. & Hilton, G. M. 2004. Using stable isotopes to investigate migratory connectivity of the globally threatened Aquatic Warbler *Acrocephalus paludicola*. *Oecologia* 138: 168–174.

Palfrey, J. 1989. Great Reed Warblers feeding from spiders' webs. *Brit. Birds* 82: 373.

Paludan, K. 1959. On the birds of Afghanistan. *Vidensk. Medd. Dansk Naturh. For.* 122: 1–332.

Panov, E. N. 1989. *Gibridizatsiya I etologicheskaya izolyatsiya u ptits.* Moscow.

Park, D. S., Kim, S. I. & Park, S. R. 1996. A song transition the geographic populations of Bush Warbler (*Cettia diphone*). *Korean J. Ecol.* 19 (2): 141–149.

Park, J. G. 2008. Taxonomic Study on Japanese Bush Warblers (*Cettia diphone*) in South Korea. *Korea National Parks Service: 2008 annual report on migratory researches*: 203–227.

Park, S. R. & Park, D. S. 2000. Song type for intrasexual interaction in the Bush warbler. *Auk* 117 (1): 228–232.

Parker, S. A. 1962. A new name for *Bradypterus barratti major* (Roberts). *Bull. Brit. Orn. Club* 82: 122.

Parker, S. A. & Harrison, C. J. O. 1963. The validity of the genus *Lusciniola* Gray. *Bull. Brit. Orn. Club* 83: 65–69.

Parkin, D. T., Collinson, M., Helbig, A. J., Knox, A. G., Sangster, G. & Svensson, L. 2004. Species Limits in *Acrocephalus* and *Hippolais* warblers from the Western Palearctic. *Brit. Birds* 97: 276–299.

Parmenter, T. & Byers, C. 1991. *A Guide to the Warblers of the Western Palearctic.* Bruce Coleman Books, Uxbridge.

Pattenden, B. 1976. The origin of British Aquatic Warblers. *Brit. Birds* 69: 228–229.

Pattenden, B. 1989. The Aquatic Warbler in Cornwall. *Cornwall Bird Report* 1988: 132–134.

Patterson, R. M. 1991. RAOU Records Appraisal Committee Opinions and Case Summaries 1988–1991. *RAOU Report No. 80.* RAOU, Melbourne.

Paz, U. 1987. *The birds of Israel.* Christopher Helm, London.

Peach, W. J., Baillie, S. R. & Underhill, L. 1991. Survival of British Sedge Warblers *Acrocephalus schoenobaenus* in relation to west African rainfall. *Ibis* 133: 300–305.

Pearson, D. J. 1971. Weights of some Palaearctic migrants in southern Uganda. *Ibis* 113: 173–184.

Pearson, D. J. 1972. The wintering and migration of Palearctic passerines at Kampala, southern Uganda. *Ibis* 114: 43–60.

Pearson, D. J. 1973. Moult of some Palaearctic warblers wintering in Uganda. *Bird Study* 20: 24–36.

Pearson, D. J. 1975. The timing of complete moult in the Great Reed Warbler *Acrocephalus arundinaceus*. *Ibis* 117: 506–509.

Pearson, D. J. 1980. Northward spring passage of Palaearctic passerines across Tsavo. *Scopus* 4: 25–28.

Pearson, D. J. 1981. Identification of first-winter Marsh and Reed Warblers. *Brit. Birds* 74: 445–446.

Pearson, D. J. 1982. The migration and wintering of Palaearctic *Acrocephalus* warblers in Kenya and Uganda. *Scopus* 6: 49–59.

Pearson, D. J. 1989. The separation of Reed Warblers *Acrocephalus scirpaceus* and Marsh Warblers *A. palustris* in eastern Africa. *Scopus* 13: 81–89.

Pearson, D. J. 1990. Palearctic passerine migrants in Kenya and Uganda: temporal and spatial patterns of their movements. In: Gwinner, E. (ed.). *Bird Migration*: 44–59. Berlin: Springer-Verlag.

Pearson, D. J. 1992. Northward passage of Palearctic songbirds through Kenya. *Proc. Pan-African Ornithol. Congr.* 7: 113–124.

Pearson, D. J. & Backhurst, G. C. 1976. The southward migration of Palaearctic birds over Ngulia, Kenya. *Ibis* 118: 78–105.

Pearson, D. J. & Backhurst, G. C. 1983. Moult in the River Warbler *Locustella fluviatilis*. *Ringing & Migration* 4: 227–230.

Pearson, D. J. & Backhurst, G. C. 1988. Characters and taxonomic position of Basra Reed Warbler. *Brit. Birds* 81: 171–178.

Pearson, D. J. & Jobson, G. J. 1980. River Warblers in song in Kenya. *Scopus* 3: 59–60.

Pearson, D. J., Ash, J. S. & Bensch, S. 2004. The identity of some *Hippolais* specimens from Eritrea and the United Arab Emirates examined by mtDNA analysis: a record of Sykes's Warbler *H. rama* in Africa. *Ibis* 146: 683–684.

Pearson, D. J., Backhurst, G. C. & Backhurst, D. E. G. 1979. Spring weights and passage of Sedge Warblers *Acrocephalus schoenobaenus* in central Kenya. *Ibis* 121: 8–19.

Pearson, D. J., Britton, P. L. & Britton, H. A. 1978. Substantial wintering populations of Basra Reed Warbler *Acrocephalus griseldis* in eastern Kenya. *Scopus* 2: 33–35.

Pearson, D. J., Finch, B. W. & Backhurst, D. E. G. 1988. A second Savi's Warbler *Locustella luscinioides* at Ngulia. *Scopus* 11: 94.

Pearson, D. J., Jackson, C. H. & Backhurst, G. C. 1998. Melodious Warbler *Hippolais polyglotta* at Ngulia, Kenya – first record for East Africa. *Scopus* 20: 43–45.

Pearson, D. J., Kennerley, P. R. & Bensch, S. 2008. A second museum specimen of Large-billed Reed Warbler *Acrocephalus orinus*. *Bull. Brit. Orn. Club.* 128(2): 136–138.

Pearson, D. J., Nikolaus, G. & Ash, J. S. 1988. The southward migration of Palaearctic passerines through northeast and east tropical Africa: A review. *Proc. Pan-African Orn. Congr.* 6: 243–262.

Pearson, D. J., Small, B. J. & Kennerley, P. R. 2002. Eurasian Reed Warbler: the characters and variation associated with the Asian form *fuscus*. *Brit. Birds* 95: 42–61.

Peiró, I. G. 1995. Patterns of abundance, body-mass dynamics and habitat use of the Reed Warbler *Acrocephalus scirpaceus* in two reed-beds of south-eastern Spain. *Ringing & Migration* 16: 100–108.

Peiró, I. G. 2003. Intraspecific variation in the wing shape of the long-distance migrant Reed Warbler *Acrocephalus scirpaceus*:

effects of age and distance of migration. *Ardeola* 50(1): 31–37.

Pennington, M. 1998. Blyth's Reed Warbler on Unst, 16th September – 1st October, and summary of previous Scottish records. *Birding Scotland* 1: 7–13.

Penny, M. 1982. *The Birds of Seychelles and outlying Islands.* Collins, London.

Pepler, G. R. M. 1976. Autumn passage of Sedge Warblers at Radipole. *Radipole* 2: 25–33.

Pepler, G. R. M. & Pepler, P. A. 1976. Sedge Warblers and Reed Warblers at Radipole in 1972. *Radipole* 1: 11–29.

Pereira, S. L. & Baker, A. J. 2006. A molecular timescale for galli-form birds accounting for uncertainty in time estimates and heterogeneity of rates of DNA substitutions across lineages and sites. *Molecular Phylogenetics and Evolution* 38, 499–509.

Perlman, Y. & Geffen, A. 2007. Basra Reed Warbler *Acrocephalus griseldis* in the Hula Valley, Israel, in 2006. *Sandgrouse* 29(2): 210–213.

Pettitt, E. E. 1919. Evidence towards double-broodedness of the Reed Warbler. *Brit. Birds* 12: 236–237.

Pettitt, R. G. 1960. Olivaceous Warbler in Co. Donegal. *Brit. Birds* 53: 311–312.

Phillips, A. R. 1968. *Cettia montana* versus *C. fortipes* (Aves: Sylviinae). *J. Bombay Nat. Hist. Soc.* 65: 223–224.

Phillips, I. 1998. Icterine Warblers on the East Coast in autumn 1997. *Birding Scotland* 1: 20–21.

Piechocki, R. & Bolod, A. 1972. Beiträge zur avifauna der Mongolei. Teil II. Passeriformes. *Mitt. Zool. Mus. Berlin* 48: 1–108.

Piechocki, R., Stubbe, M., Uhlenhaut, K. & Sumjaa, D. 1982. Beiträge zur avifauna der Mongolei. *Mitt. Zool. Mus. Berlin* 58, Suppl. Ann. Orn. 6: 3–53.

Pikulski, A. 1986. Breeding biology and ecology of Savi's Warbler *Locustella luscinioides* at Milicz fishponds. *Ptaki Slaska* 4: 2–39.

Pilastro, A., Macchio, S., Massi, A., Montemaggiori, A. & Spina, F. 1998. Spring migratory routes of eight trans-Saharan passerines through the central and western Mediterranean; results from a network of insular and coastal sites. *Ibis* 140: 591–598.

Pinilla, J. 2001. How does the extent of a partial moult vary? Some data for Melodious Warblers *Hippolais polyglotta* in central Iberia. *Ardeola* 48(1): 81–84.

Pitman, C. R. S. 1956. Some notes on Fox's Swamp Warbler *Calamocichla rufescens foxi* (Sclater). *Bull. Brit. Orn. Club* 76: 153–155.

Pitt, R. G. 1967. Savi's Warblers breeding in Kent. *Brit. Birds* 60: 349–355.

Pollo, R. 1992. [Nesting of the Sedge Warbler, *Acrocephalus schoenobaenus*, at Brusà-Vallette Marshes, Verona, N. Italy.] *Riv. Ital. Ornithol.* 62: 17–21. (Italian, English summary)

Pollock, C. M., O'Halloran, J., O'Mahony, B. & Smiddy, P. 1994. A Paddyfield Warbler off the south Irish coast. *Irish Birds* 5: 195–197.

Poluda, A. M., Tsukanova, S. V., Baev, V. A. & Zhmud, M. E. 1995. [Olivaceous Warbler in the 'Danube Floods' Nature reserve]. *Vestnik zoologii* 5/6: 85–86. (Russian)

duPont, J. E. 1971. *Philippine Birds.* Delaware Museum of Natural History, Greenville.

duPont, J. E. 1976. *South Pacific Birds.* Monograph Series No. 3. Delaware Museum of Natural History, Greenville.

Poot, M., Engelen, F. & van der Winden, J. 1999. Een gemengd broedgeval van Struikrietzanger *Acrocephalus dumetorum* en Bosrietzanger *A. palustris* bij Utrecht in voorjaar 1998. *Limosa* 72: 151–157.

Popel'nyukh, V. V. 2000. [Remarks on expansion of the range of *Acrocephalus agricola* and its appearance on the Lake Ladoga.] *Russian J. Ornithol.* Express issue 96: 18–20. (Russian)

Portenko, L. A. 1960. [*Birds of the USSR.*] Academy of Sciences, Moscow. (Russian)

Porter, R. F. 1983. Identification pitfalls and assessment problems: Aquatic Warbler. *Brit. Birds* 76: 342–346.

Pring, C. J. 1939. Abnormal nest-building of Reed-Warbler. *Brit. Birds* 32: 44.

Pratley, P. 1984. River Warbler in Norfolk. *Brit. Birds* 77: 213–214.

Pratt, H. D., Bruner, B. L. & Berrett, D. G. 1987. *A Field Guide to the Birds of Hawaii and the Tropical Pacific*. Princeton University Press, Princeton, New Jersey.

Price, T. 2008. *Speciation in birds*. Roberts and Company Publishers, Greenwood Village, Colorado.

Prigogine, A. 1980. *Bradypterus alfredi kungwensis* au Zaïre. *Gerfaut* 70: 279–280.

Pringle, J. S. 1977. Breeding of the Knysna Scrub Warbler. *Ostrich* 48: 112–114.

Procházka, P., Hobson, K. A., Karcza, Z. & Kralj, J. 2008. Birds of a feather winter together: migratory connectivity in the Reed Warbler *Acrocephalus scirpaceus*. *J. Ornithol.* 149(2): 141–150.

Proud, D. 1958. Bird Notes from Nepal. *J. Bombay Nat. Hist. Soc.* 55: 345–350.

Prokofieva, I. V. 2004. [Behaviour of *Acrocephalus schoenobaenus* while feeding nestlings and characteristics of food provided.] *Russian J. Ornithol.* Express issue 260: 402–406. (Russian)

Prokofieva, I. V. 2004. [Peculiarities of feeding and behaviour of *Acrocephalus dumetorum* when feeding nestlings.] *Russian J. Ornithol.* Express issue 266: 624–628. (Russian)

Prŷs-Jones, R. P. 1979. The ecology and conservation of the Aldabra Brush Warbler *Nesillas aldabranus*. *Phil. Trans. Roy. Soc. London (Ser. B)* 286: 211–224.

Ptushenko, E. S. 1954. [Family *Sylviidae* In: *Birds of the Soviet Union.*] Vol 6: 142–330. (Russian)

Pyman, G. A. 1966. Olivaceous Warbler in Dorset. *Brit. Birds* 59: 197–198.

Qiao, Y.-L., Liu, Y., Guo, D.-S., Zeng, X.-Q. & Zhang, E. 2006. First Chinese breeding record of Pleske's Warbler *Locustella pleskei*, from a small island off Qingdao, Shandong province. *BirdingAsia* 6: 81–82.

Quayle, E. H. 1904. Copie dactlyographiée du Journal tenu pendant la Whitney South Sea Expedition, 1920–1923. Déposée à l'American Musuem of Natural History, New York. Unpublished MS.

Radford, A. P. 1982. Reed Warbler singing at Magpie and Cuckoo. *Brit. Birds* 75: 383–384.

Raherilalao, M. J. & Goodman, S. M. 2005. Modèles d'endémisme des oiseaux forestieres des hautes terres de Madagascar. *Rev Ecol (Terre Vie)* 60: 355–368.

Raijmakes, J. M. H. 1995. Record of a European Reed Warbler at Vanderbijlpark. *Birding in Southern Africa* 47(3): 95.

Raijmakes, J. M. H. 1996. Identification aid for European Marsh Warbler and European Reed Warbler. *Safring News* 25: 21–27.

Raijmakers, J. M. H. & Raijmakers, J. H. F. A. 1994. Distribution, size and moult of migrant warblers in the southern Transvaal. *Safring News* 23: 65–71, 24: 3–12.

Raja, N. A., Davidson, P., Bean, N., Drijvers, R., Showler, D. A. & Barker, C. 1999. The birds of Palas, North-west Frontier Province, Pakistan. *Forktail* 15: 77–85.

Ramsey, E. P. 1876. Characters of a new genus and species of passerine bird from the Fiji Islands, proposed to be called *Vitia*. *Proc. Linn. Soc. New South Wales* 1: 41–42.

Rand, A. L. 1936. The Distribution and Habits of Madagascar Birds. Summary of the Field Notes of the Mission Zoologique Franco-Anglo-Américaine à Madagascar. *Bull. Amer. Mus. Nat. Hist.* 72. New York.

Rand, A. L., Friedmann, H. & Traylor, M. A. 1959. Birds from Gabon and Moyen Congo. *Fieldiana: Zoology* 41 (2): 221–411.

Randall, R. D. 1995. Greater Swamp Warbler *Acrocephalus rufescens* on the Chobe River. *Babbler* 29/30: 33.

Randall, R. D. 1999. Olive-Tree Warblers *Hippolais olivetorum* in northern Botswana. *Babbler* 35: 26.

Ranner, A. 1992. More on Moustached Warbler. *Birding World* 5: 446–447.

Rasmussen, P. C. & Anderton, J. C. 2005. *Birds of South Asia. The Ripley Guide*. Vols. 1 & 2. Smithsonian Institution and Lynx Edicions, Washington D. C. and Barcelona.

Rasmussen, P. C., Round, P. D., Dickinson, E. C. & Rozendaal, F. G. 2000. A new bush-warbler (Sylviidae, *Bradypterus*) from Taiwan. *Auk* 117(2): 279–289.

Ratnasingham, S. & Hebert, P. D. N. 2007. BOLD: the Barcode of Life Data System (www.barcodinglife.org). *Molecular Ecology Notes* 7: 355–364.

Ravokatra, M., Wilmé, L. & Goodman, S. M. 2003. Bird Weights. In: Goodman, S. M. & Benstead, J. F. (eds.). *The Natural History of Madagascar*. Pp. 1059–1063.University of Chicago Press, Chicago.

Raymer, H. 1993. The elusive River Warbler. *Witwatersrand Bird Club News* 161: 19.

Redfern, C. P. F. 1979. Survival in relation to sex in Reed Warbler populations. *Wicken Fen Group Report* 10: 34–38.

Redfern, C. P. F. & Alker, P. J. 1996. Plumage development and post-juvenile moult in the Sedge Warbler *Acrocephalus schoenobaenus*. *J. Avian Biol.* 27: 157–163.

Redfern, C. P. F. & Clark, J. A. 2001. *Ringer's Manual*. BTO, Thetford.

Redfern, C. P. F., Topp, V. J. & Jones, P. 2004. Fat and pectoral muscle in migrating Sedge Warblers *Acrocephalus schoenobaenus*. *Ringing & Migration* 22(1): 24–34.

Red'kin, Ya. A. 1998. [Remarks on *Locustella* (Sylviidae) of Arkhangel'sk Region.] *Russian J. Ornithol.* Express issue 32: 3–7. (Russian)

Reichel, J. D., Wiles, G. J. & Glass, P. O. 1992. Island extinctions: the case of the endangered Nightingale Reed Warbler. *Wilson Bull.* 104: 44–54.

Renner, S. C., Rappole, J. H., Rasmussen, P. C., Aung, T., Aung, M., Shwe, N. M., Dumbacher, J. P., Fleischer, R. C. 2008. A new subspecies of *Tesia olivea* (Sylviidae) from Chiang Mai province, northern Thailand. *J. Ornithol.* 149: 439–450.

Rguibi-Idrissi, H., Julliard, R. & Bairlein, F. 2003. Variation in the stopover duration of Reed Warblers *Acrocephalus scirpaceus* in Morocco: effects of season, age and site. *Ibis* 145: 650–656.

Rheindt, F. E. 2010. New biogeographic records for the avifauna of Taliabu (Sula Islands, Indonesia), with preliminary documentation of two previously undiscovered taxa. *Bull. Brit. Orn. Club* 130(1): 33–51.

Rheindt, F. E. & Hutchinson, R. O. 2007. A photoshot odyssey through the confused avian taxonomy of Seram and Buru (southern Moluccas). *BirdingASIA* 7: 18–38.

Richards, B. 1992. *Hippolais* identification. *Birding World* 5: 234.

Richards, J. H. & Long, R. 1964. Cetti's Warblers in Jersey. *Brit. Birds* 57: 517–518.

Richardson, C. 1990. *The Birds of the United Arab Emirates*. Hobby Publications, Dubai.

Richardson, C. T. 1993. Reed Warbler *Acrocephalus scirpaceus* breeding in Dubai, the first breeding record for the United Arab Emirates. *Emirates Bird Report* 17: 59–60.

Richardson, D. S., Burke, T. & Komdeur, J. 2002. Direct benefits the evolution of female-biased cooperative breeding in Seychelles Warblers. *Evolution* 56: 2313–2321.

Richardson, D. S., Jury, F. L., Blaakmeer, K., Komdeur, J. & Burke, T. 2001. Parentage assignment and extra-group paternity in a cooperative breeder: the Seychelles Warbler (*Acrocephalus sechellensis*). *Molec. Ecol.* 10: 2263–2273.

Riddiford, N. 1984. Plumage variations and age characteristics of River Warblers. *Brit. Birds* 77: 214.

Riddiford, N. & Findley, P. 1981. Seasonal movements of summer migrants. BTO, Tring.

Riddiford, N. & Harvey, P. V. 1991. Pallas's Grasshopper Warbler identification: some new field characters. *Birding World* 4: 324–326.

Riddiford, N. & Harvey, P. V. 1992. Identification of Lanceolated Warbler. *Brit. Birds* 85: 62–78.

Riddiford, N. & Potts, P. 1993. Exceptional claw-wear of Great Reed Warbler. *Brit. Birds* 86: 572.

Riddington, R. 1995. The Olivaceous Warbler on Fair Isle. *Birding World* 8: 218–220.

Riddington, R. 1996. The Paddyfield Warbler on Fair Isle. *Birding World* 9: 388–389.

Riley, D., Shepherd, K. & Votier, S. 1993. The Lanceolated Warbler in Norfolk. *Birding World* 6: 396–397.

Riley, J. H. 1940. Five new forms of birds from southern Annam *Proc. Biol. Soc. Washington* 53: 47–49.

Ripley, S. D. 1982. *A Synopsis of the Birds of India and Pakistan, together with those of Nepal, Bhutan, Bangladesh and Sri Lanka.* 2nd edition. Bombay Natural History Society, Bombay.

Ripley, S. D. & Rabor, D. S. 1961. The avifauna of Mount Katanglad. *Postilla* 50: 1–20.

Roberts, T. J. 1992. *The Birds of Pakistan.* Vol. 2. Oxford University Press, Oxford.

Robertson, I. 1989. Mystery Photographs 145: Lanceolated Warbler. *Brit. Birds* 82: 319–321.

Robson, C. R. 1988. Recent Reports, China. *Bull. Oriental Bird Club* 8: 32–33.

Robson, C. R. 1995. Russet Bush-Warbler *Bradypterus seebohmi*; a new species for Bhutan and the Indian subcontinent. *Forktail* 11: 161.

Robson, C. R. 2000. *A Field Guide to the Birds of South-east Asia.* New Holland, London.

Robson, C. R. 2000. From the Field. *Bull. Oriental Bird Club* 31: 49–57.

Robson, C. R. 2000. From the Field. *Bull. Oriental Bird Club* 32: 66–76.

Robson, C. R. 2001. From the Field. *Bull. Oriental Bird Club* 33: 68–78.

Robson, C. R., Buck, H., Farrow, D. S., Fisher, T. & King, B. F. 1998. A birdwatching visit to the Chin Hills, West Burma (Myanmar), with notes from nearby areas. *Forktail* 13: 109–120.

Robson, C. R., Eames, J. C., Nguyen, C. & Truong, V.A. 1993a. Further recent records of birds from Viet Nam. *Forktail* 8: 25–52.

Robson, C. R., Eames, J. C., Nguyen, C. & Truong, V.A. 1993b. Birds recorded during the third BirdLife/Forest Birds Working Group expedition in Viet Nam. *Forktail* 9: 89–119.

Robson, C. R., Eames, J. C., Wolstencroft, J. A., Nguyen, C. & Truong, V. L. 1989. Recent records of birds from Viet Nam. *Forktail* 5: 71–97.

Robson, D., Barriocanal, C., Garcia, O. & Villena, O. 2001. The spring stopover of the Reed Warbler *Acrocephalus scirpaceus* in northeast Spain. *Ringing & Migration* 20: 233–238.

Rodwell, S. P., Sauvage, A., Rumsey, S. J. R. & Braunlich, A. 1996. An annotated check-list of the birds occurring at the Parc National des Oiseaux du Djoudj in Senegal, 1984–1994. *Malimbus* 18: 74–111.

Rogers, M. J. and the Rarities Committee. Report on rare birds in Great Britain in 2006. *Brit. Birds* 100: 694–754.

de Roo, A. & Deheegher, J. 1969. Ecology of the Great Reed Warbler *Acrocephalus arundinaceus* (Linné) wintering in the southern Congo savanna. *Gerfaut* 59: 260–275.

Roselaar, C. S. 1994. Geographical variation within western populations of Clamorous Reed Warbler. *Dutch Birding* 16: 237–239.

Roselaar, C. S. 1995. *Songbirds of Turkey. An atlas of biodiversity of Turkish passerine birds.* Pica Press, Robertsbridge.

Roselaar, C. S. (Kees)., van den Berg, A. B., van Loon, A. J. & Maassen, E. 2006. [Pallas's Grasshopper Warblers in Noord-Holland in September 2002–05]. *Dutch Birding* 28: 273–283. (Dutch, English summary)

Rossinskiy, A. A. 2004 (reprinted from publication in 1917). [Biology of *Iduna caligata* Licht. and *Acanthopneuste viridanus* Blyth.] *Russian J. Ornithol.* Express issue 252: 122–139. (Russian)

Røstad, O. W. 1986. The autumn migration of the Sedge Warbler *Acrocephalus schoenobaenus* in East Finnmark. *Cinclus* 9: 57–61.

Roth, T. & Jalilova, G. 2004. First confirmed breeding record of Pallas's Grasshopper Warbler *Locustella certhiola* in Kyrgyzstan. *Sandgrouse* 26(2): 141–143.

Rothschild, W. 1982. Descriptions of seven new species of birds from the Sandwich Islands. *Ann. Mag. Nat. Hist.* 10: 109.

Round, P. D. 1983. Some recent bird records from northern Thailand. *Nat. Hist. Bull. Siam Soc.* 31(2): 123–138.

Round, P. D. 1992. The identification and status of the Russet Bush-Warbler in China and continental Southeast Asia. *Hong Kong Bird Report* 1991: 188–194.

Round, P. D. 1993. Winter records of the Manchurian Reed-Warbler *Acrocephalus* (*agricola*) *tangorum* from Thailand. *Forktail* 9: 83–88.

Round, P. D. 2008. *The Birds of the Bangkok Area.* White Lotus Press, Bangkok.

Round, P. D. & Allen, D. 2010. A record of active moult in the Streaked Reed Warbler *Acrocephalus sorghophilus.* *Bull. Brit. Orn. Club* 130(2): 145–147.

Round, P. D. & Kennerley, P. R. 2007. Large-billed Reed Warbler *Acrocephalus orinus* back from the dead. *BirdingASIA* 7: 53–54.

Round, P. D. & Loskot, V. 1994. A reappraisal of the taxonomy of the Spotted Bush-Warbler *Bradypterus thoracicus.* *Forktail* 10: 159–172.

Round, P. D. & Rumsey, S. J. 2003. Habitat use, moult and biometrics in Manchurian Reed Warbler *Acrocephalus tangorum* wintering in Thailand. *Ringing & Migration* 21(4): 215–221.

Round, P. D., Hansson, B., Pearson, D. J., Kennerley, P. R. & Bensch, S. 2007. Lost and found: the enigmatic Large-billed Reed Warbler *Acrocephalus orinus* rediscovered after 139 years. *J. Avian Biol.* 38: 133–138.

Rozendaal, F. 1987. Description of a new species of bush-warbler of the genus *Cettia* Bonaparte, 1834 (Aves: Sylviidae) from Yamdena, Tanimbar Islands, Indonesia. *Zool. Meded. Leiden* 61: 177–202.

Rozendaal, F. 1989. Taxonomic affinities of *Bradypterus montis.* *Dutch Birding* 11: 164–167.

Rozendaal, F. 1990. Mystery Photographs 34: Gray's Grasshopper Warbler. *Dutch Birding* 12: 9–11.

Rozendaal, F. G. 1999. A record of the Grey-bellied Tesia *Tesia cyaniventer* (Aves: Sylviidae) from Doi Inthanon, northern Thailand. *Nat. Hist. Bull. Siam Soc.* 47: 119–120.

Rozendaal, F. G. & Dekker, R. W. R. J. 1989. Annotated checklist of the birds of the Dumoga-Bone National Park, north Sulawesi. *Kukila* 4(2): 85–109.

Rumsey, S. J. R. 1975. Mist-netting Grasshopper Warblers. *Ringers Bulletin* 4: 104.

Rumsey, S. J. R. 1984. Identification pitfalls: Aquatic Warbler. *Brit. Birds* 77: 377.

Ruttledge, R. F. 1955a. Habits of the Grasshopper Warbler. *Brit. Birds* 48: 185.

Ruttledge, R. F. 1955b. Leg and bill colouration in the Grasshopper Warbler. *Brit. Birds* 48: 235–236.

Safford, R. J. 2001. Pp. 583–596. In: Fishpool L. D. C. & Evans, M. I. (eds.). *Important Bird Areas in Africa and associated islands: Priority sites for conservation.* Birdlife Conservation Series No.11. Pisces Publications and Birdlife International, Newbury and Cambridge.

Safford, R. J. & Evans, M. I. 1992. Birds of the Comoro Islands, April 1990. *Scopus* 15(2): 93–101.

Saitou, T. 1976a. Breeding biology of the eastern Great Reed Warbler, *Acrocephalus arundinaceus orientalis.* *Misc. Rep. Yamashina Inst. Ornithol.* 8: 135–156.

Saitou, T. 1976b. Territory and breeding density in the eastern Great Reed Warbler *Acrocephalus arundinaceus orientalis.* *Misc. Rep. Yamashina Inst. Ornithol.* 8: 157–173.

Salewski, V. & Herremans, M. 2006. Phenology of Western Olivaceous Warbler *Hippolais opaca* and Eastern Olivaceous Warbler *Hippolais pallida reiseri* on stopover sites in Mauritania. *Ringing & Migration* 23(1): 15–20.

Salewski, V., Herremans, M. & Stalling, T. 2005. Wing moult of Eastern Olivaceous Warblers *Hippolais pallida reiseri* at stopover sites at the southern fringe of the Sahara. *Ringing & Migration* 22(3): 185–189.

Salewski, V., Stark, H. & Leisler, B. 2009. Olivaceous Warblers in southeast Morocco. *Brit. Birds* 102: 116–121.

Salomonsen, F. 1928. Zwei neue *Acrocephalus* Formen aus dem indo-malayischen Gebiet. *Orn. Monatsber.* 36: 119–120.

Salomonsen, F. 1929. Bemerkungen über die Gruppe *Acrocephalus arundinaceus* L. *J. Ornithol.* 77: 267–281.

Sandford, G. & Raust, P. 2002. Oiseaux de Rimatara. *Te Manu* (Pape'ete, French Polynesia) 41: 3–4.

Sangster, G. 1997. *Acrocephalus* and *Hippolais* relationships: shaking the tree. *Dutch Birding* 19: 294–300.

Sangster, G., Hazevoet, C. J., van den Berg, A. B. & Roselaar, C.

S. 1997. Dutch avifaunal list: taxonomic changes in 1977–97. *Dutch Birding* 19: 21–28.

Sangster, G., Hazevoet, C. J., van den Berg, A. B. & Roselaar, C. S. 1998. Dutch avifaunal list: species concepts, taxonomic instability, and taxonomic changes in 1998. *Dutch Birding* 20: 22–32.

Sauvage, A., Rumsey, S. & Rodwell, S. 1998. Recurrence of Palearctic birds in the lower Senegal River valley. *Malimbus* 20: 33–53.

Schaefer, H. M., Naef-Daenzer, B., Leisler, B., Schmidt, V., Müller, J. K. & Schulze-Hagen, K. 2000. Spatial behaviour in the Aquatic Warbler (*Acrocephalus paludicola*) during mating and breeding. *J. Ornithol.* 141: 1–7.

Schäffer, N., Walther, B. A., Gutteridge, K. & Rahbek, C. 2006. The African migration and wintering grounds of the Aquatic Warbler *Acrocephalus paludicola*. *Bird Conserv. Int.* 16: 33–56.

Schaub, M., Schwilch, R. & Jenni, L. 1999. Does tape-luring of migrating Eurasian Reed Warblers increase numbers of recruits or capture probability? *Auk* 116: 1047–1053.

Schenkler, R. 1986. Neue Drosselrohrsänger *Acrocephalus arundinaceus* Ringfunde aus Afrika. *Anz. Orn. Ges. Bayern* 25: 217–219.

Schmidt, R. K. 1965. Incubation period of African Marsh Warbler *Acrocephalus baeticatus*. *Ostrich* 36: 34.

Schmidt, V., Schaefer, H. M. & Leisler, B. 1999. Song behaviour and range use in the polygamous Aquatic Warbler *Acrocephalus paludicola*. *Acta Ornithol.* 34: 209–213.

Schodde, R. & Mason, I. J. 1999. *The directory of Australian birds: passerines*. CSIRO publishing, Canberra.

Schonn, S. & Schonn, R. 1987. Zer Expansion, Brutbiologie und Oko-Ethologie des Schlagschwirls (*Locustella fluviatilis*) in Sachsen. *Beitr. Vogelkd.* 33: 1–17.

Schreiber, R. W. 1979. The egg and nest of the Bokikokiko *Acrocephalus aequinoctialis*. *Bull. Brit. Orn. Club* 99:120–124.

Schulenberg, T. S., Goodman, S. M. & Razafimahaimodison, J. C. 1993. *Genetic Variation in Two Sub-species of* Nesillas typica *(Sylviinae) in South-east Madagascar. Proc. 8th Pan-African Ornithol. Congr.* Annales du Musée Royal de l'Afrique Centrale (Zoologie) 268. Tervuren, Belgium.

Schulze-Hagen, K. 1989. Bekanntes und weniger Bekanntes vom Seggenrohrsänger *Acrocephalus paludicola*. *Limicola* 3: 229–246.

Schulze-Hagen, K. 1993. *Winter quarters of the Aquatic Warbler and habitat situation there – short review of recent knowledge*. Unpublished report. Birdlife International, Cambridge.

Schulze-Hagen, K. & Barthel, P. H. 1993. Die Bestimmung der europäischen ungestreiften Rohrsänger *Acrocephalus*. *Limicola* 7: 1–34.

Schulze-Hagen, K. & Sennert, G. 1990. Nestverteidigung bei Teich- und Sumpfrohrsänger - Ein Vergleich. *Ökol. Vögel* 12: 1–11.

Schulze-Hagen, K., Flinks, H. & Dyrcz, A. 1989. Brutzeitliche Beutewahl beim Seggenrohrsänger *Acrocephalus paludicola*. *J. Ornithol.* 130: 251–255.

Schulze-Hagen, K., Leisler, B., Birkhead, T. R. & Dyrcz, A. 1995. Prolonged copulation, sperm reserves and sperm competition in the Aquatic Warbler *Acrocephalus paludicola*. *Ibis* 137: 85–91.

Schulze-Hagen, K., Leisler, B., Schäfer, H. M. & Schmidt, V. 1999. The breeding system of the Aquatic Warbler *Acrocephalus paludicola* – a review of new results. *Vogelwelt* 120: 87–96.

Schulze-Hagen, K., Leisler, B. & Winkler, H. 1996. Breeding success and reproductive strategies of two *Acrocephalus* warblers. *J. Ornithol.* 137: 181–192.

Schulze-Hagen, K., Swatschek, I., Dyrcz, A. & Wink, M. 1993. Multiple Vaterschaften in Bruten des Seggenrohrsängers *Acrocephalus paludicola*: Erste Ergebnisse des DNA-Fingerprintings. *J. Ornithol.* 134: 145–154.

Scott, R. E. 1968a. Cetti's Warbler in Kent. *Brit. Birds* 61: 315–316.

Scott, R. E. 1968b. Cetti's Warbler in Kent. *Brit. Birds* 61: 533–534.

Scott, R. E. & Svensson, L. 1972. Emargination of the primaries of Cetti's Warbler. *Brit. Birds* 65: 178–179.

Secondi, J., Bretagnolle, V., Compagnon, C. & Faivre, B. 2003. Species-specific song convergence in a moving hybrid zone between two passerines. *Biol. J. Linn. Soc.* 80: 507–517.

Secondi, J., Faivre, B. & Kreutzer, M. 1999. Maintenance of male

reaction to the congeneric song in the *Hippolais* warbler hybrid zone. *Behav. Processes* 46: 151–158.

Seebohm, H. 1884. Further contributions to the ornithology of Japan. *Ibis* (5)2: 30–43.

Seibold, I. & Helbig, A. J. 1995. Evolutionary history of New and Old World vultures inferred from nucleotide sequences of the mitochondrial cytochrome *b* gene. *Phil. Trans. R. Soc. Lond. B.* 350: 163–178.

Seitre, R. & Seitre, J. 1991. *Causes de disparation des oiseaux terrestres de Polynésie Francaise*. Nouméa: South Pacific Regional Environment Programme (Occasional Papers. Series 8).

Selfe, G. 2003. Little Rush Warbler *Bradypterus baboecala*, new to Togo. *Bull. African Bird Club* 10: 51.

Sellin, D. 1984. Zum Vorkommen des Seggenrohrsängers in Gebiet des Peenestroms und im NSG Peenemünder Haken, Struck und Ruden. *Nat. Mecklenbg.* 27: 21–24.

Sellin, D. 1989. [Comparative investigation into the habitat structure of the Aquatic Warbler (*Acrocephalus paludicola*).] *Vogelwelt* 110: 198–208. (German, English summary)

Sellin, D. 1990. [Present occurrence of Aquatic Warbler *Acrocephalus paludicola* in the Oder River estuary.] *Vogelwelt* 111: 181–189. (German, English summary)

Senior, R. J. 1983. Sounds of Grasshopper Warbler and wood-crickets. *Brit. Birds* 76: 350–351.

Sharrock, J. T. R. 1965. Field-identification of *Hippolais* warblers. *Brit. Birds* 58: 520–521.

Sharrock, J. T. R. 1974a. *Scarce Migrant Birds in Britain and Ireland*. Poyser, Berkhamsted.

Sharrock, J. T. R. 1974b. The origin of British Aquatic Warblers. *Brit. Birds* 67: 443–444.

Sharrock, J. T. R. 1975. The origin of British Aquatic Warblers. *Brit. Birds* 68: 519.

Sharrock, J. T.R. 1976a. Lanceolated Warblers and vagrancy patterns. *Brit. Birds* 69: 109–110.

Sharrock, J. T. R. 1976b. The origin of British Aquatic Warblers. *Brit. Birds* 69: 229.

Sharrock, J. T. R. 1977a. Mystery photographs 1: Lanceolated Warbler. *Brit. Birds* 70: 34.

Sharrock, J. T. R. 1977b. Mystery photographs 4: Icterine Warbler. *Brit. Birds* 70: 163–164.

Sharrock, J. T. R. 1977c. Tail-cocking by Moustached Warblers. *Brit. Birds* 70: 349–350.

Sharrock, J. T. R. 1979. Identification of Blyth's Reed and Paddy-field Warblers. *Brit. Birds* 72: 596.

Sharrock, J. T. R. 1983. Mystery photographs 76: Thick-billed Warbler. *Brit. Birds* 76: 186–187.

Sharrock, J. T. R. 1984a. Mystery photographs 87: Great Reed Warbler. *Brit. Birds* 77: 105–106.

Sharrock, J. T. R. 1984b. Mystery photographs 89: River Warbler. *Brit. Birds* 77: 205.

Sharrock, J. T. R. 1985. Mystery photographs 105: hybrid Sedge x Reed Warbler. *Brit. Birds* 78: 434–437.

Sharrock, J. T. R., Hutchinson, C. D., Preston, K. & Barbier, P. G. R. 1970. The identification of Blyth's Reed Warbler in autumn. *Brit. Birds* 63: 214–216.

Shaw, D. 1999. The Blyth's Reed Warbler on Fair Isle. *Birding World* 12: 238.

Shaw, D. 2003. The Thick-billed Warbler on Fair Isle. *Birding World* 16: 206–208.

Shaw, D., Holt, C. & Maggs, H. 2000. The Caspian Reed Warbler on Fair Isle. *Birding World* 13: 315–317.

Sheldon, F. H., Moyle, R. G. & Kennard, J. 2001. *Ornithology of Sabah: History, Gazetteer, Annotated Checklist, and Bibliography*. Ornithological Monographs No. 52. AOU, Washington D.C.

Shibnev, Yu. B. & Gluschenko, Yu. N. 1977. [Two new species of reed warblers in the fauna of the USSR.] *Tez. Doklad. VII Vsesoyuz. Orn. Konf.* Part 1: 113. Naukova dumka, Kiev. (Russian)

Shigeta, Y. 1988. [*Bird banding manual, identification guide to Japanese birds, No. 5:* Megalurus pryeri.] Yamashina Institute for Ornithology, Abiko, Japan. (Japanese)

Shigeta, Y. 1999. [*A study on the methods for distinguishing among*

Japanese and foreign birds, 2, Japanese Bush Warbler Cettia diphone]. Yamashina Institute for Ornithology, Abiko, Japan. (Japanese)

Shigeta, Y. 2000. [*The identification manual of Japanese Bush Warblers* Cettia diphone.] Yamashina Institute for Ornithology, Abiko, Japan. (Japanese)

Shirihai, H. 1987. Identification of Upcher's Warbler. *Brit. Birds* 80: 473–482.

Shirihai, H. 1996. *The Birds of Israel.* Academic Press, London.

Shirihai, H., Christie, D. A. & Harris, A. 1996a. Identification of *Hippolais* warblers. *Brit. Birds* 89: 114–138.

Shirihai, H., Christie, D. A. & Harris, A. 1996b. *The Macmillan Birder's Guide to European and Middle Eastern Birds.* Macmillan, London.

Shirihai, H., Roselaar, C. S., Helbig, A. J., Barthel, P. H. & van Loon, A. J. 1995. Identification and taxonomy of large *Acrocephalus* warblers. *Dutch Birding* 17: 229–239.

Shirokov, Yu. V. & Malachishev, E. B. 2001. [Breeding of *Hippolais caligata* in the vicinity of Zaostrovie settlement (Lodeinopolskiy district, Leningrad Region).] *Russian J. Ornithol.* Express issue 135: 201–202. (Russian)

Showler, D. A. 1999. Population census and habitat use of Rodrigues Warbler *Acrocephalus rodericanus* (Aves: Sylviidae). Dissertation, University of East Anglia.

Showler, D. A. 2002a. Encouraging news from Rodrigues. *World Birdwatch* 24: 20–21.

Showler, D. A. 2002b. Extension of breeding activity for Rodrigues Warbler *Acrocephalus rodericanus.* *Bull. African Bird Club* 9: 64.

Showler, D. A., Côté, I. M. & Jones, C. G. 2002. Population census and habitat use of Rodrigues Warbler *Acrocephalus rodericanus.* *Bird Conserv. Internatn.* 12: 211–230.

Sibley, C. G. & Ahlquist, J. E. 1990. *Phylogeny and classification of birds: a study in molecular evolution.* Yale University Press, New Haven.

Sibley, C. G. & Monroe, B. L. 1990. *Distribution and taxonomy of the birds of the world.* Yale University Press, New Haven.

Sibley, C. G. & Monroe, B. L. 1993. *A supplement to distribution and taxonomy of the birds of the world.* Yale University Press, New Haven.

Simpson, J. H. 1973. Thick-billed Warbler in Shetland. *Scottish Birds* 7: 262.

Simmons, K. E. L. 1952. Some observations on the Olivaceous Warbler in Egypt. *Ibis* 94: 203–209.

Simmons, K. E. L. 1974. Cuckoos and Reed Warblers. *Brit. Birds* 67: 442–443.

Simms, E. 1984. The songs of three Locustella warblers. *Brit. Birds* 77: 115.

Simms, E. 1985. *British Warblers.* Collins, London.

Sinclair, I. & Langrand, O. 1998. *Birds of the Indian Ocean Islands.* Struik Publishers, Cape Town, South Africa.

Sinclair, J. C. 1976. Identification of Olive-tree Warbler. *Bokmakierie* 28: 19.

Skerrett, A., Bullock, I. & Disley, T. 2001. *Birds of Seychelles.* A&C Black, London.

Small, B. 2002. Bill shapes of Booted & Sykes's Warblers. *Birding World* 15: 170.

Smith, D. A. 1979. Call of Booted Warbler. *Brit. Birds* 72: 387.

Smith, G. 1980. Pallas's Grasshopper Warbler in Norfolk. *Brit. Birds* 73: 417–418.

Smith, K. D. 1953. *Locustella luscinioides* in Eritrea. *Ibis* 95: 698–699.

Smith, K. D. 1957. The Birds of Eritrea. *Ibis* 99: 306–337.

Smith, K. D. 1961. On the Clamorous Reed Warbler *Acrocephalus stentoreus* (Hemprich and Ehrenberg) in Eritrea. *Bull. Brit. Orn. Club* 81: 28–29.

Smith, K. D. 1964. *Acrocephalus dumetorum* in Africa. *Bull. Brit. Orn. Club* 84: 172.

Smith, K. D. 1968. Spring migration through southeast Morocco. *Ibis* 110: 452–492.

Smout, T. C. 1960. Field characters of the Icterine Warbler in late summer. *Brit. Birds* 53: 225.

Smythies, B. E. 1949. A reconnaissance of the N'Mai Hka drainage, northern Burma. *Ibis* 91: 627–648.

Smythies, B. E. 1957. An annotated checklist of the birds of Borneo. *Sarawak Mus. J.* 7: 523–818.

Smythies, B. E. 1968. *The Birds of Burma.* 2nd edition. Oliver & Boyd, London.

Smythies, B. E. 1981. *The Birds of Borneo.* 3rd edition. Sabah Society & Malayan Nature Society.

Smythies, B. E. & Davison, G. W. H. 1999. *The Birds of Borneo.* 4th edition. Natural History Publications (Borneo), Kota Kinabalu.

van Someren, V. G. L. 1956. Days with Birds. *Fieldiana: Zoology* 38: 1–520.

Sotnikov, V. N. 1996. [*Acrocephalus agricola* in the Kirov Region.] *Russian J. Ornithol.* Express issue 3: 15–18. (Russian)

Sotnikov, V. N. 1997. [*Acrocephalus arundinaceus* in the Kirov Region.] *Russian J. Ornithol.* Express issue 7: 10–11. (Russian)

Speight, G. J., Turton, J. M. & Rowland, R. 1986. *Trip report (Sabah).* Unpublished.

Spierenburg, P. 2005. *Birds in Bhutan. Status and distribution.* Oriental Bird Club, Bedford, UK.

Spina, F. 1990. First data on complete summer moult in the Great Reed Warbler *Acrocephalus arundinaceus* in northern Italy. *J. Ornithol.* 131: 177–178.

Spina, F. & Bezzi, E. M. 1990. Autumn migration and orientation of the Sedge Warbler *Acrocephalus schoenobaenus* in northern Italy. *J. Ornithol.* 131: 429–438.

Springer, H. 1960. Studien an Rohrsängern. *Anz. Orn. Ges. Bayern* 5: 389–433.

Squelch, P. & Safe-Squelch, W. 1994. Didric Cuckoo being fed by Little Rush Warblers. *East Africa Nat. Hist. Soc. Bull.* 24(3), 39–40.

Stam, D. & Voous, K. H. 1963. African record of Aquatic Warbler. *Ardea* 51: 74.

Steadman, D. W. 1999. The prehistory of vertebrates, especially birds, on Tinian, Aguiguan, and Rota, Northern Mariana Islands. *Micronesica* 31: 319–345.

Stein, H. 2004. [Partial albinistic Marsh Warbler *Acrocephalus palustris.*] *Limicola* 18: 209–210. (German, English summary)

Steiner, H. M. 1970. Die vom Schema der Passeres abweichende Handschwingenmauser des Rohrschwirls (*Locustella luscinioides*). *J. Ornithol.* 111: 230–236.

Stekher, S. G. 1916. [Biology of the Marsh Warbler (*Acrocephalus palustris* Bechst.).] *Ornitologicheskiy vestnik* (Ufa) 1: 16–24. (Russian)

Stelte, W. & Sossinka, R. 1996. [Significance of perches in the Marsh Warbler (*Acrocephalus palustris*) in its breeding habitat.] *Vogelwarte* 38: 188–193. (German, English summary)

Stenhouse, J. H. 1925. Jerdon's Reed Warbler *Acrocephalus agricola* at Fair Isle: an addition to the British avifauna. *Scottish Nat.* 1925: 173–174.

Stepanyan, L. S. 1972. [A new species of the genus *Locustella* (Aves, Sylviidae) from the east Palearctic.] *Zool. Zhurnal* 51(12): 1896–1897. (Russian, English summary)

Stepanyan, L. S. 1973. [Taxonomic notes on Stepanyan's Grasshopper Warbler *Locustella amnicola* Step.] *Byull. Mosk. Obshch. Ispyt. Prit. Otd. Biol.* 78(3): 38–44. (Russian, English summary)

Stepanyan, L. S. 1978. [*Composition and distribution of bird fauna of the USSR.* Vol 1. Passeriformes.] Nauka, Moskow. (Russian)

Stepanyan, L. S. 1983. [*Superspecies and sibling species in the avifauna of the USSR.*] Nauka, Moscow. (Russian)

Stepanyan, L. S. 1990. [*Conspectus of the Ornithological fauna of the USSR.*] Academkniga, Moscow. (Russian)

Stepanyan, L. S. 2003. [*Conspectus of the Ornithological fauna of Russia and adjacent territories (within the borders of the USSR as a historical region).*] Academkniga, Moscow. (Russian)

Stepanyan, L. S. & Matyukhin, A. V. 1984. [On the systematic position of the European populations of the Paddyfield Warbler (*Acrocephalus agricola*).] *Ornitologiya* 19: 212. (Russian)

Stevenson, T. & Fanshawe, J. 2000. *Fieldguide to the Birds of East Africa.* Poyser, London.

Steyn, P. 1994. Knysna Warbler in Newlands. *Promerops* 212: 10.

Straubhaar, M. & Fiedler, W. 1995. [Record of a Paddyfield Warbler (*Acrocephalus agricola*) on the Mettnau peninsula near Radolfzell at Lake Constance.] *Ornithol. Jahrb. Bad.-Württ.* 11: 237–238. (German)

Stresemann, E. 1931. Neue Formen aus Nord-Kansu VII. *Tribura major netrix. Orn. Monatsber.* 39: 105–107.

Stresemann, E. 1950. Birds collected during Capt. James Cook's last expedition (1776–1780). *Auk* 67: 66–68.

Stresemann, E. & Arnold, J. 1949. Speciation in the groups of Great Reed Warblers. *J. Bombay Nat. Hist. Soc.* 48: 428–443.

Stresemann, E. & Stresemann, V. 1970. Uber die Vollmauser der Rohrschwirls (*Locustella luscinioides*). *J. Ornithol.* 111: 237–239.

Stresemann, E., Meise, W. & Schönwetter. 1937. Beiträge zur Ornithologie von Nordwest-Kansu nach den Forschungen von Walter Beick in den Jahren 1926–1933. *J. Ornithol.* 85(3): 375–576.

Stuart, S. N. (ed.). 1986. *Conservation of Cameroon Montane Forests.* ICBP, Cambridge.

Stuart Baker, E. C. 1922. *The Fauna of British India, including Ceylon and Burma.* Birds Vol. 1. 2nd edition. Taylor & Francis, London.

Stuart Baker, E. C. 1924. *The Fauna of British India, including Ceylon and Burma.* Birds Vol. 2. 2nd edition. Taylor & Francis, London.

Stuart Baker, E. C. 1933. *Nidification of the Birds of the Indian Empire.* Vol. 2. Taylor & Francis, London.

le Sueur, F. 1980. Some Cetti's Warbler breeding observations. *Bird Study* 27: 249–253.

Suffern, C. 1965. The original misidentification of the Hampshire Cetti's Warbler. *Brit. Birds* 58: 516–518.

Suffern, C. & Ferguson-Lees, I. J. 1964. Cetti's Warbler in Hampshire. *Brit. Birds* 57: 365–366.

Sultana, J. & Gauci, C. 1973. The Cetti's Warbler *Cettia cetti* in Malta. *Il-Merrill* 12: 7–9.

Sultana, J. & Gauci, C. 1976. Great Reed Warbler moulting in August. *Il-Merrill* 17: 30.

Sushkin, P. P. 1925. Notes on systematics and distribution of certain Palaearctic birds. *Proc. Boston Soc. Nat. Hist.* 38: 1–55.

Svensson, L. 1968. Cetti's Warbler in Kent. *Brit. Birds* 61: 533.

Svensson, L. 1992. *Identification Guide to European Passerines.* 4th revised and enlarged edition. Svensson, Stockholm.

Svensson, L. 1993. Booted or Sykes's Warbler. *Birding World* 6: 492–493.

Svensson, L. 1997. Mystery Warblers in Tselinograd. *Brit. Birds* 90: 152–154.

Svensson, L. 1999 The Kazakh 'mystery warblers' once again. *Brit. Birds* 92: 481–482.

Svensson, L. 2001a. Identification of Western and Eastern Olivaceous, Booted and Sykes's Warblers. *Birding World* 14: 192–219.

Svensson, L. 2001b. Identifiering av små grå *Hippolais*-sångare. *Vår Fågelvärld* 5/2001: 16–30.

Svensson, L. 2003. *Hippolais* update: identification of Booted and Sykes's Warbler. *Birding World* 16: 470–474.

Svensson, L. & Millington, R. 2002. Field identification of Sykes's Warbler. *Birding World* 15: 381–382.

Svensson, L., Grant, P. J., Mullarney, K. & Zetterström, D. 1999. *The Collins Bird Guide.* HarperCollins, London.

Svensson, L., Prŷs-Jones, R., Rasmussen, P. C. & Olsson, U. 2008. Discovery of ten new specimens of Large-billed Reed Warbler *Acrocephalus orinus*, and new insights into its distributional range. *J. Avian Biol.* 39: 605–610.

Swanberg, P. O. 1945. Häckande gräs-hoppsångare (*Locustella naevia* Bodd.). *Vår Fågelvärld* 4: 149–174.

Swarth, H. S. 1934. Birds of Nunivak Island, Alaska. *Pacific Coast Avifauna* No. 22. Cooper Ornithological Club, Los Angeles.

Swinhoe, R. 1863. On new and little-known birds from China. *Proc. Zool. Soc. London*: 87–94.

Swinhoe, R. 1863a. Notes on the Ornithology of Northern Japan. *Ibis* (1)5: 442–445.

Swinhoe, R. 1863b. On new and little-known birds from China. *Proc. Zool. Soc.* 87–94.

Swinhoe, R. 1866. Ornithological notes from Formosa. *Ibis* 2(2): 392–406.

Swinhoe, R. 1870. Zoological notes of a journey from Canton to Peking and Kaglan. *Proc. Zool. Soc. London*: 427–451.

Swinhoe, R. 1871. A revised catalogue of the Birds of China and its Islands, with the Descriptions of New Species, References to former notes, and occasional remarks. *Proc. Zool. Soc. London*: 337–423.

Swinhoe, R. 1874. On some birds from Hakodadi, in northern Japan. *Ibis* (3)4: 150–166.

Swinhoe, R. 1876. On the Contents of a third Box of Birds from Hakodadi, in Northern Japan. *Ibis* (3)6: 330–335.

Sykes, W. H. 1832. Catalogue of Birds of the Raptorial and Insessorial Orders (systematically arranged), observed in the Dukhun, by Lieut. Colonel W. H. Sykes, Bombay Army. F.L.S., F.G.S., F.Z.S. M.R.A.S. *Proc. Zool. Soc. London*: 89.

Syvertsen, Ø, 1992. Status of Marsh Warbler in Norway. *Brit. Birds* 85: 89–90.

Takatsukasa, S. & Yamashina, Y. 1931. Some new birds from the Palao and Mariana Islands. *Dobutsu. Zasshi* 43: 484–487.

Tarboton, W. 2001. *A Guide to the Nests and Eggs of Southern African birds.* Struik, Cape Town.

Tasinazzo, S. 1993. Breeding ecology of Cetti's Warbler *Cettia cetti* in northeastern Italy. *Boll. Zool.* 60: 185–192.

Tekke. M. J. 1973. Aquatic Warblers breeding in the Netherlands. *Brit. Birds* 66: 540–541.

Tenovuo, J. 2006. Basra Reed Warbler – a little-known Western Palearctic bird. *Birding World* 19: 66–68.

Terpstra, K. 1988. [Paddyfield Warbler on Vlieland in September 1986.] *Dutch Birding* 10: 91. (Dutch, English summary)

Thaxter, C. B., Redfern, C. P. F. & Bevan, R. M. 2006. Survival rates of adult Reed Warblers *Acrocephalus scirpaceus* at a northern and southern site in England. *Ringing & Migration* 23(2): 65–79.

Thejaswi, S. & Shivaprakesh, A. 2004. Observations on the Rusty-rumped Grasshopper-Warbler *Locustella certhiola* (Pallas) at Mysore, Karnataka. *J. Bombay Nat. Hist. Soc.* 101 (3): 461–462.

Thévenot, M., Vernon, R. & Bergier, P. 2003. *The Birds of Morocco.* British Ornithologists' Union Checklist, No. 20. BOU, Tring.

Thewlis, R. M., Duckworth, J. W., Anderson, G. Q. A., Dvorak, M., Evans, T. D., Nemeth, E., Timmins, R. J. & Wilkinson, R. J. 1995. Ornithological records from Laos, 1992–1993. *Forktail* 11: 47–100.

Thibault, J.-C. 1988. *Menaces et conservation des oiseaux de Polynésie Française*: 87–124. In: Thibault, J.-C. & Guyot, I. (eds.). *Livre rouges des oiseaux menacés des régions françaises d'outre-mer.* Conseil International pour la Protection des Oiseaux (Monograph No. 5). Saint-Cloud.

Thibault, J.-C. & Cibois, A. 2006. The natural history and conservation of *Acrocephalus rimitarae*, the endemic reed-warbler of Rimatara Island, Oceania. *Bull. Brit. Orn. Club* 126(3): 201–207.

Thibault, J.-C. & Rives, C. 1975. *The birds of Tahiti.* Les editions du Pacifique. Papette, Tahiti.

Thomas, D. K. 1977. Wing moult in the Savi's Warbler. *Ringing & Migration* 1: 125–130.

Thomason, B., Maher, M. & Pennington, M. 2003. The Sykes's Warbler in Shetland. *Birding World* 16: 466–469.

Thompson, P. M. & Johnson, D. L. 2003. Further notable bird records from Bangladesh. *Forktail* 19: 85–102.

Thompson, P. M., Harvey, W. G., Johnson, D. L., Millin, D. J., Rashid, S. M. A., Scott, D. A., Stanford, C. & Woolner, J. D. 1993. Recent notable bird records from Bangladesh. *Forktail* 9: 12–44.

Thorpe, W. H. 1957. The identification of Savi's, Grasshopper and River Warblers by means of song. *Brit. Birds* 50: 169–171.

Thouy, P. 1978. Première capture au Maroc de l'hypolias ictèrine *Hippolais icterina. Alauda* 46: 98.

Ticehurst, C. B. 1941. Systematic notes on Indian birds, No. 10. *Ibis* (14)5: 318–319.

Ticehurst, C. B., Buxton, P. & Cheesman, R. 1922. The birds of Mesopotamia. *J. Bombay Nat. Hist. Soc.* 28: 268–295.

Tikader, B. K. 1984. *Birds of the Andaman and Nicobar islands.* Zoological Survey of India, Calcutta.

Timmins, R. J., Mostafawi, N., Rajabi, A. M., Noori, H., Ostrowski, S., Olsson, U., Svensson, L. & Poole, C. M. 2009. The discovery of Large-billed Reed Warblers *Acrocephalus orinus* in north-eastern Afghanistan. *BirdingASIA* 12: 42–45.

Tjernberg, M. 1991. Differences in singing behaviour between Lanceolated and Grasshopper Warblers. *Dutch Birding* 13: 11.

Tobish, T. G. Jr. 1985. The first record of *Locustella lanceolata* for North America. *Auk* 102: 645.

Toms, M. P., Clark, J. A. & Balmer, D. E. 1999. Bird Ringing in Britain and Ireland in 1997. *Ringing & Migration* 19: 215–255.

Tordoff, A. W. & Eames, J. C. 2001. New additions to the list of birds of Vietnam. *Bull. Oriental Bird Club* 33: 37–38.

Townsend, C. W. & Wetmore, A. 1919. Reports on the scientific results of the expedition to the tropical Pacific in charge of Alexander Agassiz on the US Fish Commission steamer *Albatross*. *Bull. Mus. Comp. Zool.* 63: 182–183.

Trainor, C. R. 2002. The birds of Adonara, Lesser Sundas, Indonesia. *Forktail* 18: 93–100.

Trainor, C. R. 2005. Birds of Tapuafu Peninsula, Roti Island, Lesser Sundas, Indonesia. *Forktail* 21: 121–131.

Trainor, C. R. & Soares, T. 2004. Birds of Atauro Island, Timor-Leste (East Timor). *Forktail* 20: 41–48.

Trainor, C. R., Imanuddin, Aldy, F., Verbelen, P. & Walker, J. S. 2009. The birds of Wetar, Banda Sea: one of Indonesia's forgotten islands. *BirdingASIA* 12: 78–93. 2005.

Traylor, M. A. 1963. *Check-list of Angolan Birds*. Campan. Diamanttes de Angola, Lisboa. Publ. Cult. No. 61.

Traylor, M. A. 1966. The race of *Acrocephalus rufescens* in Zambia. *Bull. Brit. Orn. Club* 86: 161–162.

Trias, J., Martínez, I. & Lascurain, J. 1982. Notes sobre la muda del Buscarle Comu (*Locustella luscinioides*), al delta de L'Ebre. *Butlletí del Grup Català d'Anellament* 1: 2–4.

Tristram, H. B. 1883. On the position of the Acrocephaline genus *Tatare*, with descriptions of the two new species of the genus *Acrocephalus*. *Ibis* (5)1: 38–46.

Tucker, J. J. 1978. A River Warbler *Locustella fluviatilis* 'wintering' and moulting in Zambia. *Bull. Brit. Orn. Club* 98: 2–4.

Tucker, G. M. & Heath, M. F. 1994. *Birds in Europe: their Conservation Status*. Birdlife Conservation Series no. 3. Birdlife International, Cambridge.

Tyler, S. J. 1991. Birds of Lake Naivasha 2. Foraging niches and relationships between migrant and resident warblers in papyrus swamp. *Scopus* 14(2): 117–123.

Tyler, S. J. & Tyler, L. 1997. Observations on the seasonal presence and moult of European Reed Warblers *Acrocephalus scirpaceus* at a site in southeast Botswana. *Ostrich* 68: 117–118.

Tyler, S. J., Lewis, J. M. S. & Tyler, M. 1997. First record of Basra Reed Warbler *Acrocephalus griseldis* in Botswana. *Ostrich* 68: 44–45.

Tymstra, R., Connop, S. & Chado, T. 1996. Some bird observations from central Bhutan, May 1994. *Forktail* 12: 49–60.

Udding, H.-J. & Slings, Q. L. 1994. [Pallas's Grasshopper Warbler near Castricum in October 1991.] *Dutch Birding* 16: 9–12. (Dutch, English summary)

Ueda, K. 2003. [Recent status of the Japanese Marsh Warbler in Japan.] *Strix* 21: 1–3. (Japanese, English summary)

Ueda, K. & Yamaoka, A. 1994. Polygyny in Schrenck's Reed Warbler *Acrocephalus bistrigiceps*. *Ibis* 136: 492–493.

Ueda, K. & Yamaoka, A. 1998. Decrease of song frequency after pairing in the polygynous Schrenck's Reed Warbler *Acrocephalus bistrigiceps*. *J. Yamashina Inst. Ornithol.* 30: 53–56.

Ullman, M. 1989. Identification of Upcher's and Olivaceous Warblers. *Birding World* 2: 167–170.

Urano, E. 1985. Polygyny and the breeding success of the Great Reed Warbler *Acrocephalus arundinaceus*. *Res. Popul. Ecol.* 27: 393–412.

Urano, E. 1990. Factors affecting the cost of polygynous breeding for female Great Reed Warblers *Acrocephalus arundinaceus*. *Ibis* 132: 584–594.

Urban, E. K., Fry, C. H. & Keith, S. (eds.). 1997. *The Birds of Africa*. Vol. 5. Academic Press, London.

US Fish and Wildlife Service. 1998a. *Recovery plan for the Nightin-*

gale Reed-warbler (Acrocephalus luscinia). US Fish and Wildlife Service, Portland.

US Fish and Wildlife Service. 1998b. *Recovery plan for the Nihoa Millerbird* (Acrocephalus familiaris). US Fish and Wildlife Service, Portland.

Vanderbilt, G. & de Schauensee, R. M. 1941. Zoological Results of the Vanderbilt Nihoa Expedition. Part 1. Summary of Zoological Explorations and the Birds of Nihoa. *Notulae Nature* 86: 1–14.

van der Veen, L. & Ebels, E. B. 1996. [Paddyfield Warbler on Vlieland in September 1994.] *Dutch Birding* 18: 13–16. (Dutch, English summary)

van der Vliet, R. E., van der Laan, J. & CDNA. 2002. Rare birds in the Netherlands in 2001. *Dutch Birding* 24: 325–349.

Van de weghe, J.-P. 1981. L'avifaune des papyraeis au Rwanda et au Burundi. *Le Gerfaut* 71: 489–536.

Van de weghe, J.-P. 1983. Sympatric occurrence of the White-winged Warbler *Bradypterus carpalis* and Grauer's Rush Warbler *Bradypterus graueri* in Rwanda. *Scopus* 7: 85–88.

van IJzendoorn, E. J. & de Heer, P. 1985. Herziening van de Nederlandse avifaunistische lijst. *Limosa* 58: 65–72.

van IJzendoorn, E. J. & Westhof, J. H. P. 1985. [Paddyfield Warbler from 1971 rehabilitated.] *Dutch Birding* 7: 121–128. (Dutch, English summary)

Vasiliu, G. D. 1968. Systema Avium Romaniae. *Alauda*, Paris.

Vaughan, R. E. & Jones, K. H. 1913. The birds of Hong Kong, Macau, and the West River or Si Kiang in South-East China, with special reference to their nidification and seasonal movements. *Ibis* 10(1): 17–76.

Vaurie, C. 1954. Systematic notes on Palearctic birds. No. 10. *Sylviinae*: the genera *Cettia*, *Hippolais*, and *Locustella*. *Amer. Mus. Novit.* 1691: 1–9.

Vaurie, C. 1955. Systematic notes on Palearctic birds. No. 18. Supplementary Notes on Corvidae, Timaliinae, Alaudidae, Sylviinae, Hirundinidae, and Turdinae. *Amer. Mus. Novit.* 1753: 1–19.

Vaurie, C. 1959. *The Birds of the Palearctic Fauna. A Systematic Reference. Order Passeriformes*. Witherby, London.

Vaurie, C. 1964. A survey of the birds of Mongolia. *Bull. Amer. Mus. Nat. Hist.* 127: 105–143.

Vaurie, C. 1972. *Tibet and its Birds*. Witherby, London.

Verbelen, D. & De Smit, G. 2003. [Five Lanceolated Warblers in Belgium in 1988–2000 and occurrence in Europe.] *Dutch Birding* 25: 221–234. (Dutch, English summary)

Verbelen, P. & Trainor, C. R. (in prep.). A new subspecies of Timor Bush-warbler *Bradypterus timorensis alorensis* sub. sp nov. from Alor Island, and rediscovery of the Timor Bush-warbler on Timor, Lesser Sundas.

Vercruysse, W. 1989. Mystery Photographs 31: Savi's Warbler. *Dutch Birding* 11: 68–70.

Verhoeye, J. & Holmes, D. A. 1999. The birds of the island of Flores – a review. *Kukila* 10: 3–59.

Vernet, R. 1973. Présence de l'hypolais ictèrine et mortalité de migrateurs dans le Sahara nord-occidental. *Alauda* 41: 425–426.

Vernon, C. J. 1962. Variation in the nest of *Chloropeta natalensis*. *Ostrich* 33: 52–53.

Vernon, C. J. 1970. Palaearctic warblers in the Transvaal. *Ostrich* 41: 218.

Vernon, C. J. 1989. Observations on the forest birds around East London. *Ostrich Suppl.* 14: 75–84.

Vincent, A. W. 1947. On the breeding habits of some African birds. *Ibis* 89: 163–204; 90: 284–312.

Viney, C. A. 1986. *WWF HK visit to North-west Fujian Province, PRC. 28 May – 7 June 1986*. Unpublished manuscript.

Viney, C. A. 1987. *WWF HK visit to Bao Bo Shan Reserve and environs, Guangdong Province, PRC*. Unpublished manuscript.

Vinicombe, K. 2002a. A tale of two warblers. *Birdwatch* 118: 22–25.

Vinicombe, K. 2002b. A handful of hippos: Icterine and Melodious Warblers. *Birdwatch* 122: 22–23.

Vinicombe, K. 2002c. Agrocephalus: Blyth's Reed Warbler. *Birdwatch* 124: 27–30.

Vinicombe, K. 2003. The right stripes: Aquatic Warbler. *Birdwatch* 134: 22–24.

Vinicombe, K. & Cottridge, D. 1996. *Rare birds in Britain & Ireland. A photographic record.* HarperCollins, London.

Vinicombe, K., Pennington, M. & Bradshaw, C. 2001. The Unst Blyth's Reed Warbler. *Brit. Birds* 94: 291–295.

Visser, B. 2002. The Knysna Warbler. *Africa – Birds and Birding* 7(2): 26–31.

Visser, G. V. & Hockey, P. A. R. 2002. Breeding behaviour and performance of the Knysna Warbler *Bradypterus sylvaticus* on the Cape Peninsula, South Africa. *Ostrich* 73: 83–86.

Voous, K. H. 1975. An aberrant Reed Warbler, or: on the inequality of genera in birds. *Ardeola* 21: 977–985.

Voous, K. H. 1977. *List of recent Holarctic bird species.* BOU, London.

Vo Quy, & Nguyen Cu. 1995. *Checklist of the birds of Vietnam.* Nha Xuat Ban Nong Nghiep, Hanoi.

Votier, S. C. & Moon, A. V. 1995. From the Rarities Committee's Files: Lanceolated Warbler in Norfolk and Lanceolated Warbler in Shetland. *Brit. Birds* 88: 430–438.

Votier, S. C. & Riddington, R. 1996. The two Blyth's Reed Warblers on Fair Isle. *Birding World* 9: 221–223.

Votier, S. C. & Riddington, R. 2005. Tail patterns of Reed Warblers. *Brit. Birds* 98: 99–100.

de Vries, J. A. 1987. [Paddyfield Warbler at Makkum already in October 1982.] *Dutch Birding* 9: 28. (Dutch, English summary)

Walbridge, G. & Lewington, I. 1991. Identification of Aquatic Warbler in autumn. *Birding World* 4: 237–241.

Waldeck, K. 1964. Waarneming van een Siberische Snor, *Locustella certhiola* (Pallas). *Limicola* 37: 304–307.

Waliczky, Z. & Moskát, C. 1991. [Habitat selection of the Icterine Warbler (*Hippolais icterina* Vieill. 1817) in Szigetköz.] *Aquila* 98: 135–140. (Hungarian, English summary)

Walinder, G., Karlsson, L. & Persson, K. 1988. A new method for separating Marsh Warblers from Reed Warblers. *Ringing & Migration* 9: 55–62.

Wallace, D. I. M. 1964. Field identification of *Hippolais* warblers. *Brit. Birds* 57: 282–301.

Wallace, D. I. M. 1966. Olivaceous Warbler in the Isles of Scilly. *Brit. Birds* 59: 195–197.

Wallace, D. I. M. 1972. Booted Warbler in the Isles of Scilly. *Brit. Birds* 65: 170–172.

Wallace, D. I. M. 1973. Identification of some scarce or difficult west Palearctic species in Iran. *Brit. Birds* 66: 376–390.

Wallace, D. I. M. 1978a. Mystery photographs 15: Marsh Warbler. *Brit. Birds* 71: 122.

Wallace, D. I. M. 1978b. Mystery photographs 20: Olivaceous Warbler. *Brit. Birds* 71: 355.

Wallace, D. I. M. 1981. Tail-cocking by Moustached Warblers. *Brit. Birds* 74: 446.

Wallace, D. I. M. 2000. Tail movements by eastern *Hippolais*. *Birding World* 13: 282.

Wallace, D. I. M. 2001. The identification of an *Acrocephalus* warbler. *Brit. Birds.* 94: 441–442.

Walsh, J. F. & Grimes, L. G. 1981. Observation on some Palaearctic land birds in Ghana. *Bull. Brit. Orn. Club* 101: 327–334.

Walther, B. A., Schäffer, N., van Niekerk, A., Thuiller, W., Rahbek, C. & Chown, S. L. 2007. Modelling the winter distribution of a rare and endangered migrant, the Aquatic Warbler *Acrocephalus paludicola*. *Ibis* 149: 701–714.

Walther, B. A., Wisz, M. S. & Rahbek, C. 2004. Known and predicted African winter distributions and habitat use of the endangered Basra Reed Warbler (*Acrocephalus griseldis*) and the near-threatened Cinereous Bunting (*Emberiza cineracea*). *J. Ornithol.* 145: 287–299.

Wang, J. X., Wu, S. X., Huang, G. Y., Yang, W. Y., Cai, Z. Y. Cai, S. Q. & Xiao, Q. L. 1991. [*A pictoral guide to the birds of Taiwan.*] Wild Bird Society Press of Taiwan, Taipei and Tokyo. (Chinese)

Warden, D. 1984. Reed Warblers at Chew Valley Lake, Avon. *Bristol Ornithol.* 17: 73–76.

Warden, D. 1998. Two Reed Warblers laying in same nest. *Brit. Birds* 91: 329.

Warden, D. 2003. Reed Warblers reusing nests. *Brit. Birds* 96: 303.

Wardhill, J. C. & Riley, J. 2000. Lanceolated Warbler records from Sangihe Island, north Sulawesi. *Kukila* 11: 148–149.

Wassink, A. 1979. Sedge Warbler with square-terminating supercilium. *Dutch Birding* 1: 122.

Wassink, A. 1983. Kleine Spotvogel op Terschelling in oktober 1982. *Dutch Birding* 5: 1–5.

Watabe, Y., Sasaki, Y. & Kobayashi, Y. 2005. The first record of Booted Warbler *Hippolais caligata* in Japan. *J. Yamashina Inst. Ornithol.* 37: 14–19.

Watling, D. 1983. Ornithological notes from Sulawesi. *Emu* 83: 247–261.

Watling, D. 2001. *Birds of Fiji and Western Polynesia: including American Samoa, Niue, Samoa, Tokelau, Tonga, Tuvalu and Wallis-Futuna.* Environmental Consultants, Fiji.

Watson, G. E. 1985. Replacement name for *Acrocephalus aedon rufescens* (Stegmann). *Bull. Brit. Orn. Club* 105: 79.

Watson, G. E. & Gray, B. J. 1969. Replacement name for *Acrocephalus agricola brevipennis* (Severtzov). *Bull. Brit. Orn. Club* 89: 8.

Watson, G. E., Traylor, M. A. Jr. & Mayr, E. 1986. Family Sylviidae, Old World warblers. In: Mayr, E. & Cottrell, G. W. (eds.). *Checklist of Birds of the World*, 11: 3–294. Museum of Comparative Zoology, Cambridge, Mass.

Wawrzyniak, H. & Sohns, G. 1977a. Über Gelegegrösse, Nestlingszeit, Brutfolge und -verluste beim Seggenrohrsänger, *Acrocephalus paludicola* (Vieillot). *Beitr. Vogelkd.* 20: 105–113.

Wawrzyniak, H. & Sohns, G. 1977b. *Der Seggenrohrsänger.* Ziemsen Verlag, Wittenberg-Lutherstadt.

Webber, G. L. 1964. Pairing of Reed Warblers from same brood. *Brit. Birds* 57: 253.

Weir, J. T. & Schluter, D. 2008. Calibrating the avian molecular clock. *Molec. Ecol.* 17: 2321–2328.

Welbergen, J., Komdeur, J., Kats, R. & Berg, M. 2001. Egg discrimination in the Australian Reed Warbler (*Acrocephalus australis*): rejection response towards model and conspecific eggs depending on timing and mode of artificial parasitism. *Behav. Ecol.* 12: 8–15.

Wells, D. R. 1982. Biological species limits in the *Cettia fortipes* complex. *Bull. Brit. Orn. Club* 102: 57–62.

Wernham, C., Toms, M., Marchant, J., Clark, J., Siriwardena, G. & Baillie, S. 2002. *The Migration Atlas. Movements of the birds of Britain and Ireland.* Poyser, London.

Westerdahl, H., Bensch, S., Hansson, B., Hasselquist, D. & von Schantz, T. 1997. Sex ratio variation among broods of Great Reed Warblers *Acrocephalus arundinaceus*. *Molec. Ecol.* 6: 543–548.

Westwood, N. J. 2005. Reed Warblers reusing nests. *Brit. Birds* 98: 101.

Wetmore A. 1919. Reports on the scientific results of the expedition to the Tropical Pacific in charge of Agassiz, on the U. S. Fish Commission Steamer Albatross from August 1899 to March 1900, Commander Jefferson F. Moser USN Commanding. XXI The Birds, Part 2: Annotated List of the Species. *Bull. Mus. Comp. Zool.* 63: 206–212.

Wetmore, A. 1924. A Warbler from Nihoa. *Condor* 26: 177–178.

Wetmore, A. 1925. A note on the Fanning Island Warbler. *Condor* 27: 212.

Wheeler, P. 1988. The Welches Dam warbler – a photographic assessment. *Birding World* 1: 50–53.

Whistler, H. 1945a. Materials for the ornithology of Afghanistan, Part II. *J. Bombay Nat. Hist. Soc.* 45: 61–72.

Whistler, H. 1945b. Materials for the ornithology of Afghanistan, Part III. *J. Bombay Nat. Hist. Soc.* 45: 106–122.

White, C. M. N. 1960. *A checklist of the Ethiopian Muscicapidae (Sylviinae) Part 1.* Occasional Papers of the National Museum of Southern Rhodesia, No. 24B: 399–430.

White, C. M. N. 1960. A note on *Acrocephalus baeticatus* Vieillot. *Bull. Brit. Orn. Club* 80: 21–22.

White, C. M. N. & Bruce, M. D. 1986. *The birds of Wallacea.* British Ornithologists' Union, Checklist No. 7. BOU, London.

Whitehead, J. 1893. [Letter describing the juvenile plumage of Kinabalu Bush Warbler.] *Ibis* (6)5: 281.

Whitehead, J. 1899. Field notes on birds collected in the Philippine Islands in 1893–96, part II. *Ibis* (7)5: 210–246.

Wilkinson, R. & Aidley, D. 1982. The status of Savi's Warbler in Nigeria. *Malimbus* 4: 48.

Wilkinson, R. & Aidley, D. 1983. African Reed Warbler in northern Nigeria; morphometrics and the taxonomic debate. *Bull. Brit. Orn. Club* 103: 135–138.

Williams, G. R. 1960. The birds of the Pitcairn Islands, central south Pacific Ocean. *Ibis* 102: 58–70.

Williams, M. D. (ed.). 1986. *Report on the Cambridge Ornithological Expedition to China 1985*. Unpublished.

Williams, M. D. (ed.). 2000. *Autumn bird migration at Beidaihe, China, 1986–1990*. Beidaihe International Birdwatching Society, Hong Kong.

Williams, M. D., Carey, G. J., Duff, D. G. & Xu, W. S. 1992. Autumn bird migration at Beidaihe, China, 1986–1990. *Forktail* 7: 3–55.

Williams, M. D. & Hsu, W. S. 1992. Birds at Beidaihe, late spring 1991. *China Flyway* 2: 11–14.

Williams, T. 1983. Song period of Moustached Warbler. *Brit. Birds* 76: 456.

Williamson, K. 1950. Fair Isle Bird Observatory. Notes on selected species, autumn, 1949. *Brit. Birds* 43: 52.

Williamson, K. 1954. Paddyfield Warbler at Fair Isle. *Brit. Birds* 47: 297–301.

Williamson, K. 1956. A useful field character of the Icterine Warbler. *Brit. Birds* 49: 119–120.

Williamson, K. 1957. Pallas's Grasshopper Warbler on Fair Isle. *Brit. Birds* 50: 395–397.

Williamson, K. 1965. *Fair Isle and its birds*. Oliver & Boyd. London.

Williamson, K. 1968. *Identification for Ringers 1. The genera Cettia, Locustella, Acrocephalus and Hippolais*. 3rd edition. BTO, Tring.

Williamson, K., Thom, V. M., Ferguson-Lees, I. J. & Axell, H. E. 1956. Thick-billed Warbler at Fair Isle: a new British bird. *Brit. Birds* 49: 89–93.

Wilson, J. D. 1985. Possible mimicry of Corn Bunting song by Grasshopper Warbler. *Brit. Birds* 78: 400–401.

Wilson, J. D., Akriotis, T., Balmer, D. E. & Kykros, A. 2001. Identification of Marsh Warbler and Reed Warbler on autumn migration through the Eastern Mediterranean. *Ringing & Migration* 20: 224–232.

Witherby, H. F. 1912. *Lusciniola pryeri sinensis*, subsp. n. *Bull. Brit. Orn. Club* 31: 11–13.

Witherby, H. F., Jourdain, F. C. R., Ticehurst, N. F. & Tucker, B. W. 1943. *The Handbook of British Birds*, Vol 2. 2nd edition. Witherby, London.

Wooldridge, G. E. & Ballantyne, C. B. 1952. Moustached Warblers in Hampshire. *Brit. Birds* 45: 219–220.

Wotton, S., Gibbons, D. W., Dilger, M. & Grice, P. V. 1998. Cetti's Warblers in the United Kingdom and the Channel Islands in 1996. *Brit. Birds* 91: 77–89.

Wright, B. K. 1995. The status of warblers in Kuwait. *Bull. Ornithol. Soc. Middle East.* 34: 1–7.

Wu, S. H. & Yang, H. Y. 1991. [*A guide to the wild birds of Taiwan*.] Taiwan Wild Bird Information Centre, Taipei, and Wild Bird Society of Japan, Tokyo. (Chinese)

Wu, Z. (ed.). 1986. [*The Avifauna of Guizhou*]. Guizhou People's Publishing House. (Chinese)

Wyllie, I. 1975. Study of Cuckoos and Reed Warblers. *Brit. Birds* 68: 369–378.

Yakushev, N. N., Zav'yalov, E. V. & Tabachishin, V. G. 1998. [Distribution of *Acrocephalus agricola* in the north of the Lower Povolzhie (Volga River area) during the 20th century]. *Russian J. Ornithol.* Express issue 47: 18–22. (Russian)

Yamada, N. 1942. [On the breeding of *Locustella fasciolata* with its young]. *Tori* 11: 438–442. (Japanese)

Yamashina, M. Y. 1940. Some additions to the 'List of the Birds of Micronesia'. *Tori* 10: 673–679.

Yang, Z. T. 1997. New bird records from Gansu. *Chinese Journal of Zoology* 32: 48.

Yen, Y. K. 1933. Einige neue Vögel aus China. *Orn. Monatsber.* 41: 15–19.

Yésou, P., Flohart, G. & Murdoch, D. 2007. First record of Basra Reed Warbler *Acrocephalus griseldis* for Syria. *Sandgrouse* 29(2): 214–215.

Yu, Y. T. 2002. Oriental Reed Warblers at Mai Po marshes nature reserve, Hong Kong, during autumn 1997. *Hong Kong Bird Report* 1998: 120–127.

Zatsepina, R. A. 1968. [Ecology of the Marsh Warbler (*Acrocephalus palustris* Bechstein)]. *Prirodnye resursy Volzhsko-Kamskogo kraya* 2: 84–93. Kazan. (Russian)

Zavialov, E. V. 1995. [Occurrences of Paddyfield Warbler *Acrocephalus agricola* and Cetti's Warbler *Cettia cetti* in the Saratov Region.] *Selevinia* 3(1): 41. (Russian)

Zavialov, E. V. & Tabachishin, V. G. 2007. Status of Cetti's Warbler in Saratov region, Russia. *Dutch Birding* 29: 303–305.

Zavialov, E. V., Tabachishin, V. G., Yakushev, N. N. & Mosolova, E. Yu. 2003. [Status of *Acrocephalus agricola* in Povolzhie (Volga River area).] *Russian J. Ornithol.* Express issue 235: 990–993. (Russian)

Zimmerman, D. A., Turner, D. A. & Pearson, D. J. 1996. *Birds of Kenya and Northern Tanzania*. Christopher Helm, A&C Black, London.

Zink, G. 1979. Ringing and recoveries of *Acrocephalus palustris* in Africa. *Ring* 100: 44–45.

Zhao, Z. (ed.). 1985. [*The Avifauna of Changbai Mountain*]. Jilin Provincial Science and Technology Press, Jilin. (Chinese)

Video & DVD recordings

Doherty, P. & Oddie, W. E. 1998. *The Warblers of Britain and Europe*. Video. Bird Images, Sherburn-in-Elmet.

Sound Recordings

Chappuis, C. 2000. *African Bird Sounds*. CD 10. Fifteen CD set. Societe d'etides Ornithologiques de France, Paris.

Connop, S. 1993. *Birdsongs of Nepal*. Turaco Nature Service, Cornell Laboratory of Ornithology, New York.

Connop, S. 1995. *Birdsongs of the Himalayas*. Turaco Nature Service, Cornell Laboratory of Ornithology, New York.

Gibbon, G. 2003. *Southern African Bird Sounds*. CD 5. Six CD set. Southern African Birding. Westville, South Africa.

Gillard, L. 1987. *Southern African Bird Calls*. Three cassettes. Gillard Bird Cassettes, Johannesburg.

Herremanns, M. 2001. *Guide sonore des oiseaux nicheurs des Comores*. CD. Africamuseum, Tervuren, Belgium.

Jännes, H. 2002a. *Calls of Eastern Vagrants*. Earlybird Birding Tours, Helsinki.

Jännes, H. 2002b. *Bird sounds of Goa & South India*. Earlybird Birding Tours, Helsinki.

McPherson, L. B. 1995. *Birds of Polynesia*. McPherson Natural History Unit, Christchurch.

McPherson, L. B. 1998. *More birds of Polynesia*. McPherson Natural History Unit, Christchurch.

Mild, K. 1987. *Soviet bird songs*. (Two cassettes and booklet). Stockholm.

Mild, K. 1990. *Bird songs of Israel and the Middle East*. Stockholm.

Roche, J.-C. 1971. *Birds of Madagascar*. One disc. Aubenas-les-Alpes.

Sample, G. 2003. *Field guide to warbler songs & calls of Britain and Europe*, CDs 1 & 2. Three CD set. Collins, London.

Smith, S. 2004. *Bird Recordings from Micronesia*. Privately published.

Stjernstedt, R. 1986. *Birdsong of Zambia*. Three cassettes. Powys, U.K.

Taiwan Wild Bird Association 1996. *Bird sounds of Hshueh Shan National Park*, CD 4 & 5. Hshueh Shan., Taiwan. (Chinese)

Ueda, H. 1998. *283 Wild Bird Songs of Japan*. Tokyo, Japan.

Veprintsev, B. N. 2007. *Bird sounds of Russia*: Vol. 1., European Russia, Urals and Western Siberia. Veprintsev Phonotheca of Animal Voices, Pushchino, Moscow region. (Russian)

▲ Adult Black-browed Reed Warbler, *Acrocephalus bistrigiceps*. Hunan, China, May (Zhang Jing-Ming).

INDEX

Figures in italics refer to the caption text in the colour plate section. Other figures refer to the first page only of the main entry in the species accounts.

A

abadiei, Oligura castaneocoronata 114, 538
Aberrant Bush Warbler *118*, 570
abyssinicus, Bradypterus baboecala 129
acanthizoides, Cettia 120, 580
acanthizoides, Cettia acanthizoides 120, 580
accentor, Bradypterus 58, 202
Acrocephalus 288
advena, Urosphena subulata 116, 551
aedon, Phragamaticola 92, 516
aedon, Phragamaticola aedon 92, 516
aequinoctialis, Acrocephalus 98, 441
aequinoctialis, Acrocephalus aequinoctialis 98, 441
African Reed Warbler *84*, 364
agricola, Acrocephalus 78, 329
agricola, Acrocephalus agricola 329
albiventris, Acrocephalus melanopogon 72, 289
albiventris, Cettia cetti 122, 621
Aldabra Brush Warbler *112*, 536
aldabranus, Nesillas 112, 536
alfredi, Bradypterus 46, 142
alfredi, Bradypterus alfredi 142
alishanensis, Bradypterus 56, 195
alulensis, Iduna pallida 106, 486
amnicola, Locustella fasciolata 70, 274
amyae, Acrocephalus stentoreus 94, 410
annae, Cettia 126, 610
ansorgei, Acrocephalus rufescens 88, 377
Aquatic Warbler *74*, 302
aquilonis, Acrocephalus percernis 100, 444
arundinaceus, Acrocephalus 90, 396
arundinaceus, Acrocephalus arundinaceus 90, 396
Asian Stubtail *116*, 556
astrolabii, Acrocephalus luscinius 457
atyphus, Acrocephalus 102, 453
atyphus, Acrocephalus atyphus 102, 453
Australian Reed Warbler *96*, 422
australis, Acrocephalus 96, 422
australis, Acrocephalus australis 96, 422
avicenniae, Acrocephalus scirpaceus 84, 354

B

baboecala, Bradypterus 44, 129
baboecala, Bradypterus baboecala 44, 129
badiceps, Cettia ruficapilla 126, 614

baeticatus, Acrocephalus 84, 364
baeticatus, Acrocephalus baeticatus 84, 364
Baikal Bush Warbler *52*, 165
Bamboo Warbler *46*, 142
bangwaensis, Bradypterus 48, 152
Bangwa Forest Warbler *48*, 152
banksi, Cettia vulcania 565
barakae, Bradypterus lopezi 50, 154
barratti, Bradypterus 46, 144
barratti, Bradypterus barratti 46, 144
Barratt's Warbler *46*, 144
Basra Reed Warbler *90*, 391
batesi, Iduna natalensis 509
benguellensis, Bradypterus baboecala 129
Benguet Bush Warbler *56*, 192
bensoni, Calamonastides gracilirostris 110, 522
bistrigiceps, Acrocephalus 76, *92*, 311
Black-browed Reed Warbler *76*, *92*, 311
Blunt-winged Warbler *78*, 322
Blyth's Reed Warbler *80*, 336
Bokikokiko 441
Booted Warbler *108*, 503
borealis, Cettia canturians 124, 595
Bornean Stubtail *116*, 554
Bougainville Bush Warbler *126*, 619
boultoni, Bradypterus lopezi 50, 154
Bradypterus 129
brevicaudata, Nesillas 112, 532
brevipennis, Acrocephalus 84, 369
Brown Bush Warbler *54*, 178
Brownish-flanked Bush Warbler *120*, 574
brunnescens, Acrocephalus stentoreus 94, 410
brunnescens, Cettia 120, 584
brunnifrons, Cettia 122, 591
brunnifrons, Cettia brunnifrons 122, 591

C

caffer, Acrocephalus 100, 449
caffer, Acrocephalus caffer 449
Calamonastides 522
caligata, Iduna 108, 503
camerunensis, Bradypterus lopezi 50, 154
cantans, Cettia diphone 124, 600
canturians, Cettia 124, 595
canturians, Cettia canturians 124, 595

Cape Verde Warbler *84*, 369

carolinae, Cettia 126, 617

Caroline Islands Warbler *102*, 460

carpalis, Bradypterus 44, 135

castaneocoronata, Oligura 114, 538

castaneocoronata, Oligura castaneocoronata 114, 538

castaneoptera, Cettia ruficapilla 126, 614

castaneus, Bradypterus 58, 205

castaneus, Bradypterus castaneus 58, 205

cathkinensis, Bradypterus barratti 144

caudatus, Bradypterus 58, 199

caudatus, Bradypterus caudatus 58, 199

cavei, Bradypterus cinnamomeus 149

celebensis, Acrocephalus stentoreus 96, 410

centralasiae, Locustella certhiola 66, 245

centralis, Bradypterus baboecala 129

certhiola, Locustella 66, 245

certhiola, Locustella certhiola 66, 245

Cettia 560

cetti, Cettia 122, 621

cetti, Cettia cetti 122, 621

Cetti's Warbler *122*, 621

Ceylon Bush Warbler *58*, 208

chadensis, Acrocephalus rufescens 377

chadensis, Bradypterus baboecala 129

Chestnut-backed Bush Warbler *58*, 205

Chestnut-crowned Bush Warbler *122*, 587

Chestnut-headed Tesia *114*, 538

chiangmaiensis, Tesia olivea 114, 544

Chinese Bush Warbler *54*, 173

cinnamomeus, Acrocephalus baeticatus 84, 364

cinnamomeus, Bradypterus 48, 149

cinnamomeus, Bradypterus cinnamomeus 48, 149

Cinnamon Bracken Warbler *48*, 149

Clamorous Reed Warbler *94, 96*, 410

concinens, Acrocephalus 78, 322

concinens, Acrocephalus concinens 78, 322

concolor, Cettia acanthizoides 120, 580

consobrina, Acrocephalus mendanae 444

Cook Islands Warbler *98*, 431

cunenensis, Acrocephalus gracilirostris 86, 372

cyaniventer, Tesia 114, 541

D

Dark-capped Yellow Warbler *110*, 509

davidiana, Cettia fortipes 120, 574

davidi, Bradypterus 52, 165

davidi, Bradypterus davidi 52, 165

dido, Acrocephalus mendanae 444

diphone, Cettia 124, 600

diphone, Cettia diphone 124, 600

disturbans, Bradypterus castaneus 58, 205

Dja River Warbler *44*, 140

dumetorum, Acrocephalus 80, 336

E

Eastern Olivaceous Warbler *106, 108*, 486

elaeica, Iduna pallida 108, 486

Elaphrornis 208

elgonensis, Bradypterus baboecala 44, 129

ellisii, Nesillas typica 526

eremus, Acrocephalus atyphus 102, 453

Eurasian Reed Warbler *82, 84*, 354

everetti, Cettia vulcania 118, 565

everetti, Tesia 114, 549

everetti, Tesia everetti 114, 549

Evergreen Forest Warbler *48, 50*, 154

F

familiaris, Acrocephalus 98, 428

familiaris, Acrocephalus familiaris 428

fasciolata, Locustella 70, 274

fasciolata, Locustella fasciolata 70, 274

fatuhivae, Acrocephalus mendanae 100, 444

Fiji Bush Warbler *126*, 614

flavidus, Acrocephalus atyphus 453

flaviventris, Cettia vulcania 118, 565

flavolivacea, Cettia 118, 570

flavolivacea, Cettia flavolivacea 118, 570

fluviatilis, Locustella 60, 219

fortipes, Cettia 120, 574

fortipes, Cettia fortipes 120, 574

Friendly Bush Warbler 202

funebris, Cettia ruficapilla 614

fusca, Locustella luscinioides 60, 211

fuscus, Acrocephalus scirpaceus 82, 354

G

garretti, Acrocephalus caffer 449

godfreyi, Bradypterus barratti 46, 144

gouldi, Acrocephalus australis 96, 422

gracilirostris, Acrocephalus 86, 372

gracilirostris, Acrocephalus gracilirostris 86, 372

gracilirostris, Calamonastides 110, 522

gracilirostris, Calamonastides gracilirostris 110, 522

Grande Comore Brush Warbler *112*, 532

grandis, Bradypterus 44, 140

granti, Bradypterus lopezi 50, 154

Grasshopper Warbler *62, 64*, 225

graueri, Bradypterus 44, 138

Grauer's Swamp Warbler *44*, 138

Gray's Grasshopper Warbler *70*, 274

Greater Swamp Warbler *88*, 377
Great Reed Warbler *90*, 396
Grey-bellied Tesia *114*, 541
Grey-sided Bush Warbler *122*, 591
griseldis, Acrocephalus 90, 391
guiersi, Acrocephalus baeticatus 84, 364

H

haddeni, Cettia 126, 619
hallae, Acrocephalus baeticatus 84, 364
haringtoni, Acrocephalus concinens 78, 322
harterti, Acrocephalus stentoreus 96, 410
hendersonii, Locustella lanceolata 64, 235
Henderson Island Warbler *98*, 437
Hippolais 465
Hume's Bush Warbler *120*, 584

I

icterina, Hippolais 104, 465
Icterine Warbler *104*, 465
idae, Acrocephalus percernis 100, 444
idoneus, Bradypterus mandelli 56, 182
Iduna 486
innae, Bradypterus major 54, 170
intricata, Cettia flavolivacea 118, 570

J

jacksoni, Acrocephalus gracilirostris 372
Japanese Bush Warbler *124*, 600
Japanese Swamp Warbler *72*, 282
Javan Bush Warbler *56*, 187
Javan Tesia *114*, 547

K

kaoko, Acrocephalus kerearako 431
kashmirensis, Bradypterus thoracicus 52, 159
kerearako, Acrocephalus 98, 431
kerearako, Acrocephalus kerearako 98, 431
Kinabalu Bush Warbler *58*, 202
kingi, Acrocephalus familiaris 428
Kiritimati Warbler *98*, 441
Knysna Warbler *46*, 147
kolichisi, Cettia vulcania 565
kungwensis, Bradypterus alfredi 46, 142

L

laeneni, Iduna pallida 106, 486
lanceolata, Locustella 64, 235
lanceolata, Locustella lanceolata 64, 235
Lanceolated Warbler *64*, 235
languida, Hippolais 106, 481
lantzii, Nesillas 112, 530

Lantz's Brush Warbler *112*, 530
Large-billed Reed Warbler *80*, 343
laurentei, Cettia pallidipes 116, 560
lentecaptus, Acrocephalus stentoreus 94, 410
leptorhynchus, Acrocephalus gracilirostris 86, 372
Lesser Swamp Warbler *86*, 372
levantinus, Acrocephalus stentoreus 94, 410
Little Rush Warbler *44*, 129
Locustella 211
Long-billed Bush Warbler *54*, 170
longicauda, Nesillas typica 526
longirostris, Acrocephalus caffer 449
Long-tailed Bush Warbler *58*, 199
lopezi, Bradypterus 48, 50, 154
lopezi, Bradypterus lopezi 48, 154
luscinioides, Locustella 60, 211
luscinioides, Locustella luscinioides 60, 211
luscinius, Acrocephalus 102, 457
luscinius, Acrocephalus luscinius 102, 457
luteoventris, Bradypterus 54, 178
Luzon Bush Warbler *126*, 607

M

Madagascar Brush Warbler *112*, 526
Madagascar Swamp Warbler *88*, 382
major, Bradypterus 54, 170
major, Bradypterus major 54, 170
major, Cettia 122, 587
major, Cettia major 122, 587
major, Iduna natalensis 110, 509
malindangensis, Bradypterus caudatus 199
Manchurian Bush Warbler *124*, 595
Manchurian Reed Warbler *76*, 317
mandelli, Bradypterus 56, 182
mandelli, Bradypterus mandelli 56, 182
manengubae, Bradypterus lopezi 48, 154
mariae, Bradypterus lopezi 50, 154
mariae, Nesillas 112, 534
Marsh Warbler *80*, 347
massaica, Iduna natalensis 110, 509
melanopogon, Acrocephalus 72, 74, 289
melanopogon, Acrocephalus melanopogon 72, 289
melanorhynchus, Bradypterus mandelli 56, 182
Melodious Warbler *104*, 471
mendanae, Acrocephalus 100, 444
mendanae, Acrocephalus mendanae 100, 444
meridionalis, Acrocephalus stentoreus 94, 410
Middendorff's Grasshopper Warbler *68*, 258
mildbreadi, Bradypterus cinnamomeus 48, 149
Millerbird *98*, 428
mimicus, Acrocephalus melanopogon 72, 74, 289

minor, Locustella certhiola 66, 245

Moheli Brush Warbler *112*, 534

moheliensis, Nesillas typica 526

montis, Bradypterus 56, 187

Mountain Yellow Warbler *110*, 514

Moustached Warbler *72, 74*, 289

msiri, Bradypterus baboecala 44, 129

musae, Acrocephalus caffer 449

musculus, Bradypterus castaneus 205

N

naevia, Locustella 62, 64, 225

naevia, Locustella naevia 62, 64, 225

natalensis, Iduna 110, 509

natalensis, Iduna natalensis 110, 509

Nauru Warbler *102*, 463

neglectus, Acrocephalus gracilirostris 86, 372

Nesillas 526

newtoni, Acrocephalus 88, 382

niauensis, Acrocephalus atyphus 453

Nightingale Warbler *102*, 457

nijoi, Acrocephalus luscinius 457

Northern Marquesan Warbler *100*, 444

nyassae, Bradypterus cinnamomeus 48, 149

O

oblita, Cettia flavolivacea 570

obscura, Nesillas typica 112, 526

obscurior, Locustella naevia 62, 225

ochotensis, Locustella 68, 258

ochotensis, Locustella ochotensis 68, 258

Oligura 538

olivea, Tesia 114, 544

olivea, Tesia olivea 114, 544

olivetorum, Hippolais 104, 476

Olive-tree Warbler *104*, 476

opaca, Iduna 106, 494

oreophila, Cettia vulcania 118, 565

orientalis, Acrocephalus 92, 403

orientalis, Cettia cetti 122, 621

Oriental Reed Warbler *92*, 403

orinus, Acrocephalus 80, 343

osmastoni, Cettia pallidipes 116, 560

P

Paddyfield Warbler *78*, 329

Palau Bush Warbler *126*, 610

palawana, Cettia vulcania 565

Pale-footed Bush Warbler *116*, 560

Pallas's Grasshopper Warbler *66*, 245

pallida, Cettia fortipes 120, 574

pallida, Iduna 106, 108, 486

pallida, Iduna pallida 106, 486

pallidipes, Cettia 116, 560

pallidipes, Cettia pallidipes 116, 560

palliseri, Elaphrornis 58, 208

palmarum, Acrocephalus atyphus 453

paludicola, Acrocephalus 74, 302

palustris, Acrocephalus 80, 347

Papyrus Yellow Warbler *110*, 522

parens, Cettia 126, 612

parvus, Acrocephalus gracilirostris 86, 372

percernis, Acrocephalus 100, 444

percernis, Acrocephalus percernis 100, 444

Phragamaticola 516

pistor, Acrocephalus aequinoctialis 98, 441

Pitcairn Island Warbler *98*, 434

pleskei, Locustella 68, 267

polyglotta, Hippolais 104, 471

pondoensis, Bradypterus sylvaticus 147

postremus, Acrocephalus percernis 444

priesti, Bradypterus barratti 46, 144

pryeri, Locustella 72, 282

pryeri, Locustella pryeri 72, 282

przevalskii, Bradypterus thoracicus 52, 159

R

rama, Iduna 108, 498

ravus, Acrocephalus atyphus 102, 453

rehsei, Acrocephalus 102, 463

reiseri, Iduna pallida 106, 486

restricta, Cettia diphone 124, 600

Rimatara Warbler *98*, 439

rimitarae, Acrocephalus 98, 439

ripleyi, Oligura castaneocoronata 538

riukiuensis, Cettia diphone 124, 600

River Warbler *60*, 219

robustipes, Cettia fortipes 120, 574

rodericanus, Acrocephalus 88, 388

Rodrigues Warbler *88*, 388

rubescens, Locustella certhiola 66, 245

rufescens, Acrocephalus 88, 377

rufescens, Acrocephalus rufescens 88, 377

ruficapilla, Cettia 126, 614

ruficapilla, Cettia ruficapilla 126, 614

Russet Bush Warbler *56*, 182

Russet-capped Tesia *114*, 549

S

sarmatica, Locustella luscinioides 211

Savi's Warbler *60*, 211

schoenobaenus, Acrocephalus 74, 296

scirpaceus, Acrocephalus 82, 84, 354

scirpaceus, Acrocephalus scirpaceus 82, 354

sechellensis, Acrocephalus 88, 385

Sedge Warbler *74*, 296

seebohmi, Bradypterus 56, 192

seebohmi, Cettia 126, 607

senegalensis, Acrocephalus rufescens 88, 377

sepiaria, Cettia vulcania 565

septima, Acrocephalus agricola 329

Seychelles Warbler *88*, 385

Shade Warbler *126*, 612

siebersi, Acrocephalus stentoreus 96, 410

similis, Iduna 110, 514

sinensis, Locustella pryeri 72, 282

Slaty-bellied Tesia *114*, 544

sorghophilus, Acrocephalus 76, 307

Southern Marquesan Warbler *100*, 444

sparsimstriata, Locustella certhiola 66, 245

Spotted Bush Warbler *52*, 159

squameiceps, Urosphena 116, 556

stegmanni, Phragamaticola aedon 92, 516

stentoreus, Acrocephalus 94, 96, 410

stentoreus, Acrocephalus stentoreus 94, 410

stevensi, Acrocephalus concinens 78, 322

straminea, Locustella naevia 62, 64, 225

Streaked Reed Warbler *76*, 307

stresemanni, Cettia flavolivacea 118, 570

Styan's Grasshopper Warbler *68*, 267

suahelicus, Acrocephalus baeticatus 364

subcerthiola, Locustella ochotensis 68, 258

subulata, Urosphena 116, 551

subulata, Urosphena subulata 116, 551

sudanensis, Bradypterus baboecala 44, 129

sumbae, Acrocephalus stentoreus 96, 410

sumbawana, Tesia everetti 114, 549

Sunda Bush Warbler *118*, 565

superciliaris, Tesia 114, 547

suschkini, Bradypterus davidi 52, 165

Sykes's Warbler *108*, 498

sylvaticus, Bradypterus 46, 147

sylvaticus, Bradypterus sylvaticus 46, 147

syrinx, Acrocephalus 102, 460

T

tacsanowskius, Bradypterus 54, 173

Tahiti Warbler *100*, 449

taiti, Acrocephalus 98, 437

Taiwan Bush Warbler *56*, 195

tangorum, Acrocephalus 76, 317

Tanimbar Bush Warbler *126*, 617

Tesia 541

Thick-billed Warbler *92*, 516

thoracicus, Bradypterus 52, 159

thoracicus, Bradypterus thoracicus 52, 159

Timor Bush Warbler *56*, 190

timorensis, Bradypterus 56, 190

Timor Stubtail *116*, 551

tongensis, Bradypterus baboecala 44, 129

transvaalensis, Bradypterus baboecala 129

tsanae, Acrocephalus gracilirostris 372

Tuamotu Warbler *102*, 453

typica, Nesillas 112, 526

typica, Nesillas typica 112, 526

U

ufipae, Bradypterus lopezi 50, 154

umbratica, Cettia brunnifrons 122, 591

unicolor, Bradypterus caudatus 58, 199

Upcher's Warbler *106*, 481

Urosphena 551

usambarae, Bradypterus lopezi 50, 154

V

vafra, Cettia major 587

vaughani, Acrocephalus 98, 434

vulcania, Cettia 118, 565

vulcania, Cettia vulcania 118, 565

W

weberi, Cettia flavolivacea 118, 570

Western Olivaceous Warbler *106*, 494

whistleri, Cettia brunnifrons 122, 591

whiteheadi, Urosphena 116, 554

White-winged Swamp Warbler *44*, 135

winterbottomi, Acrocephalus gracilirostris 86, 372

Y

yamashinae, Acrocephalus luscinius 457

Yellow-bellied Bush Warbler *120*, 580

Z

zarudnyi, Acrocephalus arundinaceus 90, 396